Ramsay's Catalogue

C000179619

British
Model Trains

Fourth Edition

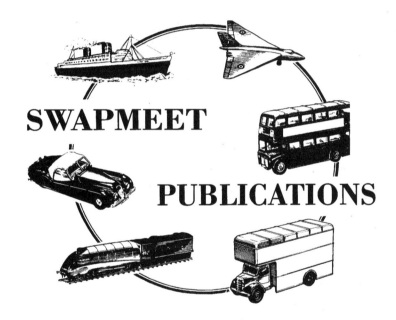

SWAPMEET

PUBLICATIONS

Swapmeet Publications
PO Box 47, Felixstowe, Suffolk, IP11 9HE
Phone (01394) 670700, Fax (01394) 670730
Website: www.swapmeet.co.uk   E-mail info@swapmeet.co.uk

Swapmeet Toys and Models, t/a Swapmeet Publications

Reg. No. 1715966. Reg. Office: 36 Rembrandt Way, Bury St Edmunds, Suffolk. Directors: E.J. Ramsay, S.E. Ramsay, Co. Sec: M.J. Ramsay BA

Originator: John Ramsay

Compiler: Pat Hammond

Technical Editor: John King

1st Edition Published 1998
2nd Edition Published 2000
3rd Edition Published 2002
4th Edition Published 2004

Copyright © 2004 owned by John Ramsay and Pat Hammond.

ISBN 0 9529352 90

Book designed by Ray Springall and John King.
Origination by Swapmeet Publications, Felixstowe.
Printed by Norwich Colour Print Ltd.

Front cover illustrations:

Tri-ang Hornby LMS Coronation 6221 'Queen Elizabeth'

Hornby O gauge LMS Compound 1185 with early unlined tender

Graham Farish N gauge 4-wheel coaches S&DJR blue

Lima Class 37 Dutch Transrail 37351 (L205193)

Bachmann Manchester Collieries 7-plank wagons
(Trafford Set of 3 with different numbers)

Bassett-Lowke by Carette locomotive and tender GNR Atlantic 351

Contents

Welcome

Welcome to the Fourth Edition of the **British Model Trains Catalogue** which covers toy trains and model railway equipment made for the British market. You will find that the catalogue has been considerably extended in response to requests by you, the buyer, to cover subjects we could not include in the Third Edition.

In the Second Edition we provided for the first time a comprehensive listing of model railway locomotives produced for the British market and in the Third Edition we extended the listing to include rolling stock as well. In addition, we have added more N gauge and 0 gauge brands including Minitrix, Lima N and Tri-ang Big Big. We have also picked up several attempts by Continental manufacturers to break into the British market with ready-to-run models but in H0 scale.

Besides ensuring that listing is comprehensive, emphasis has been given to the accuracy of the information and to the ease with which the information can be accessed. Despite our efforts, errors still creep in and we are always keen to hear of any you find.

We have been able to replace many of the question marks in the Third Edition with correct information thanks to those of you who were able and kind enough to supply it. Thanks! There are further question marks in this edition and, again, we welcome answers to these queries. They largely concern running numbers that appeared on models but which were not recorded in catalogues.

In the last edition of this catalogue we set ourselves the following targets for this edition:

1. Further update listing of current ranges.
2. Modify prices according to information available.
3. Widen further the range of makes covered.
4. Provide better information on accessories and catalogues.
5. Correct any inaccuracies that come to light.
6. Undertake further research into the histories of companies.
7. Further improve the speed with which models can be traced in the book.

I am pleased to report that all have been tackled with the exception of extending coverage of catalogues and accessories. This has not been taken further due to the lack of space due to the considerable growth there has been in new models from Hornby, Bachmann, Graham Farish, Dapol and Heljan - all of which we have included. However, these will remain our objectives for the Fifth Edition which we propose to publish in 2006.

Thanks for Your Help!

In order to get the comprehensive coverage we are always aiming for, we have had the help of about fifty volunteers who have supplied model lists, proof-read text and advised on prices. Each person has been approached as an expert in his particular field and we are very grateful for the help they have given us.

For this edition, people to whom I am particularly grateful are Bob Field who has done a lot more work on the Hornby Dublo listing, Simon Culverhouse and Dennis Lovett for extensive work on Minitrix and other N gauge makes and Martin Wrigley who has given much help with updating prices and has written our Market Review. To these and all the others who have contributed to this edition and previous editions we extend our thanks.

If you have expertise in any British make not already covered in this catalogue and would like to see your research in print, please contact me at the address below. Likewise, please write to me about any errors you find or with suggestions as to how the catalogue could be further improved. We want you to feel that this is your book and that it caters for your needs. You can either use the Comments Form that comes with the catalogue or write to me direct at the following address:

Ramsay's British Model Trains Catalogue,
PO Box 199,
Scarborough
YO11 3GT

Illustrations and Captions

In captions, the square brackets tell you in which table, in the appropriate section, you will find details of the model.

A number of illustrations in the catalogue have been loaned by auction houses and individuals and these are acknowledged in italics at the end of the caption. I should like to express my gratitude for the help we have received in the supply of illustrations and to say that we are always interested in new sources.

The remainder of the pictures have come from the Hammond Picture Library.

Beware of Prices

While everything possible has been done to obtain realistic prices, we stress throughout the catalogue that quoted prices can be misleading. They are there only because you request them! There is a considerable difference between people's perception of value depending on whether they are buying or selling and the extent to which they want the item being sold. We provide prices to give a comparison between the scarcity of models and they should not be interpreted as the price you can expect to get for your model if you sell it. Dealers often have to undertake cleaning and servicing of second-hand models they buy and can sometimes wait a long time before the right collector comes along who wants to buy it. They therefore rightly expect a good mark-up when they sell it.

Market Review

Instead of a Preface for this edition of the guide we felt that a Market Review might be more useful to our readers and we turned to Martin Wrigley of Modelfair to provide it...

Overall it's been a very interesting period since the last edition of Ramsay's British Model Trains Catalogue was published. You would think that with the quantity of new models coming into the UK market, second-hand prices would be depressed, but that is not so. It seems almost paradoxical that with large numbers of people selling off their Lima collections that there is an equal number buying them.

Ace Trains: With such small production runs it is hard to assess second-hand prices as there is so little around but, in the long term, a gradual rise in prices is expected.

Airfix: There is continuing interest in Airfix, particularly sets, wagons and coaches (both Airfix and GMR). Best examples have been selling at over the book prices.

Bachmann: There seems to be a pattern both for Bachmann and Hornby of new releases being discounted by the big retailers but a year later second-hand examples selling for more than they originally cost. A good example is the WD 2-8-0s. As the range has now all but disappeared into private ownership, prices have started to rise.

There is a lot of interest in Bachmann wagons, particularly the limited editions, and I fully expect them to reach prices of around £15, if not more, this year. With such a huge range I am sure there will be continuing interest from collectors.

Bachmann coaches are sought after and prices remain firm.

Locomotives are a bit patchy; the Class 37 is selling for around £40. The Ivatt tank is a popular model, as too are the Hall, Manor, A4 and 08 shunter.

Dapol: There is strong interest in Dapol locos, with the Castle, County, Terrier, Pug and the J94 all in strong demand. With such a bewildering range of wagons there will always be interest from collectors. Prices have yet to reflect this.

Farish 00: This is a small market which, with the arrival of the Internet, has become more international, helping to keep prices quite high. Top quality models will always command top prices.

Farish N: With the advent of Bachmann in the market, prices have started to ease off a little from the 'Wilderness period' where demand drove up values. Graham Farish N gauge locomotives are largely let down by their mechanisms. A significant proportion of second-hand examples that I receive have stripped plastic gears.

Heljan: Expensive by comparison to Bachmann and Hornby, Heljan have grabbed a premium share of the market. Second-hand prices reflect this with no sign of falling.

Hornby O: This section of the market is all about quality, originality, provenance etc. with Good examples fetching good prices on an international market.

Hornby Railways: It has been quite a ride for Hornby and they are in a stronger position now than ever. As the newer items have arrived, the expected drop through the floor of '70s and '80s products has not happened. There is interest in the older Hornby items, even down to the humble blue Class 37. To quote David Dickinson, the Hornby 50 is "as cheap as chips". I have seen retailers selling them for £60 which really is a give away price for such a wonderful model. There is worldwide interest in the Hornby range, with collectors showing interest in the wagons and coaches.

Hornby Dublo: There is strong interest in quality 3-rail items and I have sold some 3 and 2-rail locos for more than double the prices suggested in the last Ramsay's guide showing, as always, that quality counts. It is almost pointless taking into account the very top end of the market. The very high prices paid there represent the smallest part of the market and, when published, raise people's expectations.

Lima: With such a huge range there is always going to be interest from collectors. There are two forces at work currently. New better models from other manufacturers are tempting people to sell Lima, but the demise of the company and the end of production is bringing buyers to the market. I personally like Lima which is reliable and affordable. There is lots of interest in Lima coaches and wagons and prices are going up.

Mainline: The market seems to have flattened out a bit, with wagon and loco prices pretty stable. Interest in coaches is strong.

Playcraft: If I could find any, I would be able to sell them with no difficulty. This is one make to watch out for. Some of the items are, in fact, good quality models.

Replica: Top quality coaches are still holding their prices even with the new releases from Bachmann etc.. Their locos are sought after and prices are firm.

Tri-ang: Tri-ang seems to have levelled off a little, with the obvious rarities holding there prices while the run of the mill items starting to slip a little (with the exception of mint examples). There seems to be permanent interest and fascination in certain models such as Rocket, the Caley Single, 'Lord of the Isles', EM2, AL1, EMU and DMU.

Market Review Cont....

Trix: This is split into several camps with the 16V range and the later DC models all receiving strong interest in the best examples and with common or play-worn models having little value.

Wrenn: With the new book now out we can expect a big raise in interest especially as all the production figures are included in the book. The big surprise is how little was made from the mid 1980s onwards.

Martin Wrigley
http://www.modelfair.com

Acknowledgments

A work of this nature cannot be achieved by one man's efforts alone but depends upon many experts sharing their knowledge with us all. Special thanks go to Roy Chambers who wrote much of the original 0 gauge text. The text and lists that Roy and I prepared were then checked, corrected and expanded by a host of established experts whose very important contribution to this book I am pleased to acknowledge. I should particularly like to mention the following:

Rolande Allen - prices
Richard Ashby - Bachmann and Dapol wagons
Peter Baker - Lima, Bachmann and Dapol
Derrick Barratt - Hornby 0 wagons
Mike Black - Graham Farish N
Bowman Circle Members - Bowman
Richard Bradford - Wrenn
Paul & Jennifer Brookes - MasterModels
Roy Chambers - Hornby 0, Bassett-Lowke, Leeds, Milbro, Exley, Bonds, Bowman.
Jim Clark - Bachmann
Peter Corley - Graham Farish 00
Simon Culverhouse - Minitrix and other N gauge.
James Day - Playcraft
Martin Doubleday - Lone Star
Ian Dorrell - Lone Star
Terry Durrant of Lacy Scott & Knight (Auctioneers)
Merl Evans - Bachmann, Mainline and Airfix
Bob Field - Hornby Dublo (now completely overhauled)
Robert Forsythe - Bassett-Lowke, Lima H0, Minitrix
Clive Gehle - Lone Star
Peter Gomm - Airfix, Mainline etc.
Maurice Gunter - Wrenn
Peter Gurd - Hornby Dublo, Bowman and Graham Farish 00
Henk Guyt - various N gauge
Jack Holmes - prices
John Ingram - Bassett-Lowke, Leeds, Milbro, Bonds.
Stephen Knight - Kitmaster and Playcraft
Eric Large - Tri-ang TT
Brian Lee of George Kidner (Auctioneers)
Bob Leggett - Playcraft, Hornby Railways.
Allen Levy - Ace Trains
Dennis Lovett - Graham Farish N, Minitrix, Peco N, Wrenn N
Quentin Lucas - Exley 0
Robert Newson - Lone Star
Hugo Marsh of Christie's South Kensington

David O'Brien - Trix
David Peacock - Leeds Model Company
Barry Potter - prices and photographs
Tony Pritchard - Dapol
Ron Rayner - Hornby Dublo
Matthew Richter - Graham Farish N
Owen Roberts - Bowman
Paul Rouse - Tri-ang TT
Fleetwood Shaw - Bassett-Lowke
Des Sheppard - Bachmann & Dapol
Graham Smith-Thompson - Airfix, Mainline, Replica and Dapol
Nicholas Smith - Tri-ang TT
Nick Sparks - Hornby Dublo
Chris Thornburn - Trix rolling stock
John Turner - prices
Vectis Auctions - photographs and prices.
Wallis & Wallis (Auctioneers)
David Wild - Graham Farish N and various 00.
Martin Wrigley - various makes and price updates.
Martin Wykes - HO models

Considerable use was also made of the following books when I compiled the lists:

'Hornby Dublo Trains' by Michael Foster published by New Cavendish Books (ISBN 0904568180).
'The Hornby 0 Gauge System' by Chris & Julie Graebe, published by New Cavendish Books (ISBN 0904568350).
'The History of Trix H0/00 Model Railways in Britain' by Tony Matthewman, published by New Cavendish Books (ISBN 0904568768).
'Let's Stick Together' by Stephen Knight, published by Irwell Press (ISBN 1871608902).
'The Story of Wrenn' by Maurice Gunter, published by Irwell Press (ISBN 1903266424).

And, my own books published by New Cavendish Books:

'Tri-ang Railways' (2nd Edition) (ISBN 1872727298)
'Tri-ang Hornby' (ISBN 1872727581)
'Hornby Railways' (ISBN 1904562000)

Pat Hammond
Scarborough
May 2004

How to Use This Catalogue

The catalogue has been designed as a reference work and, as such, a high priority has been the ease with which models can be traced. Having said that, it helps if you have some idea as to what the model is.

The book is also principally a reference work for locomotives and rolling stock and, with a few exceptions, there is little likelihood that you will be able to use it to identify a lineside accessory.

Most models today have the manufacturer's name on them but this was not so in the case of minor manufacturers in days gone by. Nor is it always the case with non-proprietary models, for it is quite possible that your model was not originally bought ready made but was either scratch built or made from a kit. Such models are not covered by the catalogue, although Kitmaster kits have been included because they are particularly collectable in their unmade state.

Determine the size

If you do not know the name of the manufacturer, a good starting point is to look at the size of the model. Railway models are governed in size by the gauge of the track they were made to run on. You can determine the gauge of the model by measuring the distance between the backs of the wheels and referring to the section on **Scales and Gauges**.

Having determined the gauge, turn to the **Contents** page where you will find listed all the makes of that gauge that have been included, together with the number of the page on which their listing starts. The contents list is not comprehensive and there is always a chance that the make of the model you are trying to identify has not yet been covered by the catalogue. You will notice that '00' and 'H0' scales are grouped together. This is because both 00 and H0 models use the same gauge track but 00 models are made to a scale of 4mm:1ft and H0 models to 3.5mm:1ft. The former are, therefore, slightly larger than the latter when you compare like subjects.

If, having found the right part of the catalogue, you are still not sure of the make, compare the model with pictures in that section.

Looking for the Number

Having found the section you want, it does help if you know the name of the prototype that has been modelled. This will allow you to find the correct table for that model and search through it for the model variation that matches your own. If this is not the case, note the number on the side of the locomotive (or its tender) and check through the tables until you find it. This is particularly easy to do in the case of diesel and electric locomotives as these mostly have modern TOPS numbering and have been listed in numerical order.

With three of the largest product ranges (Hornby 0 gauge, Bassett-Lowke and Rovex/Tri-ang/Hornby) we have provided 'loco search' tables. All the known numbers carried by models in each of these groups have been listed in numerical order alongside the number of the table(s) in which they will be found. You will find that this is a very fast way of tracing your model.

Understanding the Tables

In 95% of cases, all the models listed in each table are structurally the same and differ only in the livery they carry or in minor added detail. You will find that the table gives you the catalogue number (if known), the name and number the model carries, its basic colour and livery together with other distinguishing features, the years it was available in shops (in italics) and a range of prices you might expect to pay for one (see **Determining Value**).

Some of the information is in code form in order to save space. Where those codes are specific to that model the codes are shown under the title of the table but where the codes are common to many models of that make they may be listed in the introduction to the section. Codes commonly used throughout the catalogue will be found under **Codes and Explanations** in the front of the catalogue.

The tables also contain information about limited and special editions (Ltd Edn and Sp Edn). Where known, this information includes the number made and (in brackets) the shop or organisation that commissioned it.

We hope that the above notes help you to find what you are looking for.

Codes and Explanations

Abbreviations

While some sections in the catalogue have their own set of abbreviations, the following codes are common throughout the guide:

Ltd Edn = Limited Edition. These are usually initiated by the manufacturer with the undertaking that the model in this form will not be repeated for a number of years. The term does not always mean that only a small number were produced. Indeed, some standard issues have been produced in smaller quantities than limited editions! The number accompanying this entry (if there is one) indicates the production run. The absence of a number indicates that we do not have that information.

Sp Edn = Special Edition. These are usually models that have been commissioned by a shop or other interested party. They also have the production figure if known and, in brackets, the name of the shop or organisation that commissioned the model.

The following codes are used for decals carried by models:

BRa - 'BRITISH RAILWAYS'.
BRb - lion astride wheel.
BRc - lion holding wheel (in a roundel on multiple units and coaches and a few diesel hydraulics). This is also known as the 'ferret and dart board' logo! In coach listing it refers to the BR red lion roundel on the side of coaches but the absence of the 'c' does not mean that the roundel is missing - only that in compiling the list there was uncertainty as to which models had one and which did not. In some tables it has been left out altogether to avoid confusion.
BRd - lion in crown (briefly used on West Coast Main Line electrics)
BRe - double arrow logo
BReLL - double arrow (large logo)

Other abbreviations used in the book include:
ECML = East Coast Main Line
Con = Construction
Dist = Distribution
I-C = Inter-City or InterCity
IC = INTERCITY
ICs = INTERCITY with swallow motif
LH = LoadHaul
Met = Metals
NSE = Network SouthEast
Rft = Railfreight,
Reg Rlys = Regional Railways
S&T = Signals & Telegraph
Trans = Transrail
WCML = West Coast Main Line

The following are abbreviations used for railway companies:

BR = British Railways
CLR = Central London Railway
CR = Caledonian Railway
EWS = English Welsh & Scottish
FGW = First Great Western (see also GWT)
GCR = Great Central Railway
GER = Great Eastern Railway
GNER = Great Northern Eastern Railway
GNR = Great Northern Railway
GWR or GW = Great Western Railway
GWT = Great Western Trains (see also FGW)
HR = Highland Railway
LBSCR = London Brighton & South Coast Railway
LMS = London Midland & Scottish Railway
LNER = London North Eastern Railway
LNWR = London & North Western Railway
LSWR = London & South Western Railway
LT = London Transport
LYR = Lancashire & Yorkshire Railway
M&GN = Midland & Great Northern Railway
Met = Metropolitan Railway
MML = Midland Mainline
MR = Midland Railway
NBR = North British Railway
NE = London North Eastern Railway
NER = North Eastern Railway
NLR = North London Railway
S&D or S&DJR = Somerset & Dorset Joint Railway
SECR = South East & Chatham Railway
SER = South Eastern Railway
SR = Southern Railway
SWT = South West Trains
VT = Virgin Trains

CN = Canadian National, Canadien National
CP = Canadian Pacific
VR = Victorian Railways (Australia)
TA = TransAustralia
TR = Tri-ang Railways
TC = Transcontinental

Colours and Liveries

While some experts on railway liveries may cringe at my use of the term 'red' or 'maroon' (shortened to 'mrn' or 'marn') instead of 'crimson lake' to describe the colour of LMS stock, this has been done so that the description is understood by the non-expert as well those knowledgeable in railway liveries. Likewise, early BR carmine and cream is listed as 'red+cream'. Distinguishing between red and maroon can be difficult especially when the model has not actually been seen.

Teak is the description used for LNER coaching stock which was unpainted light wood with a varnish finish. On some models the wood grain has been reproduced but in other cases a yellow-brown paint has been used instead.

The description 'choc+cream' stands for 'chocolate (dark brown) and cream which was the standard colour of GWR passenger stock for much of the life of the company and a similar (but different) colour scheme was used on Pullman cars.

GWR locomotives were usually finished in 'Brunswick' green which was darkish and described here simply as 'green' as the same shade became standard on British Railways (BR) locomotives used purely for passenger work. In contrast, LNER locomotives were generally 'Apple' or 'Doncaster' green which was a lot lighter and is sometimes described here as 'light green' (or lt.green). Southern Railway locomotives were usually green but the shade changed over the years and two shades commonly reproduced today on models are the early 'Olive' green and the later 'Malachite' which is a light slightly bluish green.

The use of the abbreviations 'l.' or 'lt.' as a prefix to the colour means that it is a 'light' shade while 'dark' may be referred to by 'd.' or 'dk.' prefixes and bright as 'bt'.

Running Numbers

These are the numbers carried on the side (and often the front) of locomotives and also by coaches and wagons. They are useful as a means of identifying a particular model and in a few cases 'loco search' tables have been provided to help you trace a model by its running number. The absence of a number may infer that the model did not carry one but in most cases it is because we did not know what it was. We would therefore welcome this information where it has been left out but please make sure that the number is original and has not been added after leaving the factory.

Italics

Dates are shown in italics in order to make it easier to pick these out.

Motors

All locomotive models are electric powered unless otherwise stated. **c/w** = clockwork

Prices

NA = Not Applicable or Not Available
NPG = No Price Given
(see - **Determining Value - The Impossible Task**).

Detail

The absence of detail in the description of a model is not evidence that the detail is not carried by the model. Furthermore, a feature may be mentioned on one model but not on another that also carries it. Often information is provided only where it is felt that it may be helpful in distinguishing between like models.

Listing Order

The listing of models is not always done in the same way as, in each case, we have chosen an order of listing that best suits the subject and makes it easiest for you to find what you are looking for. The method of listing is normally explained at the start of each section.

Generally speaking, however, I have moved towards a common system which lists locomotives in the order of tank engines, tender engines, diesels, electric locomotives, DMUs and EMUs. Coaches are listed with pre-nationalised stock first (GWR, LMS, LNER and SR) and then Mk1s, Mk2s, Mk3s and Mk4s. The wagons usually start with flat wagons and follow with timber open wagons, steel open wagons, hoppers, tankers, vans, brake vans and bogie wagons. But, I repeat, this is not always the case.

Dates

I have also adopted different systems for dating models but this has been determined by the level of information available. Wherever possible I have shown the span of dates when a model was available but, in some cases, models were produced in batches with hardly any carry over from year to year. This is particularly common today as manufacturers can sell more models by constantly changing their livery or the number they carry. In these cases a single date applies i.e. the year the batch was released.

Beware! The existence of an illustration of a model in a catalogue is not evidence that it was available. However, in the case of some of the earlier toy trains, I have had to use catalogue entries as a guide to availability as no other evidence is available to me.

Code 3 Models

A Code 3 model is one that has been finished outside the factory by a secondary 'manufacturer'. These are often retailers who buy a quantity of a certain model and re-release it in a modified form. To count as a Code 3 it has to have been produced in the modified form in quantity and to a common specification. This means that one off modifications do not count. Batches of 50 upwards are more usual. These often have a numbered certificate to authenticate them and to indicate how many of them were modified. These have their own niche market.

Code 3 models are not includes in the main sections of the book but in their own section at the back of the catalogue.

'Not Made'

This means that the model did not reach full production. However, it can be confusing when examples of the model turn up. This is usually because, prior to production starting, a small batch of samples was made for individuals to comment on. This is commonly the case where the models are manufactured in the Far East. These samples often find their way on to the market where they can command a high price if the model did not go into full production. This is where it pays to know your subject so that you can recognise the genuine article when you see it.

Pre-Production Models

This is a similar situation except that the models rarely look like production models. They were hand made and hand painted and were produced prior to a decision being taken on whether the subject should be put into production.

With completely new models, the sample may have been built by a model maker using plasticard or may be assembled from a proprietary model kit. It may even have been scratch built using some parts from an existing model in the range. Where it was a proposal to release an existing model in a new livery, a production model will have been taken off the production line and resprayed and detailed in the new livery as a sample for approval.

Pre-production samples (commonly referred to in the factory as 'prototypes' or 'visuals') were often finished on one side only and the writing and logos are often skilfully hand painted. Where two exist, one would have gone to the studio preparing the catalogue and the other retained in the factory for draughtsmen and engineers to refer to.

Once approved for production a 'proving' model was made. This was structurally identical to what the final production model would be and its component parts would be used in the preparation of the drawings for the toolmaker.

Pre-production models (prototypes, samples and proving models) sometimes come on the market but it is usually a problem proving that they are what someone claims them to be. While many collectors would like to buy them, uncertainty about authenticity can be a disincentive to do so.

This is really an area of collecting which requires a lot of experience in handling examples in order to recognise the genuine from the fake. Where the provenance is good they can fetch a high price and four figure sums have been known to change hands - but this is not the norm. Where there is no provenance, they may be purchased quite cheaply but there is a risk you could burn your fingers.

Determining Value - The impossible Task

For Guidance Only

The first thing to remember about quoted prices is that they are **for guidance only**. Both at auction and on swapmeet stalls, prices vary enormously and who is to say what is the exact value of a given model. What is worth £200 to one collector may be worth only £150 (or even £100) to another buyer or seller.

Swapmeet Prices

On the whole, stall holders are very knowledgeable about what they sell but each tends to be a specialist. They sometimes find themselves with models that are outside their specialised area. If advice is not at hand they have to guess at the price to put on it. This can lead to bargains for knowledgeable buyers but can also cause frustration when the object is severely overpriced.

Remember, the price seen on a model at a swapmeet is not necessarily the price at which it sells. Most stall holders are prepared to haggle. So what is the true value of the model; the price at which he bought it in, the price he put on it or the price at which you finally buy it?

Putting an accurate value to individual models is impossible. All we can do is show comparisons and that is all this price guide sets out to do.

Auction Prices

There is, usually, a fair gap between what you pay for a model and what you would expect to get for it when selling it again. We have set out prices at what we think the models will fetch at auction, prior to the addition of the buyer's premium. Even at auction, prices vary erratically depending on who is present bidding. As a result of this, we have had to deal with conflicting valuations from different auctions and, in each case, have tried to arrive at a compromise.

Auction prices can be used only for more valuable items as less valuable models are put together in groups to be sold as mixed lots. It is impossible to estimate how much of the hammer price applied to each item in the lot as some would have been more valuable than others.

eBay

Since this price guide was started, on-line auctions have grown in importance and amongst these eBay is by far the most used by model railway collectors. Here prices can be more erratic than anywhere else. This is a world-wide auction room and overseas bidders buying into a market they are unfamiliar with will sometimes take a model well over its perceived value. At other times an otherwise valuable model struggles to get anywhere near its 'normal' value. We have largely avoided using eBay prices for this reason.

Our Valuations

Our suggested values are presented in two columns to the right of each table. For reasonably recent releases, where mint boxed items may still be around, the right hand column gives a 'mint boxed' price and the left hand column an 'excellent unboxed' value. If the item was not released on its own, authentically boxed examples are unlikely to exist and so the right hand column carries an 'NA' for 'not available'. Likewise where we give a price for a boxed set of models or a train pack there is an 'NA' in the left hand column.

With many of the older, obsolete, model ranges mint boxed examples are practically an impossibility and so the two columns are used to show the price range for examples in very nice condition. There are cases where I doubt whether a model actually exists or, alternatively, I can find no example of one having been sold. In these cases the price columns are marked with an 'NPG' for 'no price given'.

Effect of Quality

Obviously, value falls as quality falls but not always by the same percentage. It depends how rare the model is and even what make it is. The lack of a box can reduce the value of a model by 40% or more. Generally the rarer the model, the more valuable the box. For poorer quality models the lack of a box has less impact on price.

The gulf between the price first class models are fetching and that paid for those of a lower standard is ever widening and in some ranges the prices of poorer quality models is actually going down. Models that have had detailing added after leaving the factory (except in the case of Code

3 models), are likely to be of lower value to collectors even though the detailing has improved the appearance of the model. The same applies to repainted models, although there are very early 0 gauge models for which a professional repaint is acceptable as few if any good unrestored examples exist in reasonable condition.

Fluctuating Prices

Prices can fluctuate from year to year and from decade to decade. With the sale of the G&R Wrenn in the early '90s, the price of Wrenn models quickly escalated but, more recently, fell to more modest levels. Since the publication of the Third Edition of this catalogue two years ago we have seen the end of Lima production and the almost immediate increase in the demand for Lima models. Thus Lima prices have risen during this time.

At auction, the sale of a famous comprehensive collection can bring out top bidders with the result that prices may rise on the day with rare and common items both selling at figures well above the norm.

High and Low Values

As already indicated, the price gap between rare and common (or poor quality) items is ever widening. This means that rare and top quality models are a much better investment than common or poor quality ones.

Train Packs

Nowadays, some manufacturers sell their models in train packs. These consist of a locomotive and some coaches or wagons but no track etc. As indicated above, the right hand column price is for the complete train pack. Multiple units (DEMUs, EMUs etc.) are sold as train packs and no price is given for individual parts of these sets. The price in the left hand column is therefore for the complete 2-car or 3-car unit without its packaging.

History of Model Train Manufacture

In the Beginning

The first commercially built model railways were imported into Britain from Germany in 1902 and were made for Bassett-Lowke by the German companies, Bing, Carette and Marklin.

Up until the First World War, the most popular gauge was 1¾" (known as gauge 1) but after the war gauge 0 really came into its own.

The war was to have a dramatic effect on the model railway industry as post-war anti-German feeling made German imports unpopular and Bassett-Lowke Ltd were forced to manufacture more of their products themselves.

It also created an opportunity for other British manufacturers to enter the fray.

The most successful of these was Meccano Ltd, a company that had been founded in 1908 to manufacture the Meccano engineering construction system. They introduced their toy trains in 1920 and these took the name of the Company's founder - Frank Hornby - and were sold as 'Hornby Trains'. Hornby, from the start, chose to manufacture in 0 gauge and early models constructed with Meccano nuts and bolts soon gave way to tinplate tab and slot construction.

First 00 Scale System

As early as 1922, Bassett-Lowke introduced to Britain a tabletop railway made in Germany by Bing and considered to be 00 gauge - i.e. half the size of the popular 0 gauge. Within a very short time this was available as an electric system. The Bing company was to fall victim to the rise of Nazi power in Germany and trading became very difficult. Out of these difficulties came a more commercial small scale system known as Trix and this was introduced to Britain in 1936, again with the assistance of Bassett-Lowke.

Within a very short time it was being made by a satellite company of Bassett-Lowke at Northampton. Meccano Ltd could see the way the wind was blowing and quickly responded with their own 00 system which they called Hornby Dublo. This was launched in 1938 and, unlike the Trix Twin system, was initially available in clockwork form as well as electric.

Post World War 2

The Second World War brought to an end all commercial model railway production but post-war Britain saw major changes in both demand and response. It was soon clear that 0 gauge was no longer the leading scale and over the years production of it gradually declined.

The new top gauge was 00 and it was to remain so to the present day.

Hornby Dublo returned after the war but while it was the market leader for a while Meccano Ltd did not recognise the importance of expanding it fast to meet the growing demands from the public. The gap in demand was quickly filled by a new system called Tri-ang Railways which was made by Rovex Scale Models Ltd, a subsidiary of Lines Bros.

The New Contender

The Tri-ang system had several advantages that would play in its favour during the struggle for market domination that lay ahead. It was a two rail system making the track look more realistic, it used plastic mouldings that could show much more detail, it was a lot cheaper while still being reliable and the range expanded quickly to offer the public plenty of choice when building a layout. Within a few years it had become the market leader.

The early post-war years saw many other companies trying to break into the model railway market. Principal amongst these was Graham Farish who marketed an 00 system with some very attractive models but which, initially, were not too reliable mechanically.

Trix in the meantime failed to respond quickly enough to the demand for realism and slowly faded. The business changed hands a few times and new investment resulted in some nice models being produced. One of its problems became obvious in the late '50s and that was its adoption of the Continental HO scale instead of British 00. This meant that when some excellent models started to arrive they looked out of scale when mixed with those of other makes. Meanwhile Tri-ang's onslaught was injuring Hornby Dublo and although Meccano Ltd made major improvements to their range, including a 2-rail system and use of plastic mouldings, its response came too late to save the Company which was being bombarded on other fronts at the same time.

Big Take-overs

In 1964 Meccano Ltd was taken over by Lines Bros. who renamed their own model railway system 'Tri-ang Hornby' and sold the Hornby Dublo tools to another of their subsidiaries - G&R Wrenn. For the next decade Tri-ang Hornby virtually had the market to itself. The only competition came from a Trix system, which limped along, and Playcraft which was made by Jouef in France and marketed in Britain by Mettoy Ltd. 1973 saw a bid by Lima to break into the British market but they made the mistake of using the smaller HO scale. Although by the 1976 Lima had changed to 00 scale, their day had not yet dawned.

In 1971, the Lines Bros. Group fell apart. Profitable Rovex, the member of the group making Tri-ang Hornby, was sold to Dunbee Combex Marx (DCM) and Tri-ang Hornby was renamed Hornby Railways. Wrenn became an independent company again and continued to manufacture Wrenn Railways for the next 20 years using the former Hornby Dublo tools. The British part of Meccano Ltd (based in Liverpool), who no longer made trains, was sold to Airfix while Meccano France (based in the Tri-ang factory in Calais) was acquired by General Mills who also owned Palitoy.

New Competition

Both Airfix and Palitoy separately judged that there was a place in the market for better quality model railways and decided to fill it. The Airfix and Mainline (Palitoy) systems were both launched in the mid '70s but it had taken them two years from announcing their intentions to supplying shops and this gave Rovex the breathing space they required to respond with their Hornby Railways system. By 1980 it was a four horse race with Hornby closely chased by Mainline and Airfix and Lima coming up on the outside. Meanwhile, trailing some way behind, was British Trix and Playcraft was now out of view.

This seems an appropriate point at which to stop and look at what else was happening.

Smaller Scales

Tri-ang had seen a need to experiment with yet smaller

scales and in 1957 had launched their TT system. This never really caught on although it was well developed as a system and was supported by manufacturers of accessories. It had died in the mid '60s.

The even smaller scale of 000 or N gauge was tried by Lone Star as a push-along system in 1957 with an electric system following in 1960. Lines Bros. were invited to buy the system but turned it down and it died out in the 1970s. Lima had produced a more sophisticated N gauge system which they had offered to Lines Bros. in the 1960s and they agreed to market it through their subsidiary, G&R Wrenn. This was sold as Wrenn Micromodels for many years.

Following the purchase of Rovex in 1971 by Dunbee Combex Marx they entered into an agreement with the German Trix company to import their Minitrix system (formerly made at Wrexham by Trix Trains) and sell it as Hornby Minitrix. New models were produced to Rovex's requirements, leaving Rovex free to concentrate on developing Hornby Railways. The arrangement was quite successful and lasted several years.

The only British company to really grasp the N gauge nettle was Graham Farish. Remember them? We last saw them in the 1950s with a nice but not too successful 00 system. This had limped along through the '60s with much shrinkage until they turned their attention to developing an N gauge system at the end of the '60s. In a virtual vacuum, but with a steadily growing demand for good N gauge models at reasonable prices, the Grafar N gauge system has expanded and now offers considerable choice to the N gauge modeller. Many small companies have developed to provide accessories, resprays etc. on the back of this system.

Before returning to 00 gauge it is worth mentioning that 0 gauge virtually petered out in the mid '60s as Hornby, Bassett-Lowke and Leeds production ground to a halt. Despite this, in the mid 1960s, Tri-ang produced their toy-like Big Big trains, the tools for which were later sent to Russia, and Lima produced some acceptable models of British outline.

The Tools Merry-go-round

In 1980 DCM were in the receivers hands and the future of the Hornby Railway system was once again in question. The same year Airfix went bust and its railway system was taken over by Palitoy and its models absorbed into the Mainline system. By 1981, Hornby were an independent company again for the first time in 30 years. Ten glorious years of expansion followed. During the 1980s Lima firmly took hold of the modern image locomotive market bringing out models of many of the better known subjects. Then, in 1990, it all changed again!

In 1984, General Mills, who owned Palitoy, had given up toy production and the assets of their Mainline system, including the Airfix tools, were sold to another up and coming company called Dapol Ltd who were by then producing their own new, high quality, models of locomotives. However, Palitoy had not owned the tools for the manufacture of their Mainline models as these belonged to Kader of China who had made them.

Enter the Dragon

Kader were interested in expanding their model railway manufacturing and in 1988 took control of the American model company, Bachmann. In 1989 they formed Bachmann Industries Europe Ltd to develop and market models in Europe through bases in Britain and Germany. The Bachmann Branchline range was launched in Britain in 1990, using the former Mainline tools. Building on these, Kader were soon manufacturing models to a quality never before seen in Britain. This was the Blue Riband range.

Once again Hornby found their commanding place in the market threatened and had to respond. To allow them to expand their range fast, and quickly improve the quality of their models, they needed to buy ready to use new tools. For these they turned to Dapol Ltd. As we have seen, Dapol had produced some high quality models of their own but also held, and used, the former Airfix tools they had bought from Palitoy along with a few Mainline tools not owned by Kader. In 1996 Hornby purchased both lots of tools and this gave them four years breathing space in which to develop their own new models. In the summer of 2000, the first of these arrived in the shops. with the promise that all new Hornby models would be to the new standard.

Graham Farish was taken over by Bachmann in 2000 and later, Dapol, having extracted the wagon tooling they required to boost their own range, sold the remainder of G&R Wrenn to Mordvale Ltd who hope to return to locomotive production. Dapol also produced their first new locomotive model for nearly ten years.

By 2002 it was clear that Lima were in difficulties and as they struggled to stay in business the Danish company, Heljan, made a bid for part of the British 00 diesel market. Other manufacturers joined in to pick off Lima's diesel subjects and produce superior versions of them.

Today, the major 00 market is dominated by Hornby and Bachmann with improved Graham Farish N gauge models being made by Bachmann. Hornby and Bachmann have everything manufactured in China. Hornby initially concentrated on upgrading its range of steam locomotives but has now joined Bachmann and Heljan in a race for control of the diesel market.

Expansion

The 0 gauge market revival continues with Ace Trains and Bassett-Lowke co-operating and smaller firms catering for the more discerning modeller.

Hornby have launched an 00 scale live steam system and hope to sell this worldwide. They see their future as an international group. They have bought Electrotren of Spain and put in a bid to buy the Lima group which includes Rivarossi, Jouef and Arnold as well as Lima itself. In Britain there is particular interest in what Hornby will do with Lima's large British range of 00 models.

The future could be very interesting.

This has been a simplified history of the principal manufacturers of ready-to-run models and toy trains and does not reflect the enormous contribution made to the industry by the scores of smaller firms that specialise in kits, materials and accessories. Without them it would be a far less interesting hobby and we hope to cover the products of more of them in future editions.

History of Collecting Model Trains

The collecting of toy trains did not really get under way in Britain until the late 1960s when operators of Hornby 0 gauge were looking for additional stock. One way in which the exchange of models was effected was through the organisation of meetings by groups of enthusiasts and this lead to the invention of a new word in the English language - the Swapmeet.

Out of this growth in interest, the Hornby Railway Collectors Association was formed in 1969 and following a period of sometimes heated argument through the pages of the Association's magazine, membership was extended to Hornby Dublo collectors, some of whom had formed the Dublo Circle. The HRCA has steadily grown over the years and is by far the largest club of its kind in the UK. It has also spawned a number of satellite organisations abroad.

The mid 1970s saw a growing interest in collecting of other makes of toy trains and the formation, in 1975, of two more organisations. The first of these was the Tri-ang Hornby Collectors Club which survived for many years, chronicling the diversities of the range, before disbanding. The other new organisation was the Trix Twin Railway Collectors Association which has flourished and remains a well supported organisation producing its own spares, special models for members and an excellent magazine.

It was not until 1978 that collectors in Britain had an organisation that catered for 'any make, any gauge, any age,'. This is the by-line of the Train Collectors Society which has stuck to its principles and not tried to set close restrictive limits to its member's interest. The result is a very friendly society that does not take itself, or its hobby, too seriously. In recent years the TCS has grown considerably in size and many collectors have seen the value of dual membership (membership of a specialist club and membership of the TCS for the wider interest)

Other specialised clubs followed with the Kitmaster Collectors Club in 1980, the Bassett-Lowke Society in 1991, the Graham Farish Circle in 1994, the Lima Collectors Society in 1995, the Wrenn Railways Collectors Club in 1998 and the Tri-ang Society, with its fairly broad interest in the products of the Lines Bros. Group, in 1999.

Recent years have seen a growing recognition, by the manufacturers, of the expanding market for new models made specially for collectors. To this end, they produce collectors editions of their models. Some, like Bachmann and Hornby have their own collectors clubs and Hornby has established collectors centres that exclusively receive some of their limited editions.

Outside the scope of this book are those British clubs that cater for collectors of foreign makes. These include the Fleischmann Model Railway Club and the Lionel Collectors Club UK.

Collectors Club

Anyone interested in collecting railway models should consider joining one of the growing number of specialist collecting clubs. The following are relevant to the systems covered by this guide:

Train Collectors Society

This is a society with a broad interest in toy and model train collecting and has the motto 'Any Make. Any Gauge, Any Age'. Founded in 1978, the Society publishes a quarterly magazine and is currently developing a spares and information service. It holds three major gatherings each year but members also exhibit at other events.
Contact : James Day, tel: 020 8209 1589
Web Site : www.traincollectors.org.uk

Airfix Collectors Club

The Club caters for collectors of any Airfix product including the model railway range and publishes a

newsletter called *Constant Scale*.
Contact : Jeremy Brook, 29 Elley Green, Neston, Nr. Corsham, Wiltshire SN13 9TX
Web Site : www.airfix-collectors-club.com

Bachmann Collectors Club

For a number of years the Company sponsored an enthusiasts club called Bachmann Times which operated at arms-length. In 2000 the club was reformed in-house under the name: Bachmann Collectors' Club. Members receive a quarterly magazine updating them on development progress and with feature articles related to the models.
Contact : Mrs Ros Hubbard, Bachmann Collectors Club, Bachmann Europe plc, Moat Way, Barwell, Leicestershire LE9 8EY.
Web Site : www.bachmann.co.uk

Bassett-Lowke Society

The Bassett-Lowke Society caters for those who collect and operate Bassett-Lowke models. It publishes a quarterly magazine called '*Lowko News*' and organises events to which members may take their stock to run.
Contact : Mr R Burgess, tel: 01473-437713.

Hornby Collectors Club

This is a club supported by Hornby Hobbies for subscribing customers. The club was formed in 1997 and publishes a full colour bimonthly magazine. Through the Club, members have the opportunity to purchase special collectors editions of models produced by Hornby.
Contact : Fiona Baulard-Cato, Hornby Collectors Club, PO Box 35, Royston, Herts SG8 5XR. Tel: 01223 208308
Web Site : www.hornby.co.uk

Hornby Railway Collectors Association

The HRCA was founded in 1969 and caters for collectors of both Hornby 0 gauge and Hornby-Dublo. It is the largest of the clubs listed here and has overseas associate organisations. The Association publishes 11 issues of its magazine each year and has a very well developed spares service.
Contact : John Harwood, tel: 01935-474830
Web Site : www.hrca.net

Kitmaster Collectors Club

Enthusiasts of the Kitmaster kit range are well catered for by the Kitmaster Collectors Club which was founded in 1980. The Club publishes a magazine called '*Signal*' twice a year and includes in the subjects covered the railway kits by Airfix and Dapol.
Contact : Steve Knight,
email: steve@kitmaster.freeserve.co.uk
Web Site : www.kitmaster-club.org.uk

Leeds Steadman Trust

The Leeds Steadman Trust is an organisation run by David Peacock to help collectors and operators of LMC models to keep them running by supplying spare parts. It is not a club but you can be placed on a mailing list for the annual price list of parts.
Contact: David Peacock,
email: dpeacock@btconnect.com

Lima Collectors Society

The Society was founded in 1995 for collectors of Lima 00 and H0 railway models produced for the British market. A bimonthly newsletter is distributed to members and a complete listing of Lima's British products is available and is regularly updated through the newsletter.
Contact : Peter Baker, tel: 01782 519267 (7pm - 9pm)
email: JacqBaker@aol.com

Tri-ang Society

The Tri-ang Society was formed in 1999 and caters for all Tri-ang products including Tri-ang Railways, Tri-ang Hornby, Tri-ang Railways TT, Big-Big Trains and Minic Motorway. The Society has a quarterly magazine and arranges displays at various model shows and vintage events.
Contact : Miles Rowland, tel 0161 976 5059
Web Site : www.tri-angsociety.co.uk

Trix Twin Railway Collectors Association

The Trix Twin Railway Collectors Association (TTRCA) was founded in 1975 and caters for enthusiasts of Trix Twin, Trix Express, Trix Trains and the models of Liliput UK. It publishes a quarterly magazine called '*Trix Twin Gazette*' and offers a spares service to its members.
Contact : Brian Arnold, tel: 0116 271 5943
Web Site : http://freespace.virgin.net/bruce.jordan/ttrca.htm

Wrenn Railways Collectors Club

The Club was founded in 1998 and caters for the collectors of all products of G&R Wrenn Ltd. It publishes a bimonthly magazine and organises gatherings for its members, contributing displays at various vintage events.
Contact : Barry Fentiman, tel: 01628 488455
Web Site : www.wrennrail.freeserve.co.uk

Magazines

As indicated above, many of the collecting organisations publish magazines for their members and there is no better way of keeping in touch with developments and the history of specific makes than through these publications. Since the demise of *Model Railway Enthusiast/Model Railway Collector* there has been no national magazine specifically catering for the toy train and railway model collector but *British Railway Modelling* carries occasional 'Classic' articles. *Collectors Gazette*, now under the same publisher, also has regular features for model railway collectors.

In addition, those with access to the Internet can read the free *Model Railway Express* magazine at www.mremag.demon.co.uk This provides daily updates of news for collectors and modellers. It also has reviews of newly released models from the collector's point of view. There are about 200 book reviews, a classified ads section and a number of articles about specific manufacturers.

Finally, there are Yahoo chat groups on the Internet with specialisms which marry with those of several of the clubs listed above.

Further Reading

When toy train collecting was in its infancy, there was a dearth of information about manufacturers and model ranges with the result that any book, however simple, that included text or pictures about toy trains, was pounced on by knowledge hungry collectors. Two such books were *'Older Locomotives (1900-42)'* [ISBN 172132088] by Peter Gomm and *'Recent Locomotives (1947-70)'* [ISBN 172132096] by Peter Randall. Both were published in 1970 by Thomas Nelson and Sons Ltd in their Troy Model Club Series for collectors and such was the demand for them that even libraries could not guarantee supplying you with a copy on loan.

While books on British manufacturers remained scarce, those on the international scene started to appear in the '70s. 1972 saw the release in Britain of the English language edition of Gustav Reder's *'Clockwork, Steam and Electric'*. This is a classic study of early toy train making and is a must for anyone with an international interest in the subject. A better illustrated book with more of a British slant is *'A Century of Model Trains'* [ISBN 0517184370] by Allen Levy and published in 1974 by Crescent Books. Another international book which is good for its mouth watering coloured photographs is Udo Becher's *'Early Tin Plate Model Railways'* [ISBN 0852426690] which was published by Argus Books in 1980. A much more general history of toy manufacturing is the very detailed *'The Toy Collector'* [ISBN 0801578469] by Louis H Hertz and published in 1976 by Hawthorn Books Inc. of New York.

Books specifically for the British collector took a step forward with F.R.Gorham's compilation of extracts from Hornby catalogues published between 1927 and 1932. Titled *'Hornby Book of Trains'* [ISBN 0090288820X] it was released by the Oxford Publishing Co. in 1973. This idea of using extracts from old publications was adopted by The Cranbourne Press Ltd. for their booklets. These were made up from Meccano Magazine and Tri-ang catalogue pages and included *'Main Line Ending'* by Peter Randall (Hornby 0 Gauge), *'Hornby Dublo Trains 1938-1939'* by Ronald Truin and *'A Short History of Tri-ang Railways'* by Tony Stanford.

Little more was available for several years and then, suddenly, there was an explosion of publishing in the late '70s starting in 1977 with the excellent *'Collectors Guide to Model Railways'* [ISBN 0852425295] by James Joyce. This remains, today, one of the best broad-brush studies of the British model railway industry, despite the fact that it needs bringing up to date. It was published by Argus books as, too, was *'Toyshop Steam'* [ISBN 085242583X] by Basil Harley, which was released the following year.

That same year saw the release of the first volume of a series of books that was to set the benchmark for specialist books on individual subjects. I refer, of course, to The Hornby Companion Series by New Cavendish. Volume 1 *'The Products of Binns Road - A General Survey'* [ISBN 0904568067] by Peter Randall provided us with the first study of Meccano Ltd and, for the first time, included full colour reproductions of three catalogues. The series went on to cover individual toy ranges from this important company as well as their paperwork and publications. There were also compendia published for some of the volumes which provided check lists of products made.

Volume 2 of The Hornby Companion Series was devoted to Meccano super models but Volume 3 was the much awaited *'Hornby Dublo Trains 1938-1964'* [ISBN 0904568180] by Michael Foster. I distinctly remember the excitement with which I waited for my volume to arrive and then shutting myself away for a week to study it.

Volume 4 was Mike & Sue Richardson's famous treatise on Dinky Toys and this was followed by what I think is the best written book in the whole series. It is of course Volume 5 *'The Hornby O Gauge System'* [ISBN 0904568350] by Chris & Julie Graebe. A better researched and illustrated book would be hard to find. The series went to seven volumes plus five compendia and several of the books have run to second editions.

A magazine popular at the time among collectors was the *'History of Model & Miniature Railways'* which built up into two bound volumes. The close-up photography for this was to spawn a number of look-alike books one of which was *'The World of Model Trains'* [ISBN 086124009X] edited by Patrick Whitehouse and Allen Levy and published by Bison Books in 1978.

A remarkable book of this period was the *'International*

Model Railways Guide' [ISBN 3920877160] which was a German publication, written in three languages (German, French and English). This was, in effect, a large catalogue of model railway manufacturers around the world illustrating in colour many (but not all) of the models available at the time (1978-79). 1979 also saw the publication of *'Mechanical Toys'* [ISBN 0600363317] by Charles Bartholomew and published by Hamlyn, but this had only limited information about toy trains.

Of special interest to Tri-ang Hornby collectors was *'The Hornby Book of Trains 25 Year Edition'* [ISBN 095065860X] which was published in 1979. It was edited by S.W.Stevens-Stratten and chapters on everything from real trains to the manufacturing process at Margate were largely written by staff at the factory - much of it by Richard Lines. The book was followed in 1983 by *'The Art of Hornby'* [ISBN 071823037X], also written by Richard Lines, which looked at catalogue and leaflet designs by Meccano Ltd for their Hornby Series and Hornby Dublo as well as for Tri-ang Hornby and Hornby Railways.

An important reference series started in 1980 was *'Cade's Locomotive Guide'* [ISBN 0905377079] which was written by Dennis Lovett and Leslie Wood. This ran to three volumes [ISBN 0905377117] [ISBN 090537715X] and was later re-released in a combined volume. The aim of the series was to provide background information about the real locomotives that are the subjects of models. After each account there were details and photographs of relevant models.

By now articles on model railway collecting were beginning to appear in the model railway press although these remained few and far between. One exception was a series by Peter Gomm called *'Tinplate Topics'* which was a regular feature in *Model Railway News* for several years and looked principally at Hornby 0 gauge. This was followed in 1984 by a series in *Model Railway Constructor* called *'Collector's Corner'* which became a regular feature and ran for several years.

Another attempt at a 'world catalogue' had come in 1983, this time in English, with the publication of *'The World Guide to Model Trains'* [ISBN 0722188242] which was compiled by Peter McHoy with the help of Chris Ellis and was published by Sphere Books Ltd.

A new major work appeared in 1984 when Roland Fuller's *'The Bassett-Lowke Story'* [ISBN 0904568342] reached the shops. This excellent book, published by New Cavendish Books, contained a considerable number of archive photographs and is a valuable reference work. For quality coloured photographs, the series by Salamanda Books Ltd cannot be beaten. The volume called *'The Collector's All-Colour Guide to Toy Trains'* [ISBN 1855010259] (1985) was compiled by Ron McCrindell and contains excellent pictures

of many rare items; most of which are in superb condition having been drawn from several famous collections.

Now for three New Cavendish books from the early 1990s. The first of these looked at the whole field of British toy manufacturers and, although railway content was small when compared with the rest, the detail provided is so good that it is a 'must' for any toy collector's library. This is *'British Tin Toys'* [ISBN 0904568865] by Marguerite Fawdry which was published in 1990 and it covers more than just tin toys!

The next is my own book *'Tri-ang Railways'* [ISBN 0904568571] which New Cavendish Books published in 1993. It is the first in a trilogy about the Rovex company better known today as Hornby plc. This first volume deals with the years from 1950 to 1965 when the product was known as Tri-ang Railways.

This was followed the next year by Tony Matthewman's beautiful volume *'The History of Trix H0/00 Model Railways in Britain'* [ISBN 0904568768]. For me the book comes a close second to Chris & Julie Graebe's Hornby 0 Gauge book for the excellence of its research and presentation. This, like *'Tri-ang Railways'* (and its sequel), was produced in landscape format to match the Hornby Companion Series.

A small book, also released in 1994, was the Shire Album Series No.255 *'Toy Trains'* [ISBN 0747800871] by David Salisbury. And another book published that year was *'Model Trains - The Collector's Guide'* [ISBN 1854227807] by Chris Ellis. Published by Magna Books, it contains an easy to follow history and some good photographs.

1996 brought with it Jeff Carpenter's privately produced volume *'Bings Table Railway'* [ISBN 1900897008], published by Diva Publishing, which provides not only a full account of the small Bing system but also the histories of many other miniature trains such as those by Karl Bub, Distler and Jep Mignon.

November 1993 had seen the launch of *Model Railway Enthusiast* which was a model railway magazine with some articles for collectors. In February 1998 content for collectors was raised to 50% of the magazine and in November 1999 to 100% when the magazine was renamed *Model Railway Collector.*

1998 saw the release of my second book *'Tri-ang Hornby'* [ISBN 1-872727-58-1], again by New Cavendish Books, and also the first edition of *'Ramsay's British Model Trains Catalogue'* [ISBN 0952835231], published by Swapmeet Publications. In 1999, two useful books on kits were published. The first of these was Steven Knight's excellent study of Kitmaster kits in *'Let's Stick Together'* [ISBN 1871608902], published by Irwell Press and the second was Arthur Ward's **'Airfix Plastic Kits'** [ISBN 0004723279] published by Harper Collins. It was also in 1999 that **'Wenman Joseph Bassett-Lowke'** [ISBN 1900622017] was published by Rail Romances who at the same time released a video recording based on films taken by W.J.Bassett-Lowke, including footage inside the factory. The book had been written by his niece Janet Bassett-Lowke.

In 2000, the first of a series of planned volumes called **'A History of Locomotive Kits'** [ISBN 0953772004] by Robert Forsythe was published by Amlor Publishing. This covers kits by K's, Nu-Cast, Wills and South Eastern Finecast. The second edition of Ramsay's Catalogue also appeared that year under new editorship.

Another 2nd edition appeared in 2001 and this was *'Tri-ang Railways'* which had had a further 32 pages of information added.

2002 was a bumper year for new books. Harper Collins published Ian Harrison's **'Hornby - The Official Illustrated History'** [ISBN 000715173X] and **'Frank Hornby - News & Pictures'** was written and published by Jim Gamble [ISBN 095420610X]. The 3rd edition of *Ramsay's Catalogue* was released - now with comprehensive listing of locos and rolling stock covering some 25 brands produced for sale in Britain over the last 80 years.

The final two books for 2002 were principally aimed at the classic tinplate collector. Firstly there was the excellent **'Christie's Toy Railways'** by Hugo Marsh which covers history and development from the earliest times. This was published by Pavilion Books [ISBN 1862055254]. The second is the magnificent English edition of Paul Klein Schiphorst's **'The Golden Years of Tin Toy Trains'** published by New Cavendish Books [ISBN 187272759X]. This contains possibly the finest collection of images of early tinplate trains ever to be assembled.

We jump now to 2004 and the release of the long awaited book on G & R Wrenn. Called **'The Story of Wrenn - From Binns Road to Basildon'** it was written by Maurice Gunter and published by Irwell Press [ISBN 1903266424]. Finally, this year will also see the publication of my third volume in the Story of Rovex and titled **'Hornby Railways'**. This is being published by New Cavendish Books and covers the years 1972-1996 [ISBN 1904562000].

Thus, from a dearth of books in 1970, today we have quite a library to choose from and there is every indication that the choice will continue to grow.

Ace Trains

HISTORY

Ace Trains originated from an arrangement to produce a limited run of electric Hornby replica 4-4-4 tank locomotives in Southern livery - the colour scheme most in demand with collectors. The parties to this arrangement were Ron Budd (the importer of Darstead Marklin style coaches) and Andries Grabowsky who acquired the Darstead business in the early 1990s.

This arrangement did not come to fruition and Allen Levy agreed to take on and expand the 4-4-4 project which was designated E/1. A company named Alchem Trains Ltd was formed in 1995 which commenced trading under the name ACE Trains.

The production and assembly of the E/1, of which both AC and DC versions were made, was initially concentrated in Taiwan and later at the Grabowsky family factory in Madras, India. The E/2, a 4-4-2 derivative of the E/1, was developed in DC only with an isolating switch allowing it to stand on the track without picking up power. The locomotives were designed to run on all types of 3-rail tinplate standard track including that by Hornby, Marklin, Bing, JEP and MDF and also have an interchangeable rear coupling.

The C/1 coach range, covering more railway systems than any former manufacturer, came on the market in 1999. The tin printing for this range was carried out by Cyril Luff in Wales who produced some of the last Hornby 0 gauge and Hornby Dublo tin printed sheets. A five-car Merseyside Express set became the last lithographed toy train product of the twentieth century. The Company introduced the first of a range of EMU units early in 2000.

Ace Trains identified a gap in the market and have been successfully filling it. They have established a market not only in the UK but around the world and have agents in a number of countries.

On May 11th, 2004, Alchem Trains Ltd changed its name to The Ace Electric Train Co. Ltd.

Further Reading

The product range is too new to have had a book written about it but there have been articles in the *HRCA Journal* from February 1996 onwards. There have also been articles in *Classic Toy Trains* (USA), *British Railway Modelling* and *Trains RM* (Japan).

LOCOMOTIVES

Motors - About 10 locos were supplied with 12V DC motors then the Company standardised their DC motor at 24V. As all Ace Trains locomotives run on 6 - 20V and draw 0.7amp the distinction became academic.

Couplings - All couplings (on locos and coaches) are replaceable except the front hook on the LMS and Metropolitan EMUs and the front buffer couplings on the E/1 and E/2 locos. The southern EMU units have replaceable couplings throughout but the coaches are without buffers as per the originals.

Cat.No.	Company, Number, Colour, Date	£	£

L1. 4-4-4 Tank Engine

This model was based on the No.2 Tank Engine in the pre-war Hornby Series, which went out of production in 1929. The original models were available only with a clockwork mechanism but the E/1 locomotives by Ace Trains have 20v electric mechanisms with remote control in AC/DC. IS = in DC only with isolating switch.

ESB/1	**SR** E492 black gloss or matt * IS - *96*	230	290
ESG/1	**SR** B604 green gloss or matt * IS - *96*	240	300
ELM/1	**LMS** 4-4-4 maroon gloss or matt IS - *96*	250	320
EMB/1	**LMS** 4-4-4 black gloss or matt - *96*	250	320
ELG/1	**LNER** 4-4-4 green gloss or matt - *96*	240	300
ELB/1	**LNER** 4-4-4 black matt - *96*	250	320
EGW/1	**GWR** 7202 green gloss or matt - *96*	250	320
ECR/1	**CR** 4-4-4 blue gloss or matt IS - *96*	290	370
EMR/1	**Metropolitan** 108 maroon gloss or matt - *96*	250	325
EET/1	**ETAT** 2-2-2 black matt - *96*	250	325
EPO/1	**PO** 2-2-2 grey matt - *96*	250	325
EPL/1	**PLM** red matt - *96*	290	370
END/1	**Nord** brown matt - *96*	250	294
END/2	**Nord** green matt - *96*	250	325
EES/1	**EST** black matt - *96*	250	325
EES/2	**EST** brown matt - *96*	250	325
ENZ/1	**NZR** black matt - *96*	270	350

* 44 of the E/1 series in Southern livery were given factory produced names at the request of customers (1996/97).

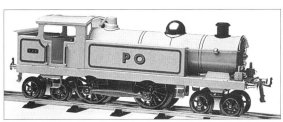

4-4-4T in French P.O. livery [L1] (Ace Trains)

L2. 4-4-2 Tank Engine

The E/2 series of locomotives were DC only and were fitted with a neutral switch allowing them to stand stationary on live track. They seem to have been based on a LNWR Whale 4-4-2T.

E/2LB	**LB&SCR** 22 brown gloss - *98*	250	320
E/2S	**Southern** 2001 green gloss - *98*	250	320
E/2LN	**L&NWR** 40 black gloss - *98*	260	350
E/2LM	**LMS** 6822 maroon gloss - *98*	200	270
E/2BR	**BR** 32085 black gloss - *98*	250	320
E/2NZR	**NZR** green gloss Sp Edn (Railmaster Exports NZ) - *98*	260	350

4-4-2T LMS Crimson Lake livery [L2] (Ace Trains)

L3. 3-Car EMUs

All units comprise a powered motor coach (DC only) with 3rd class accommodation, a first class coach and a dummy 3rd class motor coach. All are tin printed and have punched out windows. Extra trailer cars for these sets are available at £55 each.

C1E/LM	Broad Street - Richmond maroon LMS 3-car unit - *99*	250	295

C1E/Met	Baker Street - Harrow brown Metropolitan 4-car unit - *99*	250	295
C1E/S	**1528/1664/1783** green Southern 3-car unit V and L route boards carried* - *00*	260	315
C/1G	3-car German Triebwagon set - *03?*	450	495

* White and grey roof versions.

L4. A4 4-6-2

Purchasers choose their own names and numbers. Original batch was 3-rail but a 2-rail batch and a live steam model are planned for 2005. The loco body is pressure diecast and the tender is made from brass (corridor or non-corridor). The loco is fitted with matching twin 24v AC/DC motors driving all axles and with an isolating switch. Working headlights and firebox glow. Single and double chimney versions available and the second batch have smaller lamps.

	With Valances		
E/4	**LNER** Apple green - *03*	600	685
E/4	**LNER** silver grey - *03*	600	685
E/4	**LNER** pre-war Garter blue - *03*	600	685
	Without Valances		
E/4	**LNER** black restricted names - *03*	600	685
E/4	**LNER** post-war Garter blue - *03*	600	685
E/4	**BRb** 60007 'Sir Nigel Gresley' Express blue Sp Edn (A4 Society) - *03*	600	685
E/4	**BRb** Brunswick green - *03*	600	685
E/4	**BRc** Brunswick green, double chimney - *03*	600	685

A large range of names is available including: 'Sir Nigel Gresley', 'Mallard', 'Kestrel', 'Golden Plover', 'Golden Shuttle', 'Peregrine', 'Kingfisher', 'Osprey', 'Commonwealth of Australia', 'Capercaillie', 'Merlin', 'Sir Ralph Wedgwood', 'Empire of India', 'Seagull', 'Golden Eagle', 'Woodcock', 'Golden Fleece', 'Union of South Africa', 'Dominion of Canada', 'Dwight D Eisenhower', 'Dominion of New Zealand', 'Bittern', 'Silver Link' and 'Terence Cuneo'. The last of these is fictitious but chosen by Allen Levy with only 10 being made.

L5. Q Class 0-6-0 Tender Engine

Each will also be available as a train pack with three carriages.

E/5	**LNWR** black - *?*	NPG	NPG
E/5	**LBSCR** brown - *?*	NPG	NPG
E/5	**CR** blue - *?*	NPG	NPG
E/5	**LMS** - *?*	NPG	NPG
E/5	**LNER** - *?*	NPG	NPG
E/5	**GWR** green - *?*	NPG	NPG
E/5	**Southern** - *?*	NPG	NPG
E/5	**BR** black - *?*	NPG	NPG

L6. 2-6-2 Tank Engine

E/3T	**BR** - *postponed*	NPG	NPG
E/3T	**SECR** - *postponed*	NPG	NPG
E/3T	**CR** - *postponed*	NPG	NPG
E/3T	**Southern Irish** - *postponed*	NPG	NPG

COACHES

Cat.No.	Company, Number, Colour, Date	£	£

C1. 35cm Non-Corridor Stock

Tin printed. Some of the French coaches have clerestory roofs.

C/1	**LMS** maroon - *99*	50	55
C/1CL	**LMS** maroon ex-MR clerestory set of 3 - *00*	170	200
C/1	**LNER** 21397 light teak all 1st - *99*	50	55
C/1	**LNER** 1948 light teak all 3rd - *99*	50	55
C/1	**LNER** 21508 light teak brake 3rd - *99*	50	55
?	**LNER** 1948 + 21397 + 21508 light teak set of 3 - *00*	150	165
C/1CL	**LNER** ex-GER teak clerestory set of 3 - *00*	150	165
C/1	**GWR** dark brown+cream - *99*	55	65
C/1CL	**GWR** dark brown+cream clerestory set of 3 - *00*	170	200
C/1	**Southern** green brake 3rd - *99*	55	65
C/1	**Southern** green all 1st - *99*	55	65
C/1	**Southern** green all 3rd - *99*	55	65
C/1	**Metropolitan** brown - *99*	55	55

C/1	**LBSCR** brown+white - *99*	50	55
C/1	**LBSCR** brown+white brake end - *99*	55	65
?	**LBSCR** brown+white set of 3 - *00*	150	165
C/1	**Caledonian** plum+white - *99*	50	55
?	**Caledonian** plum+white set of 3 - *00*	150	165
C/1	**BR** M43277 maroon composite - *99*	50	55
C/1	**BR** M43279 maroon all 3rd - *99*	50	55
C/1	**BR** M43278 maroon brake 3rd - *99*	50	55
?	**BR** M43277 + M43279 + M43278 maroon set of 3 - *00*	150	165
?	**HRCA** 30th Anniversary set of 3 - *01*	160	180
C/1	**LNWR** brown+white - *99*	55	65
C/1	**NZR** maroon Sp Edn (Railmaster Exports NZ) - *99*	55	65
C/1F	**Etat** green sets of 3 - *99*	120	175
C/1F	**Est** aubargine+black sets of 3 - *99*	120	175
C/1F	**Est** green/brown+black sets of 3 - *99*	120	175
C/1F	**Est** brown+black sets of 3 - *99*	120	175
C/1F	**PO** green sets of 3 - *99*	120	175
C/1F	**Nord** green sets of 3 - *99*	120	175
C/1F	**SNCF** green 1st and 2nd class coaches available sets of 3 - *99*	110	175
C/1 Bge	khaki French outline baggage car - *99*	45	55

The actual price of the coaches is £55 each or £165 for three consisting of a 1st, 3rd and brake 3rd. A special HRCA 30th Anniversary set was originally priced £50 per coach or £150 the set of three.

C2a. Merseyside Express Sets

These coaches have domed roofs and litho silver windows. They have Merseyside Express name boards in the printing design except where indicated.

C/2	**LMS** maroon composite 4195 - *99*	50	60
C/2	**LMS** maroon all 3rd 4195 - *99*	50	60
C/2	**LMS** maroon restaurant car 4799 - *99*	50	60
C/2	**LMS** maroon all 1st 4183 - *99*	50	60
C/2	**LMS** maroon brake 3rd 26133 - *99*	50	60
C/2	**LMS** maroon composite, no name boards 4195 - *99*	50	60
C/2	**LMS** maroon all 3rd, no name boards 4195 - *9*	50	60
C/2	**LMS** maroon brake 3rd, no name boards 26133 - *99*	50	60
C/2	**LMS** maroon set of 3 to go with the Bassett-Lowke Mogul, Ltd Edn? - *00*	130	175
C/2	**LMS** Merseyside Express set of 5 - *00*	170	260

Merseyside Express set [C2a]

C2b. Gresley Excursion Stock

C/2	**LNER** twin coach articulated set green + white - *postponed*	NPG	NPG
C/2	**LNER** set of four coaches green + white - *postponed*	NPG	NPG

C3. LMS Stanier Main Line Coach Kits

These have lower roofs and cut-out windows. They come with a choice of the following destination boards: 'The Royal Scot', The Merseyside Express', 'The Mancunian' and 'The Yorkshireman'.

?	**LMS** maroon - *02*	NPG	35

C4a. LNER Bow Ended Stock
(clear windows)

The coaches are supplied with slots in the roof and coach roof boards to fit them carrying the name 'Flying Scotsman'. Available either with or without cut-out windows. The first batch made of Set A had no internal partitions (nip) but later ones did or you could have them retrospectively fitted. Rear working light on the brake end.

C/4/T	**LNER** 6461 teak all 1st brake nip - *03*	65	NA
C/4/T	**LNER** 61639 teak all 3rd nip - *03*	65	NA
C/4/T	**LNER** 1516 teak brake 3rd nip - *03*	65	NA
set A	Above three coaches nip - *03*	NPG	200
C/4/T	**LNER** 6461 teak all 1st brake - *03*	70	NA
C/4/T	**LNER** 61639 teak all 3rd - *03*	70	NA
C/4/T	**LNER** 1516 teak brake 3rd - *03*	70	NA
set A	Above three coaches - *03*	NPG	225
C/4/T	**LNER** 62659 teak brake 3rd - *03*	70	NA
C/4/T	**LNER** 1865 teak all 3rd open - *03*	70	NA
C/4/T	**LNER** 689 teak all 1st open - *03*	70	NA
set B	Above three coaches - *03*	NPG	225
C/4/T	**LNER** 63291 teak corridor comp - *03*	70	80
C/4/T	**LNER** 650 teak 3rd buffet car - *03*	70	80

C4b. LNER Bow Ended Stock
(print windows)

The coaches are supplied with slots in the roof and coach roof boards to fit them carrying the name 'Flying Scotsman'. A run of only 50 of each. Rear working light on the brake end.

C/4/B	**LNER** 6461 teak all 1st brake - *03*	70	80
C/4/B	**LNER** 61639 teak all 3rd - *03*	70	80
C/4/B	**LNER** 1516 teak brake 3rd - *03*	70	80
C/4/B	**LNER** 1516 teak brake 3rd - *03*	70	80
C/4/B	**LNER** 650 teak 3rd buffet car - *03*	70	80

C5. BR Mk1 Coaches

All sets include internal compartments where appropriate, Rear working light on the brake end. All with punched out windows.

C/5	**BR** 13030 red+cream full 1st - *03*	65	NA
C/5	**BR** 5029 red+cream full 3rd - *03*	65	NA
C/5	**BR** 35260 red+cream brake 3rd - *03*	65	NA
C/5	above set A of 3 - *03*	NPG	215
C/5	**BR** 302 red+cream restaurant car - *03*	65	75
C/5	**BR** 80675 red+cream full brake - *03*	65	75

C6. LNER Articulated Gresley Stock

C/6	**LNER** 1204 + 1205 teak sleeping cars London (King's Cross) - Edinburgh - *04?*	NPG	140

C7. Coronation Articulated Coaches

C/7	blue+white [C] + [B] - *04*	NPG	NPG
C/7	blue+white [A] + [G] - *04*	NPG	NPG
C/7	blue+white [D] + [H] - *04*	NPG	NPG

ACE/WRIGHT SERIES

This set new standards in a small series of ready-to-run special vehicles. The models are made of lithographed heavily varnished card applied to Ace C/1 and C/2 coaches.

CA/W. Various Stock

-	**GWR** full brake with low roof - *03?*	55	60
-	**GWR** full brake with clerestory roof - *03?*	65	70
-	**LMS** full brake Stanier c1930 - *03?*	55	60
-	**SR** parcel van c1930 with ribbed roof - *03?*	55	60
-	**LMS** ex-MR mail van clerestory - *03?*	55	60
-	**GWR** Siphon with pre-war lettering - *03?*	55	60

-	**LNER** 5219 full brake teak The Flying Scotsman - *04?*	NPG	60

WAGONS

Cat.No.	Branding, Colour, Date	£	£

W1a. Petrol/Spirit Tank Wagon

These are sold in sets of three and they will have interchangeable couplings. The bodies are lithographed in four colours and are fitted to a detailed chassis with brake gear . The chassis has dropout side frames for lubricating axle boxes.

G/1	**Ace Trains Oil** - *04*	35	NA
set 1	set of 3 (Ace + Esso yellow + Mobiloil) - *04*	NA	89
G/1	**Esso** grey - *04*	35	NA
G/1	**Wakefield Castrol** green - *04*	35	NA
G/1	**Regent** silver - *04*	35	NA
set 2	set of above 3 - *04*	NA	99
G/1	**Pratt's Spirit** brown - *04*	35	NA
G/1	**Pratt's Spirit** green - *04*	35	NA
G/1	**Pratt's High Test Sealed** orange - *04*	35	NA
set 3	set of above 3 - *04*	NA	99
G/1	**Anglo American Oil Co.** brown - *04*	35	NA
G/1	**Colas** red - *04*	35	NA
G/1	**BP Motor Spirit** yellow - *04*	35	NA
set 4	set of above 3 - *04*	NA	99
G/1	**Royal Daylight** grey - *04*	35	NA
G/1	**Redline-Gilco** dark blue - *04*	35	NA
G/1	**Shell Motor Spirit** red - *04*	35	NA
set 5	set of above 3 - *04*	NA	99
G/1	**National Benzole Mixture** ochre - *04*	35	NA
G/1	**Pool** grey - *04*	35	NA
G/1	**Colas** blue - *04*	35	NA
set 6	set of above 3 - *04*	NA	99
G/1	**BP British Petrol** green - *04*	35	NA
G/1	**BP Motor Spirit** grey - *04*	35	NA
G/1	**Power Ethyl** green - *04*	35	NA
set 7	set of above 3 - *04*	NA	99
G/1	**Esso** yellow - *04*	35	NA
G/1	**Mobiloil** grey - *04*	35	NA
G/1	**Pool Fuel Oil** black - *04*	35	NA
set 8	set of above 3 - *04*	NA	99

W1b. Milk Tank Wagon

These are also sold in sets of three and are the same as the petrol tanks but without cross strapping and riveting. They also have a smaller filler cap with a valve on either side.

G/1M	**United Dairies** white - *04?*	35	NA
set A	set of 3	NA	99
G/1M	**Express Dairy** white - *04?*	35	NA
set B	set of 3	NA	99
G/1M	**Nestles Milk** white - *04?*	35	NA
set C	set of 3	NA	99

ACCESSORIES

The Ace Constructor Series was introduced in April 2002 and the first item is an all-over glazed roof which is 1' high and 2' long and coded AC/1 (£107). A pair of platforms and ramps with four working ornamental lamp standards are also available as AC/1a (£43). The glazed roof set was later sold with an AC/1a accessory pack for £150.

A terminus building is also planned and a prototype model has been produced.

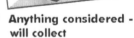

Airfix GMR

HISTORY

Airfix are best remembered for their comprehensive range of plastic construction kits but in 1971, on the collapse of the Lines Group, they had bought Meccano Ltd who, incidentally, had been stripped of all connection with the model railway industry seven years earlier. In 1975 Airfix announced their own intention of entering the ready-to-run model railway market. They had recognised a need for ready-to-run models of a finer standard than were available at the time and planned to fill the gap in the market. Unfortunately for them, the American backed Palitoy toy company, had come to the same conclusion and made similar plans.

Airfix had little experience or expertise in model railway production and so had to buy in this from professional designers or overseas companies including Bachmann of America. This resulted in their first venture being a joint project with Bachmann; a Wild West Adventure train set which made use of existing H0 Bachmann products. The Dr. X adventure set followed but this time used 00 models designed specifically for the British market.

Milestones
1971 Airfix buy Meccano Ltd.
1975 Airfix announce the launch of a ready-to-run railway system.
1976 First samples seen at toy fairs.
1976 Class 31 and Doctor X set released for Christmas.
1977 Airfix draw up their production plan.
1979 GMR name adopted and wagon production starts in the UK
1980 Airfix empire crumbles.
1981 Production ceases and Palitoy acquires the model railway tools.

In the early 1970s, the Hong Kong Trade Development Commission were looking for business for local factories and this resulted in the Hong Kong company, Sanda Kan, producing models for Airfix.

Their first samples were displayed at the Harrogate and Brighton Toy Fairs in 1976 where they received a cool reception due to their poor quality. They had been cobbled together in a hurry and bore little resemblance to what was to follow.

Mechanically the locomotives were not exceptional but the mouldings were good and brought much praise. The first locomotive release was the Class 31 in the 'Doctor X' set, which arrived in time for Christmas 1976.

In 1977, Airfix drew up an overall programme that was to give a balanced range. There were to be 5 groups: Midland, Western, Southern, Eastern and BR. Each group was going to have an express passenger, mixed traffic, goods, large tank and small tank engines. In addition, the coaches for each group were to be gangwayed (express mainline) and suburban.

The range of locomotives, coaches and wagons expanded in 1978. Not all the models were made by Sanda kan, another Hong Kong company, Cheong Tak, made the 4F, Royal Scot, Stanier and suburban coaches and were to have made a Compound followed by a Crab, Black 5 or 8F. Other planned models were the N2, Dean Goods, Schools and B1 but the Company's fortunes were now affecting future plans.

It was becoming more apparent that communication with Hong Kong and control of the finished product was not very good whereas UK production, although more expensive, would deliver as good a product, on time, to Airfix's specifications, without masses of communication and without so many hidden costs. The Company, therefore, produced some wagons themselves in the UK and the success of these proved this point and would have ultimately lead to the phasing out of overseas production.

This change happened in 1979 and, at the same time, the name of the product was altered to GMR which stood for Great Model Railways to better distinguish the product line from the Airfix kits. The new branding was launched at the Toy Fair at Earls Court and the selling line was 'Precision made by Airfix'.

The GMR assembly line was to be at Charlton (South East London) and the Dean Goods its first product. As this model was about to go into production in mid 1980, the Airfix empire was crumbling. Other parts of the Company were being closed down, moved or sold off. £7M was spent in an attempt to save Meccano and when this failed Airfix went into receivership.

Airfix/GMR exhibited for the last time at the 1981 Toy Fairs but shortly after this they ceased production. The Airfix model railway interests were acquired by its rival - Palitoy - the makers of Mainline Railways. Many models were made by Palitoy from Airfix tooling and later by Dapol and today Hornby - each adding their improvements.

Further Reading

A detailed listing of the Airfix and Mainline model railway systems was produced by the late Charles Manship in the 1980s but it is no longer available. However, there has been a series of articles by Graham Smith-Thompson, in *Model Railway Enthusiast* magazine, profiling the Airfix and Mainline ranges and other systems that later used the tools. There were six parts devoted specifically to Airfix published in the July-December issues in 1998. More recently a detailed history of the Airfix railway range by Pat Hammond was published in *British Railway Modelling*.

Collectors Clubs

The Airfix Collectors Club caters for collectors of any Airfix product including the model railway range and publishes a newsletter called *Constant Scale*. Further information about this organisation may be obtained from Jeremy Brook at 29 Elley Green, Neston, Nr. Corsham, Wiltshire SN13 9TX or by visiting them at their Website which is at http//www.djairfix.freeserve.co.uk

Dates - The dates used in the following tables are based on catalogues and price lists and factory records and should not be taken as evidence of availability.

Samples on the Market - Far East manufacturers sent samples to their customers for approval before proceeding with full production. These samples often ended up in collections and today they command a good price. Samples of models that did not reach the production stage are of greater interest to collectors.

LOCOMOTIVES

Listing - The locomotives are arranged in the order of size from smallest to largest, starting with tank engines and finishing with diesels.

Cat.No.	Number, Company, Colour, Dates	£	£
L1.	**Class 14XX 0-4-2T**		
54152	**1466** GWR green - *78-81*	20	30
54153	**1466** BRb lined green - *78-81*	22	32

The tools for this model passed to Palitoy, then Dapol, and finally Hornby who now make their own versions of the model.

Class 14XX tank [L1]

L2. Class N2 Tank 0-6-2T (see Mainline)

54154	**9522** LNER green - *	NA	NA
54155	**69531** BRb black - *	NA	NA

* Arrived too late and were sold by Palitoy in Mainline packaging. The tools for this model passed to Palitoy, then Dapol, and finally Hornby who now make their own versions of the model.

L3. Class 61XX Prairie Tank 2-6-2T

54150	**6110** Great Western green - *77-81*	18	30
54151	**6167** BRb lined black - *77-81*	20	32

The tools for this model passed to Palitoy, then Dapol, and finally Hornby who now make their own versions of the model.

L4. American 4-4-05

54170-5	**'Jupiter'** Central Pacific red + silver (CPRR) - *77-80*	20	30
54171-8	**119** Union Pacific RR red + black - *77-80*	20	30

L5. Class 2301 'Dean Goods' 0-6-0
(see Mainline)

54156	**2516** GWR green - *	NA	NA
54157	**2538** BRb black - *	NA	NA

* Arrived too late and were sold by Palitoy in Mainline packaging. The tools for this model passed to Palitoy, then Dapol, and finally Hornby who now make their own versions of the model.

L6. Class 4F 0-6-0

Some Airfix 4Fs had piston tail rod covers on the buffer beam.

54122	**4454** LMS black - *78-81*	25	30
54123	**44454** BRb (small) black - *78-80*	25	35
54122-6	**44423** BRb (small) black - *?*	NPG	NPG
54123	**44454** BRb (large) black - *80-81*	30	40

The tools for this model passed to Palitoy, then Dapol, and finally Hornby who now make their own versions of the model.

LMS Class 4F goods loco [L6]

LMS Royal Scotts Fusilier [L7]

L7. Class 6P/7P 'Rebuilt Royal Scot' 4-6-0

54120	**6103** 'Royal Scots Fusilier' LMS black - *78-81*	25	40
54121	**46100** 'Royal Scot' green BRb smoke deflectors, badly positioned decals on tender - *78-81*	25	40

L8. Class 4073 'Castle' 4-6-0

54124	**4073** 'Caerphilly Castle' Great ( ) Western green - *79-81*	35	50
54125	**4079** 'Pendennis Castle' BRb green incorrectly numbered in cat - *79-81*	35	50

'Powderham Castle' and 'Pembroke Castle' were Airfix models renamed and renumbered by Dapol but sold in original Airfix boxes. These will be found listed under Dapol.

L9. Class 31/4 Diesel A1A-A1A

54100-6	**31401** BRe blue, front code IP02 - *77-81*	15	30
54109-9	**D5531** green BRc front code C - *77-81*	15	30

Lost and Gone

With Airfix in the hands of the receivers early in 1981, they left plans for new locomotives half finished. Some of these were in a fairly advanced stage of development while others were just a glint in the eye of the designer. They included the following with planned release dates, where known:

SR Schools Class - 1982 *
LNER B1 Class 'Mayflower' 1982
LMS Compound - 1982 *
LT Underground train *
GWR 43XX Class Mogul *
SR Lord Nelson Class - 1982
WD 2-8-0 - 1983
SR U Class Mogul - 1983
LNER J69 tank - 1984
LMS Crab Mogul - 1984
SR ex-LSWR Class 02 Adams tank
LMS Black 5
LMS 8F

* pre-production mock-up exists.

The underground train was to have been sold as a 4-car set complete with a platform and accessories. It was to have been powered by a specially adapted Mabuchi motor and to this end a testing model was built.

COACHES

The Company had an unfortunate policy of withholding new models until existing stocks had diminished sufficiently. One example of this was the 2nd class open Mk2D model which was not made until stocks of the 1st class open had largely sold! Consequently it was available very late and sold out quickly.

The Airfix coaches, with very minor exceptions, were excellent scale models, moulded in plastic, assembled, spray painted and tampo printed with accurate detail. They helped to set a new standard in the ready-to-run market. They were the correct length, had flush fitting windows and proper interior detail. Errors did occur and these included the choice of bogies for the two Siphons and the colour of the LMS coaches which was much too dark. The latter was put down to the matt varnish used to finish them. A new batch, in the correct shade, was ordered but these were retained in the store until all the old stock had been cleared. By then, the Company was in the liquidators hands and Palitoy inherited the new stock which they sold in the Mainline range.

With the take-over of Airfix railway assets by Palitoy in 1981, many of the Airfix coaches were absorbed into the Mainline range, mostly as new production runs. The tools were then sold on to Dapol in the mid '80s and to Hornby in the mid '90s both of whom produced their own models from them.

At the time of the demise of Airfix there were new coach models in the pipeline in various stages of development but not yet advertised. These included:
SR Bullied Corridor Stock (3 types) - 1981
LNER Gresley Corridor Stock (3 types) - 1982
SR Birdcage Stock (2 types) - 1983
LMS Sleeper - 1983
LNER Gresley Non-Corridor Stock (2 types) - 1984

Quotes for the Bullied coaches were obtained in the UK in August 1997 and they were to have been produced in two liveries. A pre-production sample was made up from a Phoenix kit and, finished in BR(SR) green, was numbered S5806S.

Listing - Earliest styles of coaches are listed first and finishing with more modern British Railways designs.

Cat.No.	Company, Number, Colour, Dates	£	£

C1. American Passenger Cars (made by Bachmann)

These were in the 54051 Wild West set and were made by Bachmann who marketed their version of the set in America.

| (54051) | **CPRR** 3 red saloon car with trapdoor in roof - *76-78* | 8 | 14 |
| (54051) | **CPRR** 5 red exploding baggage car - *76-78* | 10 | 17 |

C2. GWR Suburban B Stock

54250	**GWR** 6869 dark brown+cream - *77-81*	8	14
54250	**GWR** 6895 dark brown+cream - *?*	8	14
54250	**GWR** 6896 dark brown+cream - *?*	8	14
54250	**GWR** 4895 dark brown+cream - *78-80*	8	14
54257	**BR** W6894W maroon - *80*	10	20

C3. GWR Auto Trailer

| 54255 | **GWR** 187 dark brown+cream - *78-81* | 8 | 14 |
| 54256 | **BR** W187W maroon Didcot sign - *78-81* | 8 | 14 |

C4. GWR Centenary Stock

54207	**GWR** 6659 dk brown+cream comp* - *80-81*	8	14
54209	**GWR** 4575 dk brn+cream brake 3rd* - *80-81*	8	14
54208	**BR** W6659W maroon composite** - *80-81*	10	17
54208	**BR** W6661W maroon composite** - *?*	10	17
54210	**BR** W4576W maroon brake 3rd** - *80-81*	10	17

* With 'Cornish Riviera Limited' coach boards (the pre-production sample models had 'Plymouth and Paddington Ocean Express'). ** With 'Paddington, Newport, Cardiff and Swansea' coach boards

C5. LMS Stanier Corridor Stock

These are LMS Period 3 coaches developed during Stanier's time as CME.

54202	**LMS** 3935 maroon comp 60' - *78-81*	8	14
54202	**LMS** 3935 maroon comp 60' - *	NA	NA
54204	**LMS** 5542 maroon brake 3rd 57' - *78-81*	8	14
54204	**LMS** 5542 maroon brake 3rd 57' - *	NA	NA
54258	**LMS** 9072 maroon vestibule 3rd 57'** - *not made*	NA	NA
54203	**BR** M3935M red+cream comp 60' - *78-81*	8	14
54205	**BR** M5542M red+cream brake 3rd 57' - *78-81*	8	14
54259	**BR** M9103M red+cream vestibule 2nd 57' * - *not made*	NA	NA

* These resulted from a colour correction ordered by Airfix but were kept in store until old stocks were used up. They were inherited by Palitoy who boxed and sold them. ** These were in the design stage at Airfix (scheduled for 1982) when they went into receivership and the models were later finished and sold by Replica Railways.

Proposed LMS vestibule 3rd [C5]

C6. LMS 57' Non-Corridor Stock

54251	**LMS** 19195 maroon comp - *79-81*	8	14
54253	**LMS** 15185 maroon brake 3rd - *79-81*	8	14
54253	**LMS** 25250 maroon brake 3rd - *?*	10	17
54254	**LMS** 25250 maroon brake 3rd - *?*	10	17
54252	**BR** M19195M maroon comp - *79-81*	10	18
54254	**BR** M25250M maroon brake 3rd - *79-81*	10	17

BR Stanier non-corridor brake end [C6]

C7. LMS 68' Dining Car (12 wheels)

These were in the design stage when Airfix went into receivership and Mainline took up the project. They were to have been released by Airfix in 1982. After Palitoy, the project next fell into the hands of Dapol who actually produced the first batch of models. Their tools, thought to have been damaged in a factory fire, were later sold to Hornby who modified them and now make the model. The model was based on an LMS Period 2 coach.

| 54260 | **LMS** - maroon - *not made* | NA | NA |
| 54261 | **BR** M236M red+cream - *not made* | NA | NA |

C8. Mk2D Stock

	Inter-City blue + grey		
54201	**BR** E3170 1st Open - *77-81*	8	14
54200	**BR** E9479 brake 2nd Open - *77-81*	8	14
54206	**BR** E5690 2nd Open - *80*	10	20

WAGONS

The same standards of accuracy that had been applied to locomotives and coaches were also applied to the wagons Airfix produced. However, for the sake of economy there was standardisation on chassis, wheels etc. 12 of the body types used no more than 4 chassis for a total of 48 models. Only spoked and solid wheels were used and, despite publicity photographs showing metal tyred and white rimmed wheels, neither type was used on production models.

Attention, however, was given to getting liveries reasonably accurate although those on some of the vans were non-authentic. These are interesting as some were re-liveried models, done in batches of 7,000 to use up surplus stocks of BR ventilated vans. Not all the liveries were fictitious. The 'English Eggs' one was seen on the LMS and the 'Lyons Tea' livery appeared on some railway containers.

Additionally, some wagons were deliberately done in very small quantities of incorrect colours to generate an interest in collecting them. It had been intended to do a batch (approximately 7,000) of each but the factory manager misunderstood and did only about 20 of each. These deliberate 'errors' are very rare and therefore command a high price.

Listing - The wagons are arranged in the order of: flats, open wagons, hoppers, tankers, vans, brake vans and bogie stock.

Cat.No.	Company, Number, Colour, Dates	£	£

W1. Lowmac MS

54330	**BR** B904662 red-brown + crate - *77-81*	4	8
54333	**BR** B904662 red-brown Conflat ISO + **Sea Land** container - *78-79*	8	14
54334	**BR** B904662 red-brown + NCL trailer - *78-79*	6	12
(54052)	**BR** B904662 red+ NCL trailer with opening doors from 54052 Dr. X pack brown - *77*	8	NA

W2. Conflat with Container

54331	**GW** 39005 dark grey + **GW** brown container BK -1829 - *78-81*	5	10
54332	**BR** B735833, B735700 red brown + **BR** furniture container - *78-81*	6	12
54337	**NE** 39324 grey + **J Miles** container* - *80-81*	6	12

* This was a non-authentic livery although the Leeds-based compa ny existed and had asked for a promotional model for their customers. It is based on the livery of the Company's vans.

GWR container wagon [W2]

W3. 5-Plank Open Wagon

Samples based on both LMS and GWR designs were made and the production model was a compromise between the two.

54372	**GW** 109458 dark grey - *78-81*	5	10
54373	**LMS** 404104 grey - *78-81*	4	8
54374	**Devizes Sand** 1 grey - *78-79*	5	10
54375	**Spencer** 24 red - *78-81*	4	8
54376	**Arnold** 156 brown - *78-81*	4	8
54377	**Harts Hill** 2 brown - *78-79*	5	10

54364	**BR** M407562 grey - *79-81*	5	10
54365	**BR** M411459 red brown - *79-81*	5	10
54388	**Alloa** 1124 yellow - *80-81*	4	8
54389	**ICI** L3110 grey - *80-81*	5	10

W4. 7-Plank Open Wagon
This was a compromise design to allow a range of liveries.

54378	**GWR** 29017 dark grey - *78-81*	5	10
54379	**LMS** 40781 grey - *79-81*	4	8
54380	**Gloucester Gas Light Company** 51 black - *78-79*	5	10
54381	**Broadoak** 460 brown - *78-79*	4	8
54381	**Broadoak** 460 grey Ltd Edn 20 - *78-79*	35	45
54382	**Highley Mining** 425 brown - *78-79*	4	8
54382	**Highley Mining** 425 grey Ltd Edn 20 - *78-79*	35	45
54383	**Hales Fuels** 241 grey - *78-81*	4	8
54383	**Hales Fuels** 241 brown Ltd Edn 20 - *78-81*	35	45
54366	**BR** P136284 grey - *80-81*	5	10
54390	**Carlton** 4372 black - *80-81*	5	10
54391	**Stalybridge** 15 brown - *80-81*	5	10
54391	**Stalybridge** 15 grey Ltd Edn 20 - *80*	35	45

7-plank wagon Broadoak [W4]

W5. NE 20T 9-Plank Mineral Wagon

54369	**NE** 31273 grey - *81*	5	10
54359	**BR** E30995, E10995 grey - *81*	5	10

W6. GWR 20T Steel Mineral Wagon

54370	**GWR** 83516 dark grey - *79-81*	5	10
54371	**BR** P339371K grey - *79-81*	4	8
?	**Avon Tyres*** black - *not made*	NA	NA

* This livery was suggested to Airfix by Palitoy who supplied a picture of it. Airfix prepared the artwork ready for a release in 1981. The artwork was amongst the assets acquired by Palitoy on the demise of Airfix and they brought out the wagon themselves.

W7. NE 21T Hopper Wagon

54367	**NE** 193258 grey - *80-81*	5	10
54368	**BR** E289595K grey - *80-81*	5	10

W8. 20T Tank Wagon
This was an authentic model of a 12' chassis tank wagon done from Railway Clearing House drawings but the liveries are not strictly authentic, belonging as they do to other styles of tanker.

54345	**Esso** 135 silver - *79-81*	8	14
54346	**Shell BP** 3967 black - *79-81*	6	12
54347	**Shell** 2373 buff - *79-81*	8	14

W9. 12T Planked Single Ventilated Van
The private owner versions were mainly re-sprayed and reprinted BR ventilated vans of which there was a large stock unsold. They were done in batches of about 7,000 at the Airfix factory in the UK. Roofs were sprayed any grey available to avoid buying paint specially for them.

54300	**BR** B751707 red brown with brown roof - *76-80*	4	8
54300	**BR** B751707, B760563 red brownwith grey roof - *78?*	4	8
54302	**Lyon's Tea** 528163 blue - *78-79*	6	12
54301	**English Eggs** 506150 dark blue - *78-81*	8	14
54303	**Blue Circle** 520112 yellow - *78-79*	8	14

54310	**Lyle's Golden Syrup** 547117 green - *80-81*	6	12
54311	**Tizer** 561772 yellow - *80-81*	6	12
54312	**Spratt's** 538422 white brown printing for name - *80-81*	6	12
54312	**Spratt's** 538422 white red printing for name Ltd Edn 20 - *80*	35	45
54313	**Huntley & Palmer** 566327 green - *80-81*	6	12
54314	**Persil** 547921 green - *80-81*	6	12
54315	**Nestle's Milk** 531179 blue - *80-81*	6	12

LMS sliding door vent van - Spratt's [W9]

W10. SR 12T Ventilated Van
54304	**SR** 44392 brown - *79-81*	5	10
54305	**BR** S44437 grey - *79-81*	5	10

W11. LMS 20T Brake Van
This model had its own unique chassis.
54361	**LMS** 730097 grey - *77-81*	4	8
54362	**BR** 114875 red brown - *77-81*	5	10

W12. GWR 20T Brake Van
This model had its own unique chassis.
54360	**BR** 114926 grey - *77-83*	4	8
54363	**GWR** 114875 dark grey Swindon - *78-81*	4	8
54363	**GWR** 56616 dark grey Oxford - *78-81*	6	12

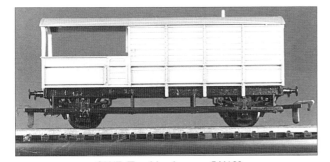

GWR Toad brake van [W12]

W13. Standard/LNER 20T Brake Van
54386	**NE** 182922 brown - *not made*	NA	NA
54387	**BR** brown+yellow - *not made*	NA	NA

W14. GWR Macaw H Bogie Bolster Wagon
54335	**BR** W107364 grey box of 2 - *81*	NA	22
(54335)	as above single unboxed	8	NA
54336	**GWR** 107364 dark grey box of 2 - *81*	NA	22
(54336)	as above single unboxed	8	NA

W15. GWR Siphon G Bogie Milk Van
As a cost cutting exercise, the two GWR Siphons were fitted with bogies from the GWR Centenary coaches. While authentic, examples on the railways so fitted were rare. The bogies should have been a 9' American type.
54306	**GWR** 1478 dark brown - *80-81*	9	14

54307	**BR** W1478 maroon - *80-81*	9	14

W16. GWR Siphon H Bogie Milk Van
54308	**GWR** 1437 dark brown - *80-81*	9	14
54309	**BR** W1429 maroon - *80-81*	9	14

W17. American Freight Cars (made by Bachmann)
These were in the 54053 Wild West Freight train set and were made by Bachmann who marketed their version of the set in America.
54270	**Union Pacific** 356 red box car - *77-78*	4	NA
54271	**Union Pacific** yellow caboose - *77-78*	4	NA

The last display of new liveries was at the 1981 Toy Fair and included some which Airfix did not have time to produce. These included the 20T steel mineral wagon in the livery of 'Avon Tyres' and the 12T ventilated van finished as 'Meccano', 'Camp Coffee' and 'Oxo'. There were also to be a 5-plank 'BAC', a 7-plank 'Perfection Soap' and a Conflat with a Fraser's container. Some of these liveries were later taken up by Palitoy.

Also planned for 1982 was an LNER type brake van which was based on vehicle ESR 49028 from which the drawings had been prepared. This was to have been followed by a 9' chassis for more accurately scaled private owner wagons. The model would have been based on a Gloucester design and was due for release during 1981.

Other wagons being considered (with the year of their proposed introduction) were:

SR 25T brake van - 1982
LNER 9' wheelbase fruit van - 1982
GWR mobile crane and jib carrier - 1983
GWR Tube wagon - 1983
GWR Ro-Rail milk wagon - 1983
16T mineral wagon - 1983
Plate wagon - 1983

It was also planned to each year add further liveries to the 5-plank, 7-plank, container and mineral wagon ranges.

ACCESSORIES
There were very few accessories for the Airfix range but they included, in 1979, a series of card lineside structures which were both available separately and provided in the train sets. The models released that first year were a signal box (54650-6), tunnel (54651-9) and a station (54652-2).

Track was supplied by Peco and Airfix supplied both battery and mains power units. At the end Airfix launched their own version of Zero 1 which was called 'MTC' which stood for Multiple Train Controller

SETS
Airfix tried hard to sell their sets and produced a total of 19 before they went into liquidation. Retailers always wanted sets made up of boxed items so that they could break up sets that did not sell and offer the items individually. As the Airfix range is relatively small and so easy to build a complete collection of, there is a growing interest in Airfix train sets. This particularly applies to those of the pre GMR days. Of special interest are the adventure sets - 'Doctor X' and the two Wild West sets which can fetch as much as £80. Another interesting set is the Cornish Riviera without the gold beading on the splashers of the locomotive or with it applied as print splasher labels. The latter were done in an emergency to cover a production mistake.

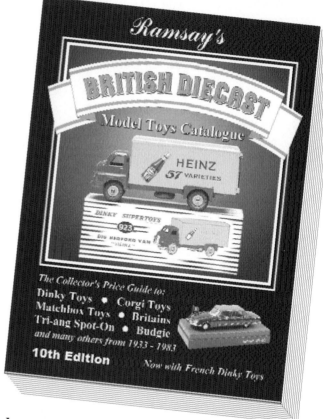

Bachmann (British)

HISTORY

The name Bachmann came from a German emigrant to the USA who, in 1835, founded a company in Philadelphia. Amongst other things, the company made tinplate toys and, many years later, was one of the pioneers of plastic goods, including toy trains. Bachmann went on to become the largest distributor of toy trains and model railways in America.

Meanwhile, in 1925, in China, a man named Ting Hsiung-chao bought a battery manufacturing company in Shanghai for US$500. During the civil war between the Nationalist and Communist factions in China he was imprisoned for political reasons by the Communists, and was unable to tend to his business, which ultimately collapsed as a result. He was eventually forced to flee from Communist China, to re-establish what became a thriving business in North Point, Hong Kong.

His company, Kader, was founded in 1948 and went on to become the largest manufacturer of toys in the Far East. In the mid 1950s, the Company started manufacturing for Bachmann and by 1987, Kader had bought Bachmann outright.

Kader Industrial Co. Ltd, one of the Kader group of companies, is now based in Kowloon Bay, very near the old airport, Kai Tak.

One British company it manufactured for was Palitoy, the owners of the Mainline Railways range which was prominent in the 1970s and early 1980s. Palitoy had an arrangement whereby they required the manufacturers to produce their own tools for their products with the tools remaining in the ownership of the manufacturing company. As a result of this, when Palitoy closed down and its model railway assets were acquired by Dapol, the latter did not acquire the Far East tools of Kader origin.

By the late 1980s, Kader were looking at the European market. With their good collection of tools for making locomotives and rolling stock for the British market, they decided to form a European company to develop the local potential. Thus, Bachmann Industries Europe Ltd was formed in June 1989 and the model railway press in Britain announced the newly launched Bachmann Branch-Line range in January 1990. Kader also acquired a number of famous European names including Liliput which is based in Altdorf, near Nuremberg, Germany. A new purpose built block has been added to the Zhong Tang factory complex, in Guangdong Province, dedicated solely to the manufacture of model railways in various gauges for the UK, Continental Europe, China and US markets. While Bachmann models are made at Zhong Tang, the parent company, Kader Industrial Co. Ltd, is still based in Kowloon Bay, Hong Kong.

While the former Mainline tools formed the basis of the Bachmann British range, the last ten years have seen considerable improvements made to the models and, at an early stage, the

Milestones
1835 Bachmann founded in Philadelphia.
1925 Ting Hsiung-chao buys a battery company in Shanghai.
1948 Ting founds Kader in Hong Kong.
1975 Kader start producing Mainline models for Palitoy.
1987 Kader buys Bachmann.
1989 Bachmann Industries Europe Ltd formed.
1990 Bachmann Branchlines launched in UK initially using former Mainline tools.
1993 Kader acquires Liliput.
1998 Bachmann Industries Europe Ltd introduce their Blue Riband range.
2000 Bachmann buy Graham Farish.

launch of many new models. This process continues with Bachmann setting a new standard for ready-to-run 00 scale models in the UK which rivals were forced to follow.

Blue Riband Models - With the ever increasing strive for higher quality in their models, in 1998, Bachmann launched their Blue Riband range. This badge is worn only by those models that Bachmann consider to be to the high standard they have set themselves to achieve and it is expected that all completely new models will fall in this category. The name comes from transatlantic shipping where the Blue Riband was awarded to the fastest liner to ply the route.

Further Reading

A series of articles was written by Graham Smith-Thompson, in *Model Railway Enthusiast* and *Model Railway Collector* magazines, profiling the Airfix and Mainline ranges and other systems that later used the tools. The first part on Bachmann models was published before the magazine ceased publication in the summer of 2000 but subsequent parts were not published. The Magazine of the Bachmann Collectors Club (see below) is developing into a useful source of information for further research.

Collectors Club

For a number of years the Company sponsored an enthusiasts club called Bachmann Times which operated at arms-length. In 2000 the club was reformed in-house under the name Bachmann Collectors Club and members receive a quarterly magazine. Further information about this may be obtained by writing to the Club at Bachmann Industries Europe Ltd, Moat Way, Barwell, Leicestershire LE9 8EY.

Dates - It is difficult to date Bachmann Branch-Line models by their appearance in catalogues as some models have not been ready for distribution until one or two years after their catalogue launch. As near as possible, in the tables below, we have given the years in which we believe the models first appeared in the shops.

A single date has been given because Bachmann operated a batch production supply system. Generally there is only an initial batch of models which, when sold-out, is not repeated. Instead, the model was either dropped from the catalogue or replaced by a similar model renumbered and generally improved in finish. Some models have been available in the shops for several years from the date of the initial production - the length of time being dependent on the popularity of the model.

Catalogue Numbers - Generally the addition of a letter suffix to a catalogue number indicates a modification of some kind to the model. This could be a change of number or an alteration to the chassis. For general release models the letters were taken from the start of the alphabet i.e. 'A', 'B', 'C' etc. but for commissioned models (specials ordered by shops or societies) lettering started with 'Z' and worked upwards from the bottom of the alphabet. (See also the note on 'Wagon Numbers' in the Wagons section as this may also apply to locos and coaches).

Buyers should be aware that box numbering errors have sometimes occurred and that boxes with a 'new' number suffix sometimes contain a model with the old number.

Boxes - wooden presentation cases (wpc) have been provided for a number of limited or special editions.

Weathering - Bachmann were one of the first to turn out models

Bachmann (British)

with a weathered finish (although Tri-ang had tried it in 1965). It started with wagons and spread to locomotive models. To save space, weathered models are coded in the text with a 'W' after the colour.

LOCOMOTIVES

Bachmann took the 'Spectrum' quality of their American range and applied it to the British models to give very superior performance far removed from the old Mainline standard. A skew armature replaceable Mabuchi can motor was fitted with an excellent gear drive and brass flywheel.

Listing - The locomotives are arranged in the order of size from smallest to largest, starting with tank engines, then tender engines and finishing with diesels, electrics and multiple units.

Class 56XX in BR green [L4]

Cat.No.	Number, Company, Colour, Date	£	£

L1. Class 57XX Pannier Tank 0-6-0PT (ex-Mainline)

imp = improved chassis.

31-900	**7760** Great Western green - *93*	25	35
31-900A	**7702** GWR green imp - *96*	25	35
31-901	**5796** BRb black - *93*	25	35
31-901A	**8700** GWR (button) green imp - *96*	25	35
31-902	**7754** BRb black - *93*	25	35
31-902A	**5775** BRc black imp - *96*	25	35
31-903	**L94** London Transport maroon imp Sp Edn 500 (LT Museum) - *99*	40	55
(30-200)	**L91** LT maroon ex sets - *91*	80	NA
(30-201)	**L99** LT maroon ex sets - *93*	30	NA

L2. Class 8750 Pannier Tank 0-6-0PT

32-200	**9643** GWR green - *99*	35	45
32-200A	**6752** GWR green blue spot - *01*	35	45
32-200B	**3715** GWR green - *03*	35	45
32-201	**8763** BRb lined black - *99*	35	45
32-202	**4672** BRc black - *99*	35	45
32-202A	**9753** BRc black - *02*	40	48
32-203	**4666** BRc black W - *03*	40	48

L2A. Class 3F 'Jinty' 0-6-0T

32-225	**47410** BRc black - *04*	NPG	48
32-226	**47354** BRb black - *04*	NPG	48
32-227	**7524** LMS black - *04*	NPG	48

L3. Class J72 0-6-0T (ex-Mainline)

Similar to the last Mainline J72 but now fitted with an open frame motor driving on centre axle. rpv = NER Ross 'pop' valves. * full length ejector pipe

31-050	**8680** LNER green - *90*	28	35
31-050A	**8680** LNER green lined - *99*	30	40
31-051	**69023** BRc/NER light green - *90*	25	35
31-052	**68680** BRb black lined - *90*	28	35
31-053	**69012** BRc black unlined - *90*	27	35
31-054	**2313** LNER black lined * - *96*	25	35
31-055	**68680** BRb green lined * - *96*	25	30
31-055A	**68737** BRb black W * - *02*	30	45
31-056	**69025** BRc black unlined * - *96*	27	35
31-056	**68723** BRc/NER light green - *03*	30	40
31-057	**8693** LNER black unlined * - *98*	30	40
31-058	**68727** BRc black W - *04*	NPG	44
(30-100)	**68745** BRb black rpv ex 30-100 freight set only - *94*	50	NA

L4. Class 56XX 0-6-2T

32-080	**5601** BRc plain green - *03*	35	45
32-077	**5658** BRc lined green - *02*	35	45
32-075	**5667** GWR green - *02*	35	45
32-075A	**6600** GWR green - *03*	35	45
32-079	**6624** BRb plain black - *03*	35	45
32-076	**6676** Great Western green - *02*	35	45

L4A. Class 45XX 2-6-2T

32-125	**4566** BRc lined green - *03*	40	50
32-125A	**4569** BRc lined green - *04*	40	50
32-126	**4560** BRb unlined black - *03*	40	50
32-127	**4550** GWR green - *03*	40	50
32-127A	**4527** GWR green - *04*	40	53
32-128	**4573** BRb plain black W - *04*	45	56

L4B. Class 4575 2-6-2T

32-135	**5531** GWR green - *04*	40	53
32-135Y	**5552** BRc lined green Ltd Edn 504 (Kernow Model Rail Centre) - *04*	45	59
32-136	**5555** Great Western green - *04*	40	53
32-137	**5559** BRb plain black - *not made*	NA	NA
32-137	**5500** BRb plain black - *04*	40	53
32-?	**5553** BRc lined green Ltd Edn 1000 (Bachmann Collectors Club) - *04*	38	52

Class VI [L5]

L5. Class V1 & V3 2-6-2T

hb = hopper bunker. csp = cranked steam pipes. West = Westinghouse pump

31-600	**7684** LNER green (V3) hb - *92*	32	45
31-601	**67601** BRc black (V1) csp - *92*	32	45
31-602	**67664** BRb black (V1) hb - *92*	32	45
31-603	**466** LNER black (V1) hb csp - *92*	34	45
31-604	**67666** BRc black (V3) hb - *96*	35	45
31-605	**67610** BRb black (V1)* csp - *96*	35	45
31-606	**448** LNER lined black (V1) - *97*	35	45
31-606A	**2911** LNER black csp (V1) - *00*	40	50
31-607	**67684** BRa green hb (V3) - *97*	30	40
31-608	**7684** LNER green hb (V3) - *99*	40	50
31-609	**67673** BRb black West hb (V1) - *99*	40	50
31-609A	**67669** BRb lined black West hb (V3) - *02*	45	55
31-610	**67645** BRb lined black csp (V1) - *02*	40	50
31-611	**67635** BRc lined black W csp (V1) - *02*	45	55

* The box indicates that this was a V3.

L6. Class 2MT Ivatt 2-6-2T

p-p = push-pull equipment.

31-450	**41221** BRb black p-p - *95*	30	45
31-450A	**41272** BRc black p-p plaque as 7000th loco from Crewe - *96*	35	50
31-450B	**41281** BRb lined black p-p - *98*	30	45
31-450C	**41224** BRc lined black p-p - *00*	40	55

31-450D	**41324** BRb fine lined black - *not made*	NA	NA
31-450D	**41324** BRc fine lined black p-p - *02*	40	55
31-450E	**41273** BRb fine lined black p-p - *02*	40	55
31-451	**41241** BRb lined black - *95*	35	45
31-451A	**41250** BRb lined black - *96*	35	45
31-451C	**41247** BRb lined black - *00*	40	55
31-451D	**41304** BRc lined black - *02*	40	55
31-452	**41313** BRc lined black - *95*	30	45
31-452A	**41202** BRc lined black - *96*	35	45
31-452B	**41233** BRc lined black - *98*	35	45
31-452C	**41304** BRc fine lined black - *01*	35	55
31-453	**1206** LMS black - *95*	35	50
31-453A	**1202** LMS black - *98*	35	50
31-454	**41286** BRb lined black - *02*	40	55

Standard Class 4MT tank [L7]

L7. Class 4MT Standard Tank 2-6-4T

DCC ready, separately fitted water tanks and very detailed cab interior. It was originally intended to produce the model with an opening smokebox door, but fearing that they would be unable to effect repairs if the door mounting were to get damaged, Bachmann released them with the door lightly glued in place. The 4MT tanks made from 2002 onwards were fitted with higher quality 3-pole motors and lower gearing. .

32-350	**80061** BRb lined black - *01*	45	60
32-351	**80097** BRc lined black - *01*	45	60
32-352	**80032** BRb lined black - *02*	45	65
32-353	**80135** BRc lined green - *02*	45	65
32-354	**80002** BRc lined black - *02*	45	65
32-354A	**80120** BRc lined black W - *03*	50	70
32-355	**80136** BRb lined black - *03*	45	65
32-356	**80038** BRc lined black W - *04*	50	70

L8. Class 2251 'Collett Goods' 0-6-0

32-300	**3202** GWR green - *98*	35	50
32-301	**2260** BRb black - *98*	35	50
32-302	**2277** BRc lined green - *98*	35	50
32-303	**2251** BRb black - *99*	35	50
32-304	**2294** GWR green - *04*	45	59
32-305	**2217** BRb black W - *04*	45	59

L9. Class J39 0-6-0

st = stepped tender.

31-850	**1974** LNER lined black - *94*	32	40
31-851	**64964** BRb black - *94*	32	40
31-851A	**64958** BRb black - *96*	35	45
31-852	**64967** BRc black - *94*	32	40
31-852A	**64970** BRc black - *96*	35	45
31-853	**1996** LNER black - *96*	35	45
31-854	**64960** BRb black - *04*	40	55
31-855	**1856** LNER lined black - *00*	35	50
31-860	**1496** LNER black st - *99*	35	50
31-861	**64838** BRb black st - *99*	35	50
31-862	**64791** BRc black st - *99*	35	50
31-864	**64841** BRc black W st - *04*	40	55

L10. Class 93XX 2-6-0

31-801	**9319** GWR green - *92*	35	45
31-802	**9308** BRb green - *92*	35	45
31-803	**7332** BRc green - *92*	35	45

L11. Class 43XX 2-6-0 (ex-Mainline)

Sprung buffers.

31-825	**4318** GWR green - *96*	30	40
31-826	**6384** BRc unlined green - *96*	30	40
31-827	**5355** GWR (button) green - *96*	30	40

31-827A	**4377** BRc lined green - *03*	40	50
31-828	**5370** BRb lined black red plates - *01*	40	50
31-829	**4331** Great () Western lined green - *01*	40	50
31-2000	**5358** BRc lined green Ltd Edn 1000 + Manor + 6 coaches - *01*	NA	200*
31-2000/2	**5358** BRc lined green from above 65 set - *01*	30	NA

* Price given is for complete Cambrian Coast Express set.

L12. LMS 'Crab' 2-6-0

DCC ready. cr = coal rail on tender. rt = riveted tender. .

32-175	**13098** LMS maroon - *03*	50	65
32-176	**42765** BRb lined black cr - *03*	50	65
32-177	**42789** BRc lined black cr, rt - *03*	50	65
32-178	**2715** LMS lined black - *04*	NPG	76
32-179	**42942** BRb lined black W cr, rt - *04*	NPG	76

Ex LMS Crab [L12]

L12A. LNER K3 2-6-0

DCC ready. gst = standard group tender. st = stepped tender.

32-275	**2934** LNER black gst - *04*	NPG	77
32-276	**61932** BRb lined black gst - *04*	NPG	77
32-277	**61907** BRc lined black st - *04*	NPG	77

L13. SR Class N 2-6-0

wpc - wooden presentation case. sst = slope sided tender. xsd = no smoke deflectors.

32-150/1	**810** SE&CR grey Ltd Edn 1000 - *98*	65	NA
32-150/2	**1863** SR green Ltd Edn 1000 - *98*	65	NA
32-150	above two locos wpc* - *98*	NA	145
32-150W	**383** CIE grey+black Sp Edn 640 (Murphy's Models) - *00*	45	65
32-150X	**376, 388** CIE LNWR black Sp Edn 640 (Murphy's Models) - *00*	45	65
32-150Y	**372, 385, 390**** CIE green Sp Edn 500 (Murphy's Models) - *00*	50	65
(00651)	CIE green ex Irish Railways set - *04*	60	NA
32-150Z	**31874 'Brian Fisk'** BRb black Sp Edn 500 (Beatties) wpc - *99*	85	110
32-151	**31860** BRc lined black - *98*	35	45
32-151A	**31816** BRc lined black - *99*	35	45
32-152	**31813** BRb lined black - *98*	35	45
32-153	**1824** SR olive green - *98*	45	60
32-153A	**1821** SR olive green - *99*	30	40
32-154	**31843** BRc lined black - *00*	35	45
32-155	**1854** SR malachite green - *00*	35	45
32-156	**31844** BRb lined black W - *02*	40	55
32-160	**1406** SR olive green xsd sst - *02*	40	55
32-161	**31862** BRb lined black sst - *01*	40	55
32-162	**31401** BRc lined black sst - *01*	40	55
32-163	**1404** SR olive green sst - *02*	40	55

* Price quoted is for the complete set in a case. ** 3 alternative numbers supplied as transfers.

L13A. Class 4 Ivatt 2-6-0

DCC ready. dc = double chimney.

32-575	**3001** LMS black dc - *04*	NPG	77
32-576	**43047** BRc lined black - *04*	NPG	77
32-577	**43160** BRb lined black - *04*	NPG	77

L14. Class V2 2-6-2

st = stepped tender. osp = outside steam pipes. wpc - wooden presentation case. dc = double chimney. spn = separate printed nameplates

31-550	**4771 'Green Arrow'** LNER green Ltd Edn 1000 wpc - *92*	110	140
31-550	**60800 'Green Arrow'** BRc green - *04*	65	80
31-551	**60800 'Green Arrow'** BRb black - *92*	50	65

Bachmann (British)

31-552	**60964 'The Durham Light Infantry'** BRc green - *92*	50	65
31-553	**60807** BRa black - *92*	45	60
31-553A	**60807** BRb black - *97*	45	60
31-554	**60903** BRc green dc - *92*	45	60
31-555	**4801** LNER green - *92*	45	60
31-556	**3650** LNER unlined black - *92*	45	60
31-557	**60884** BRb green osp - *97*	50	65
31-558	**4844 'Coldstreamer'** LNER green spn -*96*	50	65
31-559	**60800 'Green Arrow'** BRc green Ltd Edn 500 - *00*	70	80
31-560	**4806 'The Green Howard'** LNER green st - *99*	65	80
31-561	**60825** BRc green osp st - *99*	65	80
31-562	**60834** BRb lined black W st - *04*	NPG	80

Ex LNER Class V2 [L14]

L15.   Manor Class 4-6-0 (ex-Mainline)

31-300	**7802 'Bradley Manor'** GWR unlined green - *91*	35	55
31-300Z	**7816 'Frilsham Manor'** BR green, black metal work Sp Edn 500 (Brunswick Railways Ltd) - *99*	40	65
31-301	**7820 'Dinmore Manor'** BRb unlined green - *91*	35	50
31-302	**7823 'Hook Norton Manor'** BRc lined green - *91*	35	55
31-303	**7829 'Ramsbury Manor'** BRb lined black red plates - *91*	35	55
31-303A	**7829 'Ramsbury Manor'** BRb lined black red plates modified chassis - *99*	35	55
31-304	**7800 'Torquay Manor'** GWR (button) green - *96*	35	60
31-305	**7805 'Broome Manor'** GWR green - *96*	35	60
31-306	**7822 'Foxcote Manor'** BRc lined green - *96*	35	60
31-307	**7813 'Freshford Manor'** BRb black red plates modified chassis - *02*	45	65
31-2000	**7828 'Odney Manor'** BRc green Ltd Edn 1000 + Class 43XX + 6 coaches - *01*	NA	200*
31-2000/1	**7828 'Odney Manor'** BRc green from above set - *01*	70	NA

* Price shown is for complete Cambrian Coast Express set (31-2000) which was sold in a wooden presentation case

L15A.   Class 4900 Hall 4-6-0

DCC ready.

32-001	**6937 'Conyngham Hall'** BRc green - *04*	NPG	76
32-002	**5960 'Saint Edmund Hall'** BRb lined black - *04*	NPG	76
32-003	**4936 'Kinlet Hall'** GWR green - *04*	NPG	76

L16.   Class 6959 Modified Hall 4-6-0 (ex-Replica)

31-775	**6990 'Witherslack Hall'** BRb black red plates - *96*	35	60
31-776	**7915 'Mere Hall'** BRc green stepped tender - *96*	35	60
31-777	**6962 'Soughton Hall'** G()W green stepped tender - *96*	35	60
31-778	**6969 'Wraysbury Hall'** BRb green Hawksworth tender - *96*	35	60

31-779	**6960 'Raveningham Hall'** G()W green gold nameplates Ltd Edn 1000 9ct wpc - *97*	40	65
?	**'Hogwarts Castle'** ex Hogwarts Express US set - *?*	40	NA

L17.   Jubilee Class 5XP 4-6-0 (ex-Mainline)

Later with sprung buffers. sc = single chimney. dc = double chimney. en = etched nameplate. Ft = Fowler tender with coal rails. St = Stanier 4,000 gallon tender. wpc = wooden presentation case.

31-150	**5552 'Silver Jubilee'** LMS black* Ltd Edn 500 wpc - *90*	250	315
31-150A	**5699 'Galatea'** LMS maroon St Sp Edn 600 (Loco Marketing Services) red card presentation box - *96*	100	150
31-150S	**45679 'Armada'** BRc green Ft en -*01*	45	70
31-150T	**45670 'Howard of Effingham'** BRb green St en - *01*	45	70
31-150Y	above 2 locos wpc Sp Edn 250 (TMC) - *00*	NA	165
31-150U	**45732 'Sanspareil'** BRc green St en - *01*	45	70
31-150V	**45733 'Novelty'** BRb green St en - *01*	45	70
31-150Z	above 2 locos wpc Sp Edn 250 (TMC) - *00*	NA	165
31-151	**45552 'Silver Jubilee'** BRc green en St - *90*	40	55
31-152	**45568 'Western Australia'** black BRb (small) Ft - *90*	45	55
31-153	**45596 'Bahamas'** BRc green dc St - *90*	48	55
31-154	**5721 'Impregnable'** LMS maroon St - *94*	40	50
31-155	**5699 'Galatea'** LMS maroon Ft - *94*	47	55
31-155A	**5699 'Galatea'** LMS maroon Ft - *00*	35	50
31-156	**45715 'Invincible'** BRc green Ft - *97*	40	55
31-156A	**45715 'Invincible'** BRc green Ft - *99*	45	55
31-157	**5684 'Jutland'** LMS maroon St ** - *00*	45	65
31-158	**45742 'Connaught'** BRb green St** - *00*	45	65
31-159	**5711 'Courageous'** LMS black Ft ** - *03*	45	65
31-160	**45697 'Achilles'** BRc green W st - *04*	NPG	73

* 1930s livery with chrome plated fittings. The chrome plating was applied before the black paint and the latter tends to peel off. ** Single and double chimneys supplied with the model.

Jubilee Class [L17] (Bachmann)

L18.   Rebuilt Patriot Class 4-6-0 (ex-Mainline)

St = Stanier 4,000 gallon tender. xsd = no smoke deflectors.

31-200	**45528** BRa black St - *91*	38	50
31-201	**45545 'Planet'** BRc green St - *91*	45	55
31-202	**5526 'Morecambe and Heysham'** LMS black St xsd - *96*	40	55
31-203	**45528 'R.E.M.E'** BRb green St - *01*	50	65

L19.   Rebuilt Royal Scot 4-6-0 (ex-Mainline)

xsd = no smoke deflectors. St = Stanier 4,000 gallon tender. wpc - wooden presentation case.

31-225	**46102 'Black Watch'** BRb green etched brass military crest - *96*	45	60
31-226	**6133 'Green Howards'** LMS black xsd - *97*	50	65
31-227	**46162 'Queens Westminster Rifleman'** BRc green - *97*	50	65
31-228	**46141 'The North Staffordshire Regiment'** BRb green - *03*	50	65
31-275W	**46168 'The Girl Guide'** BRc green St - *01*	65	80
31-275X	**46169 'The Boy Scout'** BRb green St - *01*	65	80
31-275Y	Above 2 models Sp Edn 350 wpc (TMC) Mancunian headboard - *99*	NA*	150
31-277Z	**46159 'The Royal Air Force'** ** BR green wpc + diecast aircraft Sp Edn 500	75	90

(Annex Industries) - *00*

* Price quoted is for the pair in the presentation box. ** Commemorating the 60th Anniversary of the Battle of Britain.

L20. Rebuilt Jubilee 4-6-0

(larger boiler + double chimney)

xsd = no smoke deflectors. St = Stanier tender.

31-250	**45735 'Comet'** BRa black xsd St - *91*	45	60
31-251	**45736 'Phoenix'** BRc green St - *91*	45	60

L21. Parallel Boiler Scot 4-6-0 (ex-Mainline)

Ft = Fowler tender with coal rails. St = Stanier 4,000 gallon tender. xsd = no smoke deflectors. wpc - wooden presentation case. cre = coal rail extensions. crest = crest on cabsides, number on tender

31-275	**6100 'Royal Scot'** LMS maroon St brass bell special nameplates Ltd Edn 1000 wpc - *94*	75	90
31-275Z	**6110 'Grenadier Guardsman'** LMS maroon Ft xsd crest Sp Edn 500 (Beatties) wpc - *98*	90	110
31-276	**6134 'The Cheshire Regiment'** LMS black St curved top deflectors - *94*	40	55
31-277	**6112 'Sherwood Forester'** LMS maroon Ft xsd - *94*	40	55
31-278	**46148 'The Manchester Regiment'** BRb green St - *95*	40	55
31-279	**6130 'The West Yorkshire Regiment'** LMS maroon Ft cre angled deflectors - *96*	40	55
31-280	**6106 'Gordon Highlander'** LMS maroon St - *98*	50	65
31-281	**6255 'The Lancer'** LMS maroon Ft - *02*	55	70
31-282	**46151 'The Royal Horse Guardsman'** BRb green W St - *02*	60	75

L22. Class B1 4-6-0 (ex-Replica)

31-700	**1264** LNER green - *95*	30	45
31-700Z	**61247 'Lord Burghley'** BRc lined black W Sp Edn 500 (SMC) - *03*	55	65
31-701	**61241 'Viscount Ridley'** BRb black - *94*	40	55
31-701A	**61399** BRb black - *96*	35	50
31-702	**61354** BRc black - *94*	35	50
31-702A	**61190** BRc black - *96*	40	55
31-703	**61010 'Wildebeeste'** BRc black - *96*	35	50
31-705	**1306 'Mayflower'** LNER green Ltd Edn 2000 9ct gold plates wpc - *96*	65	80
31-706	**1041 'Roedeer'** LNER lined black - *98*	45	60
31-707	**61002 'Impala'** BRa light green - *98*	45	60
31-708	**61003 'Gazelle'** BRc lined black - *03*	45	60
31-709	**61008 'Kudu'** BRc black W - *04*	NPG	65
31-710	**61009 'Hartebeeste'** * BRc black Sp Edn 250 (Rails) wpc - *99*	75	90
31-710A	**61018 'Gnu'*** BRc black Sp Edn 100 (Rails) wpc - *99*	95	110

*61009 'Hartebeeste' and 61018 'Gnu' were finished by Fox for Rails of Sheffield.

Lord Nelson Class [L23]

L23. Lord Nelson Class 4-6-0

Final form as rebuilt by Bulleid.

31-400	**850 'Lord Nelson'** SR malachite green Ltd Edn 1000 wpc - *92*	110	150
31-401	**864 'Sir Martin Frobisher'** SR malachite green - *92*	40	55
31-402	**30851 'Sir Francis Drake'** BRb green - *92*	45	55
31-403	**30861 'Lord Anson'** BRc green - *92*	45	55
31-404	**855 'Robert Blake'** SR olive green, original small chimney - *96*	48	60
31-405	**30852 'Sir Walter Raleigh'** BRb green - *96*	45	65
31-406	**30850 'Lord Nelson'** BRc green - *98*	50	75
31-407	**856 'Lord St.Vincent'** SR malachite green - *98*	45	60

L24. Standard Class 4MT 4-6-0 (ex-Mainline)

Sprung buffers. dc = double chimney.

31-100	**75014** BRb black BR2 tender - *96*	35	45
31-100A	**75059** BRb black BR2 tender - *98*	45	55
31-101	**75023** BRc green BR2 tender - *96*	35	45
31-102	**75073** BRb black BR1B tender - *90*	35	45
31-102A	**75072** BRb black BR1B tender - *98*	45	55
31-103	**75020** BRc black dc BR2 tender - *90*	36	45
31-104	**75069** BRc green dc BR1B tender - *90*	35	45
31-105	**75078** BRc black dc BR1B tender - *90*	36	45
31-105A	**75075** BRc black dc BR2 tender - *98*	45	55
31-106	**75029*** BRc green dc BR2 tender - *90*	40	50
31-106A	**75003** BRc green dc BR2 tender - *98*	35	55
31-107	**75027** BRc green BR2 tender - *02*	40	55
31-108	**75063** BRb black W - *not made*	NA	NA
31-108	**75065** BRb black W BR1B tender - *02*	45	60

*This was supplied with brass nameplates for 'The Green Knight' which were made for Bachmann by Jackson Evans.

Standard Class 4 [L24]

L25. Standard Class 5MT 4-6-0

Optional etched nameplates, DCC ready, removable coal load and different tenders and whistle positions. The models were fitted with higher quality 3-pole motors and lower gearing. wp = without Westinghouse pump.

32-500	**73068** BRc green BR1C tender - *02*	65	85
32-501	**73158** BRc black BR1B tender - *02*	65	85
32-502	**73082 'Camelot'** BRb black BR1B, optional nameplates - *02*	65	85
32-503	**73030** BRb black BR1 tender wp - *03*	65	85
32-504	**73014** BRc green BR1 tender - *02*	65	85
32-505	**73069** BRc black W BR1C tender - *03*	65	85
32-506	**73110 'The Red Knight'** BRc lined black BR1F tender - *04*	NPG	92

L26. Class A1 4-6-2

DCC ready. Removable coal load and optional chimneys. wpc = wooden presentation case.

32-550	**60163 'Tornado'** BRc green wpc - *03*	100	120
32-551	**60158 'Aberdonian'** BRc green - *01*	65	90
32-552	**60147 'North Eastern'** BRb green - *02*	65	90
32-553	**60161 'North British'** BRb blue - *03*	65	90
32-554	**60114 'W.P.Allen'** BRa light green - *03*	65	90
32-555	**60130 'Kestrel'** BRc green - *03*	65	90
?	**60143 'Sir Walter Scott'** BRc green ex-Bachmann 15th Anniversary set - *04*	90	NA

L27. Class A4 4-6-2

The model is based on the former Trix/Liliput model mouldings, to which 112 minor modifications were made, on a Bachmann split-chassis of standard design principal. dc = double chimney. sc = single chimney. ct = corridor tender. nct = non-corridor tender. v = valances fitted. xv = no valances. bm = blackened metalwork. wpc = wooden presentation case. swb = simulated wood finish box. en = etched nameplate. lcw = large chime whistle.

31-950	**4489 'Dominion of Canada'** LNER blue v sc brass bell Ltd Edn 2000 wpc - *95*	60	95
31-950A	**60011 ''Empire of India''** BRb green Ltd Edn 500 (Rails) wpc - *99*	60	100
31-950X	**2509 'Silver Link'** LNER grey Sp Edn 500 (Southampton MC) - *03*	60	100
31-951	**60009 'Union of South Africa'** BRc green dc en and plaques - *95*	100	150

Bachmann (British)

Class A1 [L26]

31-951A	60009 'Union of South Africa' BRb green sc ct short run - 96	55	80
31-951Z	60009 'Osprey'** BRc green Sp Edn (75069 Fund) 350 swb - 98	100	140
31-952	4903 'Peregrine' blue LNER v dc st - 96	50	70
31-952	4468 'Mallard' blue LNER v dc - 04	70	91
31-952A	2512 'Silver Fox' LNER silver v st - 98	55	80
31-953	60008 'Dwight D Eisenhower' BRc green dc nct Ltd Edn 250 US wpc - 95	350	400
31-953A	60008 'Dwight D Eisenhower' BRb blue sc ct Ltd Edn 500 US wpc - 96	70	230
31-953B	4496 'Dwight D Eisenhower' LNER blue sc ct bm Ltd Edn 500 US wpc - 97	70	100
31-953C	60008 'Dwight D Eisenhower' BRb green sc Ltd Edn USA wpc - 99	60	90
31-954	60007 'Sir Nigel Gresley' BRb express blue dc - 96	50	70
31-954A	60007 'Sir Nigel Gresley' BR green Ltd Edn 1000 swb - 00	55	70
31-954A	60007 'Sir Nigel Gresley' BRb blue xv sc - 04	75	90
31-955	60013 'Dominion of New Zealand' BRb green nct lcw sc - 96	55	70
31-955	60013 'Dominion of New Zealand' BRc green nct lcw sc - 96	100	120
31-956	4482 'Golden Eagle' LNER green v sc - 97	55	70
31-957	60033 'Seagull' BRc green dc - 97	55	70
31-958	60020 'Guillemot' BRc green dc - 98	55	70
31-959	26 'Miles Beevor' LNER blue xv - 98	55	70
31-960	60017 'Silver Fox' BRc + 6 coaches Ltd Edn Elizabethan set* wpc - 96	NA	275
-	60017 'Silver Fox' BRc ex above set - 96	85	NA
31-960A	60015 'Quicksilver' BRc green W dc - 03	75	90
31-961/1	4468 'Mallard' LNER blue v Ltd Edn 1000 - 98	65	NA
31-961/2	60022 'Mallard' BRc green dc Ltd Edn 1000 - 98	65	NA
31-961	above 2 locos 160th anniversary release Ltd Edn 1000 wpc - 98	NA	165
31-962X	2510 'Quicksilver' LNER black Sp Edn 350 (Rails) swb - 99	85	100
31-962Y	4496 'Golden Shuttle' LNER black Sp Edn 350 (Rails) swb - 99	85	100
31-962Z	4 'William Whitelaw' NE black Sp Edn 350 (Rails) swb - 99	85	100
31-2001/1	4491 'Commonwealth of Australia' LNER blue from set - 00	70	NA
31-2001/2	60012 'Commonwealth of Australia' BRb blue from set - 00	70	NA
31-2001/3	60012 'Commonwealth of Australia' BRc green dc from set - 00	70	NA
31-2001	above 3 in Ltd Edn 1000 wpc - 00	NA	245

* Price given is for complete set. ** The original batch had unacceptable body mouldings and were re-bodied. However, a few of the original models have survived.

L28. WD 'Austerity' 2-8-0

Removable coal load and sprung buffers. West = Westinghouse pump fitted.

32-250	400 'Sir Guy Williams' LMR blue Ltd Edn 2000 wpc - 99	70	90
32-250X	NS4479 NS green North British type Ltd Edn 500 (Tasco Nederland BV) - 03?	90	110
32-250Y*	NS4310 NS green Vucan Foundry type Ltd Edn 500 (Tasco Nederland BV) - 00	45	110
32-250Z	NS4329 NS green North British type Ltd Edn 500 (Tasco Nederland BV) - 00	80	100
32-251	90274 BRb black - 99	70	90
32-252	90445 BRc black W - 99	75	95
32-252A	90201 BRc black W - 03	75	95
32-253	90312 BRb black - 00	70	90
32-254	3085 LNER black West - 00	70	90
32-255	78697 WD 21st Army Transport Group green*** - 00	75	95
32-255A	7199 WD WW2 Desert Sand - 02	80	100
32-256	90566 BRc black - 00	70	85
32-257	90015 BRb black W Ltd Edn - 00	70	85
32-257A	90732 'Vulcan' BRb black - 03	75	95

* The Dutch agent allocated his own number of 32.259 to this model. ** This was made as a Millennium model for sale in Hong Kong with only 200 being put on sale in the UK. *** Some were originally printed with the red and blue on the shields reversed.

Ex LNER Class A4 [L27]

L29. Class 03 Diesel Shunter 0-6-0DS (ex-Mainline)

No further Class 03 models can now be made from these tools as they were adapted to produce the Class 04 (above). ats = air tanks supplied. xhs = no hazard stripes. cx = conical exhaust. cfc = cast flared chimney

31-350	D2000 BRc green xhs cx - 91	35	45
31-351	D.2012 BRc green cx - 91	35	45
31-353	03197 BRe blue cfc ats - 91	35	45
31-352	03371 BRe blue cx ats - 91	35	45

L30. Class 04 Diesel Shunter 0-6-0DS

This model was produced by adapting the former Mainline tools for the Class 03 (below). Sprung buffers. xhs = no hazard stripes.

31-337A	D2223 BRc green - 02	30	40
31-337B	D2228 BRc green - 02	30	40
31-337B	D2228 BRc green W - 04	35	40
31-336A	D2258 BRe blue - not made	NA	NA
31-336B	D2294 BRe blue - 04	35	40
31-337	D2280 BRc green - 97	30	35
31-338	D2282 BRc green xhs - 99	30	35
31-336	D2334 BRe blue - 97	25	36
31-335	11226 BRb black xhs - 97	25	36

L31. Class 08/09 Diesel Shunter 0-6-0DS

Flywheel drive 5-pole motor and easily converted to DCC.

32-112	D3336 BRc green hinged door - 04	35	46
32-101A	D3586 BRc green hazard stripes - 01	35	45
32-101	D3729 BRc green hazard stripes - 00	30	40
32-101B	D4192 BRc green hazard stripes - 03	35	45
32-111	08243 BRe blue hinged door - 04	35	46
32-?	08507 BRe blue W Ltd Edn 1000 (Bachmann Coll. Club) - 03	40	50
32-106	08585 Freightliner green - 02	35	45
32-?	08600 'Ivor' early NSE Sp Edn 500 (ModelZone) - 03	40	50
32-102	08623 BRe blue no ladders - 00	30	40
32-107	08648 BRe Rft departmental grey - 02	35	45
32-104	08653 Rft Distribution grey - 01	35	45
32-102B	08748 BRe blue no ladders - 03	35	45
32-102A	08762 BRe blue no ladders - 01	35	45
32-105	08800 InterCity swallow grey - 02	40	50
32-103	08921 EWS red air comp cabinet new front windows deep springs - 01	35	45
32-116	09006 Mainline blue - 02	35	45
32-110	13029 BRb black hinged door - 04	35	46

32-100	**13365** BRc green - *00*	30	40
32-?	**('Cambridge')** RES grey+red Ltd Edn 500 (Model Rail) * - *01*	40	55
32-102W	**97800 'Ivor'** BRe blue+red Sp Edn 500 (Modelzone) - *04*	30	40

* This was sold through the magazine and came with a sheet of numbers by Modelmaster and a sheet by Shawplan with 'Cambridge' nameplates and logos.

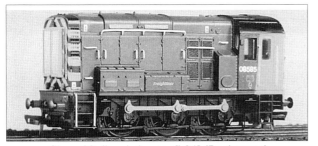

Class 08 diesel shunter [L31] (Bachmann)

L31A. Class 20 Diesel Bo-Bo

DCC ready, bogies with NEM pockets,

32-027	**D8000** BRc green discs - *04*	40	49
32-028	**D8134** BRc green boxes - *04*	40	49
32-025TF	**20042** Waterman Railways black Ltd Edn 500 - *04*	80	100
32-025	**20063** BRe blue discs - *04*	40	49
32-026	**20192** BRe blue boxes - *04*	40	49

L32. Class 24 Diesel Bo-Bo

DCC ready, bogies with NEM pockets (from 2002), roof grill and fan.

32-429	**D5011** BRc green - *03*	35	45
32-427	**D5038** BRc 2-tone green - *not made*	NA	NA
32-426	**D5054** BRc green - *01*	35	45
32-427	**D5085** BRc 2-tone green - *02*	35	45
32-428	**5087** BRe blue - *02*	35	45
32-425	**24081** BRe blue - *01*	35	45
32-425Z	**97201 'Experiment'** BRe Research Department red+blue Sp Edn 750 (Rail Express) - *01*	45	60

L33. Class 25 Diesel Bo-Bo

Roof grill and fan, DCC ready and bogies with NEM pockets (from 2002). sno= snow ploughs fitted.

32-325	**D5211** BRc green 25/1 - *03*	35	45
32-411	**D5233** BRc 2-tone green 25/2 - *01*	35	45
32-413	**D5237** 2-tone green 25/2 - *02*	35	45
32-403	**D5269** BRc 2-tone green W 25/3 - *02*	35	45
32-410	**5293** BRe blue 25/2 - *not made*	NA	NA
32-400	**D7645** BRc 2-tone green 25/3 - *01*	35	45
32-404	**D7667** BRe blue, sno 25/3 - *02*	40	50
32-402	**D7672 'Tamworth Castle'** BRc 2-tone green 25/3 - *01*	35	45
32-326	**25054** BRe blue 25/1 - *03*	35	45
32-412	**25083** BRe blue W 25/2 - *02*	35	45
32-410	**25087** BRe blue 25/2 - *01*	35	45
32-401	**25279** BRe blue 25/3 - *01*	35	45
?	**25322 'Tamworth Castle'** BRe blue, silver roof, yellow cabs 25/3 Sp Edn 1 (Model Rail) - *01*	40	55

L34. Class 37 Diesel Co-Co

DCC ready, working LED headlight, metal roof grill and fan and cast or fabricated bogies. Sprung buffers. en = etched nameplates. sno = snow ploughs. ch = centre headcode. sh = split headcode.

32-776	**D6707** BRc green sh - *04*	40	45
32-778	**D6826** BRc green ch - *04*	40	45
32-775	**37038** BRe blue sh - *04*	40	45
32-777	**37238** BRe blue ch - *04*	40	45
32-777Z	**37142** BRe blue ch Sp Edn 504 (Kernow Model Rail Centre) - *04*	NPG	68

32-?	**37403 'Ben Cruachan'** BRc green Sp Edn 900 (Bachmann Club) - *02*	45	55
32-377	**37408 'Loch Rannoch'** BReLL blue Eastfield motif 700 made - *03*	40	45
32-275W	**37411 'The Institution of Railway Signal Engineers'** BReLL blue Sp Edn (Model Rail) - *03*	50	60
32-275X	**37412 'Driver John Elliot'** Transrail triple grey en Sp Edn 500 (Geoffrey Allison) - *03*	50	60
32-375	**37419** EW&S maroon - *03*	40	45
32-376	**37429 'Eisteddfod Genedlaethol'** Regional Railways blue - *03*	40	45
32-378	**37431 'Bullidae'** IC Mainline /petroleum grey+white sno - *03*	35	40
32-380	**37671 'Tre Pol and Pen'** Railfreight Distribution tripe grey sno en BRe, St Blazey plates and nameplates - *03*	40	50
32-379	**37678** BRe Railfreight red stripe grey sno - *03*	40	45

Class 24 diesel [L32] (Bachmann)

L34A. Class 40 Diesel 1Co-Co1

DCC ready, working LED headlight, metal roof grill and fan and cast or fabricated bogies.

32-475	**D368** BRc green code boxes - *04*	50	63
32-476	**40075** BRe blue discs - *04*	50	63
32-477	**D325** BRe green split headcode - *04*	50	63

L35. Class 42 'Warship' Diesel Hydraulic B-B

Optional separate apron parts and a buffer beam accessory pack.

32-055	**D800 'Sir Brian Robertson'** BRc green - *00*	35	45
32-053	**D804 'Avenger'** BRe blue - *00*	35	45
32-056	**D806 'Cambrian'** BRc maroon - *01*	35	45
32-060	**D810 'Vanguard'** BRc maroon W - *04*	40	56
32-052	**D816 'Eclipse'** BRc green - *99*	35	40
32-050	**D817 'Foxhound'** BRc maroon - *98*	35	45
32-059	**D818 'Glory'** BRc green - *04*	40	56
32-058	**D820 'Grenville'** BRc green - *03*	35	55
32-054	**D831 'Monarch'** BRe blue - *99*	35	40
32-051	**D832 'Onslaught'** BRc green - *98*	35	40
32-057	**D870 'Zulu'** BRe blue - *02*	35	50

A small number of maroon bodies of D827 'Kelly' (not of Mainline origin) have been found.

L36a. Classes 44 'Peak' Diesel 1Co-Co1

Roof grill and fan, buffers mounted on the bogies and etched nameplates.

32-650	**D1 'Scafell Pike'** BRc green - *03*	45	55
32-651	**44008 'Penyghent'** BRe blue - *03*	45	55

L36b. Classes 45 'Peak' Diesel Electric 1Co-Co1

Roof grill and fan, buffers mounted on the bogies and etched nameplates.

31-125Z	**D55 'Royal Signals'** BRc green W Sp Edn 500 (Southampton MC) - *02*	55	65
31-125	**D67 'The Royal Artilleryman'** BRc green, cream band - *not made*	NA	NA
31-126	**45114** BRe blue, white roof - *not made*	NA	NA

L36c. Classes 45 'Peak' Diesel 1Co-Co1
(2003 model)

Roof grill and fan, buffers mounted on the bogies and etched nameplates.

32-675*	**D67 'The Royal Artilleryman'** BRc green, cream band - *04*	50	63

Bachmann (British)

32-676*	**45114** BRe blue, white roof - *04*	50	63

* These were planned in 2002 using the old tooling but not proceeded with as it was decided to retool the model. These would have been 31-125 and 31-126.

Class 45 Diesel [L36C]

L37a. Classes 46 'Peak' Diesel 1Co-Co1 (ex-Mainline)

Later models had roof grill and fan, buffers mounted on the bogies and etched nameplates. wpc - wooden presentation case.

31-076A	BRe blue - *95*	25	35
31-081	**D163 'Leicestershire and Derbyshire Yeomanry'** BRc green - *not made*	NA	NA
31-080	**D172 'Ixion'** BRc green Watermans Railway Ltd Edn 2000 wpc - *96*	50	65
31-078	**D181** BRe blue - *97*	25	35
31-077	**D193** BRc green - *97*	25	35
31-075	**46026 'Leicestershire and Derbyshire Yeomanry'** BRe blue - *94*	30	40
31-076	**46045** BRe blue - *94*	25	35
?	**97403 'Ixion'** Research red/blue Sp Edn (Rail Express) - *02*	NPG	NPG

* This was planned in 2001 using the old tooling but not proceeded with as it was decided to retool the model. This would have been 31-081.

L37b. Classes 46 'Peak' Diesel 1Co-Co1 (2003 model)

Later models had roof grill and fan, buffers mounted on the bogies and etched nameplates. wpc - wooden presentation case.

32-700	**D163 'Leicestershire and Derbyshire Yeomanry'** BRc green - *04*	50	63
32-701	**46053** BRe blue - *04*	50	63
32-70?	**97403 'Ixion'** BRe blue+red (Sp Edn (Modelzone) - *05*	50	63

L38. Class 55 'Deltic' Diesel Co-Co

4 metal roof fans, 5-pole motor/flywheel drive and sprung buffers. W=weathered

32-525A	**D9002 'The Kings Own Yorkshire Light Infantry'** BRc green - *not made*	NA	NA
32-525	**D9004 'Queens Own Highlander'** BRc 2-tone green - *03*	45	60
32-525X	**D9021 'Argyll & Sutherland Highlander'** BRc green [1A35+1A06] Sp Edn 504 (TMC) - *04*	60	75
32-525Y	as above but weathered [1A16+1E15] Sp Edn 504 (TMC) - *04*	60	80
32-525A	**55002 'The Kings Own Yorkshire Light Infantry'** BRc green - *04*	50	64
32-527	**55012 'Crepello'** BRe blue - *04*	55	64
?	**55019 'Royal Highland Fusilier'** BRe blue W Sp Edn 500 (DPS) - *04*	60	74
32-526	**55020 'Nimbus'** BRe blue - *03*	45	60

L38A. Class 57 Diesel Co-Co

DCC ready.

32-750	**57008 'Freightliner Explorer'** Freightliner green - *04*	NPG	68
32-751	**57301 'Scot Tracy'** Virgin red and grey - *04*	NPG	68
32-752	**57602** FGW green - *04*	NPG	68

L38B. Class 66 Diesel Co-Co

DCC ready.

32-725	**66135** EWS maroon - *04*	NPG	73
32-726	**66610** Freightliner green - *04*	NPG	73
32-727	**66701** GBRf blue - *04*	NPG	73

L39a. Class 158 Express Units

31-501	**158702** Express/Scotrail blue+white 2-car - *97*	40	60
31-507	**158726** ScotRail Woosh! livery 2-car - *02*	50	70
31-506	**158745** Wales & West Alphaline silver 2-car - *00*	50	70
31-506A	**158746** Wessex Trains Alphaline silver 2-car - *02*	50	70
31-503	**158757** Express/Regional Railways blue+white 2-car - *97*	40	60
31-505	**158758** First North Western blue 2-car - *00*	50	70
31-504	**158783** Central Trains green 2-car - *00*	50	70
31-500A	**158791** Regional Railways blue+white 2-car - *97*	45	65
31-504A	**158797** Central Trains green 2-car - *02*	50	70
31-513	**158811** Northern Spirit purple+gold 3-car - *99*	65	80
31-513A	**158811** Arriva purple+gold? 3-car - *02*	65	85
31-511	**158809** Express blue+white 3-car - *98*	65	85
31-500	**158860** Regional Railways blue+white 2-car - *?*	NPG	NPG
31-500B	**158868** Regional Railways blue+white 2-car - *98*	40	60
31-502	**158906** BRe West Yorks PTE Metro red 2-car - *97*	40	60

L39b. Class 159 Express Units

31-510	**159001 'City of Exeter'** NSE bright blue 3-car - *98*	65	85
31-512	**159009** SWT/Stagecoach white 3-car - *98*	65	85
31-514	**159016** SouthWest Trains white 3-car - *01*	65	85

L40a. Class 165/1 'Network Turbo'

Working LED lights and flywheel driven 5-pole motor.

31-035	**165001** Chiltern Line white 2-car - *not made*	NA	NA

Class 165/1 Turbostar [L40a] (Bachmann)

L40b. Class 166 'Network Express Turbo'

Working LED lights and flywheel driven 5-pole motor.

31-025	**166202** NSE white 3-car - *99*	65	85
31-026	**166212** Thames Trains Express white+blue 3-car - *02*	65	85

L41. Class 168/1 Clubman DMU

3-car DMU.

32-470	**168110** (58160+58460+58260) Chiltern Railways white+violet - *03*	70	90
32-471	**?** (?+?+?) Chiltern Railways white+ violet - *04*	NPG	93

L42a. Class 170 2-Car 'Turbostar' DMU

Different front apron styles and authentic running lights operation.

32-450	**170105** Midland Main teal 170/1 - *01*	50	70
32-453	**170271** Anglia Railways blue 170/2 - *03*	55	75
32-452	**1700301?** SouthWest Trains white 170/4 - *01*	50	70

32-452A	**170302** SouthWest Trains white 170/4 - *04*	55	75
32-451	**170515?** Central Trains green 170/5 - *01*	55	75
32-451A	**170514** Central Trains green W 170/1 - *04*	55	75

L42b. Class 170 3-Car 'Turbostar' DMU
Flush ribbon glazing.

32-460	**170637** (50637+56637+79637) Central Trains green 170/6 - *03*	65	85
32-461	**170424** Scotrail woosh! livery 170/3 - *01*	65	85
32-462	**170470** (50470+56470+79471) Strathclyde PTE maroon+cream 170/3 - *03*	65	85

L43. Class 220 Virgin Voyager DEMU
Non-tilting 4-car set

32-600	**220001 'Maiden Voyager'** (60301 + 60701+ 60201+ 60401) grey+red - *02*	80	100
(30-600)	**220017 'Bombardier Voyager'** grey+ red 3-car ex-set - *03*	80	NA
32-601	220032 **'Grampian Voyager'** grey+red - *04*	80	103

L44. Class 221 Virgin Super Voyager DEMU
Tilting 5-car set

32-625	**221130 'Michael Palin'** grey+red - *04*	80	120
32-626	**221115 'Louis Bleriot'** grey+red - *04*	80	123

COACHES

The earliest coaches were a number of GWR Colletts and LMS types from the former Mainline range but with different stock numbers. Some of these had also been made for Replica Railways by the tool owners - Kader. They were followed by LNER coaches of Thompson design and Bulleid stock of the Southern Region.

Running Numbers - The finest development so far is an extensive range of Mk1 coaches, in the Blue Riband series, which first appeared late in 1999. Bachmann tend to give their coaches different stock numbers when they redo a batch and this is usually reflected in the addition of a letter suffix to the catalogue number to denote the change. There have, however, been a few cases where the suffix has been missed off the box which shows, instead, the old catalogue number and there have been boxes with the new number but with a coach carrying the old running number. As always, it is as well to ensure that the contents of the box are what you expect them to be.

Cat.No.	Company, Number, Colour, Date	£	£

Collett Stock

C1a. Collett 60ft Corridor 3rd (2nd)

34-050	**GWR** 1107 choc+cream - *91*	12	22
34-050A	**GWR** ? choc+cream - *93*	12	20
34-050B	**Great Western** 1118 choc+cream Hawksworth livery - *?*	NPG	NPG
34-050C	**Great Western** ? choc+cream Hawksworth livery - *01*	12	17
34-050D	**Great Western** ? choc+cream Hawksworth livery - *03*	12	17
34-051	**GWR** (button) 1145 choc+cream Hawksworth livery - *95*	12	19
34-052	**Great Western** ? choc+cream Hawksworth livery - *04*	NPG	17
34-055	**BR** W1123 red+cream - *95*	12	19
34-056	**BR** ? red+cream - *04*	NPG	17
34-200	**BR** W562W maroon - *91*	12	22

C1b. Collett 60ft Corridor Brake End

34-075	**GWR** 1655 choc+cream 3rd - *91*	12	22
34-075A	**GWR** 1657 choc+cream 3rd - *?*	NPG	NPG
34-075B	**Great Western** 1656 choc+cream1st/3rd	12	18

	Hawksworth livery - *97*		
34-075C	**Great Western** ? choc+cream 3rd Hawksworth livery - *01*	12	17
34-075D	**Great Western** ? choc+cream 3rd Hawksworth livery - *03*	12	17
34-076	**GWR** (button) 6600 choc+cream1st/3rd Hawksworth livery - *95*	12	19
34-076	**Great Western** ? choc+cream Hawksworth livery - *04*	NPG	17
34-080	**BR** W6550 red+cream 1st/2nd - *95*	12	19
34-081	**BR** ? red+cream - *04*	NPG	17
34-175	**BR** W1657W maroon 2nd - *91*	12	22

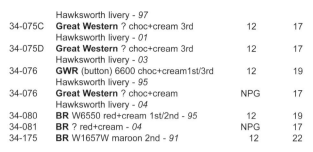

Collette 60' corridor brake end [C1b] (Bachmann)

C1c. Collett 60ft Corridor 1st

34-100	**GWR** 8095 choc+cream - *90*	12	22
34-100A	**GWR** 8099 choc+cream - *?*	NPG	NPG
34-100B	**Great Western** 8096 choc+cream Hawksworth livery - *97*	12	18
34-101	**GWR** (button) 8101 choc+cream - *95*	12	19

C1d. Collett 60ft Corridor Composite

34-125	**GWR** 7001 choc+cream - *90*	12	22
34-125A	**GWR** 7003 choc+cream - *?*	NPG	NPG
34-125B	**GWR** 7056 choc+cream - *97*	12	18
34-125C	**Great Western** ? choc+cream Hawksworth livery - *01*	12	17
34-125D	**Great Western** ? choc+cream Hawksworth livery - *03*	12	17
34-126	**Great Western** ? choc+cream Hawksworth livery - *04*	NPG	17
34-126	**GWR** (button) 7023 choc+cream - *95*	12	19
34-130	**BR** W7021 red+cream - *95*	12	19
34-131	**BR** ? red+cream - *04*	NPG	17
34-150	**BR** W7033W maroon - *90*	12	22

LMS Stock

These include LMS period 1 panelled stock and the period 3 Stanier parcel van.

C2a. LMS Panelled 57ft Corridor Brake End

34-225	**BR** M5315 maroon - *90*	12	18
34-226	**LMS** 5312 maroon end boards - *96*	12	16
34-226A	**LMS** 5284 maroon end boards - *00*	12	15
34-226B	**LMS** ? maroon end boards - *03*	12	15
34-226Y	**CIE** 1095 green - *00*	10	15
34-226Z	**CIE** 1087 green - *00*	10	15
34-275	**BR** M5267 red+cream - *90*	12	18
34-276	**LMS** 10199? maroon 1928 livery - *not made*	NA	NA

C2b. LMS Panelled 57ft Corridor Composite

34-250	**BR** M3565 maroon - *90*	12	18
34-251	**LMS** 3650 maroon end boards - *96*	12	16
34-251A	**LMS** 3572 maroon end boards - *00*	12	15
34-251B	**LMS** ? maroon end boards - *03*	12	15
34-251X	**CIE** 2096 green - *00*	10	15
34-252	**LMS** 3705 maroon end boards - *96*	12	16
34-252A	**LMS** 3591 maroon - *00*	12	15
34-252B	**LMS** ? maroon - *03*	12	15
34-300	**BR** M3672 red+cream - *90*	12	18
34-301	**LMS** 18997 maroon 1928 livery - *not made*	NA	NA
34-302	**LMS**? maroon 1928 livery - *not made*	NA	NA

Bachmann (British)

C2c. LMS Panelled 57ft Corridor All 3rd

34-251Y	CIE 1332 green - *00*	10	15
34-251Z	CIE 1336 green - *00*	10	15

C3. Stanier 50ft Parcels Van

34-325	BR M31340 red+cream - *90*	12	18
34-325	BR M31386M red LMS end boards - *96*	12	16
34-326	BR M31319M red+cream LMS type end boards - *96*	12	16
34-327	LMS 31250 maroon end board - *96*	12	16
34-327A	LMS ? maroon - *01*	12	15
34-350	BR M31261 maroon - *90*	12	18

Thompson Stock

The 1992-93 stock was released in Thompson brown livery but those made in 2000 were in pre-war LNER brown.

C4a. Thompson 63ft Corridor 3rd (2nd)

34-375	BR E1098E red+cream - *91*	12	19
34-375/1	BR E1056E red+cream - *?*	12	19
34-376	BR E1497E maroon - *91*	12	19
34-376/1	BR E1001E maroon - *?*	12	19
34-377	LNER 1047 brown - *92-93*	12	19
34-378	BRc E1550E maroon - *97*	12	18

Thompson 63' corridor 3rd [C4a] (Bachmann)

C4b. Thompson 59.5ft Corridor Composite

34-400	BR E1207E red+cream - *91*	12	19
34-400/1	BR E1236E red+cream - *?*	12	19
34-401	BR E1228E maroon - *91*	12	19
34-401/1	BR E1240E maroon - *?*	12	19
34-402	LNER 144 brown - *92-93*	12	19
34-403	BRc E1262E maroon - *97*	12	18

C4c. Thompson 63ft Corridor Brake Composite

34-425	BR E1146E red+cream - *91*	12	19
34-425/1	BR E1143E red+cream - *?*	12	19
34-426	BR E1158E maroon - *91*	12	19
34-426/1	BR E1140E maroon - *?*	12	19
34-427	LNER 138 brown - *92-93*	12	19
34-427	LNER 1142 brown - *?*	12	19
34-427/1	LNER 1112 brown - *?*	12	19
34-428	BRc E1151E maroon - *97*	12	18

C4d. Thompson 63ft Corridor Brake 3rd (2nd)

34-450	BR E1905E red+cream - *91*	12	19
34-450/1	BR E1925E red+cream - *?*	12	19
34-451	BR E1907E maroon - *91*	12	19
34-451/1	BR E1932E maroon - *?*	12	19
34-452	LNER 1908 brown - *92-93*	12	19
34-453	BRc E1910E maroon - *97*	12	18

C4e. Thompson 63ft Corridor 1st

34-475	BR E1315E red+cream - *91*	12	19
34-475/1	BR E1323E red+cream - *?*	12	19
34-476	BR E1322E maroon - *91*	12	19
34-476/1	BR E1312E maroon - *?*	12	19
34-477	LNER 1132 brown - *92-93*	12	19
34-477	LNER 138 brown - *?*	12	19
34-478	BRc E1320E maroon - *97*	12	18

C4f. Thompson 63ft BG Full Brake

Fitted with end board and step board.

34-650	BR E19E maroon - *94*	12	21
34-651	BR E12E maroon - *96*	12	20
34-651	LNER ? brown - *00*	12	18
34-651A	BR E153E red+cream - *00*	12	18
34-652	BR E18E blue - *95*	12	20
34-652A	BR E18E blue - *00*	12	18
34-653	BR E16E red - *96*	12	18
34-653A	BR E16E red - *00*	12	18
34-654	BRc E14E maroon - *97*	12	20
34-654A	BRc E14E maroon - *00*	12	18
34-655	LNER 11 brown - *00*	12	18

C4g. Thompson 2nd Corridor (flush end glazing)

34-800	BR ? red+cream - *02*	15	19

C4h. Thompson Composite (flush end glazing)

34-825	BR ? red+cream - *02*	15	19

C4i. Thompson Composite Brake (flush end glazing)

34-850	BR ? red+cream - *02*	15	19

C4j. Thompson 2nd Brake (flush end glazing)

34-875	BR ? red+cream - *02*	15	19

C4k. Thompson 1st Corridor (flush end glazing)

34-900	BR ? red+cream - *02*	15	19

Bulleid Stock

C5a. Bulleid 63ft Corridor Open Brake 3rd (2nd)

be = brown end door

34-500	BR S3945S green - *93*	12	21
34-500A	BR S3955S malachite green - *97*	12	19
34-500B	BR S3962S malachite green - *00*	12	18
34-501	BR S3948S malachite green - *93*	12	21
34-501A	BR S3949S malachite green - *97*	12	19
34-502	BR ? red+cream no red cantrail band - *96*	12	20
34-502	BR S3960 red+cream - *93*	12	21
34-502A	BR S3960 red+cream - *00*	12	18
34-503	BR S3962S red+cream - *93*	12	21
34-503A	BR S3951S red+cream - *97*	12	18
34-503A	BR ? red+cream, be - *02*	12	18

C5b. Bulleid 63ft Corridor Composite

be = brown end door

34-522	BR ? red+cream no crimson red band - *99*	12	18
34-550	BR S5871S malachite green yellow 1st class line - *93*	12	21
34-550A	BR S5870S malachite green yellow 1st class line - *99*	12	18
34-550A	BR ? malachite green - *97*	12	19
34-550B	BR S5810S malachite green yellow 1st class line - *00*	12	18
34-551	BR S5890S malachite green - *93*	12	21
34-551A	BR S5900S malachite green - *97*	12	19
34-552	BR S5907S red+cream - *93*	12	21
34-552A	BR S5907 red+cream no red cantrail band - *00*	12	18
34-552A	BR S5907 red+cream no red cantrail band, be - *02*	12	18
34-553	BR S5868S red+cream - *93*	12	21
34-553A	BR S5900S red+cream - *97*	12	18

C5c. Bulleid 63ft Corridor 3rd (2nd)

be = brown end door

34-525	BR S82S, S1085 green - *93*	12	21
34-525A	BR S127S malachite green - *97*	12	19
34-525B	BR S125S green - *?*	12	18
34-526	BR S130S, S1275 malachite green - *93*	12	21

34-526A	**BR** ? malachite green - *97*	12	19
34-527	**BR** S101 red+cream no red cantrail - *93*	12	21
34-527A	**BR** ? red+cream - *00*	12	18
34-528	**BR** S114S red+cream - *93*	12	21
34-528A	**BR** ? red+cream - *97*	12	18
34-528A	**BR** ? red+cream, be - *02*	12	18

C5d.   Bulleid 63ft Open 3rd (2nd)
EB = SR end boards.

34-575	**BR** S1504S malachite green EB - *95*	12	20
34-575A	**BR** S1504S malachite green EB - *00*	12	18
34-576	**BR** S1493S red+cream EB - *95*	12	20
34-576A	**BR** S1493S red+cream - *00*	12	18

Mark 1 Suburban Stock

C6a.   Mk1 57ft Suburban 3rd (2nd)

34-600	**BR** M46082 red unlined - *93*	12	19
34-600/1	**BR** E56128 red unlined - *94*	12	19
34-601	**BR** M46083 red unlined - *93*	12	19
34-601A	**BR** M? red unlined - *02*	12	18
34-602	**BR** M46073 maroon - *93*	12	19
34-602A	**BR** M? maroon - *02*	12	18
34-602/3	**BR** ? maroon - *94*	12	19
34-603	**BR** M46074 maroon - *93*	12	19
34-603A	**BR** M? maroon - *02*	12	18
34-604	**BR** W46199 maroon - *96*	12	19
34-604A	**BR** W46199 maroon - *00*	12	18
34-605	**BR** E46109 red unlined - *96*	12	19
34-605A	**BR** E46109 red unlined - *00*	12	18
34-606	**BR** E46127 red unlined - *96*	12	19
34-606A	**BR** E46127 red unlined - *00*	12	18

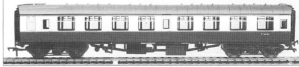

Mk1 57' suburban 3rd [C6a] (Bachmann)

C6b.   Mk1 57ft Suburban Brake 3rd (2nd)

34-625	**BR** M43259 red unlined - *93*	12	19
34-625A	**BR** M43270 red unlined - *01*	12	18
34-626	**BR** E43130 red unlined - *94*	12	19
34-626	**BR** M43257 maroon - *93*	12	19
34-627	**BR** W43102 lined maroon - *96*	12	19
34-627A	**BR** W43102 lined maroon - *00*	12	18
34-628	**BR** E53171 red unlined - *96*	12	19
34-628A	**BR** E53171 red unlined - *00*	12	18

C6c.   Mk1 57ft Suburban Open 2nd

34-675	**BR** W48029 maroon - *96*	12	19
34-675A	**BR** W48029 maroon - *00*	12	18
34-676	**BR** M48037 red unlined - *96*	12	19
34-676A	**BR** M48037 red unlined - *01*	12	18

C6d.   Mk1 57ft Suburban Composite

34-700	**BR** W41058 lined maroon - *96*	12	19
34-700A	**BR** ? maroon - *00*	12	18
34-701	**BR** M71006 red unlined - *96*	12	19
34-701A	**BR** M41004 red unlined - *01*	12	18

Blue Riband Coaches (39-XXX Series)

Mark1 Main Line Stock

C7a.   Mk1 SK Corridor 2nd (3rd)

34-725	**BR** blue+grey - *not made*	NA	NA
34-726	**BR** maroon - *not made*	NA	NA
34-727	**BR** red+cream - *not made*	NA	NA
39-025	**BR** E25039 blue+grey - *99*	15	22
39-025A	**BR** E26140 blue+grey - *01*	15	21
39-025B	**BR** E26033 blue+grey - *02*	15	20
39-026	**BR** E24538 maroon - *99*	15	22
39-026A	**BRc** E25044 maroon - *00*	15	21
39-026B	**BR** M25400 maroon - *01*	15	21
39-026C	**BR** E? maroon - *02*	15	20
39-027	**BR** M24446 red+cream - *99*	15	22
39-027A	**BR** M24467 red+cream - *00*	15	21
39-027B	**BR** M? red+cream - *02*	15	20
39-027C	**BR** E24796 red+cream - *03*	15	20
39-028	**BR** S24311 green - *00*	15	21
39-028A	**BR** S? green - *02*	15	20
39-029	**BRc** W24165 choc+cream - *00*	15	21
39-029A	**BRc** W25051 choc+cream - *02*	15	20
39-030	**BR Inter-City** M18753 grey - *02*	15	20
39-031	**BR NSE** ? bright blue - *04*	NPG	20

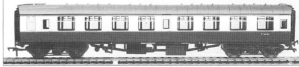

Mk1 SK Corridor 2nd [C7a]

C7b.   Mk1 SO Open 2nd (3rd)

34-750	**BR** blue+grey - *not made*	NA	NA
34-751	**BR** maroon - *not made*	NA	NA
34-752	**BR** red+cream - *not made*	NA	NA
39-050	**BR** E4357 blue+grey - *99*	15	22
39-050A	**BR** E5001 blue+grey - *01*	15	21
39-050B	**BR** ? blue+grey - *02*	15	20
39-051	**BR** E4238 maroon - *99*	15	22
39-051A	**BRc** E3850 maroon - *01*	15	21
39-051B	**BR** M4414 maroon - *01*	15	20
39-051C	**BR** M4899 maroon - *03*	15	20
39-052	**BR** M3737 red+cream - *99*	15	22
39-052A	**BR** M3788 red+cream - *00*	15	21
39-052B	**BR** ? red+cream - *02*	15	20
39-052C	**BR** M4899 red+cream - *02*	15	20
39-053	**BR** S3998 green - *00*	15	20
39-053A	**BR** S4040 green - *01*	15	20
39-054	**BRc** W3791 choc+cream - *00*	15	20
39-054A	**BRc** W4739 choc+cream - *03*	15	20
39-055	**BR Inter-City** 4909 grey - *02*	15	20
39-056	**BR Reg Rlys** 4873 blue+white - *02*	15	20
39-057	**BR NSE** ? bright blue - *04*	NPG	20
-	**ScotRail - West Highland** 4050 green +cream *see C7k coach sets*	20	NA
-	**ScotRail - West Highland** green+cream *see C7k coach sets*	20	NA
-	**ScotRail - West Highland** green+cream *see C7k coach sets*	20	NA
39-000Y(A)	**West Highland Line** IC3767C green+ cream - *see C7k coach sets*	20	NA
39-000Z(A)	**West Highland Line** IC4912C green+ cream - *see C7k coach sets*	20	NA
39-000Z(B)	**West Highland Line** IC4911C green+ cream - *see C7k coach sets*	20	NA

C7c.   Mk1 BSK Brake Corridor 2nd (3rd)

34-775	**BR** blue+grey - *not made*	NA	NA
34-776	**BR** maroon - *not made*	NA	NA
34-777	**BR** red+cream - *not made*	NA	NA
39-075	**BR** E35445 blue+grey - *99*	15	20
39-075A	**BR** M35040 blue+grey - *03*	15	20
39-076	**BR** E34168 maroon - *99*	15	22
39-076A	**BRc** E34007 maroon - *00*	15	21
39-076B	**BR** M25400 maroon - *00*	15	20

Bachmann (British)

39-077	**BR** M34655 red+cream - *99*	15	22
39-077A	**BR** E? red+cream - *99*	15	20
39-078	**BR** S35020 green - *00*	15	21
39-078A	**BR** S? green - *00*	15	20
39-079	**BRc** W34290 choc+cream - *00*	15	20
39-079A	**BRc** W34751 choc+cream - *03*	15	20
39-080	**BR Inter-City** M35465 grey - *02*	15	20
39-081	**BR Reg Rlys** 35452 blue+white - *02*	15	20
39-082	**BRc NSE?** bright blue - *04*	NPG	20
-	**ScotRail - West Highland** 9312 green+ cream *see C7k coach sets*	20	NA

Mk1 BG full brake [C7g] (Bachmann)

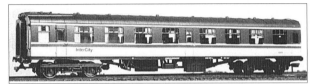

Mk1 open 2nd [C7b] (Bachmann)

C7d. Mk1 RU Restaurant Car Unclassed

34-800	**BR** blue+grey - *not made*	NA	NA
34-801	**BR** maroon - *not made*	NA	NA
39-100	**BR** E1938 blue+grey - *99*	15	20
39-101	**BR** E1926 maroon - *99*	15	20
39-101A	**BR** E1961 maroon - *03*	15	20
39-102	**BR** W1902 choc+cream - *01*	15	20
39-103	**BR** W1915 maroon - *01*	15	20
39-104	**BR** IC 1981 grey RBR - *02*	15	20

C7e. Mk1 CK Corridor Composite

39-125	**BR** E16241 blue+grey - *00*	15	20
39-126	**BRc** 15145 maroon - *00*	15	21
39-126A	**BR** M16005 maroon - *01*	15	20
39-127	**BR** M15019 red+cream - *00*	15	20
39-127A	**BR** E15271 red+cream - *03*	15	20
39-128	**BR** S15904 green - *00*	15	20
39-128A	**BR** S15566 green - *03*	15	20
39-129	**BRc** W15770 choc+cream - *00*	15	20
39-130	**BR NSE** ? bright blue - *04*	NPG	20

C7f. Mk1 FK Corridor First

39-150	**BR** E13107 blue+grey - *00*	15	20
39-151	**BRc** E13030 maroon - *00*	15	20
39-151A	**BRc** M13223 maroon - *03*	15	20
39-152	**BR** M13004 red+cream - *00*	15	20
39-153	**BR** S13143 green - *00*	15	20
39-154	**BRc** W13074 choc+cream - *00*	15	20
39-155	**BR Inter-City** M13341 grey - *02*	15	20
39-156	**BRe** Regional Rlys 13225 blue+white - *02*	15	20

C7g. Mk1 BG Full Brake

39-175	**BR** E80617 blue+grey - *00*	15	20
39-175A	**BR** M84281 blue+grey - *03*	15	20
39-176	**BR** E80798 maroon - *00*	15	21
39-176A	**BR** M80950 maroon - *01*	15	20
39-177	**BR** M80541 red+cream - *00*	15	20
39-178	**BR** S81510 green - *00*	15	20
39-179	**BRc** W81205 choc+cream - *00*	15	20
39-180	**BR Inter-City** 92151 grey NEA - *02*	15	20
39-181	**BR Regional Rlys** E92058 blue+ white NEA Parcels - *02*	15	20
39-182	**BRe** 95211 blue Newspapers NCX - *02*	15	20
39-183	**RES** 92322 red+dark grey NEX - *03*	15	20
39-184	**BRe Royal Mail** ? red NEA - *03*	15	20
39-200	**RES** 94474 red+dark grey - *01*	15	20
39-200A	**RES** ? red+dark grey - *03*	15	20
39-201	**RES Royal Mail** 94420 red+dark grey - *01*	15	20
39-201A	**RES Royal Mail** ? red+dark grey - *03*	15	20

C7h. Mk1 BCK Brake Composite Corridor

39-225	**BR** M24241 blue+grey - *01*	15	20
39-226	**BRc** E21202 maroon - *01*	15	20
39-227	**BR** M21238 red+cream - *made?*	15	20
39-227	**BR** M21026 red+cream - *01?*	15	20
39-228	**BR** S21268 green - *01*	15	20
39-229	**BR** W21067 choc+cream - *01*	15	20
39-230	**BR InterCity** 21266 grey - *02*	15	20
39-000Y(B)	**West Highland Line** IC21241C green+ cream - *see C7k coach sets*	20	NA

C7i. Mk1 RFO Restaurant First Open

39-250	**BR** E3 blue+grey - *01*	15	20
39-251	**BR** E3 maroon - *01*	15	20
39-252	**BR** M4 red+cream - *01*	15	20
39-253	**BR** S9 green - *01*	15	20
39-254	**BR** W7 choc+cream - *01*	15	20

C7j. Mk1 RMB Restaurant Miniature Buffet

39-260	**BR** ? red+cream - *04*	NPG	21
39-261	**BR** ? maroon - *04*	NPG	21
39-262	**BR** ? green - *04*	NPG	21
39-263	**BR** ? cocolate+cream - *04*	NPG	21

C7k. Mk1 Coach Sets

39-000Y	**West Highland Line** SO IC3767C + BCK IC21241C green+cream Sp Edn 360 (Harburn Hobbies) - *03*	NPG	45
39-000Z	**West Highland Line** SO IC4911C + SO IC4912C green+cream Sp Edn 360 (Harburn Hobbies) - *03*	NPG	45
-	**ScotRail - West Highland** 3 x SO + BSK green+cream Sp Edn 500 (Model Rail) - *03*	NPG	90

C8. Mk1 GUV

39-270	**RES** ? red+dark grey - *04*	NPG	21
39-271	**BR** ? maroon - *04*	NPG	21
39-272	**BR** ? blue - *04*	NPG	21

Mark1 Pullman Stock

C9a. Mk1 Pullman Kitchen FK

39-280	**BR** ? brown+cream - *04*	NPG	26

C9b. Mk1 Pullman 1st FP

39-290	**BR** ? brown+cream - *04*	NPG	26

C9c. Mk1 Pullman Kitchen 2nd SK

39-300	**BR** ? brown+cream - *04*	NPG	26

C9d. Mk1 Pullman Parlour 2nd SP

39-310	**BR** ? brown+cream - *04*	NPG	26

C9e. Mk1 Pullman Bar 2nd BSP

39-320	**BR** ? brown+cream - *04*	NPG	26

Mark2 Main Line Stock

C10a. Mk2S Corridor 1st FK
39-330	**BR** ? blue+grey - 04	NPG	22
39-331	**BR IC** ? grey - 04	NPG	22

C10b. Mk2A Corridor 1st FK
39-340	**BR** ? blue+grey - 04	NPG	22
39-341	**BR IC** ? grey - 04	NPG	22
39-342	**BR NSE** ? bright blue - 04	NPG	22

C10c. Mk2S Open 2nd TSO
39-350	**BR** ? blue+grey - 04	NPG	22
39-351	**BR IC** ? grey - 04	NPG	22
39-360	**BR** ? blue+grey - 04	NPG	22
39-361	**BR IC** ? grey - 04	NPG	22
39-362	**BR NSE**? bright blue - 04	NPG	22

C10d. Mk2S Brake Corridor 1st BSO
39-370	**BR** ? blue+grey - 04	NPG	22
39-371	**BR IC** ? grey - 04	NPG	22

C10e. Mk2S Brake Open 2nd BSO
39-380	**BR** ? blue+grey - 04	NPG	22
39-381	**BR IC** ? grey - 04	NPG	22

C10f. Mk2A Brake Open 2nd BSO
39-390	**BR** ? blue+grey - 04	NPG	22
39-391	**BR IC** ? grey - 04	NPG	22
39-392	**BR NSE**? bright blue - 04	NPG	22

C10g. Mk2S Brake Corridor 1st BFK
39-400	**BR** ? blue+grey - 04	NPG	22
39-401	**BR Reg Rlys** ? blue - 04	NPG	22
39-402	**BR NSE**? bright blue - 04	NPG	22

C10h. Mk2A Brake Corridor 1st BFK
39-410	**BR** ? blue+grey - 04	NPG	22
39-421	**BR Reg Rlys** ? blue - 04	NPG	22
39-432	**BR NSE**? bright blue - 04	NPG	22

WAGONS

As with the locomotives and coaches, wagons started with Mainline originals reproduced in a selection of new liveries. A new development was the sets of themed coal wagons and petrol tankers which are likely to become more collectable than single wagons.

The new Blue Riband wagons, which have a '37' prefix, are the bee's knees of the ready-to-run wagon world and the range is expanding fast. There have been many commissioned models (nearly all private owner open wagons) and some of these are likely to become much sought after in years to come.

Several wagons were issued with detachable loads. These containers, transformers and boilers, used as loads on wagons, were also sold separately as accessories.

Confusion surrounds some of the wagons produced in 2000 and 2001 particularly as far as their catalogue numbering goes. This is because when ordered they were allocated a 33-XXX number but by the time they arrived their specification had been raised to that of the Blue Riband range although they had not been given catalogue numbers in the 37-XXX series.

Wagon Numbers - WARNING! The numbers on wagons are mostly taken from catalogues which is not ideal as, in compiling their catalogues, Bachmann sometimes use pictures of earlier examples with the new catalogue number. Where pre-production models or photographs of real wagons have been used there is no guarantee that the production model will carry the same number. The best advice is to treat numbers quoted in this section with caution. We are keen to hear from you with suggested corrections.

Listing - While it might seem logical to keep the original wagons separate from the Blue Riband ones, this will only cause confusion for those seeking to identify unboxed examples. We have therefore listed them under types in the following order: flats, open wagons (according to size), hoppers, tankers, vans, brake vans and bogie stock. Blue Riband models are marked (B).

Cat.No.	Company, Number, Colour, Date	£	£

Flat Wagons

W1a. Conflat A
-	**BR** B702201 brown - 96	5	NA
-	**BR** B707067 brown - 96	5	NA
33-335	above 2 Conflats - 96	NA	14
-	**BR** B505461 brown - 98	5	NA
-	**BR** B505432 brown - 98	5	NA
33-335A	above 2 Conflats - 98	NA	14

W1b. Conflat A and Containers
33-325	**BR** B701739 brown + BD42724B container brown - 95	6	8
33-325A	**BR** B701283 brown + BD46541B container brown - 98	5	7
33-326	BR B506033 brown + BD6600B container crimson - 95	6	8
33-326A	**BR** B702326 brown + BD6698B container crimson W - 99	5	7
33-327	**BR** B703760 brown + AF6600B container light blue - 95	6	8
33-327A	**BR** B704933 brown + AF66008B + AF66187B containers light blue - 99	5	7
33-328	**BR** B704477 brown + AF65098B container white - 95	6	8
33-329	**GW** 36876 dark grey + B1775 container chocolate - 95	6	8
33-330-	**BR** B503829 brown + AFU16320B, AFU16327B containers white - 96	6	8

W2a. Conflat A (B)
37-980/1	**BR** B73775? brown Conflat A - 01	5	NA
37-980/2	**BR** B? brown Conflat A - 01	5	NA
37-980A	above two wagons - 01	NA	10
37-980Z	**BR** 70605? yellow shunter's running wagon Sp Edn 500 (Pennine Models) - 01	8	9

W2b. Conflat A with BD Container (B)
37-950	**BR** B708315 brown + **Speedfreight** BD47381B container grey+yellow - 01	6	8
37-951	**BR** B705549 brown + **BR** BD48964B container crimson - 01	6	8

W2c. Conflat A with AF Containers (B)
37-975	**GW** 39354 dark grey + AF2098 container **GWR** white - 01	6	8
37-975A	**GW** ? dark grey + AF? container **GWR** white - 03	5	6
37-976	**BR** B700954 brown + AFU16327B **BR** white + AF66008B pale blue containers - 01	6	8

W2d. Conflat A with BA Container (B)
BA sliding door container.
37-985	**BR** B708315? brown + BA container **Speedfreight** ? silver - not made	NA	NA

41

Bachmann (British)

Planked Open Wagons

W3a. 12T 1-Plank Wagon

33-400	**H Lees** & Son 101 red - *90*	8	10
33-400A	**H Lees** & Son 96 red - *92*	7	9
33-401	**Corsham** Quarrying 70 maroon - *92*	7	9
33-402	**BR** M460648 brown Lowfit - *92*	6	8
33-403	undecorated light grey - *92*	5	7
33-404	**LMS** 460531 brown - *97*	5	6
33-405	**Bath Stone Firms Ltd** cream - *97*	6	8
33-?	**G&KER** 31 grey Sp Edn 504 (Toys2Save) - *04*	5	6

W3b. 12T 1-Plank Wagon with Vehicle Load

33-410	**BR** B450023 + white Ford Transit Van (Herpa) load - *96*	8	12
33-411	**BR** B450050 + blue and red Ford Capri (Herpa) load - *96*	8	12
33-412	**BR** B450141 brown Triumph TR3 (Herpa) load - *97*	8	12

W3c. 12T 1-Plank Wagon with Small Container

33-950	**BR** B450027 brown + AFU19320B? container - *91*	8	10
33-951	**GW** 70031 dark grey + AF-2121 **GWR** container - *91*	8	10
33-952	**BR** B450300 brown + AF12 **BR** container - *92*	8	10
33-953	**LMS** 209340 grey + E5 **LMS** container - *91*	8	10

W3d. 12T 1-Plank Wagon with Large Container

33-975	**LMS** 209341 grey + BD1641 container maroon - *92*	8	10
33-976	**NE** 203169 brown + BD1465 container blue - *94*	7	9
33-977	undecorated dark grey - *not made*	NA	NA

W4. 1-Plank Wagon (B)

37-475	**LMS** 200345 grey - *01*	4	5
37-475A	**LMS** ? grey - *03*	4	5
37-475Z	**G&KER** 31 grey Sp Edn 504 (Toys 2 Save) - *03*	5	6
37-476	**H Lees** & Sons Ltd 105 red - *01*	5	6
37-476B	**Morris & Griffin** ? ? - *03*	4	5

W5. 3-Plank Wagon

33-450	**Cammell Laird** 630 brown - *92*	8	10
33-450A	**Easter Iron Mines** 4 brown - *96*	6	8
33-450Z	**M&GN** 470 brown + **LNER** container BD1466 On Loan to M&GN blue Sp Edn 500 (North Norfolk Railway) - *?*	15	18
33-451	**James Carter** 170 grey - *90*	8	10
33-451A	**Evan Davies** 25 light grey - *96*	6	8
33-452	**BR** W36459 brown - *92*	7	9
33-453	undecorated light grey - *92*	5	7
33-454	**SR** 62948 dark brown - *96*	6	8
(30-200)	**LT** BW231 dark grey ex set 30-200 - *91*	10	NA

3-plank wagon [W5]

W6. 3-Plank Wagon (B)

37-925	**ICI Buxton Lime** 48 light grey - *02*	4	5
37-926	**BR** M470105 brown - *01, 03*	4	5
37-926A	**BR** ? brown - *03*	4	5
37-927	**BR** M470105 brown + red BD container - *04*	4	7
37-929	**BR** ? brown + blue **LNER** BD container - *04*	4	7

W7. 5-Plank Wagon

This model was based on a 17'6" open wagon.

33-050	**Hinkley UDC** 4 red - *91*	8	10
33-050A	**Pounsbery** 1 green - *94*	6	8
33-050Z	**M&GN** 822045 brown Sp Edn 500 (North Norfolk Railway) - *94*	12	15
33-051	**Cefnmawr & Rhosymedre** 12 red - *92*	8	10
33-051A	**SR** 28422 dark brown (see table W9b - 37-050) - *not made*	NA	NA
33-052	**BR** DW280 dark grey - *91*	8	10
33-053	unfinished light grey - *95*	6	8
33-054	**English China Clays** 490 red - *95*	6	8
33-055	**Worcester New Coop** 20 red+black (see table W9b - 37-052) - *not made*	NA	NA
33-056	**Stevenson** 10 blue (see table W9b - 37-051) - *not made*	NA	NA

13T 5-plank china clay wagon [W8a]

W8a. 13T 5-Plank China Clay Wagon with Hood

The model was based on 16' open wagons and the hoods are made of stitched light blue canvas and kept in shape by a removable moulded plastic former.

33-075	**BR** B743267 brown - *91*	8	10
33-075A	**BR** B743321 brown - *94*	7	9
33-075B	**BR** B743169 brown W - *98*	6	8
33-075C	**BR** B743197 brown W - *99*	6	8
33-075D	**BR** B74397? brown W - *01*	5	7
33-080	**BR** ? brown W - *03*	5	6
33-076	**BR** B743752 brown - *92*	8	10
33-076A	**BR** B743238 brown - *94*	7	9
33-076B	**BR** B743156 brown W - *98*	6	8
33-076C	**BR** 743127 brown W - *99*	6	8
33-076D	**BR** B74327? brown 7405 - *01*	5	7
33-081	**BR** ? brown - *03*	5	6
33-07??	**BR** B743597 brown - *02*	5	6
33-080	**BR** B743169 brown W - *04*	5	6
33-081	**BR** B743141 brown W - *04*	5	6

W8b. 13T 5-Plank China Clay Wagon without Hood

33-077	**BR** B743236 brown - *92*	8	10
33-077A	**BR** B743620 brown W - *00*	6	7
33-077B	**BR** B743221 brown W 7449 - *02*	5	6
33-078	**BR** P270732 brown - *00*	7	9
33-078A	**GW** 92873 dark grey W - *02*	5	6
33-078B	**GW** 92873? dark grey W - *02*	5	6
33-079	**GW** 92971 dark grey - *96*	7	9
33-079	**BR** B743096? grey - *03*	5	6
33-082	**BR** B743357 brown W - *04*	5	6

W9a. 5-Plank Wagon with Steel Floor (B)

37-025	**Quarrite** 306 red - *98*	6	8
37-025A	**James Durnford** 37 black- *03*	4	6
37-025Y	**SLB** 702 light grey Sp Edn 250 (Virgin Trains) - *03*	5	7
37-025Z	*see below under 5-plank wagons with wooden floors*	-	-
37-026	**Tarslag** 836 grey - *98*	6	8
37-026A	**Arenig Granite** 207 red - *03*	4	6
37-027	**Penderyn** Limestone 336 grey - *99*	6	8
37-027A	**George Lovegrove** 215 red - *03*	4	6
37-028	**ICI Lime** 3034 grey - *00*	5	7
37-029	**Hopton-Wood** 2 grey - *00*	5	7
37-030	**Harry Whitehouse** 16 red - *00*	5	7

W9b. 5-Plank Wagon with Wooden Floor (B)

37-025Z	**Ogilvy Brothers** 1 dark brown Sp Edn 500 (Virgin Trains) - *04*	7	9
37-050	**SR** 28422 dark brown - *99*	5	7
37-050A	**Hugh Lumley** 21 grey - *00*	5	7
37-050A	**FH Silvey** 191 brown - *03*	4	6
37-050W	**Hill Craig** 6 brown Sp Edn (Harburn Hobbies) - *00*	10	12
37-050X	**Newark Corporation** 4 brown Sp Edn 500 (Access Models) - *00*	10	12
37-050Y	**TS Hanson** 1 red Sp Edn (B&H Models) - *00*	10	12
37-050Z	**Birmingham Railway Carriage & Wagon Co** 26892 brown Sp Edn (Warley Model Railway Club) - *00*	10	12
37-051	**E A Stevenson** 10 blue - *99*	6	8
37-052	**Worcester New Coop** 20 red - *99*	6	8
37-053	**Wood** 33 orange - *99*	6	8
37-054	**BR** P143165 grey - *99*	6	8
37-055	**Wadsworth** 53 light grey - *00*	5	7
37-056	**Joshua Gray** 3 dark brown - *00*	5	7
37-056A	**AE Moody** I dark brown? - *03*	4	6
37-056W	**JCKew** 14 grey Sp Edn (Access Models) - *01*	8	10
37-056Y	**Cafferata** 18 brown Sp Edn (Access Models) - *01*	8	10
37-056Z	**Hucknall** 3422 red Sp Edn 500 (Sherwood Models - *00*	8	10
37-057	**J&R Stone** 245 blue grey - *03*	4	6

W10. 12T Hybar Shock-Absorbing Wagon

33-225	**BR** B721326 brown Shock - *92*	8	10
33-226	**BR** B721385 brown -*94*	7	10
33-227	**BR** B724180 brown - *94*	7	10

Shock absorbing wagon [W10]

W11. 12T Hybar Shock Absorbing Wagon (B)

Fitted with sheet rails.

37-875	**BR** B721326 brown - *02*	4	6
37-876	**BR** B721385 brown - *02*	4	6

7 Plank Wagon [W12a]

W12a. 7-Plank Wagon

33-100	**Hinkleton** 1408 red - *91*	8	10
33-100A	**JL Davies** 121 red - *94*	8	10
33-100B	**Manton** 891 brown Sp Edn (Geoffrey Allison) - *96*	12	15
33-100C	**Gedling** 2598 red Sp Edn 500 (Gee Dee Models) - *98*	12	15
33-100C	**Clarke** 100 maroon Sp Edn (B&H Models) - *96*	12	15
33-100D	**Hucknall** No1 Colliery 7071 brown Sp Edn 500 (Sherwood Models) - *99*	10	12
33-100E	**Lindby** brown Sp Edn 500 (Sherwood Models) - *99*	10	12
33-100F	**WH Garton** 23 brown Sp Edn (B&H Models) - *99*	10	12
33-100G	**Pinner** 12 red Sp Edn (B&H Models) - *99*	12	15
33-100H	**Hull Corporation** 112 light grey Sp Edn (53A Models) - *98*	12	15
33-100J	**Nunnery** 1574 black Sp Edn (Geoffrey Allison) - *98*	12	15
33-100K	**Firbeck** 787 brown Sp Edn (Geoffrey Allison) - *98*	12	15
33-100L	**Welbeck** 2692 black Sp Edn (The Midlander) - *97*	12	15
33-100M	**Lincoln Wagon & Engine** light grey Sp Edn (B&H Models) - *97*	12	15
33-100N	**Kime** 5 black Sp Edn (B&H Models) - *98*	10	12
33-100O	**White** 15 grey Sp Edn (B&H Models) - *96*	12	15
33-100P	**Woodhall** 220 green Sp Edn 500 (Harburn Hobbies) - *96*	15	20
33-100Q	**Forth** 104 light grey Sp Edn 500 (Harburn Hobbies) - *96*	15	20
33-100R	**Ormiston** 199 blue Sp Edn 500 (Harburn Hobbies) - *96*	15	20
33-100S	**Rossington** 2054 light grey Sp Edn 500 (Geoffrey Allison) - *97*	12	15
33-100T	**Dinnington** 641 blue Sp Edn 500 (Geoffrey Allison) - *97*	12	15
33-100U	**Blidworth** 2444 light grey Sp Edn (The Midlander) - *97*	12	15
33-100W	**James Lewis** 19 red Sp Edn (B&H Models) - *97*	12	15
33-100WW	**North Norfolk Railway** 8572 green Sp Edn 500 (NNR) - *93*	15	20
33-100X	**Bolsover** 1190 brown Sp Edn 500 (The Midlander) - *96*	12	15
33-100XX	**Eckington** 2801 red Sp Edn (The Midlander) - *99*	10	12
33-100Y	**Lincoln Corporation** 9 red Sp Edn (B&H Models) - *97**	12	15
33-100Y	**Sheepbridge** 5101 red Sp Edn 500 (The Midlander) - *96*	12	15
33-100YY	**Staveley** 4994 black Sp Edn (The Midlander) - *99*	10	12
33-100Z	**Shireoaks** 4241 red Sp Edn (Geoffrey Allison) - *97*	12	15
33-100ZZ	**Hardwick** 637 red Sp Edn (The Midlander) - *99*	12	15

Cat No	Description		
33-101	**Shirebrook** Colliery Ltd 159 red - *91*	8	12
33-101A	**BR** M608163 grey - *96*	8	10
33-101A	**Barnsley Main** 528 brown - *93*	8	10
33-102	**Wyken** Colliery Co. 441 red - *92*	8	10
33-102A	**LMS** 609545 red brown - *96*	8	10
33-103	undecorated light grey - *95*	6	8
33-104	**Taylor** 451 brown - *92*	8	10
33-104A	**Flower & Sons** 7 grey - *96*	8	10
33-105	**Anderson** Whitstable 76 brown - *95*	8	10
33-105A	**Richard Webster** 107 red (see table W14a) - *not made*	NA	NA
33-106	**NE** 138455 grey (see table W13a) - *not made*	NA	NA

* A set of three wagons in this livery was made for B&H Models in 2004 and numbered 200, 201 and 202.

W12b. 7-Plank Wagon (Coal Trader Classics Sets)

These were sold in sets of three different wagons which were unique to the set. We provide below the mint boxed value of the set and the excellent unboxed value of the individual wagons.

Cat No	Description		
-	**Ammanford** 48 brown - *95*	7	NA
-	**Cambrian Mercantile** Collieries 114 light grey - *95*	7	NA
-	**Berthlwyd** 385 dark grey - *95*	7	NA
33-025	Coal Traders above set of 3 - *95*	NA	25
A	**Dearne Valley** 61 light blue - *99*	8	NA
B	**Cortonwood** 751 brown - *99*	8	NA
C	**Monkton** 1771 black - *99*	8	NA
33-025X	Coal Traders above set of 3 Sp Edn 500 (Geoffrey Allinson) - *99*	NA	28
A	**Chapman, Fletcher & Cawood** 980 black - *98*	8	NA
B	**Rothervale** 2563 grey - *98*	8	NA
C	**Sheffield & Eccleshall** 13 red - *98*	8	NA
33-025W	Coal Traders above set of 3 Sp End (Rails) 1st set - *98*	NA	28
A	**Thos. Black** 49 brown - *99*	8	NA
B	**Tinsley Park** 2241 brown - *99*	8	NA
C	**Thorncliffe** 3751 black - *99*	8	NA
33-025Y	Coal Traders above set of 3 Sp End (Rails) 2nd set - *99*	NA	28
A	**Staveley** Bleaching Powder 4728 grey - *98*	8	NA
B	**Staveley** Caustic Soda 7230 black - *98*	8	NA
C	**Staveley** Sand Spun Pipes 9249 grey - *98*	8	NA
33-025Z	Coal Traders above set of 3 Sp Edn (The Midlander) - *98*	NA	28
-	**Oxcroft** 721 black - *95*	7	NA
-	**Sherwood** 575 brown - *95*	7	NA
-	**Ilkeston & Heanor** 17 blue - *95*	7	NA
33-026	Coal Traders above set of 3 - *95*	NA	25
-	**'Phorpres' Bricks** London Brick 988 dark grey - *95*	7	NA
-	**Lowe & Warwick** 42 red+yellow - *95*	7	NA
-	**HC Bull & Co Ltd** 101 red - *95*	7	NA
33-027	Coal Traders above set of 3 - *95*	NA	25
-	**Blackpool Cooperative** 32 dark grey - *96*	7	NA
-	**Wigan** A147 brown - *96*	7	NA
-	**JB Scholes** 778 light blue - *96*	7	NA
33-028	Coal Traders above set of 3 - *96*	NA	25
-	**Hartnell** 22 black - *96*	7	NA
-	**Lydeard Dunkerton** 1117 dark grey - *96*	7	NA
-	**Milton** 10 dark brown - *96*	7	NA
33-029	Coal Traders above set of 3 - *96*	NA	25
-	**H Fulcher** 10 brown - *96*	7	NA
-	**Mellonie & Goulder** 307 light grey - *96*	7	NA
-	**Wrights** 135 red - *96*	7	NA
33-030	Coal Traders above set of 3 - *96*	NA	25
-	**Florence** 1017 dark grey - *97*	7	NA
-	**Grazebrook** 49 brown - *97*	7	NA
-	**Dudley Lunt** 724 blue - *97*	7	NA
33-031	Coal Traders above set of 3 - *97*	NA	25
-	**Newbold & Martell** 180 brown - *97*	7	NA
-	**Whitwick** G55 dark grey - *97*	7	NA
-	**Stockingford** 9 green - *97*	7	NA

Cat No	Description		
33-032	Coal Traders above set of 3 - *97*	NA	25
-	**Wm Shaw** 137 red - *97*	7	NA
-	**Flockton** 94 blue - *97*	7	NA
-	**South Yorkshire** 650 black+yellow - *97*	7	NA
33-033	Coal Traders above set of 3 - *97*	NA	25
-	**Yorkshire Main** 9417 red brown - *02*	6	NA
-	**Brodsworth Main** 350 red - *02*	6	NA
-	**Waleswood** 606 red brown - *02*	6	NA
37-?	Coal Traders above set of 3 Sp Edn 500 (Geoffrey Allison) - *02*	NA	22

W13a. 7-Plank Wagon with End Door (B)

Cat No	Description		
37-075	**NE** 156486 light grey - *98*	4	7
37-075	**Standard Wagon** 1923 pale yellow Ltd Edn (Bachmann Times) - *99*	10	12
37-075A	**Goldendale Iron** 598 grey - *03*	6	8
37-075V	**Tom Wright** 19 brown Sp Edn 500 (Midland Railway Soc.) - *03*	6	8
37-075W	**Newstead** 2281 grey Sp Edn (Sherwood Models) - *00*	10	12
37-075X	**Thorne - Pease & Partners** 1336 brown Sp Edn (Rails) - *00*	10	12
37-075Y	**Balgonie** 226 brown Sp Edn (Harburn Hobbies) - *00*	10	12
37-075Z	**Kinneil** 189 brown Sp Edn 500 (Harburn Hobbies) - *00*	10	12
37-076	**Gellyceidrim** 719 light grey - *98*	4	7
37-076A	**Douglas Bank Colliery** 454 brown - *03*	6	8
37-077	**ICI** Salt Works Stafford 326 brown - *99*	4	6
37-078	**Kobo** 15 grey - *99*	4	6
37-078A	**Wimberry Colliery** 2 black - *03*	6	8
37-078X	**Bachmann** 89-99 blue Ltd Edn (Bachmann) 10th Anniversary - *99*	8	10
37-079	**GW** 09244 dark grey - *00*	4	6
37-079U	**Clay Cross** Sp Edn (various)* - *01*	5	8
37-079V	**Butterley** 2301 brown Sp Edn (various)* - *01*	9	12
37-079W	**Yorkshire Main** 9417 red brown Sp Edn 500 (Geoffrey Allison) - *01*	9	NA
37-080	**JR Wood** 346 yellow - *00*	4	6
37-080R	**Edinburgh** 313 grey Sp Edn (Harburn Hobbies) - *01*	9	12
37-080S	**Moore** 113 brown Sp Edn (Harburn Hobbies) - *01*	10	12
37-080T	**Ariston** 617 brown Sp Edn (Harburn Hobbies) - *01*	10	12
37-080U	**Niddrie** 491 grey Sp Edn (Harburn Hobbies) - *01*	12	15
37-080V	**Swanwick** 2383 brown Sp Edn 500 (Gee Dee Models) - *01*	12	15
37-080V	**Renwick, Wilton & Dobson** 77 red-brown Sp Edn 500 (Virgin Trains) - *03*	6	8
37-080W	**The Derbyshire Carriage & Wagon** 110 brown Sp Edn (Bachmann Collectors Club) - *01*	12	15
37-080X	**Brodsworth Main** 350 red Sp Edn 500 (Geoffrey Allison) - *01*	10	NA
37-080Y	**Blidworth** 2323 red Sp Edn 500 (Gee Dee Models) - *01*	10	12
37-080Z	**Annesley** 195 maroon Sp Edn 500 (Sherwood Models) - *01*	10	12

*Originally commissioned by The Midlander but order subsequently cancelled. The order was then taken over jointly by Sherwood Models, Geoffrey Allison, Gee Dee Models and C&B Models.

W13b. 7-Plank Wagon (with end door) Sets (B)

Cat No	Description		
-	**Birley** 662 grey - *00*	8	NA
-	**Berkby Joliffe** 606 black - *00*	8	NA
-	**Marshell Bros** 7 black - *00*	8	NA
?	Coal Traders set of above 3 Sp Edn (Rails) - *00*	NA	30
-	**Kiveton** 2041 dark grey - *00*	8	NA
-	**Maltby Main** 298 brown - *00*	8	NA
-	**Bulcroft** 288 dark red - *00*	8	NA

-	Coal Traders set of above 3 Sp Edn (Geoffrey Allinson) - *00*	NA	30
A	**Walter Boynton** 982 brown - *01*	8	NA
B	**Walter Woodthorpe** 15 brown - *01*	8	NA
C	**Walter Boynton** 01029 brown - *01*	8	NA
37-079X	Coal Traders set of above 3 Sp Edn (B&H Models) - *01*	NA	30
-	**W.Clarke & Son** 405 brown - *03*	6	NA
-	**W.Clarke & Son** 101 black - *03*	6	NA
-	**Wm.Clarke & Son** 281 brown - *03*	6	NA
37-080W	set of above 3 Sp Edn (B&H Models) - *03*	NA	25
-	**Manchester** 8697 brown - *00*	9	NA
-	**Manchester** 8725 brown - *00*	9	NA
-	**Manchester** 8780 brown - *00*	9	NA
37-080X	Coal Traders set of above 3 Sp Edn 500 (TMC) - *00*	NA	30

W14a. 7-Plank Wagon with Fixed End (B)

37-100	**Richard Webster** 107 brown - *98*	4	6
37-100A	**WE Wise** 18 black - *03*	4	6
37-100M	**Kirriemuir Coal Society Ltd** 2 brown Sp Edn 500 (Virgin Trains) - *04*	5	7
37-100U	**Clifton** 2121 brown Sp Edn (Sherwood Models) - *00*	8	10
37-100V	**GE Parker** 1 brown Sp Edn (British Railway Modelling) - *00*	8	10
37-100W	**TE Smith** 9 dark red Sp Edn (B&H Models) - *00*	8	10
37-100X	**Pinxton** 718 black Sp Edn (Gee Dee Models) - *00*	8	10
37-100Y	**Babbington** 3144 black Sp Edn (Gee Dee Models) - *00*	8	10
37-100Z	**Woollaton** 79 red Sp Edn (Gee Dee Models) - *00*	8	10
37-101	**Parkend** 312 black - *98*	8	10
37-101A	**GW Railwaymens Coal Association** 1 light grey - *03*	5	7
37-102	**BR** P156142 grey - *99*	5	7
37-103	**James H Smart** black - *00*	5	7
37-104	**Birch Coppice** 927 red - *00*	5	7
37-105	**George & Matthews** 5 black - *00*	5	6
37-105A	**Webb, Hall & Webb** 18 blue - *03*	4	6
?	**Shipley** 1522 brown Sp Edn (Sherwood Models) - *03*	6	9
?	**Awsworth** 86 light grey Sp Edn (Sherwood Models) - *03*	6	9
?	above two models	NA	18
37-105U	**Kimberley** 4151 brown Sp Edn 500 (Warley MRC) - *01*	6	8
37-105V	**Lakeside & Haverwaithe** Sp Edn (L&HR) - *not made*	NA	NA
37-105W	**BW&Co** 1465 light grey Sp Edn 500 (Gee Dee Models) - *01*	6	8
37-105X	**Butterley** 0820 grey Sp Edn (various)* - *01*	5	7
37-105Y	**Waleswood** 606 red brown Sp Edn 500 (Geoffrey Allison) - *01*	6	8
37-2003	**James Kenworth** 47 brown Ltd Edn (Bachmann Club) - *03*	6	8
?	**Teifi Valley/Henllan** Sp Edn (Teifi Valley Railway) - *not made*	NA	NA
?	**GDOwen** Sp Edn (Teifi Valley Railway) - *01*	6	8

*Originally commissioned by The Midlander but order subsequently cancelled. The order was then taken over jointly by Sherwood Models, Geoffrey Allison, Gee Dee Models and C&B Models.

W14b. 7-Plank Wagon (with fixed end) Sets (B)

-	**Murphy Brothers** 29 brown - *01*	6	NA
-	**Murphy Brothers** 32 brown - *01*	6	NA
-	**Murphy Brothers** 33 brown - *01*	6	NA
37105Z	Coal Traders set of above 3 Sp Edn (Murphy Models) - *01*	NA	20

W15. 7-Plank Wagon with Coke Rails (B)

37-175	**BR** P238934 grey - *98*	5	7
37-175A	**BR** P368515 grey - *01*	4	6
37-175Z	**SJ Claye** 822 red Ltd Sp Edn 1000 (Bachmann Times 1999) - *00*	6	8
37-176	**P.O.P.** 217 grey - *98*	6	8
37-177	**Benzol & By-products** 1104 brown - *98*	6	8
37-178	**Stringer & Jagger** 226 red red - *98*	6	8
37-179	**New Cransley** 166 red - *98*	6	8
37-180	**S Mosley & Son Ltd** 58 grey+maroon - *00*	5	7

W16. 8-Plank Wagon with End Door (B)

37-125	**Boston Deep Sea** 86 blue - *98*	5	7
37-125Z	**Carlton** 4727 grey Sp Edn (The Midlander) - *00*	6	8
37-126	**Izal** 2915 black - *98*	5	7
37-127	**Hinkley** 19 red-brown - *99*	5	7
37-128	**BR** P238934 grey - *99*	4	6
37-129	**SC** 7961 grey - *00*	5	7
37-129A	**SC** 7961 grey - *?*	4	6
37-130	**Bagley** 38 red - *00*	4	6
37-130Z	**Shelton** 2298 red Sp Edn 500 (Haslington Models) - *01*	6	9
?	**Kinneil** 189 brown Sp Edn (Harburn Hobbies) - *00*	6	9
?	**Charles Roberts** 70001 black Ltd Edn (Bachmann Times 1997) - *98*	6	10

W17. 8-Plank Wagon with Fixed End (B)

37-150	**Stewarts and Lloyds** 6159 grey - *99*	6	8
-	**Hatfield Main** 1213 brown - *03*	6	NA
-	**Barrow Barnsley** 1708 yellow - *03*	6	NA
-	**BW&Co.** black - *03*	6	NA
37-150Y	set of above 3 Sp Edn (Geoffrey Allison) - *03*	NA	25
37-150Z	**Cooperative Society** 71 brown Sp Edn (The Midlander) - *00*	10	12
37-151	**Charles Ward** 4265 red - *99*	4	7
37-152	**AJ Salter** 202 red-brown - *00*	4	6
37-153	**Quibell Brothers** Ltd 10 red - *00*	4	6
37-154	**Musgrave** 2 grey - *00*	4	6
37-155	**Partington** 184 light grey - *00*	4	6
?	**Parker** 1 brown Sp Edn (BRM Magazine) - *00*	10	12

8 - Plank Wagon [W17]

W18. 9-Plank Coke Wagon

33-150	**Abbott** 3607 black - *91*	4	10
33-150A	**BR** 368545 grey (see table W15 - 37-175) - *not made*	NA	NA
33-151	**Flockton** 567 black - *92*	4	10
33-151A	**POP** 217 grey (see table W15 - 37-176) - *not made*	NA	NA
33-152	**Lancashire** 993 grey - *92*	4	10
33-152A	**Benzol & Byproducts** 1104 brown - *not made* (see table W15 - 37-177)	NA	NA
33-153	undecorated light grey - *95*	4	6
33-154	**Roberts Davy** 25 grey - *94*	4	8
33-155	**JA Bartlett** 2 brown - *94*	4	8
33-156	**Coalite** 401 red - *95*	4	8

Bachmann (British)

33-157	**Stringer & Jagger** 226 red - *not made* (see table W15 - 37-178)	NA	NA
33-158	**Modern Transport** 1206 dark grey - *not made* (see table W19 - 37-204)	NA	NA

8-plank wagon with coke rail [W19]

W19. 8-Plank Wagon with Coke Rail (B)

37-200	**Stamford Gas Light & Coke** 101 light grey - *98*	4	7
37-201	**Suncole** 5062 black - *98*	4	7
37-202	**The Gas Light & Coke Co.** 821 grey - *99*	4	6
37-203	**Birley** 1605 black - *00*	4	6
37-204	**Modern Transport** 110 black - *00*	4	6
37-205	**Bedwas** 621 grey - *00*	4	6

W19A. 31t OBA 5-Plank Open Wagon (B)

he = high ends.

38-040	**EWS** 110456? maroon - *04*	NPG	13
38-041	**BRe Rft** 110264 red+grey - *04*	NPG	13
38-042	**BR** Plasmore Blockfreight 110547 red+ grey he - *04*	NPG	13
38-043	**EWS** 110436 maroon he - *04*	NPG	13

Steel Open Wagons

W20. 13T Steel Sand Tippler Wagon (B)

37-350	**BR** B746752 brown Sand - *99*	4	6
37-350A	**BR** B746591 brown Sand - *02*	4	6
37-350A	**BR** B746736 brown Sand - *02*	4	6
37-351	**BR** B746609 grey Sand - *99*	4	6
37-351A	**BR** B746576? pale grey Sand - *02*	4	6
37-352	**BR** B746426 brown W Sand - *00*	4	6
37-352A	**BR** B746548 brown W Sand - *02*	4	6
37-353	**BR** B746548 grey W Sand - *not made*	NA	NA
37-353A	**BR** B746548? grey W Sand - *02*	4	6

W21. 16T Steel Mineral Wagon

33-750	**BR** B88643 brown - *90*	7	9
33-750A	**BR** B88647? brown - *94*	6	8
33-750B	**BR** B68919 brown - *96*	6	7
33-750C	**BR** B160415? brown MCV - *97*	5	7
33-751	**BR** M620248 grey - *92*	7	9
33-751A	**BR** B84198 grey - *94*	6	8
33-751B	**BR** B679900 grey - *95*	6	7
33-751C	**BR** B560287 grey - *96*	6	7
33-751D	**BR** B156124 grey - *97*	5	7
33-752	**BR** B68837? dark grey Coalite - *92*	7	9
33-752A	**BR** B68833? dark grey Coalite - *94*	6	8
33-752B	**BR** B68342 dark grey Coalite - *96*	6	7
33-752C	**BR** M622128 brown Iron Ore - *97*	5	7
33-753	undecorated - *92*	7	9
(30-201)	**BR** M620233 grey in London Transport set 30-201 - *91*	12	NA

W22. 16T Steel Mineral Wagon with End Door and Top Flaps(B)

37-225	**BR** B100071 grey - *98*	5	7
37-225B	**BR** B77701 grey - *02*	4	6
37-225B	**BR** B80200 grey - *03*	4	6
37-226	**BR** B68900 brown - *98*	5	7
37-226A	**BR** B69007 brown - *01*	4	6
37-227	**BR** B106979 grey W GWR grey - *00*	5	7
37-227A	**BR** B106979 grey W - *02*	4	6
37-228	**BR** B69190 brown W - *00*	4	6
37-228A	**BR** B68998 brown W - *02*	4	6

16T steel mineral wagon [W23]

W23. 16T Steel Mineral Wagon with End Door (no top flaps) (B)

37-250	**BR** B38066 grey - *98*	5	7
37-250A	**BR** B22571 grey - *00*	5	7
37-250B	**BR** B227229 grey - *02*	4	6
37-251	**BR** B258683 light grey MCO - *98*	5	7
37-251A	**BR** B8258683 light grey MCO - *01*	4	6
37-251B	**BR** B121830 grey MCO - *03*	4	6
37-252	**BR** B100768 olive ZHV - *made?*	NPG	NPG
37-252	**BR** ADB562927 olive ZHV - *02*	4	6
37-253	**BR** B24809 grey W - *00*	5	7
37-253A	**BR** B34807 grey W - *02*	4	6
37-253A	**BR** B25311 grey W - *02*	4	6
37-254	**BR** B266298 brown W Coal - *00*	5	7
37-254A	**BR** B564872 brown W Coal - *02*	4	6

W24. 16T Pressed Steel Mineral Wagon with End Door (B)

37-375	**BR** B746626 grey - *99*	5	7
37-375A	**BR** 391048 grey - *01*	4	6
37-375A	**BR** B100768 grey - *?*	4	6
37-375A	**BR** D101676 grey - *?*	4	6
37-375B	**BR** B80200 grey - *02*	4	6
37-376	**BR** M.O.T. 3308 brown - *99*	5	7
37-376A	**BR** M.O.T. 33327 brown - *02*	4	6
37-377	**BR** B100245 grey W - *00*	5	7
37-377A	**BR** B38751 grey W - *02*	4	6

W25. 16T Slope-Sided Steel Tippler (B)

37-400	**BR** BSCO20142 grey - *01*	4	6
37-400A	**BR** 9426 grey - *02*	4	6
37-401	**BR** BSCO20068 grey W - *01*	4	6
37-401A	**BR** BSCO9446 grey W - *02*	4	6

W26. 16T Slope-Sided Pressed Steel Mineral Wagon (B)

37-425	**BR** B197525? grey - *01*	4	6
37-425A	**BR** B8707 grey - *02*	4	6
37-426	**BR** MoT23743 brown - *01*	4	6
37-426A	**BR** MoT31763 brown - *02*	4	6
37-426A	**BR** MoT24000 brown - *02*	4	6
37-427	**Denaby** 9151 black - *03*	5	7

W27. 16T Slope-Sided Riveted Steel Mineral Wagon (B)

37-450	**BR** B11816 grey - *01*	4	6
37-450	**BR** B8128 grey - *?*	4	6

37-450A	**BR** B11532? grey - *02*	4	6
37-451	**BR** MWT11532? brown - *01*	4	6
37-451A	**BR** MWT9512? brown - *02*	4	6

W28. 27T Steel Tippler Wagon (B)

37-275	**BR** B381500 grey Iron Ore - *98*	5	7
37-275A	**BR** B381934 grey Iron Ore - *00*	5	7
37-275B	**BR** B383560 grey Iron Ore - *02*	4	6
37-276	**BR** B381293 grey Chalk - *98*	5	7
37-276A	**BR** B382883? grey Chalk - *02*	4	6
37-277	**BR** B383476 grey W Iron Ore - *00*	5	7
37-277A	**BR** B38??05? grey W Iron Ore - *02*	4	6
37-278	**BR** B381366? grey W Chalk - *00*	5	7
37-278A	**BR** B381366 grey W Chalk - *02*	4	6

W28A. MTA Box Wagon (B)

38-050	**EWS** ? maroon - *04*	10	14

W29a. Open Box Mineral Wagon MFA

This model was based on a 17'6" open wagon.

33-025	**EWS** blue (ex Mainline) - *02*	4	6
33-026	**EWS** maroon+yellow - *02*	4	6
33-027	**Rft Coal** grey+yellow - *02*	4	6
33-028	**EWS** black (ex-LoadHaul) - *02*	4	6

W29b. Open Box Mineral MFA (2004 model)(B)

38-010	**EWS** ? maroon W - *04*	NPG	7
38-011	**EWS** ? ex-Mainline - *04*	NPG	7
38-012	**EWS** ? ex-Rft - *04*	NPG	7

MEA steel box wagon [W30a]

W30a. 45t MEA Steel Box Body Mineral Wagon

33-375	**BR Rft Coal** 391045 grey+yellow - *95*	6	9
33-375A	**BR Rft Coal** 391034? grey+yellow - *96*	6	9
33-375A	**Transrail** 39? grey+yellow W, Barry WRD motifs - *01*	5	7
33-376	**BR Rft Coal** 391010 grey+yellow - *95*	6	9
33-376A	**BR Rft Coal** 391042 grey+yellow - *96*	6	9
33-377	**BR** M391158 blue - *96*	6	9
33-378	**Mainline** M391139 blue - *97*	6	8
33-378A	**Mainline** M391143 blue W - *01*	5	7
33-379	**BT** M391229 black - *97*	6	8
33-380	**EWS** 391262 maroon - *98*	6	8
33-380A	**EWS** 391250? maroon - *99*	5	7
33-380B	**EWS** 391444 maroon - *00*	5	7
33-380C	**EWS** 391389 maroon - *03*	5	7

W30b. 45t Steel Box Mineral MEA (2004) (B)

38-060	**EWS**? maroon W - *04*	5	7
38-061	**Mainline**? blue W - *04*	5	7

W31. 46t POA Box Mineral Wagon (B)

37-550	**Tiger** grey - *02*	5	7
37-551	**Yeoman** grey - *02*	5	7
37-552	**ARC** - *02*	5	7

W32. 51t POA/SSA Iron & Steel Scrap Wagon

33-425	**BR** 470068 pale blue POA - *95*	6	9
33-426	**BR** 470058 pale blue SSA - *95*	6	9
33-426A	**BR** 470096 pale blue W SSA - *99*	5	7

33-430	**BR** RLS5068 pale blue POA later style body, SR - *99*	5	7
33-430A	**BR** RLS5091 pale blue POA later style body, SR - *99*	5	7
33-432	same as above	5	7
33-431	**BR** 470005 pale blue SSA later style body - *99*	5	7
33-431A	**BR** ? pale blue SSA later style body - *03*	5	7
33-433	same as above	5	7

Open & Covered Hopper Wagons

W33. 24T Ore Hopper Wagon

33-250	**BR** P209938 grey Iron Ore - *90*	7	10
33-251	**BR** B435906 brown - *90*	7	10
33-252	**BISC** 665 dark grey - *92*	7	10
33-252	**LMS** grey - *made?*	NPG	NPG
33-253	undecorated light grey - *94*	6	9
33-254	**South Durham** 1010 black - *97*	5	8
33-255	**Richard Thomas** 9451 brown - *97*	5	8

W34. 24T Ore Hopper Wagon (B)

37-500	**BR** B436166? grey Iron Ore - *01*	4	5
37-500A	**BR?** grey Iron Ore - *03*	4	5
37-501	**RT& Co Ltd** 2016 brown - *01*	4	5

W35a. 46t HEA/HBA Hopper Wagon

It is assumed that these are HEAs unless otherwise indicated.

33-550	**BR** 360075 brown HSA - *92*	8	10
33-550A	**BR** 360711? brown W HBA - *01*	6	7
33-551	**BRe Rft** 361862 red+grey - *92*	8	10
33-551A	**BRe Rft** 360694 red+grey W - *94*	8	9
33-551A	**BRe Rft** 360? red+grey W - *01*	6	7
33-551B	**BRe Rft** 361992 red+grey HSA - *94*	8	9
33-551Z	**BRe Rft** 36? red+grey Sp Edn (Pennine Models) - *01*	8	10
33-552	**Railfreight** 360601 grey+yellow - *93*	8	10
33-552A	**Railfreight** Coal 36? grey+yellow W - *01*	6	7
33-553	**Mainline** 360955? blue - *96*	7	9
33-554	**Transrail** 361874? grey - *96*	7	9
33-555	**EWS** 361870 maroon - *98*	7	8
33-555A	**EWS** 361328 maroon - *99*	6	7
33-555B	**EWS** 360877? maroon - *01*	6	7
33-555C	**EWS** 360042 maroon - *03*	6	7
33-556	**ex Mainline** 360940 blue W graffiti one side only - *03*	6	7

46T covered hopper wagon [W36a] (Bachmann)

W35b. 46t Hopper HEA/HSA (2004 model) (B)

38-000	**EWS** ? maroon W HEA - *04*	NPG	8
38-001	**BR Rft** ? HEA - *04*	NPG	8
38-002	**BR** ? brown W HSA - *04*	NPG	8
38-003	**Mainline** ? blue HEA - *04*	NPG	8

W36a. 46t CEA Covered Hopper Wagon

33-575	**LoadHaul** 361845 orange+black - *99*	7	9
33-575	**LoadHaul** 361841? orange+black - *00*	7	8

cat. no.	description		
33-575A	LoadHaul 36? orange+black W - 01	6	7
33-576	EWS 360791 maroon - 99	7	9
33-576	EWS 360726 maroon - 00	6	7
33-576A	EWS 361024? maroon - 01	6	7
33-576B	EWS 360955 maroon - 03	6	7

33-577 EWS

cat. no.	table	cat. no.	table	cat. no.	table
33-500	W40	33-501	W40	33-505	W40
33-500A	W39	33-501A	W39	33-505A	W41
33-500W	W38	33-502	W38	33-506	W39
33-500X	W38	33-502A	W39	33-507	W39
33-500Y	W38	33-502B	W38	33-508	W38
33-500Z	W38	33-503	W38	33-509	W38
33-500Z	W38	33-504	W39	33-510	W41
		33-504A	W38	33-512	W41

	361024? maroon W - 01	7	8

W36b. 46t CEA Covered Hopper (2004) (B)

38-020	EWS ? maroon - 04	6	8
38-021	LoadHaul ? orange+black - 04	6	8

W37. BRT 35T Bulk Grain Wagon

33-125	Grainflow BRT7690 green+grey - 94	9	12
33-125A	BR 7617 brown - 96	9	12
33-126	Vat 69 5819 blue - 94	9	12
33-126A	The Maltsters Association 6026 yellow - 96	9	12
33-127	Johnnie Walker 5820 blue - 94	9	12
33-127A	Grainflow BRT7785 green+grey - 97	8	10
33-128	BR 7580 grey - 94	9	12
33-129	White Horse 5818 blue - 97	8	10
33-130	Haig 5864 blue W - 02	6	8

Tank Wagons

33-500 Series Tank Wagons Guide

The numbering of small tank wagons became a little confusing and so we provide here an index to show where you will find models numbered 33-500 to 33-512:

W38. Small Tank Wagon (Kettle Filler Cap)

33-500W	(see table W43)	NA	NA
33-500X	Briggs 18 black Sp Edn 750 (Harburn Hobbies) - 99	10	14
33-500Y	Briggs 38 black Sp Edn 750 (Harburn Hobbies) - 98	10	14
	Briggs 20 black (see table W46)	NA	NA
33-500Z	Esso 1634 buff Dalkeith posters Sp End 750 (Harburn Hobbies) - 98	10	14
33-500Z	Shell-Mex-BP Sp Edn 500 (Pennine Models) - 01	10	14
33-502	NCB Tar 597 black - 92	8	10
33-502B	Berry Wiggins 116 silver - 98	7	9
33-503	undecorated light grey - 92	8	10
33-504A	Trent Oil Products 6 buff+brown - 97	7	9
33-508	The Yorkshire Tar Distillers 597 black - 97	7	9
33-509	BOCM B7 brown - 98	7	9

W39. Small Tank Wagon (8' Gantry + Kettle Filler Cap)

33-500A	BP 22 silver - 94	7	9
33-501A	Swindon Utd Glass 5 maroon - 96	6	8
33-502A	Berry Wiggins 106 black - 95	6	8
33-504	Fina 135 silver - 92	8	10
33-506	Shell Elec. Oils 3102 dark brown - 94	7	9
33-507	DCL 241 silver - 96	6	8

W40. Small Tank Wagon

(Ladder, 8' Gantry + Kettle Filler Cap)

33-500	Royal Daylight 1534 brown - 92	8	10
33-501	Esso 3123 black - 90	8	10
33-505	Castrol Oil 131 green - 92	8	10

W41. Small Tank Wagon

(Ladder, 6' Gantry + Manhole Filler Cap)

33-505A	Brotherton 908 blue - 97	5	8
33-510	M.O.S. 195 buff - 98	5	7
33-512	Shell BP Lubricating Oil A7287 black - 99	5	6

W42. Small Tank Traffic Classics (Mixed)

-	Shell BP A5066 light grey (19d type) - 97	7	NA
-	Shell BP 4886 black (19a type) - 97	7	NA
-	Shell 4417 silver (19d type) - 97	7	NA
33-525	Tank Traffic above set of 3 - 97	NA	25
-	Esso 30 buff (19a type) - 98	8	NA
-	Power Ethyl 116 green (19a type) - 98	8	NA
-	Royal Daylight 1531 red (19a type) - 98	8	NA
33-525Z	Tank Traffic above set of 3 Sp Edn (Alton Model Centre) - 98	NA	35
-	National Benzol 734 silver (19d type) - 97	7	NA
-	National Benzol 2023 black (19d type) - 97	7	NA
-	National Benzol Mixture 576 (19a type) - 97	7	NA
33-526	Tank Traffic above set of 3 - 97	NA	25
-	Esso 1829 black (19a type) - 98	7	NA
-	Esso 2232 silver (19d type) - 98	7	NA
-	Esso 303 buff (19a type) - 98	7	NA
33-527	Tank Traffic above set of 3 - 98	NA	25
-	Berry Wiggins 150 black - 99	6	NA
-	Berry Wiggins 119 silver - 99	6	NA
-	Berry Wiggins 109 black - 99	6	NA
33-528	Tank Traffic above set of 3 - 99	NA	22

W43. Small Tank Wagon with Large Filler

33-675	Power 115 silver - 99	6	7
33-676	BP Ethyl 1448 buff - 99	6	7
33-677	Esso 981 black - 99	6	7
33-657Z	Manchester & Sheffield Tar 19 black Sp Edn (Rails) - 00	10	12
33-500Z*	Sheffield Chemical Co. 33 black Sp Edn (Rails) - 00	10	12

*This was the number carried on the box although it had already been used on another tank wagon. Bachmann literature also recorded this tank wagon as 33-500W. To make matters worse, it was one of a number of tank wagons given 33-XXX numbers that should have been in the 37XXX series as they were to Blue Riband quality.

BP 14T tank wagon [W45]

W44. 14T Tank Wagon with Small Filler (B)

37-650	ICI 315 brown - 00	6	8
37-650X	(see table W46)	-	-
37-651	Bitumuls 12 dark brown - 00	6	8
37-652	Joseph Crosfield 3 brown - 00	6	8
-	Lee & Green 1 light blue (see Table W46)	NA	NA
-	Briggs 38 black (see table W38)	NA	NA
-	Briggs 18 black (see table W38)	NA	NA
-	Esso 1634 buff Dalkeith posters (see table W38)	NA	NA
37-653	Burmah 118 black - 02	5	7
37-654	Ronuk 38 black+blue - 02	5	7
37-655	Pratts Spirit 1613 buff - 02	5	7

W45. Sets of 14T Tank Wagons (B)

-	**BP** A3472 silver twin logos - *02*	5	NA
-	**BP** 36 silver single logo boards - *02*	5	NA
-	**BP/Shell** 1223 silver, words - *02*	5	NA
37-665	set of above 3 wagons - *02*	NA	20
-	**Esso** 1345 black - *02*	5	NA
-	**Esso** 1343 black - *02*	5	NA
-	**Esso** 1921 black - *02*	5	NA
37-666	set of above 3 wagons - *02*	NA	22

W46. 14T Tank Wagon with Large Filler (B)

37-670Y	**Lindsey & Kesteven Chemical Co.** 2 black Sp Edn 500 (B&H Models) - *02*	7	9
37-670Z	**Little's Sheep Dips** 3 black Sp Edn 500 (B&H Models) - *02*	7	9
-	Above two wagons - *03*	NA	16
37-675	**Mobil** 1624 black - *00*	6	8
-	**Sheffield Chemical** 33 black (see table W43)	NA	NA
37-675W	**Briggs** 20 black Sp Edn (Harburn Hobbies) - *00*	8	10
37-675X	**Michael Nairn** 503 yellow Sp Edn (Harburn Hobbies) - *00*	8	10
-	**Manchester & Sheffield Tar** 19 black (see table W43)	NA	NA
37-675Y	**Kalchester** 101 brown Sp Edn 500 (TMC) - *00*	8	10
37-676	**Acme Dominion** 25 lemon - *00*	6	8
37-677	**Carburine** Motor Spirit 6 buff - *00*	6	8
37-678	**United Molasses** 13 brown - *02*	5	7
37-679	**BP Shell** 5075 yellow - *02*	5	7
37-680	**Esso** 1210 silver - *02*	5	7
37-650X	**Lee & Green** 1 blue green Sp Edn 750 (British Railway Modelling) - *02*	5	7

W47. 45T TTA Monobloc Tank Wagon (B)

37-575	**BP** ? green, pet. logos - *04*	NPG	8
37-576	**Esso** 57575 grey - *04*	NPG	8
37-577	**Shell BP** 67391 grey BRT - *04*	NPG	8

10T Saxa salt van [W48]

Vans

W48. 10T Covered Salt Wagon

33-175	**Stubbs Salt** 35 maroon - *92*	8	10
33-176	**Saxa Salt** 255 orange-yellow - *92*	8	10
33-176A	**Saxa Salt** 251 yellow - *96*	7	9
33-177	**Winsford Salt** - *made?*	NPG	NPG
33-177	**Chance & Hunt Ltd*** 333 brown - *92*	8	10
33-177	**Mangers Salt** 180 green - *01*	6	7
33-177	**Mangers Salt** 121 green - *02*	5	7
33-178	**ICI Salt** 3781 green blue - *92*	8	10
33-178	**DCL** 52 light grey - *02*	5	7
33-179	**Shaka Salt** 168 blue - *92*	8	10
33-180	**Union Salt** 2713 grey - *92*	8	10
33-181	**Stafford Salt Works** C26 red - *94*	7	9

* sold in a box marked 'Winsford Salt'.

W48A. Cottage Roof Wagon (B)

33-177W	**LGW** 118 red-brown Ltd Sp Edn (Harburn Hobbies) - *03*	6	8
33-177X	**The Distillers Co** 46? light grey Ltd Sp Edn (Harburn Hobbies) - *03*	6	8
33-177Y	**Leith General Warehousing Co.** 120 red-brown Ltd, Sp Edn (Harburn Hobbies) - *03*	6	8
33-177Z	**North British Storage** 56 grey Sp Edn (Harburn Hobbies) - *03*	6	8

W48B. Covered 5-Plank Lime Wagon (B)

?	**SLB** 702 grey Sp Edn 500 (Geoffrey Allison) - *04*	6	8

W49. Cattle Wagon

33-650	**BR** M14398 brown - *90*	8	10
33-650A	**BR** M14390 brown - *92*	8	10
33-650B	**BR** 266640 brown - *94*	7	9
33-650C	**BR** M14400 brown - *98*	5	7
33-651	**NE** 502860 brown large letters - *92*	8	10
33-651A	**NE** 502460? grey? - *94*	7	10
33-651B	**NE** 55787 grey large letters - *96*	6	8
33-652	**LMS** M14400 grey small letters - *92*	8	10
33-652A	**LMS** M14407 grey small letters - *94*	7	9
33-652B	**LMS** 214875 brown medium letters - *95*	7	9
33-652C	**LMS** 292372 grey large letters (boxed as 'LMS Brown') - *98*	5	7
33-653	undecorated light grey - *92*	5	7
33-654	?	NPG	NPG
33-655	**LMS** 243606 grey W* - *99*	5	6
33-656	**BR** M143820? brown W - *99*	5	6

* The box was marked - 'BR B/GREY WEATHERED'.

W50. Cattle Wagon (B)

37-700	**BR** M101376 brown - *02*	4	6
37-700A	**BR** ? brown - *03*	4	6
37-701	**LMS** ? grey - *02*	4	6
37-701A	**LMS** ? grey - *03*	4	6

GWR fruit van [W52]

W51. 12T Fruit Van

33-200	**BR** B875274 brown - *90*	8	10
33-201	**BR** W134195 brown Fisons - *92*	8	10
33-202	**LMS** 134209 grey - *?*	8	10
33-202	**GW** 134209 dark grey - *94*	7	9
33-203	undecorated light grey - *92*	8	10
33-204	**BR** W134265 brown W - *99*	5	6

W52. 12T Fruit Van (B)

37-750	**BR** W134143 brown - *01*	5	7

37-750A	BR W134143 brown - *02*	6	8
37-750B	BR W134333 brown - *03*	4	6
37-751	GW 134281 dark grey - *01*	5	7
37-751A	GW 134209 dark grey - *02*	6	8
37-751B	GW 134330 dark grey - *03*	4	6

W53.   12T Mogo Van

33-700	BR W126981 brown - *92*	8	10
33-701	BR W126901 grey - *91*	8	10
33-702	GW 126981 dark grey - *92*	8	10
33-703	undecorated light grey - *92*	8	10
33-704	GW 126342 dark grey W - *99*	5	7

W54.   12T Mogo Van (B)

37-775	BR W133971 light grey - *01*	5	6
37-775A	BR W133971 light grey - *02*	6	8
37-775B	BR? light grey - *02*	4	6
37-776	BR W126884 brown - *01*	5	6
37-776	BR W123956 brown - *01*	5	6
37-776A	BR W123956 brown - *02*	6	8
37-776A	BR W123954 brown - *02*	4	6
37-776B	BR W124000 brown - *03*	4	6

W55.   12T Single Vent Van with Sliding Doors

The doors are fixed shut.

33-625	LMS 511470 grey - *91*	8	10
33-626	BR M283322 light grey - *92*	8	10
33-627	BR B751782 brown Sunday Times - *92*	8	10
33-628	BR M504891 light grey W - *99*	5	6

W56.   12T Shock-Absorbing Single Vent Van
with Corrugated Ends

33-735	BR B852193 brown 3 short thick vertical stripes - *92*	8	10
33-736	BR B850005 brown 3 medium thin vertical stripes - *94*	7	9
33-737	BR brown 3 medium thin vertical stripes - *not made*	NA	NA

W57.   12T Single Vent Van with Sliding Doors (B)

This LMS type had a flatter roof and corrugated ends.

37-800	LMS 505960 grey - *01*	5	6
37-800A	LMS 505969? grey - *02*	4	6
37-800B*	LMS 52946 grey - *03*	4	6
37-800Z	Virgin Trains 220 white Sp Edn 500 (Virgin Trains) - *01*	8	10
37-801	BR M518972 brown - *01*	5	6
37-801A	BR M508587 brown - *02*	4	6
37-801B*	BR M508894 brown - *03*	4	6

* shown with a 'B' suffix in the catalogue but an 'A' suffix on the box.

W58.   12T Double Vent Van

33-600	BR W145548 brown - *91*	8	10
33-601	BR W133977 grey - *91*	8	10
33-602	GW 134089 dark grey - *91*	8	10
33-603	undecorated light grey - *92*	6	8
33-604	GW 35065 dark grey W - *99*	5	6

W59.   12T Shock-Absorbing Double Vent Van

33-725	GW 139576 dark grey Shock Absorbing Van No.39 - *92*	8	10
33-726	BR W139556 brown 3 medium thin vertical stripes - *94*	7	9
33-727	BR W139594 dark grey 3 long thin vertical stripes - *94*	7	9

W60.   12T Double Vent Van (B)

37-725	GW 139956 dark grey - *01*	5	6
37-725A	GW 112787 dark grey - *03*	4	6

37-726	BR W12480 brown - *01*	5	6
37-726A	BR W142689 brown - *03*	4	6
-	BR W114521 brown W	5	NA
-	BR W112818 brown W	5	NA
-	BR W116296 brown W	5	NA
37-726Z	above three Sp Edn (TMC) 503 - *03*	NA	20
33-727	GW 112787 dark grey Parto - *04*	NPG	5
33-728	BR W142218 brown - *04*	NPG	5
37-775B	BR W134030 grey - *03*	4	6

W61.   12T Planked Shock Absorbing Van (B)

37-900	BR B851440 brown - *02*	4	6
37-901	BR B851778 brown - *02*	4	6

W62.   12T Van Wide Box Van (B)

37-825	BR B784873 brown - *?*	NPG	NPG
37-826	Railfreight 230506 red+grey - *?*	NPG	NPG

W62A.   12T SR Planked Vent Van (B)

38-070	SR 48679 dark brown - *04*	NPG	7
38-071	BR S49091 brown - *04*	NPG	7

W62B.   12T SR Plywood Vent Van (B)

38-075	SR 57002 dark brown - *04*	NPG	7
38-076	BR B752698 brown - *04*	NPG	7

W62C.   12T SR 2+2 Planked Vent Van (B)

38-080	LMS 521202 light grey - *04*	NPG	7
38-081	BR M523578? light grey - *04*	NPG	7

46T VGA sliding wall van [W64]

W63.   46t VGA Sliding Wall Van

33-275	BRe Rft 210595 grey+red - *95*	7	9
33-276	BR Rft Distrib 210614 grey+yellow* - *95*	7	9
33-277	Transrail 210572 grey+yellow* - *97*	6	8

* carries Carlisle Currock wagon shop motifs (running fox).

W64.   46t VGA Sliding Wall Van (B)

37-600	EWS maroon - *00*	10	14
37-600A	EWS 210626 maroon - *03*	10	14
37-601	Transrail grey+yellow - *00*	10	14
37-601A	BRe Rft Speedlink 210595 grey+red - *01*	10	13
37-60??	BRe Rft Speedlink 210452 grey+red - *02?*	10	13
37-601Z	Lovat Spring 230527? grey+yellow Sp Edn (Harburn - Hobbies) pair of vans - *02*	NA	28
37-602	Rft Distribution 210614 grey+red - *00*	10	14
37-602A	Rft Distribution 210??4? grey+yellow W - *01*	10	14
37-603	Rft Distribution 210614 grey+yellow - *00*	10	14
37-60??	210649 W - *02?*	10	14

Brake Vans

W65.   20T GWR Toad Brake Van

33-300	BR W68805 grey - *90*	6	8
33-300A	BR W68875 grey - *96*	5	7
33-300B	GW 56683 dark grey Severn Tunnel Junc - *00*	5	7
33-300C	GW 68690 grey Dowlais Cae Harris - *03*	5	7
33-301	GW 114926 grey Cardiff - *90*	6	8
33-301A	56365 dark grey Paddington - *96*	5	7
33-301B	GW 114800 dark grey W Rhymney - *99*	5	7

33-301C	**GW** ? brown Westbury - *03*	5	6
33-301Y	**Virgin Trains** 2003 Warley red+silver Sp Edn 500 (Virgin Trains) - *03*	5	7
33-301Z	**GW** 56368 grey W Toddington Sp Edn (Cotswold Steam Preservation) - *01*	5	6
33-302	**BR** OW17455 brown - *91*	6	8
33-303	undecorated light grey - *92*	4	6
33-304	**BR** W114961 brown - *97*	5	7
33-305	**BR** W35960 grey Shrewsbury (Cotton Hill) - *01*	5	6
33-305A	**BR** W114925 grey Oxford - *03*	5	6
(30-700)	? brown ex 30-700 set - *?*	6	NA

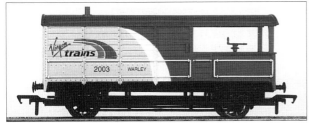

20T GWR Toad brake van [W65]

W66.   20T 16ft LNER/BR Standard Brake Van

33-350	**BR** B950880 brown (1st issue) - *90*	6	8
33-350	**BR** B953087 brown (2nd issue) - *90*	6	8
33-350A	**BR** B955044 brown - *92*	6	8
33-350B	**BR** B955044 brown - *99*	5	7
33-351	**NE** 182908 brown large letters - *90*	6	8
33-352	**NE** 260922 brown small letters, box labelled 'NE Grey' - *92*	6	8
33-352	**EN** (error)* 260922 brown - *92*	10	12
33-352A	**BR** B951759 grey - *96*	5	7
33-353	undecorated light grey - *92*	6	8
33-354	**BR** B955136? brown+yellow - *92*	6	8
33-355	**BR Rft** Distribution B964885 grey+red CAR - *92*	6	8
33-355A	**BR Rft** Distribution 201205 grey - *99*	5	7
(30-201)	**LT** B582 dark grey ex set 30-201 - *91*	10	NA

*The wrongly printed bodies were withdrawn before issue but were later sold off to the public and so may turn up occasionally, possibly fitted to a spare chassis.

W67.   20T 12ft LNER/BR Standard Brake Van

33-800	**NE** 182030 brown large letters ex sets? - *90*	8	NA
33-801	**BR** E168064 grey - *92*	8	10
33-801A	**BR** E178569 brown - *00*	4	6
33-801B	**BR** E167830? grey - *01*	5	6
33-801C	**BR** ? brown - *02*	4	6
33-801D	**BR** E178499 grey - *03*	4	5
33-802	**NE** 108061 brown small letters - *91*	8	10
33-802	**BR** E178513 brown - *03*	4	5
33-803	undecorated light grey - *not made*	NA	NA

W68a.   20T LNER/BR Standard Brake Van (B)

37-525	**BR** B955055 brown - *02*	4	6
37-526	**BR** B950002 grey - *not made*	NA	NA
37-526	**BR** B951480 grey - *01*	5	6
37-527	**NE** ? brown small letters - *02*	4	6

W68b.   20T Standard Brake Van (Flush Sides) (B)

37-535	**BR Rft** B955247 CAR grey+red - *02*	5	6
37-536	**BR** B955055 CAP brown - *02*	5	6
37-537	**BR** ? brown - *04*	5	6
37-?	**BR** RES CAR red+grey Sp Edn (Model Rail) - *02*	7	8

Bogie Wagons

W69.   Queen Mary 25T Brake Van

33-825	**BR** S56297 brown - *95*	8	10

33-825A	**BR** S56302 brown - *97*	8	9
33-825B	**BR** S56299 brown - *98*	7	9
33-825C	**BR** S54297 brown - *03*	7	9
33-826	**BR** ADS5629S green+yellow S&T Department - *95*	8	10
33-826A	**BR** ADS56299 green+yellow S&T Depart - *97*	7	8
33-827	**SR** 56282 dark brown large letters - *95*	8	10
33-827A	**SR** 56299 dark brown small letters - *97*	8	9
33-827B	**SR** 56294 dark brown large letters - *98*	7	9
33-828	**NSE** ADS56304 blue - *97*	7	8
33-829	**BR** S56302 grey+yellow - *97*	7	8
33-830	**EWS** AD58299? maroon - *99*	7	8
33-830A	**SR** 56301 dark brown - *04*	8	12

Queen Mary 25T brake van [W69]

W70.   Intermodal Bogie Wagon

33-475	**BR** Railfreight Distribution with ISO dry freight steel container - *not made*	NA	NA

W71a.   Intermodal (Euro Twin) (B)

Like the real thing these come as a pair of bogie flat wagons, semi-permanently joined, designed to carry 45' Swap Body containers. The wagon frames are diecast.

37-300	**Rft Distribution** green + 2 x 45' **ECS** European Containers maroon - *01*	22	27
37-300A	**Rft Distribution** green + 2 x 45' **Consent Leasing** - *02*	20	25
37-300B	**Rft Dist** green + 2 x 45' **ECS** - *02*	20	25
37-301	**Rft Distribution** green + 45' **Power Box** and **Sea Wheel** - *01*	22	27
37-301A	**Rft Dist** green + 2 x 45' **Axis** - *02*	20	25
37-301B	**Rft Distribution** green + 2 x 45' **Sea Wheel** (SWLU451349 + ?) green - *02*	22	27
37-302	**Rft Dist** green + 2 x 45' **Seaco** - *01*	22	27
37-302A	**Rft Dist** green + 2 x 45' **EFS** - *02*	20	25
37-302B	**Rft Distribution** green + 2 x 45' **Seaco** (SCZU145822 + ?) dark blue - *02*	20	25
37-310	**Rft Dist** green + 2 x 20' **Hamburg Sud** (SUDU370512[2] + SUDU369632[9]) - *03*	22	27
37-311	**Rft Dist** green + 2 x 20' **P&O** - *02*	20	25
37-312	**Rft Dist** green + 2 x 20' **Mediterranean Shipping Co** (MSCU116371[3] + MSCU251438[7]) - *03*	20	25
37-315	2 x **Rft Distribution** green - *03*	15	18
37-316	2 x **Rft Distribution** green W - *03*	15	18

W71b.   Intermodal Containers (only) (B)

36-101	2 x **Eucon** (45') - *04*	NPG	8
36-102	2 x **Dream Box** (45') - *04*	NPG	8
36-125	2 x **China Shipping** green CCLU 314404[5] + CCLU 304949[6] - *03*	5	7
36-126	2 x **Maersk** grey APMO282700[1] + **Maersk Sealand** MSKU206820[0] - *03*	5	7
36-127	2 x **Cosco** grey CBHU3281860[8] + CBHU328736[5] - *03*	5	7

W72.   30T Bogie Bolster Wagon

cb = commonwealth bogies. db = diamond bogies. BBC = Bogie Bolster C

33-850	**BR** ADB997648 dark grey BBC S&T Dept cb - *91*	8	10
33-850A	**LMS** 31406 grey db - *00*	6	7
33-850B	**LMS** 720717 brown db - *03*	6	7

Bachmann (British)

33-851	**BR** M290075 grey Macaw C cb - *91*	8	10
33-851	**BR** B943134 grey cb - *?*	8	10
33-851A	**BR** grey Macaw C db - *97*	7	9
33-852	**GW** 70247 dark grey Macaw B db + load - *96*	8	10
33-852A	**GW** 56302 dk.grey Macaw B db + load - *?*	8	10
33-853	**BR** B943293 brown - *96*	7	9
33-853A	**BR** brown db - *97*	7	9
33-854	**BR** DB997653 red S&T Prawn cb - *97*	7	9
33-854A	**BR** DB997636 Gulf red - *03*	6	8
33-855	**BR** B940751? grey BBC cb - *99*	6	7
33-856	**BR** B922150 brown BBC cb - *01*	6	7
33-856A	**BR** B922150? grey BBC cb - *03*	6	7

W73. 30T Bogie Bolster Wagon with Load

33-925	**BR** M290034 grey + steel beam - *91*	10	12
33-926	**LMS** 301326 grey + brown steel beam - *92*	10	12
33-927	**GW** 70240 grey + steel beam - *92*	10	12

W74a. 45T Bogie Well Wagon

33-900	**GW** 41900 dark grey Crocodile H - *92*	8	10
33-900A	**GW** 41973 dark grey Crocodile H - *98*	7	8
33-900B	**GW** 41973 dark grey Crocodile H - *00*	6	8
33-900C	**GW** ? dark grey Crocodile H - *?*	6	7
33-900D	**GW** 41901 dark grey Crocodile H - *03*	6	7
33-901	**LMS** grey - *not made*	NA	NA
33-901A	**BR** W41973 grey Weltrol WH + girders - *98*	7	8
33-901B	**BR** W41947 grey Weltrol WH - *00*	6	8
33-901C	**BR** W41900? grey Weltrol WH - *04*	NPG	7
33-902	**BR** W41973 grey Weltrol WH - *91*	8	10

W74b. 45T Bogie Well Wagon with Load

33-875	**NE** 77823 grey Flatrol M + boiler **Riley Bros** - *91*	10	15
33-876	**BR** W41975 grey Weltrol WH + dark brown boiler - *92*	10	15
33-877	**BR** W41943 grey Weltrol WH + green transformer - *92*	10	15
33-878	**LMS** 299882 grey + grey transformer - *93*	10	15

90T bogie hopper wagon [W75] (Bachmann)

W75. 90t JGA Bogie Hopper Wagon (B)

37-325	**Tilcon** NACO? grey - *01*	17	19
37-325A	**Tilcon** NACO? grey - *01*	17	19
37-325B	**Tilcon** NACO19184 grey - *02*	17	19
37-326	**RMC** RMC? orange - *01*	17	19
37-326A	**RMC** RMC? orange - *01*	17	19
37-326B	**RMC** RMC19228 orange - *02*	17	19
37-327	**Buxton** BLI? white+blue - *01*	17	19
37-327A	**Buxton** BLI? white+blue - *01*	17	19
37-327B	**Buxton** BLI19206 white+blue - *02*	17	19
37-328	**Tarmac** NACO???97 pale grey, green+ yellow flash - *02*	17	19
37-328A	**Tarmac** NACO? pale grey, blue line - *03*	16	18

W76a. 102t Thrall Steel Coil Carriers BYA (B)

37-625	**EWS** maroon - *02*	16	20

W76b. 102t Thrall Steel Strip Carriers BRA (B)

37-626	**EWS** maroon - *02*	16	20
37-628	**EWS** 964007 maroon W - *04*	16	21

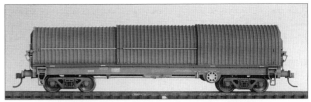

102t Thrall bulk steel strip carrier [W76b]

W77. 102t Thrall Bulk Coal Hopper HTA (B)

37-850	**EWS** maroon+yellow - *02*	16	20
37-851	**EWS** 310223 maroon+yellow W - *04*	16	21

W78. 100t Bogie Hopper Wagon HHA (B)

38-030	**Freightliner** ? grey - *04*	NPG	21
38-031	**Freightliner** ? grey - *04*	NPG	21

SETS

Initially, Bachmann sets came with a circle of track, an inexpensive controller, a standard range locomotive and rolling stock drawn from what was available at the time. None of these are of particular interest to collectors but interest in them will almost certainly grow in future years as they were not sold in very great quantities and many sets were broken up by retailers in order to sell the contents separately.

An exception to the general run was the London Transport set (30-201) of 1991 which contained the early pannier tank in LT livery and three wagons. Another exception will be the Cambrian Coast Express set (31-2000), which was originally planned by Palitoy for their Mainline range. The Bachmann set had two locomotives and six coaches together with accessories.

Bassett-Lowke 0

HISTORY

Wenman Joseph Bassett-Lowke was born in December 1877 and was a member of the boiler making family, J.T.Lowke & Co Ltd. After the death of Tom Lowke, his wife had married one Absalom Bassett who adopted her son Joseph Tom Lowke. He got on well with his stepfather and when he married and had three sons of his own he gave them all 'Bassett' as their middle name. All three sons, however, grew up using the surname Bassett-Lowke. Wenman, for some reason took the name Whynne but was often referred to simply as 'WJ'.

Whynne Bassett-Lowke trained in the family business but wanted to strike out on his own. With his father's book keeper, Harold Franklin, he founded his own model engineering company in 1899 while still serving an apprenticeship with his father. This became a limited company in 1910 with a factory base in Northampton. The Company was never large although its output was considerable. This was achieved by contracting out work to other companies that Bassett-Lowke became associated with. One of these was Winteringham Ltd, which had been established by George Winteringham in 1908 as a subsidiary, and this became Bassett-Lowke's main manufacturer.

WJ had been to the 1900 Paris Exhibition and been much impressed by the products of German manufacturers such as Marklin, Carette and Bing. A year later, all three had agreed to manufacture models to Bassett-Lowke's designs for the latter to sell in the UK. The first supply arrived in 1901 and the first locomotive was a gauge 3 model of a LNWR 4-4-0 named 'Black Prince'. WJ supplemented the supplies he received from Germany with models built in his limited facilities although, initially, these were mainly freelance subjects. By 1904 a range of 40 locomotives were being offered!

Milestones

1899 Bassett-Lowke sets up his company with Harry Franklin.
1899 B-L produces his first mail order catalogue at the age of just 22.
1900 Paris Exhibition and B-L enters into an import agreements with Stefan Bing and George Carette.
1901 B-L takes delivery of his first supply from Bing.
1901 Henry Greenly appointed Consulting Engineer and Designer to B-L.
1902 Track developed by George Winteringham.
1902 First comprehensive catalogue produced containing railway items.
1905 First exhibition stand at the Model engineering Exhibition in London.
1905 Model Railway Handbook first published.
1907 'Lowko' motor introduced.
1908 Winteringham Ltd formed as a subsidiary.
1908 B-L opens his first shop in Holborn, London.
1910 Bassett-Lowke Ltd becomes a public company.
1912 First Continental retail agency opens in Paris.
1919 Mass production plant installed for small gauge models.
1920-23 Wintringham's trademark appears on some items.
1922 Introduction of Bing Table Top Railway.
1922 Edinburgh shop opens.
1922 First American agency established in New York.
1924 Smallest model railway in the world made for Queen's dolls house.
1927 BDV gift coupon scheme sells 30,000 locos.
1927 Manchester shop opened.
1931 Robert Bindon Blood joins B-L, later to design many of the better models.
1932 Franz Bing emigrates to England.
1932 Trix Ltd founded in the UK with WJ Bassett- Lowke as a Director.
1935 Launch of Trix Twin Railway.
1941 Founding of Precision Models Ltd.
1946 Reappearance of models after the war.
1949 50th Anniversary celebrations.
1950 New BR livery appears on a B-L locomotive.
1953 Death of W.J.Bassett-Lowke.
1963 Last Bassett-Lowke catalogue released.
1965 Bassett-Lowke Ltd ceases trading.
1968 Bassett-Lowke Railways produce some prototype models.
2000 Corgi Classics re-launch the range.

The German supplies ceased during the First World War but Bing and Marklin both produced models to Bassett-Lowke's requirements after the war. However, it took Germany sometime to recover from the war and there was now considerable anti-German feeling in Britain, particularly among Bassett-Lowke's affluent middle class whose boyhood ranks had been so tragically decimated.

When German supplies did resume, Bassett-Lowke removed German trademarks and stamped the models 'Foreign Made'. Any models marked 'Bing' or 'Marklin' are likely to be from stocks supplied before the First World War. Eventually, around 1930, Winteringhams took over production and Bassett-Lowke became less reliant on imported products.

Model railways in gauges 0, 1, 2 and 3 were only part of the Bassett-Lowke business. They also made stationary engines, model ships and miniature railways. A man who came closely linked with Bassett-Lowke for many years was Henry Greenly and he was responsible for the design of some of their engines as well as the British liveries used on German models made for the British market. Another famous name associated with Bassett-Lowke was the model maker E.W.Twining who illustrated catalogues for them and later joined the Company.

Year by year the Bassett-Lowke catalogue grew and was split into different interest sections. Besides a large range of railway locomotives, rolling stock, accessories, track and sets being offered, there were the drawings and parts to enable you to construct your own models in one of a number of gauges. Models were also available with a choice of power units; namely steam, clockwork or electric.

The range of locomotives available before and immediately after the First World War was considerable and some were available for many years. Amongst the favourites were the Precursor tank, 'George the Fifth', 'Sydney', Deeley Compound (which was also available as a kit from 1909), GNR Atlantic and the Great Central locomotive 'Sir Sam Fay'.

In the early 1920s, Bassett-Lowke and Henry Greenly were instrumental in introducing 00 scale to Britain in the form of the Bing Table Top Railway. This started life as a clockwork system but was soon available with electric motors. In the mid 1930s they assisted Trix to establish a company in Britain and this became closely associated with Wintringhams where the models were made.

A different approach to marketing had been made in 1927 through Godfrey Phillips B.D.V.cigarettes, when sons were encouraged to get their fathers to smoke themselves to death to collect enough tokens for the Bassett-Lowke model of the 'Duke of York'! Bassett-Lowke made 30,000 locomotives for this promotion. It was in October this year that Bassett-Lowke opened a shop at 28 Corporation Street, Manchester. A branch they had opened earlier in Fredrick Street, Edinburgh, was closed in 1930.

As the years passed the demand for the larger gauges fell away and 0 gauge became the mainstay of Bassett-Lowke Ltd, especially after the First World War. Likewise, interest in electric traction grew and that in steam and clockwork lessened especially after the Second World War.

Some of the finest and most famous Bassett-Lowke locomotives were built during the late 1920s and 1930s; many designed by Robert Bindon Blood. Popular subjects included 'Flying

Bassett-Lowke

Scotsman', 'Royal Scot', 'Lord Nelson', a Jubilee, 'Princess Elizabeth', a Duchess, a range of A4s with different names, a Midland Compound, the 0-6-0 and 0-4-0 Standard tanks and, of course, the much loved Moguls.

Production in Northampton ceased during the Second World War and restarted sometime after the cessation of hostilities. The new British Railways livery made its appearance on a Bassett-Lowke models in 1950 and, the following year, the 4-4-0 'Princess Elizabeth' was replaced by 'Prince Charles'. Notable post-war locomotives were the Rebuilt Royal Scot, 'Spitfire' (Castle), 'Britannia', the Classes 5, 8F and 9F and 'Deltic'. These were mostly built in brass for Bassett-Lowke by Mr V Hunt and some were later rebuilt to a higher quality by Mr V Reader. These compare favourably with today's finescale 0 gauge models.

The final catalogue was published in 1963 and trading ceased in 1965; although there was an unsuccessful attempt at reviving the Company in the late 1960s under the name Bassett-Lowke Railways.

In the mid 1990s, a range of white metal models, in 1:43 scale, was produced under the Bassett-Lowke name by the then owners. These were of steam land vehicles such as a Clayton steam lorry, a Burrell steam roller and others. A showman's engine had been planned but deposits for this had to be returned when the name and intellectual assets of the company were acquired by Corgi. This acquisition provided an interesting link with the past. Corgi had been a product of Mettoy, a company which started life in 1933 in the basement and ground floor of the Winteringham factory. At the time Winteringham Ltd was, of course, the production arm of Bassett-Lowke Ltd!

At the 2000 British Toy and Hobbies Fair at Olympia, Corgi Classics launched the first of a new range of Bassett-Lowke 0 gauge locomotives and the subject chosen for the re-launch was a steam powered Mogul. All subsequent madels produced by then were electric powered.

Further Reading

The standard work is 'The Bassett-Lowke Story' by Roland Fuller and published by New Cavendish Books (ISBN 0-904568-34-2). This is thought to be out of print but available through the public library service. A recently published book of value to researchers is 'Wenman Joseph Bassett-Lowke' by his niece Janet Bassett-Lowke and published by Rail Romances (ISBN 1-900622-01-7). This same publisher has also released a video tape showing footage taken by WJ himself which includes factory scenes.

Collectors Club

The Bassett-Lowke Society caters for those who collect and operate Bassett-Lowke models. The Society publishes a quarterly magazine called 'Lowko News' and organises events to which members may take their stock to run. For further information about the Society, ring 01359 251127.

Prices - There is very limited information about prices of Bassett-Lowke models except through auctions. Where auction prices are known, the latest is given but it should be remembered that some of these are now 4 or 5 years old. These will be added to as more information becomes available. The two prices show the range for a model in good condition.

Codes - The following codes are peculiar to this section:

(F) = Freelance design. Also, 'Standard' normally implies freelance.
(B) = Made by Bing for Bassett-Lowke.
(C) = Made by Carette for Bassett-Lowke.
(L) = Made by Leeds Model Company for Bassett-Lowke.
(M) = Made by Marklin for Bassett-Lowke.
(H) = Made by Hunt for Bassett-Lowke.
litho = lithographed (printed as opposed to painted) locomotives.

Listing - The models have been separated into gauges (only gauge 0 is included in this edition) and then separate tables have been prepared for each model type. The tables are arranged so that tank engines are listed first followed by tender engines, diesels and electrics. The smallest engines (judged by the number of driving wheels (or large wheels)) are listed first starting with 0-4-0s and finishing with 2-10-0s. If you are unsure what type of locomotive you have, check the running number on the side of the locomotive or its tender against the Loco Search and it will tell you in which table to look. Models made for Bassett-Lowke by Bing, Carette, Marklin, Leeds and Hunt are all included in these lists but may also be identified in the tables by a letter code as indicated above.

Dates - The dates when models were available are very difficult to determine so long after the event and should not be taken too seriously. They also ignore breaks in availability during the two world wars when the Company was engaged in war work.

LOCOMOTIVES

Hand-Built Locomotives - In 1933, Bassett-Lowke announced a range of hand-built locomotives which could be made to order. The models would be to a very high specification including all solder construction, all external and visible details and full painting and lining. Locomotives could be had either with variable speed clockwork drive, 8-10v DC or 20v AC electric mechanisms. These are listed below together in Table L97.

Nu-Scale - In 1957, Bassett-Lowke introduced both a 2-rail electric control system and a Nu-Scale service. Nu-Scale was Bassett-Lowke's response to a changing market which required an improved, more scale, appearance for model railway locomotives which would run on BRMSB gauge 0 scale track, as well as standard Bassett-Lowke track. The changes, which increased prices by 30 to 40%, included replacing the alloy wheels with 10-spoke iron ones on the front bogie wheels, thinner driving wheel profiles (.200"), Stuart Turner wheel castings and iron ones on the tender. It also meant sprung close coupled tender drawbars, lamp brackets and lamps, whistles and extra handrails. All the standard range of locomotives, in 2 or 3-rail, were available with these improvements except for 'Prince Charles'.

Warning! - Be careful when buying models alleged to be 'Nu-Scale' versions as the term is often misused to describe a locomotive which has had some or all of its wheels changed or thinned down, has been converted to 2-rail electric or has had non-standard details added. These conversions could actually reduce the value of the model on the collector's market, rather than increase it as would be the case with a genuine Nu-Scale model.

The Nu-Scale service does not appear to have been well used judging by the infrequency with which these models turn up at auction. That said, particularly the iron 10 spoke front bogie wheels, do appear on Compounds, 'Prince Charles' and 'Flying Scotsman' locomotives where these have been obtained separately by individual customers. Collectors are advised to check the provenance most carefully.

Loco Search

The following table will help you to trace that elusive model. If you know the running number on the side of the locomotive or its tender you can look it up in the following table and the adjacent column will tell you in what section you will find it.

41125	L39	45295	L62	62453	L32a
41611	L13	46100	L68	62759	L28
41613	L13	46232	L79	63871	L54
42603	L21	48209	L85	64193	L54
42608	L21	60103	L80	68211	L13
42980	L56	61324	L63	70000	L82
43871	L54	62078	L32a	92220	L87
45126	L71	62136	L32a		

Loco Nos.	Tables	1017	L2	4072	L53
		1036	L39	4079	L73
1	L88	1063	L39	4256	L54
10	L3	1067	L39	4331	L59
11	L12	1082	L39	4390	L42
23	L90	1106	L4	4417	L55
25	L3	1108	L39	4420	L25
33	L57	1113	L39	4431	L59
36	L3	1190	L39	4460	L51
41	L10	1425	L49	4460	L63
44	L10	1442	L49	4472	L51
45	L9	1448	L53a	4472	L64
63	L3	1456	L54	4472	L80
73	L13	1652	L94	4481	L2
77	L37	1864	L57	4489	L81
78	L13	1902	L33	4490	L81
78	L16	1927	L31	4498	L81
88	L3	1930	L31	4853	L70
89	L12	1931	L31	5071	L73
94	L17	1931	L53	5320	L35
100	L2	2066	L58	5374	L13
101	L2	2241	L11	5524	L62
103	L80	2265	L32	5552	L69
112	L1	2350	L48	5573	L69
142	L36	2495	L62	5600	L66
211	L1	2509	L81	5701	L69
251	L49	2510	L81	5712	L69
298	L14	2511	L81	5765	L15
335	L13	2512	L81	6000	L74
433	L13	2524	L20	6027	L74
440	L27	2526	L20	6100	L19
441	L5	2531	L20	6100	L67
483	L40	2536	L20	6105	L19
504	L9	2603	L20	6200	L77
504	L42	2603	L21	6201	L77
504	L35c	2663	L35a	6202	L77
513	L34	2663	L35b	6220	L78
513	L35c	2664	L35a	6225	L78
601	L41	2664	L35b	6232	L79
650	L24	2670	L22	6285	L28
773	L51	2700	L55	6311	L7a
773	L76	2838	L72	6508	L51
850	L75	2848	L72	6508	L65
851	L62	2871	L62	6560	L94
864	L60	2945	L56	6750	L25
866	L60	3064	L93	6810	L10
903	L61	3400	L39	7083	L92
910	L47	3410	L44	8851	L25
930	L52	3433	L35c	8851	L51
947	L13	3433	L44	8872	L50
955	L26	3536	L20	8937	L13
982	L57	3611	L9	9405	L42a
999	L30	3611	L18	13000	L55
1000	L38	3800	L45	13007	L56
1000	L35	3801	L45	41109	L39

Cat.No.	Number, Company, Colour, Dates	£	£

Tank Engines

L1.   L&SWR Class S14 0-4-0T
(Bing for Bassett-Lowke)

Cat.No.	Number, Company, Colour, Dates	£	£
53/0	112 LNWR black steam - *21-29*	NPG	NPG
21/0	as above c/w - *21-29*	NPG	NPG
37/0	211 LNWR black electric - *21-29*	325	350
53/0	112 GNR green steam - *21-29*	NPG	NPG
21/0	as above c/w - *21-29*	NPG	NPG
37/0	211 GNR green electric - *21-29*	NPG	NPG
53/0	112 MR red steam - *21-29*	NPG	NPG
21/0	as above c/w - *21-29*	NPG	NPG
37/0	211 MR red electric - *21-29*	NPG	NPG
53/0	112 NER brown steam - *21-29*	NPG	NPG
53/0	112 CR blue steam - *21-29*	NPG	NPG
21/0	as above c/w - *21-29*	NPG	NPG
31/0	as above electric - *21-29*	NPG	NPG
37/0	211 CR blue electric - *21-29*	NPG	NPG
21/0	112 GWR green c/w - *21-29*	400	600
21/0	112 LMS maroon c/w - *24-29*	NPG	NPG
21/0	112 L&NER green c/w - *24-29*	NPG	NPG

Bing for Bassett-Lowke S14-0-4-0 tank [L1] sold for £480 (Barry Potter Auctions)

L2.   Peckett 0-4-0ST
(Carette and Bing for Bassett-Lowke)
The Carette version was slightly smaller than the Bing one.

Cat.No.	Number, Company, Colour, Dates	£	£
3104/0	100 MR maroon (B) c/w - *?*	450	650
3104/0	101 LNWR black (B) c/w - *07-09-?*	400	550
3104/0	101 MR maroon (B) c/w - *07-09-?*	350	550
3104/0	101 GNR green (B) c/w - *07-?*	500	650
3104/0	1017 green (C) c/w - *24-34*	300	400
3104/0	as above (C) electric - *24-34*	500	600
-	4481 green electric - *24-34*	400	450

L3.   Standard Tank 0-4-0T

Cat.No.	Number, Company, Colour, Dates	£	£
-	10 LMS black DC electric - *37-?*	300	360
4730/0	25 LMS black litho c/w - *37-?*	NPG	NPG
-	as above electric - *37-?*	NPG	NPG
4730/0	36 LMS black litho c/w - *37-?*	200	250
-	as above electric - *37-?*	300	450
4730/0	36 LNER black litho c/w - *37-?*	NPG	NPG
-	as above electric - *37-?*	NPG	NPG
-	88 LNER green DC electric - *37-?*	NPG	NPG
-	as above but black - *37-?*	300	400

4730/0	**63** Southern black litho c/w - *37-?*	NPG	NPG
-	as above electric - *37-?*	NPG	NPG

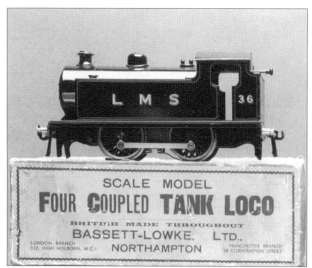

Standard 0-4-0 tank [L3] sold for £400
(Barry Potter Auctions)

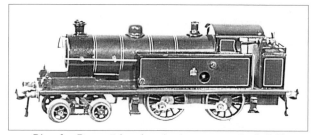

Bing for Bassett-Lowke short precursor tank [L9]
(Christies)

L4.   Class 11XX Class Dock Tank 0-4-0T
These were made to order.

-	**1106** GWR green (only about 3 made) electric - *61-63*	NPG	NPG

L5.   Class 0 Passenger Tank 0-4-4T
(Bing for Bassett-Lowke)

-	**441** NER green c/w - *14-19*	NPG	NPG

L6.   GNR Suburban Tank 0-4-4T
(Marklin for Bassett-Lowke)

-	GNR c/w - *07-?*	NPG	NPG

L7.   Class M7 Tank 0-4-4T (Bing for Bassett-Lowke)

-	**109** LSWR yellow-green c/w - *09-13*	750	900

L7A.   GWR Tank 2-4-2T (Bing for Bassett-Lowke)

-	**3611** green c/w - *09-13*	750	1600

L8.   4-4-0T (Freelance) (Bing for Bassett-Lowke)

-	GNR green c/w - *20-26*	NPG	NPG
23593/0	L&NWR black c/w - *20-26*	NPG	NPG
-	MR red c/w - *20-26*	NPG	NPG
-	CR blue c/w - *20-26*	NPG	NPG
-	GWR green c/w - *20-26*	NPG	NPG
-	NBR brown c/w - *20-26*	NPG	NPG

L9.   Short Precursor Tank 4-4-0T
(Bing for Bassett-Lowke)

-	GNR green c/w - *21-?*	NPG	NPG
-	CR blue c/w - *21-?*	NPG	NPG
-	Great Western green c/w - *21-?*	450	550
-	**MR** red c/w - *21-?*	NPG	NPG
-	**3611** L&NWR black c/w - *21-?*	NPG	NPG
-	**45**, **4221** LMS maroon c/w - *23-?*	400	600
-	**504** LNER green c/w - *?*	550	900
-	**3611** LNER black c/w - *23-?*	400	450

L10a.   Precursor Tank 4-4-2T
(Marklin for Bassett-Lowke)

-	**44** L&NWR black c/w - *09-10*	450	550
-	as above electric - *09-10?*	450	550

L10b.   Precursor Tank 4-4-2T (Enamelled)
(Bing for Bassett-Lowke)

3101/0	**44** L&NWR black c/w - *11-19?*	350	450
-	as above 3-rail 4-8v DC - *11-14?*	350	450

L10c.   Precursor Tank 4-4-2T (Lithographed)
(Bing for Bassett-Lowke)

3101/0	L&NWR black c/w - *20?*	350	450
-	as above 3-rail 4-8v DC - *20?*	350	450

L10d.   Precursor Tank 4-4-2T

3101/0	**44** L&NWR black c/w - *21-c23*	300	400
-	as above electric - *21-c23*	300	400
-	**6810** L&NWR black c/w - *21-?*	NPG	NPG
-	as above electric - *21-c23*	NPG	NPG
- *	as above electric over-painted 'LMS' - *c25*	400	500
3101/0	**6810** LMS red c/w - *25-28*	250	400
2/0	as above electric 3-rail 12vDC - *25-28*	300	450
-	**41** M&GN yellow electric - *64*	NPG	NPG
-	**9*** M&GN yellow electric - *?*	NPG	NPG

* Special order

L11.   County Tank 4-4-2T

-	**2241** GWR green one-off electric - *c50*	NPG	NPG

L12a.   LBSCR I2 Class 4-4-2T
(Bing for Bassett-Lowke)

4/0	**11** LB&SCR umber c/w - *11-25*	350	550
-	as above electric - *11-25*	450	600

L12b.   LBSCR I3 Class 4-4-2T

-	**89** LB&SCR umber electric - *69*	500	650

L13.   Standard Tank 0-6-0T (Freelance)
All the 0-6-0 standard tanks were lithographed. Some electric locomotives were fitted with a super reduction gear (40:1) for shunting and locos can be found with automatic (track operated) couplings. Likewise, some models are found with smoke units driven by a cam on the front axle. The LMS versions had a capuchon on the chimney. Pre-war electric models did not have key holes or control rod holes in the cab rear plate while post-war examples usually did, until late production orders. Catalogue number 4305/0 was used until 1940 for electric locos fitted with junior permag mechanisms.

3305/0	**5374** LMS black lined red c/w - *33-38*	250	350
4305/0	as above electric - *33-38*	350	450
4305/0	as above with Walschaerts valve gear electric - *33-38*	450	650
3305/0	**61** LMS black lined red c/w - *38-50*	250	350
5305/0	as above electric - *38-50*	350	450
5505/0	as above electric 20vAC - *38-50*	350	450
3305/0	**78** LMS black lined red c/w - *38-50*	250	350
5305/0	as above electric - *38-50*	350	450
3305/0	**335** LNER black lined red c/w - *33-38*	250	350

5305/0	as above electric - *33-38*	350	450
3305/0	**433** LNER black lined red c/w - *38-50*	250	350
5305/0	as above electric - *38-50*	350	450
3305/0	**533** LNER black lined red c/w - *47-50*	250	350
5305/0	as above electric 12vDC - *47-50*	250	350
5305/0	**8937** LNER black lined red electric 12vDC - *47-50*	300	430
3305/0	**947** Southern black lined green c/w - *38-50*	350	400
5305/0	as above electric 12vDC - *38-50*	400	500
3305/0	**68211** BRb black lined red c/w - *51-67*	250	350
5305/0	as above electric 12v DC 3-rail - *51-67*	300	350
2305/0	as above 2-rail electric - *51-67*	350	400
3305/0	**41611** BRb black lined red c/w - *51-67*	250	350
5305/0	as above electric - *57-67*	400	500
2305/0	as above 2-rail electric - *51-67*	400	500
-	as above electric Nu-Scale** - *57-65*	550	650
3305/0	LMS black lined red c/w - *59-61*	400	450
5305/0	as above electric - *59-61*	450	550
2305/0	as above 2-rail electric - *59-61*	450	550
3305/0	LNER black lined red c/w - *59-63*	400	450
5305/0	as above electric - *59-63*	450	550
2305/0	as above 2-rail electric - *59-63*	450	550
-	**41613-41617*** Longmoor Military Railway (LMR) blue electric - *?*	450	750
5305/0	**9033** LNER black lined red electric - *48-50*	450	550

* used for training at Longmoor Military Railway. It is understood that they were numbered in sequence from 41613 to 41617. ** See note on Nu-Scale in the Introduction to this chapter.

Standard 0-6-0 tank [L13]

L14. Ex-Burry Port Hudswell Clark 0-6-0T

-	**298** black prototype only, steam - *68*	NPG	NPG

L15. Class 27XX Pannier Tank 0-6-0PT

-	GWR green 2/3 rail electric - *?-50-57?*	NPG	NPG

L15A. Class 57XX Pannier Tank 0-6-0PT
(Hunt for Bassett-Lowke)

-	**5765, 5775 *** Great Western green electric - *50-63*	1600	2000

* Made to order. Other numbers probably exist.

L16. Class 3P Suburban Tank 2-6-2T

-	**78** LMS black c/w - *40-?*	800	1100
-	**78** LMS black 2P electric -*40-?*	800	1100

L17. LMS Fowler Prairie Tank 2-6-2T

-	**94** LMS black lined red c/w - *?*	2100	2900
-	as above electric 3-rail AC - *?*	2100	2900

L18. Class 36XX Class 2-4-2T
(Bing for Bassett-Lowke)

-	**3611** GWR green c/w - *11-13*	1900	2800
-	as above electric - *13-16*	1900	2800

L19. GWR 61XX Class Prairie 2-6-2T

3609/0	**6105** GWR button green c/w - *37-41?*	1100	2200
A4609/0	as above electric AC - *37-41?*	1100	2200

5609/0	as above electric DC - *37-41?*	1100	2200
-	**6100, 6101 *** Great Western green (H) electric 2/3 rail - *55-63*	800	2400

* Hand Built to order. Other numbers probably exist.

L20. Stanier 3-Cylinder 4P Tank 2-6-4T
(Marklin for Bassett-Lowke)

This was an early Stanier design and had a domeless boiler and straight rear edge to the cab doorway.

913/0/C	**2524** LMS black c/w - *35-?*	1800	2100
913/0/A	as above electric AC - *35-?*	1800	2400
913/0/D	as above electric DC - *35-?*	1800	2400
913/0/C	**2526** LMS black c/w - *c37*	2300	2800
913/0/A	as above electric AC - *c37*	2300	2800
913/0/D	as above electric DC - *c37*	2300	2800
913/0/C	**2531** LMS black c/w - *c39*	1100	1600
913/0/A	as above electric AC - *c39*	1100	1600
913/0/D	as above electric DC - *c39*	1100	1600
913/0/C	**2536** LMS black c/w - *c37*	1800	2300
913/0/A	as above electric AC - *c37*	1800	2300
913/0/D	as above electric DC - *c37*	1800	2300

L21. Stanier 2 - Cylinder 4P Tank 2-6-4T

This was a later Stanier design and had a domed boiler and a recessed upper rear edge to the cab doorway.

913/0	**2602** LMS black electric AC - *40-c50*	750	900
913/0	as above electric DC - *40-c50*	750	900
-	**2603, 2606** LMS black c/w - *40-c50*	1100	1700
913/0	as above electric AC - *40-c50*	1100	1700
913/0	as above electric DC - *40-c50*	1100	1700
-	**42603** BRb black c/w - *c50-?*	1300	1900
-	as above electric - *c50-?*	1600	1900
3618/0	**42608** BRb black c/w - *c52-c59*	850	1400
5618/0	as above electric 2/3 rail - *c52-63*	1100	1400
-	as above * Nu-Scale - *57-60*	1600	2200

* See note on Nu-Scale in the Introduction to this chapter.

4P 2-6-4 tank [L21] (Barry Potter Auctions)

L22. Bowen-Cooke Superheater Tank 4-6-2T
(Bing for Bassett-Lowke)

This was a tank version of the LNWR Prince of Wales Class built in 1911.

-	**2670** L&NWR black c/w - *14*	800	1100

Tender Engines

L23. Der Adler 2-2-2 (Marklin for Bassett-Lowke)

-	**'Der Adler'** electric - *35-?*	NPG	NPG

L24. Johnson Spinner 4-2-2
(Bing for Bassett-Lowke)

-	**650** MR maroon litho c/w - *14*	1200	1500
-	**650** MR red litho - *14*	1800	2000

L25. Freelance 0-4-0

4734/0	**4420** GWR green (B?) c/w - *c28*	NPG	NPG
4735/0	**6750** LMS maroon (B?) c/w - *c28*	NPG	NPG
4732/0	**8851** LNER green (B?) c/w - *c28*	NPG	NPG
4733/0	Southern (B?) c/w - *c28*	NPG	NPG

L25A. Freelance 0-4-0
Produced from Carette tooling acquired after Carette closed down in 1917.

6460/0	green lined in yellow steam - *c28*	NPG	NPG
6460/0	maroon lined in yellow steam - *c28*	NPG	NPG
6460/0	blue lined in white steam - *c28*	NPG	NPG
6460/0	black lined in red - *c28*	NPG	NPG

L26. Charles Dickens 2-4-0
(Marklin for Bassett-Lowke)

-	**955 'Charles Dickens'** L&NWR black c/w - *03-?*	1600	2200
-	as above electric - *03 -?*	1600	2200

L27. Standard Express 4-4-0 (Freelance)
(Bing for Bassett-Lowke)

All were steam driven.

48/0	**440** LSWR green - *22-29*	NPG	NPG
48/0	**440** 'Greater Britain' CR blue -*22-29*	NPG	NPG
48/0	**440** L&NWR black - *22-26*	NPG	NPG
48/0	**440** MR red - *22-29*	NPG	NPG
48/0	**440** GNR green - *22-29*	NPG	NPG
48/0	**440** GWR green - *22-29*	NPG	NPG

L28. Enterprise Express 4-4-0 (Freelance)
All were steam driven.

	Loco kit - *31-?*	NPG	NPG
?	SR green lined white - *31-40?*	NPG	NPG
6690/0	**6285** on tender red - *31-40*	NPG	NPG
6690/0	as above black - *31-40*	350	550
6690/0	as above green - *31-40*	250	270
6690/0	as above LNER green - *31-40*	250	400
6690/0	**62759** BRb green lined white - *c54*	300	350
6690/0	as above blue lined orange - *c54*	400	450
6690/0	as above black lined orange - *c54*	300	350
6690/0	as above black lined white - *c54*	250	300

L29. Bogie Express 4-4-0 (Freelance)
(Bing for Bassett-Lowke)

All were steam driven.

61/250/0	GWR green - *11*	NPG	NPG
61/250/0	LMS red - *24-26*	NPG	NPG
61/250/0	LNER green - *24-26*	NPG	NPG
61/250/0	GWR green - *24-26*	NPG	NPG

L30. Midland Compound 4-4-0
(Bing for Bassett-Lowke)

17/0	**999** MR maroon c/w - *10-14, ?-30*	1100	1600
-	**1000** MR maroon steam - *10-14*	850	1300

L31. Duke of York 4-4-0 (Freelance)
All examples of this model have a lithographed body. Only LMS versions carried a company designation. The 1927 locos had coupling rods with 'marine' Bing style big ends while later coupling rods were of a simplified shape. Electric models with a key hole have been converted to electric operation after purchase.

1927 'Duke of York'			
61/4710/0	light green lined black+white c/w - *27-29*	300	450
61/4710/0	as above electric - *27-29*	300	650
61/4710/0	dark green lined black+white c/w- *27-29*	300	450
61/4710/0	as above electric - *27-29*	300	650
61/4710/0	red lined black+yellow c/w - *27-29*	300	450
61/4710/0	as above electric - *27-29*	300	650
1930 'Duke of York'			
3301/0	light green lined black+white c/w - *30*	350	550
4301/0	as above electric - *30*	400	650
3301/0	dark green lined black+white c/w - *30*	350	550
4301/0	as above electric - *30*	400	650
3301/0	red lined black+yellow c/w - *30*	350	550
4301/0	as above electric - *30*	400	650
1931 'Duke of York'			
3301/0	light green lined black+white c/w - *31-32*	300	450
4301/0	as above electric - *31-32*	300	650
3301/0	dark green lined black+white c/w - *31-32*	300	450

4301/0	as above electric - *31-32*	300	650
3301/0	red lined black+yellow c/w - *31-32*	300	450
4301/0	as above electric - *31-32*	300	650

'Duke of York' [L31] (Barry Potter Auctions)

L32a. Princess Elizabeth 4-4-0 (Freelance)
The alloy wheels on this model were prone to metal fatigue and disintegration with the result that many have been re-wheeled. In such a case, if original period Bassett-Lowke iron replacement wheels have been fitted, add £50 to the value. Electric models with a key hole have been converted to electric operation after purchase. All models are lithographed.

2265 'Princess Elizabeth'			
3301/0	LMS red crest on cab c/w - *32-35*	250	350
4301/0	as above electric - *32-35*	300	550
3301/0	LNER green c/w - *32-35*	250	350
4301/0	as above electric - *32-35*	300	550

L32b. Prince Charles 4-4-0 (Freelance)
All models were lithographed and all had a key hole whether clockwork or electric.

3313/0	**62078 'Prince Charles'** BRb blue c/w - *51-53*	250	400
4313/0	as above electric - *51-53*	300	550
3313/0	**62136 'Prince Charles'** BRb dark green lined black+white c/w - *52-54*	250	400
4311/0	as above electric - *52-54*	300	550
BRb 62453 'Prince Charles'			
3313/0	dark green lined black+white c/w - *51-55*	250	400
4311/0	as above electric - *51-55*	300	500
3313/0	Brunswick green lined black+org c/w - *54-64*	250	350
4311/0	as above electric 3r - *54-64*	300	450
2311/0	as above electric 2r - *57-64*	300	550

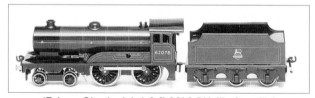

'Prince Charles' 4-4-0 [L32b] (Wallis & wallis)

L33. Black Prince 4-4-0
(Bing for Bassett-Lowke)

26/0	**1902 'Black Prince'** L&NWR black steam - *10-19*	700	900

L34. Precursor 4-4-0
(Marklin for Bassett-Lowke)

-	**513 'Precursor'** L&NWR black c/w - *07-?*	450	550

L35a. George the Fifth 4-4-0 (Soldered)
(Bing for Bassett-Lowke)
Soldered construction and hand painted. This model was also sold in the UK under the Bing name.

11/0	**2663 'George the Fifth'** L&NWR black c/w - *11-13*	300	350
11/0	as above electric - *11-19*	300	350
-	**2664 'Queen Mary'** L&NWR black painted c/w - *11*	NPG	NPG
-	as above electric - *11*	NPG	NPG

L35b. George the Fifth 4-4-0 (Lithographed)
(Carette for Bassett-Lowke)
Carette were more extravagant with rivet detail than Bing.

-	**2663 'George the Fifth'** L&NWR black c/w - *11*	NPG	NPG
-	as above electric - *11*	NPG	NPG

L35c. George the Fifth 4-4-0 (Lithographed)
(Bing for Bassett-Lowke)
This model was also sold in the UK under the Bing name and also under the Gamages name and by other shops that imported it. These included other names such as 'Apollo', GWR 3343 'Mercury', LMS 513 'Mercury', LNER 8551, LNER 504 'King George V' and LMS 1924 as well as versions similar to those listed below. Marklin also made a rather ugly 'George V' which too was not marketed through Bassett-Lowke.

2663/0	**2663 'George the Fifth'** L&NWR black c/w - *19-23*	250	300
2663/0	as above electric - *19-23*	250	300
-	**1000** MR red c/w - *19-23*	NPG	NPG
-	**2664 'Queen Mary'** L&NWR black painted c/w - *21?-?*	800	950
-	as above electric - *21?-?*	800	950
61/4710/0	**5320 'George the Fifth'** LMS maroon c/w - *24-27*	300	400
61/BL/0	as above electric - *24-27*	350	450
-	**513 'George the Fifth'** LMS maroon c/w - *26?*	NPG	NPG
-	as above electric - *26?*	NPG	NPG
-	**3433 'City of Bath'** GWR green c/w - *24-27*	250	300
-	as above electric - *24-27*	250	300
-	**504** LNER green c/w - *24-27*	250	300
-	as above electric - *24-27*	250	300

L36. McIntosh Class 140 Dunalastair IV 4-4-0
This model had an 8-wheel tender.

-	**142** C()R blue (B) c/w - *11-16*	1600	1900
142/0	**142** C()R blue c/w - *25-35*	1500	1800
142E/0	as above electric - *25-35*	1600	1900

Caledonian Railway Dunalastair [L36]
(Barry Potter Auctions)

L37. Class 72 Pickersgill 4-4-0
(Leeds for Bassett-Lowke)
This model had a 6-wheel tender.

77/0	**77** C()R blue c/w - *22-?*	NPG	NPG
77E/0	as above electric - *22-?*	NPG	NPG

L38. Deeley Class 4P Compound 4-4-0
(Bing for Bassett-Lowke)

-	**1000** MR maroon c/w - *c21-23*	NPG	NPG
-	as above steam - *12-14?, c21-23*	NPG	NPG
-	as above electric - *c21-23*	NPG	NPG

L39. LMS Standard Compound 4-4-0
Pre-war electric models did not have key holes and had their handrails cranked where they passed over the front edge of the firebox. After the war, all Compounds had key holes whether clockwork or electric and the handrails were straight. Pre-war models could be had with 20v AC mechanisms (Cat. No. A5502/0). sBt = small Bing type tender. B-Lst = Bassett-Lowke standard tender. crt = coal rail tender

3302/0	**1190** LMS maroon litho sBt c/w - *28-35*	300	450
4302/0	as above 6-8v DC - *28-35*	300	650
-	as above 20v AC - *28-35*	300	650

3302/0	**1108** LMS maroon litho B-Lst c/w - *36-40*	300	450
4302/0	as above 6-8v junior premag - *36-40*	300	650
5302/0	as above 8-10v stand premag - *36-40*	300	650
A5502/0	as above 20vAC - *36-40*	300	650
3302/0	**1108** LMS maroon litho crt c/w - *36-40*	300	450
4302/0	as above electric - *36-40*	300	650
3302/0	**1108** LMS maroon litho crt c/w - *46-47*	300	450
5302/0	as above electric - *46-47*	300	650
3302/0	**1036** LMS maroon litho crt c/w - *48-50*	300	450
5302/0	as above electric - *48-50*	300	650
3302/0	**1036** LMS brown litho crt c/w - *48-50*	300	450
5302/0	as above electric - *48-50*	300	650
3302/0	**1063** LMS brown litho crt c/w - *48-50*	300	450
5302/0	as above electric - *48-50*	300	650
3302/0	**1063** LMS maroon litho crt c/w - *48-50*	300	450
5302/0	as above electric - *48-50*	300	650
3302/0	**1082** LMS maroon litho crt c/w - *48-50*	300	450
5302/0	as above electric - *48-50*	300	650
3302/0	**1082** LMS black painted over 1082 litho red lined c/w - *48-50*	300	450
5302/0	as above electric - *48-50*	300	650
3302/0	**1082** LMS black painted over 1063 litho red lined c/w - *48-50*	300	450
5302/0	as above electric - *48-50*	300	650
3302/0	**41109** BRb black litho lined red+grey c/w - *51-65*	300	450
5302/0	as above electric 3-rail - *51-65*	300	650
2302/0	as above electric 2-rail - *57-68*	350	750
-	**41109, 41125** BRb black litho electric Nu-Scale* - *57-68*	500	850
3302/0	**41125** BRb black litho lined red+grey c/w - *60-64*	300	450
2302/0	as above electric 3-rail 12vDC - *60-64*	300	650
3302/0	**3400** GWR dark green painted over 1190 litho c/w - *34-35*	450	850
5302/0	as above electric - *34-35*	450	850
3302/0	**3400** GWR dark green painted over 1108 litho c/w - *36-39*	450	850
5302/0	as above electric - *36-39*	450	850

Pre-war hand-built quality models of the Compound will be found in Table L97. These had numbers to the customer's choice as could post-war Compounds and 41107 and 41108 are known to exist. * See note on Nu-Scale in the Introduction to this chapter.

Standard Compound [L39] (Barry Potter Auctions)

L40. Class 2P 4-4-0

17/0	**483** LMS maroon c/w - *26?-28-?*	NPG	NPG
66/0E	as above electric - *c26-28-?*	NPG	NPG

L41. LMS Class 2P 4-4-0 (altered Compound)
These were former 1108 Compound models that were over-painted. They have had their outside cylinders removed and plated over, and steam chest fairings on each side of the smokebox mounting also removed (the tin tab slots for the fairings can still be seen). The electric models were often fitted with lamp brackets not found on the Compounds.

3306/0	**601** LMS black c/w - *36-40*	300	450
4306/0	as above electric - *36-40*	300	600
5506/0	as above electric - *36-40*	300	600
4306/0AC	as above electric 20vAC - *36-40*	300	600
4306/0P	as above electric - *36-40*	300	600

L42. Ex-GNR Ivatt Express 4-4-0
(Bing for Bassett-Lowke)

L2103/0	**504** LNER green litho c/w - *24-25*	550	850
LE2103/0	as above electric - *24-25*	550	850

L2103/0	**4390** LNER green litho c/w - *27-30*	330	400
LE2103/0	as above electric - *c26-28-?*	330	400

L42A. Glen Class 4-4-0

This was a model built by the reformed Bassett-Lowke Railways in the late 1960s.

-	**9405 'Glen Spean'** LNER green 3-rail - *late 60s?*	NPG	NPG

L43. Atbara Class 4-4-0
(Bing for Bassett-Lowke)

The models did not have outside cranks.

-	**3410 'Sydney'** GWR green c/w - *04-10*	750	1100

L44. City Class 4-4-0 (Bing for Bassett-Lowke)

The models had outside frames and cranks and were of an all soldered construction. Brass bogie wheels, nameplates and safety valve cover. Typical Bing buffers with tapered shank and nickel plated.

-	**3433 'City of Bath'** Great Western green with incorrect yellow and black lining c/w - *13-15*	4200	6000
-	as above electric - *14*	4200	6000

L45. Churchward County 4-4-0
(Leeds for Bassett-Lowke)

3800/0	**3800 'County of Middlesex'** GWR green c/w - *22-25*	NPG	NPG
3800E/0	as above electric - *22-25*	NPG	NPG
3800/0	**3801 'County of Carlow'** GWR green c/w - *22-25*	400	550

Other names exist.

L46. Wainwright Class D 4-4-0
(Bing for Bassett-Lowke)

-	SE&CR green c/w - *14*	1900	2700

Markin for Bassett-Lowke 'Merchant Taylors' [L47]
(Christies)

L47. Schools Class 4-4-0
(Marklin for Bassett-Lowke)

910/0/C	**910 'Merchant Taylors'** Southern green c/w - *34-37-?*	950	1600
910/0/A	as above electric AC - *34-36-?*	1100	1700
910/0/D	as above electric DC - *34-36-?*	1100	1700

L48. NYC Vauclain Compound 4-4-0
(Carette for Bassett-Lowke)

-	**2350** NYC c/w - *05-?*	NPG	NPG

L49. GNR Atlantic 4-4-2
(Carette or Bing for Bassett-Lowke)

-	**251** GNR green (C) c/w - *07-09*	800	1100
-	as above (C) electric - *07-?*	NPG	NPG
9/0	**1425** GNR green (B) c/w - *13-14?*	500	650
-	as above (B) electric - *12-14?*	500	650
-	**1442** GNR green litho (C) c/w - *11-?*	500	850
-	as above (C) electric - *11-?*	500	850

L50. Ex-NBR Class C1 Atlantic 4-4-2

-	**8872 'Auld Reekie'** LNER green elec - *c55*	NPG	NPG

L51. Goods Loco 0-6-0 (Bing for Bassett-Lowke)

4736/0	**773** Southern green litho c/w - *28-?*	NPG	NPG
4736/0	**4460** GWR green litho c/w - *28-?*	NPG	NPG
-	**4472** LNER green litho c/w - *27-?*	NPG	NPG
4736/0	**6508** LMS maroon litho c/w - *28-?*	NPG	NPG
4736/0	**8851** LNER green? c/w - *28-?*	NPG	NPG

L52. Cauliflower 0-6-0 (Bing for Bassett-Lowke)

-	**930, 1269** L&NWR black c/w - *12-14*	NPG	NPG
-	GNR black c/w - *12-14*	NPG	NPG

L53. Fowler 4F 0-6-0

This model was of soldered construction with a paint finish.

3204/0	**4072** LMS black lined red c/w - *27-33*	400	650
4204/0	as above electric - *27-33*	400	750
5302/0	**1931** GWR green lined + copper capped chimney elec. - *27-33*	350	500

Fowler 4F 0-6-0 [L53] sold for £520
(Barry Potter Auctions)

L54. J39 0-6-0

This model was of soldered construction with a paint finish.

3205/0	**1448** LNER black lined red c/w - *27-35*	350	600
4205/0	as above electric 12v - *27-35*	350	600

L55. Standard Goods Locomotive 0-6-0

This model was of tab construction and lithographed. The LMS version had a capuchon on the chimney. The non-BR locos had a Bing type tender without the horizontal fluting found on passenger locomotives. The BR model has the later standard Bassett-Lowke tender.

	the following were lined in red		
?	**4256** black c/w - *36?*	250	450
3307/0	**4256** LMS black c/w - *36-40*	300	500
4307/0	as above 12vDC - *36-40*	350	500
A4307/0	as above 20vAC - *36-40*	350	550
5307/0	as above spur drive - *36-40*	350	550
?	**4417** LMS black c/w - *?*	250	450
4308/0	**156** LNER black electric - *36-40*	350	550
4308/0	**1448** LNER black 3-rail 12vDC - *36-40*	450	600
3308/0	**1456** LNER black c/w - *36-40*	300	450
4308/0	as above electric - *36-40*	350	550
A4308/0	as above 20vAC - *36-40*	350	550
5308/0	as above spur drive - *36-40*	350	550
	the following were unlined		
3308/0	**63871** BRb black c/w - *55-67*	250	450
5308/0	as above electric 3-rail - *55-67*	300	500
3308/0	**64193** BRb black c/w - *55-67*	250	450
5308/0	as above electric 3-rail - *55-67*	300	500
2308/0	as above electric 2-rail * - *57-67*	300	500
-	as above electric * - *57-65*	550	650
3308/0	**43871** BRb black c/w - *55-67*	250	450
5308/0	as above electric 3-rail - *55-67*	300	500
2308/0	as above electric 2-rail - *57-67*	300	500

* See note on Nu-Scale in the Introduction to this chapter.

L56. Hughes 'Crab' Mogul 2-6-0

-	**2700** LMS maroon steam - *25-?*	NPG	NPG
-	as above c/w - *25-?*	NPG	NPG
-	as above electric - *25-?*	NPG	NPG
-	**2700** LMS black steam - *25-?*	NPG	NPG
-	as above steam - *25-?*	NPG	NPG
-	as above electric - *25-?*	NPG	NPG
6660/0	**13000** LMS maroon steam - *25-39*	600	750

6670/0	as above steam - *25-39*	600	750
3601/0	as above c/w - *25-33*	550	700
4601/0	as above electric - *25-33*	700	900
4602/0	as above electric - *25-33*	700	900
4601/0	as above number on cabsides and tender 3-rail 12vDC - *25-33*	700	900
6660/0	**13000** LMS black steam - *25-39*	650	900
6670/0	as above steam - *25-39*	650	900
3601/0	as above c/w - *25-33*	600	800
4601/0	as above electric - *25-33*	800	1100
4602/0	as above electric - *25-33*	800	1100

L57. Stanier Mogul 2-6-0

-	kit steam - *?*	NPG	NPG
-	kit c/w - *?*	NPG	NPG
-	kit electric - *?*	NPG	NPG
6660/0	**2945** LMS maroon steam - *34-c41*	350	550
-	as above kit steam - *c39-c49*	650	800
-	as above c/w - *34-c41*	300	400
-	as above kit c/w - *c39-c49*	400	500
4601/0	as above electric - *34-c41*	300	400
-	as above kit electric - *c39-c49*	400	500
-	as above steam - *01*	NPG	NPG
6660/0	**2945** LMS black steam - *34-c41*	350	550
-	as above kit steam - *c39-c49*	650	800
-	as above c/w - *34-c41*	300	400
-	as above kit c/w - *c39-c49*	400	500
4601/0	as above electric - *34-c41*	300	400
-	as above kit electric - *c39-c49*	400	500
-	**5524** LMS maroon steam Fowler tend - *?*	NPG	NPG
-	**13007** LMS maroon steam - *68-69*	NPG	NPG
6661/0	**42980** BRb black lined grey+red steam - *c52-64*	550	800
-	as above c/w - *?*	NPG	NPG
-	as above electric - *?*	NPG	NPG
-	**42981** BRb black steam - *?*	NPG	750

L58. Gresley Class K3 Mogul 2-6-0

6670/0	**33** LNER green steam - *25-41*	1100	1400
3602/0	as above c/w - *25-41*	850	1400
4602/0	as above electric 12vDC - *25-41*	850	1400
6670/0	**33** LNER black steam - *25-41*	1600	1900
3602/0	as above c/w - *25-41*	1300	1700
4602/0	as above electric - *25-41*	1100	1500
6670/0	**982** LNER green steam - *26-c38*	NPG	NPG
3602/0	as above c/w - *26-28-?*	NPG	NPG
4602/0	as above electric - *26-28-?*	NPG	NPG
6670/0	**982** LNER black steam - *26-c38*	NPG	NPG
3602/0	as above c/w - *26-28-?*	NPG	NPG
4602/0	as above electric - *26-28-?*	NPG	NPG
-	**1864** LNER green steam - *46-?*	400	550
-	as above c/w - *46-?*	450	550
-	as above electric - *46-?*	450	550
-	**1864** LNER black steam - *46-50-?*	550	1050
-	as above c/w - *46-50-?*	550	1050
-	as above electric - *46-50-?*	550	1100

L59. Class K4 Mogul 2-6-0

-	**2066 'Deer Stalker'** LNER green elec - *c69*	450	550

L60. GWR Class 43XX Mogul 2-6-0

All carried Great (crest) Western on their tenders.

6680/0	**4431** green steam - *25-28-?*	420	450
3603/0	as above c/w - *25-36?*	500	550
4603/0	as above electric - *25-36?*	500	550
6680/0	**4431** black steam - *25-28-?*	NPG	NPG
3603/0	as above c/w - *25-28?*	NPG	NPG
4603/0	as above electric - *25-28?*	NPG	NPG
3603/0	**4331** green c/w - *25-36?*	500	550
4603/0	as above electric - *25-36?*	500	550

L61. Maunsell Class N Mogul 2-6-0

6685/0	**864** Southern green steam - *26-c38*	NPG	NPG
3644/0	as above c/w - *26-28-?*	NPG	NPG
4644/0	as above electric - *26-28-?*	NPG	NPG
6685/0	**864** Southern black steam - *26-c38*	NPG	NPG
3644/0	as above c/w - *26-28-?*	NPG	NPG
4644/0	as above electric - *26-28-?*	NPG	NPG
6685/0	**866** Southern green steam - *26-c38*	NPG	NPG
3644/0	as above c/w - *26-c38*	NPG	NPG
4644/0	as above electric- *26-c38*	NPG	NPG

L62. Cardean 4-6-0 (floor model)
(Carette for Bassett-Lowke)

-	**903 'Cardean'** C()R blue c/w - *09-?*	NPG	NPG

L63. Super Enterprise 4-6-0 (Freelance)

6655/0	**851** Southern green steam *37-?*	NPG	NPG
6655/0	**2495** black steam *37-40*	NPG	NPG
6655/0	**2871** LNER green steam *37-40*	NPG	NPG
6655/0	**5524** LMS maroon steam *37-40*	350	NPG
-	**45295** BRb green steam *37-?*	250	400
-	**61324** BRb black steam *37-?*	250	400

L64. 4-6-0 (Freelance) (Bing for Bassett-Lowke)
All were litho printed and clockwork.

4737/0	**4460 'Windsor Castle'** GWR green - *28*	NPG	NPG
4737/0	**4472 'Flying Fox'** LNER green - *28-?*	NPG	NPG
4737/0	**6508 'Royal Scot'** LMS maroon - *28-?*	NPG	NPG
4737/0	**773 'King Arthur'** Southern green - *28-?*	1100	1300

L65. Prince of Wales 4-6-0
(Bing for Bassett-Lowke)

49/0	**5600 'Prince of Wales'** LMS maroon c/w - *24-25*	NPG	NPG

L66. Royal Scot Class 4-6-0
Ft = Fowler tender. St = Stanier tender. sd = smoke deflectors fitted.

	LMS 6100 'Royal Scot'		
3303/0	maroon litho Ft c/w - *29-37*	850	1450
3611/0	maroon St c/w - *37-52*	850	1450
3622/0	black St c/w - *c48-52*	1300	1900
A4303/0	maroon litho Ft AC - *29-37*	550	700
4303/0	maroon litho Ft DC - *29-37*	550	700
5611/0	maroon St and sd AC - *37-52*	750	950
5711/0	maroon St and sd DC - *37-52*	750	950
5622/0	black St and sd 3-rail 12vDC - *c48-52*	1300	1600

'Royal Scot' [L66] (Christies)

L67. Rebuilt Royal Scot 4-6-0
Stanier tender and reprofiled smoke deflectors.

	BRb 46100 'Royal Scot'		
-	green c/w - *53-?*	1300	1800
5622/0	green 3-rail 12vDC - *53-56-?*	2600	3200
-	green electric* Nu-Scale - *57-60*	2100	3700

* See note on Nu-Scale in the Introduction to this chapter.

L68. Jubilee Class 4-6-0

911/0	**5552 'Silver Jubilee'** LMS black + silver (M) c/w - *35*	3100	4200
911/0/A	as above (M) electric AC - *35*	3100	4200
911/0/D	as above (M) electric DC - *35*	3100	4200

911/0	5610 'Gold Coast' LMS maroon (M) c/w - 35-?	2850	3700
911/0/A	(M) electric AC - 35-?	2850	3700
911/0/D	(M) electric DC - 35-?	2850	3700
911/0	5573 'Newfoundland' LMS maroon (M) c/w - 35-40?	2850	3700
911/0/A	as above (M) electric AC - 35-40?	2850	3700
911/0/D	as above (M) electric DC - 35-40?	2850	4700
911/0/C 3607/0	5682 'Trafalgar' LMS maroon(M) c/w - 36-40?	4200	5500
5607/0	as above (M) electric - 36-40-?	4200	5500
911/0/C 3607/0	5701 'Conqueror' LMS maroon c/w - 36-40?	2700	5200
911/0/A	as above electric AC - 36-40?	3000	5700
911/0/D	as above electric DC - 36-40?	3000	5700
911/0/C 3607/0	5712 'Victory' LMS maroon c/w - 36-40-?	3900	5200
5607/0	as above electric DC - 36-40-?	4200	5700

Rebuilt Royal Scot [L67] (Christies)

L69. LMS Black 5 4-6-0 (rebuilt from Marklin Jubilee)

	4853? LMS black c/w - 35-c40	800	1100
-	5294 LMS black elec 12vDC 3-rail - 35-c40	800	1100
-	5241 LMS black elec 12vDC 3-rail - 35-c40	NPG	2500

L70. Class 5MT 4-6-0

-	45126 BR black electric 2/3 rail - 59-63	NPG	NPG

L71. Class B17 4-6-0

-	2838 'Melton Hall' LNER green c/w - 36-c39	4700	6200
-	as above electric 3-rail 12vDC - 36-c39	4600	6200
3608/0	2848 'Arsenal' LNER green c/w - 36-c39	5000	9200
A4608/0	as above electric AC - 36-c39	5200	9200
5608/0	as above electric DC - 36-c39	5200	9900
3608/0	2853 'Huddersfield Town' LNER green c/w - 36-c39	4200	5200
A4608/0	as above electric AC - 36-c39	4200	5200
5608/0	as above electric DC - 36-c39	4200	5200

Class B17 'Melton Hall' [L71] (Barry Potter Auctions)

L72. Castle Class 4-6-0

-	4079 'Pendennis Castle' GWR green using Mogul parts c/w - 30-?	1350	1600
-	4079 'Pendennis Castle' GWR green c/w - 39-51	1600	2100
	as above electric - 39-51	1600	2100
	as above electric (H) - c55	2100	2600
-	5071 'Spitfire' GWR green electric 2/3 rail - 55-63	2100	2600
-	5071 'Spitfire' BRb green (H) - c55	2100	2600

-	5015 "Kingswear Castle" * Great Western green electric 3-rail 12vDC - 50s?	3200	3700
-	5003 'Lulworth Castle' * Great Western green electric 3-rail 12vDC - 50s?	3200	4200

* Special order.

L73. County Class 4-6-0 (Hunt for Bassett-Lowke)

-	1003 'County of Wilts' BRc green electric 3-rail 12vDC 57-63?	NPG	NPG

L74. King Class 4-6-0

912/0/C	6000 'King George V' green (M) Great()Western c/w - 35-37-?	3200	4700
612/0/A	as above electric AC (M) - 35-37-?	4200	5450
912/0/D	as above electric DC (M) - 35-37-?	4200	5450
-	6027 'King Richard' GWR green electric 2/3 rail hand built - c60-63*	2700	3200

* Made to order.

L75. Lord Nelson 4-6-0 (rebuilt from litho Royal Scot)

-	850 'Lord Nelson' Southern green c/w - 35-?	1300	1600
-	as above electric - 35-?	1300	1600

L77. Princess Royal Class 4-6-2

LMS 6200 'The Princess Royal'			
3605/0/C	maroon c/w - 35-?	3100	4200
3605/0/A	maroon electric AC Fowler tender - 35-?	3100	4200
3605/0/D	maroon electric DC Fowler tender - 35-?	3100	5000
LMS 6201 'Princess Elizabeth'			
3605/0	maroon c/w - 36-39-?	3100	5200
A4605/0	maroon electric AC - 36-39-?	3100	4700
5605/0	maroon electric DC - 36-39-?	3600	4700
-	6202 LMS maroon Turbomotive c/w - 36-c50	NPG	NPG
-	as above but 3-rail 12v electric (only one known) - c37	NPG	NPG

L78. Streamlined Princess Coronation Class

-	6220 'Coronation' LMS blue c/w - 37-c48	4200	7200
-	as above electric - 37-c48	4200	8700
3606/0	6225 'Duchess of Gloucester' LMS maroon c/w - 38?-c48	4200	5200
4606/0	as above electric AC - 38?-c48	4200	7200
5606/0	as above electric DC - 38?-c48	4200	7200
-	6227 'Duchess of Devonshire' LMS maroon c/w made to order* - ?	NPG	8700

* Made for Harold Elliott's sea-front layout at Scarborough.

L79. Princess Coronation Class 4-6-2

sd = with smoke deflectors fitted.

LMS 6232 Duchess of Montrose'			
3613/0	maroon c/w - 39-49	2100	3200
5613/0	maroon electric 12vDC 3-rail - 39-49	2100	3200
BRb 46232 'Duchess of Montrose'			
3613/0	blue sd c/w - c52	3700	5200
3613/0	green sd c/w - c54-c58	2600	3200
-	blue sd electric - c52	4200	5200
2613/0	green sd electric 2-rail - c57-c58	3100	4700
5613/0	green sd electric 3-rail - c54-c58	3100	4700
-	green sd electric Nu-Scale ** - 57-65	2600	4200
-	46245 'City of London'* BRb black smoke deflectors 3-rail 12vDC - 50s	3100	3700
-	46257 'City of Salford'* BRb black smoke deflectors 3-rail 12vDC - 50s	1300	1500

* Special order. ** See note on Nu-Scale in the Introduction to this chapter.

L80. A1/A3 Pacific 4-6-2

LNER A3 103 'Flying Scotsman'			
-	green litho c/w - c47-c50	1300	1900
-	green litho electric - c47-c50	1300	1900
LNER A1 4472 'Flying Scotsman'			
3304/0	green litho c/w - 33-c41	750	1400

4304/0	green litho electric 8vDC - *33-c41*	850	1400
5304/0	green litho 8vAC - *33-c41*	850	1400
5504/0	green litho electric 20vAC - *33-c41*	850	1400
6304/0	green litho electric 20vAC - *33-c41*	850	1400
-	green litho electric Nu-Scale - *57-65*	1600	2000
	BRb A3 60103 'Flying Scotsman'		
3310/0	blue litho c/w - *50-52*	1300	1600
-	blue litho electric 12vDC 3r - *50-52*	1300	1600
3310/0	green litho c/w - *c53-c58*	800	1300
5310/0	green litho electric 12vDC 3-rail - *c53-c58*	800	1300
2310/0	green litho electric 12vDC 2-rail - *c53-c58*	1300	1700
-	green litho electric Nu-Scale - *57-65*	1600	2100

'Duchess of Montrose' [L79] (Christies)

L81. A4 Pacific 4-6-2

2507/0	**2509 'Silver Link'** LNER silver c/w - *36-c40*	4700	8200
4606/0	as above electric AC - *36-c40*	4700	8200
5606/0	as above electric DC - *36-c40*	4700	8200
2507/0	**2510 'Quicksilver'** LNER silver c/w - *36-c40*	4700	8200
4606/0	as above electric AC - *36-c40*	4700	8200
5606/0	as above electric DC - *36-c40*	4700	8200
2507/0	**2511 'Silver King'** LNER silver c/w - *36-c40*	4700	8200
4606/0	as above electric AC - *36-c40*	4700	8200
5606/0	as above electric DC - *36-c40*	4700	8200
2507/0	**2512 'Silver Fox'** LNER silver c/w - *36-c40*	4700	8200
4606/0	as above electric AC - *36-c40*	4700	8200
5606/0	as above electric DC - *36-c40*	4700	8200
2507/0	**4489 'Dominion of Canada'** LNER blue c/w - *c38-c40*	4700	8200
4606/0	as above electric AC - *c38-c40*	4700	8200
5606/0	as above electric DC - *c38-c40*	4700	8200
2507/0	**4490 'Empire of India'** LNER blue c/w - *c38-c40*	4700	8200
4606/0	as above electric AC - *c38-c40*	4700	8200
5606/0	as above electric DC - *c38-c40*	4700	8200
2507/0	**4498 'Sir Nigel Gresley'** LNER blue c/w - *c38-c40*	4700	8200
4606/0	as above electric AC - *c38-c40*	4700	8200
5606/0	as above electric DC - *c38-c40*	4700	8200

L82. Britannia Class Pacific 4-6-2
(Hunt for Bassett-Lowke)

-	**70000 'Britannia'** BRc green hand built electric 2/3-rail - *58-?*	5200	8200

L83. German State Railways 4-6-2
(Marklin for Bassett-Lowke)

MG/0	German State Railways electric - *34-36-?*	NPG	NPG

L84. New York Central 4-6-4 (Marklin for Bassett-Lowke)

AK/0	**'Commodor Vanderbilt'** AK70/12920 New York Central black electric - *34-36-?*	NPG	NPG

L85. Class 8F 2-8-0

-	**48209** BRc black electric 2/3-rail - *60-63*	NPG	NPG

L86. French Mountain 4-8-2 (Marklin for Bassett-Lowke)

MF/0	ETAT electric - *34-36-?*	NPG	NPG

L87. Class 9F 2-10-0 (Hunt for Bassett-Lowke)

-	**92220 'Evening Star'** BRc green electric 2/3-rail - *61-63*	2300	3200
-	BRc black electric - *61-63*	NPG	NPG

Diesel and Electric Locomotives

L88. SECR Steam Railmotor
(Carette for Bassett-Lowke)

-	**1** litho steam brown - *07-09-?*	1600	1900

L89. Deltic Diesel Co-Co
It is believed that fewer than 10 Deltics were made.

-	**'Deltic'** electric blue twin electric motor bogies 3-rail 12vDC - *59-63*	2100	4700
-	**'Deltic'** BRc green - *?*	NPG	NPG

'Deltic' [L89] sold for £2,000 (Wallis & Wallis)

L90. Steeplecab Electric 0-4-0
(Bing & Marklin for Bassett-Lowke)

-	**23** CLR blue (M) electric - *03-?*	1600	1900
-	**23** CLR blue (B) electric - *04-?*	500	650

L91. Swiss Pantograph Electrics
(Marklin for Bassett-Lowke)

-	SBB 4-6-2 electric - *35-?*	NPG	NPG
-	SBB 4-4-2 electric - *35-?*	NPG	NPG
-	SBB 0-4-0 electric - *35-?*	NPG	NPG

L92. London Underground Standard EMU
Made all of brass.

-	**7073 +?+ 7072** London Transport red + cream 3-car electric 35 12vDC - *37-38*	2600	5200
-	**7073 + 7072** London Transport red + cream 2-car electric 35 12vDC - *37-38*	950	1400

L93. Southern EMU (Bing for Bassett-Lowke)

1457/0	**2601** Southern green 3-car set elec - *c28*	1400	1600

L94. Euston-Watford 1927 Stock EMU

104/0	**1652/3416/6560** LMS maroon 3-car * litho electric 3-rail 12vDC - *30-35*	1100	2000

* The centre car was a 1st/3rd.

L95. Southern EMU (Exley for Bassett-Lowke)
These were 3-car sets with 12V DC Bassett-Lowke motor bogies and B-L coach bogies.

?	**3072/3086** (11165 + ?) Southern green Portsmouth 3-car set - *?*	1300	1600
?	**3072/3074** Southern green 4RES 3-car suburban set - *53-57*	1300	1600
?	**3091/3071** Southern green 4RES 3-car suburban set - *53-57*	1600	2100
?	LMS maroon ex-Southern 4RES 3-car EMU (fictional) about 10 sets made as a special order - *c55*	1600	2200

L96. Brighton Belle Pullman EMU
The cars were made-to-order and had metal sides, metal window frames, wooden floors and roof, brass handrails, B-L bogies and full internal fittings.

-	**88** Pullman dark brown+cream driver	NA	NA
-	**87** Pullman dark brown+cream driver	NA	NA
-	**'Hazel'** Pullman dark brown+cream 1st	NA	NA
-	**'Doris'** Pullman dark brown+cream 1st	NA	NA

Bassett-Lowke

		£	£
-	**86** Pullman dark brown+cream 3rd	NA	NA
-	the above 5 cars	2600	4200

Watford set [L94] (Barry Potter Auctions)

Miscellaneous

L97. Hand-Built Locomotives

In 1933, Bassett-Lowke announced a range of hand-built locomotives which could be made to order. The models would be to a very high specification including all solder construction, all external and visible details and full painting and lining. Locomotives could be had either with variable speed clockwork drive, 8-10v DC or 20v AC electric mechanisms. Customers could choose their own running numbers and those given below are examples seen or advertised.

-	GWR 2-6-0 Mogul - *33-35*	NPG	NPG
	GWR 2-6-2T - *33-35*	NPG	NPG
-	**2793** GWR 0-6-0T - *33-35*	NPG	NPG
	LMS 2-6-0 Mogul - *33-35*	NPG	NPG
-	**6100** LMS 4-6-0 Royal Scot Class - *33-39*	NPG	NPG
-	LMS 4-6-0 Baby Scot Class - *33-39*	NPG	NPG
-	LMS 4-6-0 Rebuilt Claughton Class - *33-35*	NPG	NPG
-	**1067** LMS 4-4-0 Midland Compound - *33-35*	450	650
-	**453** 'King Arthur' Southern King Arthur Class - *33-35*	NPG	NPG
	LMS 4-6-2T CR Pickersgill - *33-35*	NPG	NPG
-	LMS 2-6-2T - *33-39*	NPG	NPG
-	LMS 2-6-4T - *33-39*	NPG	NPG
-	LMS 0-6-0 goods tender loco - *33-39*	NPG	NPG
-	**4472** 'Flying Scotsman' LNER 4-6-2 A1/A3 Class - *33-39*	NPG	NPG
-	LNER 0-6-0 goods tender loco - *33-35*	NPG	NPG
-	**453** 'King Arthur' Southern King Arthur Class - *33-35*	NPG	NPG
-	**850** 'Lord Nelson' Southern Lord Nelson Class - *33-35*	NPG	NPG
-	PLM French Windcutter Pacific - *33-35*	NPG	NPG
-	**2300** CP 4-6-2 Canadian Pacific loco - *33-35*	NPG	NPG

COACHES

As with the locomotives, many of the early coaches were imported from Germany where they were made by Bing, Marklin or Carette but, by the 1930s, Bassett-Lowke were manufacturing their own.

Carette coaches produced for Bassett-Lowke were all made before the First World War and, consequently were all in pre-grouping liveries. Some of these were toy-like but so-called 'scale' model coaches arrived in 1910. Some of Carette tools were later acquired by Bassett-Lowke to produce the LNWR and LMS travelling post offices and 12-wheeled diners in the 1920s.

Bing lithographed coaches dominated the '20s and are known as the 1921 Series. These were all steel and were produced in the pre-grouping liveries of GNR, LNWR, MR and GWR (lake). A year after the grouping in 1924, the coaches were produced in the post-grouping liveries of LMS, LNER (teak), SR and GWR (chocolate and cream) and were fitted with corridor connections.

The first coach made by Bassett-Lowke themselves appeared in 1930 and was part of the Watford EMU set. First class corridor and brake thirds were made in the liveries of all four railway companies but the LMS and SR EMUs (see 'Locomotives' section) also received a pair of suburban coaches. These were available separately as too was an LMS travelling post office.

A new design of coach was introduced after the Second World War in BR red and cream. These new coaches were made by Precision Models in Northampton who were also manufacturing the Trix Twin system at that time. Exley also made coaches for Bassett-Lowke from 1936 and these had the Exley trademark carefully removed and were packed in Bassett-Lowke boxes. More about these later.

Cat.No.	Company, Number, Colour, Dates	£	£

C1. Early Clerestory Coaches
(Carette for Bassett-Lowke)

These coaches were 10" and 12" long respectively and fitted with Maunsell type wheels and double windows.

-	**MR** maroon 1st/3rd - *?-19*	200	230
-	**MR** maroon brake - *?-19*	200	230
-	**GWR** dark brown+cream 1st/3rd - *?-19*	200	230
-	**GWR** 1334 dk.brn+cream full brake - *?-19*	200	230
-	**GNR** teak 1st/3rd - *?-19*	200	230
-	**GNR** teak brake - *?-19*	200	230
-	**LNWR** brown+cream 1st/3rd - *?-19*	200	230
-	**LNWR** brown+cream brake - *?-19*	200	230

C1A. 6-Wheel Coaches (Bing for Bassett-Lowke)

These coaches had embossed sides and three pairs of wheels. The centre pair slid from side to side to allow for tight curves. The coaches came as a set of three with crude couplings between and standard couplings at the end of the trio. The set consisted of two composite coaches and a brake 3rd but a full brake, with standard couplings at both ends, could be bought separately.

-	**LNWR** 13212 black+crm 1st/3rd comp - *?*	200	230
-	**LNWR** 13312 black+cream brake/3rd - *?*	200	230
-	**LNWR** 13312 black+cream full brake - *?*	200	230

C2. Early Freelance Coaches

These were designed to be whatever you wanted them to be and were finished for the customer accordingly. They had a curved roof which was fitted with torpedo ventilators. The windows were glazed with glass, including ground glass for the lavatory compartments. They were 13" long and the bodies and underframes were made from hard wood, the door handles were gold plated brass. The doors did not open but the coaches could be bought in kit form.

601E	teak various 1st/2nd/3rd - *?-19*	200	230
602E	teak various brake - *?-19*	200	230

C3. 1921 Series Bogie Coaches
(Bing for Bassett-Lowke)

These coaches were 13" long and of tinplate construction. They had embossed sides and compensated heavy gauge steel bogies. The black painted wheels were a heavy alloy, Maunsell type, with thick flanges and ran loose on crimped axles which were retained in covered axle boxes by crimped on washers. The roofs were clipped on and there was no provision for corridor connectors. They were fitted with Bing couplings with long single drop links, cast oval alloy buffers riveted on, with two gas cylinders and underframe stays. The coaches could be had with turned cast iron wheels and are often found with the later superior Bassett-Lowke 612/0 bogies with large diameter turned cast iron Maunsell pattern wheels and cast axle boxes. Stocks lasted well after the introduction of the later '1924' series coaches.

60/0	**MR** lake 1st corridor - *22-26*	170	250
61/0	**MR** 2783 lake 3rd/brake - *22-26*	170	250
62/0	**GWR** 132 lake 1st corridor - *22-26*	170	250
63/0	**GWR** 133 lake 3rd/brake - *22-26*	170	250

64/0	**LNWR** 1921 brown+cream 1st corridor - *21-26*	170	250
65/0	**LNWR** 1921 brown+cream 3rd/brake - *21-26*	170	250
65/0	**LNWR** 1334 brown+cream 3rd/brake - *21-26*	170	250
65/0	**LNWR** 1334 brown+cream full /brake - *21-26*	170	250
66/0	**GNR** teak 1st (12" long) - *21-26*	170	250
67/0	**GNR** teak full brake (12" long) - *21-26*	170	250
64/0	**LSWR** 1308? brown+salmon 1st/3rd corridor - *21-26*	170	250
65/0	**LSWR** brown+salmon 3rd/brake - *21-26*	170	250

C4. 1924 Series Bogie Coaches
(Bing for Bassett-Lowke)

These were also 13" long and were to the same specification as the 1921 Series (table C3) except for livery and provision of corridor connections. Each coach had one overscale bellows type coach connector made in black camera cloth which spanned between adjacent coaches. The connections were hollow and brake end coaches were provided with a clip-on closure plate. Early examples had brass buffers and brass Bing couplings and, again, improved bogies and cast iron wheels could be fitted.

60/0	**LMS** 2784 maroon 1st - *25-31*	170	200
61/0	**LMS** 2783 maroon 3rd/brake - *25-31*	170	200
62/0	**GWR** 132 cream+dark brown 1st - *28-31*	200	230
63/0	**GWR** 133, 1921, 3251 cream+dark brown 3rd/brake - 28-31	200	230
66/0	**Southern** 7001 green 1st * - *26-31*	220	270
67/0	**Southern** 7000, 7716 green 3rd/brake* - *26-31*	220	270
68/0	**LNER** 1235N teak 1st - *25-31*	170	200
68/0	**LNER** 601 teak all 1st - *25-31*	170	200
69/0	**LNER** 1234N teak 3rd/brake - *25-31*	170	200

*SR coaches introduced in 1926 were repaints of GWR lake coloured ones.

C5. 12-Wheel Dining Cars (Carette Design)

14" long, these had uncompensated folded tinplate bogies, a battery box (instead of gas cylinders), no axle boxes, cast alloy buffers riveted on, recessed vestibules, a clip-on roof, underframe stays, heavy alloy wheels running loose on crimped axles and embossed tinplate sides.

94/0	**LNWR** 13210 cream+brown - *21-24*	250	370
94/0	**LMS** 13210 maroon - *24-34*	250	370

C6. Post Office Mail Vans (Carette Design)

The length of these vans was 12¼" and they had no corridor connections. They had 4-wheel uncompensated folded tinplate bogies, gas cylinders, no underframe stays, cast buffers riveted on and a long ducket along one side. The coach had an operating pickup 'net' and delivery arm and an activating trigger beneath the coach which engaged with a ramp which was operated by the lineside delivery apparatus. Coaches came complete with mail bags and ground apparatus, electric or clockwork. The ground apparatus could be either tinplate or wooden sleepered track.

95/0	**LNWR** 1339 cream+brown - *22-24*	220	240
95/0	**LMS** 1924 maroon - *24-31*	180	200

LMS Travelling Post Office from carette tooling [C6]

C7. Post Office Mail Van - Wooden

This was to a similar specification to that used for the Carette model (table C6), with identical mechanical features, but with the coach body made of wood and with the livery transferred on. The roof was solidly fixed in place and there appeared to be no easy way of retrieving mail bags from inside the coach.

-	**LMS** 1930 maroon - *30*	300	330

C8. Short Bogie Coaches

These were to a similar specification as the 1921 and 1924 Series coaches but were only 9½" long. They were fitted with folded tinplate Carette style bogies and reduced size Bing style couplings. They were also fitted with a transverse mounted single gas cylinder.

100/0	**LNER** 524 teak full brake - *26-32*	120	250
101/0	**LNER** 525 teak 1st - *26-32*	120	250
103/0	**LNER** 526 teak 3rd - *26-32*	120	250
160/0	**LNER** teak 1st/3rd - *30-32*	120	250
160/0	**LMS** maroon 1st/3rd - *30-32*	120	250
260/0	**LNER** teak full brake, opening doors - *30-32*	120	250
260/0	**LMS** maroon full brake, opening doors - *30-32*	120	250

C9. Short Pullman Coaches
(Bing for Bassett-Lowke)

These were 12¼" long and were of tinplate construction with hinged roofs. They were interior fitted with tables and chairs and had vestibule ends, underframe trusses with two transverse gas cylinders and battery box as well as brass couplings and buffers. Bing style bogies with axles retained by press-on washers in axle covers and heavy alloy spoked wheels, were fitted. There were similar GWR, LMS and LNER coaches in this range but they were not listed in the Bassett-Lowke catalogues.

195/0	**Pullman** 'Minerva' brown+cream - *28-32*	100	120
195/0	**Pullman** 'Cassandra' brown+cream - *28-32*	100	120

C10. Prototypical Scale Wooden Coaches

Bassett-Lowke offered a high quality range of wooden coaches, of scale length, at least until around 1938. By this time, Edward Exley Ltd were supplying top of the range quality coaches. Most of the models in the Bassett-Lowke quality range were made to customer's own specifications including choice of livery and panelled and moulded sides. Bogies were the current top of the range ones consisting of 601/0, 607/0 (6-wheel) or 612/0 as appropriate. 57' and 70' coaches were available in LMS, LNER and GWR livery.

G621/0	3rd/brake end - *21-38*	NPG	NPG
G621/0	1st/3rd composite corridor - *21-38*	NPG	NPG
G621/0	dining car - *21-38*	NPG	NPG
G621/0	sleeping car - *21-38*	NPG	NPG

C11. Wooden Modern Coaching Stock Bodies

These were quality coach bodies that could be bought and finished by the purchaser. They were supplied without bogies and the body and roof were made of wood. They came ready for painting.

625/8/0	**LMS** 54' corridor 3rd/brake, old type - *28-32*	NPG	NPG
623/7/0	**LMS** 54' corridor 1st/3rd, old type - *28-32*	NPG	NPG
625/5/0	**LMS** 57' centre corridor 1st - *28-32*	NPG	NPG
625/1/0	**LMS** 57' centre corridor 1st/3rd - *28-32*	NPG	NPG
625/2/0	**LMS** 57' centre corridor 3rd/brake - *28-32*	NPG	NPG
625/3/0	**LMS** 57' centre corridor 3rd - *28-32*	NPG	NPG
625/4/0	**LMS** 50' kitchen car - *28-32*	NPG	NPG
625/28/0	**LMS** sleeping car 1st - *30-32*	NPG	NPG
625/29/0	**LMS** passenger brake van - *30-32*	NPG	NPG
625/13/0	**GWR** 57' corridor 1st/3rd - *28-32*	NPG	NPG
625/14/0	**GWR** 57' corridor 3rd/brake - *28-32*	NPG	NPG
625/15/0	**GWR** 57' corridor 1st/3rd - *28-32*	NPG	NPG
625/25/0	**GWR** 70' corridor 1st/3rd - *28-32*	NPG	NPG
625/26/0	**GWR** 70' 3rd/brake - *28-32*	NPG	NPG
625/27/0	**GWR** 70' diner 1st/3rd - *28-32*	NPG	NPG
627/1/0	**GWR** 57' corridor 1st/3rd, old type - *28-32*	NPG	NPG
627/2/0	**GWR** 57' 3rd/brake, old type - *28-32*	NPG	NPG
627/10/0	**LNER** 60' corridor 1st/3rd - *28-32*	NPG	NPG
627/11/0	**LNER** 60' corridor 3rd/brake - *28-32*	NPG	NPG
627/12/0	**LNER** 60' diner 1st/3rd - *28-32*	NPG	NPG
628/1/0	**GWR** 38'9" suburban 1st/3rd - *28-32*	NPG	NPG
628/2/0	**GWR** 38'9" suburban 3rd/brake - *28-32*	NPG	NPG
626/1/0	**Pullman** 76' saloon car - *28-32*	NPG	NPG
626/2/0	**Pullman** 76' kitchen car - *28-32*	NPG	NPG

C12. 1931 Series Bogie Coaches
(Winteringham for Bassett-Lowke)

These were 13" long and of a similar specification as the earlier steel 1921 and 1924 Series. They had a lower roof line, simplified uncompensated bogies, battery box (instead of gas cylinders), underframe trusses and lighter diecast alloy wheels pressed onto splined axles. The clip-on roofs had under-scale ventilators and rain strips. The buffers were cast alloy, riveted on and the couplings were Bing style with the long link. They also had detachable concertina corridor connections at each end of the coach. At extra cost, the coaches could be bought with improved bogies (612/0) and cast iron wheels.

-	**GWR** 9174 dark brown+cream 1st corridor - *32-40*	170	220
-	**GWR** 9310 dark brown+cream 3rd brake corridor - *32-40*	170	220
-	**LMS** 3490 maroon 1st corridor - *32-40*	140	170

-	**LMS** 9343 maroon 3rd brake corridor - *32-40* 140	170
-	**LNER** 36232 teak 1st corridor - *32-40*	140	170
-	**LNER** 62362 teak 3rd brake corridor - *32-40*	140	170
-	**LMS** 3416 maroon suburban 1st/3rd (13¾") - *32-40*	140	170
-	**LMS** 6560 maroon suburban 3rd/brake (13¾") - *32-40*	140	170
-	**Southern** 7411 green 1st corridor - *32-40*	200	240
-	**Southern** 3722 green 3rd brake corridor - *32-40*	200	240

Winteringham for Bassett-Lowke GWR coach [C12]

C13.   LMS Post Office Mail Van
(Winteringham for Bassett-Lowke)

This was 13" long and of a similar specification to the 1931 Series coaches in table C12 above. However the pickup and delivery mechanism was the same as that for the earlier Carette mail van. The concertina clip-on corridor connections were offset from the centre and the coach came with mail bags and ground operating apparatus which were the same as those for earlier TPOs. The coaches could be bought separately and were suitable for both electric and clockwork systems. There were no underframe trusses and but one battery box. Bogies and wheels were the same as for the 1931 Series. It seems that the royal cipher of 'G(crown)R' on a red post box, carried on the sides of the coach, was not changed in 1937 with the change of monarch.

107/0	**LMS** 3251 maroon - *32-40*	200	220

C14.   Standard BR Corridor Coaches
(Precision Models for Bassett-Lowke)

These were 13¾" long and featured tinplate concertina corridor connections. Called 'third class', the coaches never featured a '3' on the doors and so strictly speaking they were standard class. They had the simplified Fox pattern bogies (611/0) with MFD/0 disc pattern alloy wheels although they are often found with the better running TS/0 turned steel disc wheels or synthetic plain disc wheels for 2-rail running which was available from 1957. A particular characteristic of these coaches was the overlong, blackened, round-headed, turned brass buffers. Standard Bassett-Lowke black hook and short single link couplings were used. Curiously, these coaches did not carry a Bassett-Lowke trademark.

110/0**	**BR** 3995 red+cream 1st corridor - *50-61*	140	200
112/0	**BR** 26233 red+cream 3rd/brake - *50-61*	140	200
113/0	**BR** 9272 red+cream 3rd corridor - *50-61*	140	200

** 1st class coaches (110/0) are sometimes found in boxes labelled '111/0 1st Class Corridor Coach', but it is clear that the number '111/0' was never used for this series of coaches.

Standard BR coach by Percision Models [C14]
(Bassett-Lowke)

Coaches by Edward Exley Ltd

Bassett-Lowke bought in complete coach bodies from Exley, fitted their own bogies and wheels, removed any Exley labelling and sold them in Bassett-Lowke labelled boxes. Towards the end of production, the LMS maroon lake was becoming distinctly red and plastic components were being used. For example, battery boxes, coach ends, dynamos and vacuum tanks were introduced and, right at the end (1963-65), Bassett-Lowke (617/0) plastic

bogies were used.

There were two types of coach, the K5 and the K6. The differences, for the Bassett-Lowke marketed Exley coaches, were principally the windows. The earlier K5s had the window ventilators painted on whereas the later K6s had them punched out. On K5s and K6s coaches they sold themselves, Exley used their own bogies whereas Bassett-Lowke fitted to them with 616/0 Fox or 618/0 Gresley pattern bogies with turned steel disc wheels (Maunsell MCF/0 or plain disc TS/0). From 1957, synthetic plain disc wheel sets were available for 2-rail operation.

The following tables list the Exley coaches sold by Bassett-Lowke in their own boxes. They were produced in batches and were not all available at the same time. The running numbers varied and, because Exley coaches were sold through various retail outlets, it is not easy to determine whether any particular running numbers were unique to Bassett-Lowke.

C15.   Pre-war Coaches (Exley for Bassett-Lowke)

These were quality coaches made for Bassett-Lowke by Edward Exley Ltd. The original labels were removed and the coaches were sold in Bassett-Lowke boxes, fitted with the appropriate Bassett-Lowke bogies and wheels (usually 612/0). These coaches continued to be shown in the catalogues after the Second World War until 1950 but availability would have been both doubtful and, at best, intermittent. cc = centre corridor. sc = side corridor.

	Pullman Dark Brown & Cream	250	270
-	'Hazel' 1st class 19" - *36-40*	250	270
-	3rd class 19" - *36-40*	250	270
-	3rd/brake 19" - *36-40*	250	270
	LMS Maroon	250	270
-	Royal Mail TPO 17" with non-working apparatus - *36-40*	250	270
-	1st sc 15½" - *36-40*	250	270
-	3rd sc 15½" - *36-40*	250	270
-	1st sc brake 15½" - *36-40*	250	270
-	3rd sc brake 15½" - *36-40*	250	270
-	dining/kitchen car 2050 16½" - *36-40*	250	270
	SR green		
-	1st sc 16½" - *36-40*	320	350
-	3rd sc 16½" - *36-40*	320	350
-	1st sc brake 16½" - *36-40*	320	350
-	3rd sc brake 16½" - *36-40*	320	350
	LNER Teak		
-	dining/kitchen 16½" - *36-40*	250	270
-	1st sc 15½" - *36-40*	250	270
-	3rd sc 15½" - *36-40*	250	270
-	1st sc brake 15½" - *36-40*	250	270
-	3rd sc brake 15½" - *36-40*	250	270
	GWR Dark Brown & Cream		
-	sc 16½" long - *36-40*	300	320
-	sc brake end (16½" long) - *36-40*	300	320

C16.   Early Post-war Coaches
(Exley for Bassett-Lowke)

These early post-war coaches predate the introduction of the K5 and K6 types. cc = centre corridor. sc = side corridor.

	LMS Maroon		
-	57' cc - *47-50*	120	170
-	57' cc brake - *47-50*	120	170
-	54' sc - *47-50*	120	170
-	54' sc brake - *47-50*	120	170
-	restaurant car - *47-50*	140	200
-	sleeping car - *47-50*	120	170
	LNER Teak	120	170
-	54' sc - *47-50*	120	170
-	54' sc brake end - *47-50*	120	170
-	54' luggage van and brake end - *47-50*	120	170
-	restaurant car - *47-50*	140	200
	GWR Dark Brown & Cream		
-	57' sc - *47-50*	120	170
-	57' sc brake - *47-50*	120	170

-	full brake - *47-50*	120	170
-	restaurant car - *47-50*	140	200

C17. Post-war LMS Coaches
(Exley for Bassett-Lowke)

There were no listed LMS side-corridor 1st/brakes (K6) version from Bassett-Lowke, neither was there an LMS Engineer's inspection saloon. The LMS livery was crimson lake (maroon) of late style lined in yellow and black. The LMS decal was carried in the centre of each side. The roofs and underframing were black. cc = centre corridor. sc = side corridor.

	LMS Maroon	120	230
-	54' sc 3rd - *50-54*	120	230
-	54' sc 1st - *50-54*	120	230
-	54' sc brake/3rd - *50-54*	120	230
-	54' sc brake/1st - *50-54*	120	230
-	57' cc 3rd (K5) - *50-54*	120	230
-	57' cc 1st (K5) - *50-57*	170	320
-	57' cc brake/3rd (K5) - *50-57*	170	320
-	57' cc brake/1st (K5) - *50-57*	170	320
-	57' sleeper, 1st/3rd 716 - *50-67*	140	280
-	TPO 30244 (K6) - *54-65*	170	470
-	suburban non-corridor 3rd - *54-62*	140	280
-	suburban. non-corridor brake/3rd - *54-62*	140	280
-	suburban non-corridor 1st/3rd - *54-62*	140	280
-	corridor full brake (K5) - *54-57*	140	280
-	corridor kitchen (K5) - *54-57*	200	320
-	non-gang full brake - *54-57*	140	280
-	non-gangwayed parcels van - *54-57*	140	280
-	buffet car + pantry (K5 & K6) - *54-60*	200	300
-	suburban 6-wheeled 3rd - *54-57*	170	310
-	suburban 6-wheeled 1st/3rd - *54-57*	170	310
-	suburban 6-wheeled brake/3rd - *54-57*	170	310
-	sc 3rd (K5) - *54-57*	140	320
-	sc 1st (K5) - *54-57*	140	270
-	sc brake/3rd (K5) - *54-57*	140	290
-	sc brake/1st (K5) - *54-57*	140	280
-	sc 1st (K6) - *57-67*	140	280
-	sc 3rd (K6) - *57-67*	140	280
-	sc brake/3rd (K6) - *57-67*	140	280
-	restaurant 1st/3rd 44 (K5) - *54-57*	170	320
-	restaurant 1st (K5) - *54-57*	170	310
-	restaurant 1st (K6) - *57-65*	200	300
-	cc 3rd (K6) - *57-62*	200	300
-	cc 1st (K5&K6) - *57-62*	200	320
-	cc brake/3rd (K6) - *57-62*	200	300
-	cc brake/1st (K6) - *57-62*	200	300
-	sc1st/3rd composite - *?*	200	300

C18. Post-war GWR Coaches
(Exley for Bassett-Lowke)

There was no listed GWR K6 side corridor 1st/brake from Bassett-Lowke. The GWR livery was chocolate brown and cream with 'Great(crest)Western' at the centre of the coach sides. Roofs and underframing were black. cc = centre corridor. sc = side corridor.

	GWR Dark Brown & Cream	120	220
-	57' sc 3rd (K5) - *50-57*	120	260
-	57' sc 1st (K5) - *50-57*	120	210
-	57' sc 3rd/brake (K5) - *50-57*	120	220
-	57' sc 1st/brake - *50-54*	120	220
-	57' restaurant car 1st/3rd (K5) - *50-62*	170	310
-	57' restaurant car 1st/3rd (K6) - *50-62*	170	310
-	57' cc 3rd (K5) - *54-57*	120	220
-	suburban 3rd - *54-64*	120	220
-	suburban 3rd/brake - *54-64*	120	220
-	suburban 1st/3rd - *54-64*	120	220
-	Ocean Mail parcel van - *54-57*	120	220
-	parcels train full brake - *54-57*	120	220
-	corridor full brake - *54-57*	140	280
-	sleep car 5550? 1st - *54-57*	140	310
-	sleep car 3rd - *54-57*	140	280
-	buffet car with pantry - *54-57*	140	280
-	TPO - *54-57*	200	310
-	6-wheel suburban 3rd - *54-57*	200	310

-	6-wheel suburban 3rd/brake - *54-57*	140	280
-	6-wheel suburban 1st/3rd - *54-57*	150	30
-	57' sc 3rd (K6) - *57-62*	210	310
-	57' sc 1st (K6) - *57-62*	210	310
-	57' sc 3rd/brake (K6) - *57-62*	210	310
-	57' cc 3rd - *57-62*	230	330

C19. Post-war SR Coaches
(Exley for Bassett-Lowke)

The Southern Railway coaches had green sides and black ends, roofs and underframes. The name 'Southern' was printed in yellow as a logo in the centre of the coach sides. cc = centre corridor. sc = side corridor.

	SR Green		
-	sc 3rd - *54-57*	230	390
-	sc 1st - *54-57*	230	390
-	5600 cc 1st - *54-57*	230	390
-	sc 3rd/brake - *54-57*	230	390
-	suburban 3rd - *54-57*	210	330
-	suburban 3rd/brake - *54-57*	210	330
-	suburban 1st/3rd - *54-57*	210	330

C20. Post-war LNER Coaches
(Exley for Bassett-Lowke)

LNER coaches were not listed in Bassett-Lowke catalogues but details could be supplied on request. Two separate liveries are known to exist - Gresley/Thompson teak and LNER tourist stock green and cream. Note that the LNER Exley coaches have square cornered windows (any found with round cornered windows may be repainted LMS or GWR coaches which are more common). LNER coaches should be fitted with Gresley type bogies (618/0).

-	**LNER** teak *50-59*	140	270
-	**LNER** green+cream *55-5?*	550	750

C21. Post-war BR Coaches
(Exley for Bassett-Lowke)

British Railways coaches by Exley were not listed in the Bassett-Lowke catalogues but for a short period (1955-57) Bassett-Lowke offered to supply any of the post-grouping coaches painted in BR livery, to order. Examples are known to exist in both carmine & cream and crimson lake (maroon) livery. Look out for crimson lake examples as they are easy to miss as they look similar to LMS stock. They have slightly different lining and no decals. The coaches should be fitted with the standard Bassett-Lowke Fox pattern bogie (616/0) and either steel turned wheels or post 1957 synthetic plain disc wheels for 2-rail operation.

	BR Red & Cream		
-	standard centre corridor - *55-57*	280	380
-	1st class - *55-57*	280	380
-	brake end - *55-57*	280	380
-	full brake - *55-57*	280	380
-	restaurant car - *55-57*	280	380
-	M660 sleeping car (K5) - *55-57*	280	380
	BR Maroon		
-	centre-corridor standard - *55-57*	200	300
-	1st class - *55-57*	200	300
-	brake end - *55-57*	200	300
-	full brake - *55-57*	200	300
-	restaurant car - *55-57*	200	300
-	sleeping car - *55-57*	200	300

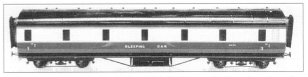

Post-war coach by Exley [C21] (Barry Potter Auctions)

Cat.No.	Company, Number, Colour, Dates	£	£

WAGONS

Up until the First World War, Carette produced many wagons for Bassett-Lowke, others were made at Winteringham's. Unfortunately too little is known about them to include details here. However a photograph has survived in the Bassett-Lowke

Bassett-Lowke

archives which shows a range of tinplate 0 gauge wagons designed for Bassett-Lowke in 1909. We have included these here for the sake of completeness but do not know if all were produced.

Both wooden and tinplate wagons were produced and were available side by side. The latter were mostly post-grouping examples and in wood you could buy a range of scale handmade wagons at a price four times that of a tinplate equivalent. Even the standard wooden wagons could be twice the price of tinplate ones. After the Second World War, some wooden wagons were available in kit form.

Today, the value of wagons has reversed with tinplate ones selling for twice the price of wooden ones. Look particularly for the 2-rail versions fitted with synthetic wheels and the 3-rail ones which have top quality Bassett-Lowke iron spoked wagon wheel sets.

W1a. Pre-war Tinplate Wagons
(Carette for Bassett-Lowke)

1341/0	LNWR 1907 grey brake van Crewe - *09-14?*	80	120
1342/0	MR M1911 grey brake van - *09-14?*	150	200
1343/0	MR 1914 grey large cattle truck - *09-14?*	150	200
1344/0	LNWR grey van - *09-14?*	NPG	NPG
1345/0	LNWR white refrigerator van - *09-14?*	NPG	NPG
1346/0	LNWR 7T goods wagon - *09-14?*	NPG	NPG
1347/0	MR grey open wagon - *09-14?*	150	200
1348/0	Greaves 130 grey pitched roof van lime & cement - *09-14?*	NPG	NPG
1349/0	1909 black tar tank wagon - *09-14?*	200	250
13410/0	LNWR pair of timber trucks - *09-14?*	NPG	NPG
13411/0	Anglo American Oil Co 405 red tanker - *09-14?*	NPG	NPG
13412/0	GNR van - *09-14?*	100	150
13413/0	Bassett-Lowke, Northampton 165 red-brown 8-plank - *09?- 14?*	150	250
13413/0	Bassett-Lowke Ltd, London & Northampton 6285 red-brown 8-plank - *19-23*	150	250
13414/0	GWR brake van - *09-14?*	NPG	NPG
13415/0	GWR 16613 grey ventilated van - *09-14?*	NPG	NPG
13416/0	GWR 8T banana van - *09-14?*	NPG	NPG
13417/0	MR bogie steel coal wagon grey - *09-14?*	150	200
13418/0	W.H.Hull & Son 405 light grey 10T 7-plank - *09-14?*	NPG	NPG
13420/0	GWR 59761 white Mica B refrigerated meat van - *09-14?*	NPG	NPG
13421/0	GNR 10959 brown 10T brake van - *09-14?*	100	150
13422/0	GNR 8T banana van - *09-14?*	NPG	NPG
13423/0	GNR 2881 brown 15T open wagon - *09-14?*	150	200
-	GNR 18335 brown 6-plank open wagon - *09-14?*	150	200
13424/0	GNR 5T fish van - *09-14?*	NPG	NPG
13425BL/0	WJ Bassett-Lowke & Co yellow van - *09?-23*	550	900
13425M/0	Colman's Mustard Traffic yellow 10T van - *09-14?*	NPG	NPG
13425S/0	Colman's Starch Traffic van - *09-14?*	NPG	NPG
13426/0	LNWR fruit van - *09-14?*	NPG	NPG
13427/0	LNWR 13445 dk.brown horse box - *09-14?*	NPG	NPG
13428/0	City of Birmingham Gas Dept. 1201 red-brown 8-plank - *09-14?*	NPG	NPG
13429/0	LNWR open carriage truck - *09-14?*	NPG	NPG
13430/0	City of Birmingham 779 grey Gas Dept. steel coke hopper - *09-14?*	NPG	NPG
13431/0	NBR 8T open wagon - *09-14?*	NPG	NPG
13432/0	GCR 8T open wagon - *09-14?*	NPG	NPG
13433/0	MR light grey 7-plank Loco Coal - *09-14?*	NPG	NPG
13434/0	MR open wagon loco coal - *09-14?*	NPG	NPG
13435/0	LYR 1930 grey 3-plank ballast wagon - *09-14?*	150	200
13436/0	LB&SCR 9083 light grey open wagon + sheet rail + LB&SCR tarpaulin - *09-14?*		
13437/0	MR ventilated van - *09-14?*	NPG	NPG
13438/0	MR 1909 grey 3-plank ballast wagon - *09-14?*	150	200
13439/0	NER 3192 grey Flatrol M + brown boiler J.T.Lowke & Sons - *09-14?*	450	900
13439/0	NER 77823 grey Flatrol M + brown boiler Bassett-Lowke Ltd - *20-23*	NPG	NPG
13442/0	MR 68 brown Eng. Dept. (ED) ballast wagon - *09-14?*	NPG	NPG
13443/0	CR 71908 brown 4-plank wagon - *09-14?*	NPG	NPG
13444/0	L&NWR brown gunpowder van - *09-14?*	NPG	NPG
13445/0	LNWR 13445 dark brown motor car van - *09-14?*	NPG	NPG
13446/0	GER 10T open wagon - *09-14?*	NPG	NPG
13447/0	LNWR grey brake van Camden - *09-14?*	NPG	NPG
13448/0	LNWR van - *09-14?*	NPG	NPG
13449/0	LNWR open wagon Loco Coal - *09-14?*	NPG	NPG

'Bassett-Lowke Ltd' 8 plank by Carette [W1a]
(Barry Potter Auctions)

W1b. Tinplate 4-Plank Open Wagons
(Carette for Bassett-Lowke)

These were 5" long and 2¼" wide and made in tinplate. They had Carette couplings and thick heavy metal solid disc wheels.

-	LNWR 1913 - *20-27*	20	30
-	LSWR - *20-27*	20	30
-	MR 7915 grey - *20-23*	20	30
-	GN 602 brown - *20-23*	20	30
-	7915 no markings grey - *20-27*	20	30

'Bassett-Lowke' 8 plank by Carette [W1a]
(Barry Potter Auctions)

W2. Tinplate Standard Wagons by Bing

These tinplate wagons were 5" long and 2¼" wide. They had Bing hook and long link couplings and heavy metal thick spoked wheels. The wagons were of an excellent quality but had distinctly short proportions.

1346/0	LNWR 850, 44865 grey 10T 5-plank open wagon - *23-26*	20	30
13433/0	MR 45321 grey 12T 7-plank open wagon,	20	30

	Loco Coal - *23-26*		
13447/0	**LNWR** grey 10T brake van, single end verandah - *23-26*	35	45
13448/0	**LNWR** grey covered goods van - *23-26*	45	55
13413/0	**Bassett-Lowke** 165 red brown 7-plank Northampton - *23-30*	170	280
13413/0	**Bassett-Lowke** 6285 grey 7-plank London & Northampton - *23-30*	80	90
13413/0	**Bassett-Lowke** 6285 grey 7-plank London, Northampton & Edinburgh - *23-30*	80	90
13416/0	**GW** 91694 green 10T 5-plank open wagon - *23-30*	20	30
1346/0	**LMS** 24320 grey 10T 5-plank open wagon - *26-30*	20	30
13433/0	**LMS** 45321 grey 12T 7-plank open, Loco Coal Only - *26-30*	45	55
13447/0	**LMS** 152540 grey 10T brake van, single end verandah - *26-30*	35	45
13448/0	**LMS** 4132 grey 10T covered goods van - *26-30*	35	45

Several of the Bing tinplate wagons were not listed in the Bassett-Lowke catalogues including 'Explosives', NE 'Refrigerator', NE cattle, LMS fish and the bogie vans - 'Fish Traffic' and 'Milk Traffic'.

W3. Cheap Tin Plate Wagons
(Bing for Bassett-Lowke)

These tinplate wagons were 5" long and 2¼" wide and were of a simplified appearance but with good quality litho printing. . They had either Bing automatic couplings or standard Bing drop link hooks with a drop link at one end only. The bases were common for both vans and wagons and carried a running number on the solebars. 73923 was the number often used but 163581 and 425071 are also found. The wheels were tinplate on spragged axles but some had Bassett-Lowke heavy alloy spoked wheels. The vans were issued with either opening or non-opening doors.

592/0	**GW** dark grey 7-plank - *28-32*	25	35
592/0	**LMS** dark grey 7-plank - *28-32*	25	35
592/0	**NE** dark grey 7-plank - *28-32*	25	35
592/0	**SR** dark grey 7-plank - *28-32*	25	35
593/0	**GW** dark grey van - *28-32*	30	40
593/0	**LMS** dark grey van - *28-32*	30	40
593/0	**NE** dark grey van - *28-32*	30	40
593/0	**SR** dark grey van - *28-32*	30	40

W4. Tinplate Standard Wagons
(Winteringham for Bassett-Lowke)

These were 5¾" long and 2¼" wide and made in tinplate. They were of scale proportions with Bing style hook and long link couplings. The wagons had heavy metal spoked wheels on splined axles and cast buffers that were riveted on. There was no representation of brake gear or vee-hangers and the wheels were painted black. The range, with the exception of the LMS open wagon, covered van and guards van, ceased in 1940 at the outbreak of the Second World War. The design of the LMS wagons was changed in 1938 and continued after the war until 1960. The wheels on these changed to the new post-war design which had a neater, more scale, appearance.

1352/0	**LMS** 24468 grey 5-plank - *30-38*	35	40
1354/0	**GW** 91694 green 5-plank - *30-40*	35	40
?	**GW** 103873 dark green van - *30-40*	35	40
1353/0	**NE** 130911 green 5-plank - *30-40*	35	40
1355/0	**SR** 9871, 10252 dark green 12T open wagon 6-plank - *30-40*	40	45
1356/0	**Bassett-Lowke** Ltd 6285* green-grey 12T 7-plank London Northampton & Manchester - *30-40*	70	90
1360/0	**LMS** 62306 grey 20T brake van verandah both ends - *30-38*	60	70
1361/0	**NE** 140517 grey 20T brake van verandah both ends - *30-34*	80	100
1361/0	**NE** 140517 red-brown 20T brake van verandah both ends - *34-40*	90	100
1362/0	**GW** 35642 grey 20T brake Toad van 0 Exeter - *30-4*	60	100
1370/0	**LMS** 29850 grey 12T van - *30-38*	60	70
?	**LMS** 291859 grey van - *?*	60	70
1371/0	**NE** 13897 green** 12T van - *30-40*	50	60
1373/0	**SR** 15757, 17741 green van - *30-40*	80	90
1380/0	**LMS** 17741, 14548 grey cattle wagon - *30-40*	60	70
1390/0	**NE** 54849, 153180 white 8T Refrigerator	120	140

	van - *30-40*		
1400/0	**NE** 451004 brown bogie Brick wagon - *30-40*	80	90
1401/0	**GW** 2007 white United Dairies milk tanker - *30-40*	480	650
1402/0	**Pratt's** Spirit petrol 1852, 21774 buff tanker - *30-35*	500	650
1404/0	**Esso** petrol 21774 cream tanker (also 1042/0) - *3?-40*	450	700
1404/0	**Mobiloil** Vacuum Oil dark green-grey tanker (also 1042/0) - *36-40*	450	700
1406/0	**NE** 77823 brown standard Flatrol bogie wagon 12" long *** - *32-40*	650	750
1406/0	**77823** brown bogie well wagon + grey cable drum and coil Enfield Cable Company 12" long - *30-40*	850	950
1406/0	**NE** 77823 grey Flatrol M + brown Callender cable drum - *30-40*	850	950
1406/0	**NE** 77823 grey standard Flatrol bogie wagon + brown boiler Bassett-Lowke Ltd, 12" - *32-40*	450	950

* 6285 was the telephone number of the Bassett-Lowke shop at 112 high Holborn, London. ** The NE van tinplate printing suffered a production problem resulting in almost all the survivors having a crazed appearance. *** The load bed was plain having no tinplate tab slots for the attachment of either the cable drum or the boiler.

'Bassett-Lowke Ltd' 7 plank by Winteringham [W4] (Bassett-Lowke)

W5. Wagon Tarpaulins

Wagon sheets, made either by Bing or Bassett-Lowke, were available for several pre- and post-grouping companies and would fit any tinplate or wooden 4-wheeled open wagon . Each company's sheet had its own number and initials and RCH diamonds parallel with the long edges. The Bing sheets also had a St Andrew's cross stretching to the corners. They were made of black linen and the printing was in white. Strings, with which to tie the sheet to the wagon's buffers, were sewn into short edges but some early sheets had elasticated ends.

-	**L&NWR** black - *20-27*	10	12
-	**MR** 139197 black by Bing - *20-36*	10	12
-	**MR** 1922 black - *20-36*	10	12
-	**GNR** 17220 black by Bing - *20-36*	10	12
-	**GNR** 1922 black - *20-36*	10	12
-	**L&SWR** 1343 black by Bing - *20-27*	10	12
-	**GWR** black - *20-36*	10	12
-	**LMS** 5231 black - *?*	10	12

W6. Methylated Spirit Tanker for Live Steam Locomotives

This was 5¼" long and consisted of a brass tank on a wooden base. It had cast WAG/0 axle guards screwed to the solebars, cast buffers screwed to the buffer beams and standard heavy alloy spoked wheels which were painted black and mounted on splined axles. The tank was secured by wire cables to the end stanchions and the wooden base. The tank carried either water or methylated spirits for operating live steam locomotives. Removing the loose cap from the top, disclosed a spring valve which, when operated, allowed the contents to flow out of the outlet pipe beneath the tank.

3112/0	**Lowko Spirit** grey+red - *22-37*	80	120
?	**Colas** black - *?*	80	120

Bassett-Lowke

Flat No 1 with boiler by Winteringham [W4] (Christies)

W7. Scale LMS (MR) High Capacity Bogie Wagon

This wagon, which was 12" long, was the type used by the Midland Railway for transportation of rails, girders and other cumbersome items. It was offered for a short period only. The bogies were cast in white metal and could be bought separately as 509/0. The wagon had low stretchers to hold loads in place.

	LMS grey - *23-24*	80	120

Wooden Goods Vehicles

Bassett-Lowke continued to offer, throughout their existence, a bespoke service for top quality, museum standard, rolling stock. However, just prior to the First World War, the Company introduced a standard range of vehicles made of best quality materials for discerning clients who preferred something rather better than the mass produced tinplate wagons. The clients also preferred models made of the same materials as the prototypes i.e. wooden tops, steel wheels and three link couplings.

The specification of the standard range of goods vehicles changed over the period. Some were plain while others had representations of sides and ends printed on. There may have been several suppliers, such as Mills Bros. and the Leeds Model Company, who produced the bodies to which Bassett-Lowke fitted the wheels, couplings and buffers. The Bassett-Lowke wooden vehicles may be recognised by the WAG/O axle guards or the use of box or pine wood with butt joins (as opposed to combed or dovetail joints). Theirs had a one piece wooden base with the tops and solebars pinned and glued on. Except for roofs, Bassett-Lowke never used plywood.

Three link couplings when fitted were not normally sprung. The coupling shanks were twisted through 90º and pinned to small wooden blocks under the wagon's floor. Other couplings included Bing style hook and long link and Stedman LF/16 single hook and single link. Wheels were generally the period Bassett-Lowke heavy alloy spoked wheels mounted on splined axles.

W8. Wooden Pre-Grouping Wagons - Pre-WW1

These were 5" long and had printed and/or painted sides.

3311	**LNWR** grey 7T 4-plank - *19-22*	20	25
3321	**LNWR** grey 10T 5-plank - *19-22*	20	25
3322	**MR** grey 10T 6-plank Loco Coal - *20-22*	20	25
3323	**GN** brown 15T 6-plank - *20-22*	20	25
3331	**LNWR** grey box van - *19-22*	25	30
3341	**LNWR** grey brake van, Crewe - *19-22*	25	30

W9. Wooden Pre-Grouping Wagons - Post-WW1

The unlettered wagons could be lettered at the request of the purchaser and at extra cost. These were also available as kits. db = dumb buffers

G501E	**GN** brown 10T 5-plank db - *19*	30	35
G501E	**GW** green 10T 5-plank db - *19*	30	35
G501E	**MR** grey 10T 5-plank db - *19*	30	35
G501E	**GC** 10T 5-plank db - *19*	30	35
G501E	**LNWR** grey 10T 5-plank db - *19*	30	35
G504E	**MR** grey high capacity bogie mineral wagon 504/0 bogies - *19*	45	55
G504E	**NER** grey high capacity bogie mineral wagon 504/0 bogies - *19-22*	45	55

G505E	**NER** 90652 white refrigerator van - *19-22*	45	55
G505E	**LNWR** white refrigerator van - *19-22*	45	55
G505E	**GNR** refrigerator van - *19-22*	45	55
G507E	grey unlettered pair of timber bolster wagons with db - *19-22*	30	35
G510	**North Eastern** 108340 brown high capacity bogie box van - *19-22*	45	55
G511E	**NER** 17827 brown 4-wheel 10T brake van, 2 verandas + duckets - *19-22*	30	35
G513E	**NBR** brown 4-wheel brake van, ducket, no veranda - *19-22*	30	35
G514E	**MR** grey 4-wheel 10T brake van, 1 veranda + 1 platform - *19-22*	30	35
G515E	**MR** M1907 grey 6-wheel 20T brake van, 1 veranda + 1 platform - *19-22*	35	45
G516E	**GW** green 4-wheel 10T brake van, 1 veranda - *19-22*	30	35
G561E	**Bassett-Lowke Ltd** London & Northampton 10T 8-plank - *19*	15	20
G561E	grey unlettered 8T open - *21-22*	15	20
G561E	grey unlettered 10T open - *21-22*	15	20
G562E	grey unlettered 10T box van - *21-22*	20	25
G582E	**LNWR** grey 10T box wagon - *19*	30	35
G582E	**MR** grey 10T box wagon - *19*	30	35
G582E	**GN** 10T box wagon - *19*	30	35
G582E	**NBR** 10T box wagon - *19*	30	35
G583E	grey unlettered cattle wagon - *21-22*	35	45
G534E	**GN** brown 4-wheel 10T brake van, 2 verandas - *19*	30	35
G585E	**LNWR** grey 4-wheel 10T brake van, 1 veranda - *19*	30	35
G535E	**GN** brown 6-wheel 20T brake van, 2 verandas - *19*	35	45
G586E	**LNWR** grey 6-wheel 20T brake van, 1 verandah - *19*	35	45

LNWR brake van [W8] (Bassett-Lowke)

W10. Wooden Scale Prototypical Models

These were 5" long and similar to those in table W9 but were of a better quality - perhaps having come from a different supplier. They were fitted with cast iron turned wheels and detailed fittings; especially the guards vans. They were forerunners to further series of quality wagons. It seems that none of the models were fitted with brake gear or vee-hangers.

03311/0	**LNWR** 1503? grey 7T open - *20-28*	25	30
03321/0	**LNWR** grey 10T open - *20-28*	25	30
03309/0	**GN** 18335? brown 15T high-sided - *23-26*	25	30
03322/0	**MR** 1311? grey 12T open, Loco Coal - *23-26*	25	30
03331/0	**LNWR** 1911? grey van - *23-26*	30	35
03341/0	**LNWR** 1809? grey brake van, 1 verandah - *20-26*	30	35
-	** open wagons - *27-40*	35	45
-	** open wagons - *27-40*	35	45
-	** brake vans - *27-40*	35	45
-	** high capacity bogie mineral wagons - *27-40*	70	80

** These had liveries painted to order.

W11. Wooden Standard Post-Grouping Wagons

3327/0	**SR** 3753 brown 12T 7-plank - *28-36*	15	25
3333/0	**SR** 15757 brown 12T van - *28-36*	20	30
3344/0	**SR** 11892 brown 20T brake van 2 verandahs - *28-36*	15	25
3352/0	**LMS** grey 10T 5-plank - *30-36*	15	25
3354/0	**GW** green 8T 5-plank - *30-36*	15	25
3353/0	**NE** brown 10T 5-plank - *30-36*	15	25
3370/0	**LMS** grey van - *30-36*	20	30
3371/0	**NE** brown van - *30-36*	20	30
3113/0	**Colas** grey black tank no valve and pipe - *30-36*	120	140
3362/0	**GW** green brake van, 7⅜" - *30-36*	20	30
3360/0	**LMS** 646 grey 10T brake van, 7½" long - *30-36*	20	30
3361/0	**NE** 451091 grey 10T ** brake van, 5½" long - *30-36*	20	30

** Catalogue picture shows '20T'.

W12. Wooden Standard Post-Grouping Wagons
(attributed to Milbro)

These wagons were 5½" long. They had no trademark showing but were almost certainly made for Bassett-Lowke by Milbro. They had Milbro axle guards screwed to the solebars and cast wheels, turned brass buffers, 3-link unsprung couplings and Milbro style wood construction. The wagons were not normally fitted with brake gear or vee-hangers although these may have been fitted at the customer's request or have been done so retrospectively. The brake vans had footboards.

-	**GW** green 12T 5-plank - *37-40*	35	45
-	**LMS** grey 12T 5-plank - *37-40*	35	45
-	**NE** grey 12T 5-plank - 37-40	35	45
-	**SR** brown 12T 5-plank - *37-40*	35	45
-	black 20T tube wagon - *37-40*	35	45
-	**LMS** red gunpowder van - *37-40*	60	70
-	**GW** green van - *37-40*	45	60
-	**LMS** 1906 grey van - *37-40*	45	60
-	**NE** grey van - *37-40*	45	60
-	**SR** brown van - *37-40*	45	60
-	**GW** green? Eng. Dept. low-sided - *37-40*	35	45
-	**LMS** grey? Eng. Dept. low-sided - *37-40*	35	45
-	**NE** grey? Eng. Dept. low-sided - *37-40*	35	45
-	**SR** brown? Eng. Dept. low-sided - *37-40*	35	45
-	grey cattle wagon - *37-40*	45	60
-	**LMS** grey 20T 6-wheel brake van 2 verandahs - *37-40*	60	70
-	**LMS** grey 10T 4-wheel brake van 2 verandahs - *37-40*	35	45
-	**NE** grey 10T, brake van, 1 verandah - *37-40*	35	45
-	**GW** 98014 green 10T brake van 2 verandahs - *37-40*	35	45
-	**SR** brown 10T brake van - *37-40*	45	60

Bakelite Wagons

These were made in self-coloured bakelite with standard Leeds Model Company axle guards mounted on separate tinplate double brackets which were tabbed to the floor of the wagon. They had non-locking alloy buffers and sprung 3-link couplings. The wagons were fitted with LMC alloy spoked or 4-hole disc wheels and had super details included on the bakelite moulding. Metal fatigue is a common problem with the buffers and wheels on these wagons and these items have often been replaced. Although dropped from the catalogue in 1940, some remained on sale in Bassett-Lowke's shops as late as 1948. (see also the chapter on the Leeds Model Company - Wagons Tables 13 and 14).

W13. Bakelite Wagons
(Leeds for Bassett-Lowke)

P10	**LMS** brown 12T 7-plank - *38-40*	15	20
P20	**NE** 37042 grey 12T 7-plank - *38-40*	15	20
P30	**GW** grey 12T 7-plank - *38-40*	15	20
P40	**SR** brown 12T 7-plank - *38-40*	20	25
P50	**NE** red 12T 7-plank - *38-40*	20	25
P80	**LMS** 606521 brown 12T van - *38-40*	15	20
P90	**LMS** 606521 brown 12T van, ventilators, brake pipes - *38-48*	20	25
P100	**LMS** maroon 6T fish van, passenger brake - *38-40*	25	30
P110	**NE** grey 12T van - *38-40*	15	20
P120	**NE** grey 12T van, ventilators, brake pipes - *38-48*	20	25
P130	**NE** red 12T fruit van, ventilators, brake pipes - *38-48*	20	25

Post-war Tinplate Wagons

The tinplate wagons in the following three tables used WF/0 8-spoked alloy wheel sets as standard but could be had with the better running WCF/0 8-spoked turned steel wheels at extra cost. From 1957, the vehicles could be had with Tri-ang manufactured synthetic 3-hole disc wheels, at a reduced cost, for 2-rail operation. All these vehicles featured standard, later pattern, Bassett-Lowke black hook and short single link couplings but Bassett-Lowke offered a replacement conversion kit (601/13/0) for scale 3-link couplings which are sometimes found on these wagons. So too are track operated hook and loop remotely controlled automatic couplings.

Tarpaulin covers (or 'sheets') were not available for the open wagons after the war.

W14. Post-war Tinplate Wagons

Although pre-war tinplate rolling stock appeared in the early post-war catalogues, none was produced except for the later 0 gauge LMS brown goods series which was introduced in 1938 and continued, albeit with modifications, until 1960. iag = black integral axle guards. sag = black separate axle guards.

1352/0	**LMS** 36721, 3672 ** brown 13T open, brown base, iag - *38-48*	20	30
1352/0	**LMS** 36721, 3672 ** brown 13T open, brown base, sag - *48-50*	20	30
1352/0	**LMS** 36721, 3672 ** brown 13T open, black base, sag - *50-60*	20	30
1370/0	**LMS** 91375 brown 12T van, brown base, ag - *38-48*	25	45
1370/0	**LMS** 91375 brown 12T van, brown base, sag - *48-50*	25	45
1370/0	**LMS** 91375 brown 12T van, black base, sag - *50-60*	25	45
1360/0	**LMS** 730273 brown 20T brake van, brown base, iag - *38-48*	30	55
1360/0	**LMS** 730273 brown 20T brake van, brown base, sag - *48-50*	30	55
1360/0	**LMS** 730273 brown 20T brake van, black base, sag - *50-53*	30	55
1364/0	**BR** 837354 grey brake van, LWB, black base, sag - *51-68*	25	35

** Due to a litho printing error some wagons have the last digit ('1') missing on one or both sides making the running number '3672'.

W15. Post-war Wooden Wagons and Kits

These wagons were available factory made or as sets of parts, for home assembly and finishing, at approximately half the price of factory made vehicles. The specification included parts made of good quality seasoned wood cut to size with planking scribed as necessary. Included in each kit were WAG/0 axle guards, WO/12 or WO/10 oval or round buffers, 601/15/0 3-link couplings, strapping, WF/0 alloy wheel sets, screws, pins, transfers and instructions. Turned steel wheels (WCF/0) were available at extra cost and synthetic 3-hole disc wheels for 2-rail operation were available from 1957 and reduced the price of the kit by 2/-. Prices are provided in this table for factory made models built from these kits and (at the bottom) any unmade kit with all parts still intact.

-	**LMS** 672149** brown 12T 5-plank - *48-56*	15	20
-	**NE** 36720** grey 12T 5-plank - *48-56*	15	20
-	**GW** green 12T 5-plank - *48-50*	15	20
-	**BR** 837483** grey 12T 5-plank - *50-65*	15	20
-	**BR** grey cattle wagon - *52-60*	20	30
-	**LMS** brown 12T van - *48-56*	25	30
-	**NE** 14972** grey 12T van - *48-56*	25	30
-	**GW** green 12T van - *48-50*	25	30

-	**BR** 108283** grey 12T van - *52-60*	25	30
-	**LMS** brown 20T brake van - *48-56*	25	30
-	**NE** 13758** grey 20T brake van - *48-56*	25	30
-	**GW** green 20T brake van - *48-50*	25	30
-	**BR** 37463** grey 20T brake van - *52-60*	25	30
-	any kit complete - *48-68*	NPG	25

** The numbers given are for known examples, however, these changed over the years and depended on the production batches.

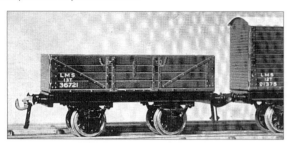

Post-war tinplate open wagon [W14] (Bassett-Lowke)

W16. Long Wheelbase Special Load Wagons

These wagons used the base of the 1364/0 guards van. All bases were black.

Vehicle A	black chained metal plates - *57-65*	15	30
Vehicle B	black + strung and wedged 2 **Hornby Liverpool Cables** drums - *57-65*	15	30
Vehicle E	black + chained large metal tube - *57-65*	15	30
Vehicle M	large log chained black - *57-65*	15	30
Vehicle N	black + chained lg square timber - *57-65*	15	30

Post-war wooden wagons and kits [W15] (Bassett-Lowke)

W17. Standard Wheelbase Special Load Wagons

These wagons used the base of 1352/0, 1370/0 and 1360/0 standard wagons; all with black bases.

Vehicle C	black + pinned **Hornby** insulated meat container - *57-65*	15	30
Vehicle D	black + chained Machinery casting (varied) - *57-65*	15	30
Vehicle F	black + chained 12 **Bassett-Lowke** wooden sleepers - *57-65*	15	30
Vehicle G	black + chained 4 **Bassett-Lowke** loco driving wheels - *57-65*	15	30
Vehicle H	black + strung and wedged **Hornby Liverpool Cables** drum - *57-65*	15	30
Vehicle K	black + pinned **Hornby** furniture container - *57-65*	15	30
Vehicle L	black + 2 chained ship propellers - *57-65*	15	30

ACCESSORIES

Bassett-Lowke produced quite an extensive range of accessories not least their various series of track which offered the public different standards according to what they could afford. Lineside equipment included stations, goods depots, level crossings, signals and platform personnel and equipment.

SETS

Train sets did not play a big part in the Company's marketing policy but starter sets were available.

Bassett-Lowke by Corgi

HISTORY

Corgi Classics purchased the tools and intellectual assets of Bassett-Lowke in 1996 and decided to introduce a range of models based on earlier Bassett-Lowke designs with the Greenly valve gear. The first was released as a steam driven model but only one steam version was made. After that all new models have had 12v electric mechanisms some fitted with smoke generators.

LOCOMOTIVES

Cat.No.	Number, Company, Colour, Dates	£	£
L1.	**LMS Mogul 2-6-0**		
99001	**42981** BRb black steam Ltd Edn 500 - *00*	350	400
99002	**2945** LMS maroon - *00*	350	460

Steam powered LMS Mogul [L1]

Cat.No.	Number, Company, Colour, Dates	£	£
L2.	**SR N Class ('Woolwich') Mogul 2-6-0**		
99003	**1846** SR green - *01*	400	500
99004	**31407** BRb black - *01*	400	500
99005	CIE lined green Ltd Edn 60 - *01*	400	500

SR Mogul [L2]

Cat.No.	Number, Company, Colour, Dates	£	£
L3.	**LMS Princess Royal Class 4-6-2**		
99006	**6201 'Princess Elizabeth'** LMS maroon Ltd Edn 350 - *02*	NPG	700
99007	**46200 'The Princess Royal'** BRb green Ltd Edn 350 - *02*	NPG	700
99008	**46206 'Princess Margaret Rose'** BRb blue Sp Edn 100 (Much Ado About Toys) - *02*	NPG	700
99009	**46203 'Princess Marie Louise'** BRb blue - *02*	NPG	700
99010	**6210 'Lady Patricia'** LMS black Ltd Edn 350 - *03*	NPG	700
?	**46205 'Lady Victoria'** BRa black - *04*	NPG	700
99013	**46208 'Princess Helena Victoria'** BRc maroon - *04*	NPG	700

Cat.No.	Number, Company, Colour, Dates	£	£
L4.	**LMS Rebuilt Royal Scot Class 4-6-0**		
99011	**46100 'Royal Scot'** BRb green 500 made - *03*	NPG	700
99012?	**6100 'Royal Scot'** LMS black - *03*	NPG	700

Cat.No.	Number, Company, Colour, Dates	£	£
L5.	**LNER Class A3 4-6-2**		
?	**'Flying Scotsman'** green - *04*	NPG	700

Bond's 0

History

Bond's are primarily known as a manufacturer of mechanisms, locomotives, rolling stock and track parts as well as being agents for other manufacturer's products. They were established in 1887 as Bond's Ltd but in April 1926 took the name Bond's O'Euston Road Ltd; their address being 254 Euston Road. The Company still exists at Midhurst, Sussex, having moved there some 30 years ago but stocks are extremely limited; the only items likely to be available are track parts.

They catered principally for the 0 gauge and larger scales but made small quantities of 00 scale from 1925. The pre-war catalogues show a wide selection of model railway items by both British and Continental manufacturers. Materials, castings, tools, lathes, milling machines and boilers were also offered for those interested in model engineering.

Bond's electric motors and gearboxes are highly regarded; in fact, they are often found fitted to other makers' locomotives. Some will have been changed during the life of the engine but others may have been installed when new, as many manufacturers were quite pleased to fulfil extra requirements, such as a Bond's motor, at extra cost. Bond's also made brass framed motor bogies as well as sprung coach bogies.

Following the Second World War, things did not get back to normal until late in 1947. The Company, by then, had changed direction, becoming more retail orientated, and during the 1950s their catalogues listed the Hornby Dublo, Tri-ang, Trix ranges as well as a wide selection of parts for not only model railways but also aircraft and boats.

The by now well known shop in Euston Road had to be closed in 1973 as the whole site was to be redeveloped and the company moved to Midhurst. Although a retail shop continued, the business now became mostly mail order.

Collectors Club

There is no collector's society for Bond's equipment but the Bassett-Lowke Society may be able to help or indicate sources of information (see details under 'Bassett-Lowke').

Repairs

A limited repair service for Bond's mechanisms is available from DM Leakey, 7 Camplin Street, New Cross, London SE14 5QX (tel. 020 7732 6453). Send an SAE with any request. Leakey

mechanisms followed similar design principles to Bonds mechanisms and, although no longer made, are equally sought after.

Prices - It is difficult to assess the value of Bond's locomotives as they are not often found for sale. The two prices shown represent the likely range for one in good condition.

New Information - We would welcome information on other locomotives and rolling stock by this manufacturer.

LOCOMOTIVES

Bond's own locomotives were offered in gauges 00, 0, 1, 2½ " and 3½" and many were made to special order. Indeed, their catalogues offered to quote for building any type "from the tiny 4mm 00 gauge electric model to a 1½" scale garden steam locomotive".

Other Gauges - The locomotives listed below were also available in gauge 1 electric and in live steam in gauges 1, 2½" and 3½".

Cat.No.	Number, Company, Colour, Dates	£	£

Peckett type dockland saddle tank [L1]

L1. Peckett Type Dockland Saddle Tank 0-6-0ST (Freelance)

Referred to as the Bonzone, the model was based on Peckett lines and had six balanced, all flanged, wheels. It also had a toolbox with a lid that opened to reveal the key winder. This box varied in position and there were slight variations in the shape of the body. It had a copper top chimney and brass dome. Post-war mechanisms were 12V.

	1, 2, 3, 4 'Bonzone'		
-	Brunswick green c/w - *28-56?*	250	350
-	Brunswick green 6-8V DC - *28-56?*	250	350
-	black c/w - *28-56?*	250	350
-	black 6-8V DC - *28-56?*	250	350
-	deep yellow c/w - *28-56?*	250	350
-	deep yellow 6-8V DC - *28-56?*	250	350
-	red-brown - *28-56?*	250	350
	unnamed		
-	Great Western green - *28-56?*	225	300
-	Southern green - *28-56?*	250	350
-	**6** dark green - *28-56?*	250	350

'The Princess Royal' [L5]

L2. Hunslet Diesel Shunter 0-6-0DS

-	**3** black electric - *32-40?*	250	300
-	**3** green electric - *32-40?*	250	300

L3. Jinty Type 3F Tank Locomotive 0-6-0T

Post-war mechanisms were 12V.

-	**7118** LMS black 6-8V DC electric - *38-60*	300	350

Jinty 3F 0-6-0T [L3]

L4. J39 Goods Locomotive 0-6-0
(Vulcan of Kendal for Bond's)

This model was made by Harry D'Arcy of Vulcan of Kendal.

-	**4811** LNER black 12V DC electric - *64-69*	150	250
-	**47260** BR black 12V DC electric - *64-69*	150	250

L5. Bond's Special Order Locomotives

The following Bond's locomotives were built to order. Post-war mechanisms were 12V.

-	**2-6-2T** 2900 LNER black 6-8V DC - *35-c55*	850	1100
-	**Bowen-Cooke 4-6-2T** ex-LNWR 6798 LMS black 6-8V - *35-c55*	350	450
-	as above but red - *35-c55*	350	450
-	**Class A3** 4472 'Flying Scotsman' LNER green 6-8V DC - *35-c55*	NPG	NPG
-	**Stanier 4-6-0 Class 5MT** 5020 LMS black 6-8V DC - *35-c55*	750	1300
-	**Princess Royal Class** LMS maroon 6200 'The Princess Royal' 6-8V - *35-c55*	2100	2300
-	as above but black - *35-c55*	2100	2300
-	**King Class** 6000 'King George V' GW green 4-6-0 6-8V DC - *35-c55*	2100	2300
-	**ex-L&Y 2-4-2T** 1384 LMS black 6-8V DC - *35-c55*	250	350
-	**Stanier 2-6-0** LMS red 6-8V DC - *35-c55*	NPG	NPG
-	as above but black - *35-c55*	NPG	NPG
-	**Lord Nelson Class** 850 'Lord Nelson' SR green 6-8V DC - *35-c55*	NPG	NPG
-	**Class N10** LNER blk 0-6-2 - *35-c55*	NPG	NPG
-	**King Arthur Class** A767 'Sir Valence' SR grn 6-8V DC - *35-c55*	NPG	NPG
-	**City Class** 3440 'City of Truro' GW green 4-4-0 6-8V DC - *35-c55*	NPG	NPG
-	**ex-CR 0-4-4T** 15201 LMS black - *?*	NPG	NPG
-	**0-4-4** 73 LSWR green - *?*	NPG	NPG
-	**Class E1** SR 0-6-0T - *?*	NPG	NPG

Ex CR 0-4-4T [L5]

Bond's continued to build models to order in gauges 0 and 1 and, in their catalogues during the 1970s, illustrated an LMS 6247 'City of Liverpool' they had built for a Mr Liverpool.

Cat.No.	Company, Type, Colour, Dates	£	£

COACHES

In the 1920s Bond's also sold a range of coach bodies of their own manufacture and stocked coaches by Marklin, Bing, Bassett-Lowke, Leeds and others. Those of German origin (especially Marklin) had their identity concealed after the First World War. In the 1930s the company offered their own range of wooden bodied hand painted coaches which were of a good quality. After the Second World War the 0 gauge range stocked by Bond's was limited to Exleys and kits by CCW and Ratio. However, they continued to sell their own coach fittings into the 1960s.

C1. Wooden Coach Bodies

These unpainted wooden bodies were sold without bogies but glazed. They were based on real prototypes and varied in length according to the subject. Fittings including bogies were available separately.

C8/A	**LMS** 57' corridor 1st - *?-32*	15	20
C8/B	**LMS** 57' corridor 1st/3rd - *?-32*	15	20
C8/C	**LMS** 57' brake 3rd - *?-32*	15	20
C8/D	**LMS** 50' all 3rd - *?-32*	15	20
C8/E	50' kitchen car - *?-32*	15	20
C8/F	**LNER** 60' corridor 1st/3rd - *?-32*	15	20
C8/G	**LNER** 57' corridor brake 3rd - *?-32*	15	20
C8/H	**LNER** 57' 1st/3rd diner - *?-32*	15	20
C8/I	**GWR** 57' corridor 1st/3rd - *?-32*	15	20
C8/J	**GWR** corridor brake 3rd - *?-32*	15	20
C8/K	**GWR** 57' 1st/3rd diner - *?-32*	15	20
C8/L	**GWR** 70' corridor 1st/3rd - *?-32*	15	20
C8/M	**GWR** 70' brake 3rd - *?-32*	15	20
C8/N	**GWR** 70' 1st/3rd diner - *?-32*	15	20
C8/O	**GWR** 57' old type corr 1st/3rd - *?-32*	15	20
C8/P	**GWR** 57' old type brake 3rd - *?-32*	15	20
C8/Q	**Pullman** coach - *?-32*	15	20
C8/R	**Pullman** kitchen - *?-32*	15	20

Ready Made Coaches

Between 1932 and the outbreak of the Second World War, Bond's advertised 'New Super Detail Coaches' in their catalogues but little detail of the types available was given. They were a range of corridor and suburban coaches and it is assumed that these were built to order in their own workshop. We know that the wooden and hand painted bodies were not all of a standard design but were specific to the companies whose livery they carried and varied in length accordingly. They had glass in the windows, corridor compartments and separate door handles fitted. They also had bogies "of special construction", metal wheels, oval brass buffers and corridor coaches had corridor connections. They were not quite so heavy in proportion as the Milbro coaches and sold at a standard price of £1-18-6. The listing below is based on very limited evidence and the editor would welcome further information.

LMS 3rd brake [C2] (Bond's)

C2. LMS Stock

		£	£
-	corridor 1st/3rd crimson - *32-40*	120	170
-	corridor all 3rd crimson - *32-40*	120	170
-	corridor brake 3rd crimson - *32-40*	120	170
-	suburban coach crimson - *32-40*	120	170
-	suburban brake crimson - *32-40*	120	170

C3. LNER Stock

Not a lot is known about these coaches

-	Gresley corridor 1st/3rd teak - *32-40*	120	170
-	Gresley corridor brake teak - *32-40*	120	170
-	suburban coach teak - *32-40*	120	170
-	suburban brake teak - *32-40*	120	170

C4. GWR Stock

-	corridor 1st/3rd dark brown+cream - *32-40*	120	170
-	corridor brake dark brown+cream - *32-40*	120	170
-	suburban coach dark brown+cream - *32-40*	120	170
-	suburban brake dark brown+cream - *32-40*	120	170

C5. SR Stock

-	corridor coach green - *32-40*	120	170
-	corridor brake end green - *32-40*	120	170
-	suburban coach green - *32-40*	120	170
-	suburban brake green - *32-40*	120	170

WAGONS

These were listed as 'True Scale Model Wagons' and described as 'models of lesser known types of goods stock'. Originally, these were made by a Sheffield company known as the Miniature Reproductions Company (M.R.Co) and were sold almost exclusively by Bond's between the late '20s and the outbreak of the Second World War. Later introductions may have been made in Bond's workshop.

The majority were made of wood and fitted with sprung 3-link couplings and oval head buffers (3/6 extra). All had turned cast iron wheels and some had metal chassis; the LMS 20 ton coke hopper was all metal. It seems that while a stock of finished wagons was kept in the shop, the models could be finished to the customer's requirements, "involving a few days delay", and this included, up to 1931, private owner liveries (1/- extra).

Unusual types include an LNER trestle wagon, LNER pulley wagon, Harwich ferry wagon, NE 40 ton hopper (also all metal) and a bogie well wagon with a length of 15½" (390mm) which had sprung bogies and sold for £1-18-6!

Bond's also sold wagons of other manufacturers.

Cat.No.	Company, Type, Colour, Dates	£	£

First Series (M.R.Co. for Bond's)

W1. Machinery Flat Wagon

-	flat top machinery truck - *28?-31*	25	30
-	ditto with spring buffers/couplings - *28?-31*	25	30

W2. Ballast and Mineral Wagons

-	**LMS** 15T ballast wagon - *26?-40*	25	30
-	as above but two end doors - *26?-40*	25	30
-	**NE** 12T ballast dropside - *26?-40*	25	30
-	**LMS** 12T mineral, door - *26?-40*	25	30
-	Private Owner wagons - *36-40*	30	35

W3. Other Open Wagons

Doors in the following open wagons were usually made to open.

-	**LNER** dropside 3-plank fish truck with Westinghouse pipes - *26?-40*	25	30
-	as above with vacuum pipes - *26?-40*	25	30
-	**GWR** 12T drop-door wagon - *26?-40*	25	30

LNER fish wagon [W3] (Bond's)

W4. Bolster Wagons

-	**NE** long single bolster - *28?-33*	25	30
-	ditto with spring buffers/couplings - *28?-33*	28	32
-	double bolster timber wagon - *26?-33*	25	30
-	6-wheel double bolster rail and timber wagon - *26?-33*	30	35
-	**LMS** 20T 6-wheel double bolster timber wagon - *26?-40*	30	35
-	ditto with spring buffers/couplings - *28?-33*	32	37

GWR 12T drop-door wagon [W3] (Bond's)

W5. Small Vans

Doors in the following covered vans were usually made to open.

-	**NE** van, 2 doors each side - *26?-40*	25	30
-	as above but ventilated van - *26?-40*	25	30
-	ditto + pipes + torpedo vents - *26?-40*	27	32
-	ditto with dual braking - *26?-40*	27	32
-	refrigerator van with end ladders - *26?-40*	30	35

W6. Early Brake Vans

These were available in different company designs.

-	**NE** short 4-wheel - *26?-33*	25	30
-	6-wheel - *26?-33*	30	35

W7. GWR Hopper Wagon

-	**GWR** hopper wagon - *28?-31*	60	70

W8. Well Wagons

This was a superb model with sprung bogies and buffers and a removable load.

-	with girder frame - *28?-40*	60	70
-	ditto with brake wheels - *31-40*	60	70
-	ditto with LMS brakes fitted - *31-32*	60	70

W9. Bogie Vans

-	bogie covered van (8 doors) - *32-40*	70	80
-	ditto with vents - *32-40*	70	80
-	ditto with vacuum pipes - *32-40*	70	80
-	ditto with brake gear - *32-40*	70	80

W10. Other Bogie Wagons

Fitted with sprung buffers and couplings.

-	bogie open wagon - *32-40*	60	70
-	bogie bolster wagon - *32-40*	60	70

Second Series

W11. Harwich Ferry Wagon

Doors in the following open wagons and covered vans were usually made to open.

-	grey - *32-40*	70	80

W12. Brake Vans

More recent style with long wheelbase, metal chassis, sprung buffers and couplings and glazed windows.

-	**SR** dark brown with platforms - *32-40*	30	35
-	**LNER** with platforms - *32-40*	27	32
-	**LMS** (modern) - *32-40*	27	32
-	**GWR** 20T - *33-40*	27	32

W13. Refrigerator Vans

Fitted with all metal chassis, ladders, vacuum pipes, sprung buffers and couplings. The LNER and GWR versions had vents at each end.

-	**LMS** - *32-40*	25	30
-	**SR** - *32-40*	25	30
-	**LNER** 139284 white - *32-40*	25	30
-	**GWR** white - *36-40*	25	30

W14. Small Hopper Wagons

Fitted with all metal body and chassis, opening hopper doors, sprung buffers and couplings.

-	**Roberts & Co** - *32-40*	80	90
-	**City of Birmingham Gas Dept.** - *32-40*	80	90

W15. Meat Van

Fitted with all metal chassis.

-	**LMS** - *32-40*	25	30

W16. Horse Box

Fitted with all metal chassis.

-	**LMS** - *32-40*	25	30

W17. Fish Vans

Fitted with all metal chassis, ladders, vacuum pipes, sprung buffers and couplings.

-	**LNER** dummy louvres - *32-40*	25	30
-	**LMS** dummy sliding doors - *32-40*	25	30

W18. Cattle Wagon

Correct open plank sides. Dummy swing doors and flap. Fitted with all metal chassis, ladders, vacuum pipes, sprung buffers and couplings.

-	**LMS** - *32-40*	25	30
-	**LNER** - *32-40*	25	30

W19. 1-Plank Container Wagons

Fitted with all metal chassis, ladders, vacuum pipes, sprung buffers and couplings.

-	**LMS + LMS** open container - *32-40*	35	40
-	**LMS + LMS** closed container - *32-40*	35	40
-	**LNER + LNER** open container - *32-40*	35	40
-	**LNER + LNER** closed contain. - *32-40*	35	40

1-plank wagon with container [W19] (Bond's)

W20. 40T Bogie Hopper Wagon

All metal with sliding hopper doors. Sprung buffers and couplings.

-	**LNER** 100011 - *32-40*	70	80

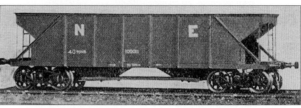

40T bogie hopper wagon [W20] (Bond's)

W21. 20T Well Wagon

All metal wagon fitted with brake handle wheels. Equalised bogies, ladders, sprung buffers and couplings.

-	**LNER** - *32-40*	70	80
-	girder load - *32-40*	25	30
-	**GWR** - *32-40*	70	80
-	diesel road roller load - *33-40*	25	30

W22. PO Lime Wagon

All metal with sliding roof door.

-	various PO names - *32-40*	35	40

W23. 20T Coke Hopper Wagon

All metal wagon fitted with sprung buffers and couplings.

-	**LMS** grey - *33-40*	70	80

W24. Trestle Wagon

Fitted with sprung buffers and couplings

-	**LNER** 14710 - *33-40*	70	80

LNER trestle wagon [W24] (Bond's)

W25. Pulley Wagon

Fitted with sprung buffers and couplings

-	**LNER** 46470 + ship's propeller - *33-40*	70	80

W26. Flat Container Wagon

Fitted with sprung buffers and couplings.

-	**GWR** 39015 + meat container - *33-40*	70	80

Bowman

HISTORY

Although they built locomotives for only 10 years, this firm's products had a major impact on the live steam locomotive market and many enthusiasts are continuing to run these engines.

Geoffrey Bowman Jenkins (born in 1891) took out his first patent in 1919. This was for driving a toy locomotive with elastic. He had also patented a number of ideas for toy steam boats, which he was successfully making in London and in 1923 he was invited to join forces with the well established firm of Hobbies Ltd at Dereham in Norfolk, who traded in materials and tools for keen amateur woodworkers. With Jenkins' ideas and Hobbies machinery and marketing the firm Bowman Models was established.

The powerful single-acting oscillating-cylinder engines were first placed in a series of successful steamboats and then developed onto horizontal stationary engines. In 1925, the first of three non-reversing model railway locomotives was placed on the market, most being powered by two oscillating cylinders. In 1927 a patent was obtained for his design of track and the following year Jenkins exhibited his models at the British Industries Fair. During this, a 4-4-0 locomotive with six coaches behind it clocked up 183 miles during the Fair. It was refuelled every 40 minutes and the success of this exercise lead directly to Bassett-Lowke developing their Enterprise 4-4-0 model to achieve a similar performance.

The scale of these locomotives was really gauge 1 which allowed for the use of a large boiler and burner (meths fired) but the wheels were built to gauge 0. At this stage, gauge 1 was on the decline so it was advantageous to have models which would run on the more popular 0 gauge track.

Most of the brass parts were made in Birmingham but assembly and finishing was done at Dereham. It was there also that the wooden parts such as sleepers and rolling stock parts were made. Initially the models were packed in wooden boxes but, later, card ones were used. These could be identified by their brown and cream striped finish.

The production of Bowman trains was run down during the early 1930s and had ceased by 1935 when Jenkins started the Jentique furniture making firm and the following year parted company with Hobbies Ltd. The only post-war production of Bowman was stationary and marine engines done at Luton. These were made until about 1950. Jenkins died in 1959. The withdrawal of Jenkins from Hobbies Ltd left a gap which was filled by Geoffrey Malins and this lead to the Mamod range.

Bowman items used to be very cheap but the market has risen over the last two years.

Collector's Club

Bowman collectors are catered for by the Bowman Circle who publish a quarterly journal and anyone interested in joining should contact Colin Wilson Tel: 01444 232647. Members of the Bowman Circle have provided much of the information given above.

Prices - The two prices shown represent the likely range for one in good condition.

LOCOMOTIVES

The largest locomotive was a 4-4-0 tender engine whilst the other three were 0-4-0 tanks, one being smaller in size and a bit nearer 0 scale. Strictly speaking the wheel arrangements were not as just described as the locomotives had no coupling rods, only connecting rods to the rear set of wheels.

Although you will go a long way before you will find a real locomotive looking quite like a Bowman, with its long thin cylinders and distinctive safety valve, Bowman locomotives were characterised by their simple design, sound engineering and superb performance.

Power and speed were effectively controlled by blanking off up to three of the burner wicks with burner caps, making the engine quite docile and able to trundle round 2ft curves without a load. Unfortunately the wick caps were often lost and in later years operated on full throttle unless substitute wick caps or plugs were fitted. This gave them a reputation for being too fast and needing plenty of stock behind them to slow them down and keep them on the track.

As evidence of their good performance, a Bowman 4-4-0 tender locomotive hauled six Bowman carriages for 183 actual miles at the British Industries Fair in the late 1920s.

Cat.No.	Number, Company, Colour, Dates	£	£

L1. 4-4-0 Tender Locomotive (Freelance)

The model carried the number on the tender and an oval badge on cabside marked 'Bowman Patent'. On later versions this was worded 'Bowman Models'. These were sold in wooden boxes.

234	**4472** LNER green also numbered **234** + others - *27-35*	150	200
234	**4472** LNER black - *27-35*	NPG	NPG
234	**4073** GWR green also numbered **234**, **4472** + others - *27-35*	250	350
234	**453** SR green also numbered **234**, **4472** + others - *27-35*	200	280
234	**13000** LMS maroon - *27-35*	175	250
234	**13000** LMS black also numbered **234**, **4472** + others - *27-35*	175	250

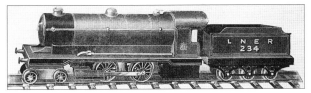

4-4-0 tender loco [L1] (Bowman)

L2. Large 0-4-0 Tank Engine (Freelance)

Outside cylinders.

265	**265** LNER green - *27-35*	120	170
265	**265** LNER black - *27-35*	120	180
265	**265** LMS maroon - *27-35*	120	160
265	**265** LMS black - *27-35*	120	170

L3. Small 0-4-0 Tank Engine (Freelance)

300	**300** LNER green - *27-35*	120	160
300	**300** LMS black - *27-35*	120	160
300	**300** LMS maroon - *27-35*	120	160
30	**30** LMS maroon - *27-35*	120	160

L4. Small 0-4-0 Tank Engine ('Baby Bowman') (Freelance)

Single oscillating cylinder on the cab floor driving the rear axle by gearing.

410	green - *32-34*	175	250

		£	£
410	black - *32-34*	NPG	NPG
Cat.No.	**Number, Company, Colour, Dates**	**£**	**£**

COACHES

Without doubt the passenger coach was the most attractive model made by Bowman. It was a bogie coach with a heavy wooden base and ends but with nicely lithographed tin sides with opening doors and a pair of large gas cylinders under the floor. No brake coach was made. The coach was built to gauge 1 proportions but for 0 gauge track. They are not common and can be more expensive to buy than the locomotives.

C1. 1st/3rd Composite

551	**LNER** 17172 teak - *27-35*	180	260
551	**GWR** 10152 dark brown+cream - *27-35*	180	260
551	**LMS** 10153 maroon - *27-35*	180	260

WAGONS

Bowman produced wagons to go with the locomotives and again, although 0 gauge, they were built to gauge 1 proportions. A range of 0 scale wagons was planned but never made. In June 1933 retailers were informed that the wagons were no longer available. The open wagon and brake van had the 'Bowman Models' badge on each end, the tank wagon was badged on the side and the timber wagons carried no badge.

Cat.No.	**Company, Colour, Dates**	**£**	**£**

W1. 5-Plank Open Wagon

661	**LMS** grey - *27-35*	30	40
661	**LNER** grey - *27-35*	30	40

W2. Brake Van

662	**LMS** grey - *27-35*	35	45
662	**LNER** grey - *27-35*	35	45

LNER goods brake van [W2] (Chris Ellis)

W3. Tank Wagon

663	**Shell** red - *27-35*	50	60

W4. Timber Wagon

664	**LMS** grey - *27-35*	25	30
664	**LNER** grey - *27-35*	25	30

Dapol N

HISTORY

Developed in great secrecy, Dapol N gauge was launched in 2003 at the Warley National Model Railway Exhibition at the National Exhibition Centre in Birmingham and was the talk of the show.

The subjects chosen so far have all been ones previously made in 00 gauge by Airfix and Hornby Dublo/Wrenn and subsequently produced by Dapol after their acquisition of the Airfix and Wrenn tooling.

LOCOMOTIVES

At the time of writing only two locomotives have been identified in Dapol's development programme. However, their 2004 catalogue shows their intention to produce others.

Cat.No.	**Number, Company, Colour, Date**	**£**	**£**

L1   Class 14XX 0-4-2T (ex-Airfix)

?	GWR 1425 green - *04?*	NPG	NPG
?	BR 1458 black - *04?*	NPG	NPG

L2 Class 73 ED

With working lights and illuminated headcode panels which light in the direction of travel.

?	- *04?*	NPG	NPG

COACHES

Cat.No.	**Company, Number, Colour, Date**	**£**	**£**

C1. GWR Suburban B Stock

NC-005	**BR** W6907W maroon - *03*	8	12
NC-006	**BR** W6970W maroon - *03*	8	12
NC-007	**GWR** 6736 brown+cream - *03*	8	12
NC-008	**GWR** 6738 brown+cream - *03*	8	12

C2. GWR Auto Trailer

NC-0??	**GWR** dark brown+cream - *04*	8	12
NC-0??	**BR** maroon - *04*	8	12

WAGONS

Cat.No.	**Company, Number, Colour, Date**	**£**	**£**

W1. GWR Gunpowder Van

NB-001	**GWR** 37985 grey - *04*	4	6
NB-002	**BR**.brown - *04*	4	6
NB-005	**LNWR** light grey - *04*	4	6
NB-006	**Elterwater Gunpowder Co.** Ltd 11 light grey - *04*	4	6

W2. SR CCT Utility Van

NB-003	**BR** S23805 green - *04*	4	12
NB-004	**BR** M527402 maroon - *04*	4	12
NB-007	**BR** S2385S green - *04*	4	12
NB-008	**BR** blue - *04*	4	12

W3. GWR Siphon G Bogie Milk Van

NC-001	**BR** W1449 maroon - *03*	8	12
NC-002	**GWR** 1443 dark brown - *03*	8	12

W4. GWR Siphon H Bogie Milk Van

NC-003	**BR** W1431 maroon - *03*	8	12
NC-004	**GWR** 1435 dark brown - *03*	8	12

Dapol 00

HISTORY

David Boyle, of Highfield Birds & Models, who in 1981 had been unsuccessful in a bid to buy the model railway division of Airfix when the Company was being broken up and sold off, founded a company of his own called Dapol. This was established to handle a large amount of Airfix stock and spares that he had been able to acquire. Boyle's ambition, all along, was to produce a range of British outline locomotives and rolling stock of a quality in performance and detail that, previously, had only been found in some Continental ranges.

Research and development had already commenced for a L&Y Pug, a GWR County Class and a J94 tank to the extent that plans had been drawn and the tools manufactured.

When Airfix stocks ran low, Boyle had new moulds made of some of the old Airfix wagons, which went on the market in November 1983. His company also commenced the production of the ex-L&Y 'Pug', which was released the following year, and the Hawksworth `County' which arrived soon after.

When Palitoy closed down in 1985, David Boyle was finally offered the Airfix models as well as the intellectual assets of Palitoy's Mainline Railways range. There followed a merging of Airfix, Mainline and Dapol products under the Dapol name. In fact, very few Mainline designs were used, except as old stock, as the tools for them belonged to the production company in Hong Kong - Kader.

Dapol next took over the remnants of some of the Trix Trains/Lilliput (UK) range in the late '80s and these included the tooling for the bodies of the E3000 and Trans-Pennine DMU, the chassis remaining with Lilliput in Austria and ending up with Bachmann.

Milestones
1981 Dapol formed by David and Pauline Boyle.
1983 Dapol market their own wagons and renamed Castles.
1984 first Dapol locos released.
1985 Dapol buy the intellectual assets of the Mainline system from Palitoy and Airfix tooling.
1986 1st catalogue published.
1988 Dapol acquire residue of British Lilliput.
1988 2nd catalogue published.
1989 3rd catalogue published.
1993 Dapol buy G&R Wrenn.
1994/5 Dapol move to Llangollen.
1995 fire at Winsford factory.
1995 4th catalogue published.
1999 David Boyle leaves Dapol.
2001 5th catalogue published.
2001 Dapol sell G&R Wrenn Ltd to Mordvale Ltd.
2001 1st new loco for 12 years.
2003 Dapol enter the N gauge market.
2004 Company moves to Chirk.

Dapol also bought the assets of G&R Wrenn in 1992 although only some wagons from the Wrenn range have been made. Some of these were sold on chassis purchased from Bachmann when the latter turned production over to their Blue Riband range. Dapol's other main production is plastic kits from the former Airfix tools. At one time they also made kits from the ex-Tri-ang Model-Land tools.

Stock was stored in various places including Boyle's own home. From time to time, forgotten boxes of obsolete stock emerged and the contents sold, often through Dapol's shop - especially at their Winsford addresses. Some of this stock was never advertised making it difficult to record what and when models were released. A severe fire at the Cheshire factory damaged a number of tools.

Dapol moved from Winsford in Cheshire to Llangollen, in Wales, where they opened an exhibition called 'Model Railway World'

which, at one time, included some of the Wrenn machines and tools which started life in the Hornby-Dublo production line at the Meccano factory in Liverpool.

Around 1996, some of the Dapol and former Airfix tools were offered to Bachmann but, subsequently, were sold to Hornby. Almost all of these are back in production out in China, having first undergone further improvements. Dapol, however, continued to produce limited runs of some of these models from their stock of parts.

In April 1999 Dapol Ltd parted company with its founder, David Boyle, and since then has been under new management with George Smith as Director of Corporate Affairs.

In 2001, with the transfer of Graham Farish production to China, it became the last British company to regularly manufacture ready to run models in the UK.

At the 2000 Warley National Model Railway Exhibition, Dapol announced one of their largest projects for several years - the production of a model of the Pendolino, the flagship of the Virgin Trains fleet. The model was delivered a year later and at about the same time, the company sold the tools, archives and intellectual assets of G&R Wrenn Ltd to Mordvale Ltd.

In January 2004 the company moved once more, this time to a new factory complex not far away at Chirk. This gave them the opportunity to dispense with much of the clutter from the past and consolidate on what had become their main product - 00 gauge private owner wagons. Additionally, with the launch of their first N gauge models at the Warley show the previous autumn, plans were put in hand to expand this range.

Confusion - As we have said, this is a very difficult range to record as there was such a mix up of old stock from other manufacturers that has been repackaged and new batches made by Dapol from the old tooling. There were also models made from duplicate tooling produced for Dapol in the Far East from samples of models sent out there for copying.

An example of the confusion is Dapol coaches which are ex-Mainline, ex-Airfix or produced by Dapol. Some of the 'Dapol' variety have a proper 'Dapol' printed on the underside. However, several have the Mainline arc with 'Railways' printed below it. The word 'Mainline' has been blanked out and 'Dapol' printed above the arc. To make matters worse, there are two versions of the (now blank) arc. In the case of one the arc is totally smooth and appears never to have had any wording on it and, in the case of the other, it looks as if the name 'Mainline' has been removed from the mould using a file as there are vertical striations where the word had been.

We have not attempted to separate out these variations in the following listing.

Further Reading

There was a series of articles by Graham Smith-Thompson, in *Model Railway Enthusiast* magazine, profiling the Airfix and Mainline ranges and other systems that later used the tools. There were four parts devoted specifically to Dapol published in the August-November 1999 issues of the magazine.

Listing - The locos are listed in order of size starting with tank engines followed by tender locos and ending with diesels and multiple units. The coaches are listed with pre-Nationalisation stock first followed by vehicles of later years. Wagons are listed in the order of: flats, open wagons, hoppers, tanks, vans, brake vans and bogie stock.

LOCOMOTIVES

Dates: We have found little information about when models first became available or when they were out of production. The dates quoted in the tables below are based on this limited knowledge, coming largely from press advertising and are for guidance only. However, one breakthrough was the discovery of a stock list prepared during the drafting of the 1995 catalogue which included many models no longer being advertised. One of the reasons for this was the haphazard stock control exercised before the present management took over. It resulted in boxes of stock being uncovered and offered for sale long after it had been thought that they were sold out. We even found models included in the 1995 catalogue which had been missing from advertised sales lists for several years and did not return to them. No doubt their inclusion was a statement of intent which Dapol were not able to fulfil largely because of the extra work that came with the acquisition of the Wrenn tools and parts. We therefore express caution in using catalogues as a means of dating and to not take too literally the dates we have given below.

Packaging - Items in the following list shown as being 'ex-Airfix stock' or 'ex-Mainline stock' were, as far as we know, sold in their original packaging.

(A) = ex-Airfix stock
(M) = ex-Mainline stock

Cat.No.	Number, Company, Colour, Dates	£	£
L1.	**Class 0F 'L&Y Pug' 0-4-0ST**		
D1	**11217** LMS black - *84-94*	30	40
D2	**51241** BRb black - *84-99*	28	38
D10	**19** L&Y black - *90-02*	28	38
D?	**821** WD black, spark arrester fitted to chimney Ltd Edn 100 - *99?*	65	85
D?	**402** black Ltd Edn 100 - *03*	40	60

The tooling was sold to Hornby in 1996 and the model reintroduced by them.

Class OF ex-Lancashire & Yorkshire 0-4-0ST [L1]

	L2	**Class 14XX 0-4-2T (ex-Airfix)**		
D19	**1466** GWR green (A) - *85-95*	20	30
D19	**1420** GWR (button) green, new chassis - *95-02*	22	35
D20	**1466** BRc green lined (A) - *85-95*	22	32
D96	**1438*** BRb black new chassis - *95-02*	25	35
?	**1401** BR black from the film 'Titfield Thunderbolt' Ltd Edn 100*** - *02*	50	70
D97	**1459**** GWR black new chassis - *95-02*	25	35
D97	**1466** GWR black new chassis - *95-02*	25	35
D97S1	**4803** GWR green Ltd Edn 100 - *99*	65	90

* also shown in catalogue as 1442. ** also shown as black 1456 in 1989 catalogue. *** This model was claimed by Dapol to be their last limited edition locomotive. The tooling was sold to Hornby in 1996 and the model reintroduced by them.

Class 14XX 0-4-2T [L2]

L3 Class 57XX Pannier Tank (ex-Mainline)
D61	**5768** BRb black (M) - *85*	30	38

L4 Class J72 0-6-0T (ex-Mainline)
D54	**581** LNER green (M) - *85-94*	20	28
D55	**68745** BRa black, Ross pop safety valves (M) - *85-94*	20	28
D56	**'Joem'** North Eastern green (M) - *85-86*	20	28
D57	**69001** BRb black enclosed safety valves (M) - *85-86*	18	26

Class J94 [L5]

L5. Class J94 'Austerity' 0-6-0ST
D7	**WD150 'Warrington'** WD* deep grey - *85-98*	25	40
D8A	**68077** BRc black, rectangular windows - *86-887*	25	40
D8B	**68034** BRb black - *86-88*	25	40
D8C	**68068** BRc black, round windows - *86-89*	25	40
D9	**68080** BR black** - *90-96*	22	38
?	**8049** LNER desert sand livery Ltd Edn 125 - *98-99*	65	85
?	**8054** LNER black Ltd Edn 125 - *98*	65	85

* Under-feeder stoker type chimney, preserved livery **With extended bunker kit and corrected balance weights. An EM wheel conversion kit was available. The tooling was sold to Hornby in 1996 and the model reintroduced by them.

Terrier 0-6-0 tank [L6]

L6. Terrier 0-6-0 tank

D69	**662** LBSC Marsh Umber - *89-95*	35	45
D70	**2635** SR lined green - *89-94*	35	45
D71	**32640** BRb lined black - *89-94*	30	40
D72	**6** GWR button green - *88-94*	35	45
D100	**82 'Boxhill'** LBSC yellow-brown - *89-95*	35	45
D101	**82 'Boxhill'** LBSC yellow-brown, as D100 but Ltd Edn - *99*	50	75
D101S1	**2659** SR black, wartime 'Sunshine' lettering, Ltd Edn 100 - *97*	75	90
D101S2	**B636** SR black Ltd Edn 100 - *99-00*	75	90
D101S3	**5 'Portishead'** GWR button green Ltd Edn 100 - *99*	80	95
D102	**55 'Stepney'** LBSC yellow-brown - *90-98*	50	65
D6A	**2655** SR dark green Ltd Edn 100 - *98-99*	75	90

The tooling was sold to Hornby in 1996 and the model reintroduced by them.

L7 Class 66XX Tank 0-6-2T (ex-Mainline)

D59	**6652** BRb black (M) - *85-94, 98*	30	35
D60	**6697** GWR green (M) - *85-89*	30	35

L8 Class N2 Tank 0-6-2T (ex-Airfix)

D51	**4744** LNER black, red lining (M) - *85-01*	28	38
D52	**69532** BRb black lined (M) - *85-01*	22	30
D53	**9522** LNER lined green (M) - *85-96*	22	30

The tooling was sold to Hornby in 1996 and the model reintroduced by them.

L9 Class 61XX Prairie Tank 2-6-2T (ex-Airfix model)

D21	**6167** BRb lined black (A) - *85-94*	20	32
D22*	**6110** Great Western green (A) - *85-94*	18	32
D23	**6167** BRc lined green (M) - *85-89*	27	35
D24*	**6169** GWR green (M) - *85-88*	27	35

* Some confusion exists as to which number applies to which loco. The tooling was sold to Hornby in 1996 and the model reintroduced by them.

L10 Class 2P 4-4-0 (ex-Mainline)

Many of the Mainline stock absorbed had only polystyrene trays and had to be put in Dapol boxes to sell.

D15	**635** LMS black, lined red (M) - *85-96*	32	42
D16	**40568** BRb lined black (M) - *85-90*	30	40
D16A	**40567** BRb lined black - *90-93*	30	38
D16B	BRb lined black - *90-93*	NPG	NPG
D16C	**40569** BRb lined black - *90-95*	32	40
D17	**563** LMS lined maroon - *86-96*	30	38
D67	**45** blue SDJR - *88-96*	32	40

The tooling was sold to Hornby in 1996 and the model reintroduced by them.

L11 Class 2301 'Dean Goods' 0-6-0 (ex-Airfix)

D18	**2516** GWR green (M) - *85-88*	28	38
D18A	**2517** Great Western green - *86-98*	25	38
D18B	**2518** GWR green - *86-94*	25	38
D18C	**2519** GWR (button) green - *86-94*	25	38
D50	**2538** BRb black (M) - *85-94*	28	38
D018S1	**2515** Great Western green, Ltd Edn 100 - *99*	65	90

The tooling was sold to Hornby in 1996 and the model reintroduced by them.

Class 2301 GWR Dean Goods 0-6-0 [L11]

L12 Class 4F 0-6-0 (ex-Airfix)

D25	**4454** LMS black (A) - *85-94*	25	30
D25	**4312** LMS black, lined red - *not made*	NA	NA
D26	**44454** black BRb (small or large) (A) - *85-94*	30	40
D98	LMS maroon - *not made*	NA	NA
D99	SDJR blue - *not made*	NA	NA

The tooling was sold to Hornby in 1996 and the model reintroduced by them.

L13. Class 43XX Mogul 2-6-0 (ex-Mainline)

D47	**5328** BRb black (M) - *85-00*	37	45
D48	**5322** Great Western green (M) - *85-90*	32	40
D49	**4358** BRb lined green (M) - *85-90*	32	40

L14. Manor Class 4-6-0 (ex-Mainline)

D44	**7808 'Cookham Manor'** GWR green (button) (M) - *85-94*	32	40
D45	**7819 'Hinton Manor'** GWR green (M) - *85-94*	32	40
D46	**7827 'Lydham Manor'** BRc green (M) - *85-94*	32	40

L15. Class 4073 'Castle' 4-6-0 (ex-Airfix)

Some of the stock of Airfix Castles (with tender drive) were renamed and renumbered by Dapol. Of these, some were sold in their original Airfix boxes while others were put into new Dapol packaging once the expanded polystyrene tray had been trimmed with a large knife!

D29	**4079 'Pendennis Castle'** BRb green (A) - *85-94*	35	50
D30	**4073 'Caerphilly Castle'** Great () Western green (A) - *83-89*	35	50
?	**4080 'Powderham Castle'** BRb green (Airfix 54125 renamed by Dapol) - *83-85*	75	100
?	**4080 'Powderham Castle'** Great () Western grn (Airfix 54124 renamed by Dapol) - *83-85*	75	100
?	**4078 'Pembroke Castle'** BRb green (Airfix 54125 renamed by Dapol) - *83-85*	75	100
?	**4078 'Pembroke Castle'** Great () Western grn (Airfix 54124 renamed by Dapol) - *83-85*	75	100

Former Airfix Castle renamed 'Powderman Castle' by Dapol [L15]

L16. Class 4073 'Castle' 4-6-0

This model had loco drive and a Hawksworth tender.

D5	**4090 'Dorchester Castle'** BRb lined green, optional double chimney - *85-95*	40	50
D6	**5090 'Neath Abbey'** G()W green - *85-93*	40	50
D107	**5090 'Isambard Kingdom Brunel'** GW green - *not made*	NA	NA

The tooling was sold to Hornby in 1996 and the model reintroduced by them.

L17. Class 1000 'Hawksworth County' 4-6-0

Hawksworth tender

D3	**1029 'County of Worcester'** G()W green single chimney - *84-94*	40	50
D4	**1027 'County of Stafford'** BRc green, double chimney - *84-94*	40	50
D68	**1019 'County of Merioneth'** BRb gloss black - *88-94*	40	50
D103	**1011 'County of Chester'** G()W green * - *90-96*	40	50

* remodelled boiler and firebox, improved finish. The tooling was sold to Hornby in 1996 and the model reintroduced by them.

Hawksworth County [L17]

Dapol 00

L18. Parallel Boiler Royal Scot 4-6-0 (ex-Mainline)

D34	**6127 'Old Contemptibles'** LMS maroon (M) - *85-94*	32	40
D35	**46137 'Prince of Wales Volunteers, South Lancashire'** BRb green (M) - *85-94*	32	40

L19. Rebuilt Royal Scot 4-6-0 (ex-Airfix)

D27	**46100 'Royal Scot'** BRb green (A) - *85-94*	25	40
D28	**6103 'Royal Scots Fusilier'** LMS black (A) - *85-94*	25	40

L20. Rebuilt Royal Scot Class 4-6-0 (ex-Mainline)

D36	**6115 'Scots Guardsman'** LMS black (M) - *85-94*	30	38
D41	**46115 'Scots Guardsman'** BRc green (M) - *85-93*	35	42
D58	**6100 'Royal Scot'** LMS maroon bell on front, name on smokebox door (M) - *85-96*	30	38

L21. Jubilee Class 5XP Class 4-6-0 (ex-Mainline)

D37	**5687 'Neptune'** LMS black, Stanier tender (M) - *85-94*	30	38
D38	**45691 'Orion'** BRc green, Stanier tender (M) - *85-98*	35	42
D42	**45700 'Amethyst'** BRb black, Fowler tender (M) - *85-95*	30	38
D43	**45698 'Mars'** BRb green, Fowler tender (M) - *85-94*	35	42

L22. Rebuilt Patriot Class 4-6-0 (ex-Mainline)

D39	**45536 'Private W.Wood V.C.'** BRa black (M) - *85-94*	35	42
D40	**45532 'Illustrious'** green BRc (M) - *85-93*	35	42

L23. Class A4 4-6-2 (ex-Trix)

D84	**4468 'Mallard'** LNER blue with valances - *not made*	NA	NA
D85	**2512 'Silver Fox'** LNER silver with valances - *not made*	NA	NA
D86	**60027 'Merlin'** BRc green - *not made*	NA	NA

L24. Class A3 4-6-2 (ex-Trix)

D87	**4472 'Flying Scotsman'** LNER green - *not made*	NA	NA
D88	**60103 'Flying Scotsman'** BRc green - *not made*	NA	NA

L25. Class A2 4-6-2 (ex-Trix)

D89	**525 'A.H.Peppercorn'** LNER green - *not made*	NA	NA
D90	**60532 'Blue Peter'** BRc green - *not made*	NA	NA

D9 & D10 - In 1985, these numbers were originally allocated to two versions of a Beyer-Garratt locomotive due to be released in 1987 but the model did not reach production and D10 was reallocated to the L&Y Pug.

D11 - In 1985 this number was allocated to a WD 2-8-0, also due for release in 1987 but about which no more was heard.

L26. Class 31/4 Diesel Electric Co-Co (ex-Airfix)

D30**	**31401** BRe blue (A) new bogie - *85*	15	30
D30	**31226** BReLL Rft plain grey - *not made*	NA	NA
D31**	**D5531** BRc green (A) - *85*	15	30
D31	**31247** BReLL Railfreight red stripe grey - *not made*	NA	NA
D32	**31217** BRe Rft Distribution grey - *not made*	NA	NA
D61	**31401** BRe blue (A) - *88-94*	15	30
D62	**D5531** BRc green (A) - *88-94*	15	30
D73	BRe Rft Distribution grey - *not made*	NA	NA

** Early code numbers used for D61 and D62. Some of the tools were amongst those bought by Hornby in 1996 but there were insufficient to make a complete model.

L27. Class 42 'Warship' Diesel Hydraulic B-B (ex-Mainline)

D64	**827 'Kelly'** BRe blue as D65 with diesel sound and klaxon (M) - *85-88*	30	40
D65	**827 'Kelly'** BRe blue (M) - *85-89*	20	30
D66	**D824 'Highflyer'** BRc green (M) - *85-87*	22	30

L28. Class 56 Diesel Co-Co (ex-Mainline)

D12	**56079** BRe blue, (M) - *85-98*	25	35
D12*	**56077** BRe blue - *?*	30	40
D13	**56086** BReLL blue, (M renumbered) - *85-93*	22	35
D14	**56075 'West Yorkshire Enterprise'** Railfreight red stripe grey - *85-88*	35	45
D14	**56077** BRe blue - *94-95*	25	35
D14A	**56064** Railfreight grey - *89-98*	30	40
D14B	**56068** Railfreight grey - *89-98*	30	40
D14C	**56090** Railfreight grey - *89-96*	30	40
D80	**56001** BRe Construction grey - *89-98*	30	40
D81	unpainted grey - *89-93*	15	25
D104	**56094** Rft Coal Sector grey - *91-95*	30	40

* also shown as D14. The tooling was sold to Hornby in 1996 and the model reintroduced by them.

Class 56 diesel in Railfreight grey [L28]

L29. Class 81 (ex-Trix)

D91	**E3000** BRd electric blue - *not made*	NA	NA
D92	BRe rail blue - *not made*	NA	NA
D93	BRe Executive grey - *not made*	NA	NA

L30. Class 124 Trans-Pennine DMU (ex-Trix)

These were assembled using mouldings made at Dapol's Winsford factory and fitted with their Sprinter motor bogie with new sideframes clipped on. The units were adapted to take Dapol coach weights to give them extra weight.

D94	BRe blue 2-car single motor - *not made*	NA	NA
D95	**NE51953/NE51954** BRc green 2-car, single motor - *94-95*	70	85
D105	**NE51953/NE51954** BRc green 2-car, 2 motors, 221 were made - *00-01*	75	90

The tools were amongst those bought by Hornby in 1996 but as the model is under scale, it is unlikely that it will be made by them.

L31. Class 150/2 Sprinter

It was not a very accurate model, particularly the front end and the body side windows, and it was not very reliable. Hornby bought the tooling but because of its reputation are unlikely to reintroduce the model unless it is from new tooling.

D82+ D82A	**150237(57237/52237)** BRe Provincial grey + blue 2-car - *92-94*	50	70
D82+ D82A	**150237(57237/52237)** BRe Provincial grey + blue improved 2-car - *93-99*	50	70
D108	Centro 2-car - *?*	NA	NA
D109	PTE 2-car - *?*	NA	NA

L32. Class 155 Super Sprinter

D83+ D83A	**155329(57329/52329)** BRe Provincial grey + blue 2-car - *92-94*	50	70
D83+ D83A	**155329(57329/52329)** BRe Regional Rlys grey + blue improved 2-car - *93-98*	50	70
D110	BRe Metro PTE maroon 2-car - *?*	NPG	NPG
D106	BRe Regional Railways grey + blue 2-car - *not made*	NA	NA

The tooling was sold to Hornby in 1996 and the model reintroduced by them.

L33. Class 390 Pendolino

Cat.No.	Company, Number, Colour, Dates	£	£
D390-1	**390001 'Virgin Pioneer'** Virgin red+grey 4-car Ltd Edn 2000 - *01-02*	70	100
D390-2	**390002 'Red Revolution'** Virgin red+grey 4-car Ltd Edn 2000 - *01*	70	100
?	**390002 'Red Revolution'** Virgin red+grey no motor Sp Edn special launch presentation sleeve - *01*	NPG	NPG
D390-3	**390006 'Mission Impossible'** Virgin red+grey 4-car Ltd Edn 200 - *03*	70	100
D390-4	**390007 'Virgin Lady'** Virgin red+grey 4-car Ltd Edn 200 - *03*	70	100
D390-5	**390010 'Commonwealth Games 2002'** Virgin red+grey 4-car Ltd Edn 200 - *03*	70	100
D390-6	**390011 'City of Preston'** Virgin red+grey 4-car Ltd Edn 200 - *03*	70	100
D390-7	**390014 'City of Manchester'** Virgin red+grey 4-car Ltd Edn 200 - *03*	70	100
-	Virgin red+grey 4-car Ltd Edn named **'Pen y darren'** one side and **'Pendolino'** specially commissioned by Virgin Trains for Railfest 2004 - *04*	NPG	NPG

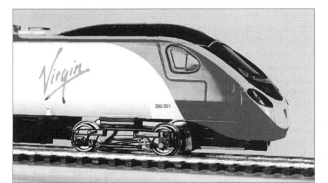

Pendolino 'Virgin Pioneer' [L33]

L34. American 4-4-0 (ex-Bachmann/Airfix)

D33	**'Jupiter'** red + silver (A) - *85-94*	20	30

COACHES

For its coaches, Dapol depended principally on old Airfix and Mainline stock and Airfix tooling. Initially they sold the large surpluses of stock they acquired from Airfix and Palitoy but then produced variations of the former Airfix models. These included Mk2D coaches in Executive livery and the 12 wheel LMS diner which was planned by both Airfix and Palitoy but not actually released until Dapol took it over. The coaches were numbered with an 'E' prefix and E41 seems to have been the highest number reached.

(A) = ex-Airfix stock
(M) = ex-Mainline stock

Cat.No.	Company, Number, Colour, Dates	£	£

C1a. GWR Centenary Coach (ex-Airfix)

E16	**GWR** 6659 dark brown+cream** (M) - *85-95*	8	14
E18	**BR** W6659W maroon* - *85-87*	10	17
E18	**BR** W6661W maroon* - *88-90*	10	16
E20	**BR** W6562W red+cream* - *90-02*	10	16
E20	**BR** W6662W red+cream* - *90-02*	10	16

*Paddington Newport Cardiff and Swansea coach boards. ** Cornish Riviera coach boards. The tooling was sold to Hornby in 1996 and the model reintroduced by them.

Ex-GWR centenary coach [C1a]

C1b. GWR Centenary Brake End (ex-Airfix)

E17	**GWR** 4575 dk.brn+cream** (M+A) - *85-02*	8	14
E19	**BR** W4576W maroon* (A) - *85-02*	10	17
E21	**BR** W4576W red+cream* - *90-02*	10	16

*Paddington Newport Cardiff and Swansea coach boards. ** Cornish Riviera coach boards. The tooling was sold to Hornby in 1996 and the model reintroduced by them.

C2. GWR Suburban B Stock (ex-Airfix)

E22	**GWR** 6869 dark brown+cream (A/M) - *85-02*	8	14
E23	**BR** W6894W maroon (A) - *85-88*	8	14
E24	**BR** W6447W lined maroon (M) - *85-02*	12	18

The tooling was sold to Hornby in 1996 and the model reintroduced by them.

C3. GWR Auto Trailer (ex-Airfix)

E25	**GWR** 187 dark brown+cream (M) - *85-98*	12	18
E26	**BR** W187W maroon (A) - *85-95*	8	14
E27	**BR** W176W red+cream (M) - *85-87*	12	18
E27	**BR** W178W red+cream - *88-90*	10	16

The tooling was sold to Hornby in 1996 and the model reintroduced by them.

C4a. LMS Stanier Corridor Composite (ex-Airfix)

E4	**LMS** 3935 maroon (A) - *87*	8	14
E4	**LMS** 3936 maroon - *88-02*	10	16
E6	**BR** M3935M red+cream (A) - *85-86*	8	14
E8	**BRc** M3868M maroon (M) - *87*	8	14
E8	**BRc** M3868M maroon - *91-02*	10	16

C4b. LMS Stanier Corridor Brake End (ex-Airfix)

E5	**LMS** 5542 maroon (A) - *85-86*	8	14
E5	**LMS** 5545 maroon - *89-92*	10	16
E7	**BR** M5542M red+cream (A) - *85-86*	8	14
E7	**BR** M5542M red+cream - *97-02*	10	16
E9	**BRc** M3868M maroon (M) - *85*	12	20
E9	**BRc** M5648M maroon - *87-02*	10	16

C5a. LMS 57' Non-Corridor Lav Coach (ex-Airfix)

E28	**LMS** 19195 maroon (A) - *85-87*	8	14
E28	**LMS** 19191 maroon - *88-02*	10	16
E31	**BR** M19195M maroon (A) - *85-92*	10	18
E31	**BR** M19199M maroon - *88-02*	10	16
E41	**BR** M16456M red - *02*	10	16
E42	**BR** M16161M red (all 2nd) - *02*	10	16

C5b. LMS 57' Non-Corr Lav Brake End (ex-Airfix)

E29	**LMS** 15185 maroon (A) - *87-?*	8	14
E29	**LMS** 25250 maroon - *95-02*	10	16
E30	**BR** M25250M maroon (A) - *86-91*	10	17
E30	**BR** M16161M maroon - *94-02*	10	16
E40	**BR** M16370 red - *02*	10	16

C6. LMS 12-Wheel Dining Car (ex-Mainline)

These were boxed in standard Dapol maroon boxes with blank labels and included a spare chassis. This was an LMS Period 2 coach.

E1	**LMS** 10440 maroon - *87-88*	15	25
E1A	**LMS** 238 maroon panelled - *88*	NPG	NPG
E2	**BR** M239M maroon - *86-90, 98-99*	15	25
E2A	**BRc** M239M maroon - *98-99*	15	25
E3	**BR** 10440 red+cream - *85-86*	20	35
?	**BR** maroon+cream - *not made*	NA	NA

The tooling was sold to Hornby in 1996 and the model reintroduced by them.

Dapol 00

12-wheel dinning car [C6]

C7.   LMS 50' Parcels Van BG (ex-Mainline)

E33	**BR** M31262M blue+grey NFV (M) - *85-02*	10	15
E34	**BR** M31398 blue NFV (M) - *85-01*	10	15
E35	**BR** red+cream (M) - *86*	15	18
E36	**BR** lined maroon (M) - *86*	15	18
E37	**LMS** 30965 maroon (M) - *86*	8	12

C8a.   BR Mk1 Corridor Coach (ex-Mainline)

E32	**BR** M1709 blue+grey (M) - *85-88*	9	13
E38	**BR** S25915 green (M) - *86*	14	17
E39	**BR** M25390 maroon (M) - *86*	10	15

C8b.   BR Mk1 Corridor Brake End BSK (ex-Mainline)

E40	**BR** M35040 maroon (M) - *85-87*	10	15

C9a.   Mk2D Open Coach FO & SO (ex-Airfix)

E10	**BR** E3170 blue+grey 1st (A) - *85-02*	8	14
E11	**BR** E5690 blue+grey 2nd (M) - *85-99*	10	20
E13	**BR ICs** E3207 executive grey 1st - *86-02*	10	16
E14	**BR ICs** E5732 executive grey 2nd - *86-02*	10	16

The tooling was sold to Hornby in 1996 and the model reintroduced by them.

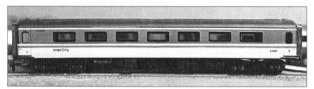

Mk2D open coach in executive grey livery [C9a] (Dapol)

C9b.   Mk2D Open Brake End BSK (ex-Airfix)

E12	**BR** E9479 blue+grey (M) - *85-02*	10	14
E15	**BR ICs** E9483 executive grey - *86-02*	12	16

The tooling was sold to Hornby in 1996 and the model reintroduced by them.

C10.   American Passenger Car (ex-Bachmann/Airfix)

E41	**CPRR** 3 red saloon car with trapdoor in roof (A) - *85-87*	8	14

C11a.   Pendolino Standard Class

Makes coaches AD or AJ for 390-001 and 390-002 and coaches AC, AD or AJ for 390-006, 390-007, 390-010, 390-011 and 390-014.

DPC-01	**Virgin** with transfers for any set - *03*	NPG	NPG

C11b.   Pendolino 2nd Class

Makes coach AF for 390-001 and 390-002.

DPC-02	**Virgin** with transfers for 390-001 and 390-002 - *03*	NPG	NPG

COACH GIFT SETS

These were introduced in 1999 to clear surplus stocks of coaches.

Mk2D Open Stock

E100	2 x E10 - *99*	NA	24
E200	2 x E12 - *99*	NA	24
E300	2 x E14 - *99*	NA	24
E400	E13 + E15 - *99*	NA	24
E500	E30 + E31- *01*	NA	24
E600	E40 + E41 - *01*	NA	24

E700	E8 + E9 - *01*	NA	24

WAGONS

Former Airfix and Mainline Wagons - Dapol had hoped to acquire the Airfix wagon tooling when Airfix collapsed but it went to Palitoy with much of it being put back into use to produce new Mainline wagons. Instead, Dapol had a series of wagons tooled up for them in Hong Kong. These may have included the 12T tanker, Mogo van, 7-plank wagon, 5-plank wagon, double vent van, SR box van, LMS brake van, GWR Toad, Conflat and container, 12T hopper wagon, large steel mineral wagon and possibly the PCA V-tank. These duplicates were very much like the Airfix and Mainline ones that were copied and it is often difficult to tell them apart. Later, Dapol acquired the Airfix tools but also tooled up at least five new wagons themselves.

The first Dapol wagons were released in 1984 and were numbered with a 'B' prefix. The wagon range was the most prolific of all the ranges produced by Dapol.

Dapol did acquire surplus Airfix stock from Palitoy and later purchased the entire Mainline stock when Palitoy ceased production of it. Some of these were then sold under the Dapol name until the stocks were used up. Dapol also obtained Airfix and Mainline wagon parts and assembled some of the wagons themselves, packaging them as Dapol wagons. No records have come to light to show the origins of these wagons and so a 'B' number can include repackaged Airfix or Mainline stock, models assembled from factory clearance parts, replica parts made by Dapol or a mixture of all these. Thus, the listing here has had to be done on a generic basis but with divisions made in the tabling only where detective work suggests that these should be. Much more research is needed and we would welcome further information on this subject.

Dapol reissued some popular Airfix wagons, often taking the opportunity to change the running number, but the printing on these reissues was sometimes of a poorer quality which helps to identify them. They also reissued some Mainline wagons but using the equivalent Dapol replica or Airfix body but with Mainline artwork.

Former Wrenn Wagons - In 1993, Dapol purchased the Wrenn company and its tooling and, while on this occasion they did not receive any completed stock, they did have all the unassembled parts from which wagons were made up and sold.

From 1997 these were sold in three different categories. Where all Wrenn parts were used they was sold as Wrenn models with a 'WR1' prefix to the catalogue number. If the wagons were made up from Wrenn bodies fitted to a Dapol chassis they were sold as Dapol wagons with a 'WR2' prefix and if new bodies were made from the Wrenn tools they were sold as Dapol models with a 'WR3' prefix. Once original parts were used up the WR1 and WR2 categories disappeared and WR3 wagons were absorbed into the main wagon series and given 'B' prefixes.

Unfortunately, I had no production records when compiling this list and depended to a large extent on catalogues and price lists. Thus, the inclusion of a wagon in the following tables is not evidence that it was actually made. It is merely an indication that Dapol listed it.

When, in 2001, Dapol sold G&R Wrenn Ltd to Mordvale, they retained all but 9 of the former HD/Wrenn wagon body tools including the following: utility van, gunpowder van, Presflo, 5-

plank wagon, banana van, mineral wagon, grain wagon, salt van and cattle van.

WRCC Models - Dapol produced wagon bodies for the Wrenn Railways Collectors Club which were supplied in Dapol boxes and with two gold printed labels. The pairs of labels carried a unique number and indicated the size of the run. The idea was that members would fit these special edition bodies to any spare Wrenn chassis they had and if they wished, boxed them in Wrenn boxes to which they affixed the gold label The bodies sold for about £6 each. Later special editions for the club were complete wagons. In all there were ten of these releases by Dapol.

Special Editions - In recent years Dapol have established themselves as the leading manufacturer of special edition wagons commissioned by shops and organisations. These are often produced in numbers no greater than 100 and quickly sell out. Due to the vast number of variations produced, we have not been able to trace every one of them and the absence of one from the tables below is not an indication that the model is rarer than others. We are always interested to learn of ones we have missed and in each case would like to know inscription, colour, running number, production quantity, year of release and who it was made for, etc. - if known.

Listing - To assist with finding models, we have arranged them in order of size starting with flat wagons, open wagons, hoppers, vans, tanks, brake vans and bogie stock. Within each table the wagons are mostly listed in catalogue order.

(A) = ex-Airfix stock

(M) = ex-Mainline stock

Cat.No.	Company, Number, Colour, Dates	£	£

W1. Lowmac MS (ex-Airfix)

The Hornby Dublo Lowmac tool was damaged and later sold with others to Morevale Ltd with G&R Wrenn Ltd.

B57	**BR** B904662 red brown + crate (A) - *85-86*	4	8
B57	**BR** dark grey + crate - *89-91*	7	9
B58	**BR** B904662 red brown + **Sea Land** container (A) - *85-86*	8	14

The tooling was sold to Hornby in 1996 and the model reintroduced by them.

W2. Conflat + B Type Container (ex-Airfix)

Duplicate tools for the wagon and container were made and one set sold to Hornby.

A4	brown+grey - unfinished - *86-03*	4	6
B91	**GW** 39324 dark grey + **C&G Ayers** container 37 green (M) - *87-92*	5	7
B399	**GW** 39005 dark grey + **C&G Ayers** container 37 dark blue - *02-03*	5	8
B100	**BR** B735700 red brown + **BR** furniture container (A) - *86-88*	6	12
B118	**BR** W36507 brown + **Pickfords** container - *87-89*	5	7
B119	**GW** 39324 dark grey + **GWR** BK1828 container - *88-92*	5	7
B119	**GW** 39005 dark grey + **GWR** container BK1828 dark brown - *95-99*	5	10
B531	**GW** 39005 dark grey + **GWR** container BK1828 dark brown - *03*	3	5
B120	**NE** 240749 grey + **J Miles** container red (A) - *88-89*	6	12
B383	**NE** 240748 grey + **J Miles** container 3 red - *02-03*	5	7
B121	**NE** 240747 brown + **LNER** container dark blue BK1828 - *88-92*	5	7
B563	**NE** 240748 grey + **LNER** container BK1828 dark blue - *03*	3	5
B129	**SR** 39115, 39155 dark brown + **SR**	5	7

	container K591 - *94-97*		
B530	**SR** 31955 dark brown + **SR** container K591 green - *03*	3	5
B162	**LMS** 300478 light grey + **LMS** container K1 maroon - *91-99*	5	7
B544	**LMS** N300478 grey + **LMS** container K1 dark brown - *03*	3	5
-	**SR** 31947 dark brown + **Earnest Reeves** brown container Sp Edn 93 (West Wales Wagon Works) - *04*	5	7
-	**Reg Stickells** green (Conflat only) Sp Edn 110 (Hythe Models) - *02*	5	7
-	**SE&CR Conflats** 105 dark brown + **W.G. Harris** container green Sp Edn (Ballards) - *03*	6	8

The tooling was sold to Hornby in 1996 and the model reintroduced by them.

LMS Conflat B with container [W2]

W3. 1-Plank Wagon + Container (ex-Mainline)

B90	**BR** B450023 red brown + **Bird's Eye** BD container (M) - *86*	5	7

W4. 1-Plank Wagon (ex-Wrenn)

B239	**BR** B459325 grey - *c95*	10	NPG
WR1-31	as above - *99*	10	17
B240	**LMS** + **LMS** container - *not made*	NA	NA
B241	**Auto Trader** 115 red brown - *c95*	12	NPG
WR1-30	**Auto Trader** 115 brown + 4 tyres - *99*	12	20
WR2-29	as above Dapol chassis - *99*	12	15

W5. 3-Plank Open Wagon (ex-Mainline)

A8	brown - unfinished - *85-89*	4	6
B23	**BR** M471363 light grey - *85-89*	4	6
B24	**LMS** 473449 red brown - *85-95*	4	6
B47	**Carter** 172 grey (M) - *85-86*	5	7
B48	**LMS** 471624 grey - *85-92*	4	6
B49	**NE** 535962 grey - *85-89*	5	8
B50	**BR** M473453 red brown, new chassis (M) - *85-87*	4	6
B96	**E.Turner** 26 cream (M) - *86-87*	5	7

W6. 5-Plank Open Wagon (ex-Airfix)

This table includes models made from the Airfix tool and from a replica tool produced in China for Dapol. We have no record as to which models were done with which tool.

A2	grey - unfinished - *84-99*	4	6
B3	**LMS** 413833 red brown - *84-97*	4	6
B11	**BR** M407562, M407580 light grey (A) - *84-03* 5		10
B13	**NE** 104021 red brown - *84-?*	4	6
B13	**NE** 214021 red brown - *?-03*	4	6
B18	**GW** 109458, 109459 dark grey (A) - *84-95*	5	10
B19	**BR** M411455 red brown - *84-90*	4	6
B38	**Arnold** 156 red brown (A) - *86-87*	4	8
B39	**Devizes Sand** 1 grey (A) - *85-87*	5	10
B40	**Spencer** 24 red (A) - *85-89*	4	8
B41	**Harts Hill** 2 brown (A) - *85-92*	5	10

B41	**Harts Hill** 2 brown - *95-02*	4	6
B42	**LMS** 404104 grey (A) - *86-92*	4	8
B42	**LMS** 404105 grey - *95-99*	4	6
B45	**BAC** 4253 red brown (M) - *85-82*	4	6
B46	**Black Rock** 46 black (M) - *85-92*	4	7
B268	**Black Rock** 46 black - *98-02*	4	6
B99	**Wadworths** 69 black - *86-89*	4	6
B126	**Webster** 341 dark brown (M) - *?*	5	8
B160	**Alloa** 1124 yellow (A) - *89-?*	4	8
B160	**Alloa** 1125 yellow - *?-99*	4	6
B163	**Warrener** 3 green - *94-02*	4	6
B177	**NE** 535962 grey - *89-03*	4	6
B179	**SR** 27348 dark brown - *89-99*	4	6
B101	**James Marriott** 14 brown - *not made*	NA	NA
B183	**James Marriott** 14 brown - *91-92, 97-02*	4	6
B199	**Higginbotham** 521 brown - *91-92, 95-02*	4	6
B397	**Penderyn Limestone** 336 grey + limestone - *02-03*	4	6
B515	**Corporation of Dundee Gas Dept**. 67 red-brown - *03*	4	6
B543	**Preston** 1 dark brown + coal - *03*	4	6
B547	**Simmonds** 23 dark brown + coal - *03*	4	6
B551	**Somerset Trading Company** 56 red + coal - *03*	4	6
-	**John North & Son** 18 red-brown, Sp Edn 200+ (Geoff Osborn) - *99*	6	8
-	**Old Radnor Lime** 126 Sp Edn (Hereford Model Centre) - *03?*	6	8

The tooling was sold to Hornby in 1996 and the model reintroduced by them.

5-plank wagon [W8]

W7. 5-Plank Open Wagon (ex-Mainline)

B67	**Timpson** 5 blue grey (M) - *85-92, 97-02*	6	8
B99	**Wadworths** 66 black (M) - *86*	5	7
B163	**Warrener** 3 - green - (M) - *89-92*	4	6
B164	**Ellis & Everard** 136 red+black (M) - *?*	4	5

W8. 5-Plank Open Wagon (ex-HD/Wrenn)

A2	grey - unfinished + coal - *02-03*	4	6
B126	**Webster** 47 grey - *95*	12	15
WR3-17	**Webster** 47 green + load - *99-02*	5	7
B149	**Consolidated Fisheries** 76 grey - *95*	12	NPG
WR1-36	as above - *99*	12	15
WR2-02	as above but Dapol chassis - *97-99*	8	12
WR1-38	**Higgs** light grey + coal - *99*	10	15
WR2-04	**Higgs** light grey + coal - *98-99*	8	10
B150	**British Soda** 14 brown - *95*	12	NPG
WR1-10	as above grey or white load- *99*	12	15
WR2-26	as above, Dapol chassis - *99*	12	15
WR3-02	**British Soda** 14 brown + load - *97-02*	5	7
B151	**Barnsley Main** 350 red - *95*	5	NPG
WR3-07	**Barnsley Main** 350 red - *98-02*	5	7
B152	**A Bramley** 6 red-brown - *95*	25	NPG
B153	**Twining** 95 red-brown - *95*	10	NPG
WR1-25	as above ochre and no shading - *99*	40	50
B154	**J Bly** black - *95*	NPG	NPG
W5000	**J Bly** black (body only) + coal Sp Edn 250 (Wrenn RCC) WRCC1 - *99*	8	10

B155	**Bassetts** 77 grey - *95*	10	NPG
WR3-16	**Bassetts** 77 grey + load - *99-02*	5	7
B156	**S Harris** 14 black - *95*	10	NPG
WR1-53	as above + load - *99*	10	18
B157	**Amos Benbow** 3 grey - *95*	10	NPG
WR3-03	**Amos Benbow** 3 grey - *97-02*	5	7
B161	**Cranston** 347 red - *95*	10	NPG
WR1-20	as above - *99*	10	15
B267	**Wolverton Mutual Society **** 29 grey Sp Edn 500 (Chris Wright) - *97-98*	4	6
B267	**Woverton Mutual Society** 29 grey Sp Edn 500 (Chris Wright) - *97-98 ****	4	6
B300	**Broughton & Plas** 630 olive green + coal, Ltd Edn 500 - *98-02*	4	6
B301	**J B Gregory** 37 red brown + coal , Ltd Edn 500 - *98-02*	4	6
B302	**Vauxhall** 292 green-grey + coal, Ltd Edn 500 - *98-02*	4	6
B303	**Vron** 175 black + coal, Ltd Edn 500 - *98-99*	4	6
B304	**Westminster** 74 grey + coal, Ltd Edn 500 - *98-02*	4	6
B305	**Llay Hall** 492 black + coal, Ltd Edn - *98-02*	4	6
B306	**Whynnstay** 551 brown + coal - *00-02*	4	6
B307	**Pounsbury** 1 green + coal - *00-02*	4	6
B313	**Nunnerley** 1 grey + coal - *00-02*	4	6
B314	**Tom Milner** 2 grey + coal - *00-02*	4	6
B338	**LMS** 404102 light grey coal - *01-03*	4	6
B347	**ICI** L3102 grey blue + coal - *01*	4	6
B369	**Alloa** 1125 cream - *02-03*	4	6
B378	**Groby Granite Co. Ltd** 471 grey + coal - *02-03*	4	6
B387	**Blake** 136 brown + coal - *02-03*	4	6
B392	**Cefn Mawr & Rhosymedre** 12 brown + coal - *02-03*	4	6
B393	**The Minera Lime Company** 125 brown + coal - *02-03*	4	6
B515	**Corporation of Dundee Gas Dept**. 67 red-brown - *03*	4	6
B515	**Corporation of Dundee Gas Dept**. 67 dark brown - *03*	4	6
(B522)	**R Webster** 303 red-brown - *03*	4	NA
B565	**Samuel Jeffries** 7 red - *04*	4	6
B577	**W.C.Gethen** 14 red - *04*	4	6
B586	**The Poenix Coal Co** 10 black - *04*	4	6
B591	**Arenig Granite** 207 red - *04*	4	6
B595	**Palmer & Sawdye** 16 grey - *04*	4	6
-	**Affleck** F Fyfe Sp Edn (Strathspey Railway) - *03?*	5	7
-	**Arbroath** 295 light grey + coal Sp Edn 500 (Virgin Trains) - *03*	4	6
-	Charles & Frank **Beadle** 28 black Sp Edn (Erith MRC) - *02*	4	6
-	**Baltic Saw Mills** 10 red brown + coal Sp Edn 330 (Ballards) - *01*	5	7
-	**Bennett & Carter** 12 grey Sp Edn (Ballards) - *03*	5	7
-	**Cambrian Railways** grey Sp Edn (Cambrian Railway Society) - *01*	10	15
-	**CIE** Sp Edn (Marks Models) - *02?*	5	7
-	**Clee Hill Granite** Sp Edn (Dartmoor Railway) - *03?*	5	7
-	**Conduit Colliery Norton Caines** 124 red-brown + coal Sp Edn 200 (Tutbury Jinny) - *02*	6	NA
-	**Crook & Greenway** Sp Edn (Glouc/Warks Railway) - *03?*	6	8
-	**Cudham** pale grey + coal Sp Edn (MRE Magazine) - *99-00*	6	8
-	**Cudham** red brown + coal Sp Edn (MRE Magazine) - *99-00*	6	8
-	**Dapol 2000** green Sp Edn (Dapol) - *00*	6	8
-	**Didcot Railway Centre** 817200 green Sp Edn 110 (DRC) - *01*	4	6
-	O **Edwards** 148 brown + coal Sp Edn	4	6

299 (Hythe Models) - *01*

-	**ECLP** red-brown Sp Edn (Mevagissey Model Railway) - *02*	5	NA
-	**ECLP** red-brown Sp Edn (Mevagissey Model Railway) - *02*	5	NA
-	**Edward Russell** 140 grey + coal Sp Edn 100 (Modellers Mecca) - *01*	6	NA
-	**English China Clays Lovering Pochin & Co Ltd** red-brown Sp Edn (Mevagissey Model Railway) - *02*	5	NA
-	**English China Clays Lovering Pochin & Co Ltd** red-brown Sp Edn (Mevagissey Model Railway) - *02*	5	NA
-	JH & E **Essen** 4 dark brown Sp Edn 250 (1E Promotionals) - *04*	5	7
-	GE **Farrant** 21 brown + coal Sp Edn 500 (Ballards) - *02*	6	8
-	**Foster Yeoman** 36 black + stone Sp Edn 125 (East Somerset Models) - *01*	6	8
-	**Foster Yeoman** 74 black + stone Sp Edn 125 (East Somerset Models) - *01*	6	8
-	H **Fulcher** 5 brown Sp Edn 250 (1E Promotionals) - *04*	5	7
-	**General Refractories** 85 off white + coal Sp Edn (TAG Models) - *02*	4	5
-	**GE** 7748 grey (Chalk marks - 'Prent. Bros 2227') Sp Edn 62 (Stowmarket Railway Club) - *03*	4	5
-	**GE** 7748 dark brown (Chalk marks - 'Prent. Bros 2227') Sp Edn 62 (Stowmarket Railway Club) - *03*	4	5
-	**Hatton's** light grey Sp Edn (Hattons) - *88*	10	15
-	**Hingley** 14 dark brown + coal Sp Edn 100 (Modellers Mecca) - *01*	6	NA
-	**Huxford & Co** 153 red + coal Sp Edn 564 (Hythe Kent Models) - *01*	4	6
-	**Isaiah Gadd** 29 dark grey Sp Edn 150 (Loddon Vale Club + WWWW) - *03*	5	7
-	**IWC** 117 black + coal Sp Edn 100 (I of W Model Railways) ex set - *01*	4	NA
-	**IWC** 68 grey + coal Sp Edn 100 (I of W Model Railways) - *01*	4	NA
-	**IWR** 29 brown + coal Sp Edn 200 (I of W Model Railways) - *02*	4	NA
-	**James MacPherson** Sp Edn (Strathspey Railway) - *03?*	6	8
-	**James Taylor** Sp Edn (Cotswold Steam Preservation Ltd) - *03?*	5	7
-	**Kent & East Sussex Rly** * grey + coal Sp Edn 215 (Hythe Models) - *02*	4	6
-	**LNER** Loco Sand Sp Edn (Stowmarket Railway Club) - *03?*	5	7
-	A T **Locke** 4 red-brown + coal Sp Edn 110 (Astolat MRC) - *03*	6	8
-	**Mid Suffolk** 16 grey Sp Edn 100 (Mid-Suffolk Light Railway) - *02*	5	7
-	**Mid Suffolk** 17 grey Sp Edn 100 (Mid-Suffolk Light Railway) - *02*	5	7
-	**Mid Suffolk** 17 dark brown Sp Edn (Mid-Suffolk Light Railway) - *02*	5	7
-	**Moira** 467 red brown + coal Sp Edn 500 (Tutbury Jinny) - *00*	6	8
-	**Nathaniel Pegg** 155 red Ltd Edn 210 (Hythe Models) - *02*	6	8
-	**Newcastle Main** 415 grey + coal Sp Edn 500 (G Allison) - *99*	4	6
-	**Newcastle Main** 415 brown + coal Sp Edn 12 (G Allison) - *99*	10	15
-	**Old Radnor Co**. 159 Sp Edn (Hereford Model Centre) - *?*	6	8
-	**Old Radnor Co**. 238 Sp Edn (Hereford Model Centre) - *?*	6	8
-	J. L. L. **Peate** 1 brown Sp Edn (Welshpool	5	7

& Llanfair Railway) - *02*

-	**Pilchard Collard** * light grey + coal Sp Edn 324 (Hythe Models) - *01*	4	6
-	**Poppitt Sands** 712 deep cream + sand Sp Edn 121 (Teifi Valley Railway) - *02*	5	7
-	**Poppitt Sands** 711 deep cream + sand Sp Edn 121 (Teifi Valley Railway) - *03*	5	7
-	**Scatter Rock** Sp Edn (The Model Shop Exeter) - *03?*	5	7
-	**Settle Speakman** Sp Edn (Haslington Models) - *00*	6	8
-	**Spaldings** 52 light grey + coal Sp Edn 200 (Tutbury Jinny) - *02*	4	NA
-	**Vectis** 34 grey Sp Edn 200 (I of W Model Railways) - *03?*	4	NA
-	**Vectis Cement Co**. 68 grey + chalk Sp Edn 200 (I of W Model Railways) - *02*	4	NA
-	L.**Williams & Son** 1 cream Sp Edn 50 (Barry & Penarth MRC) - *03*	4	6

* These were delivered unnumbered and were individually numbered by Steve Skelton of Hythe (Kent) Models. ** Produced to celebrate the 150th anniversary of Wolverton Railway Works. *** A spelling error and the wagons were sold abroad in sets.

7-plank special for Mevagissy [W9]

W9. 7-Plank Open Wagon (ex-Airfix)

This table includes models made from the Airfix tool or from a replica tool produced in China for Dapol. We have no record as to which models were done with which tool but one of the almost identical tools was sold to Hornby in 1996. Almost without exception, the models in this table were sold with a coal (or other) load infill.

A3	brown or grey - unfinished - *86-03*	4	6
B6	**LMS** 609525 red brown - *84-92*	4	6
B12	**NE** 17519 grey - *84-89*	4	6
B14	**GW** (thick) 06515 dark grey - *95-01?*	4	6
B14	**GW** (thin) 29019 dark grey - *95-01?*	4	6
B43	**Gloucester Gas Light** 51 black (A) - *85-88*	5	10
B44	**Hales Fuels** 241 grey (A) - *85-88*	4	8
B82	**Parkinson** 100 dark blue - *?-99*	4	6
B89	**David Jones** 650 red brown (M) - *86*	5	8
B89	**David Jones** 650 red brown - *95-02*	5	6
B94	**Brentnall & Cleland** 3000 black (M) - *86-02*	5	8
B101	**S J Claye** Ltd 825 red - *86-99*	4	6
B103	**Thrutchley** 2212 red - *86-92, 96-02*	4	6
B111	**LMS** 602604 grey - *89-?*	4	6
B111	**LMS** 602508 grey - *?-99*	4	6
B122	**Carlton** 4372 black (A) - *?*	5	10
B165	**Stalybridge** 15 brown (A) - *?*	5	10
B167	**Colman's** 35 yellow - *91-99*	4	6
B169	**Courtaulds** 18 green - *90-01*	4	6
B170	**Emlyn** 811 olive green - *90-02*	4	6
B171	**Bass** 56 light grey - *90-02*	4	6
B174	**Cambrian** 107 black - *89-02*	4	6
B175	**Broadoak** 460 brown (A) - *89-?*	4	8
B175	**Broadoak** 406 brown - *?-01*	4	6
B176	**Highley Mining** 425 brown (A) - *89-?*	4	8
B176	**Highley Mining** 245 brown - *?-02*	4	6
B178	**Dapol** black Sp Edn (Dapol) - *c89*	10	15
B181	**Coal Agencies** 42 black - *89-02*	4	6
B182	**Halls Swadlincote** 711 brown - *89,95*	4	6

Ref	Description		
B186	**Cory Bros** 9644 black - *91-02*	4	6
B190	**Huddersfield Co-op** 14 dark grey - *90*	4	6
B192	**Wm Evans** 174 black - *90-02*	4	6
B195	**Sutton Manor** 1075 light grey - *90,95-02*	4	6
B200	**Hendy Merthyr** 1862 brown - *91-92*	4	6
B205	**SR** 37427 dark brown - *94-95*	4	6
B265	**Normans Super Warehouse** brown - *97-98*	4	6
B316	**Blue Circle** 173 yellow - *00-03*	4	6
B318	**Sheepbridge** 6091 red - *00-02*	4	6
B319	**Chatterley-Whitfield** 1822 grey - *00-02*	4	6
B320	**Evans & Bevan** 386 grey - *01-02*	4	6
B321	**Polmaise** A260 red-brown - *01-02*	4	6
B322	**John G Boreland & Peat** 317 pale grey - *01-02*	4	6
B323	**Brightmore** 113 grey - *01-02*	4	6
B324	**Darton** 145 red - *01-02*	4	6
B325	**Phorpes Bricks** 988 black - *01-02*	4	6
B328	**SR** 37423 dark brown - *01-03*	4	6
B331	**Old Silkstone** 2401 bright red - *01-02*	4	6
B332	**Redgrave** 1386 grey - *01-02*	4	6
B333	**Rhymney** 1927 grey - *01-02*	4	6
B334	**Hartnell** 22 black - *01-03*	4	6
B335	**Dunkerton** 1117 grey - *01-02*	4	6
B337	**LMS** 602504 light grey - *01-03*	4	6
B348	**GW** 06512 grey - *01-03*	4	6
B351	**Miller & Lilley** 66 black - *01-03*	4	6
B356	**NE Loco** HB4333 grey - *01-02*	4	6
B359	**Glynea & Castle** 191 brown - *01-02*	4	6
B360	**Charles Roberts** 1910 brown - *01-02*	4	6
B361	**Sharlston** 1420 brown - *01-02*	4	6
B362	**Marlborough** 4 dark grey - *01-02*	4	6
B363	**Nicholsons** 1 dark grey - *01-02*	4	6
B367	**Hickleton** 3166 brown - *02-03*	4	6
B368	**R.Taylor** 451 brown - *02-03*	4	6
B370	**Summers** 69 black - *02-03*	4	6
B371	**John J Tims** 413 brown - *02-03*	4	6
B374	**Lewis** 0196 black - *02-03*	4	6
B374A	**Lewis** 0199 black - *02-03*	4	6
B375	**Ammanford** 24 - dark brown - *02-03*	4	6
B375A	**Ammanford** 48 - dark brown - *02-03*	4	6
B377A	**Black Park** Ruabon 329 brown - *02-03*	4	NA
B377B	**Black Park** Chirk 2021 red-brown - *02-03*	4	NA
B377	above 2 wagons in a twin pack - *02-03*	NA	12
B380	**Ilkeston & Heanor Water Board** 14 blue-grey - *02-03*	4	6
B384	**Collins Green** 417 brown - *02-03*	4	6
B390	**Lawley** 391 grey - *02-03*	4	6
B394	**Manton** 891 brown - *02-03*	4	6
B395	**Norstand** 376 maroon - *02-03*	4	6
B396	**Steam Trawlers Coal & Trading Co** 71 brown - *02-03*	4	6
B514	**Dearne Valley** 61 bright blue - *03*	4	6
B516	**United Collieries** 1506 black - *03*	4	6
B516	**United Collieries** 1506 dark grey - *03*	4	6
B519	**Beaumont** 665 red-brown - *03*	4	6
B520	**HG Smith** 24 red - *03*	4	6
B521	**Blidworth** 2323 grey - *03*	4	6
(B522)	**R Webster & Sons** 302 maroon - *03*	4	NA
B524	**Berthlwyd** 966 black - *03*	4	6
B525	**Macclesfield** 10 red - *03*	4	6
B529	**C H Taylor** 3 grey - *03*	4	6
B535	**Fred Hardisty** 2 brown - *03*	4	6
B536	**Crosfields' Perfection Soap** 84 red - *03*	4	6
B539	**Eccleshall Industrial & Provident Society Ltd** 4 dark brown - *03*	4	6
B540	**Rix & Groom** 21 red - *03*	4	6
B541	**Gortac** 29 yellow - *03*	4	6
B542	**John Heaton** 101 grey - *03*	4	6
B545	**Dinington Main** 641 grey blue - *03*	4	6
B546	**Asquith & Tompkins** 21 red - *03*	4	6
B550	**Carpenter & Son** 4 maroon - *03*	4	6
B552	**Renwick, Wilton & Co** 521 maroon - *03*	4	6
B553	**A Munday** 6 maroon - *03*	4	6
B554	**Wright's** 14 brown - *03*	4	6
B555	**Hockaday & Co** 4 black - *03*	4	6
B557	**Humber** 100 red - *03*	4	6
B558	**Old Roundwood Collieries** 312 mrn - *03*	4	6
B565	**Oldham Corporation Gas** 019 maroon - *03*	4	6
B566	**Bullcroft** red - *04*	5	6
B568	**BR** grey - *04*	5	6
B570	**Macclesfield Co-op** 41 brown - *04*	5	6
B571	**J.Potts** - *04*	5	6
B572	**F.H.Silvey** 205 light grey - *04*	5	6
B574	**S.J.Baverstock** black - *04*	5	6
B575	**H.Blandford** 7 light grey - *04*	5	6
B576	**South Wales** 20 grey - *04*	5	6
B581	**Gedling** 2598 red - *04*	5	6
B587	**E.Turner** blue grey - *04*	5	6
B589	**Kinneil** 118 red - *04*	5	6
B594	**Small & Son** blue grey - *04*	5	6
B596	**Western Valleys** 670 dark brown - *04*	5	6
B598	**Wigan Coal & Iron** A147 grey - *04*	5	6
B599	**Mold Collieries** blue grey - *04*	5	6
B603	**CT** Bamfurlong & Mains 1462 red - *04*	5	6
B604	**S.Taylor, Firth** 731 red - *04*	5	6
B608	**Webbs' Coals** black - *04*	5	6
-	**Aberbeeg Colliery** dark grey Sp Edn (South Wales Coalfield) - *04*	5	7
-	**Aberdare Graig** Coal 2 red Sp Edn 100 (David Dacey) - *03*	5	7
-	**Aberpergwm** Sp Edn (Roger Mileman) - *03?*	5	7
-	**Annesley** 162 brown, Sp Edn 100 (The Model Centre) - *03*	5	7
-	**Annesley** 173 brown, Sp Edn 100 (The Model Centre) - *03*	5	7
-	**Annesley** 195 brown, Sp Edn 100 (The Model Centre) - *03*	5	7
-	Wm. **Aplin** 2 black Sp Edn 120 (W.Wales Wgn Wks) - *03*	5	7
-	Wm. **Aplin** 5 black Sp Edn 110 (West Wales Wagon Works) - *03*	5	7
-	**Archd Bathgate & Sons** 201 brown, Sp Edn 100 (The Model Centre) - *03*	5	7
-	**Archd Bathgate & Sons** 205 brown, Sp Edn 100 (The Model Centre) - *03*	5	7
-	**Archd Bathgate & Sons** 211 brown, Sp Edn 100 (The Model Centre) - *03*	5	7
-	**Astley Green Colliery** 245 red-brown 'M' Sp Edn (Astley Green Mining Museum) - *03*	4	6
-	**Astley Green Colliery** 229 'M' Sp Edn (Astley Green Mining Museum) - *03*	4	6
-	**Astley Green Colliery** 337 'M' Sp Edn (Astley Green Mining Museum) - *03?*	4	6
-	**Atkinson & Prickett** Sp Edn (D.Hewins) - *03?*	5	7
-	**Atkinson & Prickett** (overprinted BR 1516) Sp Edn (D.Hewins) - *03?*	5	7
-	**Avan Hill** Sp Edn (Jenny's) - *03?*	5	7
-	Ed **Bannister** 1500 grey Sp Edn 100 (D Hewins) - *00*	6	8
-	**Barrow** 623 red Sp Edn 120 (Midlander) - *01*	6	8
-	**Barrow of Barnsley** buff Sp Edn 117 (Modellers Mecca) - *02*	5	7
-	**Barrow Barnsley** buff Sp Edn (Midlander) - *03*	5	7
-	**Barry Coal Coy**. black Sp Edn 120 (Barry & Penarth MRC) - *04*	4	6
-	**Barry Rhondda** 148 black, Sp Edn 130 (South Wales Coalfields) - *03*	5	7
-	**Bass** 56 light grey, Sp Edn 188 (Tutbury Jinny) ex 2 wagon pack - *02*	6	NA
-	**Betteshanger** * black Sp Edn (Hythe Models) 1st run Snowdon - *00*	4	6
-	**Betteshanger** * black Sp Edn (Hythe Models) 2nd run Chislet & Tilmanstone - *02?*	4	6
-	John T **Bingham & Co** 10 black Sp Edn	5	7

Item		
(Ballards) - 03		
Wm **Black** Sp Edn (Ayr Glass & Glazing) - 03?	4	6
Blackwell 1836 red brown Sp Edn 130 (Midlander) - 01	6	8
Blackwell 1298 red-brown Sp Edn 115 (Midlander) - 02	6	8
Blaenavon Sp Edn (Pontypool & Blaenavon Railway) - 03?	5	7
Blaen-Graigola 29 red Sp Edn 100 (David Dacey) - 03	5	7
Bliss Tweed Mills 6 green Sp Edn 159 (Banbury MR Show + WWWW) - 03	6	8
Bowes Railway Sp Edn (Bowes Railway) - 03?	4	6
Bradford & Sons 1 red Sp Edn 100 (Buffers) - 03	5	6
Bradford & Sons 2 Sp Edn (Buffers) - 03?	5	6
Burnyeat, Brown & Co Ltd 335 black Sp Edn (Lord & Butler Model Railways) ex double pack. - 02	5	NA
Burton-on-Trent Co-op 11 dark red Sp Edn 200 (Tutbury Jinny) - 01	6	8
F. W. **Butcher** 3 dull green Sp Edn (Ballards) - 02	5	7
Butterley 2322 red brown Sp Edn 102 (Midlander) - 00	6	8
Butterley 01702 grey Sp Edn 105 (Midlander) - 00	6	8
Butterley 5513 grey Sp Edn 130 (Midlander) - 01	6	8
Camerton Collieries 175 black Sp Edn 125 (E.Somerset Models) - 02	6	NA
Camerton Collieries 199 black Sp Edn 125 (E.Somerset Models) - 03	6	NA
Cannock Rugley 648 grey+red Sp Edn 200 (Tutbury Jinny) - 01	6	NA
Cardigan Mercantile Co 18 black Sp Edn (West Wales Wagon Works) - 04	5	7
Charles Bazzard & Son 192 Sp Edn 151 (West Wales Wagon Works) - 03	5	7
Chislet * black Sp Edn 440 (Hythe Models) - 01	6	8
CIE 412 grey Sp Edn (Mark's Models) - ?	6	8
City of Birmingham 1747 black Sp Edn 140 (Midlander) - 01	6	8
Clay Cross 1254 red brown Sp Edn 140 (Midlander) - 00	6	8
Clemant's Tump 2 black Sp Edn 250 (RD Whyborn) - ?	6	8
Clifton & Kersley Coal 2224 red Sp Edn 337 (Red Rose Team Soc.) - 03	5	6
Coleford Red Ash 6 black Sp Edn (RD Whyborn) - ?	8	12
as above but red (error)	NPG	NPG
Coventry Collieries 334 black Sp Edn 143 (Midlander) - 01	6	8
Crane & Company 107 bright red Sp Edn 185 (Wales & West Assn MRCs) - 04	5	6
Crawshay Bros 1120 grey Sp Edn 100 (David Dacey) - 03	5	7
Cribbwr Fawr Collieries Sp Edn (David Dacey) - 03	5	7
W. **Crocker** 2 red-brown Sp Edn (Hampton Court MRS) - 02	6	8
Crystalate 1262 yellow Sp Edn (Ballards) - 04	6	8
Cwmaman 501 black, Sp Edn 130 (South Wales Coalfields) - 03	5	7
Cwmtillery Sp Edn (Pontypool & Blaenavon Railway) - 03	5	7
Cynon Sp Edn (Jenny's) - 03?	5	7
Dalmellington Iron 351 red Sp Edn	4	6
(Ayrshire Railway Pres Group) - ?		
Dapol Virgin Pendolino white Sp Edn (Virgin) - 01	6	8
Darkhill & Elwood 50 black Sp Edn (RD Whyborn) - ?	6	8
Davies Brothers black Sp Edn 120 (Barry & Penarth MRC) - 04	4	6
Deltic Preservation Society 1977-1997 black Sp Edn (DPS) - 97	8	12
as above but blue Sp Edn (DPS) - 97	8	12
Doncaster New Royal Infirmary 3 Sp Edn 1,020 (BRM Magazine) - 02	4	6
Doncaster Works Sp Edn (Wabtec Ltd) - 03	4	6
Duffryn Rhondda Co. Sp Edn (Jenny's) - 03?	5	7
East Cannock 4016 black Sp Edn 200 (Tutbury Jinny) - 02	6	NA
Eastern Valleys Sp Edn (Pontypool & Blaenavon Railway) - 03?	5	7
ED 675 red brown Sp Edn 100 (Modellers Mecca) - 01	6	NA
Edward Eastwood Sp Edn (Midlander) - 03	6	8
WH **Edwards** 10,18,25 brown Sp Edn (TMC) - 04	6	8
Elders Steam Navigation 466 black Sp Edn 250 (RD Whyborn) - ?	6	8
G&G **Ellis** * blue Sp Edn 100 (Hythe Models 30th Anniversary) - 01	4	6
Elsecar 771 red Sp Edn 130 (Midlander) - 01	6	8
JH & E **Essen** 4 brown Sp Edn 250 (E1 Promotionals) - 04	6	8
Evans, Adlard & Co No.1 black Sp Edn 2000 (Glos & Warks Railway) - 00	6	8
Eveson 348 red-brown Sp Edn (Midlander) - 03	5	7
Fountain & Burnley Ltd 104 red brown Sp Edn 120 (Midlander) - 02	6	8
Foxfield Colliery 2 red-brown Sp Edn (Alsager Toys & Models) - 02	5	7
Frank Lomas 2 pale grey Sp Edn 500 (Peak Rail Stock Fund) - 04	5	7
G&KERy 67 dark grey Sp Edn 150 (Toys2Save) - 03	5	7
Gann & Brown * grey-blue Sp Edn 220 (Hythe Kent Models) - 01	4	6
GE 5043 grey Sp Edn 200 (Mid-Suffolk Light Railway) - 03	5	7
Gellyonen Collieries pale grey Sp Edn 100 (David Dacey) - 03	6	8
General Refractories Sp Edn (TAG Models) - 03?	5	7
Gilwen Sp Edn (David Dacey) - 03	5	7
Glyncoed 162 brown, Sp Edn 130 (South Wales Coalfields) - 03	5	7
Glyncorrwg Colliries Ltd 276 black Sp Edn (Jenny's) - 02	6	8
WT **Goolden & Co** (uniquely numbered 1-77) dark red Ltd Edn 77 (Oliver Leetham) - 03	5	7
Goldethorpe 2744 red brown Sp Edn 122 (Midlander) - 01	6	8
Granville 227 grey Sp Edn 200 (Tutbury Jinny) - 02	4	NA
Grassmoor 940 black Sp Edn 115 (Midlander) - 03	6	8
Platelayers * black Sp Edn (Great British Train Show, Ontario) - 02	4	6
Great Grimsby Coal Salt 1180 black Sp Edn 100 (D Hewins) - 00	5	7
Great Treverbyn 48 red brown + chalk Sp Edn (Railtronics) ex-set - 01-02	6	NA
Great Western Society green Sp Edn (GWS) - ?	10	15

	Item		
-	A.E.**Griffiths** 35 grey, choice of 5 loads*** Ltd Edn 96 (O Needham) - *02*	6	8
-	**Guest, Keen & Nettlefolds** 0747 black, Sp Edn 151 (South Wales Coalfields) - *03*	5	7
-	**Hall's** 1401 black Sp Edn 132 (Midlander) - *01*	6	8
-	**Harecastle** 55 brown Sp Edn 200 (Tutbury Jinny) - *03*	5	7
-	**Harris & Co** Sp Edn (Antics) - *?*	5	7
-	**Hatton's** brown Sp Edn (Hattons) - *?*	6	8
-	**Hauton Main Colliery** Sp Edn (Midlander) - *03?*	5	7
-	T A **Hawkins** 271 red brown Sp Edn 200 (Tutbury Jinny) - *01*	6	NA
-	**Helston Gas Company** 30 Sp Edn (Kernow MRC) - *03?*	5	7
-	**Helston Gas Company** 10 Sp Edn (Kernow MRC) - *03?*	5	7
-	**Herbert Hall** 111 maroon Sp Edn 200 (Modellers Mecca) ex set - *02*	5	NA
-	**Hertingfordbury** 1 buff Sp Edn 100 (Great Eastern Railway Society) - *03?*	6	8
-	The **High Brooms** red Sp Edn 300 (Ballards) - *01*	6	8
-	**Holly Bank** 62 brown Sp Edn 200 (Modellers Mecca) ex set - *02*	5	NA
-	**Houghton Main** 2029 red-brown Sp Edn 120 (Modellers Mecca) - *02*	5	7
-	**Houghton Main** 2029 red-brown Sp Edn (The Midlander) - *03*	6	8
-	**Howes Models** 1 blue Sp Edn 110 (Howes Models) - *02*	5	7
-	Wm **Hubbard** 30 black, Sp Edn 294 (Teifi Valley Railway) - *02*	5	7
-	**International Colliery** French Anthrecite dark red Sp Edn (South Wales Coalfield) - *04*	5	7
-	**Isiah Gadd** Sp Edn 159 (W.Wales Wagon Works for Loddon Vale Railway Club) - *04*	6	8
-	**Itshide** 265 black Sp Edn (Ballards) - *03*	5	7
-	James Oaks & Co Sp Edn (Haslington Models) - *03?*	6	8
-	John **Lancaster** & Co Sp Edn (Pontypool & Blaenavon Railway) - *03*	5	7
-	**Lachlan Grant** Sp Edn (Strathspey)	6	8
-	**Leadbeter** grey Sp Edn 120 (Barry & Penarth MRC) - *04*	5	7
-	**Lewis' Merthyr Navigation** Ltd 768 black Sp Edn (Lord & Butler Model Railways) ex double pack - *02*	5	NA
-	**Lightmoor** 263 grey, Sp Edn 200+ (Geoff Osborn) - *99*	5	7
-	Henry **Lodge** 214 red Sp Edn 159 (Midlander) - *01*	6	8
-	**Longbottom & Co** 703 brown, Sp Edn 100 (The Model Centre) - *03*	5	7
-	**Longbottom & Co** 716 brown, Sp Edn 100 (The Model Centre) - *03*	5	7
-	**Longbottom & Co** 728 brown, Sp Edn 100 (The Model Centre) - *03*	5	7
-	**Lydney** Sp Edn (Dean Sidings) - *?*	5	7
-	**Lysaght's** Sp Edn (Scunthorpe District MRS) - *03?*	5	7
-	**Manchester Collieries** 8692 brown, Sp Edn 100 (The Model Centre) - *03*	5	7
-	**Manchester Collieries** 8743 brown, Sp Edn 100 (The Model Centre) - *03*	5	7
-	**Manchester Collieries** 8785 brown, Sp Edn 100 (The Model Centre) - *03*	5	7
-	**Main** 568 black, Sp Edn 100 (South Wales Coalfields) - *03*	5	7
-	**Manvers Main** 3044 red brown Sp Edn (Midlander) - *02*	6	8
-	**Manx Tails** brown, Ltd Edn - *03*	NPG	NPG
-	**Martin Bros** 28 brown + chalk Sp Edn (Railtronics) ex-set - *01-02*	6	NA
-	**Mathew Grist** Sp Edn (Antics) - *?*	5	NA
-	**Measham** 1305 black Sp Edn 123 (Midlander) - *01*	6	8
-	**Medway Queen** Sp Edn (Richard Halton) - *03?*	6	8
-	**Mein, Wooding & Co** 250 black Sp Edn (Barry & Penarth MRC) - *03*	4	6
-	**Mid-Hants Rly** Sp Edn (Mid-Hants Railway) - *03?*	5	7
-	**Midland Coal, Coke & Iron** 5004 brown Ltd Edn 200 (Haslington Models) - *02*	6	8
-	W **Miles** Sp Edn (Antics) - *?*	5	7
-	**Monks Bar** 40th Anniversary Sp Edn (Monks Bar) - *03?*	5	7
-	**Moira Collieries** 1340 brown 300 Sp Edn (Tutbury Jinny) - *00*	6	8
-	**Mottramwood** 2021 red-brown Sp Edn (Midlander) - *03*	5	7
-	**Netherseal** 881 red brown Sp Edn 109 (Midlander) - *01*	6	8
-	**New Cwmgorse Colliery** 330 Sp Edn 200 (West Wales Wagon Works) - *03*	5	7
-	**New Cwmgorse Colliery** 42 dark brown Sp Edn 150 (West Wales Wagon Works) - *03*	5	7
-	**New Cwmgorse Colliery** 43 dark brown Sp Edn 150 (West Wales Wagon Works) - *03*	6	8
-	**New Hey Industrial** Sp Edn (Paul Devlin) - *?*	5	7
-	**New Medway** 19 brown Sp Edn (Medway Queen) - *03*	5	7
-	**New Medway** 19 black Sp Edn (Medway Queen) - *03*	5	7
-	F. J. **Newton** 37 grey Sp Edn 200 (Modellers Mecca) ex set - *02*	5	NA
-	**Norman's Warehouse Ltd** brown Sp Edn - *97-98*	4	6
-	**North Cornwall** 3 brown + chalk Sp Edn (Railtronics) ex-set - *01-02*	6	NA
-	**North & Rose** 19 brown + chalk Sp Edn (Railtronics) ex-set - *00-01*	6	NA
-	**North Norfolk Railway** brown Sp Edn (NNR) - *?*	6	8
-	**North Rhondda** Sp Edn (Jenny's) - *03?*	5	7
-	Norths Navigation Sp Edn 200 (MIB models) - *04*	5	7
-	**NYMR** 454491 grey Sp Edn (North Yorkshire Moors Railway) - *03*	6	8
-	**Norton & Biddulph** 3237 black Sp Edn 200 (Haslington Models) - *03*	10	15
-	**Norton & Co.** 176 black Sp Edn 300 (W.Wales Wagon Works) - *02-03*	5	7
-	**Notts & Derby** 3601 dark grey Sp Edn 195 (Sherwood Models) - *03*	5	7
-	**Notts & Derby** 3601 black Sp Edn (Sherwood Models) - *03*	5	7
-	**Nottingham Corporation Gas** 169 black Sp Edn 200 (Sherwood Models) - *02*	5	7
-	**Novis & Son** 1 red Sp Edn 1000 (Ballards) - *02*	5	7
-	**NRM** 2004 maroon Sp Edn 200 (TMC) - *04*	6	8
-	James Oakes & Co 772 black Sp Edn (Haslington Models) - *02*	5	7
-	GD **Owen** 16 dark pink + coal Sp Edn** 71 (West Wales Wagon Works) - *02-03*	5	7
-	**Parc-y-Bryn** 58 Sp Edn 250 (RD Whyborn) - *?*	6	8
-	**Parkhouse Colliery** 2993 brown Sp Edn 200 (Haslington Models) - *01*	6	8
-	**Parkyn & Peters** 35 red + chalk Sp Edn (Railtronics) ex-set - *00-01*	6	NA
-	**Pentrich** 1674 black Sp Edn 127 (Midlander) - *01*	6	8

-	John **Perry** 13 red-brown Sp Edn 345 (East Kent MRS) - 02	6	8
-	SJ **Phillips** 7 black Sp Edn 270 (West Wales Wagon Works) - 03	5	7
-	**Pilsley** 4437 red brown Sp Edn 120 (Midlander) - 01	6	8
-	**Platelayers** 2002 black Sp Edn 125 (Great British Train Show, Ontario) - 02	4	6
-	**Plymouth** Coal Sp Edn (Antics) - ?	5	7
-	**Pochin** 114 grey + chalk Sp Edn (Railtronics) ex-set - 00-01	6	NA
-	**Powell, Gwinnell & Co** 191 black Sp Edn 1000 (Cotswold Steam Preservation Society) - 02	5	6
-	**Primrose** 489 black, Sp Edn 110 (South Wales Coalfields) - 03	5	7
-	**Prince of Wales Collieries** 554 dark red Sp Edn 118 (Midlander) - 02	6	8
-	**Raunds CoOperative Society** blue Sp Edn (Kitmaster Club) - 03	6	8
-	**Rennishaw Park Collieries** red brown Sp Edn 118 (Midlander) - 01	6	8
-	**Ripponden Industrial Society** 10 black Sp Edn - ?	6	8
`	**Samuel Evers** 34 dark grey Sp Edn 200 2 (Modellers Mecca) ex set - 0	5	NA
-	**Samuel Llewellyn** 122 grey, Sp Edn 130 (South Wales Coalfields) - 03	5	7
-	**St Leger** 225th Aniviversary 86451 grey Sp Edn 225 (Leetham) Peco extension planks supplied - 01	5	7
-	**Sheffield & Eccleshall Co-operative Soc.** 13 red-brown Sp Edn (TAG Models) - 02	4	5
-	**Shipley** 1254 red brown Sp Edn 130 (Midlander) - 01	6	8
-	**Sleight** P201194 grey Sp Edn 50 (D Hewins) - 02	6	8
-	**Sleight** P201083 grey Sp Edn 50 (D Hewins) - 02	6	8
-	G H **Smith & Son (Fuel) Ltd** 24 black Sp Edn (Ballards) - 02	6	8
-	**Sneyd** 1414 red brown Sp Edn 104 (Midlander) - 01	6	8
-	**Snowdon** * grey Sp Edn 454 (Hythe Models) - 00	6	8
-	**South Crofty Mine** 26 blue Sp Edn (Blewetts of Hayle) - 02	6	8
-	**South Leicestershire** 2120 brown Sp Edn 200 (Tutbury Jinny) - 02	6	NA
-	**Southwold MRE** Sp Edn (Southwold MRC) - 03?	6	8
-	**South Yorkshire Chemical Works** 330 red-brown Sp Edn (Midlander) - 03	6	8
-	**Speechhouse** Sp Edn 250 (RD Whyborn) - ?	6	8
-	**Steamtown** black Sp Edn (Steamtown Museum Shop) - ?	6	8
-	**Stuart Coal Coy.** 95 dark brown Sp Edn 100 (Barry & Penarth MRC) - 03	4	6
-	GS **Sturgeon** 465 dark grey Sp Edn 330 (Ballards) - 01	6	8
-	**Swansea Navigation** 247 black Sp Edn 100 (David Darcey) - 03	5	7
-	**Swanwick** 551 red Sp Edn 137 (Midlander) - 01	6	8
-	**Teifi Valley** 1 dark green Sp Edn 108 (TVR) - 00	6	8
-	**Teifi Valley** 285 black Sp Edn 121 (TVR) - 01	6	8
-	**Teifi Valley** 28 black Sp Edn 97 (TVR) - 01	6	8
-	**Teifi Valley** 20 Sp Edn 91 (West Wales Wagon Works) - 03	6	8
-	**Ten Commandments** Sp Edn (Ten Commandments) - ?	6	8
-	**Tilmanstone** * brown Sp Edn 414 (Hythe Kent Models) - 00	6	8
-	**Tirpentwys** 121 Sp Edn (Pontypool & Blaenavon Railway) - 02	5	6
-	D **Thomas Lime** Sp Edn (David Dacey) - 03	5	7
-	**Tom Wright** 19 brown Sp Edn 500 (Peak Rail Stock Fund) - 03?	5	7
-	**Tonhir Maesteg** black Sp Edn (South Wales Coalfield) - 04	6	8
-	**Vartag** 312 black, Sp Edn 130 (South Wales Coalfields) - 03	5	7
-	**Victor Grey** 54 red, Sp Edn 130 (South Wales Coalfields) - 03	5	7
-	John **Vipond** 877 brown Sp Edn 100 (David Dacey) - 03	5	7
-	**Ward & Sons** 14 red Sp Edn (Ballards) - 02	5	7
-	**Warncliffe Woodmoor** 1540 red-brown Sp Edn (Midlander) - 03	6	8
-	**Warwick Coal** Ltd Sp Edn (Midlander) - 02	5	7
-	**Waterloo** 853 black, Sp Edn 100 (The Model Centre) - 03	5	7
-	**Waterloo** 932 black, Sp Edn 100 (The Model Centre) - 03	5	7
-	**Waterloo** 949 black, Sp Edn 100 (The Model Centre) - 03	5	7
-	**Wath Main** 1875 red brown Sp Edn 159 (Midlander) - 02	6	8
-	**West Goonbarrow** 28 grey + chalk Sp Edn (Railtronics) ex-set - 01-02	6	NA
-	**West of England** 126 light grey + chalk Sp Edn (Railtronics) ex-set - 00-01	6	NA
-	**Wharncliffe Woodmoor** 1540 red-brown Sp Edn (Midlander) - 02	5	7
-	**Whitstable Shipping** 21 dark grey Sp Edn 300 (EKMRS) - 01	6	8
-	**Whitstable Shipping** 22 dark brown Sp Edn 110 (EKMRS) - 02	6	8
-	**Whitwick Colliery** 1046 black Sp Edn 200 (Tutbury Jinny) - 02	6	NA
-	T L **Williams** 29 dark red Sp Edn 120 (Barry & Penarth MRC) - 03	6	8
-	W T **Williams** 6 brown Sp Edn (Hereford Model Centre) - ?	6	8
-	**Wimberry** Sp Edn (Dean Sidings) - ?	5	7
-	**Winchcombe Coal Co** 12 grey Sp Edn 1000 (Glous & Wark Railway) - 98	6	8
-	**Winchcombe Coal Co** 10 grey Sp Edn 1000 (Glous & Wark Railway) - 00	6	8
-	**Winchcombe Coal Co** 7 grey Sp Edn (Glous & Wark Railway) - 03?	6	8
-	**Windsor** black Sp Edn (South Wales Coalfield) - 04	6	8
-	**Ystradgynlais & Yniscedwyn** 779 black Sp Edn 100 (W Wales Wagon Wks) - not made	NA	NA

* These were delivered unnumbered and were individually numbered by Steve Skelton of Hythe (Kent) Models.   ** 200 were sold as solo models and the other 200 came in wagon sets.   *** The 5 loads are Dapol coal, real coal, crushed brick rubble, limestone and crystaline salt. Just 96 of each load were made.   **** These were individually numbered by W.Wales Wagon Works.   ***** 3 alternative numbers.

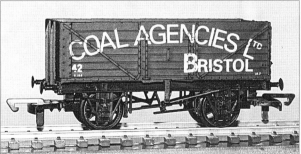

7-plank Coal Agencies [W9]

W10. 7-Plank Open Wagon (ex-Mainline)

B10	**BR** P99347 grey (M) - *84-96*	4	7
B14	**GW** 06515 dark grey (M) - *84-92*	4	7
B69	**CWS** Coal 1941 dark brown (M) - *85-89*	4	6
B70	**Perfection Soap** 82 red (M) - *85-92*	4	7
B80	**Horlicks** 1 brown (M) - *85-88*	4	7
B81	**NE Loco Coal** HB4333 grey (M) - *85-87*	4	6
B82	**Parkinson** 107 dark blue (M) - *85-?*	5	8
B166	**S.J.Moreland** 1 red+black (M) - *c89*	4	7
B167	**Colman's** 25 yellow (M) - *c89*	4	6
B168	**Persil** 258 dark green (M) - *c89*	4	6
B172	**Persil** 258 dark green (M) - *c89*	4	6
B169	**Courtaulds** 18 green (M) - *c89*	4	6
B170	**Emlyn** 813 grey (M) - *c89*	4	7
B171	**Bass** 65 grey (M) - *c89*	4	6
B172	**Patent Nut & Bolt** Co. 658 dark brown (M) - *c89*	4	7
B173	**Diamond** 34 red (M) - *c98*	4	7
B174	**Cambrian** 1078 black - *79-81*	4	7

Although S.J.Moreland, Colman's, Persil, Courtaulds, Emlyn, Bass, Patent Nut & Bolt Co., Diamond and Cambrian were illustrated in catalogues, we have found no evidence that any of them was sold in Dapol packaging although some were reissued using the Airfix body (see above).

Unidentified Wagons

The following were special edition open wagons but we do not know which body they had.

-	**Bartletts** Sp Edn (The Model Shop Exeter) - *03?*	5	7
-	**Elizabeth Meredith Jones** of Blaenau Ffestiniog Sp Edn (West Wales Wagon Works) - *04*	5	7
-	**Gresford Colliery** 638 Sp Edn (West Wales Wagon Works) - *04*	5	7
-	**Harlech Show** Sp Edn (West Wales Wagon Works) - *04*	5	7
-	**H O White** Sp Edn (West Wales Wagon Works) - *04*	5	7
-	**T Jenkerson & Sons** of Milford Haven Sp Edn (West Wales Wagon Works) - *04*	5	7
-	**Pudsey** Sp Edn (Children in Need + WWWW) - *03*	6	8
-	**Railtronics** + coal Sp Edn (Railtronocs) - *?*	6	8
-	**Richard Trevithick** 200 Sp Edn (West Wales Wagon Works) - *04*	5	7
-	**Square Wheels** Sp Edn (Square Wheels Ltd) - *03?*	6	8
-	**Thomas Thomas** Sp Edn 200 (West Wales Wagon Works) - *04*	5	7
-	**William Thomas** Sp Edn (West Wales Wagon Works) - *04*	5	7
-	**Ynys Amman** Sp Edn (West Wales Wagon Works) - *04*	5	7
-	**York Models** Sp Edn (York Model Railways) - *03*	5	7

W11. 9-Plank Coke Wagon (ex-Mainline)

B71	**Dinnington** 254 red brown (M) - *85-89*	5	8
B151	**MOY** 1851 red brown (M) - *c89*	4	7
B149	**TCD** 171 dark brown (M) - *c89*	4	7
B150	**Coalite** 552 dk.brown new chassis (M) - *c89*	5	7
B148	**Bedwas** 621 light grey (M) - *c89*	4	7
B155	**TWW** 1746 brown (M) - *c89*	4	7
B152	**Baldwin** 2030 black (M) - *c89*	4	7
B154	**Carpenter** 28 red (M) - *c89*	4	7
B153	**Arthur H.Stabler** 21 grey (M) - *c89*	4	7
B156	**CCC** 105 dark red (M) - *c89*	4	7

Although a number of other coke wagons were illustrated in catalogues we have found no evidence that any were sold in Dapol packaging.

W12. NE 20T 9-Plank Mineral Wagon (ex-Airfix)

A9	brown or grey - unfinished - *85-02*	4	6
B54	**Charringtons** 257 brown (M) - *85-88*	5	7

B55	**Gas Light & Coke** 794 grey (M) - *85-88*	5	8
B115	**BR** E10995, E30995 grey (A) - *86-?*	5	10
B115	**BR** E30996 grey - *?-02*	5	7
B114	**NE** 31273 grey (A) - *?*	5	10
B266	**NE** 31285 grey - *97-02*	5	7

The tooling was sold to Hornby in 1996 and the model reintroduced by them.

13T steel-sided wagon [W13]

W13. 13T Steel Sided Wagon

The former Hornby Dublo steel wagon body tool was lost and so Dapol had a copy made.

B236	**NTG** B486863 buff - *c95*	10	NPG
WR1-19	as above - *99*	10	15
WR2-17	as above Dapol chassis - *99*	10	12
B237	**BAC** 4253 red brown - *c95*	10	NPG
WR1-26	as above - *?*	10	15
WR3-06	**BAC** 4253 red brown - *98-02*	5	7
B238	**BR** B466865 brown - *c95*	10	NPG
WR1-50	as above - *99*	10	15
B354	**BR** Soda Ash B745543 grey + white load - *01-02*	4	6
B358	**BR** B490563 grey + coal - *01-03*	4	6
B364	**NCB** 30 grey + coal - *01-02*	4	6

W14. 16T Steel Mineral Wagon (ex-Mainline)

B27	**BR** B118301 grey (M) - *86*	4	6
B28	**ICI** 776 dark blue (M) - *86*	4	6
B73	**BR** B595150 red brown + coal (M) - *85-87*	4	6

16T steel mineral wagon [W15]

W15. 16T Steel Mineral Wagon (ex-HD/Wrenn)

B90	**Park Ward** 7 brown - *c95*	10	NPG
WR1-15	as above - *99*	10	18
B27	**BR** B54884 grey - *c95*	7	NPG
WR2-11	as above - *98-99*	7	8
WR2-10	**Shell** - *01*	8	10
B73	**BR** B54884 brown - *c95*	10	NPG
WR2-06	as above - *98-99*	10	20
B228	**GW** 110265 dark grey - *c95*	10	NPG
B229	**Esso** silver - *c95*	15	NPG
WR1-14	as above - *99*	15	20
B230	**Shell** silver - *c95*	8	NPG
WR2-10	as above - *98-99*	8	10
B346	**ICI** 268 blue grey + coal - *01*	4	6
B350	**GW** Loco 18810 grey + coal - *01-03*	4	6

B352	**BR** B54882 grey + coal - *01*	4	6
B353	**BR** B54884 brown + coal - *01*	4	6
WR2-11	as above - *01*	5	8
B398	**BR** 105530 grey Coal - *02*	4	6
B398A	**BR** 105534 grey Coal - *02*	4	6
B523	**BR** B480215? red-brown + coal - *03*	4	6
B559	**BR** B489177 red-brown Sand - *03*	4	6
-	**Virgin & Dapol** Pendolino red Sp Edn - *01*	5	7

W16. 20T Steel Mineral Wagon (ex-Airfix)

A5	brown - unfinished - *84-99*	5	7
B8	**BR** P339371K light grey (A) - *84-89*	4	8
B25	**GW Loco** 83516 grey (A) - *85-92, 97-98*	5	10
B25	**GW Loco** 83517 grey - *?*	5	7
B51	**Avon Tyres** 1 black (M) - *85-92, 97-99*	5	7
B52	**Glenhafod** 2277 black (M) - *85-92*	5	7
B53	**Blaenavon** 2441 red brown (M) - *85-94*	5	7
B53	**Blaenavon** 2441 red brown - *97-02*	5	7
B56	**Stewart & Lloyds** 3506 grey (M) - *85-89*	5	7
B83	**PJ&JP** 3619 black (M) - *85-02*	5	8
B95	**SC** 25503 dark grey (M) - *86-87*	5	8
B45	**SC** 25503 light grey-green - *c95*	5	7
-	**Teifi Valley Railway Gala** Extension Project Department - *04*	5	7

The tooling was sold to Hornby in 1996 and the model reintroduced by them.

20T steel mineral wagon PJ & JP [W16]

W17. 12T Hopper Wagon (ex-Mainline)

B68	**Hoare Bros** 101 black (M) - *85-02*	5	8
B72	**BR** Sand B436398 grey + sand (M) - *85*	5	8
B72	**BR** Sand B437319 grey + sand - *91-02*	4	6
B97	**BISC** 776 dark grey Iron Ore (M) - *86-88, 91-02*	4	6
B139	**Sheepbridge** 8251 red brown - *91-02*	4	6
B140	**BR** B435975 red brown (M) - *?*	4	6
B141	**BR** B433473 grey Ore Hop (M) - *91-02*	4	6
B142	**Cadbury Bournville** 156 blue (M) - *91-02*	5	7
B143	**Clay Cross** 72 red brown (M) - *?*	5	8

12T hopper wagon [W17]

W18. NE 21T Hopper Wagon (ex-Airfix)

A1	grey - unfinished - *84-99*	5	7
B1	**BR** E289595K light grey (A) - *84-88*	5	10
B1	**BR** E289592 light grey - *89-94*	5	7
B1	**BR** E289593K light grey - *89-94*	5	7
B59	**Norman Jackson** 10 black (M) *85-?*	5	8
B59	**Norman Jackson** 10 black - *?-99*	5	7
B60	**MOT** 1324 black (M) - *85-94*	5	7

B112	**NE** 193258 grey (M) - *88-99*	5	7
B113	**Charringtons** B421814K grey + orange (M) - *89-92*	5	7
B124	**House Coal Concentration** B429816K red brown (M) - *89-94*	5	7
B128	**BR** - ? - red brown - *?*	NPG	NPG
B201	**BR** B??6398 grey - *?*	NPG	NPG
B203	**G Weaver Transport** 152 brown - *94-00*	5	7
B207	**British Steel** 28 brown - *98-99*	5	7
B579	**British Gas** 142 red - *04*	5	6
B585	**BR** grey - *04*	5	6
B588	**MOT** black - *04*	5	6
B592	**NE** grey - *04*	5	6
B602	**British Steel** red - *04*	5	6
B606	**NCB** grey - *04*	5	6
-	**Meldon Quarry** Sp Edn (Dartmoor Railway) - *03?*	5	7
-	**North Norfolk Railway** grey Sp Edn 250 (NNR) - *?*	6	8
-	**Trago Mills Shopping Centre** grey Sp Edn 250 (Trago Mills) - *?*	6	8
-	**Trago Mills Shopping Centre** black Sp Edn 250 (Trago Mills) - *?*	6	8

The tooling was sold to Hornby in 1996 and the model reintroduced by them.

W19. 21T Hopper Wagon (ex-HD/Wrenn)

B187	**Hoveringham** red brown - *c95*	10	NPG
WR1-09	as above - *99*	10	15
B188	**Tarmac** M82 beige - *c95*	10	NPG
WR1-07	as above - *98-99*	10	15
B189	**Sykes** 7 light grey - *c95*	10	NPG
WR1-23	as above - *99*	10	45
B201	**British Steel** 28 brown - *c95*	25	NPG
B201	**British Gas** 142 dark grey - *c95*	15	NPG
WR1-44	as above - *99*	15	30
B202	**Weaver Transport** 152 brown - *c95*	50	NPG
WR1-48	**BR** B413021 dark grey - *99*	15	30

HBA hopper wagon [W20] (Dapol)

W20. HBA/HEA Hopper Wagon

This wagon was designed and tooled by Dapol.

B158	**BR** 360634 red brown HBA - *91-02*	6	8
B159	**BR** 360394 red+grey Railfreight HEA - *91-01*	6	8
B159	**BR** 361874 red+grey HEA - *not made*	NA	NA

The tooling was sold to Hornby in 1996 and the model reintroduced by them.

W21. 20T Grain Hopper Wagon (ex-HD/Wrenn)

B251	**BR** B885040 light grey - *c95*	10	NPG
WR1-49	as above - *99*	10	15
B252	**Bass Charrington** 24 maroon - *c95*	10	NPG
WR1-42	as above - *99*	10	35
B254	**Kelloggs** B885040 grey - *c95*	10	NPG
B255	**Quaker Oats** red brown - *c95*	10	NPG
B502	**BR** B885044 grey - *02-03*	5	7
B502A	**BR** B885364 - grey - *02-03*	5	7
B503	**GW** grey Grano - *02-03*	5	7
B517	**SGD** 18 grey - *03*	5	7
B528	**GW** 42315 grey Grano - *03*	5	7
B534	**LMS** 701314 grey Bulk Grain - *03*	5	7
B548	**Bass Charrington** 9 brick red - *03*	5	7
B562	**LMS** 710351 red-brown Bulk Grain - *03*	5	7

Dapol 00

20T grain hopper wagon [W21]

W22a. Ore Wagon (ex-Wrenn)

B243	**Wm.Carter** 7 black - *c95*	10	NPG
WR1-41	as above - *99*	10	17
B249	**Clay Cross** black - *c95*	50	NPG
B250	**Southdown** 17 blue - *c95*	15	NPG
WR1-24	**Hinchley** blue - *99*	10	18
B593	**IBISC Iron Ore** dark grey - *04*	5	6
B605	**NCB** black - *04*	5	6
B607	**Sheepbridge Copal & Iron** brown - *04*	5	6

W22b. Presflo Cement Wagon (ex-HD/Wrenn)

B242	**Blue Circle** grey - *c95*	10	NPG
B244	**Tunnel Bulk** grey - *c95*	10	NPG
B245	**BR** Presflo 72 grey - *c95*	10	NPG
B246	**Cerebos Salt** orange - *c95*	15	NPG
B247	**RMC** 68 grey - *c95*	30	NPG
B248	**Bulk Cement** 52 orange - *c95*	10	NPG
B578	**Blue Circle** - grey - *04*	5	6
B582	**Cerebos Salt** red - *04*	5	6
B600	**ARC** AR12640 yellow - *04*	5	6
B601	**Tunnel Cement** grey - *04*	5	6

W23. Prestwin Silo Wagon (ex-HD/Wrenn)

B190	**BR** B873000 brown - *c95*	10	NPG
B191	**Fisons** B873000 brown - *c95*	10	NPG

W24. PCA Presflo V Tank (ex-Lima?)

B196	**BOC** 1066 very pale grey - *95-03*	6	8
B197	**Albright & Wilson** light blue - *95-03*	6	8
B198	**APCM** 9344 very pale grey - *95-03*	6	8

The tooling was sold to Hornby in 1996 and the model reintroduced by them.

W25. 12T Tank Wagon (ex-Mainline)

This tank was later made by Dapol from tools, almost identical to the Mainline version, which were made in China for Dapol and are now owned by Hornby. Both ex-Mainline and Dapol made versions are included here.

B32	**United Molasses** 128 red brown (M) - *85-86*	5	7
B32	**United Molasses** 128 red brown larger letters - *91-02*	5	7
B86	**Shell Electrical Oils** SM2202 brown (M) - *86*	5	8
B86	**Shell Electrical Oils** v. dark grey - *90-02*	5	7
B87	**LMS** Creosote 304592 grey (M) - *86*	5	8
B87	**LMS** Creosote 304592? grey - *90-02*	5	7
B130	**Royal Daylight** 1534 black (M) - *91-02*	5	7
B131	**BP** 5049 grey - *91-97*	5	7
B132	**National Benzol** 731 silver - *91-95*	5	7
B133	**Crossfield** 49 green grey - *91-02*	5	7
B134	**Esso** 3066 silver white spirit - *91-95*	5	7
B135	**Shell** 4492 silver - *91-95*	5	7
B136	**Benzole By-Products** 1 buff - *91-99*	5	7
B137	**ICI** 895 dark blue - *91-99*	5	7
B138	**Ronuk** 38 blue - *91-02*	5	7

The tooling was sold to Hornby in 1996 and the model reintroduced by them.

W25A. 12T Tank Wagon (ex-Wrenn)

B580	**Yorkshire & Lincolnshire** Tar Distillation Co 4 red brown - *04*	6	7
B583	**Anglo Persian Oil** Co red brown - *04*	6	7
B590	**United Nolasses** 13 brown - *04*	6	7
B597	**Barrow** red brown - *04*	6	7

W26. 20T Tank Wagon (ex-Airfix)

A13	unfinished - *98*	5	7
B20	**Shell** 2373 buff (A) - *?*	8	14
B21	**Shell** BP 3967 black (A) - *?*	6	12
B29	**ICI** 499 dark blue (M) - *85-?*	6	8
B29	**ICI** 400 dark blue - *?-87*	6	8
B85	**Crossfield** 15 dark green (M) - *86*	6	8
B85	**Crossfield** 15 green and no number on ends of tank - *97-99*	6	8
B106	**Rainford Tar Prods.** 1 black - *87-88*	6	8
B106	**Rainford Tar Prods.** 1 brown - *97-99*	6	8
B107	**Newcastle & Gateshead** 18 black - *87-88, 96-99*	6	8
B116	**United Molasses** 86 red brown - *88-89*	6	8

The tooling was sold to Hornby in 1996 and the model reintroduced by them.

W27. 6-Wheel Tank Wagon (ex-HD/Wrenn)

B214	**Co-op** 172 white - *c95*	40	NPG
B215	**Express Dairies** 50 blue - *c95*	25	NPG
B216	**Unigate** 220 white - *c95*	50	NPG
B217	**St Ivel Gold** white - *c95*	50	NPG
B218	**Milk Marketing Board** blue - *c95*	20	NPG
B219	**UD** white also W4657P - *c95*	15	NPG
B220	**Double Diamond** red brown - *c95*	20	NPG
B221	**Skol Lager** red brown - *c95*	20	NPG
B222	**Guinness** silver - *c95*	20	NPG

W28. Salt/Lime Van (ex-HD/Wrenn)

Originally sold as 'WR3' stock it was absorbed from the Wrenn range when G&R Wrenn was sold to Mordvale in 2001.

B223	**Jas. Colman** 15 pale green - *c95*	10	NPG
B224	**ICI** Bulk Salt 25 grey - *c95*	30	NPG
WR3-05	**ICI** Bulk Salt 25 grey - *98-02*	6	7
W5101	**ICI** Salt 25 white (body only) Sp Edn 70* (Wrenn RCC) WRCC5 - *01*	8	12
B225	**DCL** 87 grey - *c95*	10	NPG
WR3-04	**DCL** 87 grey - *98-02*	6	7
B226	**Saxa Salt** 248 lemon yellow - *c95*	10	NPG
B226	**Saxa Salt** 248 yellow - *00-01*	4	6
B505	**Saxa Salt** 248 yellow - *02-03*	4	6
WR3-01	**Saxa Salt** 248 yellow - *97-91*	6	7
W4665	**Saxa Salt** 25 white (body only) Sp Edn 70* (Wrenn RCC) WRCC4 - *01*	8	12
B308	**Chance & Hunt** 333, 33 maroon - *00-02*	4	6
B309	**Stubbs Salt** 37 red - *00-02*	4	6
B366	**Shaka Salt** 119 blue - *02-03*	4	6
-	**ICI** Fleetwood Salt 12 maroon Sp Edn 250 (Toys2Save) - *04*	6	8
-	**George Brown** 1 grey Sp Edn 100 (Modellers Mecca) - *01*	6	NA
-	**GD Owen** 12 dark pink + coal Sp Edn** 400 (West Wales Wagon Works) - *02-03*	6	8
-	**G&KERy** 15 grey Sp Edn 110 (Toys2Save) - *03*	4	6
-	**Llanharry Limestone & Gravel** Coy 33 crm Sp Edn 100 (Barry & Penarth MRC) - *03*	4	6
-	**Llanharry Limestone & Gravel** Coy 37 crm Sp Edn 100 (Barry & Penarth MRC) - *04*	4	6
-	**Llywernog Silver-Lead Mining Co** 160 grey (West Wales Wagon Works) - *04*	5	7
-	**New Explosives Co Ltd** 10 grey Sp Edn 100 (Stowmarket MRC) - *02*	5	7
-	**South Wales Portland Cement & Lime Co**. Ltd 115 grey Sp Edn 120 (Barry & Penarth MRC) - *03*	4	6
-	**South Wales Portland Cement & Lime Co**.	4	6

Ltd 110 grey Sp Edn (Barry & Penarth MRC) - *03*

| - | **St Matthews School** Tuck Shop Supplies 8 yellow Sp Edn 100 (St Matthews) - *03* | 7 | 10 |

* 125 of each body were produced but only about 70 of each were usable due to faults with the others. These were returned to the factory. ** 200 were sold as solo models and the other 200 came in wagon sets.

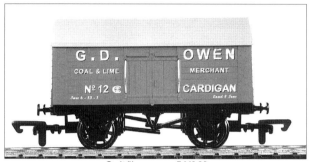

Salt/lime van [W28]

W29. Gunpowder Van (ex-HD/Wrenn)

This is a steel low sided van. Originally sold as 'WR3' stock it was absorbed into the Dapol range when G&R Wrenn was sold to Mordvale in 2001.

B207	**GW** W105780 black red X - *c95*	12	NPG
WR1-52	as above - *99*	12	15
WR2-01	as above (Dapol chassis) - *99*	8	10
B208	**BR** B887002 red brown - *c95*	10	NPG
B510	**BR** B887002 red brown - *02*	5	6
WR3-15	**BR** B887002 red brown - *99-01*	5	7
B209	**BSA** B887002 brown - *c95*	10	NPG
B210	**Standard Fireworks** B887002 brown - *c95*	12	NPG
B310	**LNWR** light grey - *00-02*	4	6
B311	**Ferrocrete** 167 -yellow - *00-03*	4	6
B312	**GW** 37985 dark grey - *00-03*	4	6
B315	**Blue Circle** 177 yellow - *00-03*	4	6
B329	**SR** 61204 dark brown - *01-03*	4	6
B330	**LSWR** 1379 red - *01-03*	4	6
B336	**LMS** 299031 light grey - *01-03*	4	6
B349	**BR** W105780 black red cross - *01-03*	4	6
B355	**NE** grey - *01-02*	4	6
B365	**Rugby** 13 black - *02-03*	4	6
B372	**Cambrian Railways** 139 black - *02-03*	4	6
B510	**BR** B887002 red-brown - *02-03*	4	6
B513	**2002 Golden Jubilee** 1952 purple - *02*	4	6
B513	**2002 Golden Jubilee** 1952 blue - *02*	4	6
B505	**Jubilee** 1952 blue, Union Jack Sp Edn 100 (Teifi Valley Railway) * - *01*	5	7
-	**Jiwbili** 2002 white, Welsh flag Sp Edn 111 (Teifi Valley Railway) * - *01*	5	7
B518	**NB** bright red gunpowder van - *03*	5	7
B518	**NB** bright red gunpowder van - *03*	5	7
B556	**Elterwater Gunpowder** 11 black - *03*	5	7
B573	**Spillers** Flour 175 white - *04*	5	6
-	**Cotton Powder Co. Ltd** var. nos. brown Sp Edn 303 (Hythe Models) - *02*	4	6
-	**Rialtronics** Sp Edn (Railtronics) - *?*	5	7
-	**Royal Leamington Spa** DB887499 grey Enparts van Sp Edn 200 (Classic Train & Motor Bus) - *02*	5	7
-	**Royal Leamington Spa** DB887499 faded blue Enparts van Sp Edn 50 (Classic Train & Motor Bus) - *04*	5	7
W5200	**Brock's Fireworks** B887008 black Sp Edn (Wrenn Collectors Club) WRCC8 - *02*	8	12
W4313P	**Standard Fireworks** B887007 light blue Sp Edn 100 (Wrenn Coll's Club) WRCC7 - *02*	8	12
W?	**Golden Jubilee** gold Sp Edn (Wrenn Collectors Club) WRCC10 - *03*	8	12
-	**R&D Models** 1977-2002 dark green Sp Edn	5	7

-	100 (R&D Models) - *02*		
-	**Trains, Models & Hobbies** white Sp Edn 108 (TM&H) - *01*	5	7
-	**Axminster Carpets** white 227? Sp Edn 200 (Buffers Model Railways) - *03*	4	6
-	**TMC** blue Sp Edn 180 (The Model Centre) - *03*	6	8
-	**BR** D887499 dark brown Sp Edn (Classic Train & Motor Bus) - *03?*	6	8
-	**BR** DB887499 light blue Enparts Sp Edn 50 (Classic Train & Motor Bus) - *03*	6	8
-	**Salvage** Sp Edn (Lord & Butler) - *03?*	5	7
-	**Platelayers** dark grey Sp Edn 125 (The Great British Train Show 2004) *04*	6	8

* See also boxed wagon sets (below).

W30. LMS Cattle Wagon (ex-Mainline)

| B157 | **BR** M12093 red brown - *?* | 4 | 6 |

W31. Cattle Wagon (ex-HD/Wrenn)

B47	**BR** B893344 red-brown - *c95*	10	NPG
WR1-04	as above - *98-99*	10	15
B58	**GW** 103240 grey - *c95*	10	NPG
WR1-03	as above - *97-99*	10	25
B500	**GW** 13813 grey - *02-03*	4	6
B501	**BR** B893344 red brown - *02-03*	4	6
B501A	**BR** B893369 red brown - *02-03*	4	6
B549	**GWR** 38659 grey Ale Wagon - *03*	4	6
-	**CIE** Sp Edn (Marks Models) - *03?*	5	7

W32. 8T Y10 GWR Fruit Van (ex-Wrenn)

This was the Hornby Dublo cattle wagon converted by Wrenn to a fruit van and represents one of 130 so converted by the GWR in 1939.

B211	**BR** B872181 grey - *c95*	15	NPG
WR1-33	as above - *99*	15	75
B212	**GW** 38200 grey - *c95*	NPG	NPG
B213	**BR** B872181 brown - *c95*	10	NPG
WR1-32	as above - *99*	10	20
B504	**GW** 38231 grey - *02-03*	4	6
B504A	**GW** 38218 grey - *02-03*	4	6
B584	**BR** brown Mex - *04*	5	7
-	**BR** W106133 red-brown Evesham Sp Edn 300 (Classic Train & Model Bus) - *03*	5	7

W33. BR Passenger Fruit Van (ex-HD/Wrenn)

| WR1-05 | **BR** W28720 blue - *98-99* | 10 | 22 |
| WR1-51 | **BR** B517112 grey - *99* | 30 | 60 |

W34. GWR 12T Goods Fruit Van (ex-Mainline)

This van has no plank effect on the sides and no protruding vents in the ends. Originally sold as 'WR3' stock it was absorbed from the Wrenn range when G&R Wrenn was sold to Mordvale in 2001.

B98	**BR** W134251 brown - Fruit - *91-02*	5	7
B261	**Fyffes** 1437 yellow - *?*	NPG	NPG
B81	**GW** 134149 grey - *89-03*	6	8

W35. 12T Banana Van (ex-HD/Wrenn)

This van has no plank effect on the sides and no protruding vents in the ends. Originally sold as 'WR3' stock it was absorbed from the Wrenn range when G&R Wrenn was sold to Mordvale in 2001.

B178	**BR** B881902 brown Banana - *?*	10	NPG
WR1-18	**BR** B881902 brown - *99*	10	35
B345	**BR** B881802 brown Banana - *01-03*	4	6
B561	**BR** B882117 brown Geest - *03*	4	6
B373	**BR** B784870 brown - *02-03*	4	6
B373A	**BR** B784879 brown - *02-03*	4	6
B385	**BR** B753479 grey - *not made*	NA	NA
B385	**BR** B753498 grey - *02-03*	4	6
B385A	**BR** B753487 grey - *02-03*	4	6
B182	**BR** Jaffa B881902 grey - *c95*	NPG	NPG
B379	**BR** Jaffa B881902 grey - *02-03*	4	6
W5105	**BR** Jaffa B881867 orange Sp Edn (Wrenn Collectors Club) WRCC6 - *02*	8	12
W?	**BR** Jaffa B881867 lemon yellow Sp Edn	8	12

	(Wrenn Collectors Club) WRCC9 - 02		
B180	**BR Fyffes** B881687 brown - 89-90	10	NPG
B264	**BR Fyffes** B881867 yellow (also B263) - c95	12	NPG
WR1-27	as above - 99	12	15
B381	**BR Fyffes** B881967 brown - 02-03	4	6
B511	**BR Fyffes** 881902 yellow - 02-03	4	6
WR3-18	**BR Fyffes** 881802 yellow - 00-01	5	7
B204	**BR Geest** B881902 grey - 94-95	10	NPG
WR1-28	as above - 99	10	50
B512	**BR Geest** B881967 grey - 02	4	6
WR3-19	**BR Geest** B881967 grey - 00-01	5	7
W?	**BR Geest** B881902 black (Body only) SP Edn 135 (Wrenn RCC) WRCC2 - 00	8	12
W5007A	**BR Geest** B881902 dark grey (body only) SP Edn 115 (Wrenn RCC) WRCC3 - 00	8	12
B263	**Tropical Fruit Co** M40 grey - ?	10	NPG
WR1-54	as above - 99	10	15
WR2-08	as above Dapol chassis - 98-99	8	10
B326	**SR** 41596 brown, dark grey roof - 01-02	6	8
B326	**SR** 41594 brown, light grey roof - 01-03	4	6
B357	**NE** 158677 light grey - 01-03	4	6

W36. GWR 12T Mogo Van (ex-Mainline)

This van has sides like the Mainline ventilated van but has end doors. It was made from duplicate tools which Hornby later bought.

B145	**BR** W105682 red-brown Mogo - 91-03	5	7
B146	**GW** 126342 grey Mogo - 91-03	4	6
B147	**Shepherd Neame** 3 cream (M) - ?	5	7

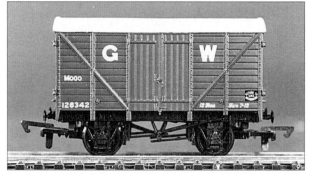

Mainline look-alike Mogo van [W36]

W37. LMS 12T Single Vent Sliding Door Van (ex-Mainline)

On the model the doors slide.

B7	**LMS** 511476 grey (M) - 84-99	4	7
B65	**ICI Salt** 2300 maroon (M) - 85-95	5	8

W38. LMS 12T Planked Single Vent Van (ex-Airfix)

On the model the doors are part of a single body moulding and so do not slide unlike those on an earlier Mainline model.

A6	grey unfinished - 84-03	4	6
B7	**LMS** 501636 grey - 84-85	5	7
B7	**LMS** 508587 grey (M) - 88-99	4	6
B9	**LMS** 511840 red brown - 84-88	4	6
B22	**BR** M501083? light grey (M) - 84-87	8	10
B61	**Tizer** 561772 yellow (A) - 85-88	6	12
B62	**Persil** 547921 green (A) - 85-92	6	12
B63	**BR** B753722, B751707 red brown (M) - 85-92	6	8
B64	**English Eggs** 506150 dark blue (A) - 85-87	8	14
B376	**English Eggs** deep blue - 02-03	4	6
B66	**Nestle's Milk** 531179 blue (A) - 85-87	6	12
B161	**Huntley & Palmer** 566327 green (A) - ?	6	12
B382	**LMS** 508587 light grey - 02-03	4	6
B382A	**LMS** 508579 light grey - 02-03	4	6
B386	**BR** M283328 grey - 02-03	4	6
B386A	**BR** M283331 grey - 02-03	4	6
B526	**LMS** 511240 grey, Egg Van - 03	4	6

B527	**LMS** 511246 grey, Fruit Van - 03	4	6
B532	**GW** 95444 grey Steam Banana - 03	4	6
B567	**LMS** brown - 04	5	6
-	**Bass** 23 light grey, Sp Edn 188 (Tutbury Jinny) ex 2 wagon pack - 02	6	NA
-	**Bass** 29 light grey, Sp Edn 200 (Tutbury Jinny) - 03	6	8
-	**Fremlin Bros** 1 white, grey roof Sp Edn (Ballards) - 02	6	8
-	**John Norton & Sons** * green Sp Edn 194 (Hythe Kent Models) - 01	6	8
-	**Trago Mills** yellow Sp Edn 250 (Trago Mills) - 89	6	8
-	same but blue Sp Edn 250 - 89	6	8
-	same but green Sp Edn 250 - 89	6	8
-	same but red Sp Edn 250 - 89	6	8
-	**Worthington** 3 brown, Sp Edn 200 (Tutbury Jinny) 03	6	8

* These were delivered unnumbered and were individually numbered by Steve Skelton of Hythe (Kent) Models.

W39. 12T Planked Single Vent Van (ex-HD/Wrenn)

This van is very like the Dapol single vent planked van in table W40 but has no bolt protruding downwards from the point where the doors join.

A11	grey - unfinished - 02-03	4	6
B235	**SR** 41596 dark brown - c95	10	NPG
WR1-61	as above - 99	10	15
WR2-09	as above but Dapol chassis - 98-99	8	10
WR1-18	**BR** B881902 brown - 02	30	35
WR1-35	**BR** 57 brown - 99	25	30
WR1-22	**BR** B545523 brown - 99	10	35
WR1-34	**BR** W145207 grey - 99	25	30
B317	**ICI Salt** 2653 red - 00-02	4	6
B339	**LMS** 511840 light grey - 01-02	4	6
B339	**LMS** 59673 red - ?	10	12
WR1-39	as above - 99	10	15
WR2-05	as above but Dapol chassis - 98-99	7	10
WR2-03	**Robertson's** 57 brown - 98-99	10	15
B389	**BR** B753889 grey - 02-03	4	6
B389A	**BR** B753896 grey - 02-03	4	6
B391	**BR** 760561 brown - 02-03	4	6
B391A	**BR** 760579 brown - 02-03	4	6
-	**CIE** 315 grey Sp Edn (Mark's Models) - ?	6	8
-	**John Norton** 9 dark green Sp Edn (Hythe Models) - 01?	6	8
-	**NYMR** NE133971 light grey Sp Edn ((North Yorkshire Moors Railway) - 01	6	8

W40. 12T Planked Single Vent Van

This wagon was designed and tooled by Dapol. It has one vent each end and has angled braces on the doors. The corner irons are also tapered and it differs from the HD/Wrenn vent van in table W39 in having a bolt protruding downwards from the point where the doors join. The tool was later sold to Hornby.

A11	? - unfinished - 98-99	4	6
B109	**BR** B760563 red brown - 88-99	4	6
B110	**BR** B753894 grey - 89-96	4	6

W41. 12T Plywood Single Vent Van

This wagon was designed and tooled by Dapol. It has no plank effect on the sides but has vents in the ends. It also has a raised data panel near the bottom left hand corner of the sides.

A10	brown or grey - unfinished - 95-03	4	6
B102	**BR** B784783 red brown - 86-99	4	6
B108	**BR** B753498 grey - 89-96	4	6
-	**Cathcart Railway Exhib.** 1968-1992 brown Sp Edn (Cathcart MRS) - 92	6	8
-	**Crewe Heritage Centre** grey Sp Edn (Crewe Centre Models) - ?	10	15
-	**North Norfolk Railway** brown Sp Edn (NNR) - ?	6	8

CHRISTIE'S

Bing for Bassett-Lowke
an example of the many rare pieces by the greatest makers sold at Christie's

Toy and Model Trains

Unrivalled experience and knowledge about toy and model trains
and free advice about buying and selling at auction

Enquiries
Hugo Marsh
hmarsh@christies.com
+44 (0)20 7752 3274

Catalogues
+44 (0)20 7389 2820

South Kensington
85 Old Brompton Road
London SW7 3LD

View catalogues
and leave bids online
at **christies.com**

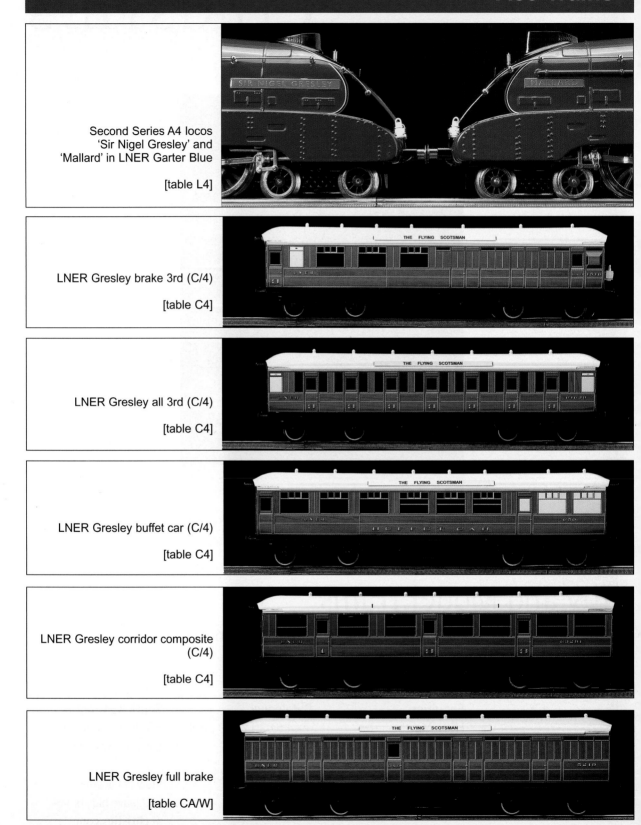

Second Series A4 locos
'Sir Nigel Gresley' and
'Mallard' in LNER Garter Blue

[table L4]

LNER Gresley brake 3rd (C/4)

[table C4]

LNER Gresley all 3rd (C/4)

[table C4]

LNER Gresley buffet car (C/4)

[table C4]

LNER Gresley corridor composite
(C/4)

[table C4]

LNER Gresley full brake

[table CA/W]

GAUGE '0' READY TO RUN

Ace Trains, PO Box 2985, London W11 2WP
telephone: 0207 727 1592 fax: 0207 792 4029
email: trainsW11@aol.com website: www.acetrains.com

acetrains

BR Class 61XX 2-6-2T 6167 (54151)   [table L3]

BR 4079 'Pendennis Castle' (54125)   [table L8]

LMS 6103 'Royal Scots Fusilier' (54120)

[table L7]

LMS Stanier non-corridor composite (45253)

[table C6]

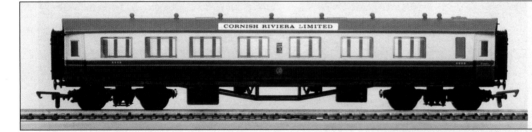

GWR Centenary composite (54207)

[table C4]

5-Plank - John Arnold & Sons (54376-1)   [table W3]

GWR Conflat + container (54331-8)   [table W2]

BR Class A1 60161 'North British' (32-553) [table L26]

BR Class 72 0-6-0T 69023 (31-051) [table L3]

BR Class 43XX 2-6-0 4377 (31-827A) [table L11]

Railfreight Class 37 37678 (32-379) [table L34]

Central Trains Class 170/6 170637 (32-460) [table L42b]

BR Class 04 D2228 (31-337B) [table L30]

Virgin Class 220 Pendolino 220001 (32-600) [table L43]

BR Class B1 61003 (31-708) [table L22]

Bachmann

BR(WR) Mk1 SO W4739 (39-054A)   [table C7b]

BR Mk1 BSK M35040 (39-075A)   [table C7c]

BR 60' Collett corridor composite W7021 (34-130)
[table C1d]

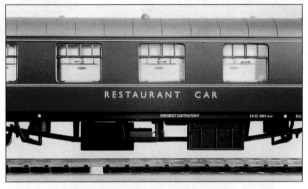

BR(LMR) Mk1 RFO M6 (39-251)   [table C7i]

BR(SR) SO S3998 (39-053) [table C7b]

BR(WR) Mk1 suburban brake 2nd W43102 (34-627)
[table C6b]

LNER
Thompson
BG 11
(34-655)

[table C4f]

RES
upgraded
Super BG
94451
(39-200A)

[table C7g]

GWR fruit van 134209 (37-751A)   [table W52]

8-Plank Boston Deep Sea Fishing (37-125)   [table W16]

BP small tank wagon 36 (37-665)   [table W45]

GWR Conflat + container (33-329)   [table W1b]

Mainline HEA with graffiti 360940 (33-556)   [table W35]

GWR 5-Plank china clay wagon 92873 (33-078)
[table W8b]

1-Plank Bath Stone Firms Ltd (33-405)   [table W3a]

3-Plank Evan Davies 25 (33-451A)   [table W5]

7-Plank coke wagon S.J.Claye Ltd 822 (37-175Z)
[table W15]

Bassett-Lowke

LMS Jubilee
5701
'Conqueror'

[table L68]

<small>Barry Potter
Auctions</small>

LNER 4-4-0
9405
'Glen Spean'

[table L42a]

LMS 2265
'Princess Elizabeth'

[table L32]

<small>Barry Potter
Auctions</small>

LMS
Fowler Class 4F
4072

[table 53]

<small>Barry Potter
Auctions</small>

LNER
Class J39
1448

[table L54]

LNER A1 Class
103
'Flying Scotsman'

[table L80]

<small>Barry Potter
Auctions</small>

LNWR brake 3rd 13312 by Bing   [table C1a]

LNWR full brake 13312 by Bing   [table C1a]

LNWR
1st/3rd
13212
by Bing

[table C1a]

LNWR
brake 3rd
1921
by Bing

[table C3]

LNWR
full brake
1334
by Bing

[table C3]

Bond's and Bowman

Bond's LMS 0-6-0T Jinty 7118   [table L3]

Bond's LMS Ex-CR 0-4-4T 15201   [table L5]

Bond's LMS 6200 'The Princess Royal'   [table L5]

Bowman
LNER brake van

[table W2]

PHOTO:
CHRIS ELLIS

GWR 5090 'Neath Abbey' (D6) [table L16]

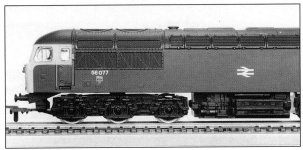

BR Class 56 56077 (D12) [table L28]

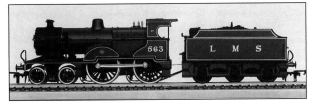

LMS Class 2P 563 (D17) [table L10]

BR Class 14XX 1438 (D96) [table L2]

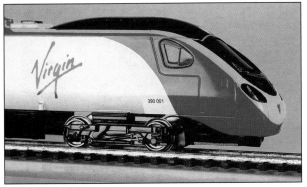

Virgin Class 390 Pendolino 390001 'Virgin Pioneer'
[table L33]

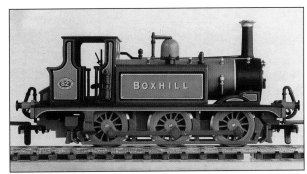

LBSC Terrier tank 82 'Boxhill' (D100)
[table L6]

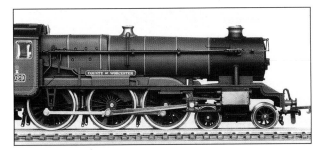

GWR County Class 1029 'County of Worcester' (D3)
[table L17]

LNER Class J94 0-6-0ST 8049
[table L5]

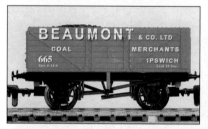

A selection from the vast range of 7-plank wagons produced by Dapol in recent years.

LMS
suburban brake 3rd
2681

[table C2]

GWR
suburban brake 3rd
6661

[table C2]

LNER
side corridor 3rd
8000

[table C17]

GWR
full brake corridor
1120

[table C14]

LNER suburban 1st/3rd 223   [table C1]

LMS suburban brake 3rd 271   [table C1]

SR Portsmouth EMU 3080   [table L2]

SR suburban EMU 3074   [table L2]

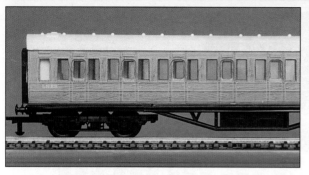

LNER mainline composite 75674 (10622)   [table C7]

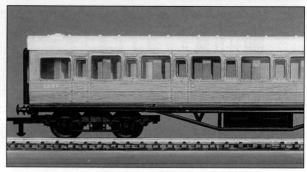

LNER mainline composite 75674 corridor side (10622)
[table C7]

5-Plank A.Sharpe   [table W13]   PHOTO: CHRIS DIXON

LNER brake van 157691 (13022)   [table W18]

Single vent van Terry's (12314)   [table W16]

7-Plank J.R.Wood & Co. (12116)   [table W13]

BR
Golden Arrow
34090
'Sir Eustace
Missenden'

[table L6]

BR Class 08 'Thomas 1' (1006)   [table L24]

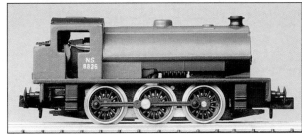

NS Class Austerity 0-6-0ST 8826 (101B)   [table L8]

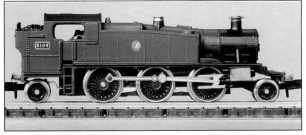

GWR Class 61XX 6104 (1603)   [table L9]

BR Class 57XX 0-6-0PT 7777 (1115)   [table L5]

SR freelance 0-6-0T 2579 (1703)   [table L3]

EWS Class 47 47744 (802C)

[table L32]

BR Class 40 40106 'Atlantic Conveyor' (8114)

[table L30]

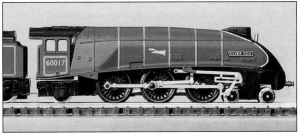

BR Class A4 60017 'Silver Fox' (18611)   [table L19]

BR Class 8F 48331 (1905)

[table L23]

BR BB Class 34089 '602 Squadron' (1515)

[table L22]

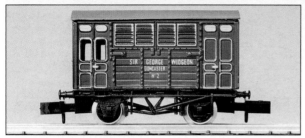

Horse box Sir George Widgeon (2711)   [table W20]

Caib PCA Cerestar PR10017 (4212)   [table W16]

Shell/BP Tar tank (2813)   [table W18]

PGA British Industrial Sand BIS 7842 (4511) [table W14]

PGA Yeoman PR14435 (4412)   [table W13]

Presflo Cerebos Salt (3513)   [table W11]

GWR steel mineral wagon 110134 (2204)   [table W9]

7-Plank British Railway Modelling   [table W7]

7-Plank Barrow Barnsley   [table W7]

7-Plank Gray Brothers   [table W7]

BR Class 37
D6607
'Ben Cruachan'
(317-156)

[table L26]

BR Class 37
37417
'Highland
Region'
(317-155)

[table L26]

Regional
Railways
Class 37
37429
'Eisteddfod
Genedlaethol'
(317-154)

[table L26]

EWS
Class 37
37419
(317-153)

[table L26]

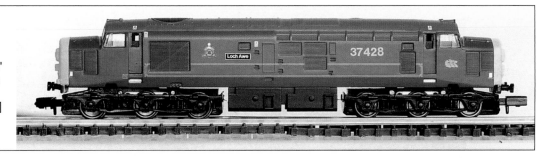

Class 37
37428
'Loch Awe'
(317-151)

[table L26]

Graham-Farish by Bachmann

Regional Railways Mk1 BG E92058 (374-031)

[table C3b]

RES Mk1 BG 92322 (374-032)   [table C3b]

Virgin Mk2E BSO 9516 (374-675)   [table C5a]

7-Plank Flower & Sons Ltd (373-177)   [table W2]

7-Plank Kobo (373-176)   [table W2]

PGA Railease PR14466 (373-036)   [table W10]

PCA Tunnel Cement RLS10321 (373-001)   [table W12]

InterCity Mk1 RMB 1832 (374-103)

[table C3e]

BR Class A4
60030
'Golden Fleece'
(2211)

[table L7]

BR Class AL1
E3002
(2245)

[table L15]

BR Class 4MT
2-6-4T
80033
(2218)

[table L4]

BR
WC Class
34005
'Barnstaple'
(2235)

[table L8]

BR Duchess
46245
'City of London'
(2226)

[table L6]

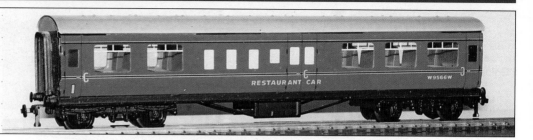

BR(WR)
restaurant car
W9566W
(4049)

[table C2]

BR(LMR)
Mk1 open 1st
M3002
(4062)

[table C6]

BR(ER)
Mk1 full brake
E81312
(4075)

[table C9]

BR(LMR)
Mk1 suburban
composite
M41012
(4083)

[table C10]

BR(LMR)
Mk1 Stove
M32958
(4076)

[table C11]

SR 5-plank coal wagon 19260 (32025)   [table W1]

BR cable wagon Liverpool Cables (32086)   [table W12]

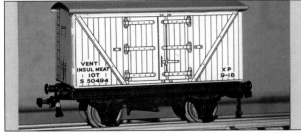

BR(SR) meat van S50494 (32065)   [table W5]

Power Ethyl small tank (32080)   [table W4]

BR(LMR) high-sided wagon M608344 (32030)   [W2]

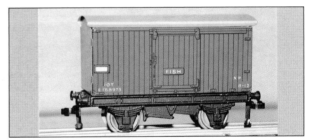

BR(ER) horse box E2337 (32060)   [table W5]

GWR cattle wagon 106324 (32020)   [table W5]

LMS meat van 19631 (32060)   [table W5]

Esso small tank wagon (32081)   [table W4]

LNER horse box 2337 (32060)   [table W5]

24a

W42. GWR 12T Planked Double Vent Van
(ex-Mainline)

This van has two vents at each end and no angled braces on the doors. Duplicate tools were made in China. One set was sold to Hornby in 1996 and the model reintroduced by them.

B4	**LMS** 521202 red brown - *84-88*	4	6
B92	**BR** W141826 red brown (M?) - *86, 91-02*	4	6
B93	**BR** W133971 grey (M?) - *86-02*	4	6
B144	**GW** 123507 grey - *91-03*	5	7
-	**Shepherd Neame** 3 cream Sp Edn 400 (East Kent MRS) - *02*	6	9
TMCD 001	**CLA Game Fair** green Sp Edn 137 (TMC) - *03*	6	8

W43. SR 12T Double Vent Box Van (ex-Airfix)

This van has an elliptically curved roof, the sharpest curves being just above the sides. For B17, two sizes of 'SR' may be found. It is thought that the tooling was sold to Hornby in 1996.

A7	grey - brown roof, unfinished - *84-02*	4	6
B15	**GW** 144886 dark grey - *84-95*	4	6
B16	**BR** S44437 grey (A) - *84-92*	5	10
B17	**SR** 273843 dark brown - *84-?*	4	6
B17	**SR** 44393 dark brown - *?-94*	4	6
B327	**SR** 273840 dark brown - *01-02*	4	6

W44. CCT Utility Van (ex-HD/Wrenn)

B340	**BR** S2514S blue - *01-03*	8	12
B341	**Southern** S2279S green - *01-03*	8	12
B342	**BR** M527071 red - *01-03*	8	12
B388	**BR** S2380S green - *02-03*	8	12

W45. 10T Quadruple Vent Meat Van

This wagon was designed and tooled by Dapol and the body tool later sold to Hornby.

A14	red - unfinished - *98-03*	3	5
B26	**BR** B870074 red - *85-99*	4	6
B180	**BR** B681687? red brown - *89-90*	4	6

W46. 12T Mica B Refrigerator Van (ex-HD/Wrenn)

B231	**BR** 150721 grey Insulmeat - *c95*	NPG	NPG
B232	**BR** W145207 white Mica B - *c95*	15	NPG
B233	**GW** 59828 white Mica B - *c95*	10	NPG
B234	**Birds Eye** 312 blue - *c95*	10	NPG
WR1-12	**Young's** 78 white - *99*	10	15
WR1-13	W59850 plain green - *99*	25	35
WR2-07	**Eskimo** W59850 white - *98-99*	8	10

W47. Blue Spot Van (ex-HD/Wrenn)

Originally sold as 'WR3' stock it was absorbed from the Wrenn range when G&R Wrenn was sold to Mordvale in 2001.

B256	**BR** E87231 white Insulfish - *c95*	10	NPG
B507	**BR** E87232 white Blue Spot - *02-03*	5	7
WR3-09	**BR** E87232 white Blue Spot - *99-01*	5	7
B261	**BR** grey - *c95*	NPG	NPG
B259	**BRe** E87003 blue Red Star - *c95*	15	NPG
B508	**BRe** E87160 blue Red Star - *02*	5	7
WR3-10	**BRe** E87160 blue Red Star - *99-01*	5	7
B262	**BRe** E87003 blue Exp. Parcels - *c95*	15	NPG
B506	**BRe** E87160 blue Exp. Parcels - *02*	5	7
WR3-08	**BRe** E87160 blue Exp. Parcels - *99-01*	5	7
B260	**BRe** E67840 beige BRT - *c95*	10	NPG
WR1-06	as above - *98-99*	10	20
WR3-14	**BRe** E87539 ochre BRT - *00-02*	5	7
B258	**Ross** white - *c95*	10	NPG
B257	**North Sea Fish** E67840 blue - *c95*	10	NPG
B509	**North Sea Fish** E87642 white - *02-03*	5	7
B533	**BRe** E88005 blue Express Parcels NRV - *03*	5	7
B537	**BR** E75575 brown Van Fit - *03*	5	7
B538	**BR** E87486 light blue Insulvan - *03*	5	7
B564	**BR** E75575? brown Van Fit ballast cleaner van - *03*	5	7
WR3-11	**North Sea Fish** E87642 white - *00-01*	5	7
?	**Findus** E87232 white - *02*	5	7
WR3-12	**Findus** E87232 white - *00-02*	5	7

?	**Ross** E87234 white - *02*	5	7
WR3-13	**Ross** E87234 white - *00-02*	5	7
-	**BRe** ADB975419 red (Barrowhill Depot) Sp Edn 120 (O.Leetham) - *02*	6	8
-	**BR** ADB975418 yellow (Shirebrook Depot) Sp Edn 120 (O.Leetham) - *02*	6	8
-	**BR** M87793 red brown RBV barrier wagon Sp Edn 93 (O.Leetham) - *02*	6	9
-	**BR** E? ice blue with black lettering Sp Edn 70 (O.Leetham) - *02*	6	8
-	**BR** E? ice blue with white lettering Sp Edn 70 (O.Leetham) - *02*	6	8
-	**York Model Railway** 2004 light blue Sp Edn (YMR) - *03*	5	7
-	**Virgin Trains** red + silver Sp Edn 500 (Virgin for Crewe Open Day) - *03*	6	8

Blue Spot van [W47]

W48. GWR 20T Toad Brake Van (ex-Airfix)

B33	**BR** 114926 grey (A) - *85-02*	4	8
B104	**GW** 56835 grey Rhymney - *87-88*	5	7
B105	**GW** 114925 grey Saltney - *86-92*	5	7
B105	**GW** 114925? grey Saltney - *98-99*	5	7
B117	**GW** 68976 dark grey Park Royal - *88-89*	5	7

The tooling was sold to Hornby in 1996 and the model reintroduced by them.

W49. GWR 20T Brake Van (ex-Mainline)

B34	**BR** W68855 light grey (M) - *85-99*	5	7
B35	**BR** W68816 red brown (M) - *?*	5	7

W50a. LMS 20T Brake Van (ex-HD/Wrenn)

B2	**LMS** 730973 red brown - *84-97*	10	12
WR1-46	as above - *99*	10	15

W50b. LMS 20T Brake Van (ex-Airfix)

B5	**BR** M730836 grey - *84-86*	5	7
B5	**BR** M? grey - *97-98*	5	7
B123	**LMS** 730097 grey (A) - *92-95*	4	8
B127	**BR** 114875 brown + yellow (A) - *92-95*	5	10
B185	**BR** red brown - *94-95*	5	7

The tooling was sold to Hornby in 1996 and the model reintroduced by them.

W51a. Short Brake Van (ex-Mainline)

B31	**BR** E168064 grey (M) - *85-88*	4	6
B37	**NE** 182030 - red brown - *85-89*	4	6

W51b. LNER/Standard Brake Van (ex-Mainline)

B30	**BR** B951480 dark brown (M) - *85-88*	5	7
B36	**BR** B950880 grey (M) - *85-87*	5	7

W52a. LNER/Standard Brake Van (ex-HD/Wrenn)

This had a diecast chassis.

B30	**BR** B950350 red brown - *c95*	10	NPG
B36	**BR** B932103 grey - *c95*	15	NPG
WR1-47	as above - *99*	15	40
B206	**SR** 32831 dark brown - *c95*	10	NPG
WR1-01	as above - *97-99*	10	18

W52b. BR Standard Goods Brake Van

(short wheel base) (ex-HD/Wrenn)

This had a diecast chassis.

B31	**NE** 128105 grey - *c95*	10	NPG
WR1-02	as above - *97-99*	10	18

W53. GWR Macaw H Bogie Bolster (ex-Airfix)

A12	grey - unfinished - *98-99*	5	7
B88	**BR** W107364 grey - *86-92*	8	10

The tooling was sold to Hornby in 1996 and the model reintroduced by them.

W54. GWR Macaw B Bogie Bolster (ex-Mainline)

B75	**BR** W84921 grey + girder (M) - *85-87*	8	10
B125	**GW** 107291 dark grey Macaw B, (MS?) - *90-92*	8	10

W55. GWR Crocodile H Well Wagon (ex-Mainline)

B74	**GW** 41973 dark grey Crocodile H + marine boiler (M) - *85-88*	9	12

W56. GWR Siphon G Bogie Milk Van (ex-Airfix)

B78	**BR** W1478 maroon (A) - *85*	9	14
B78	**BR** W1457 maroon (M) - *85-86*	10	15
B78	**BR** W1452 maroon - *88-01*	10	15

The tooling was sold to Hornby in 1996 and the model reintroduced by them.

W57. GWR Siphon H Bogie Milk Van (ex-Airfix)

B76	**GW** 1435 brown - *85*	9	14
B76	**GW** 1437 brown (M) - *85-86*	10	15
B76	**GW** 1437 brown - *90-01*	10	15
B262	**GW** 1437 brown - *?*	NPG	NPG
B79	**BR** W1429 maroon (A) - *85-86*	9	14
B79	**BR** W1429 maroon - *88-02*	10	15

The tooling was sold to Hornby in 1996 and the model reintroduced by them.

W58. American Caboose (ex-Bachmann/Airfix)

B84	**Union Pacific** yellow - (A) - *85-88*	4	6

WAGON PACKS

In 1999, Dapol offered a range of wagon packs in an attempt to move some of the more stagnant items in their stock. They also had rather a large number of the GWR and BR Class 14XX locos and used up some of these in 'loco and wagon' packs which contained one of three versions of the loco, a BR liveried toad brake van and two other wagons.

P1. Wagon Packs

B400	**BR** toad, 7-plank B&C, BR plywood van, BR 9-plank mineral - *99-02*	NA	20
B401	**BR** toad, 7-plank Thrutchley , 10T BR meat, 20T Rainford Tar brown - *99-02*	NA	20
B402	**BR** toad, 7-plank Coal Agencies , 10T BR meat, NE 9-plank mineral - *99-02*	NA	20
B403	**BR** toad, 7-plank Broadoak , 10T BR meat, 20T Joseph Crosfield - *99-02*	NA	20
B404	**BR** toad, BR plywood van, 7-plank Emlyn, 20T Newcastle Gas - *99-02*	NA	20
B405	**BR** toad, 7-plank Emlyn, BR plywood van, BR + NE 9-plank minerals - *99-02*	NA	20
B409s	4 Welsh wagon set - *01-02*	NA	20
B522	**Webster** brown twin pack 7-plank 302 + 5-plank 303 - *03*	NA	15
-	5-plank **Spalding Colliery** + 7-plank **Granville** Ltd Edn (Tutbury Jinny) - *02*	NA	14
-	7-plank **Whitwick Colliery**+ 7-plank **South Leicester** Ltd Edn (Tutbury Jinny) - *02*	NA	14
-	7-plank **East Cannock** + 5-plank **Conduit** Ltd Edn (Tutbury Jinny) - *02*	NA	14
-	7-plank **Cannock Rugeley** + 7-plank **Hawkins** Ltd Edn (Tutbury Jinny) - *02*	NA	14
-	**Bass** 7-plank + van Ltd Edn 180 (Tutbury	NA	15

	Jinny) - *02*		
-	set of 4 x 7-plank - **Herbert Hall, F. J. Newton, Holly Bank, Samuel Evers** Sp Edn 200 (Modellers Mecca) - *02*	NA	20
-	set of 4 - **North & Rose, Parkyn & Peters, Pochin, West of England** Sp Edn (Railtronics) - *00-01*	NA	25
-	set of 4 - **Great Treverbyn, Martin Bros, North Cornwall, West Goonbarrow** Sp Edn (Railtronics) - *01-02*	NA	25
-	2 wagons - **Camerton Collieries** 175+199 black + coal Sp Edn 125 (East Somerset Models) - *02*	NA	14
-	**GD Owen** dk.red 7-plk and salt van Sp Edn 200 (West Wales Wagon Works) - *02-03*	NA	15
-	2 Mink vans - **Jubilee 1952** + **Jiwbili 2002** Sp Edn 50 (Teifi Valley Railway) - *01*	NA	15
-	**IWC** 117 + 68 Sp Edn 100 (I of W Model Railways) - *01*	NA	15
-	**IWR** + **Vectis Cement** Co Sp Edn 200 (I of W Model Railways) - *02*	NA	25
-	7-planks **Lewis' Merthyr Navigation** 768 + **Burnyeat, Brown & Co** 335 Sp Edn (Lord & Butler Model Railways) - *02*	NA	15
-	four 5-planks 2 x **English China Clays Lovering Pochin & Co** Ltd + 2 x **ECLP** Sp Edn (Mevagissey Model Railway) - *02*	NA	27
-	2 LMS style vent vans * **Worthington 3** brown + **Bass** 29 grey Sp Edn 200 (Tutbury Jinny) - *03*	NA	15

P2. Loco + Wagon Gift Sets

B406	**GWR** 14xx + toad + 2 wagons - *99-02*	NA	45
B407	as above but shirt button - *99-02*	NA	45
B408	as above but BR black tank - *99-02*	NA	45

SETS

Dapol sets went under the prefix 'F' in their catalogue numbering scheme and tended to be made up with surplus stock, including Airfix, Mainline and Dapol models (often mixed) in order to use up stock. In selling sets, like other companies, Dapol found it difficult to compete with Hornby whose name was familiar to first-time buyers. In 1983 there were just three sets but these rose to ten by 1987. While a few were added as more were dropped, the sets were not pushed very hard from this time on and were soon dropped from the advertising. If they did not sell well they are likely to become collectable in the future and prices are only now beginning to rise as Dapol becomes more collectable. Do not be surprised if you get offered little more than the value of their contents, for one. If this is the case, the best advice is to hang on to them and hope that their value will rise.

Exley 0

HISTORY

This firm is primarily known for its coaching stock in 00 and 0 gauge and was founded at Bradford by Edward Exley around 1922. Initially the products were locomotives, in live steam, clockwork and electrically powered, in gauges 0 and 1, which were made to order.

By the 1930s, 0 gauge coaches had joined the range of products, and both locos and coaches were available 'off the shelf' as well as to order. During this period the company started supplying Bassett-Lowke with models, including the range of 0 gauge coaches which the latter company sold as their 'scale range'! It should be remembered that this was in the days before current consumer legislation, and as we have seen elsewhere in this catalogue, Bassett-Lowke bought in much of their range of products from other manufacturers and sold them through their catalogues under their own name. At the same time a business relationship was formed with J S Beeson, Mills Bros., Leeds Model Company and others, with much cross fertilisation of products between the parties involved.

In the later 1930s, partly as a result of Vivien Boyd-Carpenter having joined the company, high quality 00 coaching stock was added to feed a growing market in this new scale.

During the Second World War, work turned to the war effort and scale model ships for naval recognition use were made. With the return of peace, the Company retooled in 1945 to produce their railway models again. The underframes and bogies of the early post war coaches were improved from those of the pre-war era, and around 1950 the tooling for the coach bodies was also upgraded to the style most commonly found today.

Edward Exley Ltd also produced industrial models to commissioned orders, which included charabancs, industrial installations, large diesel engines, etc., and continued to supply Bassett-Lowke with 'scale' coaches.

In the early post war years the sales department was in Worksop, Nottinghamshire, with Boyd-Carpenter running this part of the business, although the works were still in Bradford. By 1952, however, Edward Exley (Sales) Ltd had moved to Baslow in Derbyshire and Edward Exley had resigned as a Director of the Sales Company in July 1955 after a disagreement. However, Edward continued to manage the works in Bradford. Furthermore, the catalogue carried the statement 'This Company is not now a manufacturing undertaking'. Lists of coaches in 00 and 0 scale were issued by the factory but these were headed 'Exley of Bradford'.

Locomotives had continued to be available after the war, mainly to order, but in the late 1950s Edward Exley sold the loco construction part of the business to Stanley Beeson, who had made locos for a number of Exley clients. Coaches were listed until 1962 when there was a terrible fire on 24th June which destroyed the Bradford premises and most of the tools. At this point Edward Exley decided to retire. A note in the 1962-63 catalogue, reporting the fire, indicated the company's intention to rebuild the factory but it seems that this did not happen. At this same time Edward Exley Ltd became the sole suppliers of Milbro products which are covered elsewhere in this book.

The company at Baslow continued to offer coaches but discontinued the 00 gauge range as the manufacturing facility was lost in the fire. The 7mm models were listed as available until the death of Boyd-Carpenter in January 1995, but were being made to order by outside workers. It has to be said that quality of the coaches made after 1962, once a hallmark of the company name, was variable, and to the purist no true Exleys were made after the destruction of the Bradford factory.

After the death of Boyd-Carpenter, Edward Exley Ltd ceased trading at Baslow, and all the shares and remnants of the company were purchased by Quentin and Tricia Lucas from Fife. In the latter half of the 1990s they rebuilt the company, trading in original Exley models, carrying out restorations, and selling modern finescale 0 gauge kits, models and components. Quentin specialised in the 0 gauge Exley market, and Tricia in 00. They were a familiar sight at model railway exhibitions and at selected Train Fairs and Auctions, and operate a mail order service too. In January 1999 they moved the business to near Berwick-upon-Tweed, and not long after this wound up the company when they retired.

Dates - Only post-war coaches are listed here at present as more research is required on pre-war production. Approximate dates of availability (for guidance only) are given in the tables and none are given after the factory burnt down in 1962.

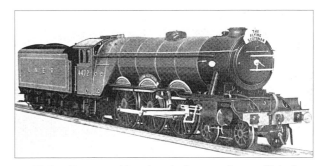

'Flying Scotsman' handmade for a customer (Exley)

LOCOMOTIVES

The majority of the Exley locomotives were hand-built, true to prototype and made to order. In the early days of the company many of them were built by Edward himself, this was his first love in the business, but by the 1930s many were built by employees in the factory, and by other contemporary builders such as Mills Bros. and Stanley Beeson. As a result of almost no records being kept, exact production details have been impossible to obtain.

Pre-war, the Exley catalogue listed the following locos as available in both 0 gauge and gauge 1: Royal Scot, LNER A3, LMS Compound, LNWR Hardwicke, LNER N2, LMS Prince of Wales, LNER 10000, LMS Princess Royal, GNR Single, GWR King, Caledonian 4-6-0, SR Lord Nelson, GWR 2-6-2T, GWR Castle, and a freelance steam 0-4-0 Saddle Tank. All of these were listed as stock items, and others were advertised as built to order.

Post-war catalogues show an LNER 'Flying Scotsman', a Southern 4-6-0 'Lord Nelson', a Southern Schools Class, a 36XX Class GWR 2-4-2T and a number of overseas locomotives for special purposes. Further known products were a NBR J35 and an LMS 2-6-4T. Catalogue illustrations post-war were usually of locos that had been supplied to customers, rather than an indication of what may be available from stock. As mentioned above, the locomotive building part of the Bradford business was sold to Stanley Beeson in the late 1950s.

Prices - It is difficult to assess the value of Exley locomotives as they are not often found for sale, nor are they easy to identify. They are very well crafted models with nicely finished detail but they rarely carry the makers mark and, when buying, one relies more on the provenance. The price for an Exley locomotive model is entirely dependent upon this as well as originality, condition, and the price the buyer and seller are prepared to negotiate. Naturally locos identified positively as 'Beeson for Exley' attract premium prices. The two prices shown represent the likely range for one in good condition.

Cat.No.	Company, Number, Colour, Dates	£	£

L1a. 0-4-0DS (Freelance)
This model had a square bonnet and radiator.

?	**LNER** 717 green - ?	150	200
?	**LMS** black - ?	150	200
?	private owner livery - ?	150	200

L1b. 0-4-0ST (Freelance)
This model had the same body as the above diesel shunter but different fittings to make it look like a steam engine and with outside cylinders.

?	**Newman Bros**. orange - ?	100	150

L2. Southern EMU (Exley for Bassett-Lowke)
These were sold as 2-car sets with 12V DC Bassett-Lowke motor bogies and B-L coach bogies. Although made for Bassett-Lowke, they were also sold by Exley. The motor and trailer cars of the Portsmouth set were 3rd class centre corridor brake ends suitably modified, and many were sold with normal SR corridor coaches in the middle, to create the image of the prototype train. A similar suburban set was made from two suburban coaches in the same way, again often with additional non corridor coaches added. The suburban set is much rarer than the Portsmouth set. Prices quoted should be adjusted where additional coaches have been added to the basic 2 car sets.

?	**Southern** green 3080(11157+11171) Portsmouth 2-car set - 53-60?	1100	1500
?	**LMS*** maroon - c55	1600	2200
?	**Southern** green 3064, 3074(3990+?), 2-car suburban set - 53-60?	1300	1700

* A very small number of the corridor EMUs were turned out to special order in LMS livery (thought to be less than 10 sets). This was entirely a fictional subject and did not represent any known LMS prototype EMU but, nevertheless, makes a fine looking set.

Portsmouth-Waterloo set [L3] (Christies)

L3. Miscellaneous Locomotives
MTO = made to order

?	0-6-0ST (freelance) private owner - ?	150	200
?	**GWR** 4-6-0 King Class green - ?	850	1300
?	**LMS** 4-4-0 Compound 1126 red - ?	400	600
?	**NBR** 848 0-6-0 Class J35 dark blue - ?	400	600

?	**LMS** 2-6-4T black - ?	500	700
?	**GCR/LNER** Class 04/05 ROD 2-8-0 5012, 5412 black - 30-50	670	750
-	**LMS** Patriot 4-6-0 5504 'Royal Signals' maroon MTO - 30-50	NPG	NPG
-	**LNER** A4 4498 'Sir Nigel Gresley' blue 3-rail 12V DC, brass, MTO - 57	2600	4300
-	**LNER** A1 2573 'Harvester' green 3-rail 12V DC, brass, MTO - 57	2700	4300
-	**Portsmouth** 2-car EMU set 331+313 green - ?	650	750
-	**LNER** Sentinel steam railcar 'Fair Maid' green+cream - ?	NPG	NPG

COACHES
Exley coaches were made from aluminium using a wrap-round technique so that roof, sides and solebars were one. This was attached to a wooden floor which pre and early post-war sat high inside the coach body, but from about 1950 sat just above solebar level.

Pre-war the ends were an alloy casting showing the end planking detail; bowed if the prototype was. They incorporated a cast lug which screwed to the underside of the floor. From around 1950, using a heavier alloy, the end castings were changed to a more modern pattern which was based on the LMS Stanier coach end. These were retained by copper wires cast into the end at solebar level. The heavier cast ends, with integral buffers also became plastic in the late 1950s.

The windows were glass, held in place by spring clips and should not be taken apart - unless by someone experienced in doing so.

Before the war, battery boxes were usually blocks of wood with little or no underframe detail. Post-war, pressed metal battery boxes were introduced, initially with an open bottom and an indication of truss rodding. Bogies were mounted on a central spigot bolted through the wooden floor.

These construction methods were modified with the introduction of the K5 and K6 series of the '50s. There has been much speculation about the significance of K5 and K6 but, suffice to say, the principal difference between them is that K5 and earlier coaches have painted on the glass window ventilators whereas K6, and the plastic range, have window ventilators stamped out from the metal of the coach side. However, this is not an infallible rule as many K5 coaches have stamped metal vents! K6 coaches, and K5 metal vents, do attract a price premium over those with painted vents. The K5 and K6 series also had different bogies but we have not distinguished between them here.

Apart from modified bogie fittings with the advent of the split pin, the underframes became more detailed and were an all metal construction. The bodies were lowered on the bogies so that no daylight showed underneath and material for the interiors changed in the late 1950s so that they now had coloured seats in metal. The final modification to the coaches themselves was the utilisation of plastic for coach ends, bogies and parts of the underframe, and they now carried the 'BFD EXLEY MODDEX' trade mark.

A variety of bogies have been used with Exley coaches over the years. Pre-war the Exley bogie had pressed steel and cast side frames. They had a central spigot socket and wire bracing and the axle ends were suspended on spring steel wire. Exley coaches sold by Bassett-Lowke were fitted with their range of bogies.

Post-war, Exley bogies developed to the familiar 'V' shaped central stretcher for split pin attachment. These had cast side frames and wire end stretchers, but still with spring steel wire support to the axle ends. Again, coaches sold by Bassett-Lowke were fitted with their post-war compensated bogie. Today, post-war coaches appearing on the market are about evenly divided between the 2 bogie types, and this has no effect upon value.

Quite a variety of coaches were made in the liveries of the big four railway companies and latterly in the crimson & cream and maroon BR colour schemes; although BR coaches generally are far less common. Available to special order were coaches for the pre-grouping companies and freelance concerns. The rare availability on the market of these specials makes it impossible to provide a realistic price guide for them, however, good to excellent examples have changed hands recently at prices between £500 and £1200 each, depending upon the livery they carried and their rarity.

The coaches made before 1940 tend to be more accurate to the prototype whereas after the introduction of the K5 series, which were largely based upon the LMS Stanier profile, it became a matter of changing livery, rainstrips and window positions.

Exley coaches are always impressive, run well and, in their day, were the leaders in their field. More recently, handbuilt scale coaches have overtaken Exleys for the finescale enthusiast, but they still have a major following amongst operators, as well as among collectors.

Prices - At this stage we cannot give a price guide to all the types of coach made but we have given an indication of value, of coaches manufactured after the 2nd World War. The values given refer to coaches in good to excellent condition. Those in poor, altered and well used condition are worth much less.

We apologise for the incompleteness of this section but much more research is required.

Cat.No.	Company, Nos., Type, Colour, Date	£	£

Post-War K5/K6

C1. Suburban 6-Wheel Coaches 31'

-	LMS all 3rd maroon - *54?*	250	350
-	LMS 271 brake 3rd maroon - *54?*	250	350
-	LMS 1st/3rd maroon - *54?*	250	350
-	LMS Brake Stove R maroon - *54?*	300	400
-	LNER 222 all 3rd teak - *54?*	250	350
-	LNER brake 3rd teak - *54?*	250	350
-	LNER 223 1st/3rd teak - *54?*	250	350
-	SR all 3rd green - *54?*	250	500
-	SR brake 3rd green - *54?*	250	500
-	SR 1st/3rd green - *54?*	250	500
-	GWR all 3rd dark brown+cream - *54?*	250	350
-	GWR brake 3rd dark brown+cream - *54?*	250	350
-	GWR 1st/3rd dark brown+cream - *54?*	250	350

C2. Suburban Brake 3rd 50'

-	GWR 6661 dark brown+cream - *50?-62*	250	350
-	LMS 2681 maroon - *50?-62*	250	350
-	LNER brown - *53?-62*	300	375
-	SR 3806, 3807, 4442 green - *50?-62*	400	650
-	BR maroon - *59?-62*	NPG	NPG

C3. Suburban 1st/3rd 50'

-	GWR dark brown+cream - *50?-62*	250	350
-	LMS 1620 maroon - *50?-62*	250	350

-	LNER brown - *53?-62*	300	375
-	SR 7632 green - *50?-62*	400	650
-	BR maroon - *59?-62*	NPG	NPG

LNER 6-wheel suburban coach [C1]

C4. Suburban Full 3rd 50'

-	GWR dark brown+cream - *50?-62*	250	350
-	LMS 19161, 20011 maroon - *50?-62*	250	350
-	LNER brown - *53?-62*	300	375
-	SR 1999 green - *50?-62*	400	650
-	BR maroon - *59?-62*	NPG	NPG

C5a. Restaurant Car Kitchen 1st 57'

-	LMS 45, 4203 maroon - *50?-62*	250	400
-	SR 6577 green - *50?-62*	450	900
-	BR red+cream - *61?-62*	500	600

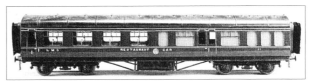

LMS restaurant kitchen car 1st [C5a]

C5b. Restaurant Car Kitchen 1st 69'

-	LMS 20 maroon - *?*	NPG	NPG

C6. Restaurant Car 1st/3rd Kitchen 57'

-	GWR choc+cream - *50?-62*	300	375

C7. Kitchen Car 50'

-	LMS 31221 37771 maroon - *50?-62*	325	400
-	LMS 30075, 30088 maroon - *50?-62*	325	470

C8. Buffet Car (with bar and pantry)

-	LMS maroon - *50?-62*	300	400
-	SR 1250, 1254 green - *50?-62*	450	900
-	LNER 21601 green+cream - *50?-62*	300	430
-	LNER 21602, 21603 green+cream - *50?-62*	300	380
-	BR maroon - *59?-62*	NPG	NPG

C9. Travelling Post Office 57'

-	GWR 818? dark brown+cream - *50?-62*	370	525
-	LMS 30220? maroon - *50?-62*	350	425
-	LNER 988 brown - *57?-62*	800	1000
-	BR red+cream - *58?*	500	575
-	BR maroon - *59?-62*	NPG	NPG

C10. Ocean Mails Van 57'

-	GWR 1196? dark brown+cream - *50?-62*	400	475
-	BR maroon - *59?-62*	NPG	NPG

C11. Parcels Train Brake Van 57'

-	GWR dark brown+cream - *50?-62*	300	350
-	BR maroon - *59?-62*	NPG	NPG

GWR Ocean Mails van [C10]

C12. Non-Gangwayed Full Brake 50'

-	**GWR** dark brown+cream - *50?-62*	250	325
-	**LMS** maroon - *50?-62*	250	300
-	**LNER** 303 brown - *53?-62*	250	350
-	**SR** 441 green - *53?-62*	350	650
-	**BR** crimson+cream - *58?-59?*	350	400
-	**BR** maroon - *59?-62*	NPG	NPG

C13. Parcels Train Non-Gangwayed 50'

-	**GWR** dark brown+cream - *57?-62*	300	350
-	**LMS** maroon - *50?-62*	250	300
-	**LNER** brown - *59?-62*	250	350
-	**SR** green - *50?-62*	350	650

C14. Corridor Full Brake 57'

-	**GWR** 224,1120 dark brown+cream - *50?-62*	325	350
-	**BR** maroon - *59?-62*	NPG	NPG

C15. Corridor Full Brake 50'

-	**LMS** 25 maroon - *50?-62*	250	300
-	**LNER** brown - *53?-62*	300	250
-	**SR** green - *50?-62*	350	650
-	**BR** red+cream - *58?*	375	450
-	**BR** maroon - *59?-62*	NPG	NPG

C16. Side Corridor 3rd Brake End 57'

-	**GWR** 5518? dark brown+cream - *50?-62*	250	300
-	**LMS** 3000, 6464, 6656 maroon - *50?-62*	300	350
-	**LNER** brown - *53?-62*	350	300
-	**SR** green - *50?-62*	375	650
-	**BR** red+cream - *57?-58?*	425	500
-	**BR** maroon - *59?-62*	350	400

C17. Side Corridor Full 3rd 57'

-	**GWR** 212, 3000 dark brown+cream - *50?-62*	250	300
-	**LMS** 1592 maroon - *50?-62*	250	300
-	**LNER** 8000, 8107 brown - *53?-62*	350	400
-	**SR** 5480?, 8000, 8400, 8673, 8883, 8888, 8672 green - *50?-6*	300	580
-	**BR** red+cream - *57?-58?*	425	500
-	**BR** maroon - *59?-62*	350	400

C18. Side Corridor Full 1st 57'

-	**GWR** dark brown+cream - *50?-62*	250	300
-	**LMS** 8777 maroon - *50?-62*	250	300
-	**LNER** 8004 brown - *53?-62*	350	380
-	**SR** 8531, 8771 green - *50?-62*	375	650
-	**BR** red+cream - *57?-58?*	475	550
-	**BR** maroon - *59?-62*	350	400

C18A. Side Corridor 1st/3rd Composite 57'

-	**LMS** 3032, 4440 maroon - *50?-62*	250	350

C19. Centre Corridor 3rd Brake End 57'

-	**LMS** maroon - *50?-62*	250	350
-	**LNER** green+cream - *53?-62*	475	550
-	**SR** green - *50?-62*	700	650
-	**BR** red+cream - *58?*	525	600
-	**BR** maroon - *59?-62*	350	400

C19A. Centre Corridor 1st Brake End 57'

-	**LMS** 3032, 8811 maroon - *50?-62*	250	350

C20. Centre Corridor Full 3rd 57'

-	**GWR** 2033? dark brown+cream - *50?-62*	300	380
-	**LMS** maroon - *50?-62*	250	350
-	**LNER** green+cream - *53?-62*	475	550
-	**SR** 6611 green - *50?-62*	400	680
-	**BR** red+cream - *58?*	525	600
-	**BR** maroon - *59?-62*	350	400

C21. Centre Corridor Full 1st 57'

-	**LMS** maroon - *50?-62*	250	350
-	**BR** maroon - *59?-62*	NPG	NPG

C22. Sleeping Car 1st/3rd 57' & 69'

-	**LMS** maroon 57' -*50?-62*	250	350
-	**LMS** 744, 3425 maroon 69' - *60?-62*	375	450

C23. Sleeping Car Full 1st

-	**GWR** 6560? dark brown+cream - *50?-62*	375	620
-	**LNER** 6461 brown - *57?-62*	350	430
-	**LNER** 6463 brown - *57?-62*	300	350
-	**BR** maroon - *59?-62*	NPG	NPG

C24. Sleeping Car Full 3rd

-	**GWR** dark brown+cream - *50?-62*	375	450
-	**LNER** brown - *57?-62*	350	425
-	**BR** maroon - *59?-62*	NPG	NPG

C25. Engineer's Inspection Saloon 50'

-	**LMS** maroon - *57?-62*	400	450
-	**BR** maroon - *59?-62*	NPG	NPG

LMS Engineer's inspection saloon [C25]

Other coaches in pre-grouping and private liveries were available to order.

K5 Series Coaches

C26. Side Corridor Composite

-	**BR** M3030M red+cream - *?*	500	650
-	**BR** M3044M red+cream - *?*	600	800
-	**BR** M3040M red+cream - *?*	400	455

C27. Side Corridor All-3rd

-	**BR** M3040M red+cream - *?*	400	500

C28. Side Corridor Brake 3rd

-	**BR** M6432M red+cream - *?*	450	600

C29. Side Corridor Brake Composite

-	**BR** M3344M red+cream - *?*	400	600

Fleischmann H0 (British)

HISTORY

The German model manufacturer decided to attempt a break into the UK market in 1977 and produced a model of a Warship diesel locomotive and three Bulleid coaches. This was a strange combination but apparently they could have been seen together when they ran out of Waterloo in the mid 1960s.

Unfortunately, Fleischmann produced their models in HO scale and not the slightly larger British 00 scale. As a result of this, the models did not sell well in Britain but in both liveries, and with their original catalogue numbers, they have remained in the Fleischmann catalogue and were still being advertised in the 2000/2001 German edition and on the Fleischmann website in 2004.

The locos and coaches were available separately and were not available in a set.

Included in the boxes of both locomotives were three alternative headboards. These were for Torbay Express, Cornish Riviera Express and The Mayflower.

An HO scale West Country locomotive was also planned in 1977. This was to have been 'Blackmore Vale' but, with sales of the Warship being so poor, the project was abandoned. The Bulleid coaches were produced to go with this model had it gone ahead.

Class 42 'Glory' [L1]

LOCOMOTIVES

Cat.No.	Number, Company, Colour, Dates	£	£
L1.	**Class 42 'Warship' Diesel-Hydraulic B-B**		
4247	**D818 'Glory'** BRe blue - 77-01?	50	110
4246	**D821 'Greyhound'** BRc green - 77-01?	50	110
L2.	**West Country 4-6-2**		
-	**'Blackmore Vale'** green - not made	NA	NA

Class 42 'Greyhound' [L1]

COACHES

These were based on BR built stock preserved on the Bluebell Railway in Sussex. The models had snap-in corridor end boards and a sheet of rub-down transfers representing 'set' numbers.

Cat.No.	Company, Number, Colour, Dates	£	£
C1a.	**Bulleid 1st/3rd Composite**		
5146	**BR** S5751S green - 77-01?	10	25

Bulleid 1st/3rd [C1a]

C1b.	**Bulleid Corridor 3rd**		
5147	**BR** S130S green - 77-01?	10	25

Bulleid 3rd [C1b]

C1c.	**Bulleid Open Brake 3rd**		
5148	**BR** S4279 green -	10	25

Bulleid brake 3rd [C1c]

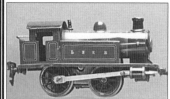   

Graham Farish 00

HISTORY

The Company was founded by Thomas Graham Farish in 1919, at the end of the Great War with a view to cashing in on the new interest in radio. In those days, if you wanted a wireless, you built your own and there was, therefore, a market for radio components. Remember, this was six years before the BBC came into being. Marconi, the radio pioneer, was a personal friend of Graham Farish.

The business was initially in Catford but in 1922 it moved to Masons Hill in Bromley, Kent. At its peak, the company was producing over 35,000 radio components per day. The boom lasted for about fifteen years before competition from off the shelf radio sets took away much of their business. The company gradually turned over to other products such as electric fires of which over 8,000,000 were made and it is interesting to note that two of the company's senior managers were Donald Morphy and Charles Richards who later left to form Morphy-Richards. The company developed the first successful submarine aerial and were one of the first to use the early type of plastic known as bakelite.

During the Second World War they made hand grenades, shell and land mine casings, electronic equipment and an important sideline was 'Snap Vacuum Closures'. These consisted of a tinned lid, a rubber sealing ring and a reusable clip and they were used for sealing glass jars for storing preserved fruit. These were particularly useful during the war and over 1,000,000,000 were made! Other items manufactured up to 1949 included water pumps for ornamental fountains, underwater lights, lightning conductors for buildings, metal flower baskets and, in 1949, the Plantoid plant food pellets! Much sought after today are 60 or more figures that were made in 1953 to celebrate the Coronation.

With peace had come the need to look for new products for the company's fourteen toolmakers and four hundred production workers, not to mention the diecasting and other machines that had grown in number during the war. The steel and chromium needed for electric fire production were in short supply but alloy for casting and the new plastics were available. Like others, Graham Farish saw the potential of the model railway market and in particular they saw a need for a 2-rail electric system and good quality 2-rail flexible track. Here were products which required the available materials, the design and electrical skills within the Company and which were labour intensive - in other words, ideal for Graham Farish to tackle.

In 1948 Graham Farish announced their proposed 'Scale Model Railroads' and demonstrated their new 'Formo' flexible track on a massive layout at the 1948 British Industries Fair at Earls Court. This type of track was a first in the British market and track production became a very big part of the Company's output in those early days and right through 1960s when Formoway was one of the best on the market. It was said that 60 miles of track was sold by them each year and at one stage the Company was manufacturing 13 types of point.

The GP5 train sets of 1949, with their Black 5 locomotives, were Britain's first 2-rail ready-to-run 00 gauge electric model railways. They came in four versions - goods or passenger (with 4-wheel coaches) and with or without track and the set's contents were available separately the following year together with transfers for the rolling stock.

No sooner had the Company started train set production, than it was hit by material shortages due to Korean War. It is also possible that some staff were directed back onto war work. The GWR Prairie, when it arrived in March 1952, was initially available only as a kit and a 3-rail version of the kit was also proposed. The body casting for the Prairie was contracted out to Universal Engineering of Nottingham and it is possible that other early work was put out.

The GP5 loco was also followed by a Bulleid Pacific, a GWR King and a New York Hudson 4-6-4. Early wagons were diecast, the first series of five being released in 1949 but had gone by March 1951. They were replaced by three low-sided or flat wagons in 1952. Perhaps the best remembered item of early rolling stock was the cellulose acetate bodied Pullman car which distorted with age to give it a double bow to the roof. These were particularly attractive models and remained firm favourites over the years. It was claimed that over 100,000 of them were made in the early '50s. There were also bogie suburban coaches and the first Brookdale building kits arrived in 1951 and West's metal figures in 1952.

The Formo 3-rail set

By the summer of 1953, stocks in shops were not moving and everywhere prices were being slashed. At the factory, production of 2-rail models was halted and, in November, a 3-rail train set with an oval of track, like that of Hornby Dublo, was released onto the market. After being the first in the market with a 2-rail system, this move has surprised historians for many years but, with difficulty in

Graham Farish 00

selling the 00 system, Graham Farish had turned to what other companies such as Meccano Ltd and Trix were successfully selling - 3-rail! It should be born in mind that Tri-ang Railways, with their successful 2-rail system, had been launched only a year before and it was too early to see the impact of this.

The new 3-rail system was sold under the Formo name, rather than that of Graham Farish, possibly because they were successfully selling their track under that name and hoped that success would rub off. Literature was published carrying the name 'Formo Ltd' but with the Bromley address. The range consisted of a Southern 0-6-0 Q Class loco and some wagons and tinplate track which looked rather like that made at the time by Marklin. The loco and rolling stock were available separately or in a boxed set. The wagons were from the same moulds as the earlier Graham Farish 2-rail vehicles but had diecast non-insulated wheels and the name 'Formo' cast into the underside of the chassis. The 3-rail system did not sell and was quickly dropped.

Possibly the Company had hoped to develop the 2-rail system further but the poor motor design made the stocks they were holding difficult to sell. In 1958 Graham Farish disposed their remaining complete and unmade stock through one of their subsidiaries, Hutchinson Roe of Bromley, who sold the models and parts cheaply to the public. The Formo set for example was offered at £2.17.6 instead of £5.12.3. They also invited orders for Pullman coaches they could assemble from parts in stock. It seems that S. French & Sons Ltd. of Tolworth had bought a lot of the remaining stock by the following year and offered it to the public. Hutchinson Roe & Co. had the same address (Masons Hill, Bromley) as Graham Farish Ltd. Indeed, the latter had no fewer than ten subsidiaries in 1951 including Formo Products Ltd, Grafar Products Ltd and West & Short Ltd who made the platform accessories.

After a break of eight years, and having cleared the factory of the old stock, the return to serious 00 modelling for Graham Farish came in 1961 with the release of the Prairie tank with a much improved motor and chassis and a new Pannier tank. The revised range also included the first series of four plastic wagons and the Pullman cars, now in rigid polystyrene. Suburban and mainline coach kits were also available in the 1960s and mail and baggage coaches were also planned. By now the Company was selling a much improved quality Formoway track which had a moulded plastic sleeper web and a good range of points.

In 1964, the Graham Farish moved to a former armaments factory at Holton Heath in Dorset, not far from Poole. Here a number of factory units were developed. Throughout the 1960s the Company published their handbook which both contained modelling tips and promoted their products. A 21st Anniversary edition of this was published in 1969 to celebrate the 21 years Farish had been involved in the model railway industry. At this time Peter Graham Farish was Sales Director and Dudley Dimmock (who had previously been associated with Bassett-Lowke) was General Manager of the Models Division.

In 1970 Graham Farish launched their N gauge system and a range of nicely printed 00 rolling stock followed in 1973. However, in 1975, it was decided to phase out production of 00 models after Peter Graham Farish had visited the Brighton Toy Fair and learned of the plans by both Airfix and Palitoy to enter the 00 gauge market. It was decided that the 00 market was about to be flooded and that Graham Farish would do better to concentrate all its efforts on N gauge. The last 00 model to be made at Holton Heath was a special edition van in 1980. 00 stock was no longer advertised after 1981.

Tom Graham Farish's son Gordon, who was a naval architect, had established the Romney Boats business in 1959 and this occupied one of the factory units at Holton Heath. When Tom retired in 1973, Gordon disposed of the boat business and joined his brother Peter in running Graham Farish Ltd. Gordon retired first and moved to South Africa and Peter Graham Farish continued with the business on his own. Wishing to retire, himself, in the summer of 2000, Peter sold Graham Farish Ltd to Bachmann Industries Europe Ltd. Today, the Graham Farish name is solely associated with their dominant N gauge system which is described elsewhere in this book.

Metal Fatigue: Like other manufacturers, Graham Farish had problems with diecast components. Chassis are especially prone to mazak disintegration which results in the 'growth' of parts. This can result in the distortion of the chassis or body and breakage of small components like the tender front gearbox of the GP5. The problem cannot be cured but if not evident now may well never occur. it may be restricted to, say, a pony truck which can be replaced. It is advisable to check carefully for any evidence of this problem: our guide values assume that the item is in good sound condition with no trace of fatigue.

Further Reading
To date we are unaware of any books published on the Graham Farish system but there have been a number of magazine articles.

Dates: we have found little evidence of when models first became available and particularly when they were out of production. Those quoted in the tables below are based on this limited knowledge, coming largely from catalogues and press advertising, and are for guidance only.

Listing - The models are now arranged in the order adopted else where in this book.

Couplings - These were like a cross between the early type IIb Tri-ang couplings and their later tension-lock type which were adopted as the British standard after 1965. Consequently Graham Farish models will couple to most British post 1965 makes.

LOCOMOTIVES
The first locomotive, an LMS Black 5, was initially available only in train sets. As a scale model it was not bad for the time even if mechanically poor and lacking a good finish - not helped by the embossed cabside numbers. It had a diecast body but plastic tender body and it was claimed that it was designed to BRMSB standards. It has been suggested that some components were war surplus.

The tender drive motor unit of this model, as well as in the Bulleid, King and Hudson locomotives, was revolutionary. It consisted of an enclosed permanent magnet rotor with two coils of wire both above and below which, in turn, were connected to two contact blades which oscillated via the rotor shaft between four electrical contacts. These were connected to the two electrical plunger pick ups situated below the tender side frames. Two pieces of steel rod were situated either side of the coils which, in theory, returned the rotor to its starting point. The drive from the tender was via a spring drive and centrifugal clutch to reduction gears and by pinion shaft to the locomotive's driving wheels.

3-Rail Operation: The 3-rail Q Class 0-6-0 had a 5-pole conventional design motor with easily replaceable brushes. It was said at the time to be similar to the Pittman DC.60 motor. It had a 30:1 reduction worm set with a single-start square thread steel worm running in a 15mm diameter brass wheel. The model also had plunger type power collectors.

There is evidence that later models of the King, Bulleid Pacific and Prairie tank were being prepared for 3-rail operation as examples of both have turned up with the gear bracket extended backwards ending in a vertical cylindrical boss bored to accept a pick-up plunger similar to those on tenders. Some tender base plates also carry a marking which would be where the power supply wire would pass. There is no evidence of these models actually being sold fitted for 3-rail operation.

Later Mechanisms: The 5-pole motor used in the later Prairie and Pannier tanks was developed in 1957 and was very like the Tri-ang X04 in design. It employed Alcomax magnets, a drum commutator, bronze bearings and carbon brushes. The chassis had plated, see-through, wheels, Tufnol worms for quiet running and phosphor bronze power collectors There was a choice of scale (BRMSB standards) or universal wheels. The bodies were diecast and fitted with nickel handrails, connecting rods and crossheads.

Cat.No.	Number, Company, Colour, Dates	£	£

L1. GWR Class 94xx Pannier Tank 0-6-0

This was an excellent model with a choice of scale or universal wheels. The subject was also chosen early on for the N gauge range.

BE1W	9410 GWR green - 61-79	25	40
-	GWR green no number - ?	30	45
BE1BR	9410 BRb black - 75-79	40	60

L2. GWR Class 81xx Prairie Tank 2-6-2

This started life as a kit and was initially a poor performer, possibly because the metal body shell interfered with eddy currents, from the unorthodox motor, restricting the available power. Due to this, few of the early '50s models have survived in working order and on many the cast drive gearbox suffers from metal fatigue. The 1960s model, fitted with a conventional motor, was a good performer and a nice looking model, especially with scale wheels. 1950s models had plunger pickups but the 1960s models had wipers on the wheels.

-	8103 black kit - 51-53	NA	60
-	8103 green kit - 51-53	NA	60
-	8103 kit - 51-53	NA	60
-	8103 BRb black - 52-53	40	65
-	8103 GWR green - 52-53	30	55
-	8105 Great Western green new motor and chassis - 61-71	30	55
-	8105 BR green new motor and chassis - 61-71	30	55

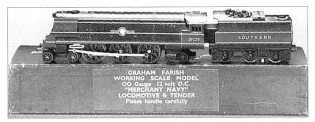

Merchant Navy loco and box [L6] (Barry Potter Auctions)

L3. Southern Class Q 0-6-0

This was the only 3-rail locomotive made by Graham Farish and was strongly built to withstand heavy use. It had a 5-pole conventional motor and a diecast mazak body for loco and tender. Power collection was with plungers on the centre rail and, in effect, it offered Dublo operators a fourth locomotive to run. The name 'Formo' was cast into the smokebox and the cabsides.

-	**Formo** BRb black - 53	80	NA
-	**Formo** BRb green - 53	125	NA
-	**Formo** BRb black rear splashers extended to cab - 53	100	NA

L4. King Class 4-6-0

Mechanically this model was similar to the Bulleid Pacific. The safety valve cover was strange in having only the top half with a copper finish. All models, irrespective of the name they carried, had '6000' cast into the cab sides.

-	**6000 'King Charles'** Great () Western green - 51-53	70	120
-	**6000 'King Charles'** BRb blue - 51-53	80	140
-	**6000 'King John'** Great () Western green - 51-53	70	120
-	**6000 'King John'** BRb blue - 51-53	80	140
-	**6000 'King Henry V'** Great () Western green - 51-53	70	120
-	**6000 'King Henry V'** BRb blue - 51-53	80	140
-	**6000 'King George V'** Great () Western green + bell - 51-53	70	120
-	**6000 'King George V'** BRb blue + bell - 51-53	80	140
-	**6000 'King George V'** Great () Western green no bell - 51-53	70	120
-	**6000 'King George V'** BRb blue no bell - 51-53	80	140
-	**6000** BRb green - ?	NPG	NPG
-	**6000** BRb black - ?	NPG	NPG
-	**6000** kit - ?	NPG	NPG

L5. 'GP5' Class 5MT (Black 5) 4-6-0

Known by Graham Farish as the 'GP5', the locomotive was propelled by a tender-mounted motor driven as described above. It had strangely designed central drivers with thicker rims and traction tyres and also had poor representation of valve gear. Power was collected from the track by a single sprung pickup each side. On the numberless first batch, the valve gear top pin was secured in a hole in part of the footplate casting and the cab floor brace plate was initially too thin to carry the chassis and subsequently snapped within a few months. This problem was overcome by strengthening the brace and, at the same time, the cab number 44753 was cast into the body moulding and the valve positioning hole became a slot. The chassis was also modified regarding its fixing to the cab floor and one of the pinions driving the wheels was deleted. The incorrect number '44753' belonged to a member of the class fitted with Caprotti valve gear and yet a more suitable number '44758' was used in illustrations.

-	**44753** BRb black thin cab floor brace plate - 49	35	60
-	BRb black unpainted numbers - 49-51	30	50

L6. Bulleid Pacific 4-6-2

The same model was passed-off as a West Country, Battle of Britain and a Merchant Navy Class although in real life the last of these should have been larger. Mechanically it was similar to the GP5.

-	**21C25 'Brocklebank Line'** SR green - 50-53	60	170
-	**21C103 'Plymouth'** SR green - 50-53	60	180
-	**21C90 'Sir Eustace Missenden'** SR green - 50-53	60	170
-	**21C90 'Sir Eustace Missenden'** SR green Golden Arrow** + flags - 50-53	140	220
-	**35017 'Belgian Marine'** SR green Golden Arrow + flags - ?	NPG	NPG
-	**35017 'Belgian Marine'** BRb blue - 50-53	70	200
-	**35027 'Port Line'** BRb blue - 50-53	70	200
-	**34101 'Exeter'*** BRb blue - 50-53	70	200
-	BRb green - ?	NPG	NPG
-	no markings blue - ?	NPG	NPG
-	kit - ?	NPG	NPG

* The number should have been '34001'. **You could have any Bulleid Pacific finished as a Golden Arrow locomotive for an extra 5/-.

L7. New York Central Hudson 4-6-4 (H0)

This model was noted for its scale wheels, Baker's valve gear detail and considerable body detail. Unlike its predecessors, the model had power collection from the tender wheels and axles. It was sold in a wooden box with a sliding lid.

-	**5405** New York Central black - *52-53*	120	200
-	**5405** New York Central black with 5-pole motor - *54*	130	240

Class 94xx Pannier [L1]

COACHES

Coaches came in three phases - 1950s, 1960s and 1970s. In the early 1950s there were heavy plastic bodied 4-wheel and bogie suburbans, Pullman cars and a coach for the New York Central Hudson. The suburban bogie coaches survived as kits into the 1960 phase when main line coach kits arrived and an improved version of the Pullman cars were introduced. The final phase came in the 1970s when the suburban and main line stock were produced as ready-to-run models in all plastic lighter form and with nicely printed liveries.

The coaches in the final stage had plug-fit reversible bogies. One end had a Farish version of the hook and bar coupling while the other end would take a Tri-ang coupling unit and there was a centre hole which would take a Peco or Dublo coupling.

Cat.No.	Company, Number, Colour, Dates	£	£

C1. 4-Wheel Suburban Stock

These coaches were 6" long and made for only a few months. They had a bakelite body, tin roof and metal sideframes.

-	**BR** red 1st - *49*	35	45
-	**BR** red 3rd - *49*	35	45
-	**BR** red composite - *49*	35	45
-	**BR** red 3rd luggage - *49*	35	45

C2a. Pullmans

After sometime, these developed a strange double bow to the roof. This has been caused by the vehicle having a solid diecast chassis and floor unit which, due to metal fatigue, has grown in length over the years, distorting the plastic roof in the process. The prices below recognise that Pullmans in perfect condition are virtually unheard of and, if found, would sell for around £50 each. Pullmans made before late 1952 had no printed surround to the name board. The Golden Arrow (GA) versions have 'Golden Arrow' at one end and 'Fleche D'Or' at the other. Early Pullman cars were issued ready named and had the name rubber-stamped on the end of the box. A little later they were issued unnamed but with a sheet of name transfers (as was also the case later when the Pullmans were reissued - table C2b).

-	**'Iolanthe'** choc+cream - *50-53*	20	35
-	**'Lydia'** choc+cream - *50-53*	20	35
-	**'Minerva'** choc+cream - *50-53*	20	35
-	**'Pauline'** choc+cream - *50-53*	20	35
-	**'Phyllis'** choc+cream - *50-53*	20	35
-	**'Iolanthe'** choc+cream GA - *51-53*	25	45
-	**'Lydia'** choc+cream GA - *51-53*	25	45
-	**'Minerva'** choc+cream GA - *51-53*	25	45
-	**'Pauline'** choc+cream GA - *51-53*	25	45
-	**'Phyllis'** choc+cream GA - *51-53*	25	45
-	**Wagon Lits** blue - *51-53*	30	50
-	**Pullman** TC No.94 choc+crm - *52-53*	20	35

C2b. Pullmans (Reissued)

Pullmans made in the 1960s were made with the more stable polystyrene and the saloons came with blank nameboards and a choice of names as transfers.

B64	choc+cream 1st parlour - *62-75*	15	30
B65	TC No.94 choc+cream brk end - *62-75*	15	30

The choice of names was: Alice, Belinda, Fingall, Gladys, Ibis, Iolanthe, Joan, Lydia, Minerva, Niobe, Penelope, Phyllis and Rosamunde. The choice of numbers for the brake car was: No. 27, No. 36, No. 54, No. 55, No. 62, No. 63, No. 67, No. 68, No. 69, No. 70, No. 71, No. 72, No. 77, No. 78, No. 79, No. 80, No. 81 and No. 82.

C3. Stainless Steel Stock (H0)

These had plastic bodies and the same metal bogies as the tender of the Hudson loco in table L7. These are very rarely found in perfect condition and this is recognised in the prices suggested below.

-	**New York Central** 3029 silver - *52-53*	30	40
-	**Chesapeake & Ohio** 3029 silver - *not made*	NA	NA

C4. Bogie Non-Corridor Suburban Stock

These were similar in appearance to the 4-wheel coaches but were twice as long. They were probably based on an LMS design and were well-detailed models, complete with seats, compartment partitions and fittings in relief - all part of the basic body moulding. They had a metal roof and floor and most had 'LMS', 'Southern', '1st', '3rd' etc. heat printed onto their sides. Early ones had a riveted fixing for Pullman type bogies while later ones (and the kits) had a nut and bolt attachment and smaller, improved, bogies. They were made in large quantities and collectors should be aware that many have received subsequent alterations by their owners.

-	**LMS** maroon 1st - *52-53*	5	12
-	**LMS** maroon 3rd - *52-53*	5	12
-	**LMS** maroon composite - *52-53*	5	12
-	**LMS** maroon brake 3rd - *53*	5	12
-	**SR** green 1st - *52-53*	5	12
-	**SR** green 3rd - *52-53*	5	12
-	**SR** green composite - *52-53*	5	12
-	**SR** green brake 3rd - *53*	5	12
-	**BR** red 1st - *52-53*	6	15
-	**BR** red 3rd - *52-53*	6	15
-	**BR** red composite - *52-53*	6	15
-	**BR** red brake 3rd - *53*	6	15
A40*	black composite kit - *63?-74*	NA	15
A41*	black brake end kit - *63?-74*	NA	15

* These kits used the original suburban coach one-piece body moulding, steel floor and diecast under-gear but had a lighter tinplate roof and bogies simplified for home construction.

C5. Main Line Stock

Although substantially similar to the A40/A41 kits (above), they used a new body moulding which was fractionally longer and with different window spacing.

A42	black composite kit - *70?-74*	NA	15
A43	black brake end kit - *70?-74*	NA	15

C6. Bogie Non-Corridor Suburban Stock

These were outwardly similar to the earlier coaches (table C4 above) but were of a much lighter construction with all plastic parts. They were reduced in height and weight by removal of the solebar and the use of a new design of plug-in solebar/bogie mounting and side truss/battery box. They also had a plastic roof and were issued in the liveries of the big four and BR.

10601	**LMS** maroon comp (BR60M) - *75-81*	6	15
10611	**LMS** 20485 maroon brake (BR61M) - *75-81*	6	15
10602	**LNER** teak comp (BR60N) - *77-81*	6	15
10612	**LNER** teak brake (BR61N) - *76-81*	6	15
BR60W	**GWR** choc+cream composite, simple livery - *75-77*	6	15
10604	**GWR** 7053 choc+cream composite, detailed livery (also BR60W) - *77-81*	6	15
BR61W	**GWR** choc+cream brake end, simple livery - *75-77*	6	15
10614	**GWR** choc+cream brake end, detailed livery (also BR61W) - *77-81*	6	15
10603	**SR** green composite (BR60S) - *75-81*	6	15
10613	**SR** green brake end (BR61S) - *75-81*	6	15
10605	**BR** red composite (BR60) - *77-81*	8	18
10615	**BR** red brake end (BR61) - *77-81*	8	18

C7. Main Line Stock

These were almost identical to the suburban stock in table C6 above but one side showed the larger corridor windows.

Cat.No.	Company, Number, Colour, Dates	£	£
10621	**LMS** maroon comp (BR62M) - *75-81*	6	15
10631	**LMS** maroon brake (BR63M) - *75-81*	6	15
10622	**LNER** 75674 teak comp (BR62N) - *76-81*	6	15
10632	**LNER** teak brake (BR63N) - *76-81*	6	15
BR62W	**GWR** choc+cream composite, simple livery - *75-77*	6	15
10624	**GWR** choc+cream composite, detailed livery (also BR62W) - *77-81*	6	15
BR63W	**GWR** choc+cream brake end, simple livery - *75-77*	6	15
10634	**GWR** choc+cream brake end, detailed livery (also BR63W) - *77-81*	6	15
10623	**SR** 1787 olive green composite (BR62S) - *75-81*	6	15
10631	**SR** 2763, 2783 olive green brake 3rd (BR63S) - *75-81*	6	15

WAGONS

The first series of wagons was released with the couplings in their original nickel silver condition. Apart from being overscale they were rather obtrusive and within a few months were painted black prior to assembly. A second series of diecast wagons arrived in 1952 but a year later, production had ceased. Besides coupling and body colour variations, all early rolling stock could have either plain plastic or nickel silver rimmed plastic wheels.

Although some publicity material showed wagons and vans with markings implying the existence of a fruit van, refrigerated van, insulated van, fish van and wagons with company lettering, it is understood that only the eight plain unmarked wagons and vans listed in tables W1 to W8 below were released.

A third series of wagons came with the revival of the system in 1961 and these had plastic bodies on diecast chassis and came unprinted but with transfers you could apply. The final series started in the 1970s and was quite extensive. The wagons were all plastic except for the couplings and had factory finished liveries.

Cat.No.	Company, Number, Colour, Dates	£	£

Diecast Wagons
1st Series

All except the brake van had a realistic looking brake lever each side and the separate underframe on the surviving examples sometimes suffers from metal fatigue.

W1. 5-Plank Wagon

-	light grey - *49-51*	2	4
-	dark grey - *49-51*	2	4
-	light brown - *49-51*	2	4
-	dark brown - *49-51*	2	4
-	red brown - *49-51*	2	4

W2. 7-Plank Wagon

-	light grey - *49-51*	2	4
-	dark grey - *49-51*	2	4
-	light brown - *49-51*	2	4
-	dark brown - *49-51*	2	4
-	red brown - *49-51*	2	4

W3. Steel Mineral Wagon

-	light grey - *49-51*	2	4
-	dark grey - *49-51*	2	4
-	light brown - *49-51*	2	4
-	dark brown - *49-51*	2	4
-	red brown - *49-51*	2	4

W4. Goods Van

-	red brown, grey roof - *49-51*	3	5
-	light grey, white or cream roof - *49-51*	3	5
-	grey, white or cream roof - *49-51*	3	5
-	'Formo'* - *53*	4	NA

*This has 'Formo' cast into box on the underside of the body which is of a slightly different construction, the dummy underframe now being incorporated in the body moulding with separate coupling and axle carrier unit at one end.

W5. Brake Van

-	red brown - *49-51*	3	5
-	black - ?	NPG	NPG
-	'Formo'* brown - *53*	4	NA

*This was the same as the Formo wagon described above in table W4.

2nd Series

These followed in 1951-52 or 53 and were produced in lower numbers with the result that they are harder to find. They had a tinplate floor, no handbrake gear and were very prone to metal fatigue.

W6. Match Truck

A plain flat wagon.

-	brown - *52-53*	6	NA
-	chocolate - *52-53*	6	NA
-	light grey - *52-53*	6	NA

W7. 3-Plank Wagon

Announced and illustrated in the first catalogue but not made until the 2nd series.

-	brown - *52-53*	6	NA
-	chocolate - *52-53*	6	NA
-	light grey - *52-53*	6	NA

W8. Bolster Wagon

Similar to the match truck (table W6) but with a single bolster cast into the body. Also provided with two pins and a chain.

-	brown - *52-53*	6	NA
-	chocolate - *52-53*	6	NA
-	light grey - *52-53*	6	NA

Plastic Wagons
3rd Series

The first plastic wagons were fairly short lived. They had unprinted self-coloured polystyrene bodies and were not unlike Trackmaster or early Tri-ang wagons in appearance. Transfer sheets were available allowing the purchaser to apply the finish of one of the big four companies but not BR. Some of the bodies were later used in the 4th series of wagons (below in tables W13-W18). They had a two-part diecast chassis which had been chemically blackened and which had four vertical locating pins for the body (again like Trackmaster or Tri-ang). Unnecessarily they had open axleboxes which rather spoilt the appearance. The chassis may be identified by a small 'GF' on the back of the solebar. The wagons were sold in a roll of corrugated paper and a thin printed outer paper wrapper.

W9. Tarpaulin Wagon

This was a 7-plank wagon with a wire tarpaulin rail.

-	grey - *62-64*	6	10
-	red brown - *62-64*	6	10

W10. Steel Mineral Wagon

-	grey - *62-64*	6	10
-	red brown - *62-64*	6	10

W11. Fast Goods Van

-	grey - *62-64*	6	10
-	red brown - *62-64*	6	10

Graham Farish 00

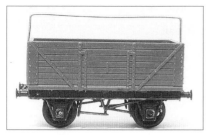

3rd series wagon - tarpaulin [W9] (Peter Gurd)

W12. Brake Van
-	grey - *62-64*	6	10
-	red brown - *62-64*	6	10

4th Series

This series was of all plastic construction. Early examples had the axles in clips which were part of the floor moulding but later ones had the axles held by the side frames. Vans and brake vans may be found either with excessive roof heights or with later corrected ones. This time they were released from the factory already decorated but, again, no BR liveries.

W13. 5-Plank Wagon
12001	**LMS** grey (also B20M) - *74-81*	4	6
12002	**NE** red brown (also B20N) - *74-81*	4	6
12003	**SR** chocolate (also B20S) - *74-81*	4	6
12004	**GW** dark grey (also B20W) - *74-81*	4	6
12011	**D.Pitt** 2 grey - *79-81*	4	6
12012	**Spiers** 513 yellow-orange - *79-81*	4	6
12013	**Snow** black - *76-81*	4	6
-	**Sharp** grey Sp Edn (Neal's Toys) - *80-81*	7	10

W14. 7-Plank wagon
12101	**LMS** brown (also B21M) - *73-81*	4	6
12102	**NE** red brown (also B21N) - *73-81*	4	6
12103	**SR** 5079 chocolate (B21S) - *73-81*	4	6
12104	**GW** dark grey (also B21W) - *73-81*	4	6
12111	**Frost** 31 black (also B21/1) - *75-80*	4	6
12112	**Pritchard** 26 green (B21/2) - *75-81*	4	6
12113	**Bullcroft** 9471 red (B21/3) - *75-81*	4	6
12114	**Joseph Ellis** 150? red brown (also B21/4) - *75-80*	4	6
12115	**South Leicester** 378 red brown (also B21/5) - *75-80*	4	6
12116	**Wood** 1410 yellow (B21/6) - *75-81*	4	6
B12112	**Sleight** 79 grey - *79-81*	4	6
12123	**Powell Gwinnell** black - *79-81*	4	6
12124	**Ocean** 918 black - *79-81*	4	6
12125	**Ormiston** 54 blue - *81*	4	6
12126	**Staveley** 8716? black - *79-81*	4	6

W15. 16T Steel Mineral Wagon
12201	**LMS** 616014 red brown (also B22M) - *73-81*	4	6
12204	**GW** 110134 dark grey (also B22W) - *73-81*	4	6
12211	**SC** 07217 grey - *79-81*	4	6

W16. Single Vent Van
12301	**LMS** 701 grey (also B23M) - *73-81*	4	6
12302	**NE** 186547? red brown (also B23N) - *73-81*	4	6
12303	**SR** chocolate (also B23S) - *73-81*	4	6
12304	**GW** 95253 dark grey (also B23W) - *75-81*	4	6
12311	**Bass** 14 grey (also B23/1) - *74-81*	4	6
12312	**Worthington** 5 chocolate (also B23/2) - *74-81*	4	6
12313	**Knorr** white (also B23/3) - *75-81*	4	6
12314	**Terry's** chocolate (also B23/4) - *75-81*	4	6
12315	**Zoflora** green (also B23/5) - *75-80*	4	6
12316	**Fyffes** yellow (also B23/6) - *75-80*	4	6
B23/7?	**Railmail** yellow Sp Edn - *77*	4	6

W17. Twin Vent Van
12401	**LMS** 7126 grey (also B24M) - *74-81*	4	6
12403	**SR** chocolate (also B24S) - *74-81*	4	6
12404	**GW** dark grey (also B24W) - *74-81*	4	6
12411	**Sportsman** white - *77-80*	4	6
12412	**Gibbs SR** blue - *77-80*	4	6
12413	**John West** green+pink - *77-80*	4	6
-	**Beatties** black Sp Edn - *80*	4	6

W18. Brake Van
13021	**LMS** grey (also B31M) - *73-80*	4	6
13022	**NE** 157691 red brown (B31N) - *73-80*	4	6
13023	**SR** 158732 dk.brown (B31S) - *73-80*	4	6

ACCESSORIES

Various model railway ancillary items were released between 1949 and 1952 which included a series of three building kits. These were:

Brookdale passenger station
Brookdale goods depot and signal cabin
Red Roofs and Timbers (villas)

Each kit included a full set of building papers and supplementary sheets consisting of brick papers, doors and windows etc. and all that was required to complete each kit was balsa wood and glue.

Up until 1950, only a battery control unit was available but the introduction of the new controller/transformer finished in chromium plate and black stove enamel made operating the railway more practical. It had a reverse lever and a four position speed lever which, although it gave much better overall control of running trains, slow running was still a problem. This was overcome by the 'fingertip controller' which used in conjunction with the transformer/controller unit made engine movements and especially shunting more practical.

West & Short Ltd made a range of diecast accessories that were exclusively marketed by Graham Farish. The range included railway personnel, passengers, a railway horse wagon, platform seats, a range of signals, street lamps and a goods depot crane. These were sold in brightly illustrated card boxed. The Graham Farish connection was printed on the packaging and this adds to the value of these.

By the late '60s, the Company was selling printed card shop fronts, plastic tunnel mouths and moulded station roofs. There were also six sets of building papers. These later accessories in original packaging are of interest to collectors.

SETS

The first four sets all contained the GP5 LMS Black 5 locomotive. The choice was between 6 wagons or 3 4-wheeled coaches and these combinations were available with or without track. Of these the goods set with track is the most common and sells for £80-£120. It seems that very few passenger sets were made and hardly any of the sets released without track have survived.

In 1953, a hard to find 3-rail set was sold under the name 'Formo' and this contained the Q Class 0-6-0 locomotive, 7-plank wagon, steel mineral wagon, van, brake van and an oval of tinplate track. In very good condition this would be expected to sell at between £120 and £150.

Graham Farish N

HISTORY

The history of the Graham Farish company has been covered elsewhere in this book (see 'Graham Farish 00') and we pick up the story in 1970.

What had previously been referred to as 000 gauge (being approximately half the size of 00) was renamed 'N' gauge in the early 1960s. By 1970 there were already Continental N gauge systems catering for the British market but these were a sideline to larger ranges for customers in Continental Europe and America. All were sold through British companies (Lima/Wrenn, Minitrix/Trix Trains and Rivarossi/Peco). All too often they involved compromises, including those of scale and use of common parts not strictly correct in a British setting.

What was needed was a complete N gauge system made specifically for the British Market. Graham Farish recognised this need and the opportunity it provided them with at a time when they were struggling to maintain a toehold in the British 00 market. There had been the pioneering Lone Star in the late '50s and early '60s but this did not provide the quality that serious modellers were seeking and especially the N Gauge Society which had been founded in 1967. The Society set standards for Graham Farish to work to.

> ### Dating Models from their Packaging
> 71-73 alphanumeric numbering and blue and yellow packaging.
> 73-77 now called 'Grafar'.
> 78 all figure catalogue numbers used and return to 'Graham Farish' name. Gold on black packaging using a clear plastic tube with rigid plastic ends.
> 79-80 black card window boxes used.
> 81-92 the same but colour scheme now yellow on black.
> 93-00 the same but an additional yellow stripe on the box.

The Company were based at Holton Heath near Poole in Dorset and their main product at the time was Formoway track which was a principle competitor for Peco track. The public heard little of the Company's N gauge plans until its advertisement appeared in the model railway press in the autumn of 1970. Initially, 32 wagons and a Pannier tank were planned but many other accessories were proposed including an N gauge handbook.

The Pannier tank was released early in 1971 and the GER Holden 0-6-0 tank and some 4-wheel coaches followed in time for Christmas. Early wagons and coaches came unprinted but there were dry transfers (made by Lettraset) available to detail them. Suburban bogie and main line coaches followed in 1972 but by September that year the unprinted wagons and coaches were being supplanted by so called 'Superstock' which left the factory with a paint finish and ready printed by the silicone pad method. The first wagons in private owner liveries quickly followed but were initially available only in mixed sets of three.

The range of locomotives and rolling stock quickly expanded and included diesel and electric locomotives in the liveries of the privatised companies and modern rolling stock to go with them. An interesting innovation was the range of Magnum layouts which were large printed cards which included a set design onto which you could lay your track, A large range of N gauge card buildings was also available.

In the summer of 2000, Peter Graham Farish took a well deserved retirement and sold Graham Farish Ltd to Bachmann Industries Europe Ltd. Production was transferred to China. Work now started on upgrading the range. The resulting models are listed separately.

Further Reading

For a more in depth study of the variations that occurred in the design of the Graham Farish range for the British market and the types of packaging used, you are recommended to obtain a copy of Monty's Amateur Collectors Guide to Graham Farish N Gauge. This is the result of an extensive study of the subject and is obtainable from S.Culverhouse, 17 Church Street, Clowne, Chesterfield S43 4JR.

Catalogue Numbers - The numbering system changed two or three times in the early days, causing confusion, but settled down to a simple four-figure number in 1978. It is therefore likely that models released before 1978 may be found with differing catalogue numbers although the box content remains the same.

The four digit system worked on the basis that the last digit referred to the variation. This worked well for up to 9 variations but after this letters of the alphabet were used or, alternatively, the numbering continued into five digits for '10', '11' etc. Near the end, an 'FA' prefix was being used and some boxes had a 'FA' number on a printed yellow label one end of the box and a cut out sticker with a Bachmann number on the other end. These were amongst the last models made at Holton Heath.

Variations meant livery changes and not changes in names and running numbers. Thus a given catalogue number could be applied to models with different names and numbers so long as the livery was the same.

An additional '0' was sometimes added in front of three figure numbers to bring them up to four digits. Here we have tended to leave out the surplus '0'.

Couplings - The European standard N gauge coupling was adopted from the start and this was altered towards the end of 1972. Initially these were sprung but, in order to avoid paying a license fee for use of the design which was owned by Arnold, the springs were dropped after a while, the sprung coupling returning in 1981.

Listing - The locos are listed in order of size starting with tank engines followed by tender locos and ending with diesels, electrics and multiple units. The coaches are listed with pre-Nationalisation stock first followed by vehicles of later years. Wagons are listed in the order of: flats, open wagons, hoppers, tanks, vans, brake vans and bogie stock.

Graham Farish by Bachmann

Following their purchase of Graham Farish Ltd in 2000, Bachmann released a list of planned locomotives as follows:

Class 4P Compound 4-4-0 41147 black BRb lined
Class 47 Diesel Co-Co 47708 'Waverley' black Fragonset
Class 57 Diesel Co-Co 57011 'Freightliner Challenger' green
Class 37 Diesel Co-Co 37609 blue DRS, yellow ends
Class 37 Diesel Co-Co 37428 'Great Scottish' maroon EWS LMS
    type livery
HST Class 43 43047+43058 jade Midland Mainline 3-car
HST Class 43 43096+43109 navy GNER 3-car
Class 20 Diesel Bo-Bo 20312 blue DRS yellow ends
Class 20 Diesel Bo-Bo D8163 green BRc small yellow ends
Castle Class 4-6-0 7033 'Hartlebury Castle' green BRb

(transfer no.14411)

Class 25 Diesel Bo-Bo 25322 'Tamworth Castle' green BRc 2-tone green

Princess Coronation 'Duchess' Class 4-6-2 46255 'City of Hereford' blue BRb

Class 50 Diesel Co-Co 50017 maroon VSOE Northern Pullman (LMS Royal Scot type livery)

Class 8F 2-8-0 3107 black LNER (no. on buffer beam)

Class 8F 2-8-0 48045 black BRc Fowler tender

Class 40 Diesel 1-Co-Co-1 D306 'Atlantic Conveyor' green BRc half yellow ends

Class 33 Diesel 33109 'Captain Bill Smith RN' blue BRe, yellow ends

Class A3 4-6-2 60051 'Blink Bonny' green BRc double chimney

Class A3 4-6-2 60080 'Dick Turpin' blue BRb

Class 158 DMU 1525 Northern Spirit 3-car

Class 158 DMU 1550 Central Trains 2-car

Class 158 DMU 1551 dk.blue First North Western 2-car

Class 159 DMU 1526 Southwest Trains 3-car

Class 31 Diesel A1A-A1A 31601 'Bletchley Park' black Fragonset

Class A4 4-6-2 60017 'Silver Fox' blue BRb

Many of these models, and some refinished rolling stock, were produced at the Holton Heath works using parts available. Some went out with four figure catalogue numbers handwritten on a cut out gummed label while others were given Bachmann six figure numbers printed onto gummed labels using a computer. We understand from Bachmann that, with so much going on at the time as British production was wound down, no comprehensive record of these batches was kept. The question of what was produced during the closing days will make an interesting study and models made during this period are going to be the most sought after by collectors in years to come. This includes some locomotives with blackened rims on the driving wheels which Bachmann requested. Unfortunately the bogie and tender wheels remained in their former bright metal condition.

Bachmann discovered that much work would have to be done to the existing tooling to upgrade the models to a standard expected of their company and so work started on this. At the same time development of new models started, be it at a slower pace. All new and improved models are made in China and these started to appear during late 2001.

As far as this guide is concerned we have included in this section all those models that were made at Holton Heath including a few sold under the Bachmann numbering system. Any models made in China will appear in the next section - **'Graham Farish by Bachmann'**.

LOCOMOTIVES

Except for Class 94XX pannier tanks made in 1971, the locomotives had a split chassis design. The combined motor and chassis unit was used from 1978 with the Prairie tank being the first model to use it. The locomotives had 3-pole motors until March 1984, after which, 5-pole motors were fitted to all Graham Farish locomotives.

During the period 1996-97, there was an unsuccessful experiment with unpainted locomotives.

Cat.No.	Number, Company, Colour, Dates	£	£

L1. Standard Tank 0-6-0T (Freelance)
This was made from the former Holden tank tooling which was altered for the purpose. It consequently looked very like a J69 but with slight structural changes.

NE3M	**583** LMS lined maroon - 75-76	25	40
NE3S	**187** Southern lined green - 75-76	25	40

L2. Promotional Tank 0-6-0T (Freelance)
This was a cheap to produce, non-powered model.

-	The **Shredded Wheat** Company black non powered - 89-99	25	NA
-	No1 **'The Gaffer 1994'** bright red powered ex-8530 set - 94	25	NA

L3. General Purpose Tank 0-6-0T (Freelance)
This replaced the Standard tank as the 'all things to all men' model in the range and was larger than its predecessor.

NE7M	**16389** LMS lined maroon - 78	25	40
1701	**16389** LMS lined maroon- 78-00	25	40
1706	**7313** LMS black - 78-00	25	40
NE7N	**2801** LNER lined green - 78	25	40
1702	**2801** LNER lined green - 78-00	25	40
-	**2801** LNER blue ex set 85311 - ?	30	NA
NE7S	**2579** Southern lined green - 78	25	40
1703	**2579** Southern lined green - 78-00	25	40
NE7BR	**47313** BRb lined black - 78	25	40
1705	**47313** BRb lined black - 78-00	25	40

Larger general purpose tank [L3]

L4. 94XX Class Pannier Tank 0-6-0PT
This was based on a Hawkesworth design and early models had a Mabuchi can motor fitted a cast metal chassis. From 1972, a split chassis design was used.

NE1	*GWR green - 71	30	45
NE1GN	*GWR green - 72-74	30	45
NE1W	*GWR green - 75-77	30	45
1104	**9405** GWR green - 78-00	35	50
NE1BK	*BRb black - 72-74	30	45
NE1BR	*BRb black - 75-77	30	45
1105	**9401** BRb black - 78-00	35	50

These * models were supplied unnumbered and with a sheet of transfers with the following numbers: 8427, 9400, 9406, 9410, 9426, 9427.

L5. 57XX Class Pannier Tank 0-6-0PT

1114	**5768** Great Western green Churchward cab - 95-00	35	50
1115	**7777** BRb black Churchward cab - 95-00	35	50
1124	**6752** GWR green Collett cab - 96-00	35	50
1124	**8751** GWR green Collett cab - 96-00	35	50
1125	**4782** BRc black Collett cab - 96-00	35	50
1125	**4672** BRc black Collett cab - 96-00	35	50
111A	**L99** London Transport maroon Ltd Edn 500 (red label) Churchward cab - 96	55	77

L6. 3F Class Jinty 0-6-0T

1731	**7277** LMS black - 96-00	35	50
1735	**47394** BRb black - 96-00	35	50
1731A	LMS black - 99-00	35	50

L7. Holden J69 Class Tank 0-6-0T

The body tool was altered in 1975 to provide a standard tank that could be passed off in various liveries (see L1).

NE2BL	**372** GER lined blue - *72-74*	30	45
NE2E	**372** GER lined blue - *75*	30	45
NE2GN	**1672** LNER lined green - *72-74*	30	45
NE2NE	**1672** LNER lined green - *75*	30	45
NE2BK	BRb lined black - *72-74*	30	45
NE2BR	BRb lined black - *75*	30	45

NCB Austerity tank [L8]

L8. J94 Class 0-6-0ST

1016	**68079** BRb black - *86-00*	35	50
1017	**61** NCB blue, red rods - *86-00*	35	50
(8540)	**07 'Robert'** Industrial green x-sets - *86-00*	35	50
?	**196** LMR blue ex-set 8531 - *99-00*	35	50
101B	**NS8826** Dutch? dull green - *?*	40	60

L9. 61XX/81XX Class Prairie Tank 2-6-2T

The 81XXs were rebuilds of the 61XXs and had smaller wheels but there is no difference to be seen on the models.

1603	**6104** GWR (button) green - *00*	35	50
1604	**3112** GWR lined green - *77-00*	35	50
NE6W	**8106** GWR green - *78*	35	50
1604	**8106** GWR green - *78-00*	35	50
NE6BR	**8100** BRc lined green - *78*	35	50
1605	**8100** BRc lined green - *78-00*	35	50
1605	**6115** BRc lined green - *77-00*	35	50
?	**6105** BRb unlined green - *84*	40	60
1606	**8102** BRc lined black - *79-00*	40	55
16011	**6135** BRb lined green - *00*	NPG	NPG
16011	**6127** BRb lined green - *00*	35	50
16012	**6104** GWR (button) green - *00*	35	50
0661	**6113** BRb lined black - *?*	35	50

L10. Standard Class 4 Tank 2-6-4T

1655	**80064** BRb lined black - *91-00*	40	55
1656	**80079** BRc lined black- *91-00*	40	55

L11. 4P Class Compound 4-4-0

1201	**1111** LMS lined maroon - *80-00*	40	55
1206	**1118** LMS black - *80-00*	40	55
1205	**40938** BRb lined black - *80-00*	40	55
12011	? BRc black - *00*	40	55
1207	**67** SDJR dark blue - *82-90*	65	80
1217	**375** Caledonian Railway blue - *81-90*	60	75

L12. 4F Class 0-6-0

1841	**4232** LMS black - *93-00*	40	55
1841	**4269** LMS black - *93-00*	40	55
1845	**44370** BRc black - *93-00*	40	55
-	**4210?** LMS black ex-set 8524 - *98-99*	45	NA

L13. 5F Class 'Crab' 2-6-0

1851	**2715** LMS lined black - *93-00*	40	55
1855	**42806** BRb black - *93-00*	40	55
185A	**13071** LMS maroon Ltd Edn *500* (red label) - *94*	45	60

18511	? BRc black - *00*	45	60

Hall class [L14]

L14. Hall Class 4-6-0

NE4W	**6998 'Burton Agnes Hall'** Great () Western green - *75-77*	50	65
1404	**6998 'Burton Agnes Hall'** Great () Western green - *78-80*	50	65
1404	**6960 'Raveningham Hall'** Great () Western green - *80-00*	50	65
NE4BR	**7915 'Mere Hall'** BRb black - *75-77*	50	65
1405	**7915 'Mere Hall'** BRb black - *78-00*	50	65
140A	**6994 'Baggrave Hall'** BRc green Sp.Edn (silver label) - *99-00*	60	80
14011	**5955 'Garth Hall'** BRc green - *00*	NPG	NPG

** an unfortunate choice as 'Burton Agnes Hall' was built in 1949 and so did not receive GWR livery until it was preserved.

L15a. Castle Class 4-6-0

1442	**5014 'Goodrich Castle'** BRc green - *99-00*	55	70
1444	**7029 'Clun Castle'** Great () Western green - *82-00*	55	70
1445	**4082 'Windsor Castle'** BRc green - *82-85*	55	70
1446	**7029 'Clun Castle'** BRc green - *?*	55	70
1446	**5042 'Winchester Castle'** Great () Western green - *83-00*	55	70
1447	**5037 'Monmouth Castle'** BR grn - *83-00*	55	70
14411	**7033 'Hartlebury Castle'** BRb green - *00*	60	80

L15b. King Class 4-6-0

This was the same model as the Castle but had a King Class front bogie specially tooled for it.

1414	**6023 'King Edward II'** GWR button green - *00*	60	80
1415	**6023 'King John'** BRb green - *00*	60	80

L16. Black 5 4-6-0

1801	**5041** LMS black - *78-00*	55	70
1805	**44911** BRc lined black - *79-00*	55	70
1805	**44923** BRc lined black - *78-00*	55	70
1805	**45296** BRc lined black - *78-00*	55	70
1806	**4806** LMS lined maroon - *81-89*	55	70
1806	**5041** LMS lined maroon - *81-89*	55	70
18011	**5303** LMS lined black - *00*	60	80
18012	**44896** BRb lined black - *00*	60	80

Duchess class [L17]

L17. 'Duchess' Class 4-6-2

1811	**6242 'City of Glasgow'** LMS black - *82-00*	60	75
1811	**6255 'City of Hereford'** LMS black - *83-00*	60	75
1814	**46244 'King George VI'** BRc green - *82-00*	60	75
1815	**46247 'City of Liverpool'** BRc maroon Sp Edn (silver label) - *00*	65	80
1816	**46229 'Duchess of Hamilton'** BRc maroon - *82-00*	60	75

1817	**46221 'Queen Elizabeth'** BRb blue - *82-90*	60	75
18111	**46255 'City of Hereford'** BR blue - *00*	65	80

L18. A3 Class 4-6-2

1822	**4472 'Flying Scotsman'** LNER light green - *87-00*	60	75
1825	**60103 'Flying Scotsman'** BRc green -*87-00*	60	75
1827	**60052 'Prince Palatine'** BRb green, German smoke deflectors - *87-00*	60	75
18211	**60080 'Dick Turpin'** BRb blue - *00*	65	80
18212	**60051 'Blink Bonny'** BRc green - *00*	65	80

L19. A4 Class 4-6-2

1862	**4498 'Sir Nigel Gresley'** LNER blue as preserved - *99-00*	60	75
1865	**60025 'Falcon'** BRc green - *99-00*	60	75
1865	**60003 'Andrew K. McCosh'** BRc green + 'The Capitals Ltd' headboard - *00*	65	NA
18611	**60017 'Silver Fox'** BRb blue - *00*	60	75

L20. Streamlined Bulleid Pacific 4-6-2 (1st Version)

This model was passed off as both a light and a heavy Bulleid Pacific. The body tool was damaged and later replaced by an improved one. This version has the two cab windows each side the same size.

NE5BR	**34066 'Spitfire'** BRb green - *77*	60	75
1505	**34066 'Spitfire'** BRb green - *78-92*	60	75
NE5S	**21C17 'Belgian Marine'** SR green - *77*	60	75
1503	**21C17 'Belgian Marine'** SR green - *78-92*	60	75
NE5SR	**21C1 'Channel Packet'** SR green - *77*	60	75
1503	**21C1 'Channel Packet'** SR green - *78-80*	60	75
NE5GA	**21C1 'Channel Packet'** SR green, Golden Arrow Ltd Edn - *77*	70	85
1513	**21C1 'Channel Packet'** SR green, Golden Arrow Ltd Edn - *85*	70	85
1507	**35001 'Channel Packet'** BRb blue - *80-92*	60	75

L21. Streamlined Bulleid Pacific 4-6-2 (2nd Version)

Following damage to the original body tool, this second version was tooled up. This version has the two cab windows each side different sizes.

1523	**21C4 'Cunard White Star Line'** SR green - *00*	65	80
1525	**34065 'Hurricane'** BRb green - *00*	65	80

L22. Rebuilt Bulleid Pacific 4-6-2

1513	**35028 'Clan Line'** BRc green - *97-00*	60	75
1515	**34089 '602 Squadron'** BRc green - *97-00*	60	75
151A	**34012 'Launceston'** BRc green Sp Edn (silver label) - *99-00*	65	80
-	**35027 'Port Line'** BRc green ex set 8526 - *00*	65	NA

L23. 8F Class 2-8-0

1901	**8177** LMS black - *86-00*	55	70
1902	**3537** LNER black - *87*	55	70
19011	**3107** LNER black - *00*	60	75
1905	**48476** BRc black - *86-00*	55	70
1905	**48331** BRc black - *86-00*	55	70
19012	**48473** BRc black - *00*	60	75

L24. Class 08 Diesel Shunter 0-6-0

1001	**7130** LMS black - *79-85*	30	45
1003	**54** Southern black - *79-80*	40	55
1005	**D4019** BRc red rods green - *79-00*	35	50
1006	**08500 'Thomas 1'** BR red York Wagon Repair Depot - *91-99*	35	50
1007	**08113** BRe blue, yellow rods - *79-00*	35	50
1007	**08493** BRe blue, yellow rods - *79-00*	35	50
1008	**08834** BRe Rft Distribution grey - *91-00*	35	50
100F	**08957** EWS maroon+yellow Sp Edn (silver label) - *99*	40	55
100G	**08921** EWS maroon+yellow Sp Edn (silver label) - *99*	40	55

Class 08 shunter [L24]

L25. Class 20 Diesel Bo-Bo

8204	**D8144** BRc green, yellow ends - *82-00*	40	55
8205	**20142** BRe blue - *82-00*	40	55
8205	**20215** BRe blue - *82-00*	40	55
8208	**20215** BRe Rft red stripe, grey Sp Edn - *91-93*	45	60
82011	BRc green half ends Sp Edn - *00*	45	60
82012	DRS blue Sp Edn - *00*	45	60

L26. Class 25 Diesel Bo-Bo

8304	**D7645** BRc 2-tone green - *83-00*	40	55
8305	**25326** BRe blue - *83-00*	40	55
8305	**25288** BRe blue - *83-00*	40	55
83011	**D7672** BRe blue - *00*	45	60

L27. Class 31 Diesel A1A-A1A

8064	**D5558** BRc green - *95-00*	45	60
8065	**31140** BRe blue - *95-00*	45	60
8066	**31205** BR Rft red stripe grey - *00*	50	65
8067	**31421 'Wigan Pier'** Regional Railways blue+grey - *95-00*	45	60
8011	**31601 'Bletchley Park Station X'** Fragonset - *00*	50	65
806A	**31552** BRe Civil Engineering grey+ yellow Sp Edn (silver label) - *97*	50	65
806B	**31466** EWS maroon+yellow Sp Edn (silver Label) - *99*	45	60

L28. Class 33 Diesel Bo-Bo

8312	**33025 'Sultan'** BRe Civil Engineering grey+yellow Sp Edn (silver label) - *96*	50	65
8314	**D6572** BRc green - *87-00*	45	60
8315	**33012** BRe blue - *87-00*	45	60
8315	**33035** BRe blue - *87-00*	45	60
8316	**33056 'The Burma Star'** BRe Rft Construction grey - *90-00*	45	60
8317	**33205** BRe Rft Distribution grey - *90-00*	50	65
831A	**33030** EWS maroon Sp Edn (silver label) - *99*	50	65
83111	**D6525 'Captain Bill Smith RNR'** BRe blue (also 371-125) - *00*	45	60

L29. Class 37 Diesel Co-Co

8014	**D6736** BRc green split head code - *81-88*	45	60
8015	**37035** BRe blue - *81-91*	45	60
8035	**37408 'Loch Rannoch'** BReLL blue - *00*	50	65
8036	**37699** BRe Rft Coal grey Canton motifs - *90-98*	45	60
8036	**37696** BRe Rft Coal grey Canton motifs - *99-00*	45	60
8037	**37887** BRe Rft Petroleum grey Ripple Lane motifs - *90-00*	45	60
8038	**37906** BRe Rft Metals grey Canton motifs - *90-00*	45	60
803D	**37055 'Rail Celebrity'** Mainline blue Sp Edn (silver label) - *97*	50	65

803E	**37408 'Loch Rannoch'** EWS maroon+yellow Sp Edn - *99*	50	65
80311	? DRS blue - *00*	50	65
80312	? Great Scottish LMS maroon - *00*	50	65

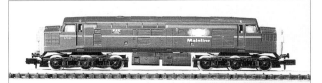

Class 37 diesel [L29]

L30. Class 40 Diesel 1-Co-Co-1

8114	**40106 'Atlantic Conveyor'** BRc green, yellow nose Sp Edn - *86-88*	50	65
8115	**D348** BRc green - *86-00*	50	65
8116	**40015 'Aquitania'** BRe blue - *86-99*	50	65
8117	**40145** BRe blue - *86-99*	50	65
81111	**'Atlantic Conveyor'** BRc green - *00*	50	65

L31. Class 43 HST

8122	**43185 'Great Western' + 41007+ 43031** FGW green+ivory 3-car - *99-00*	55	70
8125	**253007(W43015+W41015+W43014)** *BRe I-C blue+grey 3-car - *81-98*	55	70
8125	**253007(W43015+W42263+W43014)** BRe I-C blue+grey 3-car - *81-98*	55	70
8165	BRe blue+grey driving car only - *84-00*	35	50
0735	BRe blue+grey dummy driving car only - *84-00*	10	14
8126	**W43014+?+W43014** BRe I-C Executive grey 3-car - *83-90*	55	70
8126	**43129+W42023+43130** BRe I-C Executive grey 3-car - *83-90*	55	70
8126	**43129+W41015+43130** BRe I-C Executive grey 3-car - *83-90*	55	70
8166	BRe I-C Executive grey driving car only - *84-00*	35	50
0736	BRe I-C Executive grey dummy driving car only - *84-00*	10	14
8127	**43080+43081** ICs grey 3-car - *90-00*	60	75
8127	**43070+43071** ICs grey 3-car - *90-00*	60	75
8128	**43084+42108+43084 'County of Derbyshire'** Virgin red 3-car - *99-00*	60	75
81211	Midland Mainline green 3-car - *00*	70	85
81212	GNER navy 3-car - *00*	70	85

* both end cars powered.

L32. Class 47 Diesel Co-Co

8001	**47708 'Waverley'** BRe ScotRail grey - *88-99*	45	60
8002	**47813 'SS Great Britain'** First Great Western green - *99-00*	45	60
8004	**D1662 'Isambard Kingdom Brunel'** BRc 2-tone green code 1B28 - *81-00*	45	60
8005	**47455** BRe blue - *81-99*	45	60
8006	**47712 'Lady Diana Spencer'** BReLL blue Ltd Edn - *81*	55	NA
8007	**47583 'County of Hertfordshire'** BReLL blue - *82-99*	45	60
8008	**47231 'The Silcock Express'** BRe Railfreight Distribution grey Tinsley motif - *88-99*	45	60
8018	**47582 'County of Norfolk'** BRe Network SouthEast bright blue - *89-92*	45	60
8022	**47710 'Lady Godiva'** Waterman Railways black Sp Edn (silver label) - *96*	50	65
8023	**47125** Rft Distribution grey tunnel & Tinsley motifs - *95-00*	45	60
8024	**47598** BRe NSE bright blue - *91-99*	45	60

8025	**47594** BRe RES red Crewe Diesel motif - *92-00*	45	60
8026	**47487** BRe InterCity Exec. grey - *88-92*	45	60
8027	**47479 'Track 29'** BRe Parcels red+dark grey - *91-98*	45	60
8028	**47834 'Fire Fly'** ICs grey - *91-00*	45	60
800A	**47814 'Totnes Castle'** Virgin red - *99-00*	50	65
801A	**47817** Porterbrook purple+white Ltd Edn 500 (red label) - *99*	55	70
802C	**47744** EWS maroon+yellow Sp Edn (silver label) - *98*	50	65
80211	**47747 'Graham Farish'** Virgin red Sp Edn - *00*	50	65
80212	**47701 'Waverley'** Fragonset - *00*	50	65

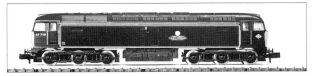

Class 47 diesel [L32]

L33. Class 50 Diesel Co-Co

8404	**50003 'Temeraire'** BReLL blue - *83-88*	50	65
8405	**50024 'Vanguard'** BReLL blue - *83-99*	45	60
8406	**50007 'Sir Edward Elgar'** BRe green GWR style - *84-99*	45	60
8408	**50002 'Superb'** NSE blue - *90-99*	45	60
84011	**50017 'Royal Oak'** LMS maroon - *00*	45	60

L34. Class 52 'Western' Diesel Hydraulic

8424	**D1002 'Western Explorer'** BRc green - *85-88*	45	65
8424	**D1036 'Western Emperor'** BRc green - *85-88*	45	65
8425	**D1070 'Western Gauntlet'** BRe blue - *85-88*	45	65
8426	**D1062 'Western Courier'** BRc maroon - *85-99*	45	65
8426	**D1065 'Western Consort'** BR maroon - *99-00*	45	65

L35. Class 55 Deltic Co-Co

8414	**D9021 'Argyll & Sutherland Highlander'** BRc 2-tone green - *84-00*	45	60
8414	**55013 'Royal Scots Grey'** BRe blue - *?*	45	60
8415	**55013 'Black Watch'** BRe blue - *84-99*	45	60
8416	**55009 'Alcydion'** BRe blue, white window surrounds - *84-88*	45	60
814A	**9016 'Gordon Highlander'** Porterbrook purple+white Ltd Edn 500 (red label) - *00*	50	65

Class 56 diesel [L36]

L36. Class 56 Diesel Co-Co

8055	**56076** BRe blue - *93-00*	45	60
8056	**56059** BRe Rft Construction grey - *93-00*	45	60
8057	**56092** BRe Rft Coal grey Toton motifs - *93-00*	45	60
805D	**56055** LoadHaul black+orange Sp Edn (silver label) - *97*	50	65
805E	**56057 'British Fuels'** EW&S maroon Sp Edn (silver label) - *97*	50	65

Graham Farish N

L37. Class 57 Diesel Co-Co
Same model as Class 47 (above)

804A	**57001 'Freightliner Pioneer'** green Freightliner Sp Edn (silver label) - *99*	45	60
80411	**57011 'Freightliner Challenger'** Freightliner green - *00*	50	65

L38. Class 87 Electric

883A	**87009 'City of Birmingham'** Virgin red - *99-00*	50	65
8837	**87001 'Royal Scot'** ICs grey - *99-00*	50	65
8835	**87101 'Stephenson'** BRe blue - *99-00*	50	65

L39. Class 90 Electric

8825	**90019 'Penny Black'** RES red - *95-00*	50	65
8827	**90015 'BBC North West'** ICs grey - *95-00*	50	65
8828	**90022 'Freightconnection'** BRe Rft Distribution grey - *95-00*	50	65
882A	**90013 'The Law Society'** Virgin red Sp Edn - *99-00*	55	70

L40. Class 91 Electric

8807	**91004** ICs grey - *90-00*	50	65
8807	**91005** ICs grey - *90-00*	50	65
8807	**91007** ICs grey - *90-00*	50	65

L41. Class 101 DMU

8133	**W50304+W50329** BRc green half yellow panel 2-car - *82-00*	50	65
8143	**W50304+W59122+W50329** BRc green half yellow panel 3-car - *82-00*	55	70
?	**M50313+M59124+M56055** BRc green 3-car powered or non-powered - *00?*	55	70
8153	BRc green half yellow panel driving car only - *85-00*	35	50
8135	**M50303+M50330** BRe blue+grey 2-car - *82-00*	50	65
8145	**M50303+M59130+M50330** BRe blue+grey 3-car - *82-00*	55	70
?	**53751+59128+51437** BRe blue+grey 3-car - *?*	55	70
8155	BRe blue+grey driving car only - *85-00*	35	50
8136	**M50330+M50303** BRe blue 2-car - *82-00*	50	65
8146	**M50330+M59130+M50303** BRe blue 3-car - *82-00*	55	70
?	**M50330+M59130+M50303** BRe blue 3-car non-powered - *?*	55	70
8156	BRe blue driving car only - *85-00*	35	50
8137	**E56063+E50202** BRe white+blue 2-car - *82-88*	50	65
8147	**E56063+E59070+E50202** BRe white+blue 3-car - *82-88*	55	70
8157	BRe white+blue driving car only - *85-00*	35	50
8131	**101653(54358+51426)** Regional Railways blue+white 2-car - *91-00*	50	65
?	**101653(54358+51426)** Regional Railways blue+white 2-car non-powered - *92-00*	50	65
8148	**L832 (51226+59570+51499)** Network South East bright blue 3-car - *91-00*	55	70
814A	**101304(51224+59090+53241)** Strathclyde PTE orange Ltd Edn 500 (red label) - *92*	60	75

L41a. Class 101 Driving Car (unpowered) (DTC)

0903	**BR** green - *85-?*	10	14
0905	**BR** blue+grey - *85-?*	10	14
0906	**BR** blue - *85-?*	10	14
0907	**BR** white+blue - *85-?*	10	14

L41b. Class 101 Driving Car (unpowered) (DMC)

0923	**BR** green - *85-?*	10	14
0925	**BR** blue+grey - *85-?*	10	14
0926	**BR** blue - *85-?*	10	14

0927	**BR** white+blue - *85-?*	10	14

L42. Class 158 DMU

8707	**158865 (52360+57860)** Regional Railways blue+white - *92-00*	55	70
8707	**158860 (52865+57865)** Regional Railways blue+white - *92-00*	55	70
0887	**158865 (52360+57860)** Regional Railways blue+white non-powered - *92-00*	55	70
8707	**158860 (52865+57865)** Regional Railways blue+white non-powered - *92-00*	55	70
?	Thai Rail blue+white (export only) - *92-00*	70	100

L43. Class 159 DMU

8748	**159007(52879+58724+57879)** NSE bright blue 3-car - *94-00*	55	70

L44. AEC Diesel Railcar

8174	**No.19** GWR button brown+cream - *85-00*	45	60
8175	**W24W** BRc green - *86-88*	45	60
8175	**W28W** BRc green - *86-88*	45	60
8176	**W27W** BR red+cream - *85-88*	45	60

COACHES

The first coaches were 4-wheeled ones, like those initially released in 1949 for the old 00 gauge system. The first announcement of bogie coaches came early in 1972 and by the end of the year, the full range was available in painted and tampo printed finish as the 'Superstock' range.

The GF MK1s were originally produced with the windows on a printed strip inserted into the body side and this allowed virtually any type to be modelled. At some point in the 1980s, they were revised to feature a totally clear body shell with the entire livery printed on.

Cat.No.   Company, Number, Colour, Dates   £   £

4-wheeled coach [C1a]

C1a. 4-Wheeled Coach (Freelance)
These appear to have been based on a Great Northern Railway design.

NR50T2	light brown 2nd - *71-72*	5	9
NR50T3	light brown 3rd - *71-72*	5	9
NR50M2	maroon 2nd - *71-73*	5	9
NR50M3	maroon 3rd - *71-73*	5	9
NR50G2	green 2nd - *71-73*	5	9
NR50G3	green 3rd - *71-73*	5	9
NR50B2	brown 2nd - *71-73*	5	9
NR50B3	brown 3rd - *71-73*	5	9
NR50/3	teak 3rd - *72-73*	5	9
NR66M	**LMS** maroon 3rd - *78*	7	9
661	**LMS** maroon 3rd - *78-88*	7	9
NR66N	**LNER** 3567 teak 3rd - *78*	7	9
662	**LNER** 3567 teak 3rd - *78-88*	7	9
NR66S	**SR** 5303 green 3rd - *78*	7	9
663	**SR** 5303 green 3rd - *78-88*	7	9
NR66W	**GWR** dark brown+cream 3rd - *78*	7	9
664	**GWR** dark brown+cream 3rd - *78-88*	7	9
667	**S&DJR** 18 dark blue 3rd - *81-88*	10	12

668	**CR** maroon+white 3rd - *81-88*	10	12
-	**The Shredded Wheat Co** yellow 3rd * - *89*	5	8
-	**Poole No1** dk.blue, yellow stripe ex set 8350 * - *94-99*	7	9

* These coaches were specially made for train sets (8350) and had a new chassis with non-universal couplings consisting of a hook one end and an oval loop the other. The couplings on the Shredded Wheat coaches had a small circular loop.

C1b. 4-Wheeled Brake (Freelance)

These appear to have been based on a Great Northern Railway design.

NR51T	light brown - *71-73*	5	9
NR51M	maroon - *71-73*	5	9
NR51G	green - *71-73*	5	9
NR51B	brown - *71-73*	5	9
NR51/1	teak - *72-73*	5	9
NR67M	**LMS** 376 maroon - *78*	7	9
671	**LMS** 376 maroon - *78-88*	7	9
NR67N	**LNER** 7894 teak - *78*	7	9
672	**LNER** 7894 teak - *78-88*	7	9
NR67S	**SR** 3725 green - *78*	7	9
673	**SR** 3725 green - *78-88*	7	9
NR67W	**GWR** 253 dark brown+cream - *78*	7	9
674	**GWR** 253 dark brown+cream - *78-88*	7	9
677	**S&DJR** 14 dark blue - *81-88*	10	12
678	**CR** dk.red+white - *81-88*	10	12
-	**The Shredded Wheat Co** * yellow - *89*	5	8

* These coaches were specially made for train sets and had a new chassis with non-universal couplings consisting of a hook one end and a loop the other.

C2a. 57' Suburban Composite (Freelance)

NR60M	**LMS** 7094 maroon - *72-78*	6	8
601	**LMS** 7094 maroon - *78-79*	6	8
606	**LMS** 16093 maroon panelled - *82-00*	6	8
NR60N	**LNER** 52347 teak - *76-78*	6	8
602	**LNER** 52347 teak - *78-00*	6	8
NR60S	**SR** 7253 green - *72-78*	6	8
603	**SR** 7253 green - *78-00*	6	8
NR60W	**GWR** 7053 dark brown+cream - *72-78*	6	8
604	**GWR** 7053 dark brown+cream - *78-80*	6	8
604	**GWR** 273 dark brown+cream - *78-80*	6	8
604	**GWR** 269 dark brown+cream lined - *79-00*	6	8
604	**GWR** 270 dark brown+cream lined - *79-00*	6	8
NR60BR	**BR** M6743 red - *78*	6	8
605	**BR** M6743 red - *78-00*	6	8
608	**CR** maroon+white panelled - *81-?*	9	12

C2b. 57' Suburban Brake End (Freelance)

NR61M	**LMS** 3762 maroon - *72-78*	6	8
611	**LMS** 3762 maroon - *78-79?*	6	8
616	**LMS** 20354 red panelled - *82-00*	6	8
NR61N	**LNER** 34789 teak - *76-78*	6	8
612	**LNER** 34789 teak - *78-00*	6	8
NR61S	**SR** 2597 green - *72-78*	6	8
613	**SR** 2597 green - *78-00*	6	8
NR61S	**SR** 2697 green - *72-78*	6	8
NR61W	**GWR** 7294 dark brown+cream - *72-78*	6	8
614	**GWR** 7294 dark brown+cream - *78-80*	6	8
614	**GWR** 849 dark brown+cream lined - *79-00*	6	8
614	**GWR** 854 dark brown+cream lined - *79-00*	6	8
NR61BR	**BR** M2570 red - *78*	6	8
615	**BR** M2570 red - *78-00*	6	8
618	**CR** maroon+white panelled - *81-?*	9	12

C3a. 57' Main Line Composite (Freelance)

NR62M	**LMS** 9485 maroon - *72-78*	6	8
621	**LMS** 9485 maroon - *78-81*	6	8
626	**LMS** 6143? maroon panelled - *82-00*	6	8
NR62N	**LNER** 75674 teak - *76-78*	6	8
622	**LNER** 75674 teak - *78-00*	6	8
NR62S	**SR1707?** green - *72-78*	6	8
623	**SR1707?** green - *78-00*	6	8
NR62W	**GWR** 2387? dark brown+cream - *72-78*	6	8
624	**GWR** 2387? dark brown+cream - *78-80*	6	8

624	**GWR** 709 dark brown+cream lined - *79-00*	6	8
NR62BR	**BR** M5801 red+cream - *76-78*	6	8
625	**BR** M5801 red+cream - *78-00*	6	8

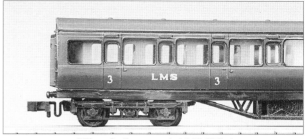

57' main line coach LMS [C3a]

C3b. 57' Main Line Brake End (Freelance)

NR63M	**LMS** 9854 maroon - *72-78*	6	8
631	**LMS** 9854 maroon - *78-81*	6	8
636	**LMS** 6587 maroon panelled - *82-00*	6	8
NR63N	**LNER** 45623 teak - *76-78*	6	8
632	**LNER** 45623 teak - *78-00*	6	8
NR63S	**SR** 2763 green - *72-78*	6	8
633	**SR** 2763 green - *78-00*	6	8
NR63W	**GWR** 2778? dark brown+cream - *72-78*	6	8
634	**GWR** 2778? dark brown+cream - *78-79*	6	8
634	**GWR** 276 dark brown+cream lined - *79-00*	6	8
NR63BR	**BR** M5911 red+cream - *76-78*	6	8
635	**BR** M5911 red+cream - *78-00*	6	8

C4a. Pullman 1st Dining Car

The Pullman Cars were supplied with a choice of transfers.

NR64	**Pullman** brown+cream unnamed - *77-78*	7	9
646	**Pullman** brown+cream unnamed - *78-00*	7	9
646	**Pullman** 'Coral' brown+cream - *99?*	7	9
646	**Pullman** 'Barbara' brown+cream- *99-00*	7	9
646	**Pullman** 'Agatha' brown+cream x-set - *99*	7	NA
?	**Wagon Lits** blue - *80*	10	12

C4b. Pullman 3rd Brake

The Pullman Cars were supplied with a choice of transfers.

NR65	**Pullman** brown+cream unnamed - *77-78*	7	9
656	**Pullman** brown+cream unnamed - *78-00*	7	9
656	**Pullman** 'Irene' brown+cream - *99-00*	7	9
656	**Pullman** 'Fortune' brown+cream x-set - *99*	7	NA

C5a. Mk1 Corridor 2nd (SK)

681	**BRc** M24583 maroon - *81-00*	6	8
681	**BRc** M25250 maroon - *81-00*	6	8
068C	**BR** M25168 maroon Sp Edn - *99-00*	6	8
683	**BRc** S24316 green - *81-00*	6	8
068A	**BRc** S24319 green Sp Edn - *99-00*	6	8
684	**BRc** W24167 dark brown+cream - *81-00*	6	8
685	**BR** E24772 blue+grey - *81-00*	6	8
686	**BR** W24335 red+cream - *82-00*	6	8
068B	**BR** W25238 red+cream - *99-00*	6	8
686	**BR** W24753 maroon+cream - *82-00*	6	8

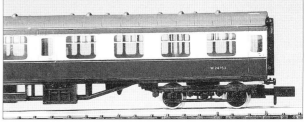

Mk1 corridor 2nd [C5a]

C5b. Mk1 Brake End (BCK)

691	**BRc** M21033 maroon - *81-00*	6	9
691	**BRc** 21236 maroon - *81-00*	6	9
693	**BRc** S21179 green - *81-00*	6	9
694	**BRc** W21072 dark brown+cream - *81-00*	6	9
695	**BR** E21008 blue+grey - *81-00*	6	9
696	**BR** W21021 maroon+cream - *82-00*	6	9
696	**BR** W24753 red+cream - *82-00*	6	9
069A	**BR** M21237 red+cream Sp Edn - *99-00*	6	9
069C	**BR** M25238 red+cream Sp Edn - *99-00*	6	9

C5c. Mk1 Buffet (RMB)

751	**BRc** M1859 maroon - *83-00*	6	9
751	**BRc** M1825 maroon - *83-00*	6	9
753	**BR** S1873 green - *83-00*	6	9
753	**BR** S1849 green - *83-00*	6	9
753	**BR** W1822 green - *83-00*	6	9
754	**BR** W1822 dark brown+cream - *83-00*	6	9
755	**BR** E1834 blue+grey - *83-00*	6	9

C6. Mk1 Full Brake (BG)

771	**BR** M80723 maroon - *84-00*	7	9
772	**BR** Scot Rail 92086 grey (blue stripe) - *88-00*	7	9
772	**BR** Scot Rail 92047 grey (blue stripe) - *88-00*	7	9
773	**BR** S81542 green - *84-00*	7	9
773	**BR** S81292 green - *84-00*	7	9
774	**BR I-C Exec** 92043 grey - *88-00*	7	9
774	**BR I-C Exec** 92075 grey - *88-00*	7	9
775	**BR** W80657 maroon+cream - *84-00*	7	9
775	**BR** W80657 red+cream - *84-00*	7	9
776	**BR** E81125 blue+grey - *84-00*	7	9
776	**BR** E81231 blue+grey - *84-00*	7	9
777	**BR Newspapers** packing van NCV M80560 blue - *84-00*	7	9
777	**BR Newspapers** packing van NCV M80826 blue - *84-00*	7	9
778	**BR Express Parcels** E81231, E81125 blue+grey - *84-00*	7	9
787	**Post Office Parcels** 92212 red NEX - *91-00*	7	9

C7. Mk1 57ft GUV

4101	**BR** M86105 maroon - *93-00*	7	9
4105	**BR** 93356 blue NXV - *91-00*	7	9
4106	**BR RES** 93999 red+black NQX - *91-00*	7	9
4107	**Post Office** 93263 red NJX - *91-00*	7	9

Mk1 GUV [C7]

C8. Post Office Sorting (POS)

797	**Post Office** 80387 NSX red - *91-00*	7	9

C9a. Mk2e Tourist 2nd Open (TSO)

801	**BR ScotRail** 5653, 5662 grey (blue stripe) - *88-00*	7	9
802	**BRe Regional Railways** 5505, 5520 blue +white - *96-00*	9	12
804	**Virgin** 5903 red - *99-00*	9	12
805	**BR I-C** M5775, M5776 blue+grey - *84-00*	7	9
806	**BR I-C** 5749 executive grey - *88-89*	8	10

807	**BR ICs** 5628, 5756 exec grey - *90-00*	7	9
808	**BR NSE** 5523, 5525 bright blue - *88-00*	7	9

C9b. Mk2d 1st Open (TFO)

811	**BR ScotRail** 3248 grey (blue stripe) - *88-00*	10	12
812	**BRe Regional Railways** blue+white - *96-00*	9	12
814	**Virgin** 3278 red - *99-00*	9	12
815	**BR I-C** M3199 blue+grey - *84-00*	10	12
816	**BR I-C** *executive* 3191 grey - *88-89*	8	10
817	**BR ICs** 3177 grey - *90-00*	10	12
818	**BR NSE** 13443, 13514, 13525 blue - *88-00*	10	12
818	**BR NSE** 5523 (error) blue - *?*	12	15

C9c. Mk2 Brake 1st Open (BFO)

080A	**Virgin** 9521 red Sp Edn - *99*	9	12

C9d. Mk2 Refreshment 1st Open (RFO)

081A	**Virgin** 1200 red Sp Edn - *99*	8	10

C10a. Mk3 Open Trailer Second (TS)

701	**BR ScotRail** 12023, 12026 grey (blue stripe) - *88-00*	6	8
702	**FGW** 42079, 42080 [b] green+ivory - *99-00*	8	10
702	**GWT** 42079 [c] green+ivory - *99-00*	8	10
705	**BR I-C** W42023 blue+grey - *81-00*	6	8
706	**BR I-C** W42023 grey - *83-90*	6	8
706	**BR ICs** 42253 grey - *84-90*	6	8
707	**BR ICs** 42219 grey - *90-00*	6	8
708	**Virgin** 42109 red - *99-00*	8	10
070A	**FGW** 42079 green Sp Edn - *99*	8	10

C10b. Mk3 Open Trailer First (TF)

722	**FGW** 41007 green - *99-00*	8	10
725	**BR I-C** W41015 blue+grey - *81-00*	6	8
726	**BR I-C** W41015 grey - *83-90*	6	8
727	**BR ICs** 41108 grey - *90-00*	6	8
728	**Virgin** 41165 red - *99-00*	8	10
070A	**GWT** 41007 [h] green - *99-00*	8	10

C10c. Mk3 Trailer Guard 2nd (TGS)

767	**BR IC** 44079 grey+black - *90-00*	6	8
768	**Virgin** 44076, 44087 red - *99-00*	8	10

C10d. Mk3 Trailer Rest. Unclassified (TRUB)

745	**BR I-C** W40301 blue+grey - *82-00*	6	8
745	**BR I-C** W40325 blue+grey - *82-00*	6	8
746	**BR I-C** W40301 exec grey - *83-90*	6	8

C10e. Mk3 Trailer Rest. Unclassified (TRFB)

747	**BR ICs** 40715 grey+black - *90-00*	6	8
748	**Virgin** 40401 red - *99-00*	8	10

C10f. Mk3a Sleeper (SLEP)

765	**BR I-C** 10536 blue+grey - *82-99*	7	9
765	**BR I-C** 10623 blue+grey - *82-99*	7	9

C11a. Mk 4 Open First (FO)

827	**BR ICs** 11209 grey - *90-00*	7	9

C11b. Mk 4 Tourist Second Open (TSO)

837	**BR ICs** 12406 grey - *90-00*	7	9

C11c. Mk 4 Standard Open End (TSEO)

857	**BR ICs** 12203 grey - *90-00*	7	9

C11d. Mk 4 Restaurant/Buffet (RFM)

847	**BR ICs** 10300 grey+black - *90-00*	7	9

C12. Mk4 Driving Van Trailer (DVT)

867	**BR ICs** 82204 grey+black - *91-00*	9	12

C13. Class 101 Centre Car (TS)

Cat.No.	Company, Colour, Dates	£	£
0913	**BR** green - *85-?*	10	14
0915	**BR** blue+grey - *85-?*	10	14
0916	**BR** blue - *85-?*	10	14
0917	**BR** white+blue - *85-?*	10	14
0918	**BR** NSE bright blue - *88-?*	10	14

WAGONS

The wagons first started to appear at the end of September 1970 and were then added to month by month. Initially these were unprinted but a sheet of rub-on transfers, sufficient for 32 wagons, was also available in black or white. From the start, the wagon chassis was also available on its own. It was not long before wagons were leaving the factory in a range of colourful private owner liveries thanks to the introduction of silicone pad printing. Some of the private owner wagons were initially released only in mixed sets of three but some of these were later available individually.

Cat.No.	Company, Number, Colour, Dates	£	£

W1. Match Truck

NR4	unprinted (transfers) red brown - *70*	3	5

W2. Long Flat and Container

4005	**OOCL** container - *88-?*	4	6
4005	**Dart** container - *88-?*	4	6
4005	**CP Ships** container - *88-?*	4	6
4005	**Merzario** container - *88-?*	4	6

W3. Container

NR2	unprinted (transfers) brown - *70*	5	7
NR2	unprinted (transfers) grey - *70*	5	7

W4. 3-Plank Wagon

NR17	unprinted (transfers) light grey - *70-71*	3	5
NR17	unprinted (transfers) maroon - *70-71*	3	5

W5. 5-Plank wagon

ex3 = from a 3 wagon set

NG8	unprinted (transfers) grey - *70-72*	3	5
NG6	unprinted (transfers) brown - *70-72*	3	5
NG6	unprinted (transfers) grey - *70-72*	3	5
NG9	unprinted (transfers) red-brown - *70-72*	3	5
NG10	unprinted (transfers) brown - *70-72*	3	5
NR20M	**LMS** 166187 light grey - *72-78*	3	5
2001	**LMS** 166187 light grey - *78-00*	3	5
NR20M	**LMS** 165417 light grey - *72-78*	3	5
2001	**LMS** 165417 light grey - *78-00*	3	5
NR20N	**NE** 600047 red-brown - *72-78*	3	5
2002	**NE** 600047 red-brown - *78-00*	3	5
NR20S	**SR** 5087 dark brown - *72-78*	3	5
2003	**SR** 5087 dark brown - *78-00*	3	5
2004	**GW** 15074 dark grey - *78-00*	3	5
2005	**BR** B475908 dark grey - *87-?*	3	NA
2011	**Pitt** 2 grey ex3 - *73-00*	3	NA
2012	**Spiers** 513 yellow ex3 - *78-00*	3	NA
2013	**Snow** black+red ex3 - *78-00*	3	NA

5-plank wagon [W5]

W6. Sheet Rail Wagon

NR9	unprinted (transfers) red-brown - *made?*	NPG	NPG

7-plank wagon [W7]

W7. 7-Plank wagon

ex3 = from a 3 wagon set

NR7	unprinted (transfers) brown - *70-72*	3	5
NR7	unprinted (transfers) grey - *70-72*	3	5
NG11	unprinted (transfers) grey - *70-72*	3	5
NG12	unprinted (transfers) red-brown - *70-72*	3	5
NG13	unprinted (transfers) brown - *70-72*	3	5
NR21M	**LMS** 313154 red-brown - *72-78*	3	5
2101	**LMS** 313154 red-brown - *78-00*	3	5
NR21N	**NE** 131457 red-brown - *72-78*	3	5
2102	**NE** 131457 red-brown - *78-00*	3	5
NR21S	**SR** 5079 dark brown - *72-78*	3	5
2103	**SR** 5079 dark brown - *78-00*	3	5
NR21W	**GW** 102784 dark grey - *72-78*	3	5
2104	**GW** 102784 dark grey - *78-00*	3	5
2105	**BR** B785911 brown - *87-?*	3	5
NR21/5	**Frost** 31 black - *75-78*	3	5
2111	**Frost** 31 black - *78-?*	3	5
NR21/4	**Pritchard** 26 black - *75-78*	3	5
2112	**Pritchard** 26 black - *78-00*	3	5
NR21/3	**Bullcroft** 9471 red - *75-78*	3	5
2113	**Bullcroft** 9471 red - *78-00*	3	5
2114	**Ellis** - *not released*	NA	NA
NR21/6	**South Leicester** 373 red brown - *75-78*	3	5
2115	**South Leicester** 373 red brown - *78-?*	3	5
NR21/1	**JRWood** 1410 yellow - *75-78*	3	5
2116	**JRWood** 1410 yellow - *78-00*	3	5
NR21/2	**Parker & Probert** 80 brown - *75-78*	3	5
2117	**Parker & Probert** 80 brown - *78-00*	3	5
NR21/9	**Lebon** 328 white ex3 - *75-78*	3	NA
2118	**Lebon** 328 white ex3 - *78-?*	3	NA
NR21/9	**Dutton Massey** 313 dark grey ex3 - *75-78*	3	NA
2119	**Dutton Massey** 313 dark grey ex3 - *78-?*	3	NA
NR21/10	**Cam Rys** grey ex3 - *75-78*	3	NA
2120	**Cam Rys** grey ex3 - *78-?*	3	NA
NR21/10	**Dombey** No.77 green ex3 - *75-78*	3	NA
2121	**Dombey** No.77 green ex3 - *78-?*	3	NA
NR21/11	**Sleight** 79 grey ex3 - *75-78*	3	NA
2122	**Sleight** 79 grey ex3 - *78-?*	3	NA
NR21/11	**Powell Gwinnell** black ex3 - *75-78*	3	NA
2123	**Powell Gwinnell** black ex3 - *78-?*	3	NA
NR23/2	**Ocean** 918 black ex3 - *78*	3	NA
2124	**Ocean** 918 black ex3 - *78-00*	3	NA
NR21/12	**Ormiston** 34 navy blue ex3 - *78*	3	NA
2125	**Ormiston** 34 navy blue ex3 - *78-?*	3	NA
NR21/12	**Staveley** black ex3 - *78*	3	NA
2126	**Staveley** black ex3 - *78-?*	3	NA
2127	**Earl of Rosslyns** No.353 brn - *78-?*	3	5
2128	**Alloa** yellow - *86-?*	3	5
2129	**Ebbw Vale** 6158 black - *86-?*	3	5
2130	**Harrods** 64 brown - *86-?*	3	5
2131	**General Refractories** 97 yel - *86-01*	3	5
2132	**Courtaulds** 19 green - *86-?*	3	5
2133	**Prince of Wales** 1857 lt.grey - *?*	3	5
2134	**Princess Royal** 4608 red-brown - *?*	3	5
2136	**Richard Thomas** 6871 black - *99-00*	3	5
2137	**Carlton Main** 5014 red - *99-00*	3	5
2138	**Fulton** 795 black - *99-00*	3	5

2139	**Geo. Mills** 15 black - *99-00*	3	5
2140	**Grey Bros.** 52 caramel - *?*	3	5
2141	**Barrow Barnsley** 720 cream - *?*	3	5
2146	**Renishaw** 917 brown - *99-00*	3	5
2147	**Dinnington Main** blue - *99-00*	3	5
2149	**Ilkeston & Heanor Water Board** 17 blue - *99-00*	3	5
?	**JK Harrison** 134 red - *?*	3	5
?	**Wm Harrison** 2227 grey - *?*	3	5
-	**British Railway Modelling** 2000 - *00-01*	3	5

W8. OAA/OBA Long Open Wagon

3805	**BR Rft** 100033 grey+red OAA - *88-?*	6	8
3806	**BRe** 100054 brown OAB - *88-?*	6	8
3807	**EWS** 200831 maroon OAB - *98-?*	6	8

W9. Steel Mineral Wagon

An all-welded version was modelled, with top hinged doors at sides and ends.

NR8	unprinted (transfers) light grey - *70-71*	3	5
NR8	unprinted (transfers) red-brown - *70-71*	3	5
NR22M	**LMS** 616014 red-brown - *72-78*	3	5
2201	**LMS** 616014 red-brown - *78-00*	3	5
NR22W	**GW** 110134 dark grey - *72-78*	3	5
2204	**GW** 110134 dark grey - *78-00*	3	5
2205	**BR** B565010 dark grey MCO - *88-?*	3	5
2211	**SC** 07217 dark grey - *79-?*	3	5

W10. Open Presflo Type Hopper Wagons

3411	**BISC** 395 very dark grey - *82-00*	3	5
3412	**NCB** 57 dark grey - *82-00*	3	5
3413	**Sheepbridge** light brown - *82-00*	3	5
3414	**Tarmac** 91 fawn - *82-00*	3	5

W11. Presflo Closed Hopper Wagon

3505	**BR** brown CSA - *88-?*	4	6
3511	**ARC** AR12649 yellow - *82-00*	4	6
3512	**Blue Circle Cement** yellow - *82-00*	4	6
3513	**Cerebos Salt** red - *82-00*	4	6
3514	**Tunnel Bulk Cement** grey - *82-00*	4	6

W12. MEA or HEA

The components for this wagon were made in Poole but assembled by Bachmann staff in Barwell following closure of the Poole factory on 23 December 2000.

373-500	**EWS** 361320 maroon - *01*	NPG	7
373-501	**Railfreight** Coal 360501 grey - *01*	NPG	7

W13. PGA Aggregate Hopper Wagon

4411	**ARC** ARC14284 sand - *93-?*	5	7
4412	**Yeoman** PR14435 grey+blue - *93-?*	5	7
4413	**ECC Quarries** PR143?? blue - *99-00*	5	7
4414	**Tilbury** TRL14612? white+brown - *99-00*	5	7

W14. PGA 38T Covered Hopper Wagon

4511	**British Industrial Sand** white - *93-?*	5	7
4512	**Tullis Russel** BS7842 blue - *93-?*	5	7

W15. Sand, Salt & Lime Wagon

?	**Dunlow Lime** brown - *80-?*	4	6
2911	**NE** Sand grey - *81-?*	4	6
2912	**Saxa Salt** yellow - *81-?*	4	6
2913	**Dunlow** Lime black? - *81-?*	4	6
2914	**South Wales** Lime white - *81-?*	4	6

W16. PCA Presflo Tanker

4211	**Rugby Cement** PR10041 grey - *93-00*	5	7
4212	**Cerestar** PR10017 white - *93-00*	5	7
4213	**Castle Cement** grey - *99-00*	5	7
4214	**ICI** Mond white - *99-00*	5	7

W17. PCA Bulk Powder V Tanker

4311	**Albright & Wilson** blue - *93-00*	5	7
4312	**Tiger** TRL9473 yellow - *93-00*	5	7
4313	**BR** 9150 grey - *99-00*	5	7
4313	**BR** 9226 grey - *99-00*	5	7
4314	**Lever Bros.** TRL10527 purple - *99-00*	5	7
4315	**Ketton Cement** yellow - *99-00*	5	7

W18. Tar Wagon

NR15	unprinted (transfers) black - *70*	NPG	NPG
2811	**Burnden** black - *81-?*	4	6
2812	**R S Clare** 19 black - *81-?*	4	6
2813	**Shell BP** black - *81-00*	4	6
2814	**Esso** black - *81-?*	4	6

Tar tank [W18]

W19. Cattle Van

NR13	unprinted (transfers) dark grey - *70-72*	4	6
NR26M	**LMS** 22719 green-grey - *72-78*	4	6
2601	**LMS** 22719 green-grey - *78-00*	4	6
2601	**LMS** red-brown - *78-00*	4	6
NR26S	**SR** 53710 dark brown - *72-78*	4	6
2603	**SR** 53710 dark brown - *78-00*	4	6
NR26W	**GW** 106325 dark grey - *72-78*	4	6
2604	**GW** 106325 dark grey - *78-00*	4	6
?	**GW** 10632 dark grey - *?*	6	8

W20. Horse Box

This model was based on a horse box on the London, Tilbury & Southend Railway and had a 10' chassis and glazed windows. The chimney on the roof was omitted.

NR14	unprinted (transfers) pale blue - *70-72*	3	5
NG30	unprinted (transfers) red brown - *71-72*	3	5
NG30B	unprinted (tfs) pale blue - *71-72*	3	5
NG30G	unprinted (transfers) green - *71-72*	3	5
NG30F	unprinted (transfers) fawn - *71-72*	3	5
2711	**Sir George Widgeon** 2 brown - *78-00*	3	5

W21. Fish Van

NG12	unprinted (transfers) red - *70-72*	4	6
NG26	unprinted (transfers) red - *70-72*	4	6
NG27	unprinted (transfers) white - *71-72*	4	6
NR25N	**NE** 27456 brown - *72-78*	4	6
2502	**NE** 27456 brown - *78-00*	4	6

W22. 12T Single Vent Van

ex3 = from a 3 wagon set

NR10	unprinted (transfers) brown - *70-72*	4	6
NG10	unprinted (transfers) grey - *70-72*	4	6
NR23M	**LMS** grey Refrigerator - *72-78*	4	6
2301	**LMS** grey Refrigerator - *78-00*	4	6
2301	**LMS** grey 505969 - *78-00*	4	6
2301	**LMS** red-brown - *78-00*	4	6
NR23N	**NE** 186547 red brown - *72-78*	4	6
2302	**NE** 186547 red brown - *78-00*	4	6
NR23S	**SR** 50567 dark brown - *72-78*	4	6
2303	**SR** 50567 dark brown - *78-00*	4	6
NR23W	**GW** 45677 dark grey - *72-78*	4	6
2304	**GW** 45677 dark grey - *78-00*	4	6
2305	**BR** E568011 brown - *88-?*	3	5
2311	**Bass** 14 light grey - *78-00*	3	6
2312	**Worthington** 5 dark brown - *78-00*	3	6

2313	**Knorr** white - *78-00*	3	5
2314	**Terrys** brown - *78-?*	3	5
2315	**Zoflora** green - *78-?*	3	5
2316	**Fyffes** yellow - *78-00*	3	NA
2317	**Fremlin Bros**. 1 white - *78-00*	3	5
2318	**Allsops** 4 ivory - *78-00*	3	5
?	**Rail Mail** green - *?*	4	6
?	**Rail Mail** buff - *?*	4	6

W23.   12T Twin Vent Van

NR11	unprinted (transfers) brown - *70-72*	3	5
NR11	unprinted (transfers) grey - *70-72*	3	5
NR?	unprinted (transfers) black - *70-72*	4	6
NG24	unprinted (transfers) grey - *70-72*	3	5
NG24	unprinted (transfers) red brn - *70-72*	3	5
NR24M	**LMS** 7126 dark grey - *72-78*	3	5
2401	**LMS** 7126 dark grey - *78-00*	3	5
2401	**LMS** red-brown - *78-00*	3	5
NR24S	**SR** 52953 dark brown - *72-78*	3	5
2403	**SR** 52953 dark brown - *78-00*	3	5
NR24W	**GW** 93252? dark grey - *72-78*	3	5
2404	**GW** 93252? dark grey - *78-00*	3	5
2411	**Anglo Sportsman** white - *79-00*	3	5
2412	**Gibbs SR** navy - *79-01*	3	5
2413	**John West** green+red - *79-00*	3	5

W24.   VAB/VBA Long Van

3905	**BR Rft** 200631 red+grey VBA - *88-?*	6	8
3906	**BRe** 200163 brown VAB - *88-?*	6	8
3907	**EWS** maroon VBA - *99-00*	6	8

VBA van in EWS livery [W24]

W25.   GWR Brake Van

NR16	unpainted (transfers) grey - *71-72*	4	6
NR13DG	unpainted brown - *71-72*	4	6
NR31	**GW** 114926 mid.grey* Plymouth - *72-78*	4	6
3104	**GW** 114926 dark grey* Plymouth - *78-00*	4	6
3105	**BR** 114920 grey** - *82-00*	4	6
3104	**BR** 114926 grey** - *82-00*	4	6

* white and light grey roof variations. ** with or without handrails painted white.

W26.   LBSC Brake Van

3001	**LMS** red-brown - *79-00*	4	6
3003	**SR** 55657 grey - *79-00*	4	6
3003	**SR** brown - *78-00*	4	6
3106	**BR** M734658 brown - *88-?*	4	6

W27.   Freightliner Flats with Containers

3605	**OOCL + OCL + Freightliner*** - *83-?*	6	8
3616	**Ford + Danzas**** - *83-?*	6	8
3609	printed 20' containers - *83-?*	6	8
3619	printed 30' containers- *83-?*	6	8
3639	unprinted 20' containers- *83-?*	6	8
3639	unprinted 30' containers- *83-?*	6	8

* other container combinations include Dart, Zanussi and Hapag-Lloyd.   **Other
containers used include ACL, Ford, OOCL and a 30' Freightliner.

W28.   Bogie Sulphate Wagon

NR32N	**NE** red-brown - *78*	4	6
NR32BR	**BR** grey - *78*	4	6
3202	**NE** red-brown - *78*	4	6
3205	**BR** E164857 brown - *79-00*	4	6
3205	**BR** E164857 grey - *79-00*	4	6
3211	**GWR** 54004 dark grey Loco Coal - *79-00*	4	6
3212	**NE** 163542 brown Brick - *79-83?*	4	6

Bogie sulphate wagon [W28]

W29.   TEA Bogie Tank Wagons

3701	**Texaco** red - *83-?*	6	8
3702	**Shell BP** grey - *83-?*	6	8
3703	**Esso** silver - *83-?*	6	8
3704	**Esso** black - *83-?*	6	8
3705	**Shell BP** black - *83-?*	6	8
3706	**Total** red - *83-?*	6	8
3708	**BP** BPO87566 green Sp Edn (silver label) - *91-?*	8	10

W30.   NE Bogie Van

3302	**NE** 102496 red-brown York - *78-00*	5	7

W31.   Set of Three Wagons

NR21/7	Wood, Parker & Probert, Bullcroft - *75-?*	NA	20
NR21/8	Pritchard, Frost, South Leicester - *75-?*	NA	20
NR21/9	Lebon, Worthington, Dutton Massey - *75-?*	NA	20
NR21/10	Dombey, Snow, Cam Rys - *75-?*	NA	20
NR21/11	Sleight, Pitt, Powell Gwinell - *75-?*	NA	20
NR21/12	Ormiston, Rosslyn, Staveley - *78-?*	NA	20
NR23/1	Fyffes, Bass, Spiers - *75-?*	NA	20
NR23/2	Sir G Widgeon, Ocean, Fremlins - *78-?*	NA	20
NR23/3	Knorr, Terrys, Zoflora - *78-?*	NA	20
2999	6 PO wagons + vans - *83-?*	NA	30
3799	assorted bogie tankers - *83?*	NA	25

ACCESSORIES

The Liveway track was released at the same time that the first wagons appeared in the autumn of 1970 and the first lineside feature, a pair of tunnel mouths, arrived in May 1971. The Snap power unit was on sale early in 1972.

SETS

The first four train sets arrived in time for Christmas 1971 and consisted of passenger and freight versions with either of the tank engines.

Graham Farish
by Bachmann

HISTORY

In the summer of 2000, Peter Graham Farish sold Graham Farish Ltd to Bachmann Industries Europe Ltd. While retaining the Houlton Heath premises as the Graham Farish headquarters, production was transferred to China and work started on upgrading the range. It had been planned to carry on making the inherited range, gradually updating it, but as adaptations had to be made before the tooling from Poole could be used on the modern machines in Hong Kong it was decided that the models should be upgraded individually before any products were released.

Bachmann had announced an extensive range of new versions of existing models at the time of the take-over but only a few of these materialised at the time, those with the old Graham Farish catalogue numbering being included in the previous section of this catalogue. The pre-production models of these were exhibited at the 2002 British International Toy & Hobby Fair in London. As a result of the transfer of production to China and the need to upgrade tooling, there was a gap in the market as shelves in model shops were emptied of remaining Graham Farish stock.

The first models from Hong Kong started to arrive in the second half of 2001 when a few wagons and improved HSTs reached the shops. Early in 2002 we also learnt that work had started on a completely new steam model - an LNER Class V2.

Listing - The locos are listed in order of size starting with tank engines followed by tender locos and ending with diesels, electrics and multiple units. The coaches are listed with pre-Nationalisation stock first followed by vehicles of later years. Wagons are listed in the order of: flats, open wagons, hoppers, tanks, vans, brake vans and bogie stock.

LOCOMOTIVES

Cat.No.	Number, Company, Colour, Date	£	£

Tank Engines

L0. General Purpose Tank 0-6-0T (Freelance)
This was the 'all things to all men' model in the original Graham Farish range and was reintroduced for a cheap train set.

(370-025)	**268** Southern green ex-set - *03*	20	NA

Class 57XX pannier tank [L1]

L1. 57xx Class Pannier Tank 0-6-0PT

371-900	**5710** GWR (button) green -*02*	35	45
371-900	**7702** GWR green - *02*	35	45
371-901	**8763** BRb lined black - *02*	35	45
371-901	**5775** BRc lined black - *02*	35	45
371-902	**8700** GWR (button) green - *02*	32	40
371-903	**5796** BRb plain black - *02*	32	40

L2. 8750 Class Pannier Tank 0-6-0PT

371-925	**8763** BR lined black - *02*	35	45
371-926	**6752** GWR green - *02*	40	50
371-927	**4672** BRc plain black - *02*	32	40
371-928	**9643** GWR green - *02*	32	40

L3. 94xx Class Pannier Tank 0-6-0PT

371-950	**8424** BRb plain black - *02*	35	45
371-951	**9401** GWR green - *02*	35	45
371-952	**9436** BRc plain black - *03*	35	45
371-953	**9409** GWR green - *03*	35	45

L4. 3F Class 'Jinty' 0-6-0T

372-200	**47338** BRc plain black - *04*	32	40
372-201	**47483** BRb plain black - *04*	32	40

L5. J94 Class 0-6-0ST

372-500	**8051** LNER black - *not made?*	NA	NA
372-501	**68006** BRb plain black - *not made*	NA	NA
372-501	**68012** BRc plain black - *not made*	NA	NA
372-501	**68079** BRb plain black - *03*	35	42
(370-050)	**68040** BRc plain black ex-set - *03*	35	NA

Class 94 0-6-0ST [L5]

L6. 61xx Prairie Tank 2-6-2T

371-975	**6135** BRb lined green - *03*	40	48
371-976	**6104** GWR (button) green - *03*	40	48
371-977	**5153** BRc lined green - *03*	35	45
371-978	**6116** Great Western green - *03*	35	45
(370-075)	**5136** BRc lined green ex-set - *03*	40	NA

Class 61XX Prairie tank [L6]

L7. 4MT Standard Tank 2-6-4T

372-525	**80097** BRc lined black - *04*	45	55
372-526	**80032** BRb lined black - *04*	45	55

Tender Engines

L8. Fowler 4F Class 0-6-0

372-050	**44018** BRb plain black - *04*	42	55
372-051	**44388** BRc plain black - *04*	42	55
(370-175)	**44143** BRb black ex-Freight set - *03*	45	NA

L9. Fowler 4P Compound 4-4-0

372-100	**41157** BRc lined black - *?*	NPG	NPG

L10. Midland Crab 2-6-0

Fowler tender.

372-225	**42932** BRc lined black - *04*	65	80
372-226	**13098** LMS maroon - *04*	65	80

L10A. V2 Class 2-6-2

First of a new range of high quality N gauge steam outline models. Has both a single flywheel with damper and a flywheel equivalent Maschima can motor.

372-600	**60800 'Green Arrow'** BRc green - *04*	70	90
372-601	**60807** BRb lined black - *04*	70	90
372-602	**4844 'Coldstreamer'** LNER green - *04*	70	90

L11. 49xx Class Hall 4-6-0

372-000	**5955 'Garth Hall'** BRc green - *03*	50	65
372-001	**4931 'Banbury Hall'** GWR green - *not made*	NA	NA
372-001	**4970 'Sketty Hall'** Great () Western green - *03*	50	65

L12. Castle Class 4-6-0

372-025	**7033 'Hartlebury Castle'** BRb green single chimney - *03*	50	60
372-026	**4080 'Powderham Castle'** BRc green double chimney - *03*	45	60
(370-150)	**7004 'Eastnor Castle'** BRc green double chimney ex Bristolian set - *03*	45	NA

L13. King Class 4-6-0

372-550	**6021 'King Richard II'** BRb blue - *03*	45	55
372-551	**6008 'King James II'** BRc green double chimney - *03*	45	55

L14. Black 5 4-6-0

Stanier tender.

372-125	**5305** LMS lined black - *04*	65	85
372-126	**44896** BRb lined black - *04*	65	85

L15. Duchess Class 4-6-2

Double chimney.

372-175	**46255 'City of Hereford'** BRb blue - *03*	60	70
372-176	**6234 'Duchess of Abercorn'** LMS maroon, no smoke deflectors - *03*	70	80
372-177	**46252 'City of Leicester'** BRc green - *04*	55	70
372-178	**46259 'Duchess of Hamilton'** BRc maroon - *04*	55	75
(370-100)	**46245 'City of London'** BRb green ex-Royal Scot set - *03*	60	NA

L16. A3 Class 4-6-2

gsd = German smoke deflectors. GN = GNR type tender.

372-375	**60051 'Blink Bonny'** BRc green double chimney - *?*	NPG	NPG
372-376	**60080 'Dick Turpin'** BRb blue - *?*	NPG	NPG
372-377	**60066 'Merry Hampton'** BRb green GN - *03*	55	75
372-378	**60103 'Flying Scotsman'** BRc green gsd corridor tender - *03*	55	75

L17. A4 Class 4-6-2

No valances. Corridor tender.

372-350	**60017 'Silver Fox'** BRb blue - *made?*	NPG	NPG
372-351	**60022 'Mallard'** BRb express blue - *03*	65	80
372-352	**60009 'Union of South Africa'** BRc green - *03*	60	75

372-353	**60027 'Merlin'** BRc green - *04*	60	70
372-351A	**'Mallard'** LNER blue with plaque - *04*	65	90

Class A3 'Dick Turpin' [L16]

L18. Unrebuilt WC/BB Class 4-6-2

372-275	**21C101 'Exeter'** SR malachite green - *04*	65	90
372-276	**34064 'Fighter Command'** BRc green - *04*	65	90
372-277	**34051 'Winston Churchill'** BRb green - *04*	65	90

L19. Rebuilt Merchant Navy Class 4-6-2

372-300	**35018 'British India Line'** BRb green - *04*	65	75
372-301	**35024 'East Asiatic Co'** BRb blue - *not made*	NA	NA
372-301	**35005 'Canadian Pacific'** * BRb blue - *04*	65	75
(370-225)	**35022 'Holland America Line'** BRc green ex-Atlantic Coast Express set - *03*	65	NA

*This model carries different colour number plates on each side.

L20. 8F/06 Class 2-8-0

Ft = Fowler tender. St = Stanier tender.

372-150	**3107** LNER black St - *04*	65	85
372-151	**48045** BRc black Ft - *04*	65	85

Diesels

L21. Class 08 Diesel Shunter 0-6-0

371-001	**D3729** BRc green - *02*	30	38
371-006	**08585** Freightliner green - *02*	28	35
371-004A	**08623** BRe blue - *02*	28	35
371-007	**08645** BRe Departmental grey - *02*	28	35
371-000	**08653** Railfreight Distribution grey - *02*	30	38
371-005	**08800** ICs dark grey+white - *02*	28	35
371-002	**08921** EWS maroon - *not made*	NA	NA
371-002	**08933** EWS maroon - *02*	30	38
371-008	**13029** BR black - *04*	28	35
371-003A	**13365** BRc green - *03*	28	35

Class 08 EWS [L21]

L22. Class 20 Diesel Bo-Bo

New crisper finish compared with Graham Farish original model.

371-026	**D8134** BRc green - *04*	48	
371-025	**20312** DRS blue - *?*	48	58
371-027	**?** BR Rft grey+yellow - *?*	48	58
371-028	**?** DRS blue - *?*	NPG	58

L23. Class 25 Diesel Bo-Bo

371-075	**D5237** BRc 2-tone green - *04*	48	63
371-076	**D7667** BRe blue weathered - *04*	45	60
(370-200)	**25322 'Tamworth Castle'** BRe blue, yellow cabs, silver roof, ex-Diesel Freight set - *03*	48	NA

Graham Farish by Bachmann

L24. Class 31 Diesel Co-Co

371-?	**5500** BR - ?	NPG	64
371-101	**31410** BR Regional Railways - 04	55	64
371-100	**31601 'Bletchley Park'** Fragonset Rlys - ?	55	64

L25. Class 33 Diesel Bo-Bo

371-126	**33021 'Eastleigh'** BRe Fragonset red BRe logo + Eastleigh motif - 04	45	58
371-127	**33035 'Spitfire'** NSE blue Eastleigh motif - 04	45	58
371-125	**33109 'Captain Bill Smith RNR'** BR blue - made?	NPG	NPG

Class 33 'Captain Bill Smith RNR' [L25]

L26. Class 37 Diesel Co-Co

371-156	**D6607 'Ben Cruachan'** BRc green Eastfield motif - 03	50	65
371-?	**D6700** (NRM Rail 200) - 04	NPG	NPG
371-155	**37417 'Highland Region'** BReLL blue Inverness motif - 03	50	65
371-153	**37419** EW&S maroon+yellow - 03	50	65
371-151	**37428 'Loch Long'/'Loch Awe'** EWS Great Scottish dark maroon - 03	50	65
371-152	BRe Dutch grey+yellow - ?	NPG	NPG
371-154	**37429 'Eisteddfod Genedlaethol'** Regional Railways blue+grey - 03	50	65
371-150	**37609** DRS blue - ?	NPG	NPG

L27. Class 40 Diesel 1-Co-Co-1

371-?	**D200** - ?	NPG	70
371-175	**D306 'Atlantic Conveyor'** BRc green - ?	60	70
371-176	**40052** BRe blue - 04	60	70

L27A. Class 42 Diesel Hydraulic B-B

371-601	**D804 'Avenger'** BRe blue - ?	60	72
371-600	**D815 'Foxhound'** BRc maroon - ?	60	72

L28. Class 43 HST InterCity 125

371-475	**MML** 43047+42157+43058 'Midland Pride' green+cream 3-car - 01	65	90
371-475A	**MML** 'Midland Pride' green+cream 3-car - 04	65	75
371-476	**GNER** 43096+42064+43109 navy blue 3-car - 01	65	90
371-477	**FGW** 43004 + TS + 43025 purple - 02	65	90
371-477	**FGW** 43029 + 42072 + 43031 purple - not made	NA	NA
371-478	**Virgin** 43084 + TS + 43161 red+black WCML - 02	65	90
371-478	**Virgin** 43089 + 42127 + 43091 red+black WCML - not made	NA	NA
371-478A	**Virgin** Challenger red+black 3-car - 03	65	90
371-479	**BR ICs** grey 3-car - 03	65	90

L28A. Class 44 Diesel Co-Co

371-201	**D1 'Scafell Pike'** BR green - ?	65	75
371-200	**44008 'Penyghent'** BRe blue - ?	65	75

L28B. Class 45 Diesel Co-Co

371-575	**'The Royal Artillaryman'** BRc green - ?	65	75
371-576	**45114** BRe blue - ?	65	75

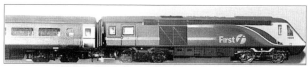

HST in First Great Western livery [L28]

L28C. Class 46 Diesel Co-Co

371-585	**D163 'Leicestershire and Derbyshire Yeomanry'** BRc green - ?	65	75
371-586	**46053** BR blue - ?	65	75

L29. Class 47/57 Diesel Co-Co

371-231	**D1505** BRc 2-tone green weathered - 04	55	65
371-229	**47150** Freightliner green - 02	55	65
(370-125)	**47534 'Crewe Traction Depot'** RES red+ black ex-Royal Mail set - 03	60	NA
371-230	**47635 'The Lass of Ballochmyle'** BReLL blue - 04	60	74
371-227	**47701 'Waverley'** Fragonset black - 02	50	60
371-225	**47747 'Graham Farish'** Virgin red - not made	NA	NA
371-226	**47832 'Tamar'** FGW green - 02	55	65
371-228	**57011 'Freightliner Challenger'** Freightliner green - 02	55	65

Class 57 'Freightliner Challenger' [L29]

L30. Class 50 Diesel Co-Co

371-251	**50004 'St Vincent'** BReLL blue - 03	55	65
371-250	**50017** LMS maroon+gold - 03	55	65
371-?	**50033 'Glorious'** - ?	NPG	72

L30A. Class 52 Western Diesel Hydr. Co-Co

This has a new mechanism and crisper well detailed finish than Graham Farish version.

371-400	**D1023 'Western Fusilier'** BRc maroon - 04	60	70
371-401	**D1030 'Western Musketeer'** BRe Swindon chromatic blue - 04	60	70

L30B. Class 55 Diesel Co-Co

371-275	**D9000 'Royal Scots Grey'** BRc 2-tone green - 03	58	68
371-276	**55006 'The Fife & Forfar Yeomanry'** BRe blue - 03	58	68

L30C. Class 56 Diesel Co-Co

371-301	**56074 'Killingley Colliery'** LoadHaul black+ orange weathered - 04	58	67
371-300	**56105** EW&S maroon+yellow - 04	55	65

L31. Class 60 Diesel Co-Co

371-350	**60052 'Glofa TWR'** EWS maroon - ?	62	75
371-350	**60078 'Glofa TWR'** Mainline blue - ?	62	75

L32. Class 66 Diesel Co-Co

371-375	**66010** EW&S maroon+yellow - ?	62	75
371-376	**66502** Freightliner green - ?	NPG	NPG

Electrics

L33. Class 87 Electric Bo-Bo

371-750	**87001 'Royal Scot'** Virgin red - ?	65	75

L34. Class 90 Electric Bo-Bo

371-776	**90004 'City of Glasgow'** Virgin red - ?	65	75
371-775	**90030 'Crewe Locomotive Works'** EWS maroon+yellow - ?	NPG	NPG

L35. Class 91 Electric Bo-Bo

371-810	**91004 'Grantham'** GNER navy + DVT trailer - ?	NA	84
(371-810)	**91004 'Grantham'** GNER navy - ?	65	NA
(371-810)	**GNER** navy DVT trailer - ?	10	NA
371-800	**91026 'York Minster'** GNER navy - ?	65	75

Multiple Units

L36. Class 101 DMU

371-500	**BRc** green 2-car - ?	60	75
371-500	**ScotRail** 2-car - ?	60	75
371-501	**BR Regional Railways** blue 2-car - ?	60	75

L37a. Classes 158 DMU

371-525	**Northern Spirit** 158811(57811+52811 +58711) purple 3-car - 02	60	75
371-550	**Central Trains** 158783(57783+52783) green 2-car unit - 02	65	86
371-550A	**Central Trains** 158797(?+?) green 2-car unit - 04	65	86
371-551	**First North Western** 158758 (57758+ 52758) blue 2-car unit - 02	55	70
371-552	**Alphaline Wales & West** 158745 (57745+52745) silver 2-car unit - 02	55	70
371-553	**Wessex Trains Alphaline** silver 2-car unit - 02	65	86
371-554	**ScotRail** white+purple Woosh! livery 2-car unit - 04	65	86

L37b. Classes 159 DMU

371-526	**Southwest Trains** 159 - 3-car - 03	65	86

L38. Class 170 Turbostar DMU

371-425	**MML** 1701?? teal green 170/1 2-car - 04	65	84
371-426	**Central Trains** 1705?? green 170/5 2-car - 04	65	84
371-427	**SouthWest Trains** 1703?? white+blue 170/3 2-car - 04	65	84
371-428	**Scotrail** 1704?? Woosh! livery 170/4 3-car - 04	70	92

Class 170 Turbostar [L38]

L39. GWR Railcar

371-625	**W22W** BRc green - ?	40	52

COACHES

Cat.No.	Company, Number, Colour, Date	£	£

C1a. Pullman Parlour Car

374-200	**Pullman** dark brown+cream - ?	NPG	NPG
374-201	**Pullman** dark brown+cream - ?	NPG	NPG

C1b. Pullman Parlour Brake

374-225	**Pullman** dark brown+cream - ?	NPG	NPG
374-226	**Pullman** dark brown+cream - ?	NPG	NPG

C2a. 57' Suburban Coach

374-277	**BR** M? red all 3rd - 04	8	11
374-278	**BR** M? red composite - 04	8	11
(370-075)	**BR** ? red ex-set - 03	10	NA
374-275	**BR** W? maroon lined composite - 04	8	11
374-276	**BR** W? maroon lined all 2nd - 04	8	11

C2b. 57' Suburban Brake 2nd/3rd

374-301	**BR** M? red - 04	8	11
(370-075)	**BR** ? red ex-set - 03	10	NA
374-300	**BR** W? maroon lined - 04	8	11

C3a. Mk1 Open 2nd (SO)

374-000	**BR** M? red+cream - ?	NPG	NPG
374-002	**BR** W? brown+cream - ?	NPG	NPG
374-003	**BR** E? maroon - ?	NPG	NPG
374-001	**BR** S? green - ?	NPG	NPG
374-005	**Reg Rlys** ? blue+grey - ?	NPG	NPG
374-004	**InterCity** ? grey+beige - ?	NPG	NPG

C3b. Mk1 Full Brake (BG)

374-026	**BR** M? red+cream - 03	9	12
374-026A	**BR** M80549 red+cream - 04	9	12
374-029	**BRc** W? brown+cream - 03	9	12
374-027	**BR** E? maroon - 03	9	12
374-027A	**BR** E80792 maroon - 04	9	12
374-028	**BR** S? green - 03	9	12
374-025	**BR** E80617 blue+grey Newspapers - 03	9	12
374-031	**Reg Rlys** E92058 blue+grey NEA - 03	9	12
374-030	**Inter-City** 92151 grey+beige NEA* - 03	9	12
374-032	**RES** 92322 red+dark grey NEX - 03	9	12
(370-125)	**RES** ? red+dark grey ex-set - 03	9	NA

* Box marked NHA but model marked NEA.

Mk1 BG intercity [C3b]

C3c. Mk1 Corridor 2nd (SK)

374-050	**BR** M24446 red+cream - 02	9	12
374-050A	**BR** M? red+cream - 03	9	12
374-050B	**BR** E24807 red+cream - 04	9	12
374-052	**BR** W24165 brown+cream - 02	9	12
374-052A	**BR** W? brown+cream - 03	9	12
374-052B	**BR** W25093 brown+cream - 04	9	12
(370-150)	**BR** ? brown+cream ex-set - 03	9	NA
374-053	**BR** E24538 maroon - 02	9	12
374-053A	**BR** E? maroon - 03	9	12
374-053B	**BR** M25437 maroon - 04	9	12
(370-100)	**BR** ? maroon ex-set - 03	9	NA
374-051	**BR** S24311 green - 02	9	12
374-051A	**BR** S24324 green - 04	9	12
(370-225)	**BR** ? green ex-set - 03	9	NA
374-055	**BR** ? blue+grey - 03	9	12
374-055A	**BR** E25011 blue+grey - 04	9	12
374-054	**BR Intercity** ? grey+beige - 03	9	12

C3d. Mk1 Corridor Brake Comp (BCK)

374-075	**BR** M21026 red+cream - 02	9	12
374-075A	**BR** M? red+cream - 03	9	12
374-077	**BR** W21067 brown+cream - 02	9	12
374-077A	**BR** W? brown+cream - 02	9	12

Graham Farish by Bachmann

(370-150)	BR ? brown+cream ex-set - 03	9	NA
374-078	BR E21202 maroon - 02	9	12
374-078A	BR E? maroon - 03	9	12
(370-100)	BR ? maroon ex-set - 03	9	NA
374-076	BR S21268 green - 02	9	12
374-076A	BR S21271 green - 04	9	12
(370-225)	BR ? green ex-set - 03	9	NA
374-080	BR ? blue+grey - 03	9	12
374-079	BR Intercity ? grey+beige - 03	9	12

C5c. Mk2 Trailer 2nd Open (TSO)

374-727	BR IC ? blue+grey Mk2E - 04	9	12
374-725	Virgin 5966 red+black Mk2E - 04	9	12
374-726	FGW ? green Mk2D - 04	9	12

C5d. Mk2 Trailer 1st Open (TFO/FO)

374-752	BR IC ? blue+grey Mk2F FO - 04	9	12
374-750	Virgin 3381 red+black Mk2E TFO - 04	9	12
374-751	FGW ? green Mk2E TFO - 04	9	12

Mk1 corridor brake composite [C3d]

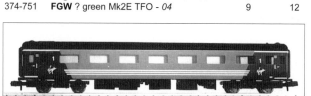

Mk2 trailer 1st open [C5d]

C3e. Mk1 Mini Buffet (RMB)

374-100	BR M? red+cream - not made	NA	NA
374-101	BR W? brown+cream - 03	9	12
374-102	BR W? brown+cream - not made	NA	NA
374-102	BR E? maroon - 03	9	12
374-103	BR E? maroon - not made	NA	NA
374-100	BR S? green - 03	9	12
374-101	BR S? green - not made	NA	NA
374-104	BR ? blue+grey - 03	9	12
374-105	BR ? blue+grey - not made	NA	NA
374-103	BR Intercity ? grey+beige - 03	9	12
374-104	BR Intercity ? grey+beige - not made	NA	NA

C3f. Mk1 Corridor 1st (FK)

374-150	BR M? red+cream - ?	NPG	NPG
374-152	BR W? brown+cream - ?	NPG	NPG
374-153	BR E? maroon - ?	NPG	NPG
374-151	BR S? green - ?	NPG	NPG
374-155	BR Regional Railways? blue - ?	NPG	NPG
374-154	BR Intercity 1832 grey+beige - ?	NPG	NPG

C3g. Mk 1 Corridor Brake 2nd (BSK)

374-175	BR M? red+cream - ?	NPG	NPG
374-177	BR W? brown+cream - ?	NPG	NPG
374-178	BR E? maroon - ?	NPG	NPG
374-176	BR S? green - ?	NPG	NPG
374-180	BR Regional Railways? blue - ?	NPG	NPG
374-179	BR Intercity ? grey+beige - ?	NPG	NPG

C3h. Mk1 Corridor 2nd (CK)

374-250	BR M? red+cream - ?	NPG	NPG
374-252	BR W? brown+cream - ?	NPG	NPG
374-253	BR E? maroon - ?	NPG	NPG
374-251	BR S? green - ?	NPG	NPG

C4. Mk1 General Utility Van (GUV)

374-125	BRe W? blue Express Parcels - 03	9	11
374-126	BR M93337 blue+grey Intercity Motorail - 03	9	11
374-127	BR RES 95197 red+dark grey - 03	9	11
(370-125)	BR RES ? red+dark grey ex-set - 03	10	NA

C5a. Mk2 Brake 2nd Open (BSO)

374-677	BR IC ? blue+grey Mk2F - 04	9	12
374-675	Virgin 9516 red+black Mk2F - 04	9	12
374-676	FGW ? green MK2D - 04	9	12

C5b. Mk2 Buffet Open 1st (RFB/RMBF)

374-702	BR IC ? blue+grey Mk2F RMBF - 04	9	12
374-700	Virgin 1208 red+black Mk2F RFB - 04	9	12
374-701	FGW ? green Mk2D RMBF - 04	9	12

C6a. Mk3 Trailer Standard (TS)

347-329	BR ICs ? grey+beige - ?	NPG	NPG
347-327	GNER 42057 [C] navy blue - 01	9	12
347-328	Virgin 42171 [?] red+black - 02	9	12
-	Virgin 42127 [?] red+black ex-pack - 02	9	NA
374-325	MML 42149 [C] green+cream - 01	9	12
347-326	FGW 42025 [C] purple - 02	9	12
-	FGW 42072 [?] purple ex-pack - 02	9	NA

C6b. Mk3 Trailer 1st (TF)

347-354	BR ICs ? grey+beige - ?	NPG	NPG
347-352	GNER 41091 [G] navy blue - 01	9	12
347-353	Virgin 41081 [?] red+black - 02	9	12
374-350	MML 41064 [G] green+cream - 01	9	12
347-351	FGW 41005 [H] purple - 02	9	12

C6c. Mk3 Trailer Buffet 1st (TRFB)

347-379	BR ICs ? grey+beige - ?	NPG	NPG
347-378	GNER 40705 [F] navy blue - 01	9	12
347-377	Virgin 40732 red+black - 02	9	12
347-375	MML 40729 [F] green+cream - 01	9	12
347-376	FGW 40707 [F] purple - 02	9	12

C6d. Mk3 Trailer Guard's Standard (TGS)

347-404	BR ICs ? grey+beige - ?	NPG	NPG
347-403	GNER 44098 [A] navy blue - 01	9	12
347-402	Virgin 44076 [A] red+black - 02	9	12
347-400	MML 44041 [A] green+cream - 01	9	12
347-401	FGW 44023 [A] purple - 02	9	12

C6e. Mk3 Trailer Buffet Standard (TRSB)

374-425	Virgin ? red+black - ?	NPG	NPG

C6f. Mk3 Trailer Buffet 1st (TRB)

374-450	FGW ? purple - ?	NPG	NPG

C6g. Mk3 Sleeper Car (SLEP)

374-475	FGW ? purple - ?	NPG	NPG
374-476	Scotrail Caledonian ? purple - ?	NPG	NPG

C6h. Mk3 Restaurant Buffet First (RFM)

374-500	Virgin ? red+black - ?	NPG	NPG

C7a. Mk4 Open Standard (Disabled) (TSOD)

374-525	GNER ? navy blue - ?	NPG	NPG

C7b. Mk4 Open Standard (End) (TSOE)

374-550	GNER ? navy blue - ?	NPG	NPG

C7c. Mk4 Open Standard (TSO)

374-575	GNER ? navy blue - ?	NPG	NPG

C7d.   Mk4 Open 1st (FO)

374-600	**GNER** ? navy blue - *?*	NPG	NPG

C7e.   Mk4 Trailer Modular Buffet 1st (TRFM)

374-625	**GNER** ? navy blue - *?*	NPG	NPG

C8.   Mk4 Driving Brake Van (DLV)

374-650	**GNER** ? navy blue - *?*	NPG	NPG

WAGONS

Cat.No.	Company, Number, Colour, Dates	£	£

W1.   5-Plank Wagon

373-150	**EA Stevenson** 10 blue - *01*	4	5
373-151	**Worcester Co-op** 20 red - *01*	4	5
373-152	**Hopton-Wood Stone** 2 grey - *01*	4	5
373-153	**ICI Lime** 3034 grey - *01*	4	5
373-154	**Harry Whitehouse** 16 red - *02*	3	4
373-155	**Joshua Grey** 3 brown - *02*	3	4
373-156	**BR** P143165 grey - *02*	3	4
373-157	**Tarslag** 836 grey - *02*	3	4
(370-200)	**BR** ? grey ex-Diesel Freight set - *03*	3	NA
(370-025)	**Carlton Main** 5014 red ex-set - *03*	3	NA

W1A.   6-Plank Wagon

373-175Z	**Royal Leamington Spa** 22 red Ltd Edn 500 - *04*	3	4

W2.   7-Plank Wagon

373-175	**ICI Salt** 326 brown - *01*	4	5
(370-200)	**ICI Salt** ? brown ex-Diesel Freight set - *03*	4	5
373-176	**Kobo** 15 grey - *01*	4	5
373-177	**Flower & Son** 7 grey-green - *01*	4	5
373-178	**Cosy Fires** 778 grey - *01*	4	5
373-179	**Lunt** 724 grey+black - *02*	3	4
373-180	**Sycobrite** 650 yellow+black - *02*	3	4
373-181	**Florence Coal & Iron** 1017 grey - *02*	3	4
373-182	**Gellyceidrim** 719 light grey - *02*	3	4
373-?	**James Kenworthy** 47 brown Ltd Edn (Bachmann Club) - *03*	3	4
(370-050)	**JR Wood Co** 346 yellow ex-set - *03*	3	NA
(370-175)	**South Leicester** 373? red ex-set - *03*	3	NA

7-plank wagon [W2]

W3.   Coal Traders Wagon Sets

373-900	6 assorted coal wagons - *02*	NA	20

W4.   7-Plank with Coke Rail

373-375	**P.O.P** - *?*	NPG	NPG
373-376	**Stringer & Jaggar** - *?*	NPG	NPG

W5.   31T 5-Plank Open Wagon OAA

373-400	**BRe** 100013 brown - *03*	4	5
373-401	**Railfreight** 100090 grey+red - *03*	4	5

W6.   16T Steel Mineral Wagon

This wagon has pressed steel end and side doors.

373-200	**BR** B38066? grey - *02*	4	5
373-202	**BR** B258683 light grey MCO - *02*	4	5
(370-175)	**BR** ? grey ex-set - *03*	3	NA
373-200A	**BR** B38059 grey - *04*	4	5
373-201A	**BR** B68998 brown Coal - *04*	4	5

W7.   46t Open Mineral Wagon MEA

373-576	**Rft Coal** 391045 grey+yellow - *02*	5	7
373-576A	**Railfreight** Coal ? grey+yellow - *?*	NPG	NPG
373-577	**Mainline** M391139 blue - *02*	5	7
373-577A	**Mainline** ? blue - *?*	NPG	NPG
373-575	**EWS** 391262 maroon - *02*	5	7
373-575A	**EWS** ? maroon - *?*	NPG	NPG

W7A.   24t Open Box Mineral Wagon MFA

373-877	**Rft Coal** 391070 grey+yellow - *03*	5	6
373-875	**EWS** 391102 in Mainline blue - *03*	5	6
373-876	**EWS** 391572 maroon - *03*	5	6

24T MFA open box wagon [W7A]

W8.   46t Hopper HEA/HSA

See also the HEA listed in the earlier Graham Farish N section.

373-502	**BR** 360075 brown HSA - *02*	5	7
373-503	**BRe Railfreight** ? red+grey - *02*	5	7
373-503A	**Railfreight** ? red+grey - *?*	NPG	NPG
373-501	**Railfreight** Coal 360501 grey+yellow - *02*	5	7
373-501A	**Railfreight** Coal ? dark grey - *?*	NPG	NPG
373-504	**ex-Mainline** ? blue + graffiti - *03*	5	7
373-500	**EWS** 361320 maroon+yellow - *02*	5	7

W9a.   46t Hopper HAA

373-900	**BR** ? brown - *04*	5	7
373-902	**Railfreight** Coal ? yellow - *04*	5	7
373-901	**EWS** ? maroon - *04*	5	7

W9b.   46t Covered Hopper CEA

373-475	**LoadHaul** orange+black - *?*	NPG	NPG
373-476	**EWS** maroon - *?*	NPG	NPG

W10.   Bulk Aggregate Hopper PGA

373-025	**Caib** grey - *03*	4	6
373-026	**Tarmac Quarry Products** green - *03*	4	6
373-027	**ARC** yellow - *03*	4	6

W10A.   51t Aggregate Hopper PGA

373-035	**Redland** - *not made?*	NA	NA
373-036	**Railease** PR14466 white - *03*	4	6

W11.   Presflo

373-525	**Rugby Cement** - *not made?*	NA	NA
373-526	**Blue Circle** - *not made?*	NA	NA
373-527	**Pozzoianic** - *not made?*	NA	NA

W12.   Bulk Powder PCA

373-000	**Alcan** 55552 silver - *03*	4	6
373-003	**Alcan** 55552 silver - *04*	4	6
373-001	**Tunnel Cement** RLS10321 white - *03*	4	6
373-004	**Tunnel Cement** ? white - *04*	4	6
373-002	**Blue Circle** DP102 pale grey - *03*	4	6
373-005	**Blue Circle** pale grey - *04*	4	6

| 373-003 | **Blue Circle** (unbranded) BCC11118 pale white - *04* | 4 | 6 |
| 373-002A | **Rugby Cement** PR9420 white - *04* | 4 | 6 |

PCA bulk powder tank [W12]

W13. Taper Bulk Powder PCA
373-075	**Blue Circle** 9343 pale grey - *03*	4	6
373-077	**Blue Circle** (unbranded) APCM9138 pale grey - *04*	4	6
373-075A	**Ketton Cement** PR9468 yellow - *04*	4	6
373-076	**Rockware Glass** 10563 blue - *03*	4	6

W14. 10T Salt Van
| 373-350 | **Shaka Salt** - *?* | NPG | NPG |
| 373-351 | **Stafford Salt Works** - *?* | NPG | NPG |

W15. 12T Cattle Van
373-250	**LMS** M14390 light grey - *03*	3	4
373-252	**NE** 56787 grey - *03*	3	4
373-251	**BR** B891416 brown - *03*	3	4
(370-175)	**BR** ? brown ex-set - *03*	3	NA

W16. 12T Fish Van
| 373-225 | **NE** brown - *?* | NPG | NPG |

W17. 12T LMS Single Vent Van
373-100	**LMS** 505969 grey - *02*	4	5
373-103	**LMS** 505953 light grey - *04*	3	4
(370-050)	**LMS** ? light grey ex-set - *03*	3	NA
(370-025)	**Worthington** 5? brown ex-set - *03*	3	NA
373-101	**BR** M504891 grey - *02*	4	5
373-104	**BR** M504883 light grey - *04*	3	4
(370-200)	**BR** ? grey ex-set - *03*	3	NA
373-102	**BR** ? brown - *03*	4	5
373-105	**BR** E568037 brown - *04*	3	4

12T LMS single vent van [W17]

W18. 12T GWR Twin Vent Van
373-125	**GW** 139956 dark grey - *02*	4	5
373-128	**GW** 139948 dark grey - *04*	4	5
373-130	**BR** W134035 grey - *04*	4	5
373-127	**BR** ? light grey - *?*	NPG	NPG

373-126	**BR** W124480 brown - *02*	4	5
373-129	**BR** W124483 brown - *04*	4	5
(370-175)	**BR** ? brown ex-set - *03*	3	NA

W19. 29T VBA/VBB Box Van
| 373-050 | **Railfraight** brown VBB - *03* | 4 | 5 |
| 373-051 | **Railfreight Coal** olive green VBA - *03* | 4 | 5 |

W20. 20T Toad Brake Van
373-325	**GW** 56683 grey Severn Tunnel Junc.- *02*	5	7
373-325A	**GW** 114800 grey Rhymney - *03*	5	7
373-327	**BR** W35960 grey Shrewsbury (Coton Hill) - *03*	5	7
373-326	**BR** W11496 brown - *?*	NPG	NPG
373-326A	**BR** W11496 brown - *03*	5	7
(370-175)	**BR** ? brown ex-set - *03*	5	NA
373-328	**BR** ? brown S&T Department - *04*	5	7

20T Toad brake van [W20]

W21. 20T Brake Van
(370-025)	? teak ex-set - *03*	3	NA
373-301	**BR** M? grey - *?*	NPG	NPG
373-300	**BR** S? brown - *?*	NPG	NPG
(370-050)	**BR** ? brown ex -et - *03*	3	NA

W22. 63' Bogie Flat + Containers
| 373-451 | 3 x 20' **BR Railfreight** containers - *04* | NPG | NPG |
| 373-450 | 2 x 30' **Railfreight** containers - *04* | NPG | NPG |

W23. 50T Bogie Sulphate Wagon
| 373-425 | Sulphate ? ? - *?* | NPG | NPG |

W23A. 90t Bogie Hopper Wagon JGA
373-800	**Tilcon** ? ? - *?*	NPG	NPG
373-801	**RMC**? ? - *?*	NPG	NPG
373-802	**Buxton Lime** ? ? - *?*	NPG	NPG

W23B. 104t Bogie Steel Carriers BYA/BRA
| 373-825 | **EWS** ? maroon coil BYA - *?* | NPG | NPG |
| 373-826 | **EWS** ? maroon strip BRA - *?* | NPG | NPG |

W23C. 102t Bulk Coal Hopper HTA
| 373-850 | **EWS** ? maroon - *?* | NPG | NPG |

W24. 100T Bogie Tanker
| 373-550 | **Shell BP** 4001 grey - *04* | NPG | NPG |
| 373-551 | **Fina** 508 grey - *04* | NPG | NPG |

Heljan 00 (British)

HISTORY

Based in Sonderso, Denmark, Heljan has made quality kits, in their own factory, for over 40 years. More recently it expanded into ready to run locomotives and rolling stock of a high quality, especially for the Scandinavian market. In 2001 it decided to tackle the UK market with an 00 gauge Class 47 diesel.

Heljan were initially approached by a syndicate of UK H0 modellers concerning the possibility of producing diesels in H0 scale. This proved to be uneconomical due to the small number of people interested in this scale in Britain but 00 scale was felt to hold possibilities. Initially, Heljan had been asked to make a Class 37 diesel but the project later changed to a Class 47. When the sponsors dropped out, the Company decided to go ahead with an 00 gauge model anyway. This was developed quite quickly and arrived in the shops in May 2001. The models are designed and tooled in Denmark and the tools are then shipped out to China for production. The models are assembled and finished in China and then shipped back to Denmark. The blue loco boxes state 'Made in Denmark' and the outer boxes say 'Made in China'. After the first batch of models was distributed the packaging was redesigned to afford greater protection to the models.

Numbering - All catalogue numbers are prefixed with '1100' but are abbreviated here to save space.

LOCOMOTIVES

The locomotives have a heavy diecast Continental chassis with H0 bogies, a 5-pole Buhler motor, Cardan shaft drive, pickups on both bogies, moulded plastic bodies with a high level of detail, working headlights, finescale blackened wheel sets, flush glazing, separately moulded handrails and other detail, NEM coupling sockets, tension-lock couplings and are DCC ready.

Cat.No.	Number, Company, Colour, Date	£	£

L1. Class 35 Hymek Bo-Bo

Centrally mounted 5-pole motor with twin flywheels. DCC ready. NEM sockets with tension-lock couplings.

3505	**D7009** BRc green - *04*	55	79
3500	**D7017** BRc 2-tone green - *03*	55	79
3508	**D7035** BRe blue full yellow ends - *04*	55	79
3502	**D7036** BRe blue small yellow panel white window frames - *03*	55	79
3501	**D7039** BRc 2-tone green small yellow panel - *03*	55	79
3507	**D7040** BRe blue small yellow ends, grey windows - *04*	55	79
3503	**D7042** BRe blue full yellow ends - *03*	55	79
3506	**D7044** BRc green, small yellow ends - *04*	55	79
3504	**D7097** BRc green, full yellow ends - *04*	55	79

Class 47 Freightliner 47258 'Forth Ports Tibury' [L2]
(Rail Express)

L2. Class 47 Co-Co (Late Body)

This model regularly suffered damage in transit from the factory and the company released a pack of spare parts for them to be repaired. Later models had redesigned packaging which gave better protection. esn = etched stainless steel nameplates. EB = early body (1965 to 1982 period). The completely new body features radiator slats as before but with authentic interchangeable illuminated four character headcodes and a boiler flue outlet. The current chassis has been adapted to include under-slung boiler water tanks and a full buffer beam cowling. LB = late body. IB = intermediate body without water tanks and with unmodified cabs, together with marker light panels and headlamps. . IBf = intermediate body with flush No.2 end.

4700	**D1100** BRc 2-tone green small yellow panels EB - *02*	65	89
4701	**D1662 'Isambard Kingdom Brunel'** BRc 2 x green small yell panels EB - *02*	65	89
4730	**D1932** BRe blue EB - *02*	65	89
4702	**D1942** BRc 2-tone green small yellow panels EB - *02*	65	89
4703	**1934** BRc 2-tone green, full yellow ends 0000 headcode EB - *02*	65	89
4731	**47059** BRe blue EB - *02*	65	89
4732	**47076 'City of Truro'** BRe blue EB - *02*	65	89
4732	**47077 'North Star'** BRe blue EB - *not made*	65	89
4675	**47079** Freightliner grey IBf - *not made*	65	89
4831	**47094** Rft Petroleum grey IB - *02*	65	89
4661	**47145 'Merrdin Emrys'** Tinsley blue - *05*	NPG	NPG
4680	**47193** Freightliner green - *05*	NPG	NPG
4664	**47200 'The Fosse Way'** Cotswold Rail silver - *05*	NPG	NPG
4802	**47211** Railfreight grey yellow ends IB - *03*	65	89
4805	**47212** Railfreight Petroleum IB - *03*	65	89
?	**47237** DRS blue IBf Sp Edn (Rail Express) - *03*	65	89
4630	**47245 'Institute of Export'** Rft Distribution European grey LB - *01*	65	89
4640	**47258 'Forth Ports Tilbury'** Freightliner green LB - *02*	65	89
4733	**47278** BRe blue, pale grey roof EB 0000 headcode - *02*	65	89
4663	**47298** DRS blue - *05*	NPG	NPG
4695	**47299 'Ariadne'** BR blue - *05*	NPG	NPG
4677	**47321** unbranded triple grey IBf - *not made?*	65	89
4677	**47321** old Freightliner Distrib. IBf - *03*	65	89
4675	**47334** old Freightliner grey IBf - *03*	65	89
4803	**47340** Railfreight red stripe grey IB - *03*	65	89
4804	**47361 'Wilton Endevour'** Railfreight Distribution grey Thornaby motif IB - *03*	65	89
4678	**47375 'Tinsley Traction Depot'** Railfreight Distribution - *05*	NPG	NPG
4800	**47591** BReLL blue IB - *03*	65	89
4806	**47593 'Galloway Princess'** InterCity grey IB - *03*	65	89
?	**47596 'Aldeburgh Festival'** BRe blue, grey roof IB Sp Edn 750 (47401 Project) - *03*	65	89
4801	**47636 'Sir John de Greame'** BReLL blue small numbers IB - *03*	65	89
4821	**47643** ScotRail red stripe grey IB - *02*	65	89
4679	**47711 'County of Hertfordshire'** NSE revised blue LB - *02*	65	89
4679	**47711 'County of Hertfordshire'** NSE revised blue IBf - *03*	65	89
4662	**47714** Anglia turquoise - *05*	NPG	NPG
4807	**47715** ScotRail blue stripe grey IB - *03*	65	89
4650	**47744** EWS maroon - *02*	65	89
4620	**47778 'Irresistible'** RES red LB - *01*	65	89
4622	**47781 'Isle of Iona'** Rail Express System - *05*	NPG	NPG
4621	**47782** RES red LB - *01*	65	89
4698	**47787 'Windsor Castle'** EWS maroon no headcode recesses esn Ltd Edn 1000 LB - *02*	65	89
4651	**47792 'Robin Hood'** EWS - *05*	NPG	NPG
4660	**47798 'Prince William'** EWS dark purple LB - *02*	65	89
4610	**47805** InterCity swallow grey LB - *01*	65	89

Heljan 00 (British)

4601	**47806** Virgin red+dark grey LB - *01*	65	89
4610	**47807** InterCity swallow grey LB - *?*	65	89
4676	**47810 'Porterbrook'** Virgin - *05*	NPG	NPG
4670	**47815 'Abertawe Landore'** First Great Western dark green LB - *02*	65	89
4611	**47826 'Springburn'** Intercity - *05*	NPG	NPG
4665	**47829** Police livery white LB - *03*	65	89
4667	**47840** BRe blue LB - *03*	65	89
4600	**47843 'Vulcan'** Virgin red+dark grey LB - *01*	65	89
4668	**47847** BReLL Heritage blue LB - *03*	65	89
4666	**47851** BRc Heritage green LB - *03*	65	89
-	**47853/D1733 'Rail Express'** BRe XP64 blue no headcode recesses esn LB Sp Edn 750 (Rail Express) - *02*	65	89

47 Virgin Trains 47843 'Vulcan' [L2] (Rail Express)

WAGONS

Cat.No.	Company, Number, Colour, Date	£	£
W1.	**Dogfish**		
4085	DB993016 - *04*	NPG	20
4086	DB983192 Mainline on hopper - *04*	NPG	20
4087	DB993314 Mainline on solebar - *04*	NPG	20
4088	DB993057 - *04*	NPG	20
4089	DB993413 - *04*	NPG	20
4090	DB993634 - *04*	NPG	20

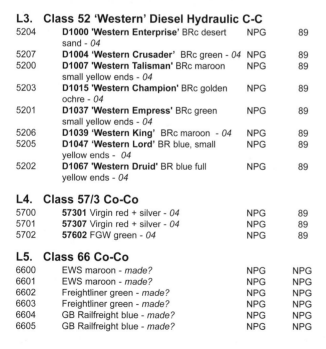

Class 47 Intercity 47805 and Railfreight Distribution 47245 [L2] (Rail Express)

L3. Class 52 'Western' Diesel Hydraulic C-C

5204	**D1000 'Western Enterprise'** BRc desert sand - *04*	NPG	89
5207	**D1004 'Western Crusader'** BRc green - *04*	NPG	89
5200	**D1007 'Western Talisman'** BRc maroon small yellow ends - *04*	NPG	89
5203	**D1015 'Western Champion'** BRc golden ochre - *04*	NPG	89
5201	**D1037 'Western Empress'** BRc green small yellow ends - *04*	NPG	89
5206	**D1039 'Western King'** BRc maroon - *04*	NPG	89
5205	**D1047 'Western Lord'** BR blue, small yellow ends - *04*	NPG	89
5202	**D1067 'Western Druid'** BR blue full yellow ends - *04*	NPG	89

L4. Class 57/3 Co-Co

5700	**57301** Virgin red + silver - *04*	NPG	89
5701	**57307** Virgin red + silver - *04*	NPG	89
5702	**57602** FGW green - *04*	NPG	89

L5. Class 66 Co-Co

6600	EWS maroon - *made?*	NPG	NPG
6601	EWS maroon - *made?*	NPG	NPG
6602	Freightliner green - *made?*	NPG	NPG
6603	Freightliner green - *made?*	NPG	NPG
6604	GB Railfreight blue - *made?*	NPG	NPG
6605	GB Railfreight blue - *made?*	NPG	NPG

Hornby 0

These models were made by Meccano Ltd at Binns Road, Liverpool, between 1920 and 1962.

HISTORY

Hornby Series was started by Frank Hornby, the inventor of Meccano, in 1920 and during a time, following the First World War, when there was strong anti-German feeling. Hitherto, toy trains had been principally imported from Germany by companies like Bassett-Lowke. Although marked 'made in England', the first cheap tinplate LNWR 0-4-0 tender locomotive and coaches, sold under the Hornby name, were based on German designs. However, the backbone of the new Hornby range was the more expensive, better made, nut and bolt constructed series of 0-4-0s in LNWR, GNR and MR company colours. These set a quality standard which was to remain until the demise of Hornby 0 gauge in the early 1960s'.

In 1910, Hornby had taken on two very competent men in key positions within the company. Beardsley was in charge of production and Jones dealt with sales. This proved to be a powerful combination.

Most of the locomotives were freelance in design and although all were beautifully made and finished, some, like the No.3s and the 4-4-2s, were peculiar in character. The products of more prototypical appearance were the No.2 special tender locomotive 4-4-0, the No.4 Schools Class 'Eton' and the top of the range 4-6-2 'Princess Elizabeth'. The latter was introduced in 1937, packed in a very attractive wooden box and cost £5.5.0 at a time when the average weekly wage was about £2.

At the other end of the scale, the market was catered for by the 'M' series, still very nicely made but much more basic.

The locomotives were supported by a large and colourful range of rolling stock, buildings and other

Milestones

1901 Frank Hornby invented Meccano.
1908 Meccano Ltd founded.
1914 Meccano Ltd moves to Binns Rd, Liverpool.
1915 Frank Hornby announces he is to make steam engines.
1920 Toy train production starts at Binns Road.
1922 Zulu trains first appear.
1923 Post-grouping liveries.
1924 'Hornby Series' name adopted.
1924 First tab and slot models appear.
1925 Metropolitan electric model introduced.
1926 M Series arrives.
1927 No.3 Pullman sets.
1927 'Hornby Lines' produced in Meccano's American factory.
1928 Meccano Ltd sell their American factory to A.C.Gilbert.
1928 First Southern Railway liveries.
1929 No2 Special locomotives.
1930 Meccano make a bid for the Canadian market.
1931 Automatic couplings.
1932 Electrically lit accessories.
1932 Countryside sections.
1933 Colour changes on many models.
1934 Automatic reversing in electric locos.
1936 Death of Frank Hornby and Roland Hornby becomes Chairman and George Jones becomes Managing Director.
1937 'Princess Elizabeth' and 'Eton' released.
1938 Arrival of Hornby Dublo points to the future.
1939 First year with no new 0 gauge models.
1941 Toy production closes down.
1946 post-war products reach the shops and are now called 'Hornby Trains' or just 'Hornby'.
1951 Plastic wheels introduced to rolling stock.
1952 M Series models reappeared.
1954 BR liveries begin to appear.
1957 No.50 series wagons arrive as a last ditch attempt to retain interest in Hornby 0 gauge.
1962 Possibly last year of 0 gauge tinplate production.
1964 Lines Bros. invited to take over Meccano Ltd.
1965 Hornby name transferred to Tri-ang Railways to give Tri-ang Hornby.
1965 Meccano Ltd release a plastic Percy Play Train.

accessories; the private owner wagons being particularly attractive. There was also a good range of colourful catalogues (including The Hornby Book of Trains series) and sales leaflets to whet the appetite.

On the death of Frank Hornby, in 1936, his son Roland replaced him as Chairman and George Jones was appointed Managing Director. With a marketing man in charge, Hornby continued to expand its base particularly with the 00 scale Hornby Dublo range introduced in 1938. On the death of Jones after the war, Beardsley became Managing Director and George Jones marketing skills were very much missed during the 1950s.

After the Second World War the product name had changed from 'Hornby Series' to 'Hornby Trains'. The large locomotives did not return and only 0-4-0 locomotives were made. Bogie rolling stock was scarcer and the range of accessories more limited. The reason was not a shrinkage in the market, indeed, in the first few years after the war the Hornby 0 gauge system was selling quite well. However, trains were no longer the toys of the better-off but had become the toy that every boy wanted. To feed this fast expanding market, and to be more suitable for the typical suburban home, the smaller 00 gauge held preference. Thus British 00 gauge quickly displaced 0 gauge as the country's most popular scale and as the demand for 00 increased, that for Hornby 0 gauge waned.

At the Meccano factory in Liverpool, special attention was now being given to expanding the Hornby-Dublo range which, for a while in the early 1950s, enjoyed its place as the market leader in Britain. Hornby 0 gauge limped on into the 1960s but production had already ceased when, in 1964, Meccano Ltd invited the toy manufacturing giant, Lines Bros. Ltd, to take them over.

'Princess Elizabeth' [L19] (Barry Potter)

After several months studying the problems at the Meccano factory, Lines Bros. decided to develop the Dinky Toy and Meccano ranges but to not restart the loss-making railway production lines. Instead they set about disposing of the large unsold stocks that had built up in the factory and, until the late 1960s, Hornby 0 Gauge wagons and accessories could be bought for very attractive prices.

Further Reading

For further reading on this subject, the most complete study will be found in *'The Hornby 0 Gauge System'* by Chris and Julie Graebe and published by New Cavendish Books (ISBN 0 904568 35 0). By the same authors and publishers there is also the *'Gauge 0 Compendium'* (ISBN 0 904568 90 3) which lists model variations and is an excellent guide to dating variations. Both books contain many more variations than we have been able to include here and are strongly recommended for an in-depth study of Hornby 0 Gauge.

Collectors Club

You may also wish to join the Hornby Railway Collectors Association (HRCA) who publish, for their members, an excellent monthly magazine, called *The Hornby Railway Collector*, devoted to the toy train and model railway products of Meccano Ltd. Details of this organisation may be obtained from the membership secretary, John Harwood, on Tel: 01935 474830.

Series Numbering - Meccano Ltd used '0', '1', '2' etc. to denote series with the higher number being used for higher standard models. Having started with '1', '0' was used when they decided to produce a cheaper series and when they wanted to produce a series even further down market they adopted the prefix 'M'. Top of the range were No.2 bogie wagons and No.2 electrically lit lineside accessories. With coaches and locomotives the numbering went even higher to '3' and '4'. Many special wagons do not have a series number.

Zulu - This was an early cheaper range which was superseded by No.0 and M3 items.

M Series - As we have seen, these form the bottom end of the range being cheaper, smaller and more toy-like than their relatives and were introduced to compete with the cheaper tin trains of Wells, Brimtoy, etc. The series which started with the M3 goods set late in 1926, was colourful and a complete system in its own right with locomotives, rolling-stock, buildings and other accessories.

The M items were later divided into the M1/M3 range and M0 items which were even simpler and cheaper. The M1/M3 items had rudimentary drop-link couplings while M0 models had a simple tab and slot coupling. None of the M items had buffers

Today, the series is probably more admired by toy-collectors than model railway collectors. M0 and M1 are the only product series names carried through to the post-war locomotives at the recommencing of manufacture in 1946.

No one is sure what the 'M' referred to but it has been suggested that it was derived from 'minor' or even 'mechanical', which was used when selling the products abroad instead of the term 'clockwork'.

The 'British Express' was an unusual variation within this series as it was especially made for chain stores and shops which were not normal Hornby outlets. In order to perpetuate this price cutting, these M0 products had special tin printings and were devoid of maker's marks.

Prices - The chance of finding mint boxed Hornby 0 gauge is so small that the use of the 'mint/boxed' column (right hand one) for this purpose would have no meaning. We have therefore used both price columns to indicate the price range one may expect for examples in very good condition (except for 'Princess Elizabeth' models which had a much higher rate of box survival).

Pricing 0 gauge Hornby is extremely difficult. Due to the large range of variations in colour and transfer positions most sellers are unaware of the rarity of some of these and so they can be bought quite cheaply. This means that prices range greatly and limiting the value of prices quoted here.

Wheels - the earliest items of rolling stock had pressed silver tinplate wheels which were replaced by black tinplate wheels around 1928. Some of the more expensive items were fitted with realistic cast wheels with white painted rims. United Dairies and Colas tank wagons are examples. Cast Maunsell type wheels were also catalogued and sold separately at 3d per pair for the more discerning to fit to their stock. Snowploughs always had cast

wheels to improve traction necessary to drive the rotating plough.

Couplings - Early models had a drop-link type coupling which required each item to be connected to its neighbour by hand. Around 1931, 'automatic' couplings were introduced which allowed vehicles to couple on their own when shunted together. It seems that the changeover from one coupling type to the other was not instantaneous but took place over a number of years thus allowing old stock to be cleared. Not all vehicles were converted to automatic couplings.

No 2 Special loco - LMS compound [L16] (Barry Potter)

Loco Search by Type

If you know the type of Hornby 0 gauge locomotive you are looking for, this table will tell you in which section you should look.

Locomotive.	Wheels	Table
'George V' Tender Loco	0-4-0	L4
'Princess Elizabeth'	4-6-2	L19
'Silver Link', Tender Loco	0-4-0	L5
'Zulu' Tender Loco	0-4-0T	L8
'Zulu' Tank	0-4-0	L9
LE1	0-4-0	L21
LE2	0-4-0	L22
M0 Tender Loco	0-4-0	L1
M1 Tender Loco	0-4-0	L2
M3 Tender Loco	0-4-0	L4
M3 Tank	0-4-0T	L6
Metropolitan	0-4-0	L20
No.0 Tender Loco	0-4-0	L8
No.00 Tender Loco	0-4-0	L4
No.1 Tank	0-4-0T	L9
No.1 Tender Loco	0-4-0	L10
No.1 Special Tank	0-4-0T	L11
No.1 Special Tender Loco	0-4-0	L12
No.101 Tank	0-4-0T	L7
No.2 Tank	4-4-4T	L13
No.2 Special Tank	4-4-2T	L15
No.2 Tender Loco	4-4-0	L14
No.2 Special Tender Loco	4-4-0	L16
No.20 Tender Loco	0-4-0	L1
No.30 Tender Loco	0-4-0	L3
No.3C Tender Loco	4-4-2	L17
No.4 'Eton' Tender Loco	4-4-0	L18
No.40 Tank	0-4-0T	L7
No.50 Tender Loco	0-4-0	L10b
No.501 Tender Loco	0-4-0	L10b
No.51 Tender Loco	0-4-0	L10b
Streamlined Tender Locos	0-4-0	L5

No2 Special loco 'County of Bedford' [L16] (Barry Potter)

Loco Search by Running Number

In order to help you find your Hornby 0 Gauge locomotive we have listed below, in the left column, the numbers that appear on the side of models (running numbers) and, in the right column, the number of the table(s) in which you will find the model.

Loco Nos	Tables				
0-4-0	L9a	2290	L10b	6161	L1
2	L20	2301	L12	6201	L19
6	L15	2323	L15	6380	L8
29	L9b	2329	L15	6418	L11
70	L11	2449	L8+10a	6600	L6+7
111	L9b	2509	L5	6781	L15
201	L16	2526	L2+4	6954	L15
234	L16	2527	L4	7140	L9b
326	L9a+9b	2586	L11	7202	L13
4-4-4	L13	2595	L1	7283	14
460	L6,7,13	2663	L4	7391	L5
463	L9a	2691	L12	8108	L11
483	L4	2694	L12	8123	L11
492	L15	2700	L12	8324	L8+10a
500	L8	2710	L4,8+10a	8327	L8+10a
516	L11	2711	L14	8329	L15
551	L8	2728	L2+4	8712	L12
600	L8	2810	L8+10b	9319	L10b
623	L9a+9b	2900	L9b	10655	L21+22
700	L16	2930	L2	15500	L11
793	L8+10a	3031	L2	16045	L11
826	L9b	3132	L2	31240	L17
850	L17	3133	L2	31290	L17
900	L18	3233	L1	31801	L17
1000	L10b	3435	L2	45746	L3
1019	L13	3580	L11	50153	L10b
1179	L12	3821	L16	60199	L10b
1185	L16	3917	L5	60985	L1
1368	L12	4073	L17	82011	L7
1452	L4	4300	L10b	A129	L11
1504	L8	4312	L12	A179	L12
1534	L13	4472	L1+17	A504	L8+10b
1759	L16	4525	L12	A600	L9a
1784	L15	4560	L9b	A759	L8,10+16
1842	L10b	4700	L12	A760	L14
2051	L13	4703	L15	A950	L11
2052	L13	4797	L8	B28	L11
2091	L15	5096	L8+10a	B343	L12
2107	L13	5097	L8	B604	L13
2115	/ L9b	5097	L10a	B667	L9a
2120	L11	5154	L15	E29	L9b
2162	L11	5165	L13	E111	L9b
2180	L15	5399	L8	E126	L6+7
2221	L15	5500	L11	E492	L13+15
2243	L13	5508	L8	E509	L8+10a
2251	L8	5600	L8+10b	E510	L14
2270	L6+7	6097	L10b	E793	L8+10b
		6100	L1+17	E850	L17

LOCOMOTIVES

Cat.No.	Number, Company, Colour, Dates	£	£

L1. M0 and No.20 Type Tender Locomotives 0-4-0

These were tinprinted, without cylinders and rods but having a fixed key until 1936. From then on it had fitted cylinders, connecting (not coupling) rods and a removable key. The tenders carried numbers only, with no railway companies decals. The British Express trains were produced for sale to non-Hornby agents and so carried no Meccano Ltd identification.

M0	4472 green, black base, cutout cab windows c/w - 30-32	20	30
M0	2595 green, red or green base c/w - 33-36	25	35
M0	2595 green, cylinders, round printed splashers (1938-41) c/w - 36-41	25	35
M0	6100 red, black base, cutout cab	20	30
	windows c/w - 30-32		
M0	6161 red, red or green base c/w - 33-36	25	35
M0	6161 red, cylinders c/w - 36-37	25	35
M0	6161 red, cylinders, round printed splashers c/w - 38-41	25	35
M0	6161, 2595 red or green, wheels unpainted c/w - 46-54	15	30
-	3233 red British Express Locomotive, black base, no cylinders or trademark, c/w - 32-36	300	350
20	60985 BRb green lined out in orange +black, black chassis c/w - 54-68	25	45

L2. M1 Tender Locomotives 0-4-0

These tin-printed models were sturdier than the M0, the early examples being copied from a Bing design. The engines had a non-reversible clockwork mechanism, without rods and there were no cylinders or company decals - only numbers. They were almost all green with black chassis and lined out in black and white. The M1 was revised from 1930 with a more modern shaped body (with single piece forming boiler and cab) and a new reversing mechanism. In 1934 two inexpensive electric motors were introduced, EM120 (20 volt) and EM16 (6 volt), both AC.

M1	2526 on tender and cab side, green, black base, cast chimney unpainted wheels c/w - 26-32	30	60
M1	2728 as above - 27-29	30	60
M1, M2930	2930 as above, tin chimney - 29-32	30	60
M1	3031 on tender green or red new shape, blk base, red wheels, c/w - 30	30	70
M1	3132 as above but tin printed windows - 31-33	30	60
M1	3132 as above dark red - 31-33	30	60
M1	3132 as above green or red but green base - 33-34	30	60
M1	3132 as above dark red - 33-34	40	60
M1	as above but 3133 + green - 33-34	30	40
M1	3435 green or red, bases green, red or black c/w - 34-41	30	40
EM16	as above green 6v - 34-38	75	200
EM16	as above red 6v - 34-38	80	215
EM120	as above green 20v - 34-38	90	210
EM120	as above red 20v - 34-38	100	230
M1	3435 green, black base, Hornby on cabsides, red wheels, c/w - 46-58	20	30
M1	3435 red, black base, Hornby on cabsides, red wheels, c/w - 46-58	25	40

L3. No.30 Type Tender Locomotives 0-4-0

Initially designed in 1954 to replace the one-piece pressing M1, it was late being issued and failed to stop the Hornby decline. The No 30 had a larger, squarer, separate cab, an improved tender and was finished in BR green with lion and wheel emblem on the tender. However, the mechanism was the same as the M1 but had very crudely cast con-rods.

30	45746 green, lined orange+black with black chassis + wheels c/w - 56-65	30	55

L4. No.00 and M3 (George V) Tender Locomotives 0-4-0

This was an 0-4-0 locomotive with outside cylinders. It was a very early tin-printed design and was based on a Bing original. It was finished in early company colours and had an under-scale tender. A clockwork reversing mechanism was fitted until 1924 after which a larger non-reversing mechanism was fitted. It was referred to as the No.00 engine in 1925 (nothing to do with '00' scale), becoming the M3 tender locomotive in 1926 and finally being paired with the larger M1 style tender with modified open coal rail. Coupling rods were fitted in 1927. No railway company markings were used on the engines in the last two years of the model, when the colour was enamelled instead of tin-printed. There were many sub-variations, especially in the last two years of production, and below we have listed only the main ones.

00, M3	1452 on cab GNR on tender, green c/w - 20-26	100	150
00, M3	483 on tender MR crest on cab, red c/w - 20-26	100	150
00, M3	2663 on cab 'George the Fifth', LNWR on tender, black c/w - 20-26	100	150
M3	2526, 2728 on M1 style tender, cutout coal rails, green c/w - 26-28	70	100

M3	**2527, 2710** on M1 style tender, MR crest on cab, cutout coal rails, red c/w - *26-28*	70	100
M3	**2710, 2527, 2663** on an M1 style tender **'George the Fifth'**, cutout coal rails, black c/w - *26-28*	80	120
M3	**2728, 2710** (red or black) on tender, No.0 style body, green c/w - *28-29*	60	90

L5. 'Silver Link' and other Streamlined Locomotives 0-4-0

The streamlined 0-4-0 tender locomotives were clockwork and belonged to the 'M' series. It was an 'M' sheep in wolf's clothing! It was heart breaking when you think of the real A4's. They were sold in sets with special articulated coaches. Those for 'Silver Link' were silver, numbered 1584 and 1585 and carried the name 'The Silver Jubilee'.

0	**2509** on loco **'Silver Link'** LNER silver c/w - *36-41*	230	380
0	**7391** on loco + tender, 2 greens c/w - *37-40*	200	300
0	**3917** on loco + tender, maroon+cream c/w - *37-40*	200	300

L6.   M3 Tank Locomotives 0-4-0T

This was an 0-4-0 locomotive without cylinders and connecting rods until 1936. Earlier locos that were repaired at factory were often fitted with rods. It had a tin-printed body and no handrail knobs. The engine was fitted with 8-spoke red wheels except between 1932 and 1936 when they were 12-spoke. From 1936, cylinders and rods were fitted.

M3	**2270 LMS** red c/w - *31-41*	50	110
EM36	as above 6v - *34-41*	120	170
EM320	as above 20v - *32-34*	130	180
M3	**460 LNER** green c/w - *31-41*	55	155
EM36	as above 6v - *34-41*	140	260
EM320	as above 20v - *32-34*	150	270
M3	**6600 Great Western**, green c/w - *31-41*	60	160
EM36	as above 6v - *34-41*	110	210
EM320	as above 20v - *32-34*	130	200
M3	**E126 Southern** dark green c/w - *31-41*	70	140
EM36	as above 6v - *34-41*	140	170
EM320	as above 20v - *32-34*	150	180

101 tank loco LNER 460 [L7] (Barry Potter)

L7.   No 101 and No.40 Tank Locomotives 0-4-0T

A post-war 0-4-0 tank locomotive with cylinders, connecting rods and coupling rods, this was a continuation of the pre-war M3 with the same mechanism and body with minor changes in the tinprinting.

101	**2270 LMS** red c/w - *47-54*	45	110
101	**460 LNER** green c/w - *47-54*	45	105
101	**6600 GW** green c/w - *47-54*	80	275
101	**E126 SR** green c/w - *47-54*	70	290
40	**82011 BRb** lined black c/w - *54-60*	40	110
40	**82011 BRc** lined black c/w - *60-65*	40	110

Note: Red lining sometimes has pinkish metallic finish.

L8.   Zulu and No.0 Tender Locomotives 0-4-0

Early examples of this 0-4-0, with outside cylinders and a coal rail tender, had 'Zulu' on the smokebox door but this was later replaced with 'Hornby'. Up until 1928 the wheel splashers were over the rear wheels only but from then on they stretched to cover both sets. In 1931 the whole locomotive was redesigned (see below) and from now on the tender coal rails were not cut out. All locos were lined out but were made without cylinders until 1937 when outside cylinders were reintroduced to the range. There were many variations of this model only some of which are listed below. Note: In most

production runs of Hornby models that were fewer black locomotives and so they normally sell for 30% to 50% more than the coloured ones. Rare numbers such as 1504, add further value.

-	**'Zulu'** on splashers in red/gold, black c/w - *23-24*	95	140
0	**2710** on tender, **LMS** on splashers, red c/w - *24-29*	100	150
0	**2710** on tender, **LMS** on splashers, black c/w - *24-29*	120	170
0	**2710 LNER** green c/w - *24*	90	110
0	as above but lined c/w - *25-27*	85	105
0	as above but red wheels c/w - *28-29*	80	100
0	**2710 LNER** black c/w - *24*	120	170
0	as above but lined c/w - *25-27*	115	165
0	as above but red wheels c/w - *28-29*	100	160
0	**2710 GW** on splasher, diecast GWR type safety valve, green c/w - *26-29*	110	220
0	**E509** on tender **Southern** black, red wheels c/w - *28-31*	190	260
0	**A759** on tender **Southern** green, red wheels, c/w - *28-31*	160	230
0	**8327, 8324, 600 LMS** on tender, red c/w - *29-31*	85	130
0	**8327, 8324, 600 LMS** on tender, black c/w - *29-31*	140	200
0	**5097, 5096 + LNER** on tender, green c/w - *29-31*	85	130
0	**5097, 5096 + LNER** on tender, black c/w - *29-31*	140	200
0	**2449** on cab, **Great () Western** on tender, green c/w - *29-31*	130	235
0	**600, 8324, 500, 551, 5600 LMS** red redesigned body c/w - *31-41*	100	140
E06	as above 6v - *34-35*	150	200
E020	as above 20v - *34-41*	190	240
0	**600, 8324, 500, 551, 5600 LMS** black redesigned body c/w - *31-41*	160	210
E06	as above 6v - *34-35*	220	270
E020	as above 20v - *34-41*	270	310
0	**6380, 2810, 5508, 4797 LNER** green redesigned body c/w - *31-41*	100	155
E06	as above 6v - *34-35*	150	200
E020	as above 20v - *34-41*	190	240
0	**6380, 2810, 5508, 4797 LNER** black redesigned body c/w - *31-41*	160	210
E06	as above 6v - *34-35*	220	270
E020	as above 20v - *34-41*	270	310
0	**2251, 5399 Great()Western** green redesigned body c/w - *31-41*	130	235
E06	as above 6v - *34-35*	170	270
E020	as above 20v - *34-41*	240	310
0	**A504, 1504, E793, 793 Southern** green redesigned body c/w - *31-41*	120	200
E06	as above 6v - *34-35*	220	600
E020	as above 20v - *34-41*	270	650
0	**A504, 1504, E793, 793 Southern** black redesigned body c/w - *31-41*	150	220
E06	as above 6v - *34-35*	250	630
E020	as above 20v - *34-41*	300	680

No 0 loco SR E509 [L8] (sold for £840) (Barry Potter)

L9a. No.1 Tank Locomotives 0-4-0T (original body)

These were 0-4-0 tank locomotives with cylinders and connecting rods. A brass dome was carried until 1928 (except Zulu) after which it was painted. There were wire handrails on the smokebox with brass knob each side and the body was enamelled. In 1931 it received a revised body (see 9b below). Mechanisms: Clockwork 1922-41, 6 volt DC. 1929-31.

1	**'Zulu'** on tank in red/gold, red edge to spectacles, black c/w - *22-23*	130	280
1	**'Zulu'** on smokebox front, LMS black c/w - *23-24*	130	160
1	**0-4-0 + LMS** on tank, red c/w - *24-26*	80	145
1	as above but black c/w - *24-26*	70	150
1	**623, 326 LMS** black, wheels black or red c/w - *26-31*	70	210
E16	as above but 6v DC - *29-34*	240	300
1	**0-4-0 LNER** green c/w - *24-26*	70	170
1	as above but black c/w - *24-26*	80	210
1	**623, 326, 463 LNER** green c/w - *26-31*	70	170
1	as above but black c/w - *26-31*	80	210
E16	**463 LNER** green 6v DC - *29-34*	180	250
E16	as above but black 6v DC - *29-34*	300	900
1	**Great Western** green c/w - *26-31*	80	155
E16	as above 6v DC - *29-34*	240	340
1	**Great()Western** green c/w - *30-31*	100	170
E16	as above 6v DC - *30-31*	260	355
1	**A600, B667** on tanks Southern green c/w - *28-31*	100	120
1	as above but black c/w - *28-31*	100	120
E16	as above green 6v DC - *29-34*	260	300
E16	as above black 6v DC - *29-34*	260	300

No 1 tank with original body [L9a] (Barry Potter)

L9b. No.1 Tank Locomotives 0-4-0T (revised body)

In 1931 a revised body design was adopted for the No.1 tank which was heavier looking with lower chimney, dome, cab and flared bunker. Control rods were now above the bunker (not through its bunker plate as previously). No black body versions were made after 1936. Mechanisms: Clockwork 1931-41; 6 volt DC. 1931-34; E16 (6 volt); 1934-36 LST1/20 (20 volt); 1934-41 E120 (20 volt).

1	**7140, 623, 326, 2115 LMS** red c/w - *31-41*	95	145
EPM16	as above 6v - *34-35*	130	180
LTS1/20	as above 20v - *32-34*	170	330
E120	as above 20v - *34-41*	180	350
1	**7140, 623, 326, 2115 LMS** black c/w - *31-41*	90	225
EPM16	as above 6v - *34-35*	190	250
LTS1/20	as above 20v - *32-34*	240	300
E120	as above 20v - *34-41*	240	300
1	**826, 2900 LNER** green c/w - *31-35*	80	180
EPM16	as above 6v - *34-35*	130	180
LTS1/20	as above 20v - *32-34*	150	220
E120	as above 20v - *34-35*	150	220
1	**826, 2900 LNER** darker green c/w *36-41*	80	180
E120	as above 20v - *36-41*	150	220
1	**826, 2900 LNER** black c/w - *31-41*	90	230
EPM16	as above 6v - *34-35*	200	650
LTS1/20	as above 20v - *32-34*	300	900
E120	as above 20v - *34-41*	300	900
1	**4560 Great Western** green c/w - *31-34*	80	130
EPM16	as above 6v - *34-35*	210	250
LTS1/20	as above 20v - *32-34*	230	300
1	**4560 GWR** button green c/w - *35-41*	80	165
E120	as above 20v - *35-41*	180	240
1	**E111, 111, E29, 29 Southern** green c/w - *31-41*	100	350
EPM16	as above 6v - *34-35*	200	400
LST1/20	as above 20v - *32-34*	220	420
E120	as above 20v - *34-41*	220	420
1	**E111, 111, E29, 29 Southern** black c/w - *31-41*	135	380
EPM16	as above 6v - *34-35*	400	500
LST1/20	as above 20v - *32-34*	450	600
E120	as above 20v - *34-41*	450	600

No 1 tank with revised body [L9b] (Barry Potter)

L10a. No.1 Tender Locomotives 0-4-0 (original body)

The No.1 0-4-0 locomotive had cylinders and connecting rods and was similar to No.0 locomotive but with brass handrail knobs instead of diecast ones. They had cylinders on all variations and the bodies were enamelled. Some early examples had nickel base plates. In 1931, a completely revised and modernised body was fitted (see 10b). Mechanism: Clockwork 1920-31. N&B = nut and bolt construction

1	**2710 LNWR** style black N&B ML Ltd c/w - *20-23*	170	220
1	**2710 GN** style green, N&B some had red sides to running plate ML Ltd c/w - *20-23*	170	220
1	**2710 MR** style maroon, N&B ML Ltd c/w - *20-23*	130	200
1	**2710 CR** style blue, N&B, ML Ltd c/w - *20-23*	230	280
1	**2710** on cabsides **LMS** on RH splasher red or black c/w - *23-24*	100	150
1	**2710** on tender **LMS** on both splashers red or black c/w - *25-29*	100	150
1	**2710** on cabsides **LNER** on RH splasher red side plates, green c/w - *23-24*	100	150
1	**2710** on tender **LNER** on both splashers, red sides till '26, c/w green - *25-29*	100	150
1	**2710** on tender **LNER** on both splashers, black c/w - *24-29*	150	180
1	**8324** on cabside **LMS** on coal-rail tender, long splashers, red c/w - *29-31*	100	150
1	**8327** on cabside **LMS** on coal-rail tender, long splashers, black c/w - *29-31*	150	180
1	**5096 + LNER** on cabside, long splashers, green c/w - *29-31*	100	150
1	**5097 + LNER** on tender, 232 on cabside, long splashers, black c/w - *29-31*	150	180
1	**8324 + LNER** on tender, 232 on cabside, long splashers, green c/w - *30-31*	200	240
1	**2710** on coal rail tender **GW** on splasher, crest on cab, green c/w - *26-29*	150	180
1	**8327** on coal rail tender, **Great()Western**	150	180

black c/w - *26-29*

1	**2449** on cabside **Great()Western** coal rail tender, long splashers, green c/w - *29-31*	150	180
1	**A759 + Southern** on tender green c/w - *28-29*	200	240
1	**E509 + Southern** on tender black + green lining c/w - *28-29*	250	300
1	**A759 + Southern** on coal rail tender 232 on cabside long splashers, green c/w - *29-31*	200	240
1	**E509 + Southern** on coal rail tender 232 on cabside, long splashers, black c/w - *29-31*	250	300

Note: There were numerous detailed variations on the No.1 tender locomotives.

No 1 loco in Midland Railway red [L10a] (Barry Potter)

L10b. No.1, No.501, No.50 and No.51 Tender Locomotives 0-4-0

The new body for the No1 tender locomotive, introduced in 1931, had a larger diameter boiler, long splashers, low chimney and dome and a cab with two windows each side. Driving wheels were normally red and a heavier type tender with solid top rails was used. The No.501 was a post WWII continuation of the No.1. The enamel was finished with a matt varnish (as were the very late No.1's from 1939). Electric 20 volt versions, numbered E502, are quite rare, having all been sent for export. No black liveries were made in the 501 series and wheels were black except for the LNER c/w locomotive which was produced with green wheels. New details were: a centre lamp bracket above the front coupling and lamp brackets on the rear of the tender. The No 50 and 51 were basically the same as the No.501 but updated with the introduction of BR liveries, emblems and numbers, being smartly lined out and finished in gloss. They were made only in clockwork. Mechanism: Clockwork 1931-41, E16 (6 volt) 1934-35, E120 (20 volt) 1934-41. N&B = nut and bolt construction

1	**1000** on cabside **LMS** on tender red c/w - *31-41*	100	280
1	**2290** on cabside **LMS** on tender black c/w - *31-36*	100	280
1	**5600** on cabside **LMS** on tender red c/w - *36-41*	100	280
E16	**1000, 2290** on cabside **LMS** on tender red 6v - *34-35*	200	300
E16	as above but black 6v - *34-35*	170	270
E120	**1000, 2290, 5600** on cabside **LMS** on tender, red 20v - *34-41*	240	380
E120	as above but black 20v - *34-41*	200	320
1	**2810** on cabside **LNER** on tender green (darker from '36) c/w - *31-35*	90	135
1	as above but darker - *36-41*	90	135
1	**6097** on cabside, **LNER** on tender, black c/w - *31-36*	95	370
1	**1842** on cabside, **LNER** on tender green c/w - *39-41*	80	120
E16	**2810, 6097** on cabside, **LNER** on tender, green 6v - *34-35*	160	325
E16	as above but black 6v - *34-35*	240	300
E120	**2810, 6097, 1842** on cabside, **LNER** on tender, green 20v - *34-41*	140	260
E120	as above but black 20v - *34-41*	280	360
1	**4300** on cabside, **Great()Western** on tender, green c/w - *31-34*	95	160
E16	as above 6v - *34-35*	240	450
E120	as above 20v AC - *31-34*	270	550
1	**4300** on cabside, **GWR** button on tender, green c/w - *35-38*	100	160
E120	as above 20v - *34-38*	270	550
1	**9319** on cabside **GWR** button on tender, green c/w - *38-41*	95	160

E120	as above 20v - *38-41*	270	550
1	**E793** on tender **Southern** green c/w - *31-33*	170	240
1	**793** on tender **Southern** green c/w - *33-41*	130	200
E16	as above 6v - *34-35*	360	700
E120	as above 20v - *34-41*	460	800
1	**A504** on tender **Southern** black - *31-36*	310	350
E16	as above 6v - *34-35*	350	600
E120	as above 20v - *34-36*	400	650
501	**5600** serif on cab **LMS** red c/w - *48*	65	170
E502	as above 20v - *48*	225	355
501	**5600** sans-serif on cab **LMS** red c/w - *49-54*	65	170
E502	as above 20v - *49-54*	225	355
501	**1842** serif on cab **LNER** green c/w - *48*	75	165
E502	as above 20v - *48*	190	375
501	**1842** sans-serif on cabside **LNER** green c/w - *49-54*	75	165
E502	as above 20v - *49-54*	190	375
501	**9319** on cab **G()W** green c/w - *48-49*	300	350
E502	as above 20v - *48-49*	400	550
50	**60199 BRb** black lined red+grey c/w - *54-61*	75	175
51	**50153 BRb** green lined orange+black c/w - *54-61*	75	190

Note: There were numerous detailed variations on the No.1 tender locomotives.

No 1 loco GWR 4300 [L10b] (Barry Potter)

L11. No.1 Special Tank Locomotives 0-4-0T

These were heavy 0-4-0 locomotives with cylinders and connecting rods. They were larger than other 0-4-0 tanks and had more powerful mechanisms. They were finished in the four railway company colours, and in black liveries (except for the GWR version). Red and black engines had red wheels while green engines had green wheels. Mechanisms: Clockwork 1929-41, EPM16 (6 volt) 1934-39, and E120 special (20 volt) 1934-41.

1	**6418 LMS** sans-serif letters and numbers shadowed, red c/w - *29-30*	130	230
1	**2120 LMS**, serif letters and numbers, shadowed, red c/w - *30-34*	130	230
1	**15500 LMS**, serif letters and numbers, shadowed, red c/w - *34-36*	140	280
EPM16	as above 6v - *34-36*	220	350
E120	as above 20v - *34-36*	250	400
1	**70** (serif) **LMS** red c/w - *36-41*	130	230
EPM16	as above 6v - *36-39*	220	350
E120	as above 20v - *36-41*	250	400
1	**70** (sans-serif) **LMS** red c/w - *37-39*	140	280
EPM16	as above 6v - *37-39*	220	330
E120	as above 20v - *37-39*	240	380
1	**16045 LMS** (sans-serif) black c/w *29-30*	180	360
EPM16	as above 6v - *34-35*	270	450
E120	as above 20v - *34-35*	320	490
1	**16045 LMS** (serif) black c/w - *30-36*	180	360
EPM16	as above 6v - *35-36*	270	450
E120	as above 20v - *35-36*	320	490
1	**8123 LNER** green 7 bands c/w - *29*	120	360
EPM16	as above 6v - *34*	210	430
E120	as above 20v - *34*	240	480
1	**8123 LNER** green 8 bands c/w - *30-35*	110	350
EPM16	as above 6v - *35*	210	430
E120	as above 20v - *35*	240	480
1	**2162 LNER** green c/w - *35*	140	380
EPM16	as above 6v - *35*	270	450
E120	as above 20v - *35*	230	500
1	**2162 LNER** darker green c/w - *36-41*	130	370

EPM16	as above 6v - *36-39*	230	450
E120	as above 20v - *36-41*	260	500
1	**8108 LNER** black c/w - *29-30*	130	380
1	**2586 LNER** black c/w - *30-36*	150	410
EPM16	as above 6v - *34-36*	350	470
E120	as above 20v - *34-36*	400	520
1	**3580 Great Western** green 7 boiler bands c/w - *29*	130	240
1	**3580 Great Western** green 8 boiler bands c/w - *30*	130	240
1	**5500 Great Western** number not on plate green c/w - *30-31*	140	250
EPM16	as above 6v - *30-31*	310	390
E120	as above 20v - *30-31*	320	440
1	**5500 Great Western** green c/w - *32-35*	140	250
EPM16	as above 6v - *32-35*	310	390
E120	as above 20v - *32-35*	320	440
1	**5500 GWR** button green c/w - *36-41*	140	250
EPM16	as above 6v - *36-39*	310	390
E120	as above 20v - *36-41*	320	440
1	**A950 Southern** sans-serif letters, green with white+black lining c/w - *29-30*	210	320
1	**B28 Southern** serif letters, green with white+black lining c/w - *30-35*	240	420
EPM16	as above 6v - *34-35*	400	1000
E120	as above 20v - *34-35*	520	1300
1	**516 Southern** green with white+black lining c/w - *35-41*	210	320
EPM16	as above 6v - *35-39*	350	850
E120	as above 20v - *35-41*	450	1150
1	**A129 Southern** black with green lining c/w - *29-30*	590	770
1	**A950 Southern** now with serif letters, black c/w - *30-36*	700	900
EPM16	as above 6v - *34-36*	800	1200
E120	as above 20v - *34-36*	1000	1400

No 1 Special tank SR B28 [L11] (Barry Potter)

L12. No.1 Special Tender Locomotives 0-4-0

These were similar to the previous models but with splashers over the wheels instead of side tanks. They were paired with a four-wheeled tender that was larger than that used with other 0-4-0 models. Other details were those already described for the No.1 Special Tank Loco except that 6 volt mechanisms were not fitted to this model.

1	**4312, 4525** plain gold on cab, **LMS** shadowed serif on unlined tender, red c/w - *29-30*	130	330
1	**4312 LMS** (serif), lined tender, red c/w - *30-31*	130	330
1	**8712** on cabside **LMS** (serif), lined tender, red c/w - *31-35*	130	330
E120	as above 20v - *34-35*	500	550
1	**2700 LMS** letters on lined tender, red c/w - *35-41*	110	310
E120	as above 20v - *35-41*	300	400
1	**4525 LMS** gold on tender, blk c/w - *29*	180	495
1	as above letters shadowed c/w - *30-36*	180	480
E120	as above 20v - *34-36*	500	550
1	**2694 + LNER** on tender, small no. on cab, blk boiler bands, green c/w - *29*	120	220

1	as above, white boiler bands - *30-31*	100	200
1	**1368** on cab, **LNER** on tender, green c/w - *31-35*	120	220
E120	as above 20v - *34-35*	300	550
1	as above but darker green c/w - *36-41*	120	220
E120	as above 20v - *36-41*	300	550
1	**2691** in gold + **LNER** on tender, oval on cabsides, black c/w - *29-36*	280	440
E120	as above 20v - *34-36*	500	650
1	**2301 Great()Western** on tender, green c/w - *29-35*	230	500
1	**4700 Great()Western** on tender, green c/w - *34-35*	200	470
E120	as above 20v - *34-35*	390	595
1	**4700 GWR** button on tender, green c/w - *36-41*	190	450
E120	as above 20v - *36-41*	390	595
1	**A179** on cab **Southern** green c/w - *29-35*	240	400
E120	as above 20v - *34-35*	800	1500
1	**1179 + Southern** on tender, green c/w - *35-41*	240	800
E120	as above 20v - *35-41*	550	1650
1	**B343 + Southern** on tender, black lined green c/w - *29-36*	550	800
E120	as above 20v - *34-36*	950	3500

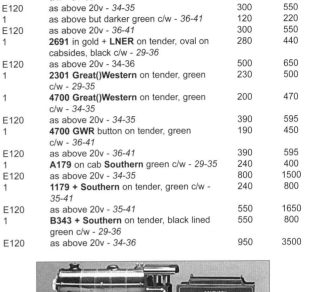

No 1 Special loco SR 1179 [L12] (Barry Potter)

L13. No.2 Tank Locomotives 4-4-4T

This was the only 4-4-4 locomotive made by Hornby and had the character of tank engines of the early years of the 20th century, especially on the LNWR. Produced from 1923-29 in clockwork only, there were many detail variations including 24 on LMS locos alone! We have not been able to deal with all of them here. Two lamps were fixed on front of the locomotive from 1924 onwards.

2	**1019 LM&SR** red part lined c/w - *23*	170	350
2	**LM&S** red part lined c/w - *23*	170	350
2	as above but black black c/w - *23*	160	280
2	**4-4-4 LMS** red fully lined c/w - *24-26*	150	320
2	as above but black c/w - *24-26*	140	260
2	**2052 LMS** crest on bunker, red c/w - *26-28*	150	320
2	as above but black c/w - *26-28*	140	260
2	**2107, 2051, 2052 LMS** on bunker plate, later on tank, red c/w - *28-29*	150	320
2	as above but black c/w - *28-29*	140	260
2	**L&NER** green with red side plates, lined bunker c/w - *23*	200	320
2	**1534 L&NER** green with red side plates, lining c/w - *24-25* lined tanks c/w - *23*	200	320
2	**4-4-4 L&NER** green + red side plates, full	180	300
2	as above but black c/w - *24-25*	170	420
2	**4-4-4 LNER** green, full lining c/w - *25-26*	180	310
2	as above but black c/w - *25-26*	170	420
2	**460 LNER** green with crest on cab c/w - *26*	200	320
2	as above but black c/w - *26*	180	440
2	**460, 5165 LNER** green with crest on bunker c/w - *27-29*	230	450
2	as above but black c/w - *27-29*	170	370
2	**Great Western** green crest on cab c/w - *26*	150	420
2	**7202, 2243 Great()Western** green c/w - *27-29*	120	380
2	**B604 Southern** green c/w - *28-29*	250	700
2	**E492 Southern** black c/w - *28-29*	300	900

No 2 tank GWR 2243 [L13] (sold for £410) (Barry Potter)

L14. No.2 Tender Locomotives 4-4-0

These were elegant 4-4-0 locomotives of early 20th century character. They were powered by clockwork only, except for a very special orders. Produced between 1921 and 1929, they had a six-wheeled coal rail tender which usually carried the number '2711'; although there are other variations. For the first two years, the locos were made in pre-grouping colours (GN - green, MR - red, CR - blue, LNWR - black) but, after this, the colours of the four grouped companies were introduced. Black engines were again available for all companies except the GWR. The driving wheels were covered by long splashers and the domes were mainly brass. The model was of nut and bolt construction, using Meccano nuts and bolts. The locos had two fixed front lamps from late 1924 onwards. Electric Models : These exceptionally rare examples were Hornby's first venture into electric mechanisms. No sound price guide is available on the electric versions as they are very rare and usually in poor condition when found. £1300 is a very broad guide.

2	2711 on brass cab plate MR style red, Meccano transfers, c/w - 21-23	190	550
2	as above LNWR style black - 21-23	350	800
2	as above CR style blue - 21-23	450	1200
2	as above GNR style green, red valences - 21-23	380	920
2	2711 metal on cab, red, LM&S on splashers, pre-group tender c/w - 23	200	550
2	as above but black c/w - 23	250	870
2	red as above but trademark transfer on RH and LMS on LH splasher - 23	200	550
2	as above but black - 23	250	870
2	red as above but LMS on splashers and tender c/w - 24	200	550
2	as above but black c/w - 24	250	870
2	red as above but number only on tender, crest on cab c/w - 24-29	150	450
2	as above but black - 24-29	240	750
2	2711 GN crests on splashers, metal cabside number, green c/w - 23	250	500
2	2711 (metal on cab) L&NER on LH and GN crest on RH splasher, green c/w - 23	250	550
2	2711 (metal on cab) L&NER on both splashers and tender, green c/w - 23	220	500
2	2711 on tender LNER on both splashers, green c/w - 24-29	180	450
2	2711 LNER on splashers, crest on cabsides, black c/w - 24-27	200	600
2	2711 LNER crest on cab, no letters on splashers, black c/w - 28-29	200	600
2	2711 on tender, GW on splashers, GWR crest on cab, green c/w - 26	260	380
2	2711 on tender, Great()Western on splashers, 7283 on cab, green c/w - 27-28	260	380
2	7283 on cabsides, Great()Western on tender, green c/w - 29	340	750
2	A760 + Southern on tender, green c/w - 28-29	470	900
2	E510 + Southern on tender, black c/w - 28-29	960	1500

No 2 tender loco LMS 2711 [L14] (Barry Potter)

L15. No.2 Special Tank Locomotives 4-4-2T

This was a 4-4-2 updated replacement for the No.2 tank and was produced from 1929 until 1941. Larger driving wheels were fitted to the later improved mechanisms and smokebox bulbs were used from 1933 onwards. It was a heavier looking engine than the No.2 with higher boiler and lower chimney, dome and cab. It had no outside cylinders but there were two fixed front lamps until 1930 when they were replaced by four brackets front and rear. Mechanisms: powered by clockwork, 6V 30-34, 6V E26 34-41, 20V LST2/20 33-34, 20V E220 34-41. The early electric motors had protruding brushes.

2	2323 + LMS sans-serif, red c/w - 29-30	150	300
2	2180 + LMS serif, red c/w - 30-36	145	280
2, E26	as above 6v - 30-36	180	270
LST 2/20	as above 20v - 33-34	210	370
E220	as above 20v - 34-36	210	370
2	6954 + LMS serif, red c/w - 36	145	280
E26	as above 6v - 36	180	300
E220	as above 20v - 36	200	350
2	6954 + LMS serif, matt red c/w - 40-41	145	280
E26	as above 6v - 40-41	180	300
E220	as above 20v - 40-41	200	350
2	6954 + LMS sans-serif matt red c/w - 37-39	145	280
E26	as above 6v - 37-39	180	2300
E220	as above 20v - 37-39	200	350
2	6781 LMS sans-serif, black c/w - 29-30	190	270
2	6781 LMS serif, black c/w - 31-36	190	250
2, E26	as above 6v - 30-36	210	340
LST 2/20	as above 20v - 33-34	240	425
E220	as above 20v - 34-36	240	425
2	6 LNER green c/w - 29-32	125	220
2	1784 LNER green, green wheels c/w - 32-35	135	260
2, E26	as above 6v - 32-35	180	270
LST 2/20	as above 20v - 32-34	200	320
E220	as above 20v - 32-35	200	320
2	1784 LNER darker green, green wheels c/w - 36-38	135	260
E26	as above 6v - 36-38	180	270
E220	as above 20v - 36-38	200	320
2	1784 LNER darker matt green, green wheels c/w - 39-41	135	260
E26	as above 6v - 39-41	180	270
E220	as above 20v - 39-41	200	320
2	5154 + LNER gold on tank, red lining, black wheels, black c/w - 29-36	145	245
2, E26	as above 6v - 30-36	260	290
LST 2/20	as above 20v - 33-34	325	350
E220	as above 20v - 34-36	325	350
2	4703 Great Western, green c/w - 29-30	250	300
2	2221 Great Western green c/w - 30-31	130	230
2	as above 6v - 30-31	170	300
LST 2/20	as above 20v - 30-31	200	380
2	2221 plate on cabside Great Western green c/w - 32-36	130	230
2, E26	as above 6v - 32-36	170	300
LST 2/20	as above 20v - 32-34	200	380
E220	as above 20v - 34-36	200	380
2	2221 on cabside GWR button, green (late ones matt) c/w - 36-41	130	230
E26	as above 6v - 36-41	170	300
E220	as above 20v - 36-41	200	380
2	8329 on bunker + Southern sans-serif, green c/w - 29	220	350
2	8329 + Southern on tanks serif, green c/w - 30-33	180	300
2	as above 6v - 30-33	210	470
2	2329 Southern green c/w - 33-35	160	300
2, E26	as above 6v - 33-35	210	470
LST 2/20	as above 20v - 33-34	250	550
E220	as above 20v - 34-35	250	550
2	2091 Southern green c/w - 35-38	160	300
E26	as above 6v - 35-38	210	470
E220	as above 20v - 35-38	250	550
2	2091 Southern matt green c/w - 39-41	160	300
E26	as above 6v - 39-41	210	470
E220	as above 20v - 39-41	250	550
2	E492 on bunker + Southern sans-serif, red	NPG	NPG

	wheels, black c/w - *29*		
2	**E492 + Southern** on tanks serif, wheels (early red late black), black c/w - *30-33*	200	550
2	as above 6v - *30-33*	350	650
2	**492 Southern**, black c/w - *33-36*	200	550
2, E26	as above 6v - *33-36*	300	550
LST 2/20	as above 20v - *33-34*	350	650
E220	as above 20v - *34-36*	350	650

The production of black 'goods' engines was stopped after 1936 but they were obtainable by special order at extra cost.

No 2 Special loco 'Bramham Moor' [L16] (Christies)

No2 special tank [L15] (Barry Potter)

L16. No.2 Special Tender Locomotives 4-4-0

These were 4-4-0 tender locomotives and were Hornby's first real venture into true-to-type models. They were and are a very attractive and popular range embodying the character of the prototypes. Mechanisms: Clockwork 1929-41, E220 (20 volt) 1934-41, 6V special order.

2	**700 LMS** black Class 2P no cylinders, special order, beware imitations - *38*	3000	4000
	LMS 1185 Compound - maroon		
2	sans-serif, red drivers + running plate, unlined tender c/w - *29-30*	300	420
2	serif, black drivers + running plate, lined tender c/w - *31-36*	330	570
E220	as above 20v - *34-37*	380	800
2	sans-serif, black drivers + running plate, lined tender c/w - *37-38*	330	570
E220	as above 20v - *37-38*	380	800
2	serif, black drivers + running plate, lined tender, matt finish c/w - *39*	330	570
E220	as above 20v - *39*	380	800
	LNER 234 'Yorkshire' - green		
2	LNER + number on tender, small cab numberplates c/w - *29*	500	950
2	LNER on tender, number on cabside, green running plate c/w - *30-31*	500	950
2	LNER on tender, number on cabside, black running plate c/w - *31-35*	500	950
E220	as above 20v - *34-35*	780	1900
2	LNER special order black with white lining - *31-32*	3000	4000
	LNER 201 'Bramham Moor'- green		
2	LNER c/w - *35-36*	400	630
E22	as above 20v - *35-36*	680	1300
2	LNER darker green c/w - *36-41*	400	630
E220	as above 20v - *36-41*	680	1300
	3821 'County of Bedford' - green		
2	Great()Western, green running plates, red nameplates c/w - *29-30*	600	1100
2	Great()Western, black running plates, black nameplates c/w - *30-36*	350	700
E220	as above 20v - *34-36*	600	1200
2	GWR button, black running plates c/w - *36-41*	350	700
E220	as above 20v - *36-41*	600	1200
	SR Class L1 - green		
2	**A759** lined cab unlined tender c/w - *29*	1000	1500
2	**A759** lined tender c/w - *30-35*	700	1275
E220	as above 20v - *34-35*	1300	2300
2	**1759** lined tender c/w - *35-41*	700	1275
E220	as above 20v - *35-41*	1300	2300

L17. Riviera Blue Train and No.3 Tender Locomotives 4-4-2

These 4-4-2 tender engines were of rather odd freelance appearance with their large cylinders and double thickness running plates. They were nothing like the top expresses they are named after. This was almost 'badge engineering', and ironically they were coupled to the excellent No 2 special tenders (except for the 'Nord' which has a bogie tender and was made for the Riviera 'Blue Train' Set). Mechanisms: Clockwork 26-40, 3E 4 volt 26-29, 3E 6 volt 29-34, E36 6 volt 34-36, E3/20 20 volt 33-34, E320 20 volt 34-40.

	Nord 31240 - brown		
3C	**31801** on tender, black running plate, brass domes c/w - *26-27*	200	330
3E	as above 4v - *26-27*	250	440
3C	**31801** on tender, brown running plate and domes c/w - *28-29*	210	330
3E	as above 4v - *28-29*	250	440
	Nord 31801 - brown		
3C	brown smokebox c/w - *29*	210	330
3E	as above 6v - *29*	250	440
E3/20	as above 20v - *29*	260	460
3C	black smokebox c/w - *30-33*	210	330
3E	as above 6v - *30-33*	250	440
E3/20	as above 20v - *30-33*	260	460
3C	black smoke deflectors c/w - *34-36*	230	380
E36	as above 6v - *34-36*	250	440
E320	as above 20v - *34-36*	260	460
3C	brown deflectors + smokebox c/w - *36-38*	230	380
E320	as above 20v - *36-38*	260	400
E320	**3.1290** brown deflectors + smokebox, cab lined gold only, 20v - *38-41*	380	500
	LMS 6100 'Royal Scot' - maroon		
3C	crest on cab and number on coal rail tender c/w - *27-29*	220	400
3E	as above 4v - *27-29*	250	440
3C	gold number on cab and number or LMS on tender c/w - *29-30*	220	400
3E	as above 4v - *29-30*	250	440
3C	gold number on cab and number or LMS on lined tender c/w - *30-32*	220	400
3E	as above 6v - *30-32*	250	440
3C	gold number on cab and number or LMS (shaded) on lined tender c/w - *33-36*	220	400
3E, E36	as above 6v - *33-36*	250	440
E3/20	as above 20v - *33-34*	300	480
E320	as above 20v - *34-36*	300	480
3C	smoke deflectors, gold number on cab and number or LMS shaded on lined tender c/w - *36-38*	300	500
E320	as above 20v - *36-40*	350	550
	LNER 4472 'Flying Scotsman' - green		
3C	LNER + number on coal-rail tender, crest on cab, grn smokebox c/w - *27*	190	350
3E	as above 4v - *27*	270	435
3C	LNER + number on coal-rail tender, crest on cab, black smokebox c/w - *28*	190	350
3E	as above 4v - *28*	270	435
3C	LNER + number on coal-rail tender, gold number on cab, black smokebox c/w - *29*	190	350
3E	as above 4v - *29*	270	435
3C	LNER on No2 tender, gold number on cab, black smokebox c/w - *30-32*	190	350

3E	as above 6v - 30-32	270	435
3C	LNER shadowed on No2 tender, gold number on cab, black smokebox c/w - 33-36	190	350
3E, E36	as above 6v - 33-36	270	435
E3/20, E320	LNER shadowed on No2 tender, gold number on cab, black smokebox 20v - 33-36	210	420
3C	as above but darker green c/w - 36-41	260	420
E320	as above 20v - 36-41	350	465
3C	with smoke deflectors, rare - 34-36?	NPG	NPG
E320	black, extremely rare, fakes! - 37	2500	3500

4073 'Caerphilly Castle' - green

3C	Great()Western coal-rail tender, green smokebox c/w - 27-28	250	430
3E	as above 4v - 27-28	250	550
3C	Great()Western, black smokebox, brass whistle c/w - 29	260	450
3E	as above 6v - 29	250	550
3C	Great()Western, black smokebox, brass whistle, No.2 tender c/w - 30-36	260	450
3E, E36	as above 6v - 30-36	250	550
E3/20, E320	Great()Western, black smoke box, brass whistle, 20v - 33-36	300	650
3C	GWR button c/w - 36-38	260	450
E320	as above 20v - 36-38	300	650
3C	GWR button, nameplate black+gold c/w - 39-41	260	450
E320	as above 20v - 39-41	300	650

SR E850 'Lord Nelson' green

3C	coal-rail tender c/w - 28-29	240	380
3E	as above 4v - 28-29	300	420
3C	No.2 Special tender c/w - 29-33	230	360
3E	No as above 4v - 29-33	300	420

SR 850 'Lord Nelson' green

3C	c/w - 33-36	240	380
3E, E36	6v -33-36	300	420
E3/20	20v - 33-34	400	480
E320	20v - 34-36	400	480
3C	smoke deflectors fitted c/w - 36-41	260	430
E320	as above 20v - 36-41	450	530

No 3 tender loco 'Caerphilly Castle' [L17] (Wallis & Wallis)

L18. No.4 'Eton' Tender Locomotive 4-4-0

This was a 4-4-0 'Schools' Class tender locomotive. A most attractive and popular model, it was Hornby's final engine based on a prototype. The tender (a No.2 special) was incorrect for prototype. Mechanisms: Clockwork and E240 (20 volt motor).

4	**900 'Eton' Southern** grn c/w - 37-41	500	900
4	as above 20v - 37-41	630	1400
4	**900 'Eton' Southern** black, mainly for export, fakes! - 37-41	3000	5000

L19. 'Princess Elizabeth' Tender Locomotive 4-6-2

The 4-6-2 Princess Royal Class locomotive was Hornby's largest and most impressive piece of motive power. However, incorrect proportions on the locomotive give a distorted appearance to line of boiler and firebox. Early wooden presentation cases were red with blue lining and marked in gold - 'Meccano Ltd. Liverpool Princess Elizabeth'. Boxes from the middle period of production were red with cream lining and late ones were blue with green lining. Both of the latter had a nice printed description and picture inside the lid. Prices - these include the wooden presentation case. Mechanism: 20 volt electric motor.

-	**6201 'Princess Elizabeth' LMS** (serif) maroon, cab inside sand - 37	1230	2100
-	as above but sans-serif - 38	1230	2100
-	as above but cab inside maroon - 39-40	1230	2100

L20. Metropolitan Locomotive 0-4-0

This was an 0-4-0 with its wheels tucked under its skirt instead of being a double bogied model like the real locomotive. One wonders what could have been achieved if Hornby had developed a motor bogie like Bassett-Lowke and the Leeds Model Company. This was Hornby's first production electric motored model as well as its first prototypical one. It was colourful and attractive but it initially worked on 125 volt AC! Re-railing without the controller turned off could give you an additional thrill! This would appear to be the only Hornby Series locomotive not to be fitted with automatic couplings in later days. Mechanisms: 1925-29 H.V. (125), 1926-39 clockwork, 1927-29 4V, 1929-39 6V, 1938-39 20V. In about mid production, clockwork and 6 volt motors were improved.

2 Metropolitan - maroon

1, HV	125v AC - 25, 27-29	300	480
2, LV	4v - 27-29	300	480
3, C	rear windows not punched out, coupling rods c/w - 26-39	200	350
LV, E36	protruding brush-caps 6v - 29-39	300	480
E320	20v - 38-39	340	520

There were numerous mechanical variations of this model but the main ones are listed above.

Metropolitan electric loco [L20] (Barry Potter)

L21. LE1 Swiss Type Locomotives 0-4-0

Here was an 0-4-0 locomotive with a Swiss type body for overhead power collection. Dummy pantographs were fitted and there were coupling rods on the clockwork models but rarely on electric ones. This was a somewhat odd production model which lasted only four years and had five colour changes in this time! These were dark green, light green, red, cream and blue and the roofs were grey, cream, red or yellow. Mechanisms: 1932-36 LEC1, clockwork. 1932-34 LE1/20, 20V. 1934-36 LE120, 20V.

LEC1	**10655** various colours c/w - 32-36	450	700
LE1/20	as above 20v - 32-34	500	800
LE120	as above 20v - 34-36	500	800

L22. LE2 Continental Locomotives 0-4-0

Another 0-4-0 locomotive and a very strange looking object being basically a Metropolitan loco without the skirts. Apart from the 'Princess Elizabeth', it was the sole Hornby model not to have a clockwork version. The body was fitted with overhead pantographs and it carried the same transfers as LE1. Some models had coupling rods and the body colours that may be found are dark green, light green, red or cream. roof colours were grey, cream or blue. Mechanisms: 1932-34 LE2/20, 20V 1934-36 LE220, 20V.

LE220	**10655** Swiss, Metropolitan body various colours 20v - 32-36	650	1850

COACHES

Until the middle of the 1920s, rolling stock was of nut and bolt (Meccano type) construction. After that, tabs and slots were used to join pieces together when items were assembled. Below we provide a means of identifying the age of coaches by their structure and finish.

Cat.No.	Company, Number, Colour, Date	£	£

M Series Coaches (4-wheel)

C1a. M0 Pullman Coaches

This was a small coach with no buffers, tin hook and loop couplings, cream and brown livery and named 'Joan' or 'Zena'.

M0	red or green roof, marked Hornby Series - 30-41	10	14
No.0	as above but with automatic couplings - 31-41	10	14
M0	grey roof, marked Hornby - 46-54	8	12
No.21	**BR** red+cream same body no names - 54-59	5	10

C1b. M1/2 and M1 Pullman Coaches

This was larger than the M0 Pullman coach. All had drop-link couplings, cream and brown livery and were named 'Pullman' (1926-28), 'Marjorie', 'Aurelia' or 'Viking'.

M1/2	yellow+green+cream, red or brown roofs and bases - 26-41	15	22
M1	white or grey roofs and black bases - 46-57	15	22

1921 No1 passenger coach [C2a]

No1 Coaches (4-wheel)

C2a. 1921 No.1 Passenger Coaches

These were of nut and bolt construction, had brass numbers on the doors, grey roofs, coats of arms on the sides, cut-out windows and 4 silver wheels.

No.1	CR orange-brown, ochre doors - 21-23	80	110
No.1	GN orange-brown, ochre doors - 21-24	60	75
No.1	LNWR brown+ white - 21-23	60	75
No.1	as above tinprinted doors - 23-24	60	75
No.1	MR maroon, brown-pink doors - 21-24	60	75

C2b. 1924 No.1 Passenger Coaches

This had a completely different body of tab and slot construction and a full brake was also made from now onwards. The coaches had grey clerestory roofs (until 1929), three opening doors in each side and printed windows. The wheelbase was short for the length of body making them look toy-like.

No.1	LMS red, clerestory roof - 24-28	40	55
No.1	LNER brown, clerestory roof - 24-28	40	55
No.1	GWR brown+cream, clerestory roof - 24-28	55	70
No.1	LMS 1136? red - 28-34	30	45
No.1	LNER brown - 28-34	30	45
No.1	GWR brown+cream - 28-34	35	50
No.1	SR 1728 green - 28-32	55	70
No.1	SR 2891 green - 32-34	55	70

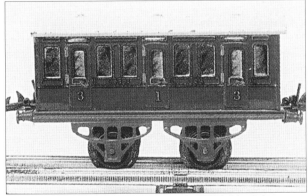

1924 No1 passenger coach [C2b] (Vectis)

C2c. 1934 No.1 Passenger Coaches

These coaches were completely redesigned models which were wider and higher than previous ones, with wheels further apart, non-opening doors and closed axle springs. Roofs were grey (lighter shade after the war) and post-war versions were marked 'Hornby' or 'Hornby Trains'.

No.1	LMS red+yellow+black detail - 34-41	25	40
No.1	LNER light brown wood-grain - 34-41	30	45
No.1	GWR brown+cream - 34-41	50	65
No.1	SR green+yellow printed detail - 34-41	80	95

No.1	LMS red - 47-59	20	35
No.1	LNER light brown - 47-59	20	35
No.1	GWR brown+cream - 47-49	70	85
No.1	SR green - 47-49	90	120
No.41	BR red+yellow lining, no black lined panels - 54-58	20	25
No.51	BR red+cream - 54-58	30	45

No 1 Coach GWR [C2c] (Barry Potter)

C2d. 1928 No.1 Pullman Coach

Both coach and brake end versions were made over a long period so mums and dads must have loved them but to kids they were hideous! They had rounded roof ends and recessed end doors. They had brown and cream tin-printed sides and were named 'Corsair', 'Cynthia', 'Niobe', 'Ansonia' or 'Aurora'. Roofs were cream, grey, red, green or blue.

No.1	opening doors - 28-35	20	30
No.1	non-opening doors - 35-41	20	30

No.2 Bogie Coaches (with compensating bogies)

The passenger coaches were 1st/3rd composites and the brake coaches were all 3rd class. They were similar in style and colour to the 1934 No.1 coaches but twice as long.

C3a. 1921 No.2 Pullman and Dining Saloon.

These were the first bogie coaches to be made by Hornby and were a light cream and green and had greenish grey roofs. They were of nut and bolt construction and had celluloid windows. Until 1923 the doors were fixed but from then they were hinged.

No.2	Pullman crests, green+cream - 21-25	90	130
No.2	Pullman crests as above but scrolled box around name - 25	90	130
No.2	Pullman crests as above but livery now brown+cream - 25-27	90	130
No.2	CR crest Dining Saloon green+cream - 21-23	100	140
No.2	GN crest Dining Saloon green+cream - 21-23	100	140
No.2	LNWR crest Dining Saloon green+cream - 21-23	100	140
No.2	MR crest Dining Saloon green+cream - 21-23	90	130
No.2	Pullman crests Dining Saloon green+cream - 23-25	90	130

No 2 Dining saloon [C3a] (Barry Potter)

C3b. Metropolitan Coaches

This was a suburban bogie coach with a fine wood grain tin-printed finish made specially to go with the Metropolitan electric locomotive. Two versions were made - 1st class and brake/3rd. They had grey roofs, yellow windows, brass buffers, drop-link couplings and were available in both lit and unlit versions.

-	**Met** 1st class brown coach - *26-39*	180	250
-	**Met** brake 3rd brown coach - *26-39*	180	250

C3c. 1928 No.2/3 or No.2 Special Pullmans

These replaced the No.2 and No.3 Pullmans in sets. They had a restyled body with smaller, better shaped, windows which had more elegant window frames. They had square accumulator boxes beneath the coach instead of cylinders. They also had snap-on roofs, seven windows in their sides and they had a curved roof with rain gullies and ventilators. All were brown and cream and a brake end (or composite) was now produced. They were called No.2/3 Pullmans until 1930/31 when they were renamed No.2 Special Pullmans.

No.2/3	**Pullman** all cream upper half, cream roof with blue vents, named '**Iolanthe**' - *28-30*	90	130
No.2/3	**Pullman** all cream upper half, cream roof with blue vents, named '**Iolanthe**' or '**Zenobia**' - *29-30*	90	130
No.2/3	**Pullman** brake, all cream upper half, cream roof with blue vents, named '**Arcadia**' - *28-30*	90	130
No.2/3	**Pullman** brake, all cream upper half, cream roof, blue vents, named '**Arcadia**' or '**Alberta**' - *29-30*	90	130
No.2	**Pullman** brown above windows, grey roof, named '**Iolanthe**', '**Zenobia**' or '**Grosvenor**' - *30-35*	120	180
No.2	**Pullman** as above but named '**Zenobia**', '**Grosvenor**' or '**Loraine**' - *35-41*	120	180
No.2	**Pullman** brake, brown above windows, grey roof, named '**Arcadia**', '**Alberta**' or '**Montana**' - *30-35*	120	180
No.2	**Pullman** as above but named '**Alberta**', '**Montana**' or '**Verona**', luggage compartment now all brown - *35-41*	120	180

No 2 Special Pullman brake car [C3c] (Wallis & Wallis)

C3d. 1935 No.2 Passenger Coaches

These were the first Hornby bogie coaches for general passenger stock of the four railway companies despite the fact that Bing and Bassett-Lowke had issued theirs in the early 1920s. The coaches consisted of a 1st/3rd composite and an all 3rd brake end.

No.2	**LMS** red + black/yellow lining - *35-41*	125	170
No.2	**LNER** light brown teak effect - *35-41*	150	195
No.2	**GWR** brown+cream with badge in lower half - *35-41*	180	250
No.2	**SR** green + yellow/black lining - *35-41*	200	300
No.2	**LMS** red + black/yellow lining - *48-50*	155	200
No.2	**LNER** light brown teak effect - *48-50*	185	240
No.2	**GWR** brown+cream with badge in lower half - *48-50*	225	295
No.2	**SR** green + yellow/black lining - *48-50*	250	350

C3e. 1937 No.2 Corridor Coaches

This was a later design to go with the larger express locomotives. They had longer windows and the end panels were cut to take the 'concertina' type corridor connections. All were composites except the Southern coach which was an all-3rd. There were destination board brackets above windows and the roofs white except LMS ones which were grey. The coaches consisted of a 1st/3rd composite and a 1st/3rd brake end.

No.2	**LMS** red + yellow lining, black chassis (matt after 1939) - *37-41*	100	160
No.2	**LNER** light brown teak effect, yellow + black panelling - *37-41*	125	180
No.2	**GWR** brown and cream with badge in lower	160	220

half - *37-41*

No.2	**SR** green + yellow panelling, brake coach had deep orange around door windows - *37-41*	200	300

No 2 passenger brake coach [C3e] (Dreweatt & Neate)

No.3 Bogie Coaches

C4a. Riviera Blue Train & Mitropa Coaches

The Riviera Blue Train coaches were the first Hornby coaches to be made with corridor connectors and were for use with the Nord locomotive. Two types, a sleeper and a diner, were available but these were structurally the same but with different celluloid strips at the windows. From 1931 onwards, they were fitted with compensating bogies and a Mitropa version of each was produced in red livery. The latter had white roofs and were a strange choice because Hornby did not have an appropriate locomotive to pull them. They could perhaps have been put behind the Nord as a through train!

No.3	**CIE** Dining Car, blue - *26-41*	150	190
No.3	**CIE** Sleeping Car, blue - *26-41*	150	190
No.3	**Mitropa** Schlafwagen, red+gold - *31-41*	500	600
No.3	**Mitropa** Speisewagen, red+gold - *31-41*	500	600

C4b. No.3 (No.2) Pullman & Saloon Coaches

Based on the Riviera Blue body, these Pullmans originally came with the No.3 train sets. They also had corridor connections and brown corridor end plates but used the same transfers as the No.2 Pullmans and carried the same livery with cream roofs. From 1930 the No.3 was renamed the 'No.2 Pullman Coach' and LMS and LNER 1st class end vestibule saloon coaches were made to the same design.

No.3	**Pullman**, large crests, drop-link couplings - *27-28*	60	80
No.2	**Pullman**, small crests, automatic couplings - *30-41*	60	80
No.2	**LMS** No.402 red saloon - *30-41*	60	80
No.2	**LNER** No.137 brown saloon - *30-41*	60	80

No 2 Pullman car [C4b] (Wallis & Wallis)

WAGONS

The first Hornby 0 gauge wagons appeared in 1920 and were of nut and bolt construction. These were in liveries representing pre-grouping companies and were priced 3/9 each.

Company Lettering - Meccano Ltd were quick to introduce the new liveries after Grouping in 1923; LNER and LMS being the first to appear followed by GWR and SR. Around 1928, 'LNER' was dropped in favour of 'NE'.

Earlier lettering on pre-grouping stock consisted of white painted tinplate letters stamped out and fixed to the sides of vehicles by the tongue and slot method. This changed to transfers around 1925 and around 1928 to transfers with shaded white lettering. On some later vehicles, gold transfer lettering was used.

As the range evolved, realism was further pursued by overall tinprinting. The SR vans are good examples where this method achieved both realistic colouring and detail representation.

Transfer Dating - most wagons carry transfers and the position in which these were placed varied according to the period in which the batch of wagons was being made. The position can help to date the wagon but space does not allow us to include the many variations here. We refer you to Chris and Julie Graebe's *Hornby Gauge 0 Compendium* published by New Cavendish Books which provides extensive listing of these along with dates.

Base Writing - A number of earlier vehicles had their description, e.g.. 'Cattle Truck', in small white letters on each side of their underframe.

Chassis - Over the years five basic types of wheelbase were fitted to the standard wagons, the main visual difference being the representation of springs and axleboxes. In addition there were longer, narrower, bases used on a few wagons and denoted here by an 'L' suffix.

> **Type 1:** (1921-25) Solid and plain. These had deep solebars and unfretted axle supports. Extra slots for drop-link couplings were added sometime in 1921 and a further revision was made the following year for thinner axles. Last stocks were used up in 1925 (T1).
> **Type 2:** (1922-41) An open chassis with embossed and pierced springs etc. (T2).
> **Type 2L:** (1924-49) This was a little used long and narrow wheelbase found on open wagons in the mid '20s, double wine wagons and M series open wagons (T2L).
> **Type 3:** (1930-40) Introduced at the time auto couplings came in. Solid with embossed springs (not cut-out) and can also be found on some wagons released immediately after WW2 (T3).
> **Type 3L:** (1934-41) this had a long narrow wheelbase and was made from a carriage chassis. It saw very little use on wagons (T3L).
> **Type 4:** (1949-57) Simple embossed spring shapes which did not show leaves as the previous type did. This was the post-war version of the T3 (T4).
> **Type 4L:** This was a long base used on M wagons after the war (T4L).
> **Type 5:** (1957-63) Known as the No.50 wheelbase, this had cast ends and buffers, no brake rod connecting the axleboxes but had a separate silver coloured brake lever (T5).

Dating wagons by their bases can be harder than it might seem due to stocks of old bases sometimes coming back into use on later wagons in order to use them up.

Watch out for Replicas - The colourful and attractive private owner wagons were a very effective way for manufacturers to advertise as they were toy versions of real wagons on the railways in the '20s and '30s. Hornby usually encouraged the companies, whose names appeared on the vans, to contribute towards the cost of the transfers.

Many of these are now much sought after. The Coleman's Mustard van was based on the first nut and bolt No.1 van and had a very short life before being replaced by the Seccotine van in 1925. A number of replica Coleman's vans are around and so buyer beware! If the Coleman's van is not a nut and bolt item it is by definition a replica but some replicas are nut and bolt vans that have been repainted.

Early Chassis Types

Type 1 brass buffers and hook coupling plus early round trade mark clip on lettering.

Type 1 with drop link coupling

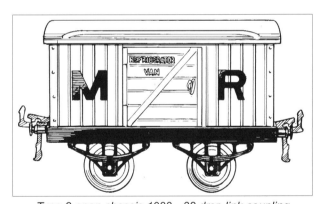

Type 2 open chassis 1923 - 32 drop link coupling

Type 3 closed chassis 1933 - 62 with automatic couplings which were introduced in 1931.

143

\Some of the private owner transfers were also applied to Dinky toys including 'Seccotine', 'Palethorpes', 'Shell', Esso' and 'Pratts'.

There was a more sophisticated tank wagon which was larger and had more detail including ladders. The transfers were United Dairies or Nestles Milk on white tanks and Colas on blue or red tanks. Genuine examples of the latter are quite rare and so beware of reproductions!

In general, wagons in Southern Railway (SR) livery are much rarer than the others and some sell for very high prices. Consequently replicas exist - so beware!

M0 Freight Stock

The M0 series were small, toy-like, tinplate wagons designed to go with the M0 locomotives. They were to a smaller scale while still being 0 gauge and so they look small alongside the other 0 gauge wagons. They were printed in red before the war and mostly in green during the post-war period (but some were red). The couplings were very simple consisting of a broad loop at one end of the wheelbase and a hook at the other.

Cat.No.	Company, Number, Colour, Dates	£	£
W1.	**M0 Wagon (open wagon)**		
M0	red on black base - 30-41	10	15
M0	green on black base - 33-41	10	15
M0	British Express Wagon - 32-36	10	20
M0	red on black base - 46-54	5	10
M0	green on black base - 46-54	5	10
W2.	**M0 Rotary Tipping Wagon**		
M0	green on black base - 35-36	10	15
M0	green on red base - 36-41	10	15
M0	blue top on red base - 36?	10	15
M0	green top on red base - 52-64	5	10
W3.	**M0 Side Tipping Wagon**		
M0	yellow on black base - 35-36	10	15
M0	same but green base - 36-41	10	10
M0	yellow top on green base - 52-64	5	10
W4.	**M0 Petrol Tank Wagon**		
M0	**Shellmex and BP** cream on black base - 35-36	10	25
M0	same but red base - 36-38	10	25
M0	**Shell or BP** cream on red base - 38-41	10	25
M0	**Shell or BP** silver on red base - 52-60	10	25
W5.	**M0 Crane Truck**		
M0	blue crane, black base - 35-36	10	15
M0	same but green base - 36-41	10	15
M0	same but post-war - 52-54	5	10

No.20 Freight Stock

A wagon used only in the No.20 post-war train set.

W6. No.20 Wagon (open wagon)
This was very like the M0 wagon but was now in a BR livery.

No.20	**BR** grey - 54-64	5	10

W7. No.20 Crane Truck
This was very like the M0 wagon but was now in a BR livery.

No.20	blue crane on green base - 54-64	5	10

M/M1 Freight Stock

The only wagons made to go with the M1 train sets were open wagons. Early ones had plain grey enamelled bodies printed in white and later ones had tin-printed bodies that showed planking and bracing detail.

W8a. M Wagon (early)
This used the long thin base and had an enamelled grey open wagon body with or without buffers. They had drop-link couplings. Letters printed in white on a plain grey body.

M	**LMS** W grey - 26-27	5	10
M	same with gold 'LMS' - 27-29	5	15
M	**NE** W grey - 29	5	10
M	**GW** W grey -26-27	5	20
M	same with gold 'LMS' - 27-29	5	15
M	**SR** W grey - 29	20	35

W8b. M1 Wagon (late)
Long thin tin-printed wagons and carrying the number 12530.

M	**LMS** plain grey - 29-30	5	10
M1	**LMS** detailed grey - 30-33, 35-41	5	10
M	same but green base - 33-35	5	10
M	**NE** plain grey - 29-30	5	10
M1	**NE** detailed grey - 30-33, 35-41	5	10
M1	same but green base - 33-35	5	10
M	**GW** plain grey - 29-30	5	20
M1	**GW** detailed grey - 30-33, 35-41	5	20
M1	same but green base - 33-35	5	20
M	**SR** plain grey - 29-30	20	35
M1	**SR** detailed grey - 30-33, 35-41	20	35
M1	same but green base - 33-35	20	35

W8c. M1 Wagon (post-war)
This was similar to the late pre-war M1 wagons but with different printing. Usually black interiors.

M1	**LMS** buff or grey - 46-48	5	10
M1	**LMS** brown - 48-57	5	10
M1	**LNE** buff or grey - 46-48	5	10
M1	**LNE** brown - 48-57	5	10

No.30 Freight Stock

These were 1956 replacements for the M1 wagons and were of a completely new design. They were available only in the No.30 train sets and had loop and hook couplings like the M0 wagons.

W9. No.30 Wagon (open wagon)
This was like the No.1 timber wagon but without buffers.

M30	**BR** grey - 56-64	5	10

W10. No.30 Van
Found in the M11 set, this was like the No.1 fibre wagon but without buffers.

M30	**BR** brown - 56-64	10	15

M3 Freight Stock

These enamelled wagons were available only in M3 goods train sets and could not be bought separately. Consequently individual boxed examples will not be found. They can be recognised by the absence of buffers on all but the pre 1927 open wagons.

W11. M3 Wagon (open wagon)
Long and thin, these open wagons were grey enamelled and, from 1927, were not fitted with buffers. They had drop-link couplings and gold transfers.

M3	**LMS** detailed grey T2L - 31-33, 35-41	15	25
M3	same but green base - 33-35	15	25
M3	**NE** detailed grey T2L - 31-33, 35-41	15	25
M3	same but green base - 33-35	15	25
M3	**GW** detailed grey T2L - 31-33, 35-41	15	25
M3	same but green base - 33-35	15	25

| M3 | **SR** detailed grey T2L - *31-33, 35-41* | 30 | 45 |
| M3 | same but green base - *33-35* | 30 | 45 |

W12. M3 Tank Wagon
This was like the No.1 Shell tank wagon but without buffers.

| M3 | **Shell** red T3 *31-36* | 20 | 35 |
| M3 | **Royal Daylight** red T3 *36-41* | 20 | 35 |

W13. M3 Timber Wagon
This was like the No.1 timber wagon but without buffers.

| M3 | red base green stanchions T3 *31-39* | 15 | 25 |
| M3 | black base red stanchions T3 *39-41* | 15 | 25 |

W14. M3 Fibre Wagon
Found in the M11 set, this was like the No.1 fibre wagon but without buffers.

| - | **LMS** grey T3 *35-41* | 25 | 45 |

No.0 Freight Stock

While to the same scale and basic design as the No.1 wagons, the No.0 series were a cost cutting exercise. They were tin-printed instead of being enamelled, had non-opening doors and a cheaper chassis, sometimes without buffers. Some of the latter were designated 'M1' and others, for tank goods sets, were labelled 'M3'.

W15. No.0 Open Wagon
This replaced the Zulu open wagon and was tin-printed; first plain and then with detail.

No.0	**LMS** plain grey T2 - *29-30*	10	20
No.0	**LMS** detailed grey T2 - *30*	15	30
No.0	now with T3 base - *30-41*	10	20
No.0	**NE** plain grey T2 - *29-30*	10	20
No.0	**NE** detailed grey T2 - *30*	15	30
No.0	now with T3 base - *30-41*	10	20
No.0	**GW** plain grey T2 - *29-30*	10	20
No.0	**GW** detailed grey T2 - *30*	15	30
No.0	now with T3 base - *30-41*	10	20
No.0	**SR** plain grey T2 - *29-30*	25	45
No.0	**GW** detailed brown T2 - *30*	15	30
No.0	now with T3 base - *30-41*	10	20

W16. No.0 Rotary Tipping Wagon
Unlike the No.1 rotary tipping wagon, this had curved tipper supports.

No.0	**Meccano** blue T2 (red) - *34-35*	20	30
No.0	blue T2 (red) - *35-39*	10	20
No.0	now with black base - *39-41*	15	25

W17. No.0 Refrigerator Van
Tin-printed with fixed doors.

No.0	**LMS** grey T3 - *37-41*	40	70
No.0	**NE** white T3 - *37-41*	40	70
No.0	**GW** white Mica B T3 - *37-41*	60	80
No.0	**SR** buff T3 - *37-41*	60	110

W18. No.0 Milk Traffic Van
Tin-printed with sliding doors until 1935, then fixed.

No.0	**GW** grey T3 (black) - *31-33*	40	70
No.0	same but green base - *33-55*	40	70
No.0	**GW** brown T3 - *35-41*	30	50

W19. No.0 Meat Van
Tin-printed with sliding doors until 1935, then fixed.

No.0	**LMS** grey T3 (black) - *31-33, 35-41*	40	60
No.0	same but green base - *33-35*	40	60
No.0	**NE** brown T3 - *37-41*	50	70
No.0	**GW** grey Mica T3 - *37-41*	80	150

W20. No.0 Fish Van
Tin-printed with sliding doors until 1935, then fixed. Normally a black base.

No.0	**NE** grey T3 (black) - *31-33*	40	70
No.0	as above but green base - *33-35*	40	70
No.0	**NE** red-brown T3 - *35-41*	40	70

| No.0 | **GW** red-brown T3 - *37-41* | 50 | 100 |
| No.0 | **LMS** red T3 - *37-41* | 50 | 100 |

No.0 meat van [W19] (Vectis)

W21. No.0 Banana Van
Tin-printed with no sliding door. It had a black base and white or grey roof and was marked 'Avonmouth' in black or white.

| No.0 | **LMS** grey T3 *35-41* | 40 | 70 |

No.1 Freight Stock

This was the basic series characterised by embossed, stamped, detail with an enamel finish. Where applied, they had quality transfer markings and vans had sliding doors.

W22a. No.1 Flat Truck

No.1	**LMS** grey T3 - *34-41*	5	15
No.1	**LMS** 219493 brown T3 - *48*	10	15
No.1	now with T4 base - *48-54*	5	15
No.1	**NE** grey T3 - *34-41*	5	15
No.1	**NE** 35968 brown T3 - *48*	10	15
No.1	now with T4 base - *48-54*	5	10
No.1	**GW** grey T3 - *34-41*	5	20
No.1	**GW** grey T3 - *48*	20	40
No.1	now with T4 base - *48-54*	15	30
No.1	**SR** brown T3 - *34-41, 48*	25	45
No.1	now with T4 base - *48-54*	25	45
No.1	**BR** brown T4 - *54-59*	5	10

Flat wagon with cable drum [W22b] (Barry Potter)

W22b. No.1 Flat Truck with Cable Drum

No.1	**LMS** grey T3 + Bl cable drum - *34-41*	20	30
No.1	same but Liverpool Cables - *37-39*	30	45
No.1	**LMS** 219493 brown T3 + Liverpool drum - *48*	20	30
No.1	now with T4 base - *48-54*	10	20
No.1	**LMS** + Electric Cables drum - *?*	250	300
No.1	**NE** grey T3 + Bl cable drum - *34-41*	20	30

No.1	same but Liverpool Cables - *37-39*	30	45
No.1	**NE** 35968 brown T3 + Liverpool drum - *48*	20	30
No.1	now with T4 base - *48-54*	10	20
No.1	**GW** grey T3 + BI cable drum - *34-41*	25	40
No.1	same but Liverpool Cables - *37-39*	20	30
No.1	same but post-war - *48*	30	60
No.1	now with T4 base - *48-51*	30	60
No.1	**SR** brown T3 + BI cable drum - *34-41*	35	70
No.1	same but Liverpool Cables - *37-39*	35	70
No.1	same but post-war - *48*	55	100
No.1	now with T4 base - *48-51*	35	70
No.1	**BR** brown T4 + Liverpool Cables - *54-59*	10	20

W22c. No.1 Flat Truck with Container

The container was of wood and covered with printed paper.

No.1	**LMS** grey T3 + LMS container - *36-41*	20	40
No.1	**LMS** brown T3 + LMS container - *48*	25	40
No.1	now with T4 base- *48-54*	15	30
No.1	**NE** grey T3 + LNER container - *36-41*	20	40
No.1	**NE** brown T3 + LNER container - *48*	25	40
No.1	now with T4 base- *48-54*	15	30
No.1	**GW** grey T3 + GWR container - *36-41*	25	50
No.1	**GW** grey T3 + GWR container - *48*	50	90
No.1	now with T4 base- *48-51*	40	80
No.1	**SR** brown T3 + SR container - *36-41*	35	70
No.1	same but post-war - *48*	190	230
No.1	now with T4 base - *48-51*	160	210
No.1	**BR** brown T4 + furniture container - *55-59*	15	30
No.1	**BR** brown T4 + insulated meat container - *55-59*	15	30

Flat wagon with furniture container [W22c] (Barry Potter)

W23. Fibre Wagon

Examples without buffers were for the M series.

-	red T3 - *31-33*	15	25
-	blue T3 - *33-39*	15	25
-	black T3 - *39-41*	15	25

W24. No.1 Lumber Wagon

This was a base with a pair of red or black bolsters. Some were inscribed 'No.1 Lumber Wagon'.

No.1	olive green T2 - *23-24*	20	40
No.1	**LMS** olive green T2 - *24-30*	10	20
No.1	**L&NER** olive green T2 - *24*	60	120
No.1	**LNER** olive green T2 - *24-26*	20	40
No.1	**NE** olive green T2 - *26-30*	10	20
No.1	**GW** olive green T2 - *26-30*	20	40
No.1	**SR** brown + blue bolsters T2 - *28-30*	90	170
No.1	brown + blue bolsters T2 - *30*	60	120
No.1	olive green T2 - *30*	30	60
No.1	same with T3 base - *30-33*	10	20
No.1	light green + yellow bolsters T3 - *33-39*	10	20
No.1	black + red bolsters T3 - *39-41*	10	20
No.1	same but post-war - *48*	10	20
No.1	now with T4 bases - *48-57*	8	20

W25. No.1 Timber Wagon

This was a flat base with two vertical projections each side to retain a planks load. Some were inscribed 'Timber Wagon'.

No.1	olive T2 with olive stanchions - *22-24*	20	40
No.1	**LMS** olive green T2 - *24-30*	10	20
No.1	**LNER** olive green T2 - *24-26*	20	40
No.1	**NE** olive green T2 - *26-30*	10	20
No.1	**GW** green & red T2 - *26-30*	10	20
No.1	**SR** brown T2 - *28-30*	80	160
No.1	brown T2 with red stanchions - *30*	70	150
No.1	olive T2 with red stanchions - *30*	30	60
No.1	now with T3 base - *30-31*	25	50
No.1	now red with yell stanchions - *31-32*	20	40
No.1	same with green stanchions - *31-39*	10	20
No.1	now black with red stanchions - *39-41*	6	20
No.1	now black with red stanchions - *47-48*	10	20
No.1	now with T4 base - *48-59*	6	20

W26. Gas Cylinder Wagon

Inscription or lettering on side of cylinders. The position of 'Gas Cylinders' and company lettering varies.

-	red T2 - *23-24*	10	20
-	**LMS** red T2 - *24-30*	10	20
-	**L&NER** red T2 - *24*	20	40
-	**LNER** red T2 - *24-26*	10	20
-	**NE** red T2 - *26-30*	10	20
-	**GW** red T2 - *26-30*	20	40
-	**SR** green T2 - *28-30*	70	140
-	red T3 - *30-33, 39-41, 48*	10	20
-	as above but with blue base - *33-39*	10	20
-	red T4 - *48-57*	5	20

W27a. Open Wagon (1st type)

These wagons started life as constructional trucks, square-ish in shape, had silver wheels, brass buffers and clip-on letters. From 1922-23 they had thinner axles.

-	**LNWR** grey T1 - *20-23*	30	60
-	now with T2 base - *22-23*	30	50
-	**MR** grey T1 - *20-23*	30	60
-	now with T2 base - *22-23*	30	50
-	**GN** grey T1 - *20-23*	35	60
-	now with T2 base - *22-23*	30	50
-	**CR** grey T1 - *21-22*	50	100
-	**LBSC** grey T1 - *21-22*	400	500
-	**GE** grey T1 - *21-22*	50	100
-	**SECR** grey T1 - *21-22*	250	350

W27b. Zulu Wagon (1st type)

The letters were sprayed on but otherwise these were similar to the 1920 open wagons. The body was fixed to the base by eyelets and fitted with cast buffers.

| No.1 | **LNW** W grey T1 - *22-23* | 30 | 60 |

Open wagon (1st type) [W27c] (Vectis)

W27c. Open Wagon (1st type)

This was as the 1920 wagon but with transfers and cast or brass buffers.

-	**LMS** W grey T1 - *23-24, 26-27*	20	45
-	same with T2 base - *23-24*	20	45
-	**LNER** W grey T2 - *23-24*	20	45
-	same with T2 base - *23-26*	20	45
-	**NE** W grey T2 - *26-27*	20	45

-	**GW** W grey T1 - *26*	25	50
-	same with T2 base - *26-27*	25	50

W27d. Open Wagon (2nd type) (Long)

These were long thin wagons with transfers. Some had brass buffers and other with cast ones.

-	**LMS** grey T2L - *24-25*	25	45
-	**LNER** grey T2L - *24-25*	25	45

W27e. Open Wagon (3rd type)

This was a new design of enamelled body introduced late 1925 and of tab construction with transfers.

-	**LMS** G grey T2 - *27-30*	10	20
No.1	now with T3 base - *30*	15	25
No.1	now with white 'LMS' - *30-32*	10	20
No.1	now with green base - *33*	15	25
-	**NE** G grey T2 - *27-30*	10	20
No.1	now with T3 base - *30*	15	25
No.1	now with white 'NE' - *30-32*	10	20
No.1	now with green base - *33*	15	25
-	**GW** G grey T2 - *27-30*	15	25
No.1	now with T3 base - *30*	15	30
No.1	now with white 'GW' - *30-32*	15	30
No.1	now with green base - *33*	15	30
-	**SR** G brown T2 - *27-30*	25	45
No.1	now with T3 base - *30*	25	45
No.1	now with white 'SR' - *30-32*	25	45
No.1	now with green base - *33*	25	45

W27f. Open Wagon (4th type) (Tin-printed)

A tin-printed range introduced in 1932. The planking, ironwork and sole bar detail were now printed on. Variants exist.

No.1	**LMS** grey T3 - *32-41*	10	20
No.1	**LMS** buff T3 - *47-48*	10	20
No.1	**LMS** brown T3 - *48*	10	20
No.1	now with T4 base - *48-49*	10	20
No.1	**LMS** (small) brown T4 - *49-54*	5	20
No.1	**NE** grey T3 - *32-41, 48*	10	20
No.1	now with T4 base - *48-49*	5	20
No.1	**NE** buff T3 - *47-48*	5	20
No.1	**NE** (small) grey T4 - *49-54*	5	20
No.1	**GW** grey T3 - *32-41*	10	30
No.1	**GW** buff T3 - *47-48*	30	50
No.1	**SR** brown T3 - *32-41*	25	45
No.1	**SR** brown T3 - *47-48*	30	55
No.1	**BR** grey T4 - *54-58*	5	20

W28a. Sheet Rail Open Wagon B

As above but with sheet rail added. Lettering was always white and the rail was blue or black.

B	**LMS** black T3 (green) - *31-33*	20	40
B	**LMS** blue T3 (green) - *33-35*	20	40
B	now with black base - *35-41*	20	40
B	**NE** black T3 (green) - *31-33*	20	40
B	**NE** blue T3 (green) - *33-35*	20	40
B	now with black base - *35-41*	20	40
B	**GW** black T3 (green) - *31-33*	25	50
B	**GW** blue T3 (green) - *33-35*	25	50
B	now with black base - *35-41*	25	50
B	**SR** black T3 (green) - *31-33*	50	90
B	**SR** blue T3 (green) - *33-35*	50	90
B	now with black base - *35-41*	50	90

W28b. Wagon with Sheet Rail

Post-war version of above.

-	**LMS** brown T3 - *48*	20	30
-	**LMS** (small) brown T4 - *49-54*	10	20
-	**NE** grey T3 - *48*	20	30
-	**NE** (small) grey T4 - *49-54*	10	20
-	**BR** grey T4 - *54-58*	10	20

W29. Coal Wagon

This was the same as the No.1 open wagon but fitted with a load of embossed coal. G = company letters in gold transfers.

-	**Meccano** G red T3 - *31-36*	75	110
-	as above but white transfer - *40?*	120	180
-	**Hornby Railway Company** G red or maroon T3 - *36-40*	100	120
-	as above but white transfer - *40-41*	100	150

W30. Hopper Wagon

Some early examples were inscribed 'Hopper Wagon'. G = company letters in gold transfers.

-	grey T2 - *23-24*	45	60
-	**LMS** G grey T2 - *24-27*	45	60
-	**LMS** G green T2 - *27-30*	20	30
-	now with T3 base - *30-39*	20	30
-	same with black base - *39-40*	20	40
-	now with white 'LMS' - *40-41*	20	40
-	now with white 'LMS' - *48*	25	60
-	now with T4 base - *48-54*	10	20
-	**LNER** G grey T2 - *24-26*	40	60
-	**LNER** G green T2 - *26-27*	40	60
-	**NE** G green T2 - *27-30*	20	30
-	now with T3 base - *30-39*	20	30
-	bow with black base - *39-40*	20	40
-	now with white 'NE' - *40-41*	20	40
-	**GW** G grey T2 - *26-27*	45	70
-	**GW** G green T2 - *27-30*	45	70
-	now with T3 base - *30-39*	30	60
-	bow with black base - *39-40*	30	60
-	now with white 'GW' - *40-41*	30	60
-	**SR** G red T2 - *28-30*	70	140
-	now with T3 base - *30-40*	55	110
-	now with white 'SR' - *40-41*	75	150
-	**BR** grey T4 - *48-59*	10	20

W31. No.1 Rotary Tipping Wagon

Early ones inscribed 'Rotary Tipper'.

No.1	grey T2 (black) - *23*	30	60
No.1	**McAlpine** grey T2 (black) - *23-26*	20	45
No.1	same with olive green base - *23-26*	20	45
No.1	now with orange base and top - *26-29*	20	45
No.1	**Meccano** orange T2 - *29-30*	55	110
No.1	now with T3 base - *30-32*	55	110
No.1	now with blue base + yell top - *32-36*	55	110
No.1	**Trinidad Lake Asphalt** buff T3 (blue) - *36-39*	20	45
No.1	now with black base - *39-41, 48*	20	45
No.1	now with T4 base - *48-59*	10	25

W32. Side Tipping Wagon

These had drop-link couplings and black or red lining. Early ones were inscribed 'Tilting Wagon'.

-	grey T2 (black) - *23-24*	20	60
-	**McAlpine** grey T2 (black) - *24-27*	25	45
-	**McAlpine** blue T2 (blue) - *27-30*	25	45
-	**Robert Hudson** blue T2 (blue) - *29-30*	25	45
-	now with T3 base - *30-33*	25	45
-	**Robert Hudson** yell T3 (blue) - *33-38*	25	45
No.1	**McAlpine** yellow T3 (blue) - *38-39*	25	45
No.1	now with black base - *39-41, 48*	25	45
No.1	**McAlpine** buff T4 (black) - *48-56*	15	25
No.1	**McAlpine** green T4 (black) - *57-64*	15	25

W33. Barrel Wagon

This was sold as a Continental type wagon. The long thin wagon base with auto couplings was used. 2 chains secured the wooden barrels on the T2L wheelbase and a single chain on the T3L one.

-	blue barrels T2L (red) - *31-33*	10	20
-	yellow barrels T2L (red) - *33-35*	10	20
-	same with green barrels - *33-35*	10	20
-	yellow barrels T3L (red) - *35-37*	10	20
-	same with green barrels - *35-37*	10	20
-	**Castrol** yell barrels T3L (red) - *37-41*	30	40
-	same with green barrels - *37-41*	30	40

W34. Single Wine Wagon

-	green with red barrels T2 - *29-30*	60	140
-	now with T3 base - *30-35*	50	120

Single wine wagon [W34] (Barry Potter)

W35. Double Wine Wagon

Long thin wheelbase.

-	green with red barrels T2L - *28-39*	50	100
-	black with red barrels T2L - *39-41*	50	100

Petrol tank with early chassis [W36] (Vectis)

W36. Petrol Tank Wagon

-	**Shell Motor Spirit** red T1 - *22-23*	50	80
-	**Shell Motor Spirit** red T2 - *25-30*	20	35
No.1	**Shell Motor Spirit** red T3 - *30-36*	20	35
No.1	**Shell Motor Spirit** red T3 - *48*	90	135
No.1	now with T4 base - *48-50*	80	110
-	**BP Motor Spirit** Petroleum cream T2 - *27-30*	50	120
-	**BP Motor Spirit** Petroleum cream T3 - *30-32*	90	135
-	**BP Motor Spirit** cream T3 - *32-36*	90	135
No.1	**Shellmex BP Motor Spirit** cream T3 - *36-38*	35	65
No.1	**Shell Lubricating Oil** yell T4 - *55-57*	25	45
-	**Pratt's Motor Spirit** green T2 - *25-30*	45	90
-	**Pratt's Motor Spirit** orange T3 - *30*	55	110
-	**Pratt's High Test** orange T3 - *31-33*	45	90
-	now yellow T3 - *33-36*	35	65
-	**National Benzole** yellow T2 - *23-29*	35	65
No.1	**National Benzole** silver T4 - *53-55*	15	30
-	**Redline** dark blue T2 - *28-30*	45	90
-	now with T3 base T3 - *30-32*	45	90
-	**Redline-Glico** dark blue T3 - *32-41*	45	90

-	**Castrol** green T3 - *30-41*	50	100
-	**Mobiloil** grey T3 - *31-41*	45	90
-	**Royal Daylight** red T3 - *36-41*	20	35
No.1	**Royal Daylight** grey T3 - *47-48*	220	320
No.1	**Esso** cream T3 - *36-41*	65	130
No.1	**Esso** silver T4 - *50-53*	12	25
No.1	**Power Ethyl** green T3 - *38-41*	180	270
No.1	**Pool** grey T3 - *40-41*	45	90
No.1	**Pool** grey T3 - *47-48*	120	170
No.1	**Manchester Oil Refineries** green T4 - *55-57*	35	65

Power tank wagon [W36] (Barry Potter)

W37a. Milk Tank Wagon

This was a better quality tank wagon with ladders.

-	**United Dairies** white+grey T2 - *29-31*	360	450
-	**United Dairies** white+blue T2 - *29-31*	360	450
-	now with T3 base - *31-37*	360	450
-	**Nestle's Milk** white+green T3 - *36-41*	400	550
-	**Nestle's Milk** white+blue* T3 - *36-41*	380	500

* Also seen with black base.

United Dairies tank wagon [W37a] (Barry Potter)

W37b. Bitumen Tank Wagon

A better quality tank wagon.

-	**Colas** 33 blue T2 red stays - *29-30*	300	500
-	same with blue stays - *30-36*	300	500
-	**Colas** 33 red T3 (blue) - *36-39*	500	800
-	same with black base - *39-41*	500	800

W38. Cement Wagon

This was a van with a pitched roof and had 'Cement Wagon' on it in white or gold in various positions. The position of company lettering also varied.

-	**Cement** grey T2 - *22-24*	30	55
-	**LMS/Cement** grey T2 - *24-27*	25	50

-	as above but red T2 - *27-30*	25	50
-	**LNER/Cement** grey T2 - *24-27*	25	50
-	as above but red T2 - *27-30*	25	50
-	**GW/Cement** grey T2 - *26-27*	30	60
-	as above but red T2 - *27-30*	30	60
-	**SR/Cement** red T2 - *28-30*	85	170
-	**Cement** red T2 - *30*	40	60
-	now with T3 base - *30-37*	25	50
-	**Portland Blue Circle Cement** yellow T3 - *37-41*	20	40
-	same post-war - *48*	20	40
-	now with T4 base - *48-57*	15	25

W39. No.1 Cattle Truck
G = gold transfers.

No.1	grey T2 (olive green) - *23*	20	40
No.1	**LMS** G grey T2 (olive green) - *24-25*	20	40
No.1	now without writing - *25-27*	20	40
No.1	**LMS** G grey+blue T2 (blue) - *27-30*	20	40
No.1	now with T3 base - *30-32*	20	40
No.1	now with red base - *32-33*	20	40
No.1	now with green base - *33-34*	20	40
No.1	**LMS** G grey T3 (black) - *34-39*	10	20
No.1	now with while letters - *39-41*	20	40
No.1	**LMS** (small) brown T3 (black) - *48*	15	30
No.1	now with T4 base - *48-54*	10	20
No.1	**LNER** G grey T2 (olive green) - *24-25*	20	40
No.1	now without writing- *25-26*	20	40
No.1	**NE** G grey T2 (olive green) - *26-27*	20	40
No.1	**NE** G grey+blue T2 (blue) - *27-30*	10	20
No.1	now with T3 base - *30-32*	10	20
No.1	same with red base - *32-33*	15	30
No.1	now with green base - *33-34*	15	30
No.1	**NE** G grey T3 (black) - *34-39*	10	20
No.1	now with while letters - *39-41*	15	30
No.1	**NE** (small) brown T3 (black) - *48*	20	40
No.1	now with T4 base - *48-54*	10	20
No.1	**GW** G grey T2 (olive green) - *26-27*	20	40
No.1	**GW** G grey+blue T2 (blue) - *27-30*	20	40
No.1	now with T3 base - *30-32*	20	40
No.1	now with red base - *32-33*	20	40
No.1	now with green base - *33-34*	20	40
No.1	**GW** G grey T3 (black) - *34-39*	20	40
No.1	now with while letters - *39-41*	20	40
No.1	**GW** (small) grey T3 (black) - *48*	70	120
No.1	now with T4 base - *48-51*	40	80
No.1	**SR** G brown T2 (black) - *28-30*	50	95
No.1	now with T3 base - *30-33*	50	95
No.1	**SR** G brown+green T3 (green) - *33-34*	50	95
No.1	now with black base - *34-35*	50	95
No.1	**SR** G brown T3 (black) - *34-39*	50	95
No.1	now with while letters - *39-41*	50	95
No.1	**SR** (small) brown T3 (black) - *48*	75	130
No.1	now with T4 base - *48-51*	50	95
No.1	**BR** brown T4 - *54-57*	8	20

W40. No.1 Milk Traffic Van
This was inscribed 'Milk Traffic' until 1925. Earliest ones had an internal clip for cans. 4 milk churns, made specially for the van, were supplied with it.

No.1	grey T2 (olive green) - *23-24*	20	40
No.1	**LMS** grey T2 (olive) - *24-27*	20	40
No.1	**LMS** blue T2 (green) - *27-30*	20	40
No.1	**LNER** grey T2 (olive) - *24-26*	20	40
No.1	**NE** grey T2 (olive) - *26-27*	20	40
No.1	**NE** blue T2 (green) - *27-30*	20	40
No.1	**GW** grey T2 (olive) - *26-27*	20	40
No.1	**GW** blue T2 (green) - *27-30*	20	40
No.1	**SR** green T2 (black) - *28-30*	45	90
No.1	**SR** 2435 green T3 black) - *48*	85	170
No.1	same with green base - *48*	95	190
No.1	same with T4 base - *48-54*	35	65
No.1	**BR** maroon T4 - *54-57*	20	40
No.1	blue T2 (green) - *30*	20	40

No.1	now with T3 base - *30-33*	10	20
No.1	now with red base - *33-35*	10	20
No.1	now with black base - *35-41*	10	20
No.1	green T3 - *48*	20	40

GWR gunpowder van [W41] (Barry Potter)

W41.   Gunpowder Van
This had 'Gunpowder Van' on white and the position of this was moved over time and was sometimes absent. W = company lettering white. G = company lettering gold.

-	**LNWR** red T1 inscription in black - *22*	150	200
-	as above but white inscription - *22*	150	200
-	now with T2 base - *22-24*	150	200
-	**LMS** W red T2 - *24-27*	35	60
-	now with gold 'LMS' - *28-30*	40	100
-	now with T3 base - *30-39*	60	100
-	now with white 'LMS' - *39-40*	70	110
-	**LNER** W red T2 - *24-26*	130	180
-	**NE** W red T2 - *26-27*	150	200
-	now with gold 'NE' - *27-30*	40	100
-	now with T3 base - *32-39*	60	100
-	now with white 'NE' - *39-41*	70	110
-	**GW** W red T2 - *26-27*	50	100
-	now with gold 'GW' - *27-28*	60	120
-	**GW** G grey T2 GPV + red cross - *28-29*	100	180
-	now with T3 base - *30-39*	60	120
-	now with white 'GW' - *39-41*	80	150
-	**SR** G red T2 - *28-30*	150	260
-	now with T3 base - *30-39*	150	260
-	now with white 'SR' - *39-41*	180	310

W42.   Private Owner Vans
This was of nut and bolt construction. and most versions may be found with either sliding or hinged doors.

-	**Coleman's Mustard** pale yellow T2 (white) - *23-24*	450	750
-	**Seccotine** blue with orange or red roof T1 (black) - *25*	250	370
-	same with T2 base - *23-31*	250	370
-	now with T3 base - *31-34*	250	370
-	**Carr's Biscuits** dark blue or blue-grey body + roof T2 (black) - *24-30*	150	210
-	now with T3 base - *30-41*	100	210
-	**Crawford's Biscuits** red body + roof T2 (black) - *24-31*	150	210
-	now with T3 base - *31-34*	150	210
-	as above but 'By Appointment' added - *34-38*	150	210
-	as above but 'By Appointment to the Late King' - *38-41*	150	260
-	**Jacob & Co's Biscuits** maroon T2 (black) - *24-30*	200	320
-	now with T3 base - *30-40*	125	210
-	as above but brown - *40-41*	150	260
-	**Fyffes Bananas** yellow with red or white roof T3 (green, red or black) - *31-41*	75	160
-	**Cadbury's Chocolate** * blue with white roof	150	230

	T3 (black or green) sliding doors - *32-41*		
-	**Palethorpe's Sausages** maroon body T3	250	420
	(black) sliding doors - *38-41*		
-	**Huntley & Palmers** **	200	320

* May be found with serif or sans-serif (later) style letters. ** This was one of only a few private owner wagons produced by the French factory

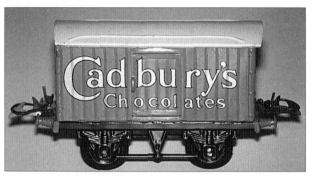

Cadburys chocolates van [W42] (Lacy Scott & Knight)

W43. No.1 Luggage/Goods Van

This was of nut and bolt construction and during the mid '20s it usually carried the inscription 'Luggage Van' either on the vans doors or base. W = company lettering white. G = company lettering gold.

No.1	**MR** (clip-on) grey T1 - *21-23*	30	60
No.1	now with T2 base - *23-24*	30	60
No.1	**LMS** W grey T2 - *24-27*	20	40
No.1	same with gold 'LMS' - *27-30*	20	40
No.1	same with T3 base - *30-39*	20	40
No.1	now with white 'LMS' - *39-41*	20	40
No.1	**LMS** (small) brown T3 - *48*	30	60
No.1	same with T4 base - *48-54*	10	30
No.1	**LNER** W grey T2 - *24-26*	20	40
No.1	**NE** W grey T2 - *26-27*	20	40
No.1	now with gold 'NE' - *27-30*	20	40
No.1	now with T3 base - *30-39*	20	40
No.1	now with white 'NE' - *39-41*	20	40
No.1	**NE** (small) brown T3 - *48*	30	60
No.1	same with T4 base - *48-54*	10	30
No.1	**GW** W grey T2 - *26-27*	20	40
No.1	now with gold 'GW' - *27-30*	20	40
No.1	now with T3 base - *30-39*	20	40
No.1	now with white 'GW' - *39-41*	20	40
No.1	**GW** (small) grey T3 - *48*	120	220
No.1	same with T4 base - *48-51*	70	150
No.1	**SR** G brown T2 - *28-30*	70	150
No.1	now with T3 base - *30-39*	70	150
No.1	now with white 'SR' - *39-41*	70	150
No.1	**SR** (small) brown T3 - *48*	180	230
No.1	same with T4 base - *48-51*	45	80
No.1	**BR** brown T4 - *54-57*	10	20

W44a. Refrigerator Van

This was of nut and bolt construction with clip-on letters and with or without the inscription 'Refrigerator Van'.

-	**MR** white T1 - *23*	35	65
-	**MR** white T2 - *23-24*	35	65

W44b. Refrigerator Van

Tab and slot construction and lettering in black (except G = gold). It was inscribed 'Refrigerator Van'.

-	**LMS** white T2 - *24-30*	30	60
-	now with T3 base T3 - *30-41*	30	60
-	same but base and roof blue - *33-34*	40	80
-	**LMS** (small) buff T3 - *48*	20	40
-	now with T4 base - *48-54*	20	40
-	**LMS** white T4 base - *48-54*	40	60
-	**LNER** white T2 - *24-27*	30	60
-	**NE** white T2 - *27-30*	30	60
-	now with T3 base - *30-41*	30	60
-	same but base and roof blue - *33-34*	40	80
-	**NE** (small) white T3 - *48*	20	40
-	now with T4 base - *48-54*	20	40
-	**GW** white T2 - *26-30*	40	80
-	now with T3 base T3 - *30-41*	40	80
-	same but base and roof blue - *33-34*	50	90
-	**SR** G pink T2 - *28-29*	650	850
-	**SR** white T2 - *29-30*	130	180
-	now with T3 base - *30-34*	130	180
-	**SR** pink T3 - *34-41*	340	450
-	**BR** white T4 - *54-57*	20	40

SR refrigerator van [W44b] (Barry Potter)

W45. LNWR Brake Van (single ended)

This was of nut and bolt construction and had a black base (green 1933-34) and white roof (grey post-war). There was a hinged door at one end and pairs of windows at both ends. W = white lettering sprayed on. G = gold transfer lettering. Post-war examples had very small lettering and lamp brackets fitted on the sides and ends.

-	**LNW** W grey T1 - *22-23*	30	45
-	now with T2 base - *23-24*	30	45
-	**LMS** W grey T2 - *24-27*	10	20
-	now with gold 'LMS' - *27-30*	10	20
-	same with T3 base - *27-33*	10	20
-	now with white 'LMS' - *34-41*	5	10
-	**LMS** (small) 1663 brown T3 - *48*	20	40
-	now with T4 base - *48-54*	10	20
-	**GW** W grey T2 - *26-27*	10	20
-	now with gold 'GW' - *27-30*	10	20
-	same with T3 base - *30-32*	10	20
-	now with white 'GW' - *32-41*	10	20
-	**GW** (small), grey T3 - *48*	140	180
-	now with T4 base - *48-51*	100	150

W46. GN Brake Van (double ended)

Nut and bolt construction. Black base (green 1933-34) and white roof. Hinged door and large single window at each end. W = white lettering sprayed on. G = gold transfer lettering. Post-war examples has very small lettering and lamp brackets fitted on the sides and ends.

-	**GN** W brown T1 - *22-23*	40	80
-	now with T2 base - *23-24*	40	80
-	**LNER** W brown T2 - *24-27*	20	40
-	**NE** G brown T2 - *27-30*	10	20
-	now with T3 base - *30-32*	10	20
-	now with white 'NE' - *32-41*	10	20
-	**NE** small, brown T3 - *48*	10	20
-	now with T4 base - *48-54*	10	16
-	**SR** G brown T2 - *28-30*	40	90
-	now with T3 base - *30-33*	40	90
-	now with white 'SR' - *32*	50	100
-	**SR** G dark brown T3 - *33*	50	100
-	now with white 'SR' - *33-41*	40	90
-	**SR** small, brown T3 - *48*	150	230
-	now with T4 base - *48-51*	120	230

-	BR E22604 brown T4 - *54-57*	10	20

W47.   Crane Truck

-	grey T2 - *23-24*	30	50
-	**LMS** grey T2 - *24-27*	20	40
-	**LMS** brown+blue T2 - *27-30*	20	40
-	**LNER** grey T2 - *24-26*	30	60
-	**NE** grey T2 - *26-27*	20	40
-	**NE** brown+blue T2 - *27-30*	20	40
-	**GW** grey T2 - *26-27*	30	50
-	**GW** brown+blue T2 - *27-30*	30	50
-	**SR** brown+blue T2 - *28-30*	55	110
-	brown+blue T2 - *30*	20	40
-	same with T3 base - *30-33*	10	20
-	blue+yellow T3 - *33-35*	10	20
-	blue T3 - *35-38*	10	20
-	grey T3 - *38-41*	10	20
-	red T3 - *48*	20	40
-	now with T4 base - *48-57*	8	20

W48a.   Rotary Snow Plough
Inscribed 'Snow Plough'.

-	grey T2 (black) - *23-24*	70	100
-	**LMS** grey T2 (black) - *24-26*	80	150
-	**LNER** grey T2 (black) - *24-26*	80	150
-	**GW** grey T2 (black) - *26*	100	180

W48b.   Rotary Snow Plough (tin-printed)
Tin-printed and inscribed 'Snow Plough'.

-	**LMS** grey T2 (black) - *26-27*	100	150
-	now with green base - *27-30*	100	150
-	**LNER** grey T2 (black) - *26*	100	150
-	**NE** grey T2 (black) T2 - *26-27*	70	100
-	now with green base - *27-30*	70	100
-	**GW** grey T2 (black) - *26-27*	150	200
-	now with green base - *27-30*	150	200
-	**SR** grey T2 (green) - *28-30*	220	350
-	grey T2 (green) - *30*	80	120
-	now with T3 base - *30-32*	50	80
-	now with red base - *32-33*	50	80
-	yellow T3 (green) - *33*	80	120
-	now with blue base - *33-36*	80	120
-	now with black base - *36-41*	50	80
-	two tone green - *?*	120	160

Rotary snow plough [W48b] (Barry Potter)

No.2 Freight Stock

W49a.   Trolley Wagon
This was a well wagon with a bolster on each raised platform over the bogies. Most were inscribed '50 Ton Trolley'.

-	**LMS** G grey with red bolsters - *24-27*	20	40
-	**LMS** G brown + blue bolsters - *27-30*	20	40
-	**NE** W grey with black bolsters - *23*	30	50
-	same with red bolsters - *23-24*	20	40
-	same with gold 'NE' - *26-27*	20	40
-	**NE** G brown with blue bolsters - *27-30*	20	40

-	**LNER** G grey with red bolsters - *24-26*	30	45
-	**GW** G grey with red bolsters - *26-27*	30	60
-	**GW** G brown + blue bolsters - *27-30*	30	60
-	**SR** G brown with blue bolsters - *28-30*	120	160
-	brown with blue bolster - *30-33*	15	30
-	red with green bolsters - *33-39*	30	60
-	grey with green bolsters - *33-39*	15	30
-	red with red bolsters - *39-41*	15	30
-	grey with red bolsters - *49-50*	200	300

Trolly wagon [W49a] (Barry Potter)

W49b.   Trolley Wagon + Cable Drums
This was the trolley wagon with two cable drums in the well. The drums were the same as those used on the flat truck. The cable drum being made of wood and the detail provided by printed paper stuck to the surface. Most were inscribed '50 Ton Trolley'.

-	red with green bolsters + Bl Cables - *36-37*	40	60
-	same with Liverpool Cables - *37-39*	40	60
-	grey with red bolsters + Bl Cables - *39-41*	40	60

W50.   No.2 Timber Wagon
Some were inscribed 'No.2 Timber Wagon'.

No.2	olive green - *22-24*	30	50
No.2	**LMS** olive green - *24-27*	30	60
No.2	now with red stanchions - *27-30*	30	60
No.2	**L&NER** olive green - *24*	30	60
No.2	**LNER** olive green - *24-26*	30	60
No.2	**NE** olive green - *26-27*	30	60
No.2	now with red stanchions - *27-30*	30	60
No.2	**GW** olive green - *26-27*	40	80
No.2	now with red stanchions - *27-30*	30	60
No.2	**SR** brown with red stanchions - *28-30*	120	160
No.2	olive with red stanchions - *30-33*	30	60
No.2	red with green stanchions - *33-39*	30	50
No.2	grey with red stanchions - *39-41*	20	40

W51.   No.2 Lumber Wagon
This was the bogie base with 2 (usually red) bolsters and three logs chained to the bolsters.

No.2	olive green - *23-24*	30	60
No.2	**LMS** olive green - *24-30*	30	60
No.2	**LNER** olive green - *24-26*	30	60
No.2	**NE** olive green - *26-30*	30	60
No.2	**GW** olive green - *26-30*	40	80
No.2	**SR** light brown - *28-29*	120	160
No.2	**SR** dark brown - *29-30*	120	160
No.2	olive green - *30-33*	30	60
No.2	yellow - *33-39*	15	30
No.2	grey - *39-41, 49-50*	30	60

W52.   No.2 High Capacity Wagon

No.2	**LMS** Loco Coal grey - *36-41, 49-50*	50	80
No.2	**LMS** Loco Coal brown - *?*	120	160
No.2	**NE** Brick Wagon red-brown - *36-41, 49-50*	60	90
No.2	**GW** Loco Coal grey - *36-41*	75	100
No.2	**GW** Loco Coal grey - *49-50*	150	200

W53.   No.2 Cattle Truck

No.2	grey on olive green - *23-24*	30	60
No.2	**LMS** W grey on olive green- *24-27*	30	60
No.2	**LMS** W grey+blue on blue - *25-27*	30	60
No.2	now with gold 'LMS' - *28-33*	40	80
No.2	as above but green base - *33-35*	30	60
No.2	now with grey base - *35-38*	30	60
No.2	as above but white letters - *38-41*	45	90

No.2	now with black base - *39*	30	60
No.2	**LNER** W grey on olive green- *24-26*	30	60
No.2	**NE** W grey on olive green - *26-27*	30	60
No.2	**NE** W grey+blue on blue - *25-27*	30	60
No.2	now with gold 'NE'- *28-33*	40	80
No.2	as above but green base - *33-35*	30	60
No.2	now with grey base - *35-38*	30	60
No.2	as above but white letters - *38-41*	30	60
No.2	now with black base - *39*	30	60
No.2	**GW** W grey+olive green - *26-27*	50	90
No.2	**GW** W grey+blue - *27-28*	50	90
No.2	now with gold 'GW' - *28-33*	50	90
No.2	as above but grey+green - *33-35*	50	90
No.2	now with grey base - *35-38*	50	90
No.2	as above but white letters - *38-41*	50	90
No.2	now with black base - *39*	50	90
No.2	**SR** G brown - *28-39*	90	150
No.2	as above but white 'SR' - *39-41*	90	150
No.2	**SR** brown+green - *33-34*	90	150
No.2	brown - *49-50*	50	75

-	same without 'LMS' - *49-50*	60	100
-	**LNER** grey + red cross - *24-27*	45	70
-	**NE** G brown+blue + red cross - *27-32*	50	90
-	now without red cross - *32-33*	50	90
-	**NE** G green+blue - *34-37*	30	60
-	**NE** G grey - *37-41*	40	70
-	**GW** grey + red cross - *26*	50	80
-	**GW** G brown+blue + red cross - *27-32*	50	80
-	now without red cross - *32-33*	60	100
-	**GW** G green+blue- *33-41*	50	80
-	**SR** G brown + red cross - *28-31*	100	160
-	now without red cross - *31-33*	100	160
-	**SR** G green+blue - *33-37*	100	160
-	**SR** G grey - *37-41*	110	180

Breakdown van and crane [W55 (Barry Potter)

No 2 cattle truck [W53] (Barry Potter)

W54. No.2 Luggage/Goods Van

Early versions were inscribed 'Luggage Van'.

No.2	grey + olive green - *23-24*	60	100
No.2	**LMS** W grey+olive green - *24-27*	50	90
No.2	**LMS** W blue - *27-28*	60	100
No.2	now with gold 'LMS' - *28-33*	60	100
No.2	**LMS** G grey - *33-39*	50	90
No.2	**LMS** W grey - *38-41*	50	90
No.2	**LMS** brown - *48-50*	80	120
No.2	**LNER** W grey+olive green - *24-26*	50	90
No.2	**NE** W grey+olive green - *26-27*	60	100
No.2	**NE** W blue - *27-28*	60	100
No.2	now with gold 'NE' - *28-33*	60	100
No.2	**NE** G grey - *33-35*	50	90
No.2	same with grey base - *36-38*	50	90
No.2	**NE** W grey with grey base- *38-41*	50	90
No.2	**NE** brown - *48-50*	80	120
No.2	**GW** W grey+olive green - *26-27*	60	120
No.2	**GW** W blue+olive green - *27-28*	60	120
No.2	now with gold 'GW' - *28-33*	60	120
No.2	**GW** G grey - *33-36*	60	120
No.2	same with grey base - *36-38*	60	120
No.2	**GW** W grey - *39*	60	120
No.2	**GW** W grey with grey base - *38-41*	60	120
No.2	**SR** G brown - *28-39*	250	350
No.2	now with white 'SR' - *39-41*	250	350

W55. Breakdown Van & Crane

This bogie wagon had the van body at one end and a crane at the other end. G = gold transfers. Early doors were hinged and later ones sliding.

-	grey with red cross - *23-24*	45	70
-	now without red cross - *23-24*	45	70
-	**LMS** grey + red cross - *24-27*	40	70
-	**LMS** G brown+blue + red cross - *27-32*	40	70
-	same without red cross - *32-33*	45	70
-	**LMS** G green+blue - *34-37*	30	60
-	**LMS** G grey+black - *38-41*	40	70
-	**LMS** brown with red crane - *49-50*	60	100

No.50 Freight Stock

This was a new series of tin-printed four wheels wagons produced late in the life of Hornby 0 gauge and all were fitted with the T5 wheelbase.

W56a. No.50 Flat Truck

No.50	**BR** brown - *57-64*	15	30

W56b. No.50 Flat Truck with Cable Drum

No.50	**BR** brown + Liverpool drum - *57-64*	25	40

W57. No.50 Flat Truck with Container

No.50	**BR** brown + furniture container - *57-64*	20	30
No.50	**BR** brown + insulated meat container - *57-64*	20	30

W58. No.50 Gas Cylinder Wagon

No.50	red - *57-64*	10	20

W59. No.50 Lumber Wagon

No.50	red bolsters - *57-64*	10	20

W60. No.50 Wagon (open wagon)

Tin-printed.

No.50	**BR** grey - *57-64*	15	30

W61. No.50 Hopper Wagon

No.50	**BR** grey - *57-64*	15	30

W62. No.50 Rotary Tipping Wagon

No.50	**Trinidad Lake Asphalt** buff - *57-64*	15	35

W63. No.50 Side Tipping Wagon

No.50	**McAlpine** green - *57-64*	15	30

W64. No.50 Saxa Salt Wagon

No.50	**Saxa Salt** yellow - *57-64*	60	80

W65. No.50 Tank Wagon

No.50	**Shell Lubricating Oil** yellow - *57-64*	25	45
No.50	**Manchester Oil Refineries** green - *57-61*	45	85

W66.	**No.50 Cattle Truck**		
No.50	**BR** brown T5 - *57-64*	20	40

W67.	**No.50 Goods Van**		
No.50	**BR** brown - *57-64*	20	40

W68.	**No.50 Refrigerator Van**		
No.50	**BR** white - *57-64*	20	40

W69.	**No.50 BR Goods Brake Van**		
This was tin-printed with no opening doors.			
No.50	**BR** brown T5 - *57-63*	15	30

W70.	**No.50 Crane Truck**		
No.50	red jib on black base - *57-64*	15	30

ACCESSORIES

Hornby 0 Gauge was a very complete system providing scores of lineside features with which to embellish your train and track. Some of these are now quite rare, as they are the items that were thrown away when your mother gave your trains to your younger cousins.

Hornby No2 'Bristol' station

Many of the accessories continued in production throughout the life of the Company; obviously with many style and colour variations, including a fair number during the post-war period. The 'Hornby' (or 'Meccano' on very early examples) trade marks appeared on all but the smallest pieces so identification is fairly easy. In this catalogue we are unable to provide a complete listing (with description and price) of all variations or even all products but the following is a basic listing giving you some idea of what is of interest and roughly what it is worth. With the exception of fields, hedges, trees, tunnels and cuttings which are made of wood and fabric, all of Hornby's accessories were made from printed tinplate.

Buffers - No.1 buffers were the short spring type in various colours (£3-£5) while No.2 buffers were the long hydraulic type as seen in large terminus stations (£15-£20). There were also versions of both types with electric lamps coded No.1E (£25-£30) and No.2E (£40-£60).

Countryside Sections - These were made from thick card and printed paper and came in various shapes to fit around the track (£20-£40 per piece).

Cuttings - There were straight and curved sections of the embankments that formed the cuttings (£40-£80).

Engine Sheds - These were Hornby's finest buildings and were made between 1928 and 1941. They were constructed of printed tinplate and featured a late 19th Century industrial building, the best having a roof ventilator and smoke vents. The No.2 engine shed was twice the length of the No.1 and may be found with either clockwork 2-rail fittings or electric 3-rail with electric interior lighting (£150-£600).

Footbridges and Lattice Girder Bridge - Over the years these were made in blues, creams and white. The No.2 footbridge had two signals on it (£30-£65). The much larger lattice girder bridge was made only between 1921 and 1934 (£90-£150).

Goods Platform - This had a rectangular platform and a simple building shape on which the detail was printed. It had a gabled overhanging roof and came in various colours. The No.2 version had an operating crane and sliding doors while a No.2E also had an electric light (£60-£300).

Hedges and Trees - Hedges were made from dyed loofah fixed to a wooden base to fit around fields. The trees were of similar construction but had lead bases to give them stability (£6-£12).

Island Platform - This had a long platform with ramps at either end and two posts supporting a central canopy. Before the war the posts were latticed but after the war they were plain. They may be found in various colours and with an assortment of names. There was also an electrically lit version (£80-£350).

Lamp Standards - These had latticed posts and hanging glass globe lamps; two in the case of the No.2 version. The standard models were non-lighting (£60-£90) but there were No.1E and No.2E lit versions, with simpler brackets, lampshades and bulbs, as well (£70-£150)

Level Crossings - The No.1 and No.E1 level crossings had single track, one for 2-rail clockwork and the other for 3-rail electric respectively. There was also a 3-rail No.E1E which had lamps on the gates (£10-£30). It is therefore logical that the No.2 level crossing had double track with No.2, No.E2 and No.E2E versions (£30-£100) being available. Over the years there were many variations in the attractive printing on the bases, showing road and verges, while gates were white with red diamonds.

Loading Gauge - Early loading gauges (1920s) had round bases but later ones were square. While the posts were white, the bases were usually blue, but green and black examples may be found (£40-£60).

Platelayers Hut - This was an attractive feature with its red brick finish, chimney, blue roof and green door which opens on some models (£40-£75).

Platform Crane - This was an operating crane on a square base with steps. Some came in bright colours (£15-£30).

Platform Accessories - There were platform machines (ticket and nameplate), pillar box, fire hut, seats and luggage consisting of hampers and trunks - all made in printed tinplate (£8-£35 each). Between 1924 and 1926 the trunk was made with a 'Carlisle' label on it. This version is much sought after and has been valued at £90.

Watchman's Hut - The hut had an open front and was blue with a red roof. It came with a shovel and poker hanging on its sides and a brazier standing in front (£25-£35).

Signal Cabins - All the signal cabins had a gabled roof and a chimney stack. No.1 had printed windows while on the No.2 version they were pierced and the cabin had separate steps. The box was unnamed except for those made between 1924 and 1928 which carried the name 'Windsor'. The No.2E had a lamp inside while the Control Cabin had an opening roof and a base for a lever frame (£25-£85).

Signal Gantries - The No.1 signal gantry was of simple construction consisting of two supporting posts and four signal posts which push-fitted together on the gantry (£30-£50). The No.2 gantry was larger with lattice posts and had railings and a ladder. The signals were worked by a series of wires (£250-£450). There was also a No.2E which had electric lights behind each signal (£1,000-£2,000).

Signals - There were many colour variations although the main part was always white - single arm, double arm, home, distant and bracket. Most post-war examples have non-latticed posts (£10-£50). There were also electrically lit examples (£50-£120).

Stations - Many variations in stations were made during 1923-41 and 1948-57. These included variations in colour and printing, the latter providing an interesting study of changing clothes fashion and car design etc.. Sadly, the long gable ended shape with two chimneys (missing from cheaper stations) is less interesting than stations designed by other manufacturers such as Bing and Marklin. Fences, an open booking hall concourse and electric lamps may be found on some Hornby stations. Prices vary from £60-£90 for fairly basic units to £120-£250 for more elaborate ones.

Staff and Passengers - These were cast in lead, the size of them being slightly reduced around 1938. The range included six station staff, six passengers, six engineering staff and five train and hotel staff. There were also sets of farmyard animals, a shepherd and sheep. Single figures in good condition sell for £5-£10 while boxed sets range from £50-£120 depending on which set it is.

Telegraph Pole - This was over-scale and was fixed to a square tinplate base. Until 1929 the two cross bars were tin after which they were cast in lead (£30-£45 each).

Tunnel - Between 1924 and 1931 the tunnel was printed tin to represent moorland (£70-£90) but from then until 1937 the picture represented countryside with hikers (£70-£120). From 1932, up to the Second World War, many were made of wood and fabric and finished with coloured sawdust. The latter were made in various lengths and available curved or straight (£20-£60).

Viaduct - This was single track and the centre section had grey or green girder sides. There were ramp sections at both ends and they came with either clockwork (£30-£35) or electric (£70-£80) track.

Water Tank - During the 1930s the No.1 water tank was red with a green base, black ladder and yellow or buff column. Post-war it was black and red with a plastic column (£15-£35). The No.2 water tank was more like gauge 1 in scale and came with a blue or green base and column and a red or yellow tank (£75-£85). There was also a No.2E version with a blue electric light fitting on the tank (£800-£1200).

SETS

If one counts the many company and colour variations, Meccano Ltd produced 223 different Hornby 0 gauge train sets before the outbreak of World War 2 and a further 34 after the war.

The Hornby train sets were released in attractive packaging and very early boxes were brown or maroon with pictures of locomotives tastefully embossed in gold on their lids.

From 1921 onwards inspiring coloured pictures of fast-moving prototypical trains appeared on most sets and only from 1925 until 1931 did Hornby show their own products on the lid. These were a 2711 4-4-0 in LMS livery, with smoke coming from the chimney, pulling No.2 Pullman cars at speed through a country scene.

The 'Royal Scot' and 'Flying Scotsman' were the most common images on set boxes and were continued in 1945. In this last period, a No.41 tank passenger set had the picture of a Castle Class locomotive on the box lid while another 0-4-0 locomotive set showed a Britannia Class engine racing along the word 'Hornby'. This was before the Trade Description Act and one thing is for sure - the contents did not match the picture!

Boxes for sets had stoutly made compartments and each contained a circle of clockwork or electric track. There were also a small box of track clips, a locomotive and either coaches or wagons. Clockwork sets also had a key in a packet and some sets had a packet of locomotive lamps and/or coach connectors. The sets contained a 'tested' label, guarantee slip, instructions and an application form for the Hornby Railway Association which the purchaser was invited to join.

Collecting sets is a specialist's field which is ignored by many who prefer to run their trains. Constant use of the contents of sets can lead to destructive and devaluing wear and tear. Replacement inserts are available for some boxes through the Hornby Railway Collectors Association.

A rough guide to the value of a run-of-the-mill set is the sum of the contents plus a bit extra for the box. A 3C set of the late '30s, containing a 4-4-2 and two coaches has a value of £550-£850 in nice condition; depending on the exact contents. A rare electric set containing a large locomotive will be upwards of £1000. On the other hand, pre-war clockwork sets with No.1 locomotives (either tender or tank) are valued at £150-£250.

M series items are generally inexpensive and small attractive sets, with good pictures on their lids, sell for £40-£60.

There are obviously more post-war 0-4-0 sets about in good order and one can expect to pay between £100-£150; unless it is uncommon in which case it could cost as much as £200.

Some of the pre-war sets were given impressive names of real named trains. These include 'The Pines Express' on a No.1 0-4-0 passenger set of 1939, 'The Dover Pullman', 'The Golden Arrow' and the 'Cornish Riviera', all of which contained various No.3 4-4-2s with bogie coaches or Pullman cars. From 1945 the romantic names disappeared but the enticing pictures remained.

Hornby-Dublo

These models were made by Meccano Ltd at Binns Road, Liverpool, between 1938 and 1964.

HISTORY

In pre-Second World War Britain, 0 gauge ruled supreme but as early as the 1920s a bid had been made to have a smaller gauge accepted. That was the Bing Table Top Railway which was a victim of the growth of Nazi influence in Germany. The German Trix system sprang from the Bing version and when the inventors fled to Britain to avoid Nazi persecution a British version of the system was developed at Northampton in association with Bassett-Lowke.

Seeing the possible risk this created for Hornby's market, Meccano Ltd decided to launch their own 00 scale system. Thus, in 1938, Hornby Dublo was born.

Initially it was a small version of the 0 gauge system except that the locomotives had cast metal bodies, the track looked like that sold by Marklin and the buildings were made of wood. Both clockwork and electric sets were available before the war but the couplings could not be uncoupled automatically. Pre-war locomotives were limited to a valanced LNER A4 Pacific named 'Sir Nigel Gresley' and an 0-6-2 tank engine which looked like an LNER Class N2 but which, in true Hornby tradition, was available in the liveries of the big four companies (with detail concessions to the GWR).

After the war, the Peco automatic coupling was adopted as standard and the buildings, when they reappeared, were diecast in aluminium. Clockwork did not reappear but the long awaited LMS 'Duchess of Atholl' did.

In 1953 the system was 'Nationalised' and the old liveries, which had been gradually dropped until only LMS was left, were finally replaced by BR ones. One of Hornby Dublo's finest locomotives was soon to appear - the 2-6-4 Standard tank. The Castle, 8F and Bo-Bo diesel quickly followed. By 1957 it was clear that Hornby Dublo was loosing ground to the Tri-ang Railways system and something drastic had to be done. The first change was the adoption of plastic for wagon bodies, the first, the grain wagon, appearing the following year.

The possibility of a 2-rail electric system had been discussed as

long ago as 1938 but was not adopted until 1959. Plastic buildings arrived the same year and the Super Detail coaches followed the year after. Too late it was realised that the system was not gaining the loyalty of beginners whose parents were being wooed by the low prices of Tri-ang and Playcraft sets. In a last ditch attempt to save the system, in 1963 two beginners sets were launched but, with unsold stock piling up in the factory, production of the Hornby Dublo system was halted.

With Meccano Ltd facing strong competition in the areas of railways (Tri-ang), diecast cars (Corgi) and construction systems (Lego) it had nowhere to go and consequently invited Lines Bros. (the makers of Tri-ang) to take them over - which they did. The name Hornby was transferred to the Tri-ang Railways system. This was done in the guise of an amalgamation but the only Hornby-Dublo models to be adopted into the newly named Tri-ang Hornby range (and then only for a few years) were the terminus station and the E3000. Thus Tri-ang Railways carried on, renamed Tri-ang Hornby (later renamed Hornby Railways), and the Hornby products in the shops today are therefore direct descendants of Tri-ang Railways and not Hornby Dublo. The name 'Hornby Dublo', was retained by Tri-ang although not used again and it is still owned by Hornby Hobbies who are also still based in Margate.

The Hornby Dublo tools were sold to Tri-ang subsidiary, G&R Wrenn, and formed the basis of the Wrenn Railways model range which started to appear in the late 1960s and is described elsewhere in this book.

At the time Meccano Ltd were taken over by Tri-ang they had various models planned. With the approval of Hornby Hobbies, two of the proposed locomotives have now been produced by Michael Foster, in association with the Hornby Railway Collectors Association (HRCA), using former Hornby-Dublo chassis. These are the V2 and the 56XX 0-6-2 tank.

Further Reading

Anyone interested in further study of this important and popular model railway system is recommended to read 'Hornby Dublo Trains' by Michael Foster and published by New Cavendish Books (ISBN 0 904568 18 0). There is also a compendium to this work by Alan F Ellis, called 'Hornby Dublo Compendium', which is also published by New Cavendish Books (ISBN 0 904568 80 6). A small but comprehensive listing of the post-war 3-rail system will be found in Tony Oakes' 'Post-war 3-rail Collectors Guide', published by Mayfield Publishing (ISBN 0 9516757 0 2).

Milestones
1901 Frank Hornby invents Meccano.
1914 Meccano Ltd moves to Binns Rd, Liverpool.
1915 Frank Hornby announces he is to make `toy trains.
1920 Toy train production starts at Binns Road.
1938 Launch of electric and clockwork Hornby Dublo through Meccano Magazine.
1941 Toy production closes and this sees the end of the clockwork system.
1947 Post-war Hornby-Dublo reach the shops and with it a new automatic coupling.
1948 Duchess of Atholl released.
1950 New motors introduced.
1953 Change to British Railways liveries.
1957 'Bristol Castle' released.
1957 Dublo Dinky Toys arrive.
1958 The first plastic wagons appear.
1958 Head and coachboards introduced.
1958 First diesel added to the range (Class 20).
1959 First plastic building appears.
1959 2-rail electric system introduced.
1960 Ringfield motor announced.
1960 Plastic couplings first appear.
1962 Decals on loco models now show only left facing lion.
1963 First beginners sets released
1964 Last model, the AL1 electric, released after other Hornby Dublo production had stopped.
1964 Lines Bros. Ltd. invited to take over Meccano Ltd.
1964 Official end of 3-rail system.
1965 Announcement of 'amalgamation' with Tri-ang Railways.
1966 Hornby Dublo tools sold to G&R Wrenn.

BR Standard horse box [W30]

Collectors Club

You may also wish to join the Hornby Railway Collectors Association (HRCA) who publish, for their members, an excellent monthly magazine, called *The Hornby Railway Collector*, devoted to the toy train and model railway products of Meccano Ltd. Details of this organisation may be obtained from the membership secretary, John Harwood, on Tel: 01935 474830.

Prices - The chance of finding mint boxed Hornby Dublo is relatively small and so the use of the 'mint/boxed' column (right hand one) for this purpose would have little meaning. We have therefore used both price columns to indicate the price range one may expect for examples in very good condition - top quality examples being in their original and correct box. We do, however, refer you to the section on values near the front of the book.

Dates - The dates used in the following tables are those when models were being advertised by the manufacturer or, in the case of short term variations, when it is thought likely they were made. Although they are thought to be fairly accurate, they are for guidance only and should not be taken too literally. There were large unsold stocks in the factory after production ceased and these took several years to clear. This time is not included in the dates given.

Couplings - pre-war models had flat sprung metal couplings while post-war they were fitted with Peco style couplings. These were metal until 1961 but had been altered in design in 1954 to give them greater depth. In 1961 rather clumsy plastic couplings replaced the metal ones but these were unpopular and in 1963, a coupling with a thinner profile and made of Delrin was introduced.

Wheels - Rolling stock initially had diecast mazak wheels, forced onto steel axles without insulating bushes, making them unsuitable for 2-rail systems. Mazak was replaced by sintered iron in 1950. The wheels were held in place by metal tabs bent over the underside of each axlebox. In 1957, one-piece wheels/axle nylon mouldings appeared for the first time, and were used in both disc and spoked form on rolling stock, again held in place by tabs.

2-rail/3-rail - Unless otherwise stated, all of the locomotives in this section have three rail power contact (i.e. power is collected from a centre rail and returned through the wheels via the outer rails) . Clockwork models (c/w) are suitable for use on both systems but not on 2-rail track at the same time as it is being used for electric locomotives. Rolling stock with metal wheels was suitable only for 3-rail operation while those with plastic wheels could be used on either 3-rail or 2-rail layouts.

Export Models - Couplings were attached with a rivet but models for export in 1962-63 usually had their couplings fixed on with screws so that they could be changed. They also had an export label on the end of the box and had different catalogue numbers. Bogie and open wagons could not be made this way, nor could locomotives with couplings attached to bogies. No 3-rail locos are known with screw-fitted couplings, other than those diesel and electric types which had them anyway. Models in boxes marked with export labels have been known to sell at prices many times higher than the equivalent for the home market. For example, in 2003, a group of four different 2-rail tank wagons in export boxes sold for £600.

Oddities - Errors do turn up from time to time and include such things as inverted printing on the side of the flat wagon, incorrect printing of the mineral wagon, mismatching bogies on bogie wagons and mismatched body sides on various items of rolling stock. Coaches with ends lacking printing detail appear to be corrections of wrongly assembled coaches.

Buyer beware! Some oddities can be 'manufactured' by the unscrupulous. For example: chassis can be swapped around as too can roofs. Many coach and van roofs were interchangeable and so models may be found with the wrong roof colour. Before buying one as a 'rarity' make sure that it can not have been 'manufactured' by a bit of roof swapping.

With the arrival of 2-rail models, the bodies of 2-rail and 3-rail locomotives were often swapped over by retailers to offer their customers choice. The only exceptions to this were the Class R1 0-6-0T which had no 3-rail equivalent, the plain green Deltic type diesel which was unnumbered and the EMU which shared a common number.

LOCOMOTIVES

Other Identification Aids - Pre-war and early post-war models did not have the model number (e.g. EDL7) under the running board while later ones did. On early post-war tank locomotives the maker's decal, on the back of the bunker, was a gold block with a red border and inscribed 'Hornby Meccano Ltd, Made in England'. This was replaced by a silver coloured decal with a red border, in late 1949, when the motor changed. 'Sir Nigel Gresley' only ever had a silver-backed label on both loco and tender (some pre-war tenders had none).

1After-Sale Factory Variations - Hornby Dublo variations marked '1' resulted from the model being returned to the factory for a repair and a revised part being used, thus altering the model. Others include 'Sir Nigel Gresley' with black driving wheels, 'Duchess of Montrose' with nickel-plated driving wheels and the 0-6-2 tank no coal in the bunker but nickel-plated driving wheels.

Cat.No.	Number, Company, Colour, Dates	£	£

L1. Starter Tank 0-4-0T

All starter locomotives were 12v DC electric and were available only in sets.

(2001)	BRd black, riveted couplings ex 'Ready to Run' set - *63-64*	25	NA
(2001)	BRd black, clipped couplings ex 'Ready to Run' set - *63-64*	25	NA
(2002)*	blue, map of Australia, from Commonwealth set for Australia - *64*	90	NA

* Those sold in the UK through non-Meccano dealers were coded 2002 but some that reached Australia were coded 2003. The latter had power units wound for Australian power supply.

Class R1 0-6-0T [L2]

L2. Class R1 0-6-0T

2206	31337 BRc black 2-rail - *59-64*	50	70
2206	as above but red buffers - *63-65*	75	100
2207	31340 BRc green 2-rail 31337 on front - *59-61*	50	70
2207	as above but **31340** on front - *61-65*	40	60
2207	as above but red buffers - *63-65*	60	80

L3. Class N2 0-6-2T (and similar)

p-wb = pre-war body (one without notch in buffer beam for post-war coupling). p-wc = pre-war couplings.

Southern

DL7	**2594** olive green p-wc c/w - *38-40*	700	800
EDL7	**2594** olive green p-wc - *38-41*	600	700
EDL7	**2594** olive green p-wb - *48*	500	700
EDL7	**2594** on bunker olive green - *48*	550	700
EDL7	**2594** malachite green - *48-53*	250	800

LMS

DL7	**6917** black p-wc c/w - *38-40*	400	450
EDL7	**6917** black p-wc - *38-41*	300	400
EDL7	**6917** black, serif letters - *47-49*	175	250
EDL7	**6917** black, sans serif letters - *49-53*	50	100

LNER

DL7	**2690** black p-wc c/w - *38-40*	450	550
EDL7	**2690** black p-wc - *38-41*	300	400
EDL7	**9596** black very rare - *47-48*	300	NPG
EDL7	**9596** green - *48-49*	110	175
EDL7	**9596** green letters changed - *50-53*	110	175

GWR

DL7	**6699** green p-wc c/w - *38-40*	700	800
EDL7	**6699** green p-wc - *38-41*	500	600
EDL7	**6699** green p-wb - *48*	NPG	NPG
EDL7	**6699** green - *47-53*	200	700
EDL7	**6231** green 'Atholl' number and not on plate, very rare* - *53-54*	700	900

BR

EDL7	**E9560** BRa green - *53?*	NPG	NPG
EDL7	**69567** BRb gloss black no coal - *53-54*	100	150
EDL17	**69567** BRb matt black no coal - *54-61*	40	70
3217	**69567** BRc matt black with coal - *61-62*	150	300
2217	**69550** BRc black 2-rail small safety valve coal in bunker - *60-63*	80	150
2217	**69550** BRc black 2-rail large safety valve dome coal in bunker - *63-64*	100	150

*Thought to have been an export-intended disposal of remaining GWR-type 0-6-2T bodies, unsuited to BR livery, with surplus '6231' numbers deputising for lack of '6699' ones.

N2 tank [L3]

L4. Class 4MT Standard Tank 2-6-4T

EDL18	**80054** BRb black - *54-61*	60	80
2218	**80033** BRc black 2-rail* - *59-65*	90	120
3218	**80059** BRc black - *61-64*	300	400

* There is a rare version of 80033 on the casting for 80054 with a different chimney.

Canadian Pacific Duchess [L6]

L5. Castle Class 4-6-0

EDLT20	**7013 'Bristol Castle'** BRc green - *57-61*	90	120
2220	**7032 'Denbigh Castle'** BRc 2-rail green -	120	200

	59-60		
2221	**4075 'Cardiff Castle'** BRc 2-rail green - *60-65*	100	150
3221	**5002 'Ludlow Castle'** BRc green - *61-64*	300	400

L6. Duchess 4-6-2

A different nameplate, with smaller letters, was used for a short time on this model around 1949.

LMS 6231 'Duchess of Atholl'

EDL2	maroon, horseshoe magnet - *48-49*	125	300
EDL2	maroon block magnet and 'EDL2' under cab roof - *49-51*	125	300
EDL2	nameplate with yellow letters on maroon - *50*	300	425
EDL2	lump replaced depression beneath one nameplate (factory error) - *51?*	150	325
EDL2	maroon longer nameplate and rib along footplate edge* - *51-53*	125	300
EDL2	+ defectors 'EDL12' in cab roof'** - ?	350	500
EDL3	**1215** Canadian Pacific black revised smokebox*** - *52-63*	400	600
EDL12	**46232 'Duchess of Montrose'** BRb gloss green - *53-54-58*	100	150
EDL12	as above but matt green - *54-58*	60	130
L12	as above but 'L12' under cab roof - *58-61*	80	120
2226	**46245 'City of London'** BRc maroon 2-rail**** - *59-64*	150	300
3226	**46247 'City of Liverpool'** BRc maroon - *61-65*	275	400
3226	as above but numbered '**46245**' on left-hand cab - *64*	475	600

*This was the final 'Duchess of Atholl' body casting which had been designed with a BR livery and 'Duchess of Montrose' in mind (the rib was to aid lining). Introduction of the BR livery was delayed due to shortages resulting from the Korean War. ** These were models re-bodied in the Service Department using a 'Duchess of Montrose' body, spraying it maroon and then fitting smoke deflectors because the body had been modified to take them. *** These were used in three batches of sets but were also available as solo releases in 1953, the tender being sold separate from the loco. The loco body casting used was the final version for the 'Duchess of Atholl' still with 'EDL2' in the cab roof. **** 'City of London' had 2 styles of cab lining.

L7. Class A4 4-6-2

Around 1950 the nameplates, for a short period, had rounded end borders. Some post-war examples of the A4 from sets released around 1949 have tenders with pre-war lettering (red shaded).

EDL1	**4498 'Sir Nigel Gresley'** LNER blue valances and p-w couplings - *38-41*	300	480
DL1	as above but clockwork - *38-41*	600	800
EDL1	**7 'Sir Nigel Gresley'** LNER blue horseshoe motor - *48-50*	80	120
EDL1	as above but block-magnet motor + 'EDL1' inside cab roof - *50-53?*	80	120
EDL1	as above but 'EDL11' inside cab roof and raised front numberplate'	300	400
EDL1	prewar loco, postwar tender' - *48-53*	150	200
EDL11	**60016 'Silver King'** BRb gloss green - *53-54*	100	150
EDL11	ditto but no raised front no. plate * - *53-54*	NPG	NPG
EDL11	**60016 'Silver King'** BRb matt green - *54-58*	85	120
EDL11	ditto but no raised front no. plate * - *54*	NPG	NPG
L11/3211	**60022 'Mallard'** BRc green** - *58-61*	100	150
3211	ditto but now with plated driving wheels and thin handrails - *61-64*	250	320
2211	**60030 'Golden Fleece'** BRc green 2-rail - *59-65*	120	200

* An extra '1' stamped under the cab roof to read 'ED11'. These possibly resulted from the use of old tooling while the EDL11 tool was under repair. ** On early examples of 'Mallard' the tender wheels are zinc but these were later changed for plastic ones - possibly with the arrival of 'Golden Fleece'.

L8. Rebuilt West Country Class 4-6-2

'Barnstaple' stocks were taken into the Tri-ang Hornby range with the model being included in the 1966 Tri-ang Hornby catalogue.

2235	**34005 'Barnstaple'** BRc green 2-rail - *61-66*	150	250
3235	**34042 'Dorchester'** BRc green - *61-64*	250	350

L9. Class 8F 2-8-0

LT25/ 3225	**48158** BRc black - *58-61*		90	120
2225	**48109** BRc 2-rail black - *59-60*		75	150
2224	**48073** BRc 2-rail black - *60-65*		75	150
3224	**48094** BRc black - *61-64*		250	350

Class 8F 2-8-0 [L9]

L10. Starter Diesel Shunter 0-4-0DS

This was a Class 08 diesel body on an 0-4-0 chassis and has a shortened body housing so as to fit the chassis, with side rods omitted.

(2004)	yellow ex 'Ready to Run' set - *64*	35	NA
(2005)	as above but from sets sent to Australia - *64*	35	NA

L11. Class 08 Diesel Shunter 0-6-0DS

Both single and 2-part coupling rods may be found, the former being the older. The body differs from the Wrenn one (which was from different tooling) in having 'Hornby Dublo - Meccano Ltd - Made in England' inside.

2231	**D3302** BRc green 2-rail - *61-63*	60	80
2231	ditto 2-piece coupling rod - *63-65*	60	80
3231	**D3763** BRc green* - *61-63*	100	150
3231	ditto 2-piece coupling rod - *63-64*	100	150

* D3763 may be found with transfer numbers instead of heat-printed ones. These are thought to have been due to the heat-printing not coming out properly first time round.

L12. Type 1 (Class 20) Diesel Bo-Bo

L30/3230	**D8000**** BRc green - *58-62*	70	120
L30/3230	**D8000** BRc green no buffers* Canadian - *59-62*	550	700
L30/3230	**D8000** BRc green no buffers* no motor Canadian - *59-62*	650	800
2230	**D8017** BRc green 2-rail - *59-62*	80	150

*These were released for the Canadian market and had the buffers sawn-off leaving rounded studs instead. They were both sold in the normal 3-rail blue box and were not particularly successful. A further batch of 2-rail models (powered and non-powered) were sent over in normal UK boxes in 1962. Some of these non-powered examples are very strangely assembled with motor bogies but with the armature missing.

L13. Met-Vic Diesel Co-Bo

Stocks of the 2-rail version were taken into the Tri-ang Hornby range with the model being included in the 1966 Tri-ang Hornby catalogue.

2233	**D5702** BRc green 2-rail* - *61-66*	100	150
3233	**D5713** BRc green - *61-64*	150	250

* A rare variation has a pair of strengthening ribs to the outline of the battery box between the bogies.

L14. Deltic Type Diesel Co-Co

2232	BRc green 2-rail - *61-64*	80	120
2232	the same with plastic bogie side frames - *64-65*	100	140
3232	BRc green - *61-64*	120	180
2234	**D9012** 'Crepello' BRc 2-tone green 2-rail - *62-64*	130	280
3234	**D9001** 'St Paddy' BRc 2-tone green - *62-65*	300	400

Deltic type diesel [L14]

L15. Class AL1 Electric

2245	**E3002** BRd blue 2-rail - *64-65*	300	500

L16. Class 501 Suburban EMU

Caution: Examples with a different livery or number have been altered after leaving the factory and are therefore not listed here.

2250+ 4150	**S65326+S77511** BRc green 2-car unit 2-rail - *62-65*	150	475
2250	power car with green rear end moulding instead of black - *?*	180	500
3250+ 4150	**S65326+S77511** BRc green 2-car unit - *62-64*	300	600
3250	power car with green rear end moulding instead of black - *?*	330	650

COACHES

The first coaches were lithographed tinplate (including windows). Construction was tab-and-slot and the bogies were diecast, as were the wheels. Pre-war diecasting often contained impurities that later led to metal fatigue resulting in much pre-war rolling stock diecastings becoming crazed or crumbling.

The LMS coaches, introduced after the war, were the first to have punched out and glazed windows, a feature which the Gresley stock never achieved. Tinplate was retained for coach production right to the end although the final range of Super Detail Mk1 coaches had only tinplate sides. The only plastic coaches produced were Pullman cars.

Cat.No.	Company, Number, Colour, Dates	£	£

C1. Gresley Stock

All had printed windows and curved round ends in typical Gresley style. p-wc = pre-war couplings. LNER versions had white roofs and BR versions, grey ones. The all 3rd LNER coaches were introduced after the change to BR livery in order to use up a residue of tinprinted parts produced for the articulated coaches.

	LNER teak		
D251	42759 D1 composite pre-war couplings - *38-41*	70	120
32010	as above, post-war couplings - *48-53*	25	40
D252	45401/45402 D2 all 3rd+brake 3rd articulated p-wc - *38-41*	500	850
D252	45401/45402 D2 all 3rd+3rd/brake articulated export only - *48-49*	750	1000
-	45402/45401/45402 articulated brake+3rd+ brake* - *not made*	NA	NA
32011	45402 D1 brake/3rd brown ends - *48-53*	25	40
32011	45402 D1 brake/3rd teak** ends - *48-53*	40	55
32012	45401 D1 all 3rd brown ends - *early 54*	25	40
32012	45401 D1 all 3rd teak ends - *late 54*	25	40
32012	as above with grey roof - *late 54-55*	35	50
	BR red+cream		
32013	E42759E D11 composite Gresley bogies - *53-54?*	20	25
32013	as above but BR bogies - *54?-56*	20	25
32014	E45402E D11 brake/3rd Gresley bogies - *53-54?*	20	25
32014	as above but BR bogies - *54?-56*	20	25

* A pre-production sample was made, after the war, from two 2-car units at Binns Road and sent to Canadian Meccano Ltd. office for their approval but the project was abandoned. ** These teak ends were from the articulated coaches and lacked the dark brown corridor detail. They were used up on all 3rd coaches but, by error, some were used on the brake/3rd coaches.

Gresley all 3rd coach [C1]

C2. Stanier Stock

Although planned for release before the last war, it was not released until after hostilities had ended. All had punched out and glazed windows. Early LMS coaches had a silver grey roof while later ones had a pale grey one. p-wc = pre-war couplings. The BR coaches gained plastic wheels in 1958, before the change to red boxes with 4XXX numbers.

LMS maroon (D3)

-	4183 composite p-wc - *not made*	-	-
32015	4183 composite dark metalic coloured roof - *48-49*	40	60
32015	as above but light metalic roof - *50-51*	40	60
32015	as above but light grey roof - *52-53*	30	50
-	26133 brake/3rd p-wc - *not made*	-	-
32016	26133 brake/3rd dark metalic coloured roof - *48-49*	40	60
32016	as above but light metalic roof - *50-51*	40	60
32016	as above but light grey roof - *52-53*	30	50

BR red+cream

32017	M4183 D12 comp LMS bogies - *53*	20	25
32017	as above but BR bogies - *53-58*	12	18
4005	as above but plastic wheels - *58-61*	18	35
4005	as above but plastic couplings - *61*	40	50
32018	M26133 D12 brake/2nd/3rd LMS bogies - *53*	20	25
32018	as above but BR bogies - *53-58*	12	18
4006	as above but plastic wheels - *58-61*	15	35
4006	as above but plastic couplings - *61*	30	45
32097	W9562 restaurant car plastic wheels - *57-64*	15	25
4048			

BR brown+cream

32094	W15862 D21 composite - *57-58*	15	25
4009	as above but plastic wheels - *58-61*	20	40
4009	as above but plastic couplings - *61*	40	50
32095	W34481 D21 brake/2nd - *57-58*	15	25
4010	as above but plastic wheels - *58-61*	15	35
4010	as above but plastic couplings - *61*	30	45
32096	W9572 D20 restaurant car plastic wheels - *57-64*	20	30
4047			

BR maroon

32022	M4193 D22 composite - *57-58*	20	25
4013	as above but plastic wheels - *58-62*	25	40
4013	as above but plastic couplings - *61*	40	50
32023	M26143 D22 brake/2nd - *57-58*	20	25
4014	as above but plastic wheels - *58-61*	25	40
4014	as above but plastic couplings - *61*	40	50
4049	W4966W red restaurant car red window detail, plastic wheels - *59-61*	30	40
4049	as above, cream window detail (factory error) - *59*	20	30

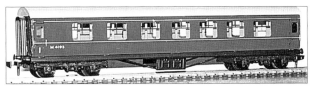

Stanier type coach [C2]

C3. Suburban Stock

Suburban stock was a post-war introduction and originally had printed windows. These were improved by stamping out and glazing them in 1956. These were eventually replaced by super detail coaches in 1962. These models are hard to find without scratch marks at their ends caused by staples used box assembly. pw = plastic wheels. They gained plastic wheels in 1958, before the change to red boxes with 4XXX numbers.

32090	**BR** maroon D13 composite printed windows - *54-57*	15	25
32090	as above but with Gresley bogies (factory error) - *?*	30	40
32092	as 32090 but glazed D14 - *56-58*	20	30
32092	as above but windows in one end - *56-57*	30	40
4021	as D14 but plastic wheels - *59-65*	15	25
32091	**BR** maroon D13 brake/3rd/2nd printed windows - *54-57*	15	25

32093	above but glazed D14 - *56-58*	15	25
4022	as above but plastic wheels - *59-65*	15	25
4025	**BR** S41060 green comp - *59-65*	25	40
4026	**BR** S43374 green brake/2nd - *59-65*	25	40
4026	as above but with plain ends - *?*	35	50

C4. Travelling Post Office

This was available only in the TPO set which included the lineside apparatus and mail bags. The value suggested in the right-hand column is for the complete set.

32098	**BR** W807 maroon coach only - *57-59*	15	20
4401	as above but plastic wheels one side - *59-65*	15	20

C5. Pullman Cars

These had all plastic bodies and were later made by Wrenn and were based on 1928 vehicles built for LNER use. The prototypes were transferred to steam-hauled services on the Southern Region in the 1950s. Watch out for broken buffers (imperfect mouldings) on these models. Early Pullman cars had Gresley compensating bogies and a three colour coat of arms but, by 1963, BR bogies were being used and a single colour was being used for the coat of arms.

4035	**Pullman** 'Aries' brown+cream 1st class Gresley bogies - *61-63*	20	30
4035	as above but BR bogies and one colour crest - *63-65*	20	30
4036	**Pullman** Car 74 brown+cream 2nd class Gresley bogies - *61-63*	20	30
4036	as above but BR bogies and one colour crest - *63-65*	20	30
4037	**Pullman** Car 79 brown+cream brake 2nd Gresley bogies - *61-63*	20	30
4037	as above but BR bogies and one colour crest - *63-65*	20	30

Super Detail Corridor Stock

These had plastic roofs, underframes and body ends but tinplate sides. They were modelled on BR Mk1 stock but were of a reduced length. Most BR and WR side corridor stock had compensating bogies.

Caution: examples with a different livery of number to any given in the tables below have been altered after leaving the factory and consequently are not listed here.

C6. BR Mk1 Passenger Coaches

BR maroon			
4052	E15770 composite* - *60-65*	20	30
4053	E35173 brake/2nd* - *60-65*	20	30
4062	M3002 1st open - *61-65*	25	30
4063	M3716 2nd open - *61-65*	25	30
BR chocolate & cream			
4050	W15870 composite* - *60-65*	20	30
4051	W34290 brake/2nd* - *60-65*	20	30
4060	W3085 1st open - *61-65*	25	30
4061	W3984 2nd open - *61-65*	25	30
BR green			
4054	S15573 composite - *62-65*	35	50
4055	S35001 brake/2nd - *62-65*	35	50

* Introduced with compensating bogies and found, usually, only in sets.

BR Mk1 passanger coach [C6]

C7. BR Mk1 Sleeping Car

Found only with compensating bogies.

4078	**BR** W2402 maroon - *61-65*	20	30

C8. BR Mk1 Restaurant Car

4070	**BR** W1910 brown+cream - *63-65*	110	130
4071	**BR** E1939 maroon - *63-65*	120	180

C9. BR Mk1 Passenger All Brake

Found only with compensating bogies.

4075	**BR** E81312 maroon - *61-65*	20	30

C10. BR Mk1 Suburban Stock

4081	**BR** S46291 green composite - *62-65*	50	70
4082	**BR** 543381 green brake 2nd - *62-65*	50	60
4082	as above but S43381* - *62-65*	110	130
4083	**BR** M41012 maroon comp - *62-65*	50	70
4084	**BR** M43277 maroon brk/2nd - *62-65*	45	60

* It is possible that these were hand altered at the factory.

C11. BR Mk1 Stove 6-Wheeled Passenger Brake

4076	**BR** M32958 maroon - *63-65*	100	150

WAGONS

Initially wagons were all lithographed tinplate with the flat spring pre-war couplings. Construction was tab-and-slot and the chassis and bogies were diecast, as were the wheels. Pre-war wagons frequently suffer from metal fatigue which has caused the diecast chassis to crumble and so care must be taken when buying these. The tinplate wagons reappeared after the war, open wagons, vans and brake vans in train sets only in 1947 and all solo models the following year for export only (and the UK market in 1949). They now had Peco couplings and, in some cases such as the tank wagons, with black instead of coloured caps.

Prior to 1953 customers had a wide choice of wagons as they were produced in the liveries of the big four companies but, that year, the whole system changed to BR liveries and where there had previously been four open wagons or vans there was now only one. This was partly compensated for with the release of the first of a series of wagons with diecast bodies, starting that year with the mineral wagon and bogie bolster.

The original diecast standard 10' wagon chassis was a rather crude affair with no daylight visible between the brake rods. Late in the day, this was improved but the chassis could not compare with plastic ones made by other manufacturers at the time.

The first Hornby Dublo vehicle to have a plastic body was the grain wagon which arrived in 1958. Once plastic wagons started to appear, wagons with larger wheelbases followed and these had plastic chassis made specially for them and were to a high standard. A plastic standard 10' wagon chassis was made at the very end but this was for wagons in the starter sets. Tinplate survived to the end for just one wagon - the 4-wheel tanker in all its variations.

Cat.No.	Company, Number, Colour, Dates	£	£

Tinplate Series

W1. D1 Open & Coal Low-Sided Wagons

The coal version of the wagon had a single moulding representing the top of a coal load. This had the ends turned down to act as feet to hold the 'coal' surface near the rim of the wagon. As it was a separate moulding it was interchangeable. p-wc = pre-war couplings

-	**LMS** 210112 brown p-wc - *38-41*	25	35
-	as above with coal - *38-41*	25	35
32075	**LMS** 210112 brown - *47-51*	15	25
32025	as above with coal - *48-51*	15	25
32075	**LMS** 210112 lighter brown - *51-53*	15	25
32025	as above with coal - *51-53*	15	25

-	**SR** 19260 dark brown p-wc - *38-41*	40	100
-	as above with coal - *38-41*	40	100
32075	**SR** 19260 dark brown - *47-50*	30	100
32025	as above with coal - *48-50*	30	100
-	**GW** 109458 grey p-wc - *38-41*	25	35
-	as above with coal - *38-41*	25	35
32075	**GW** 109458 grey - *47-50*	20	35
32025	as above with coal - *48-50*	20	35
-	**NE** 404844 green-grey p-wc - *38-41*	25	35
-	as above with coal - *38-41*	25	35
32075	**NE** 404844 green-grey - *47-51*	15	18
32025	as above with coal - *48-51*	15	18
32075	**NE** 404844 grey - *51-52*	15	18
32025	as above with coal - *51-52*	15	18
32075	**BR** E404844 grey - *54-58*	10	12
32025	as above with coal - *54-58*	10	12

Coal wagon [W1]

W2. D2 High Sided Wagon (7-plank)

The coal version of the wagon had a single moulding representing the top of a coal load. This had the ends turned down to act as feet to hold the 'coal' surface near the rim of the wagon. p-wc = pre-war couplings

-	**LMS** 608344 brown p-wc - *38-41*	25	35
-	as above with coal - *38-41*	25	35
32055	**LMS** 608344 brown - *48-51*	15	20
32030	as above with coal - *48-51*	15	20
32055	**LMS** 608344 lighter brown - *51-53*	15	20
32030	as above with coal - *51-53*	15	20
-	**NE** 91508 grey p-wc - *38-41*	40	50
-	as above with coal - *38-41*	40	50
32055	**NE** 91508 grey - *48-51*	30	50
32030	as above with coal - *48-51*	30	50
32055	**BR** M608344 grey - *54-58*	10	15
32030	as above with coal - *54-58*	10	15

W3. D1 Tube Wagon

32076	**BR** W73349 brown - *56-58*	10	15
4690	as above but plastic wheels - *59-60*	10	15

W4. D1 Short Tank Wagon

This was the only wagon to retain its tinplate body with cast ends to the end of production. p-wc = pre-war couplings.

-	**Esso** buff p-wc buff cap - *38-41*	80	150
32081	as above post-war black cap - *48-51*	80	100
36676	**Esso** silver - *52-58*	12	20
4676	as above but plastic wheels - *59-62*	15	25
4676	as above but open brake-gear - *62-64*	20	30
-	**Power Ethyl** green p-wc green cap - *38-41*	80	150
32080	as above post-war black cap - *48-51*	70	120
32080	**Power*** green - *54-55*	15	35
32080	as above but in 'Power Petrol' box - *55*	NA	100
-	**Royal Daylight** red p-wc red cap - *38-41*	80	150
32070	as above post-war black cap - *48-51*	100	120
32070	**Esso Royal Daylight** red - *52-55*	16	30
32082	**Shell Lubricating Oil** yellow - *55-58*	16	25
4678	as above but plastic wheels - *59-62*	16	25
4678	as above but open brake-gear - *62-64*	18	25
32083	**Vacuum** red - *55-56*	17	35
32084	**Mobil Oil** red - *56-57*	17	30

32084	**Mobil** red (cat.4677) - *57-58*	17	30
32084	as above but plastic wheels - *59-62*	15	20
32084	as above but open brake-gear - *62-64*	20	30
4680	**Esso** black plastic wheels - *60-62*	20	20
4680	as above but open brake-gear - *62-64*	25	35

* Power tank wagons were sold in 'Power Ethol' boxes for a long time after introduction. 'Power Petrol' boxes are extremely rare.

Short tank wagon - Power [W4]

W5. D1 Closed Vans

Vans have white roofs except for the LMS versions which started silver grey and finished light grey and the BR vans which had light grey roofs. The SR meat van was available for a while with the LMS silver grey roof and examples sell at a higher price than those with white roofs, however, as roofs were interchangeable, it is not included in the list below. p-wc = pre-war couplings

	LMS		
32040	508194 brown goods van p-wc - *38-41*	25	35
32040	as above, post-war couplings - *48-51*	15	25
32040	as above but lighter brown - *51-53*	15	25
32065	19631 brown meat van p-wc - *38-41*	25	35
32065	as above, post-war couplings - *47-53*	15	20
32020	710018 brown cattle van p-wc - *38-41*	45	65
32020	as above, post-war couplings- *48-53*	80	120
	SR		
32040	48277 dark brown goods p-wc - *38-41*	75	85
32040	as above, post-war couplings - *47-50*	80	120
32065	51298 buff meat van - *48-53*	60	80
	LNER		
32035	168975 brown fish van p-wc - *38-41*	25	35
32035	as above, post-war couplings- *48-53*	18	25
32060	2337 teak horse box p-wc - *38-41*	25	35
32060	as above, post-war couplings - *48-53*	18	25
32040	182153 brown goods van p-wc - *38-41*	25	35
32040	as above, post-war couplings- *47-53*	18	25
	GWR		
32040	112699 green-grey goods van p-wc - *38-41*	55	75
32040	as above, post-war couplings - *47-50*	50	70
32020	106324 green-grey cattle van p-wc - *38-41*	25	35
32020	ditto post-war, 2 sml windows - *48-51*	30	40
32020	as above but now grey - *51-53*	30	40
32020	as above but 1 long window - *52-53*	30	40
	BR		
32020	B893344 brown cattle van - *56-58*	12	18
32035	E168975 brown fish van - *54-58*	12	16
32040	B755414 brown goods van - *54-58*	12	16
32060	E2337 red horse box - *54-58*	12	16
32065	S50494 white meat van - *54-58*	12	16

W6. D1 Long Wheelbase Van

32058	**BR** W28798 brown - *54-58*	15	25
4326	as above but plastic wheels - *59*	20	30

W7. D1 GWR Goods Brake Van

-	**GW** 68796 grey Park Royal no chimney, pre-war couplings - *38-41*	45	65
32045	as above, post-war couplings - *47-50*	50	70

32047	**BR** W68796 grey Park Royal, with chimney - *56-58*	10	18

Long wheel base van [W6]

W8. D1 LMS Goods Brake Van

p-wc = pre-war couplings

-	**LMS** 730026 brown, no chimney, pre-war couplings - *38-41*	25	35
32045	as above but post-war - *47-51*	15	25
32045	as above but lighter brown - *51-53*	15	25
32045	**BR** M730026 grey plain roof - *53-54*	15	25
32045	as above with chimney* - *54-58*	10	12
32049	**Canadian Pacific** 437270 black caboose - *54-61*	100	250

* Rain strips also added.

W9. D1 LNER Goods Brake Van

p-wc = pre-war couplings

-	**NE** 178717 brown, pre-war couplings, no chimney - *38-41*	25	35
32045	ditto but post-war, white roof - *47-51*	15	20
32045	as above but grey roof - *53*	25	30
32046	**BR** E178717 brown, white roof - *53*	25	30
32046	as above but plain grey roof - *53-54*	15	25
32046	as above with chimney* - *54-58*	8	16

* Rain strips also added.

W10. D1 SR Goods Brake Van

p-wc = pre-war couplings

-	**SR** 55975 dk.brown, no chimney, pre-war couplings - *38-41*	125	150
32045	as above but post-war couplings, one window on end - *47-50*	100	150
32045	as above but window each side of end door (factory error*) - *48*	100	120

* This detail comes from the LMS brake van. More usually they are found with the wrong detail at one end only.

W11. D1 Bogie Brick Wagon

p-wc = pre-war couplings. All but one version had brown chassis.

-	**NE** N163535 brown p-wc - *38-41*	60	70
-	as above with black chassis*	150	160
32050	as above post-war - *48-53*	15	20
32050	**BR** E163535 brown - *53*	25	30
32050	as above but black chassis - *54-58*	10	16

* These were pre-war wagons returned for repair after the war.

Diecast Wagons

W12. D1 Low-Sided Wagon

The flat wagon with wooden cable drums had six holes in the base through which the drums were held in place with Meccano green string. Around 1960 the number of holes was reduced to two and black tube elastic was used to fix the drums. pw = plastic wheels.

32085	**BR** B459325 brown - *53-58*	8	12
4645	as above but plastic wheels - *59-64*	12	15
32087	**BR** B459325 brown + maroon furniture container - *56-58*	10	15
4647	as above but plastic wheels - *59-64*	15	20

32088	**BR** B459325 brown + white Insul-meat container - *56-58*	10	15
4648	as above but plastic wheels - *59-64*	15	20
4649	**BR** B459325 brown + tractor load, plastic wheels - *59-64*	40	55
32086	**BR** M486 grey + Liverpool Cables wood drums - *53-59*	10	15
4646	as above but plastic wheels - *59-62*	12	18
4646	**BR** M486 grey, Aluminium Wire & Cable plastic drums + wheels - *61-64*	30	40
4646	as above but wood drums with silver advert - *61*	200	300

Low-sided wagon with tractor [W12]

W13. Double Bolster Wagon
pw = plastic wheels.

32052	**BR** B920022 grey - *56-58*	10	15
32052	as above but plastic wheels - *59*	10	15
4615	**BR** B920022 grey + timber pw - *59-64*	15	20

W14. D2 Mineral Wagon

32056	**BR** B54884 grey - *53-58*	10	15
32056	as above, markings at wrong end - *53*	25	30
32056	wagon number and weights panel reversed on one side (error) - *53?*	25	30
4654	Rail Cleaning Wagon** black - *64*	300	550

** Beware of forgeries

W15. D1 Bogie Well Wagon

32053	**BR** B901006 grey diamond bogies - *55-58*	10	15
32053	as above but plate bogies - *58*	15	20
4605	as above but plastic wheels - *59-64*	10	20

W16. D1 Bogie Bolster Wagon
Early models had the stanchions 3mm longer than standard. While the shortening undoubtedly saved metal, it was probably done to stop them poking out of their boxes, with a card insert to keep them tight fitting.

32051	**BR** M720550 grey diamond bogies - *53-58*	10	15
32051	as above but plate bogies - *58-59*	20	25
4610	as above but plastic wheels - *59-64*	15	20

W17. Breakdown Crane

4620	**BR** No.133 + DE961665 matt red - *59-61*	40	50
4620	as above but gloss red, red box - *61-?*	70	120
4620	as above but yellow box top* - *?-64*	70	180

* This should contain a gloss red crane with delrin couplings, all diecast hook and plastic grips on the metal handles. Not all gloss cranes had plastic grips or delrin couplings.

SD6 Plastic Wagons

W18. Lowmac Machine Wagon

4652	**BR** B904631 gloss brown ballast weights beneath - *61-64*	10	15
4652	as above but matt brown ballast weights - *61-64*	10	15

W19. 5-Plank Open Wagon

4670	**BR** B477015 grey - *58-62*	8	12
4670	as above but open brake-gear - *62-64*	10	16
4635	**BR** B477015 grey + coal - *58-62*	10	18

4635	as above but open brake-gear - *62-64*	10	20
4660	**The United Glass Bottle Manufacturers** 82 yellow - *58-61*	8	12
4660	as above but open brake-gear - *61-62*	15	20
4660	**United Glass** 82 yellow - *62-64*	35	45
-	yellow, plastic chassis ex sets - *63-64*	10	NA

W20. Steel Open Wagon

4640	**BR** B486865 brown - *58-62*	10	15
4640	as above but open brake-gear - *62-65*	12	16
-	buff, plastic chassis ex sets - *63-64*	8	NA

W21. Mineral Wagon

4655	**BR** B54884 grey - *58-62*	10	12
4655*	as above but open brake-gear - *62-64*	25	35
4656	**BR** B550200 brown open brake gear - *62-64*	30	45

* Watch out for chassis swapping. The body should be riveted to the chassis.

W22. 21T Hopper Wagon

4644	**BR** B414029 grey - *63-64*	60	100
4644	as above, reversed transfers - *?*	100	125
4644	with nicks in end support rib - *?*	70	110

W23. Grain Wagon
Make sure that the small lugs at the base of the grain container are not missing.

4625	**BR** B885040 grey Grain - *58-64*	15	25

W24. Presflo Wagon

4626	**BR** brown Presflo - *61-64*	10	18
4627	**ICI** blue green Bulk Salt - *61-64*	10	18

Prestwin silo wagon [W25]

W25. Prestwin Silo Wagon

4658	**BR** B873000 brown Prestwin - *62-64*	12	18

Chlorine tank wagon [W26]

W26. Chlorine Tank Wagon

Care must be taken when cleaning this model as the paint easily comes off!

4675	**ICI** 124 white end supports - *60-64*	10	18
4675	as above but cream supports - *60-64*	10	18

W27. 6-Wheel Tank Wagon

4657	**UD** off-white high supports - *62-63*	28	50
4657	**UD** off-white high and low supports - *63-64*	22	40
4657	**UD** off-white low supports - *64*	60	80

W28. Ferry Tank Wagon

Check that the top piping is not missing.

4679	**Traffic Services Ltd** 500836 silver - *60-64*	15	25

W29. Saxa Salt Wagon

4665	**Saxa Salt** 248 yellow - *58-62*	10	15
4665	as above but open brake-gear - *62-64*	15	25

W30. Cattle Wagon

4630	**BR** B893344 brown - *58-64*	12	15

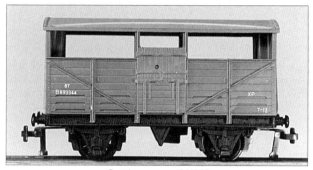

Cattle wagon [W30]

W31. BR Standard Horse Box

This model is often missing the horse or has door lugs broken off.

4316	**BR** S96412 green + horse - *60-64*	60	85
4315	**BR** E96435 maroon + horse - *60-64*	60	80

W32. Gunpowder Van

4313	**BR** B887002 brown open brake gear - *62-64*	15	18

W33. Banana Van

4301	**BR** B881967 brown open brake-gear - *62-64*	20	25

W34. Passenger Fruit Van

4305	**BR** W2910 maroon - *60-64*	20	30

W35. Ventilated Van (and Packing Van)

4325	**BR** B757051 brown white roof - *58-62*	10	14
4325	as above but open brake gear - *62-65*	10	14
4318	**BR** DE545523 red grey roof* - *62-64*	20	30

* packing van for breakdown crane.

SR utility van [W36]

W36. SR Utility Van

This model had a plastic wagon. The under-van brake gear etc. was fragile on this model and easily broken. Also watch out for broken buffers (imperfect mouldings).

4323	**BR** S2380S green CCT - *61-64*	35	50

W37. 6T Mica B Refrigerator Van

4320	**BR** W59850 white/cream - *58-62*	10	16
4320	as above but open brake gear - *62-65*	10	16

W38. Blue Spot Fish Van

This model had a plastic chassis. The under-van brake gear etc. was fragile on this model and easily broken. Also watch out for broken buffers (imperfect mouldings).

4300	**BR** E87231 white or cream Insul-fish - *61-64*	25	35

W39. WR Goods Brake Van

4312	**BR** W56421 grey Southall RU - *58-64*	10	14
4312	**BR** W35247 brown - *not made*	NA	NA

W40. LMR Goods Brake Van

4310	**BR** M730012 grey - *58-61*	10	14
4310	**BR** M730012 brown - *62-64*	35	50
4310	**BR** M730973 brown - *62-64*	35	50

W41. BR Standard Goods Brake Van

4311	**BR** B950350 brown - *59-64*	10	15
-	red, short plastic chassis ex starter sets - *63-64*	10	NA

W42. Caustic Liquor Bogie Tank Wagon

4685	**ICI** 5710 blue-green diamond bogies - *62*	150	200
4685	as above but plate bogies - *62-64*	60	95

ACCESSORIES

Pre-war wooden station buildings, which were made with either a red or green roof, are the most sought-after lineside accessories. They include: the main station building, the arched roof, island platform (green roof), engine shed and goods depot (£200-£250), red roof island platform and the through station (£150-£175), platforms from the central station (£20-£40), sets of boxed staff or passengers figures (£75-£100), wooden signal cabin (£50-£75), tunnels (340-£50), buffer-stops (£15-£20) and signal (£7-£12).

After the war the buildings were made of cast aluminium. These included the through station (£50-£70), island platform (£30-£40), straight platform extensions for either (£35-£45), footbridge or red roof signal cabin (£20-£30), green roof signal cabin (£120 -£150), metal girder bridge (£40-£50), 6 station staff or 6 passengers (£25-£30) and level crossing (£10-£15). Also from this period is the turntable (£35-£40).

Terminus station kit

Hornby-Dublo

Plastic kits for stations and lineside buildings came in 1959 replacing the aluminium ones. Most expensive are the large terminus station (£150-£300), station extension canopy in red and yellow box (£400-£500), the same in a white box (£180-£250), plastic girder bridge (£400-£500) and set of 12 railway staff (£50-£60). Other items from this period to look for include: 2-road engine shed (£60-£70), engine shed extension kit (£30-£50), suburban station kit (£30-£40), plastic tunnel (£50-£100), double track tunnel (£100-£140), island platform kit (£30-£40), goods depot kit (£30-£50), buff coloured water crane (£35-£45), buffers with electric lights on them (£8-£12), 12 plastic passengers and goods (£30-£40), lighting kit (£10-£15), set of 12 gradient and mile posts (£40-£50), set of 6 lineside notices (£25-£35) and box of 12 telegraph poles (£50-£75).

Signals sell for between £7 and £18 while lever switches are £4-£5 or, in the case of green coloured ones, £5-£6.

The most expensive item of track is the clockwork track point at £15-£20 each. Pre-war 3-rail points, in contrast, are £6-£12 and other pieces of track usually sell at between £1 and £2 each. Of post-war track, the most demanded are 3-rail straights (£1-£2), hand points (£5-£10) and electric points (£10-£15). There is little demand for 2-rail plastic sleeper track.

NEVERWAZZAS

These are models that were not made by Meccano Ltd but have been produced by enthusiasts in the style Hornby Dublo or as miniaturisation of Hornby 0 gauge wagons. While some are one-offs, others are produced in limited runs for sale to other enthusiasts. Some are merely repaints while others have structural alteration. A number of interesting ones are based on models that Meccano Ltd. planned to produce but, in the end, did not. These include two locomotives - a V2 and a GWR 0-6-2 tank. There are also a double level crossing and a log carrier using a coach chassis. Some excellent replica boxes have been produced by Tony Cooper including boxes for some neverwazzers. Recommending values is very difficult and really outside the scope of this book but at auction the boxed double level crossing will fetch £100-£150 while neverwazza wagons tend to be a lot cheaper at around £25 each.

SETS

As one might expect, pre-war train sets fetch the highest prices. Clockwork passenger DP1 sets are priced £1,000-£1,250 and DG1 clockwork goods sets sell for £300-£900; with the level of price depending on which livery is carried. Pre-war electric passenger EDP1 sets are £900-£1,250 but, again the goods sets vary: EDG7 GWR and LMS (£300-£900), EDG7 LNER and SR (£700-£900) while EDGA7 GWR sets are in the £500-£750 price range.

Amongst post-war sets, ones to look out for are the very first ones released in 1947 and 1948. They differ slightly, in various ways, from those produced after 1948 and the date on instruction leaflets will help to identify them. For these the prices are as follows: LNER passenger EDP1 (£600-£800), LMS passenger EDL7 (£300-£400), LNER goods EDL7 (£500-£900) and SR goods (£1,000-£1,500).

Other post-war pre-Nationalisation sets are priced: LNER passenger EDP1 (£150-£200), LMS passenger EDL2 (£120-£160), LMS, LNER and SR goods EDL7 sets (£300-£900), GWR goods EDL7 (£300-£500). Either of the Canadian Pacific sets sells for £650-£850.

As with the solo models, the BR liveried sets replaced the pre-Nationalisation ones in 1953 following which the range of sets grew quite fast. The following are some of the sets worth looking for: EDP15 with matt locomotive finish (£150-£200), G19 (£350-£450), P15 or P20 (£350-£450), P22 (£250-£350), 2015, 2020, 2021, 2022, 2025, 2033, 2034, 2035, 2049 or 2050 (£200-£300) and 2035 (£1,000-£1,250). Other sets are mostly priced £100-£125 for good boxed examples. Others that have turned up at auction mint boxed are 2023 (£140) and 2030 (£120).

EDG7 SR goods set (Barry Potter Auctions)

Jouef 00 (British)

HISTORY

Jouef was a French company and its earlier models made for the British market will be found under 'Playcraft' They were manufactured in H0 scale for the British company - Mettoy Ltd. Late Playcraft was mainly from the Jouef Continental range and packaged in Jouef boxes specially for the British market.

Playcraft eventually died-out in the early 1970s but this was not the end of the company's involvement in the British market. By 1977 they had produced a Class 40 diesel and some Mk3 coaches. These are unlike most models made for the British market by a Continental manufacturer in being to 00 scale and not H0. Although, some of the Continental models were for a while made in BR blue livery in the mid 1970s, these were displaced when the more suitable 00 models arrived. These had been manufactured in France and the moulds later transferred to Ireland.

With the help of a grant from the Irish government, Jouef opened a factory at Shannon Airport International Trading Estate in Ireland. One account says that this was in 1978 and another refers to it being in 1980. The company was called Hobby Developments Ireland (HDI) and they produced a variety of products and published a catalogue. The company did not survive long but did offer 18 different locomotive types before its demise in 1981. One interesting H0 model was the German V200 sold as a Warship Class loco in BR corporate blue as 825 'Intrepid'.

The idea had been to not just assemble models from parts made in France but to manufacture the parts in Ireland, right down to the packaging. It was felt that this would make the models cheaper in Ireland and Britain. Certainly Continental models have been found with 'HDI' on their bases.

In November of 1986, Hobbyphoto of Dublin were selling off the remaining stock. The tools for the British outline models were purchased from the liquidators and by April 1987 The Southern Model Railway Company of Blessington, County Wicklow, were advertising a limited run of the Class 40 locomotive in either green of blue livery.

Thought had been given to introducing a Pacific loco in the form of a Gresley A1 and A3 for 1978 but the project was abandoned. Both were to be turned out in 'strict LNER livery'.

LOCOMOTIVES

Only one loco was produced in a choice of two liveries. The green version came unfinished with a sheet of transfers which included: 2 BRc totems, 2 'Mauretania' nameplates, 4 D285 numbers, 2 'Empress of Britain' nameplates, 4 D210 numbers, 1 'Empress Voyager' headboard and 6 white ovals apparently to cover the buffer heads which are sprayed red.

Cat.No.	Details and Dates	£	£

L1. Class 40 Diesel 1Co-Co1
The models came with a choice of two headboards one of which was Irish Mail. The model had a 5-pole motor, working headlights and glazed windows. The model also had a floating bogie

Cat.No.	Details and Dates	£	£
8912	**D285** blue BRe - 77	15	25
8913	green + transfers - 78	NA	30
8913	**D210 'Empress of Britain'** green BRc - 78	20	NA
8913	**D211 'Mauretania'** green BRc - 78	20	NA

L2. Class A1/A3 2-6-4
?	LNER A1 - *announced but not made*	NA	NA
?	LNER A3 - *announced but not made*	NA	NA

COACHES

Cat.No.	Colour, Company, Dates	£	£

C1. BR Mk3 Stock
5751	blue+ grey BR 1st - 77	10	15
5752	blue+ grey BR 2nd - 77	10	15
5753	blue+ grey BR buffet - 78	10	15

Class 40 [L1] & Mk3 coack [C1]

Kitmaster

HISTORY

Nene Plastics Ltd was founded in Raunds by T. Eric Smith in 1940, immediately prior to his call-up for war service. On his return he set about developing and launching his Rosebud Dolls range. In 1954 a new injection moulding plant was brought into operation. The following year the name of the company was changed to Rosebud Dolls Ltd. with a target of 5 million dolls per year.

In 1958, Rosebud Kitmaster was formed to make kits using spare capacity in the injection moulding room. The subject was chosen because kits were a growing market and at that time locomotive kits in plastic were not being done by anyone else. In the UK, the kits were available between 1959 and 1962 and were moulded in polystyrene. They were complementary to a range of railway kits made by Airfix but were much more expensive. The subjects were chosen by Dennis Franklin who was Rosebud's Assistant Technical Manager and who took charge of the Kitmaster project. He travelled far and wide choosing and studying the models to be made and obtaining official drawings for them.

A crucial error was an early decision to model only in a 'constant' 00 scale which meant that models of foreign locomotives would not sell abroad where H0 scale was the norm. The foreign outline models were generally of little interest to the British public and, with tools costing between £6,000 and £10,000 per model, income from sale of these kits fell a long way short of repaying the development costs.

Trix had made a similar mistake in modelling in H0 for the British market and an interesting connection with Trix Products Ltd was through the latter's chief designer, Michael Catalani. He had designed the new range of Trix plastic coaches but was not prepared to move to Birmingham when that company was moved there. Instead, he went to work for Rosebud Kitmaster for three weeks before being lured back by his previous employer. While at Rosebud he was involved with the design of the Pullman cars.

Initially, the Kitmaster kits were released at a rate of one a month but after the first year the strain of this was beginning to show. As a result of pressure put on them a number of skilled staff left. Up until the release of the Beyer-Garratt model in 1960, the pattern making was done in-house but, after that, it was subcontracted to freelance model makers. Most of these patterns were made in brass by model-maker Jack Gain.

Class 4MT Mogul (Tony Wright)

The Kitmaster project was clearly over ambitious and badly planned as described above. Within a short time this was creating financial strains on the Company. The policy of a new model every month required large amounts of capital for new tools and Rosebud Kitmaster had been slow in getting their distribution and marketing sorted out. As a result, money was not coming in to the Company as fast as it was going out with the result that a crisis was looming.

The solution was to sell the Kitmaster business and the obvious buyer was Airfix Ltd. Late in 1962 the Kitmaster tools and stock were sold to that company. Some of the surplus kits were released to the public through a Shredded Wheat promotion conducted by the Hermes Supply Company; a subsidiary of Airfix Ltd.

A number of the British subjects were absorbed into the Airfix kit range and were later acquired by Palitoy and then by Dapol, who are still making them!

By 1964 things were looking desperate for Rosebud Dolls Ltd and in June that year the Receiver was called in. The Company remained in administrative receivership, with the doll business recovering, until July 1967 when it merged with Mattel Inc. (famed for Barbie doll) to form Rosebud Mattel Ltd. (renamed Mattel (UK) Ltd in 1971).

Further Reading

The book *'Let's Stick Together'* by Stephen Knight contains everything you are ever likely to want to know about the Kitmaster range and what happened to the kits in later years. This very thorough work was published in 1999 by Irwell Press (ISBN 1-871608-90-2) and is strongly recommended to anyone interested in further study.

Collectors Clubs

Enthusiasts of the Kitmaster kit range are well catered for by the Kitmaster Collectors Club which was founded in 1980. The Club publishes a magazine called *'Signal'* twice a year and includes in the subjects covered the railway kits by Airfix and Dapol. The Club has a website at www.kitmaster-club.org.uk and for enquiries regarding membership fax: 01787 478226.

KITS

Dates - The dates given below are those when the kit is believed to have first been available in the shops. Remaindered stock was available in shops, often for considerable periods, after the demise of Kitmaster.

Prices - The two prices given show the range of prices one can find on unmade kits; the second column being for mint examples in their original cellophane wrapping.

Cat.No.	Details and Dates	£	£

1. 00 Kits

Note that Continental outline models are to 4mm/1ft in this table.

Cat.No.	Details and Dates	£	£
1	**L&M 0-2-2** 'Rocket' yellow - *59*	15	25
2	**0-6-0DS** D3421 black - *59*	15	25
4	**Princess Coronation** Class 46225 'Duchess of Gloucester' black - *59*	35	50
5	**Schools** Class 30919 'Harrow' black - *59*	5	15
6	**ex-L&Y 0-4-0ST** 51212 black - *59*	5	12
7	**Class 6100** 2-6-2T 6167 black - *59*	5	12
8	**Italian Class 835** 0-6-0T 162 black - *59*	35	50
9	**Stirling Single** 4-2-2 No.1 green - *59*	35	50

Kitmaster

10	**Prototype Diesel** 'Deltic' blue - *60*	35	50
11	**Battle of Britain** Class 34057 'Biggin Hill' black - *60*	15	25
12	**Swiss Crocodile** Series Be6/8 13305 black - *60*	25	35
13	**Mk1 Corridor Composite** Coach M16001, M15627, M15019, M15243, W15111, W15598, W15430, E15307, E15144, E16017 maroon - *60*	10	20
13	**Mk1 Corridor Composite** Coach S15042, S15573, S15888, S15903, S15580, S15873 green - *60*	15	25
14	**Mk1 Corridor 2nd** Coach M25589, M24133, M24405, M24861, W24165, W24341, W24719, E24222, E24531, E25027 maroon - *60*	10	20
14	**Mk1 Corridor 2nd** Coach S24320, S24305, S24169, S24326, S24318, S24311 green - *60*	15	25
15	**Mk1 Corridor Brake 2nd** Coach M35114, M34090, M34105, M34671, W34152, W34297, W34763, E34422, E34590, E35157 maroon - *60*	10	20
15	**Mk1 Corridor Brake 2nd** Coach S34256, S34621, S34158, S34945, S34279, S35020 green - *60*	15	25
19	**German Baureihe Class 23** 23001, 23008, 23014 black - *60*	35	50
22	**Class 9F** 2-10-0 92220 'Evening Star', 92203, 92134 black - *60*	15	25
23	**French 241P Mountain** 241P.026, 241P.027, 241P.029 black - *60*	35	50
24	**GWR City Class** 3440 'City of Truro' black - *60*	15	25
25	**LMS Beyer-Garratt** 2-6-6-2 7971, 7987, 47994 black - *61*	70	100
26	**J94 0-6-0ST** 68022, 68028, 68051, 68076 black - *61*	15	25
28	**Mk1 Restaurant Car** M4, M5, M6, S9, W7, W8, E1, E2, E3, E10, E11 maroon - *61*	15	25
28	**Mk1 Restaurant Car** M4, M5, M6, S9, W7, W8, E1, E2, E3, E10, E11 green - *61*	25	35
30	**Class 4MT** BR Mogul 76000, 76093, 76114 black - *61*	25	35
31	**Midland Pullman** Power Car A F blue - *61*	35	60
32	**Midland Pullman** Kitchen Car B E blue - *61*	50	70
33	**Midland Pullman** Parlour Car C D blue - *61*	25	35
35	**USA 0-6-0T** - *not made*	NA	NA
36	**Class A3** 'Flying Scotsman' - *not made*	NA	NA

2. H0 Kits

Note that these are genuine 3.5mm/1ft models.

3	**Early American General** 4-4-0 'General' black - *59*	35	50
27	**DB B4yge Coach** - *61*	5	10
29	**SNCF A9 myfi/1958 Coach** silver - *61*	5	10
34	**New York Central Hudson** J3a 4-6-4 5405 black - *61*	70	100
37	**Canadian National** U-4-A - *not made*	NA	NA

3. TT Kits

16	**Rebuilt Royal Scot** 46100 'Royal Scot', 46110 'Genadier Guardsman', 46169 'The Boy Scout' black - *60*	35	50
17	**Mk1 Corridor Brake 2nd** M35114, M34090, M34105, M34671, W34152, W34297, W34763, E34422, E34590, E35157 maroon - *60*	5	10
17	**Mk1 Corridor Brake 2nd** S34256, S34621, S34158, S34945, S34279, S35020 green - *60*	5	10
18	**Mk1 Corridor Composite** M16001, M15627, M15019, M15243, W15111, W15598, W15430, E15307, E15144, E16017 maroon - *60*	5	10
18	**Mk1 Corridor Composite** S15042, S15573, S15888, S15903, S15580, S15873 green - *60*	5	10
20	**Mk1 Corridor 2nd** M25589, M24133, M24405, M24861, W24165, W24341, W24719, E24222, E24531, E25027 maroon - *60*	5	10
20	**Mk1 Corridor 2nd** S24320, S24305, S24169, S24326, S24318, S24311 green - *60*	5	10
21	**Mk1 Restaurant Car** M4, M5, M6, S9, W7, W8, E1, E2, E3, E10, E11 maroon - *60*	5	10
21	**Mk1 Restaurant Car** M4, M5, M6, S9, W7, W8, E1, E2, E3, E10, E11 green - *60*	5	10

4. Presentation Sets

P1	**100 Years of British Steam** 'Rocket', 'Duchess of Gloucester' and Stirling Single - *59*	100	150
P2	**Battle of Britain Set** 34057 'Biggin Hill' and 3 Mk1 coaches - *60*	NPG	200
P3	**Royal Scot Set** (TT) Rebuilt Royal Scott and 4 Mk1 coaches - *61*	NPG	300

5. Motor Kits

KM1	Motor Bogie 00 - *60*	10	15
KM2	Motor Box Van 00 - *60*	10	15
KM3	Motor Bogie TT - *not made*	NA	NA

Footnote: Airfix produced two locomotive kits of their own, not using Kitmaster tools. These were the Park Royal Railbus (R201) in green (1960) which sells for £15 in good condition and £25 when mint and the 204HP Drewry shunter (R7) in black (1961) for which you might expect to pay £7 for a good example or £10 for a mint one.

Boxed kits

Leeds (LMC)

HISTORY

The Leeds Model Company was started by Rex Stedman, an engineer. It had been founded in 1912, hand making models but, due to the war, tool making did not get underway properly until 1919; Stedman doing most of the design work himself. During the war Stedman worked on aircraft design and aerial photography. With the coming of peace, Stedman moved his fledgling company to new premises at Balm Road, Hunslet, in Leeds. With the financial help of a wealthy model railway enthusiast, G.P.Keen, the Company was incorporated in March 1920 as The Leeds Model Company Limited and Keen became its chairman.

In Britain, the Leeds Model Company ranked third, after Hornby and Bassett-Lowke, during the 1920s and '30s, the emphasis being on reasonably affordable 0 gauge models rather than toy trains. The principles Stedman adopted were that his designs must provide the widest possible product range, at minimum cost to give the customer maximum choice at the lowest possible price. To achieve this he had to produce standard models that shared parts and could look good in a range of liveries. The result was a series of freelance tank engines which were released in the early '20s.

Next, Stedman needed to make an impact in the market to get noticed and his choice was a Great Central Railway 4-4-0 Director Class, 437 'Charles Stuart Wortley'. Using much of the same tooling he went on to make another Great Central locomotive - the 4-6-0 'Sir Sam Fay'.

Production went on apace with Stedman doing most of the design work himself. Besides producing their own models to sell, LMC also sold a large range of parts for customers to build their own models.

The Company produced a full range of rolling stock, accessories and wooden sleepered track. The rolling stock made by the Company falls into three categories. The early high quality handmade wagons offered through their catalogues, started before the First World War, remained available, be it in a much restricted range, until after the Second World War. Many of these handmade models were also available in gauge 1 as well as 0 gauge.

LMC are best known for their lithographically printed, paper

Mansted Foundry

In the mid 1920s, after G.P.Keen had given up the chairmanship of the Leeds Model Company, Rex Stedman built locomotives specifically for Keen's own 0 gauge model railway which he had at home and called 'K Lines'. These unique and mainly freelance models, produced in the mid to late 20s, were supposed to come from a fictitious Mansted Foundry, the first part of the name being an anagram of 'Stedman'.

The name 'Mansted Foundry' was inscribed on the models along with the serial number. A report in the model railway press at the time indicated that some parts were supplied by Winteringhams who were part of the Bassett-Lowke group, and with whom G.P.Keen also had business links.

The bodies of the locomotives were brass instead of tinplate and the 20V DC mechanisms had cobalt steel magnets and 8-pole armatures.

K Lines was broken up a number of years ago, following the death of Keen, but several of the Mansted Foundry models have survived. Probably Stedman's finest work was an LNER Garrett.

A further link with Bassett-Lowke occurred in the early 1920s when LMC made two locomotive models exclusively for the Bassett-Lowke range.

---

covered, wooden wagons and coaches which were available between 1923 and 1966 (an embossed card NE open wagon had actually been made from 1920 but was soon dropped). Kits were available up to the time the Company ceased trading.

The third type of rolling stock arrived in the late '30s and had bodies moulded in bakelite with the detail added with transfers. This was the first time this material had been used for rolling stock production and the result was very pleasing. It continued as the True Scale range after the war.

Their cast metal wheels are much closer to scale and have finer flanges than either Hornby or Bassett-Lowke products. Some locomotives had smoke units fitted after the Second World War, pre-empting Tri-ang by a number of years.

In 1925 The Leeds Model Company merged with the Bristol Model Co. and Stedman was reduced from Managing Director to Chief Engineer and Designer. The Bristol directors, headed by Hugh Leader, had money to invest in new designs and are largely responsible for the appearance of GWR locomotives in the range including a Churchward 4-4-0 County for Bassett-Lowke. This was followed by a Caledonian Railway Class 72 Pickersgill 4-4-0. Whilst under the agreement with Bassett-Lowke LMC could not sell these two models in their own range, they did use the tooling to produce their own GWR Mogul and Pickersgill 0-6-0. Also, from 1925, an 8V DC mechanism was available as well as the clockwork one.

Things, however, did not continue to run smoothly. Stedman had invested heavily in producing models of the pre-grouping companies but by 1924 the public had been wanting the liveries of the Big Four. During an acute financial crisis in 1928, Rex Stedman left LMC and set up a new company called R.F.Stedman & Co Ltd at Jack Lane, Hunslet, Leeds. At the same time, The Leeds Model Company started cutting its prices by up to 20%. A few months later Stedman purchased the entire stock and plant as well as trade mark of LMC. He continued to manufacture under the name of R.F.Stedman & Co Ltd and work now went into extending and updating the range of models with the new liveries. The changes included a switch from clockwork to electric mechanisms and the dropping of the expensive to produce hand-built rolling stock.

In 1927 Stedman had visited the Bing factory in Nuremberg and been impressed by the new developments in die casting with alloys. However, in 1931, he again relinquished control of the Company (this time for good) and the name reverted to Leeds Model Company or, later, just 'LMC'. George Simpson now took over as Managing Director with R.S.Moore as Chairman.

As a sign of their success, LMC was the victim of Japanese imitation when Stromlite marketed copies of several models in the 1930s. These included 'Sir Sam Fay', the 0-4-0ST, Brighton Belle set and several of the coaches and wagons.

Bakelite had been considered for wagon production as long ago as 1925 but was not used by the LMC until the late 1930s. Trix, of course, had been using it for their track bases since the mid ''30s but LMC were the first company in the UK to produce coach and wagon bodies in the material.

After the war, the Leeds Model Company concentrated on supplying retailers with their models instead of supplying the public direct. Model parts for scratch builders became available again, followed by the standard locomotive range. Shortage of

Leeds (LMC)

materials and a shrinking market meant that the large scale models were no longer viable and so did not reappear. Instead, a standard 4-4-0 was designed and tooled up.

In 1954 LMC became Ellemsee Accessories supplying a wide range of parts for 0 gauge scratch builders. Stedman himself had returned to modelling after the war forming a new company in 1949 called S&B Productions ('S' stood for Stedman) who are particularly remembered for their signal parts for the 00 market.

Despite an initial post-war rallying of demand for 0 gauge railways, the 1950s saw the popularity of the newer 00 gauge explode into a major industry. Against this competition, those companies who were totally committed to the 0 gauge market stood little chance of success. While the Company survived until 1966 before being wound up, the product range was shrinking from the mid '50s so that there was not much left at the end.

Buyers Beware! - Sadly the description of a model for sale today as 'possibly Leeds' is often a misnomer and should be described as 'origin unknown'! Beware! LMC models are very well constructed from tinplate and the chief fault is flaking paint due to poor cleaning and priming before they were painted. In consequence of this, professional repaints are relatively common and do not greatly affect the value of Leeds locomotives. However, original paint work can be stabilised by a carefully applied light spray of matt or satin finish varnish.

The electric mechanisms of the earlier models had brass side frames but in the 1930s these were replaced by diecast parts some of which, over the years, have suffered from swelling and cracking due to impurities in the alloy. This is sometimes difficult to see, however, so do look carefully for distortion and cracks and ask, when buying, if the locomotive is in good working order.

Further Reading

We are unaware of a book on the Leeds Model Company but there have been several articles written about it. Two articles appeared in Model Railway Constructor, one in the August 1981 issue and the other in May 1984. The first was by David Peacock of the Leeds Stedman Trust and the second by David Peacock and Adrian Stedman - Rex Stedman's son. David Peacock, to whom we are indebted for much of the information provided here, has also written a series of articles called 'Leeds Lines' for the *Gauge O Guild Gazette* - the magazine of the Gauge O Guild.

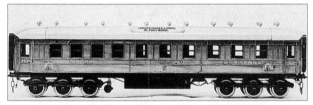

Hand built ECJS sleeping carriage C1920 (Leeds Steadman Trust)

Collecting Organisation

The Leeds Stedman Trust is an organisation run by David Peacock to look after the Stedman archives and to help collectors and operators of LMC models to keep them running by supplying spare parts. It is not a club but you can be placed on a mailing list for the annual price list of parts. The E-mail address for the Leeds Stedman Trust is dpeacock@btconnect.com

Prices - The prices quoted show the range that examples in good condition usually sell within.

Dates - It is difficult to be accurate with these as catalogues provide only a rough guide to what was available each year and a catalogue for each year is not available. Dates quoted should therefore be taken only as a guide.

Rolling Stock Bogies - Most early coaches had a fitted plywood bearing pad between the bogie and the floor of the coach but these were missing on later ones. There were at least three different types of bogies used:

1. Full white metal castings (1919-1922/3) which were fitted to hand-built stock and possibly retrofitted by owners to some early litho stock.

2. White metal dummy axleboxes and springs and a tinplate carrier (1922-35). During this long period of production tools became worn or were replaced and this shows in the castings. The tinplate carrier also varied in height. These were fitted to all litho coaching and bogie wagon stock, except the GWR Siphon G and Monster bogie vans which had American style bogies made by replacing the usual axle boxes by an integral white metal equalising bar and square axle boxes.

3. Fully diecast zinc units for bakelite coaches and LMS and GWR litho stock (from 1936/7).

LMC also made both tinplate (CO18) and diecast (CO14) 6-wheel bogies and, while these were available to scratch builders, in the factory they were fitted only to special coaches made to order. Similarly, diamond bogie frames (WO/20 and WO/22 - equalised) were also available for scratch builders and were fitted to the top of the range bolster and high capacity bogie vans.

Cast iron wheels were available for all the bogies at an extra cost.

Rolling Stock Wheels - Dissatisfied with the coarse standards of the day, Rex Stedman launched his own range of white metal wheels in 1915. These were closer to scale and had finer flanges than either Hornby or Bassett-Lowke products. However, white metal was not a particularly suitable material and soon Stedman was experimenting with zinc alloys. This lead to redesigning both coach and wagon wheels for the litho stock of the late '20s.

Wheels on wagons dating from 1928 which carry the word 'Remod' on them, and have a tyre width of 5.5 mm, were from a batch of zinc alloy wheels bought from Bing to tide the company over until their own casting plant was operational. This was working in 1929 and the rolling stock wheels being turned out had a tyre width of 5 mm. The zinc alloy wheels had finer spokes and a bronze look about them and were nearly as good as the optional cast iron wheels used on locomotive models.

In 1930, Stedman introduced a new range of locomotive zinc alloy wheels which he called 'Newalloy' and it is thought that, by 1935, LMC were using this material for a finer scale range of coach and wagon wheels with a tyre width of just 4 mm. There were three types of rolling stock wheels available: both spoked and disc wagon wheels and Maunsell coach disc wheels.

As far as we know, all standard rolling stock made in the factory was fitted with non-insulated wheels (i.e. for 3-rail operation).

Metal Fatigue - LMC wheels frequently suffered from a process popularly called 'metal fatigue' caused by impurities in the alloy mix. Some 80% of wheels (even higher immediately after the last war) show signs of disintegration or loosening on the axle. As a result, many coaches and wagons around today have been re-wheeled.

Woodworm - Later LMC vehicles were made of plywood bought from Finland. It has been prone to woodworm infestation and this should be born in mind when buying these later models. For some strange reason, reported examples have often been LNER subjects but, in fact, the problem occurs on any of the plywood bodies.

Litho Sheets - Original LMC/Steadman litho coach and wagon papers are still relatively inexpensive and an interesting line to collect. These sheets have a unique patina, which is very difficult to colour photocopy, and have self-sticky backs.

Repairs and Restoration - Repairs to wooden rolling stock can be easily and sympathetically achieved. Principle problems are fatigue of the glue, warping, detached bogies, fatigued buffers and wheels and broken couplings and buffer beams. All can be rectified: re-gluing as necessary, introducing pine strips internally along the corner edges and fixing them with PVA glue and by replacing missing and broken parts. The latter may be available from the Leeds Stedman Trust (see above) or by salvaging them from scrap vehicles. Warping is difficult to rectify but not impossible. On coaches and vans it can be achieved by gluing a horizontal wooden tie-plate internally, just below the roof line, remembering to leave spaces at either end of the vehicle to give access to the inside.

LOCOMOTIVES

Locomotives were built in heavy gauge soldered tinplate and all were fitted only with Stedman's own design of clockwork motor until 1925 when a 6-8V DC mechanism was available as an alternative. This had a laminated 3-pole motor and a permanent magnet field which was self reversing. They had an adjustable double centre rail pickup suitable for raised or level centre rails. 20V AC mechanisms, with a hand reverse switch, were supplied between 1934 and 1939. When Stedman bought back his company in 1929, he set about modernising the range and one of his decisions was to drop the clockwork mechanism. Wheels were cast iron until 1929/30 and then cast alloy ones, called Newalloy, were fitted. They were insulated from 1959 and smoke units were fitted to some locomotives from late 1949.

Catalogue Numbering - The 'LO' prefix was used up until 1937/8 after which 'LA' or 'LD' prefixes were used according to whether an AC or DC mechanism was fitted.

Freelance or 'Standard' Models

As we have seen, LMC produced a series of cost saving tank locomotives which were basically freelance in design and available in a variety of liveries. The character of individual railway companies was established by the changing of chimneys, domes and other detail fittings.

Cat.No.	Number, Company, Colour, Dates	£	£

L1. Standard Saddle Tank 0-4-0ST (Freelance)

One of the most distinctive of the freelance models was the 0-4-0 tank which is easy to recognise because of its very square appearance although it was one of the models copied by Stromlite. This was the very basic 'starter' locomotive in the range and its unusual shape was almost certainly chosen to give plenty of room for the clockwork motor. There was a choice of a clockwork or (from 1925) DC electric mechanism. Between 1934 and 1939 an AC mechanism was also available. In addition to the liveries listed below, freelance liveries were also supplied to customer's requirements.

LO/150	NER green? - *22-24*	180	230

Cat.No.	Number, Company, Colour, Dates	£	£
LO/151	L&NWR black - *22-24*	180	230
LO/152	MR black - *22-24*	180	230
LO/153	5 GCR green? - *22-24*	180	230
LO/154	GNR green? - *22-24*	180	230
LO/155	GER blue? - *22-24*	180	230
LO/156	No3 CR blue - *22-24*	120	170
LO/157	6 LB&SCR brown? - *22-24*	180	230
LO/158	60 SE&CR green? - *22-24*	180	230
LO/159	4 GWR green? - *22-24*	120	170
LO/160	78, 73 LNER green - *25-40?*	120	170
LO/160	78, 73 LNER black - *25-40?*	120	170
LO/161	93 LMS black - *25-40?*	120	170
LO/162	701 GWR green - *25-40?*	180	230
LO/163	75 Southern green - *25-40?*	180	230
LO/163	31117 Southern black - *25-40?*	180	230
LD/10	68116 BR ex train sets - *c50-66*	180	230
LD/10	68116 BR ex sets, smoke - *c50-66*	180	230
LD/10	68113 BR ex sets shorter, outside cylinders smoke - *c50-66*	180	230
L/10	loco kit - ?	180	230
-	**'Leeds Model Company'** green - *c50-66*	NPG	NPG

Standard tank [L1]

The freelance, or 'Standard' range, included several wheel combinations, the largest being 4-6-0. There were two distinct series of these. The first, starting in 1920, had high mounted boilers (to take a tall and powerful clockwork mechanism), high side tanks and squat cabs with ribbed roofs. Another feature of this series is the clearly displayed 'LMC' trade mark which was less obvious on the second series. The original plan was to top wind these locos through the cab roof (the very earliest 4-4-0Ts have a key hole covered with a ventilator plate) but the idea was dropped. Electric drive was available from 1925 and all models had standard 1½" driving wheels. It is possible that some of the pre-grouping liveries listed in the catalogue, and therefore included in our tables, were never made unless hand painted. Archive material includes NE, LNWR and GCR examples.

L2. Standard Tank 4-4-0T (Freelance)

This was Stedman's first locomotive which he started in 1919. It had clockwork or (from 1925) 6-8v electric mechanisms available. Enamelled finish.

LO/100	723 North () Eastern green - *20-23?*	230	250
LO/101	3267, 3268 L&NWR black - *20-23?*	280	300
LO/102	2908 MR red - *20-23?*	360	380
LO/103	276 GCR green - *20-23?*	360	440
LO/103	GNR green? - *20-23?*	360	380
LO/105	52 GER blue? - *20-23?*	360	380
LO/106	CR blue - *20-23?*	360	380
LO/107	910 LB&SCR brown - *20-23?*	360	380
LO/108	695 SE&CR green? - *20-23?*	360	380
LO/109	6412 LNER lined green - *25-32*	220	250
LO/109	2686 LNER green - *25-32*	280	370
LO/109	78, 6412 LNER black - *25-32*	160	250
LO/110	3754 LMS red - *25-32*	300	330
LO/110	LMS black - *25-32*	300	330

LO/111	GWR green - *25-32*	350	380
LO/112	**2664** Southern green? - *25-32*	280	250
?	**2686** green - *25-32*	300	370

L3.   Standard Tank 4-4-2T (Freelance)

This was said to look like an L&NWR Precurser tank or one of the LB&SCR tanks used on express duties. Clockwork or (from 1925) 6-8v electric mechanisms available. Enamelled finish.

LO/120	**3495** L&NWR black c/w - *20-23?*	330	360
LO/121	LB&SCR brown c/w - *20-23?*	360	380
LO/122	**276** Great()Central green c/w - *20-30?*	190	380
LO/123	**3754** LMS lined red - *25-32*	360	380
LO/124	Southern green - *25-32*	360	380
LO/125	**6412** LNER green - *25-32*	360	380
LO/125	**9064** LNER black - *25-32*	360	380
LO/126	GWR green - *25-32*	360	380

L4.   Standard Tank 4-6-0T (Freelance)

Clockwork or (from 1925) 6-8v electric mechanisms available.

LO/130	**690** North () Eastern green - *20-23?*	330	360
LO/131	**2673** L&NWR black - *20-23?*	360	380
LO/132	**271** GCR green - *20-23?*	360	380
LO/133	**386, 396** LNER lined green - *25-32*	330	360
LO/134	LMS red - *25-32*	330	360
LO/134	LMS black - *25-32*	330	360

Standard 4-6-0 tank [L4] (Leeds Steadman Trust)

L5.   Standard Tank 0-4-4T (Freelance)

Clockwork or (from 1925) 6-8v electric mechanisms available.

LO/170	**314** L&SWR green? - *20-23?*	360	380
LO/171	MR red - *20-23?*	360	380
LO/172	SE&CR green? - *20-23?*	360	380
LO/173	**23, 185, E453, E508** SR lined green - *25-32*	360	380
LO/173	**E508** Southern black - *25-32*	360	380
LO/174	LMS red - *25-32*	360	380

L6.   Standard Tank 0-6-2T (Freelance)

Clockwork or (from 1925) 6-8v electric mechanisms available.

LO/180	**510** LB&SCR brown - *20-23?*	360	380
LO/181	GNR green? - *20-23?*	360	380
LO/182	GER blue? - *20-23?*	360	380
LO/183	**E148** Southern green - *25-32*	360	380
LO/184	**5769, 9354, 9356** LNER green - *25-32*	360	380

Production of the first series standard tanks ended in 1932 and the second series was delayed until 1935 because of a disastrous factory fire at the Jack Lane Works on 29th June 1932. This second range, in tables 7-12 below, was nearer to scale in appearance and the wheel arrangements and locomotive numbering related to prototype examples. Company character, however, was still achieved by the changing detail of fittings but a particular characteristic of this series that separates it from the last is the tall dome fitted to each model. They are the product by which LMC is best remembered but, ironically, although designed by Stedman, they were not produced until after he had left the Company. A reduced selection of these tank engines was

continued in the late 1940s until the closure of LMC although towards the end only kits were available.

After 1949 it is likely that the interchangability of parts increased as castings became used up. In later years lining was simplified or left off altogether. AC and DC versions available. Bodies only were also available.

L7.   Ex-GCR Class G5 0-4-4T

LD/10	**8120** LNER black, red lining - *35-39*	230	280

Other numbers were applied.

L8.   Ex- LSWR Adams Class T1 0-4-4T

LD/22	**126** SR black, yellow lining - *35-39*	280	620
LD/22	**126** SR green, yellow lining - *50-60*	280	620

Other numbers were applied.

L9.   Ex-GER Class F4 2-4-2T

LD/11	**7102** LNER black, red lining - *35-39*	230	280

Other numbers were applied.

L10.   Ex-L&YR 2-4-2T

LD/21	**6720, 6723, 10763** LMS black, red lining - *35-60*	160	280
LD/21/S	**6720, 6723, 10763** LMS black + smoke - *52-?*	160	280
L/21	kit - *35-60?*	NPG	NPG

Other numbers were applied.

Ex-L&YR 2-4-2T [L10] (Wallis & Wallis)

L11.   Ex-GCR Class N5 0-6-2T

-	**524** GCR black, red lining - *?*	300	330
LD/12	**5773** LNER black, red lining - *35-60*	300	330
LD/12	**5773** LNER green, black and white lining - *52-54?*	300	330
L/12	kit - *50-?*	NPG	NPG

Other numbers were applied.

L12.   Ex-L&YR 0-6-2T

LD/20	**6530** LMS red, black lining - *?*	280	330
LD/20	**6550** LMS red, yellow lining - *?*	280	330
LD/20	**6530** LMS black, red lining - *35-60*	170	330
LD/20/S	**6530** LMS black + smoke - *52-?*	170	330
LD/20	BRb black, red lining - *52-?*	170	330

Other numbers were applied.

Ex-L&YR 0-2-2T [L12]

L13. Standard Tank 0-6-0T (Freelance)

This model was close to a Jinty in appearance. It could be bought with or without a smoke unit. Those with, had an 'S' suffix to the catalogue number. The model had a 12V DC mechanism and bodies only were also available

LD/15	**8410, 8415, 8418** LMS black, posing as a Jinty - *48-60*	120	170
LD/16	**8305, 8302** LNER green, posing as a J72, black and white lining - *48-60*	120	170
LD/17	**126, 259, 269, 75** SR green, lining - *48-60*	180	230
LD/17	**216** SR black, yellow lining - *?*	180	230
LD/18	BRb black - *c50-60*	120	170
L/15	LMS black kit - *c50-60*	NPG	NPG

Other numbers were applied. A GWR version is known to exist but this was not catalogued.

After the Second World War, the Leeds Model Company introduced a basic inside cylinder 4-4-0 tender locomotive with an affinity to their pre-war Director Class model, however, there was no provision for GWR fans! In fact, the 1948 catalogue carried an apology to these people and a promise to provide some GWR locomotives as well as describing present productions as a 'stop gap' measure. The shape of the model was obviously wrong for the GWR. Within a short time the model was being offered with outside cylinders as an alternative and the model was also available in BR livery. Other names and numbers were available on these late products.

L14. 4-4-0 Tender Loco (Freelance)

This post-war standard locomotive model was based roughly on the pre-war Director Class but was also thought to have a close resemblance to an LMS 2P and a Southern L1. From late 1949 the model was offered with a smoke unit fitted although the 1952 catalogue shows that only the models with outside cylinders were so fitted. The LMS, LNER, SR and tender bodies were also available on their own. The model had a 12V DC mechanism. oc = outside cylinders.

LD/50	**570, 621** LMS lined black - *47-54*	120	170
?	**564** LMS black 12vDC - *?*	250	NPG
LD/50/S	**570** LMS lined black, oc + smoke - *52-54?*	120	170
-	**570** LMS red - *50-60*	120	170
LD/51	**2683, 2685** LNER green, lined black+ white - *47-60*	120	170
LD/51/S	**2683, 2685, 2686, 2608** LNER green, lined black+white, oc + smoke - *52-54?*	120	170
LD/52	**1756** SR green, lined yellow + black - *47-60*	170	220
LD/52/S	**1756, 1783, 1754** Southern green, lined yellow, oc + smoke - *52-54?*	170	220
LD/53	GWR green - *52-54?*	170	220
LD/53/S	GWR green, oc + smoke - *53-54?*	170	220
LD/53	**30875, 60734** BRb black - *52-54?*	120	170
LD/53/S	**60734** BR black, oc + smoke - *52-54?*	120	170
L/50	LMS loco kit - *52-54?*	NPG	NPG
L/51	LNER loco kit - *52-54?*	NPG	NPG
L/52	SR loco kit - *52-54?*	NPG	NPG
L/49	tender kit - *52-54?*	NPG	NPG

Freelance 4-4-0 in SR livery [L14]

Scale Models

The development of the Director and Sir Sam Fay classes has already been described above, and these were certainly the mainstay of the Scale range, but several other scale model locomotives were made by the Leeds Model Company during the years from 1920 to 1939. Some of them were generally available while others were only made to order.

After the war only few prototypical locomotives were introduced. Most examples were reasonably detailed and could be further enhanced if required. Special models were manufactured to order and you got what you paid for. These included, in 1952, a nice 4-6-0 County Class and enthusiasts of the LMS were also tempted by the introduction of a 'special order' 4-6-0 Jubilee Class.

L15. Classes D10 (Director) and D11 (Improved Director) 4-4-0

The D11 cab versions (with 2 windows each side) had Ross pop safety valves replacing the larger GCR twin lever units. From 1930 alloy wheels were fitted and from 1935, diecast frames replaced brass ones. While mass production of the model ceased in 1939, it was available by a special order from the mid 1950s. Choice of clockwork or electric mechanism. One was specially named 1925 'John Arnott' and presented to the Lord Mayor of Leeds on 28 November 1925.

	Great () Central green D10		
LO/200	**429 'Sir Douglas Haig'** - *22-24*	500	600
LO/200	**436 'Sir Berkeley Sheffield'** - *22-29*	500	600
LO/200	**437 'Charles Stuart Wortley'** - *22-26*	500	600
	LNER green D10		
LO/201	**5437 'Sir Berkeley Sheffield'** - *25-29*	500	600
LO/201	**5437 'Charles Stuart Wortley'** - *25-37*	500	600
LO/201	**5437** on cab **'Prince George'** - *28-31*	500	600
LO/201	as above but no. on tender - *31-39*	500	600
	LNER green D11		
LO/202	**5501 'Mons'** - *29-39-?*	550	750
LO/202	**5503 'Somme'** - *29-39-?*	550	750
LO/202	**5504 'Jutland'** - *29-39-?*	550	750
LO/202	**5505 'Ypres'** - *29-39-?*	550	750
LO/202	**5506 'Butler Henderson'** - *29-39-?*	450	550

Other names and numbers could be had at an extra cost of 1/6.

Class D11 'Butler Henderson' [L15]

L16. Robinson Class B2 (B19) 4-6-0

Clockwork or 6-8v electric mechanisms available.

	Great () Central green + maroon		
LO/352	**423 'Sir Sam Fay'** - *?*	NPG	NPG
LO/352	**427 'City of London'** - *?*	NPG	NPG
	LNER green		
LO/352	**5423 'Sir Sam Fay'** - *29-39, c54-60*	450	550
LO/352	**5427 'City of London'** - *29-39*	550	750
LO/352	**5423 'City of Lincoln'** * - *29-39*	550	750
LO/352	**5426 'City of Chester'** * - *29-39*	550	750
LO/352	**5425 'City of Manchester'** * - *29-39*	550	750
LO/352	**5428 'City of Liverpool'** * - *29-39*	550	750

* Initially these were an optional extra for which there was a charge of 1/6.

L17. Robinson Class B3 4-6-0

Standard Leeds 8-pole 8V motor and engraved brass nameplates.

	LNER green		
LO/356	**6169 'Lord Faringdon'** - *26-35?*	550	750
LO/356	**6164 'Earl Beatty'** - *26-35?*	550	750
LO/356	**6166 'Earl Haig'** - *26-35?*	550	750
LO/356	**6168 'Lord Stuart of Wortley'** - *26-35?*	550	750
LO/357	**6165 'Valour'** * - *26-35?*	550	750

* Nameplates engraved 'In memory of G.C.R. employees, 1914-1918'.

L18. GWR Class 43XX Mogul 2-6-0

Clockwork or 6-8v electric mechanisms available.

LO/348	**4362, 6362, 4371** * Great Western green - *26-39?, c54-60*	380	440

Customers were offered any number between 6362 and 6369 but those shown are ones seen.

GWR Class 43xx Mogul [L18]

L19. CR Pickersgill Goods 0-6-0

Based on a Caledonian Railway goods locomotive. Choice of clockwork or electric mechanism.

LO/358	**17602, 17604, 17608** * LMS black - 27-39, c54-60	380	440

*Customers were offered any number between 17560 and 17660 but those indicated above are ones seen.

L20. GWR Hawksworth County Class 4-6-0

Fitted with smoke apparatus.

LD/54	**1024 'County of Pembroke'** * Great Western green - 52-60	550	750
LD/54	**1010 'County of Caenarvon'** * GWR green - 52-60	550	750

*Customers were offered any name. In GWR livery 'Caenarvon' should have been spelt 'Carnarvon' as the spelling was not changed to the former until November 1951.

Super Detailed Models

These were models constructed by a special department at the works and handled individually. They were made to order only and each was built to its own specification. There was usually an option to have further detail added at extra cost.

L21. GNR/LNER A1 4-6-2

High quality enamel finish, lined by hand. Made to special order only. Customers were offered any name/number and those given here are known to exist.

LO/300	**1470 'Great Northern'** GNR green - 22-28	650	950
LO/300	**4472 'Flying Scotsman'** LNER green - 29-39	650	850

L22. Claughton Class 4-6-0

Made to special order only.

LO/351	**2222 'Sir Gilbert Claughton'** L&NWR black c/w or electric - 22-32	550	850
	LMS maroon		
LO/351	**5900 'Sir Gilbert Claughton'** - 25-35	500	650
LO/351	**5931 'Captain Fryatt'** - 25-35	550	750
LO/351	**5919 'Lord Kitchener'** - 25-35	550	750
LO/351	**un-named** - 25-35	550	750

L23. Raven A2 Pacific 4-6-2

Made to special order only.

	LNER green		
LO/?	**2402 'City of York'** - 24-27	850	1300
LO/?	**1471 'Sir Fredrick Banbury'** - 24-27	850	1300

Customers were offered any number.

Raven Class A2 'City of York' [L23]

L24. GNR Atlantic 4-4-2

Made to special order only.

LO/353	**1443** * L&NER green - 25-35?	500	600
LO/?	**'St Cuthman'** LNER green c/w - c33	550	750
LO/?	**1471 'Sir Fredrick Banbury'** GNR green elec - 25-?	550	750
LO/?	**1421** GNR green electric - 25-?	550	750

Customers were offered any number.

L25. Star or Abbey Class 4-6-0

Made to special order only. The customer chose the name.

LO/354	**Great ()** Western green - 25-35?	550	750

L26. Castle Class 4-6-0

Made to special order only.

LO/355	**4078 'Pembroke Castle'** * Great () Western green - 25-35?	550	750

*customer's choice

L27. Urie 4-6-2T

Made to special order only.

-	**516** LSWR green - c29	NPG	NPG
-	**E516** Southern green - c29	NPG	NPG

L28. Jubilee Class 4-6-0

Made to special order only.

	LMS maroon		
-	**5553 'Canada'** - 52-60	550	750
-	**5581 'Biha and Orissa'** - 52-60	550	750

Customers were offered other names.

L29. Sentinel-Cammell Rail Car

Wooden body covered with lithographed paper providing detail. Black roof.

SC/1	**233 'Nettle'** LNER green+cream - 35-60	120	170

Sentinel-Cammel railcar 'Nettle' [L29] (LMC)

L30. Pullman Brighton Belle EMU

Wooden body covered with lithographed paper providing detail.

	Pullman brown & cream		
CD/154	**Car No.89** drive car - 35-50	90	130
CD/155	**Car No.88** drive car - 35-50	90	130
CD/156	**'Hazel'** 1st class car - 35-50	50	70
CD/157	**'Doris'** 1st class car - 35-50	50	70
CD/158	**Car No.86** 3rd class - 35-50	50	70
CD/159	Above 5-car train - 35-50	400	550
CD/153	**Cars Nos. 88 + 89** 2 - 35-50	170	260

L31. Class 3150 Prairie Tank 2-6-2T

-	**3169** GWR (button) green - 53-60	280	400

L32. Class 57XX Pannier Tank 0-6-0PT

-	GWR green - 59-60	140	200

L33. Class 51XX Prairie Tank 2-6-2T

-	GWR green - 59-60	140	200

L34. Princess Royal Class 4-6-2

-	**'The Princess Royal'** - 59-60	NPG	NPG

L35. McIntosh Class 140 Dunalastair IV 4-4-0

-	**140** CR blue - ?	650	800

COACHES

The very first Leeds coaches were made of painted wood but these were eclipsed by the new range made with lithograph paper prints pasted onto boxwood sides and, later, a thinner plywood. Initially MR, NER and LNWR coaches were produced but later those of the Big Four took precedence. A set of Pullman cars based on the Brighton Belle were introduced in 1935.

From 1929, both suburban and corridor coaches were made and LNER lithographed articulated sets were introduced in 1925. Other articulated coach sets were made by cutting and splicing the lithos of full length coaches.

In the late 1930s, as we have seen, Leeds scored another first by using bakelite instead of wood for their coaches.

Roof Ventilators - Two types were used: torpedo and shell. Up until 1928, all coaches either had torpedo vents or none at all. From 1928, all GWR coaches had shell vents and these were fitted to LMS bakelite coaches when they were introduced. Full brakes had 8 ventilators and pre-grouping coaches had 12. They were arranged down the centre line on LMS open stock and offset on GWR, SR and LNER coaches with side corridors. Over the years roofs have become turned round and swapped over and care should be taken to ensure that you have the right roof for the coach.

Buffers - The 1st series standard coaches (table C1 below) had pre-grouping thin buffers which, when bought separately had the catalogue number CO/10. Those in tables 2, 3 and 4 had non-locking buffers which had the catalogue number WO/11.

Trusses - The under-floor trusses on the 1st Series Standard coaches, whether solebar type or individual, had facsimiles of the tension bar boss protruding downwards. All later trusses, with the exception of those for True-Scale coaches did not have these protrusions.

Corridor Connections - These, introduced in 1930, were standard only on bakelite coaches. They were not as good as others on the market and comprised steel end plates joined by a single cloth bellows, with No.4 screw holes in the plate which adjoined the coach end door and ¼" diameter clearance holes in the other end for screwdriver access. Their part number was CO/30. Over the years those of other makes, including the better looking Exley type, have been used and so it is worth checking whether yours are genuine LMC.

Cat.No.	Company, Number, Colour, Dates	£	£

Original 1921 North Eastern Railway coach [C1]
(Leeds Steadman Trust)

C1. 1st Series Standard Coaches

These were 1' long bogie non-corridor coaches made of wood with litho printed paper pasted on to provide the colour and detail. The first series coaches were characterised by having their ends turned under. Early models had tinplate solebar, integral with the truss and solebar detail provided by a litho paper. Later models had wooden solebars painted black.

CO/106	**NER** 840 red composite - *21-28*	60	70
CO/107	**NER** 106 red full brake - *21-28*	70	80
CO/120	**LNWR** 2307 cream+brown comp - *21-28*	70	80
CO/121	**LNWR** 5410 cream+brown full brake - *21-28*	80	90
CO/137	**MR** 159 maroon full brake - *21-28*	70	80
CO/137	as above overprinted '**LMS**' 159 maroon - *25-28*	80	90
CO/136	**MR** 578 maroon composite - *21-28*	70	80
CO/136	as above overprinted '**LMS**' 578 maroon - *25-27*	80	80
CO/135	**LMS** 358 maroon brake 3rd - *28-30*	60	70

C2. Twin & Triple Sets

The individual coaches were 9¾" long and had short under-floor trusses as a result. They were made up into two or three coach articulated sets. A selling point at the time was that they took up less room on the track. The LMS and GWR versions were made from cutting and splicing the standard coach lithos while those for the LNER sets were specially printed lithos and they had white tinplate roofs. The catalogue numbers changed over the years and those shown are for 1937. The intermediate bogies were the same as the standard tinplate bogies but with the usual central 'top hat' bolster turned through 90° and soldered to each end of the bogie.

CO/150	**LNER** 6021N+6022N teak twin articulated set (brake+comp) - *25-39*	100	140
CO/152	**LNER** 6021N+6022N+6023N teak triple articulated set (brake+comp+comp) - *25-39*	120	170
CO/151	**GWR** (button) 6927+3275 brown+cream twin articulated set (brake+comp) - *31-39*	140	170
CO/153	**GWR** (button) 6927+3275+3275 brown+cream triple articulated set (brake+comp+comp) - *31-39*	170	200
CO/148	**LMS** 15478+3395 maroon twin articulated set (brake+comp) - *34-39*	140	170
CO/149	**LMS** 15478+3395+3395 maroon triple articulated set (brake+comp+comp) - *34-39*	170	200

C3. 2nd Series Standard Coaches

This was the new series of coaches released in 1929. They were the same length as the first series but had straight ends and no litho papers on the solebars. Initially they had tinplate bogies but from 1938, diecast bogies were used. To economise, corridor coaches used the suburban stock litho on the compartment side and so it was necessary for the corridor and suburban coaches to have the same number.

C3a. GWR Panelled Coaches

These had a panelled effect and the GWR coat of arms. They were replaced by standard coaches with the button logo in 1934.

CO/138	**GWR** 3275 brown+cream corridor coach - *27-33*	70	80
CO/139	**GWR** 6927 brown+cream corridor brake - *27-33*	70	80
CO/140	**GWR** 3275 brown+cream suburban coach - *27-33*	70	80
CO/141	**GWR** 6927 brown+cream suburban brake - *27-33*	70	80

C3b. Standard Coaches

These were made of wood with litho printed paper stuck to the sides and a tinplate roof.

CO/142	**SR** 4526 green corridor coach - *27-35*	60	70
CO/143	**SR** 2127 green corridor brake - *27-35*	60	70
CO/144	**SR** 4526 green suburban coach - *27-35*	60	70
CO/145	**SR** 2127 green suburban brake - *27-35*	60	70
CO/106	**LNER** 2253 teak corridor coach - *31-39*	35	45
CO/107	**LNER** 3627 teak corridor brake - *31-39*	35	45
CO/108	**LNER** 38295 teak suburban coach - *31-39*	25	35
CO/109	**LNER** 38364 teak suburban brake - *31-39*	25	35
CO/134	**LMS** 18572 maroon*corridor coach - *31-39*	35	45
CO/135	**LMS** 18503 maroon*corridor brake - *31-39*	35	45
CO/136	**LMS** 3395 maroon*suburban coach - *31-39*	35	45
CO/137	**LMS** 15478 maroon*suburban brake - *31-39*	35	45
CO/138	**GWR** (button) 3275 brown+cream corridor coach - *34-39*	35	45
CO/139	**GWR** (button) 6927 brown+cream corridor brake - *34-39*	35	45
CO/140	**GWR** (button) 3275 brown+cream suburban coach - *34-39*	35	45
CO/141	**GWR** (button) 6927 brown+cream suburban brake - *34-39*	35	45

* often faded or discoloured to brown with age.

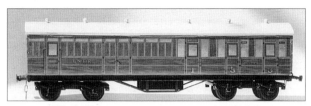

Standard LNER suburban brake [C3b]

C4. Pullman Cars

These were 14" long and among the most detailed and attractive models in the LMC range. The five listed below make up the Brighton Belle set. Litho papers, besides being available separately for these five, were also sold without names or numbers for those who wanted to choose their own.

CD/154	**Pullman** 89 brown+cream driver** - *35-39*	90	140
CD/155	**Pullman** 88 brown+cream driver** - *35-39*	90	140
CO/156	**Pullman** 'Hazel' brown+cream 1st - *35-39*	45	70
CO/157	**Pullman** 'Doris' brown+cream 1st - *35-39*	45	70
CO/158	**Pullman** 86 brown+cream 3rd - *35-39*	45	70

** these are also featured as a pair in Part 1 of the catalogue under the catalogue number CD/153 while the complete five car train was catalogued as CD/159.

C5. True Scale Coaches

These had moulded bakelite bodies and glazed windows. They were under scale length and examples may be found that have been lengthened by cutting a section out of another coach and adding it in. These were initially available between 1937 and 1940. They were self coloured bakelite and the black parts (or cream also in the case of GWR) were over-painted as appropriate. After the war all coach bodies were made black and the livery colour(s) painted on, so the LNER was dropped. BR (blood and custard) was introduced after 1949 or so. SR coaches never had window frets, all the others did, but some later GWR sets had the frets painted on the window glass. Lining, numbers, company insignia were all hand applied transfers. In the case of numbers, a large range was available as transfers. scp = self coloured bakelite for coach sides, other colours painted on. bp = black bakelite, liveries painted on.

CM/50	**LMS** maroon vestibule 3rd, scp - *37-40*	45	60
CM/50	**LMS** maroon vestibule 3rd, bp - *46-66*	45	60
CM/51	**LMS** maroon vestibule 3rd brake, scp - *37-40*	45	60
CM/51	**LMS** maroon vestibule 3rd brake, bp - *46-66*	45	60
CM/52	**LNER** teak saloon, scp - *39-40*	90	120
CM/53	**LNER** teak saloon brake, scp - *39-40*	90	120
CM/54	**GWR** brown+cream saloon, scp - *37-40*	45	60
CM/54	**GWR** brown+cream saloon, bp - *46-66*	45	60
CM/55	**GWR** brown+cream saloon brk, scp - *37-40*	45	60
CM/55	**GWR** 5065? brown+cream saloon brake, bp - *46-66*	45	60
CM/56	**SR** green 3rd saloon, scp - *37-40*	60	80
CM/56	**SR** green 3rd saloon, bp - *46-66*	60	80
CM/57	**SR** green 3rd brake, scp - *37-40*	60	80
CM/57	**SR** green 3rd brake, bp - *46-66*	60	80
CM/52	**BR** red+cream saloon, bp - *50-66*	45	70
CM/53	**BR** red+cream saloon brake, bp - *50-66*	45	70

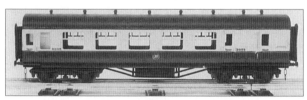

True Scale Bakelite coach [C5]

C6. Rigid Litho Coach

These were made up from a single litho printed card, folded to form the sides and roof, and held in place by diecast ends and a timber floor. The litho was to the existing 1931 design (see table C3 above). Window apertures were cut out and glazed and it had the 1935 bogies, non-locking buffers, roof vents and 3-link couplings. It was also available as a kit without bogies.

?	**LMS** 3395 maroon suburban - *48-50*	NPG	NPG

WAGONS

The methods of manufacture of wagons were the same as those used for coaches.

Buffers - All wagons had non-locking buffers.

Handmade Wagons

For those who wanted top quality models LMC made them by hand, initially entirely of wood, but later using as near as possible the materials used for the real wagon - or so they claimed. The following is a list of handmade wagons, made between 1922 and 1927, that appeared in the LMC catalogues. Most of them were also available in gauge 1 until 1928 and these would have 'W1' prefixes to their catalogue numbers.

Cat.No.	Company, Number, Colour, Dates	£	£

W1. Handmade Wagons

Some of these wagons date from 1918 and possibly some from as early as 1912 but records of production in the early days of the company are unavailable and so we have been conservative with the dates quoted. The lengths quoted below are taken over the buffers.
TCS = to customers specification

WO/500	standard open wagon, all companies or TCS 5½" - *22-28*	25	30
WO/510	10T box van, all companies or TCS 5½" - *22-28*	25	30
WO/520	**GNR** 10T 4-wheel brake van 5½" - *22-28*	30	35
WO/520	**NER** 10T 4-wheel brake van 5½" - *22-28*	30	35
WO/520	**LNWR** 10T 4-wheel brake van 5½" - *22-28*	30	35
WO/520	**MR** 10T 4-wheel brake van 5½" - *22-28*	30	35
WO/521	**LNWR** 20T 6-wheel brake van 6¼" - *22-28*	30	35
WO/521	**MR** 20T 6-wheel brake van 6¼" - *22-28*	30	35
WO/521	**GNR** 20T 6-wheel brake van 6¼" - *22-28*	30	35
WO/540	**NER** high cap bogie wagon 11" - *22-28*	35	40
WO/540	**MR** high cap bogie wagon 11" - *22-28*	35	40
WO/540	**GNR** high cap bogie wagon 11" - *22-28*	35	40
WO/545	pair of single bolster timber wagon, all companies 10" - *22-28*	30	35
WO/550	stores department drop side wagon, all companies 10 ½" - *22-28*	25	30
WO/551	**LNER** tube wagon 6⅜" - *26-28*	30	35
WO/555	**MR** 30T bogie timber truck, diamond bogie frames 11" - *22-28*	40	45
WO/560	**NER** high capacity box wagon, diamond bogie frames 11" - *22-28*	45	50
WO/561	standard cattle wagon, all companies or TCS 5½" - *22-28*	30	35
WO/562	**GWR** Syphon G 14¾" - *26-28*	45	50
WO/563	**GWR** Syphon H 14¾" - *26-28*	45	50
WO/570	standard oil tanker **'Royal Daylight'** (hand painted) 6" - *22-28*	170	180
WO/570	standard oil tanker **'BP'** (transfers) 6" - *26-33*	170	180
WO/575	standard rectangular tar wagon 5" - *22-28*	40	45
WO/580	ballast wagon, all companies or TCS 6½" - *25-28*	30	35
WO/585	**LNER** horse box 6⅜" - *25-28*	40	45
WO/586	**GWR** horse box 6⅜" - *26-28*	40	45
WO/590	**GWR** shunter's truck 4⅝" - *25-28*	30	35

Early hand-built 4-plank wagon [W1]
(Leeds Stedman Trust)

By the 1930s, high quality wagons were still made to order but there was no list of types available in the catalogue. By now they were referred to as 'Super Detail' wagons and catalogues carried a photograph of a GWR drop-door 7-plank wagon numbered 63051 as an illustration of the quality that could be achieved in the 'Super Detail Goods Vehicle Department'. They offered to produce a wagon within two weeks of an order being placed.

Litho Wagons

Wagons made after the First World War were initially embossed paper on pine, but by 1923 wagons covered with litho printed paper, spayed with matt varnish, were produced and the variety of these grew over the years. The wooden wagon bodies had lock jointed corners and sides grooved to locate the floor. Non-lock buffers and three link couplings were fitted.

W2. Embossed Litho Open Wagon

-	**NE** M132 grey - *c20*	30	35

W3a. Litho Open Wagon - 1st Series

These had 4⅝" long bodies, a wheelbase of 2⅝" and the interiors were painted to match the colour of the litho paper. These pre-grouping wagons had the litho paper butting up to the corner. All were 5-plank wagons with standard buffers and single link couplings fitted.

WO/50	**NE** V363 light grey - *23-32*	20	25
WO/51	**LNWR** 8004 grey green - *23-32*	20	25
WO/52	**MR** 12709 light grey - *23-32*	20	25
WO/53	**GC** 8124 blue grey - *23-32*	25	28
WO/54	**GN** 33225 bauxite - *23-32*	20	25
WO/55	**GW** 12509 blue grey - *23-32*	25	28

W3b. Litho Open Wagon - 2nd Series

These had 4⅝" long bodies, a wheelbase of 2⅝" and the interior was painted black (except the LMS ones which were painted pale grey to match the litho paper. These post-grouping wagons had the paper wrapped round the corner to simulate a stanchion. With one exception, all were 5-plank wagons. Non-lock buffers and three link couplings fitted.

WO/56	**SR** 12340 brown 8-plank wagon - *28-35*	25	25
WO/57	**GW** 109458 dark brown - *28-66*	20	20
WO/58	**NE** 36503 black - *28-66*	15	20
WO/59	**LMS** 304719 grey - *28-66*	20	25

W4. Litho Bogie Open Wagon

WO/253	**LMS** 13768 light grey 30T steel high capacity wagon - *29-36*	45	60
WO/254	**NE** 51001 red oxide brick wagon - *29-36*	60	70

W5. Litho Private Owner Open Wagon

These were said to be to Railway Clearing House design.

WO/60	**R.F.Stedman & Co Ltd** 36 bright green - *29-36*	35	40
WO/61	**J.R.Wood & Co Ltd** 300 orange Stedman plates - *29-34*	30	35
WO/61	**J.R.Wood & Co Ltd** 300 orange LMC plates - *34-38*	30	35
WO/62	**Brentnall & Cleland** 684 black Stedman plates - *29-34*	30	35
WO/62	**Brentnall & Cleland** 684 black LMC plates - *34-66*	30	35
WO/63	**Warrens** 1603 brown - *34-39*	30	35
WO/64	**Coote & Warren** 2176 brown - *34-39*	30	35
WO/65	**Manchester Collieries** 12001 maroon - *35-58*	25	30
WO/66	**Cawoods** 1499 black - *36-66*	20	25
WO/67	**Michael Whitaker Ltd** 100 red - *36-66*	20	25
-	**Hargreaves Coal** 2340 black Sp Edn* - *27*	NPG	NPG

* Ordered specially by a Leeds based coal company associated with the Whiting family. It had Stedman plates, white lettering and planking lines and the end papers were identical to those of the 'Cawoods' wagon.

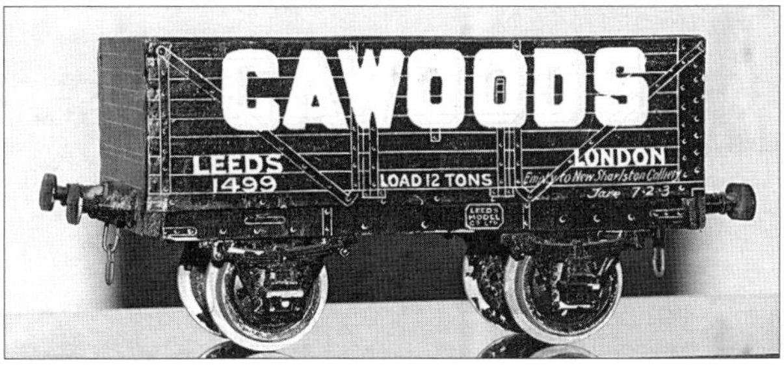

Litho private owner wagon Cawoods [W5]

W6. Litho Pre-Grouping GWR Box Van

The body of this van was 4⅝" long.

WO/170	**GWR** 1408 blue grey tin roof double axleguards - *23-28*	25	30

W7. Litho Box Van

These vans had bodies $4\frac{13}{16}$" long, a 2¾" wheelbase, although these dimensions have been known to vary slightly. The roof was white.

WO/170	**LMS** 260723 light grey sliding single door - *29-39*	25	30
WO/171	**GW** 114294 dark green double door, double vent - *29-39*	20	25
WO/172	**NE** 140092 dark green single sliding door - *29-39*	20	25
WO/173	**SR** 44556 brown triple door, single vent - *29-39*	20	25

GWR cattle wagon [W8]

W8. Litho Cattle Wagon

These had $5\frac{5}{16}$" long bodies, a 3" wheelbase and had white roofs.

WO/174	**NE** 150882 light brown - *29-39*	20	25
WO/175	**SR** 764 brown - *29-39*	20	25
WO/176	**GW** 106324 dark green - *29-39*	20	25
WO/177	**LMS** 107877 light grey - *29-39*	20	25

W9. Litho Brake Vans

These were individual designs to suit each company and all had white roofs. Litho papers for the NER and GWR brake vans were still available in the late 1950s.

WO/200	**NER** 71911 bauxite - *23-30*	30	35
WO/201	**LNWR** 382 grey - *23-31*	30	35
WO/202	**MR** M946 light grey - *23-31*	30	35
WO/200	**LMS** 917 light grey no platforms - *31-39*	30	35
WO/201	**GW** 17954 grey Toad Cardiff - *31-39*	25	30
WO/202	**NE** 71911 bauxite (same as NER brake van), no platforms - *31-39*	20	25
WO/203	**SR** 55975 brown with platforms - *31-39*	25	35

W10. Litho GWR Siphon G

WO/250	**GW** 1270 brown American bogies spoked wheels - *30-39*	45	60

W11. Litho GWR Monster

WO/251	**GW** 591 brown American bogies spoked wheels - *30-39*	45	60

GWR Monster [W11]

W12. Litho LNER 25T High Capacity Box Van

WO252   **NE** 102497 grey spoked wheels - *31-39*   40   45

True Scale Wagons

There were two mouldings, an open wagon and a box van. Before the war, self coloured bakelite was used which had detail, such as running numbers and broad diagonal stripes to show drop ends, applied as transfers. Post war models had a thin white line painted on the diagonal strapping at the drop end and the livery colour range was painted onto black bakelite. They had non-locking buffers and 3-link couplings.

The bodies could also be bought separately, ready printed, to fit to your own chassis or to make up into larger wagons by joining bodies together. After the war, catalogues showed examples of bogie stock made in this way.

W13. True Scale Standard 7-Plank 12T Mineral Wagon

A range of running numbers was available on a sheet of transfers. scp = self coloured bakelite with other detail painted on. bp = black bakelite, liveries painted on.

WM/1	**LMS** 51432, 604707* bauxite scp - *37-40*	15	20
WM/2	**NE** 588263* dark grey scp - *37-40*	15	20
WM/3	**GW** 245157 dark grey scp - *37-40*	15	20
WM/4	**SR** brown scp - *37-40*	15	20
WM/5	**NE** red oxide fitted with brake pipes scp - *37-40*	25	30
WM/1	**LMS** bauxite bp - *46-66*	15	20
WM/2	**NE** dark grey bp - *46-66*	15	20
WM/3	**GW** dark grey bp - *46-66*	15	20
WM/4	**SR** brown bp - *46-66*	15	20
WM/5	**NE** red oxide fitted with brake pipes bp - *46-66*	20	25

* example of number seen.

W14. True Scale Standard 12T Van

The moulding on the vans showed vertical planking, dummy sliding doors with moulded rollers, slide bar, stops and T end stanchion. A range of running numbers was available on a sheet of transfers. scp = self coloured bakelite with other colours painted on. bp = black bakelite, liveries painted on.

WM/8	**LMS** 190875* bauxite goods van scp - *37-40*	15	20
WM/9	**LMS** bauxite goods van brake pipes ventilators scp - *37-55*	20	25
WM/10	**LMS** maroon 6T fish van brake pipes scp - *37-40*	25	30
WM/11	**NE** dark grey goods van scp - *37-40*	15	20
WM/12	**NE** red oxide goods van brake pipes scp - *37-40*	20	25
WM/13	**NE** red oxide fruit van brake pipes ventilators scp - *37-55*	20	25
WM/14	**GW** dark grey goods van scp - *37-40*	15	20
WM/15	**SR** brown goods van scp - *37-40*	20	25
WM/8	**LMS** bauxite goods van pb - *46-66*	15	20
WM/10	**LMS** maroon 6T fish van brake pipes pb - *46-66*	25	30
WM/11	**NE** dark grey goods van pb - *46-66*	15	20
WM/12	**NE** red oxide goods van brake pipes pb - *46-66*	20	25
WM/14	**GW** dark grey goods van pb - *46-66*	15	20
WM/15	**SR** brown goods van pb - *46-66*	20	25

* example of number seen.

True Scale standard 12T van [W14]

W15. True Scale Handmade Brake Vans

Brake vans for the bakelite range were handmade in the factory - before the war in wood and after the war in tinplate. Pre-war, there were three types offered - LMS in bauxite, LNER in red oxide and SR in brown. Only the LMS van was offered after the war (those for the other three companies were to have followed but did not arrive). Initially, the post-war brake van had the long wheelbase (7½" overall) but, from about 1950, a shorter version (6" overall), was produced to accompany the boxed goods train sets. A choice of numbers was available on sheets of transfers.

WF/50	**LMS** bauxite 20T express goods brake - *c37-40*	45	60
WF/51	**NE** red oxide 20T express goods brake - *c37-40*	60	70
WF/52	**SR** brown 25T goods brake - *c37-40*	60	70
WF/50	**LMS** bauxite 20T express goods brake 7½" - *c46-66*	45	60
WF/50	**LMS** bauxite 20T express goods brake 6" - *c50-66*	45	60
?	**BR** bauxite 20T goods brake 6" - *c50-66*	35	45

ACCESSORIES

A full range of brass/steel, wooden sleepered, track was made. The electric type had the centre third rail raised 3mm above the running rails. Wooden stations, goods depots, signal boxes, huts, tunnel mouths and signals provided the enthusiast with a complete railway system.

Lima N (British)
Wrenn Micromodels

HISTORY

Lima commenced production of an Italian range of 1:160 N gauge in 1966. From the start it was a 12v 2-rail system and was available in the UK.

Lines Bros., the makers of Tri-ang Hornby, did not actually want to make N gauge but they did wish to keep their finger on the pulse. As early as the Summer of 1964 Lines had been approached by Stan Perrin of Lone Star to ask if they would take the Treble-O-Lectric system off their hands.

Perrin thought that Rovex would be able to make his trains cheaper than he could but the men at Rovex did not agree. The offer came at the time they were realising that their own TT system was not going to be profitable and a time when they were considering how they could merge the Tri-ang and Hornby-Dublo systems. On 14th August 1964 the offer was diplomatically turning down.

In 1967, however, Lines did a deal with Lima under which Lima N gauge would be sold through the Rovex subsidiary, G & R Wrenn Ltd and, in exchange, Lima would be allowed to make Tri-ang Big-Big trains under licence.

The Lima agreement was different from the Lone Star proposal. From the start it was clear that the trains were to be made by Lima and just marketed as Micromodels under the name of G & R Wrenn Ltd. A good range of track, locomotives and rolling stock would be available by June 1967 together with two boxed sets which would include British outline models. The first of the British locomotives was to be the AL1 type Bo-Bo 3001.

Rumours about Tri-ang Hornby entering the N gauge field had been rife for sometime when the 1967 Toy Fair opened and the first models were seen. A full page advertisement for the 'new' system was to be found in July model railway magazines but all the models illustrated with drawings were of Continental outline. A fully illustrated coloured brochure and a price list were also available.

The following month a magazine advert included photographs of the first three wagons to be included in the British range. These were a mineral wagon, a brake van and a BP tank wagon. The first two were clearly models of British prototypes, the standard BR brake van having been adopted for the model. The tank wagon was clearly an existing Continental model produced in a familiar livery.

By November the promised two sets were offered for the Christmas trade. Set No1 had the E3001 and 2 coaches and set No2 had the same loco but with four wagons. At the same time the loco was available as a solo purchase.

It was not until the Summer of 1968 that we heard any more about new British outline models and then it was the availability of the two coaches in maroon livery and a Buffet car in both maroon and blue/grey. Then, in November, the Wrenn full page advertisement showed the British and Swedish 2-6-4 tanks, a parlour car Wagon Lits and one of the BR Mk1 coaches in blue and grey livery.

Rovex continued to sit on the fence with regard to N gauge and Graham Farish saw an opportunity and took it to become Britain's leading developer of the system. Wrenn's association with Lima continued for a while after the collapse of Lines Bros. and the cutting loose of G&R Wrenn as an independent company.

Rovex under new management reviewed its N gauge policy but were still unconvinced that there was a good market for it. However when Trix closed down their operations in Britain and were looking for a British company to import their British Minitrix range, Rovex seemed the obvious choice and thus Hornby Minitrix appeared in the shops.

Wrenn withdrew from the Lima agreement in 1977 and Eisenmann & Co. Ltd became the British importers of Lima N gauge. From 1983 Richard Kohnstam Ltd took it over but production of the British range ceased two years later as it could not compete with Graham Farish and Hornby Minitrix. Around 1991 a new attempt at launching a British range under the Lima MiniTrains label came to nothing.

Further Reading

A more detailed account of the range and its history will be found in an excellent guide by Simon Culverhouse which was first published in 2004. This lists the full range and includes details on catalogues, train sets, track and accessories which will not be found here. The guide is available from 17 Church Street, Clowne, Chesterfield S43 4JR.

Packaging

Although sold under the Wrenn Micromodels name, the models carried the name 'LIMA' on their undersides and the grey and yellow packaging was inscribed "Made in Italy by Lima for G+R Wrenn Limited, Basildon, Essex, England."

The sets, locos and rolling-stock came in window boxes but other models had simple end flap boxes. All had the catalogue number and contents roughly printed onto a white panel on the box ends.

In the early '70s, the livery of the packaging changed to dark blue and orange and all reference to Lima was dropped. Around this time, the locomotives and rolling stock were sold in clear plastic boxes which had proved popular on the Continent for smaller scale models. Other changes in packaging style followed.

Dates: The dates quoted below are those when we believe the models were initially released.

Catalogue Numbers: Items were given new catalogue numbers in 1978 and three digit prefixes were added. These prefixes have not been included here.

LOCOMOTIVES

The small size of locomotive prototypes in Britain meant that it was difficult to fit the existing motor inside models of them. The

Lima N (British)

result was British locomotives which had an 'over fed' look to them.

Cat.No.	Number, Company, Colour, Date	£	£

L1. GWR Class 94XX Pannier Tank 0-6-0PT

240	**9400** GWR green - *not made*	NA	NA
241	**9420** BR black - *not made*	NA	NA

L2. LNER Class J50 Tank 0-6-0T

254	**8920** LNER green - *not made*	NA	NA
255	**68920** BRb black - *not made*	NA	NA

L3. BR Class 4MT Tank 2-6-4T

This was a badly proportioned model due to it having to accommodate a motor which was too large.

228	**8230** GWR green - *68*	25	40
252/227	**80033** BR black - *77*	25	40
251	**S1** Swedish - *68*	NPG	NPG
253	**383** Pennsylvania - *70*	NPG	NPG
257	**Ci.66** DB black - *not made*	NA	NA

Class 4MT tank [L3] (Lima)

L4. LMS Class 4F 0-6-0

258	**4547** LMS black - *75*	20	30
259	**11683** LMS red - *not made*	NA	NA
259	**4683** LMS red - *75*	18	30
260	**1905** black (Australian) - *83*	NPG	NPG

L5. GWR King Class 4-6-0

256	**6000 'King George V'** GWR green - *not made*	NA	NA
256	**6009 'King Charles II'** BRb green - *not made*	NA	NA
257	**6009 'King Charles II'** BRb blue - *not made*	NA	NA
257	**? 'King ?'** Caledonian blue - *not made*	NA	NA

L6. Diesel Shunter 0-4-0

Based on a German design.

210	**D2785** BRc green - *73*	15	20
211	**D2790** BRe blue - *73*	15	20

L7. Centre Cab Diesel Bo-Bo

Based on a German design but looking similar to a Clayton Class 17.

212	**D8900** BRc green - *73*	30	40
213	**D8915** BRe blue - *73*	30	40

Centre cab diesel [L7] (Lima)

L8. Class 31 Diesel A1A-A1A

214	**D5509** BRc green - *73?*	35	50
209	**D5518** BRe blue - *70?*	35	50
209	**D5572** BRe blue - *not made*	NA	NA
218	**2158** RENFE green+yellow - *76*	NPG	NPG
245L	**31004** BRe blue - *not made*	NA	NA
245	**31246** BReLL blue - *83?*	40	60
244L	**31275** BR Railfreight Coal - *not made*	NA	NA
242L	**31402** BRe blue - *not made*	NA	NA
240L	**31423** BR Mainline - *not made*	NA	NA
241L	**31541** BR 'Dutch' grey+yellow - *not made*	NA	NA
243L	**31970** BR Research - *not made*	NA	NA
?	**?** CIE deep yellow - *?*	NPG	NPG

L9. Class 52 'Western' Diesel Hydraulic C-C

299	**D1000 'Western Enterprise'** BRc desert sand - *not made*	NA	NA
244	**D1003 'Western Pioneer'** BRc green - *not made*	NA	NA
242	**D1016 'Western Gladiator'** BRc maroon - *not made*	NA	NA
243	**D1071 'Western Renown'** BRe blue - *not made*	NA	NA

L10. Class 55 'Deltic' Diesel Co-Co

253	**D9003 'Meld'** BRc green - *78*	60	70
217	**9006 'The Fife & Forfar Yeomanry'** BRe blue - *78*	60	70
217	**9009 'Alycidon'** BRe blue - *not made*	NA	NA

L11. Class 81/86 Electric Bo-Bo

205	**E3001** BRd electric blue - *not made*	NA	NA
205	**E3185** BRd electric blue - *67*	50	70
249	**86235 'Novelty'** BReLL blue - *83*	60	75

Class 81 [L11] (Lima)

COACHES

These were quite accurate 1:160 scale models and had bright metal wheels with oversize flanges. Up until 1980 the liveries used had an exaggerated brightness but these were darkened from 1980 onwards. Early examples had correct running numbers.

Cat.No.	Company, Number, Colour, Date	£	£

C1. Pullman (Continental Type)

Based on the Wagon Lits vehicles as used on the Victoria-Paris services in the UK.

355	**Pullman** 'Anne' brown+yellow - *not made*	NA	NA
355	**Pullman** 'Cecilia' brown+yellow - *76*	12	15
356	**'Golden Arrow'** 23085 blue+grey - *76*	12	15

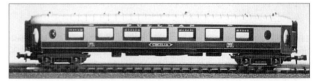

Pullman 'Cecilia' [C1] (Lima)

C2a. Mk1 Corridor Composite (CK)

306/307	**BR** 15865 blue+grey - *67*	12	15
306	**BR** W43671 blue+grey - *80*	12	15
314	**BR** 15865 maroon - *68*	12	15
314	**BR** M26810 maroon - *80*	12	15
361	**GWR** 3015 brown+cream - *76*	12	15
361	**BR** W24624 brown+cream - *80*	12	15
357	**BR** 15865 red+cream - *75*	12	15
357	**BR** M24628 red+cream - *80*	12	15
352	**BR** 534257 green - *78*	12	15
352	**BR** S37483 green - *80*	12	15
353	**BR** 534257 green - *73*	12	15
354	**Pennsylvania** 1410 red+gold -*68*	NPG	NPG
364	**Wabash** 142 grey+blue - *68*	NPG	NPG
374	**Baltimore & Ohio** 186 blue+grey - *68*	NPG	NPG
384	**Santa Fe** 1418 grey+red - *68*	NPG	NPG
394	**New Haven** 1410 grey+red - *68*	NPG	NPG
?	**CIE** deep yellow - *?*	NPG	NPG

C2b. Mk1 Brake 2nd (BSK)

306	**BR** 35024 blue+grey - *67*	12	15
307	**BR** 35024 blue+grey - *74*	12	15
307	**BR** W43281 blue+grey - *80*	12	15
315	**BR** 72234 maroon - *not made*	NA	NA
315	**BR** 35024 maroon - *70*	12	15
315	**BR** M25290 maroon - *80*	12	15
362	**GWR** 5104 brown+cream - *76*	12	15
362	**BR** W24328 brown+cream - *80*	12	15
362	**BR** W24756 brown+cream - *80*	12	15
358	**BR** 35024 red+cream - *75*	12	15
358	**BR** M24374 red+cream - *80*	12	15
352/353	**BR** S1297 green - *73*	12	15
353	**BR** S75469 green - *80*	12	15
355	**Pennsylvania** 7093 red+gold -*68*	NPG	NPG
365	**Wabash** 2697 grey+blue - *68*	NPG	NPG
375	**Baltimore & Ohio** 86 blue+grey - *68*	NPG	NPG
385	**Santa Fe** 2602 grey+red - *68*	NPG	NPG
395	**New Haven** 2609 grey+red - *68*	NPG	NPG
?	**CIE** deep yellow - *?*	NPG	NPG

C2c. Mk1 Buffet Car (RMB)

313	**BR** 1823 blue+grey - *68*	12	15
313	**BR** W43212 blue+grey - *80*	12	15
316	**BR** 1823 maroon - *68*	12	15
316	**BR** M26427 maroon - *80*	12	15
363	**GWR** 5208 brown+cream - *76*	12	15
363	**BR** W24756 brown+cream - *80*	12	15
359	**BR** 1823 red+cream - *75*	12	15
359	**BR** M34276 red+cream - *80*	12	15
354	**BR** S1297 green - *73*	12	15
354	**BR** S33760 green - *80*	12	15

Mk1 buffet car [C2c] (Lima)

C2d. Mk1 Full Brake (BG)

368	**BR** M80855 blue+grey - *77*	12	15
368	**BR** W43462 blue+grey - *80*	12	15
367	**LMS** 30964 maroon - *77*	12	15
367	**BR** M26747 maroon - *80*	12	15
366	**GWR** 4476 brown+cream - *77*	12	15
366	**BR** W24589 brown+cream - *80*	12	15
369	**BR** M80855 red+cream - *77*	12	15
369	**BR** M34752 red+cream - *80*	12	15

WAGONS

Reliveried Continental tanks and silos made their appearance in the catalogues along with various other Continental designs. It is likely that versions of these wagons made for other countries turned up in Britain but we have listed here only the Continental type wagons marked in the catalogues as being for Britain. Specifically British outline wagons were also made and these are listed separately.

The mineral wagon and brake van are overscale as they were copies of Tri-ang Hornby wagons which Lima draughtsmen wrongly took to be H0 scale. However, for later BR wagons, BR drawings were used and these are to 1:160 scale.

Cat.No.	Company, Number, Colour, Date	£	£

Continental Style Wagons

W1. Twin Bolster Wagon

482	brown + 3 pipes - *69*	6	92
483	brown + timber - *69*	6	9

W2. Open Wagon (no doors)

725	**BR** WT3 grey - *?*	3	5

W3. Steel Open Wagon (with doors)

725	**BR** WT3 blue - *not made*	NA	NA
725	**BR** WT3 grey - *75*	3	5
726	**NCB** WT3 grey+red - *76*	3	5

W4. Twin Silo Wagon

461	? Cement - *73*	3	5
729	**Blue Circle** yellow - *75*	3	5

W5. Small Tank Wagon

451	**Esso** silver - *68*	4	6
451	**Esso** silver/red - *75*	5	7
452	**Shell** yellow - *68*	4	6
454	**BP** green - *67*	4	6
455	**Texaco** red - *77*	5	7
780	**Gulf** white+red - *75*	5	7
782	**ICI Chemicals** white - *76*	5	7
784	**Mobil LP Gas** cream - *79*	5	7
781	**Mobil Oil** white - *75*	5	7

Small tank wagon [W5] (Lima)

W6. Van (lwb)

462	**East Anglian Meat** light green - *76*	4	6

W7. Refrigerator Van (lwb)

479	**Coca-Cola** white - *76*	4	6
474	**Schweppes** 2416S beige - *76*	4	6
463	**Grimsby Fish** NE26426 blue - *77*	4	6

Lima N (British)

W8. Liner Train Flat + Containers

484	**Freightliner** x3 grey+red (N484) - *69*	8	12
487	**Kuhne & Nagel+ACL+Sealand** - *73*	8	12
795	**Pickfords+Fyffes+Containerway** -*73*	8	12
485	**CNC+Danzas+LEP** - *73*	8	12
486	**Hapag Lloyd+CTI+DB** - *73*	8	12
486	**Hapag Lloyd+RENFE+DB** - *76*	8	12
486	**Fyffes+Danzas+Freightliner** - *?*	8	12
486	**Hapag Lloyd+Danzas+Freightliner** - *?*	8	12
486	**Hapag Lloyd+CTI+Freightliner** - *?*	8	12
486	**Hapag Lloyd+CTI+CNC** - *?*	8	12
486	**CIE+RENFE+DB** - *?*	8	12
760	**ACL+CP Ships** - *79*	NPG	NPG
796	**ACL+TNT+RACE** - *79*	NPG	NPG

W9. Ferry Van

400	**BR** TFV2 brown - *75*	5	7

W10. Car Carrier

481	**Sitfa** + 6 cars - *73*	18	25
792	**British Leyland** black + 6 cars - *76*	18	25

W11. USA Type Gondola Brick Wagon

420/720	**London Brick** red - *73*	5	7

USA type gondola brick wagon [W11] (Lima)

W12. Bogie Tanker

622	**Amoco** A1090 white - *80*	7	9
623	**Texaco** J62417 red - *not made*	NA	NA
625	**Milk** 152 blue+yellow - *80*	6	8

British Style Wagons

W13. 7-Plank Open Wagon

601	**Clay Cross** 1791 brown - *77*	3	5
602	**Glasshoughton** yellow - *77*	3	5
602	**Black Park** brown - *80*	4	6
603	**Evans & Bevan** 1759 black - *77*	3	5
604	**Oxford District Gas** 18 green - *77*	3	5
604	**Barrow Barnsley** yellow - *80*	4	6
605	**Dearne Valley** 61 blue - *77*	3	5
606	**GWR** 122060 grey - *77*	3	5
607	**JK Harrison** red - *79*	4	6
608	**PW Spencer** yellow - *79*	4	6
609	**Pinxton** 930 black - *79*	4	6
610	**Buxton Gas Dept** 24 grey - *79*	4	6
407	**North Thames Gas** 57200 brown - *75*	3	5
734	**Hall & Dean** 115 yellow - *74*	3	5
735	**Caxton** 32 lime green - *74*	3	5
738	**Kendall & Co**. 26 grey - *75*	3	5
-	**CIE** brown - *80*	NPG	NPG

The 1980 illustration is not of a 7-plank wagon but looks more like a ventilated van without a roof. It is not known whether any of the CIE wagons were made in N gauge

W14. 16T Mineral Wagon

406	**BR** B554430 grey - *67*	3	5
407	**BR** B54564 brown - *not made*	NA	NA

W15. Vee Cement Tank Wagon

630	**Blue Circle** grey - *not made*	NA	NA
631	**Ketton Cement** yellow - *not made*	NA	NA
632	**Castle Cement** white - *not made*	NA	NA

633	**Albright & Wilson** green - *not made*	NA	NA
634	**Lever Bros**. purple - *not made*	NA	NA
635	**BR** 9398 grey - *not made*	NA	NA

W16. Horse Box

616	**GWR** 5463 brown - *not made*	NA	NA
616	**GWR** 546 brown - *80*	9	12
617	**LMS** red - *78*	9	12
619	**SR** green - *not made*	NA	NA

W17. Ventilated Van

412	**LNER** 167349 brown - *not made*	NA	NA
476	**Tate & Lyle** green - *76*	4	6
477	**LMS** 59673 red - *76*	4	6
611	**Typhoo Tea** S1200 red - *77*	4	6
612	**Homepride** SHP2225 blue+white - *not made*	NA	NA
613	**Michelin** M1245 brown - *not made*	NA	NA
614	**St Ivel** 68837 white - *77*	4	6
615	**GWR** 59701 grey - *77*	5	7
618	**Lucas Batteries** M3245 black - *81*	4	6
619	**Birds Custard** blue - *81*	4	6
736	**Ford** S52272 blue - *74*	4	6
737	**Fyffes** yellow - *74*	4	6
739	**Castrol** GTX grey - *80*	4	6
740	**SR** 45826 brown - *75*	5	7
?	**CIE** brown - *80*	NPG	NPG

W18. CCT Van

868	**Tartan Arrow** white+red - *not made*	NA	NA
869	**BR** E94606 blue - *80*	5	7
870	**BR** M94823 maroon - *80*	5	7

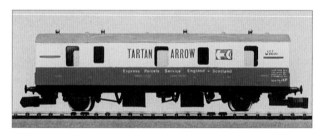

CCT van [W18] (Lima)

W19. 20T GWR Brake Van

410	**GWR** 47342 grey - *not made*	NA	NA
410	**GWR** 114756 grey - *75*	5	7

W20. 20T BR Standard Brake Van

405	**BR** B954521 brown - *67*	3	5
?	**CIE** grey - *80*	NPG	NPG

W21. GWR Siphon G

862	**GWR** 2792 brown - *80*	7	9
863	**Palethorpes** 2766 dark brown - *81*	7	9
864	**BR** W2982 blue - *80*	7	9
865	**BR** W2938W brown - *80*	7	9
865	**BR** M2928 maroon - *80*	7	9
867	**BR** RDW150423 blue Enparts - *80*	7	9

Wrenn Micromodels set by Lima

Lima H0 (British)

HISTORY

Following some success with N gauge in Britain (sold through G&R Wrenn) Lima decided to try and compete in the British 00 market which by 1973 had only one principal supplier. As in the rest of Europe, Lima's middle scale was H0 and so they produced their first British models in this smaller scale. This meant that they looked too small alongside the British 00 models of other manufacturers and Lima realised that in order to compete in the UK they would have to change to 00 scale. Lima 00 had completely replaced H0 in the British catalogue in 1977.

Because of its short life, the Lima British outline H0 range did not extend to any great size and, coming as it did from a company that made models for many countries, there was some compromising done which resulted in certain foreign subjects turning up in British liveries. Only models in UK liveries or of British subjects in foreign liveries are listed here.

The lists have been made from the full range of catalogues including the Lima Irish Collection issue of 1979/80 and Wrenn price lists of the mid '70s (Wrenn were UK agents for Lima until Eisenmann took it over).

Some models in the H0 range were up-scaled for the 00 system and sometimes they took their catalogue number with them. Today, interest in Lima H0 British models is increasing and after a long period when you could hardly give them away, we are at last seeing their prices rise. This especially applies to mint boxed models as will be seen from the prices quoted here.

Dates: Those given are those when we believe the models were sold and do not always tie up with their appearance in the catalogues. Some models such as the Deltic, J50 and King were shown in the 1976 catalogue as H0 models but were in fact 00 scale when they arrived. They have therefore been included in our Lima 00 lists.

LOCOMOTIVES

Cat.No.	Number, Company, Colour, Dates	£	£

L1. US Tank 0-4-0T

1710	**40106** red white lining, headlamp, outside cylinders - *74-76*	15	20
1711	**4572** SR green, headlamp, outside cylinders full valve gear - *76*	18	25
?	**4572** SR green, headlamp, outside cylinders simplified valve gear, ex sets - *76*	15	NA

These engines also came with NMRA couplings.

L2. Class 4F 0-6-0

Tender drive with a pancake type motor.

1701	**4547** LMS lined black - *74-78*	22	30
1702	**4168** LMS lined red - *not made*	NA	NA
1702L	**4683** LMS lined red (2 shades) - *74-76*	15	25
1707	**628** CIE black - *77-79*	35	NPG
1715	**1908** black as Australian Class 219 - *76-83*	35	45

L2A. King Class 4-6-0

1713	**6000 'King Charles'** BRb green - *not made*	NA	NA
1704	CR blue - *not made*	NA	NA
1704	**'King Charles'** BRb blue - *not made*	NA	NA

L3. Continental Diesel Shunter 0-4-0DS

American design (Plymouth MDT). Simplified versions without handrails and the roof not painted black are from train sets. These were still being sold after 1977.

1650	**D2790** BRe blue - *74-76*	12	15
1651	**D2785** BRc green - *74-76*	12	15

L3A. German Class V100 Diesel B0-Bo

This was a centre cab loco. It was probably supposed to be a Class 14 or 17.

-	**D8900** BRe blue ex starter sets - *75*	15	NA
-	**D8900** BRc green ex starter sets - *75*	15	NA

L4. Class 33 Diesel   Bo-Bo

1646	**D6514** BRc green, white window surrounds *76*	25	35
1646	**D6514** BRc green with yellow ends and window surrounds - *76*	40	50
8015	CIE orange+black - *76*	40	50
8049	**D6524** BRe dark blue no lights, ex sets - *73-76*	15	20
8049/L	**D6524** BRe chromatic blue with lights - *73-74*	20	30

Class 33 [L4]

L5. Class 55 Deltic Diesel Co-Co

Planned for release in H0 and orange-brown packaging printed ready but then the decision was taken to produce the 00 scale.

1645	**9009** BRe blue - *not made*	NA	NA

COACHES

The choice of running numbers was sometimes haphazard but the Mk1s and Mk2s were attractive models.

Cat.No.	Company, Number, Colour, Dates	£	£

Original Continental Style Coaches

C1. Pullman (panelled sides)

9146	**'Louise'** dark brown+yellow - *75-76*	5	10
9199	**'Anne'** dark brown+yellow - *75-76*	5	10
9200	**'Golden Arrow'** 23085 green+grey - *75*	5	10

C1b. Pullman (smooth sides)

9146	**'Louisa'** dark brown+yellow - *76*	5	10
9200	**'Golden Arrow'** 23085 blue+grey - *76*	5	10
9200	**'Golden Arrow'** 23085 green+grey - *76*	20	25

C1A. Coaches

These were 18cms long. Continental coaches produced in British liveries for use in early starter train sets. These were later produced with tension-lock couplings.

-	**LMS** red+yellow - *76*	5	NA
-	**LMS** maroon - *76*	5	NA
-	**SR** green - *76*	5	NA
-	**BR** blue+grey - *76*	5	NA

C2. Travelling Post Office

970	**BR** W80062 blue+grey Royal Mail - *73-75*	8	12

British Design Coaches

C3a. Mk1 Corridor Composite

9145	**BR** 15210 red+cream - *75-76*	5	10
9145	**BR** 15215 red+cream - *not made*	NA	NA

Lima H0 (British)

9152	**BR** S15865 green - *76*	5	10
?	**BR** W5449 blue+grey - *not made*	NA	NA
9146	**LMS** 2257 maroon - *75-76*	5	10
9151	**GWR** 5014 dark brown+cream - *76*	5	10
5346	**CIE** green - *not made*	NA	NA
5347	**CIE** orange+black - *not made*	NA	NA

C3b. Mk1 Brake 2nd

9320	**BR** 34100 red+cream - *75-76*	5	10
9327	**BR** S1297 green - *76*	5	10
9327	**BR** S15895 green - *not made*	NA	NA
?	**BR** blue+grey - *not made*	NA	NA
9321	**LMS** 5051 maroon - *75-76*	5	10
9326	**GWR** 5103 dark brown+cream - *76*	5	10

C3c. Mk1 Restaurant Buffet Car

?	**BR** red+cream - *not made*	NA	NA
9235	**BR** S3056 green - *76*	5	10
9232	**BR** W1652 blue+grey - *76*	5	10
9232	**BR** M1704 blue+grey - *not made*	NA	NA
9234	**LMS** 270 maroon - *76*	5	10
9233	**GWR** 9542 dark brown+cream - *76*	5	10

C4a. Mk2b Open Coach TSO
8 windows per side.

9136	**BR** W5449 blue+grey - *73-76*	5	10
9144	**CIE** orange+black - *75-?*	15	25

Mk2 TSO [C4a]

C4b. Mk2b Brake 1st BFK

9137	**BR** W16084 blue+grey - *73-76*	5	10

C4c. Mk2b Open 1st FO
7 windows per side.

9135	**BR** W13493 blue+grey - *73-76*	5	10

WAGONS

Original Continental Style Wagons

These often differed from the 00 versions of them in having Continental couplings instead of the British tension-lock type.

Cat.No.	Company, Number, Colour, Dates	£	£

W1. Continental 4-Wheel Container Wagon

2871	2 x 20' **Freightliner** containers - *made?*	NPG	NPG
2871	2104290324 + 40' **Freightliner** grey+red - *75-76*	5	6
2852	2104290324 + **Scotch Beef+LHB** blue+ orange - *75-76*	5	6

W2. Continental LWB Mineral Wagon

3173	**NCB** Cardiff 1879 light grey - *76*	4	5
3175	**BRe** 100027 brown - *73-76*	3	5

W3. Continental Covered Hopper

3194	**BR** brown - *not made?*	NA	NA

W4. Continental Twin Silo Wagon

2805	**Prestwin** brown - *73 (made?)*	4	6
2805	**Prestwin** grey - *73-74*	4	6
2805	**Blue Circle** 7504 yellow (yellow circle on blue background) - *75*	8	12
2805	**Blue Circle** 7504 yellow (blie circle) - *75?*	3	5

W5. Continental 3-Cask Beer Wagon

2822	**Watneys** P650513 red+brown - *73-76*	4	6

W6. Continental Small Tanker

2713	**Shell** 557128 yellow + black stripe - *73-76*	3	5
2713	**Shell** 557128 yellow - *73-76*	3	5
2715	**BP** green - *73-76*	3	5
2720	**ICI** Chemicals C1182 white - *76*	4	6

W6A. Continental LWB Tank

2713	**Mobiloil** red ex-sets - *75-76*	3	NA
2715	**Shell** yellow ex-sets - *75-76*	3	NA
2720	**Texaco** red ex-sets - *75-76*	4	NA
2720	**BP** dark green ex-sets - *75-76*	4	NA

W7. Continental Ferry Van

3155	**East Anglian Meat** E75 lime grn - *76*	4	6
3162	**BR** 217021003910 brown - *76*	3	5
3162	**BR** 217021003910 brown converter van - *78*	5	7

W8. Continental Refrigerator Van

3118	**Schweppes** 2416S yellow - *76*	3	5

W9. Continental Car Transporter

9057	**British Leyland** 518098800213 black - *76*	10	15
9053	**BR Motorail** 518098800213 blue - *74-76*	10	15

W10. Continental Bogie Tanker

2904	**Shell Covengas** yellow - *75*	6	8
2904	**Shellgas** yellow - *76*	5	7
2911	**Traffic Services Ltd** green - *75*	7	9
2911	**Milk** 152D blue - *76*	6	8
2913	**Amoco** A1090 white - *76*	6	8

W11. Continental Bogie Ferry Van

3194	**Traffic Services Ltd** cream - *74-76*	8	12
3194	**BR Railfreight** BRT yellow - *76*	8	12

British Design Wagons

W12. 12T 7-Plank Open Wagon

3176	**Hall & Dean** 115 yellow - *74-76*	4	6
3177	**Caxton** 52? lime green - *74-76*	4	6
3178	**North Thames Gas** 357260 - brown - *75-76*	4	6
3179	**Kendall** 26 grey - *75-76*	4	6
3180	**BR** grey - *75-76*	4	6
3511	**VR** (Australian) blue - *78-83*	15	20
?	**CIE** brown - *made?*	NPG	NPG

W13. 12T Corrugated End Van

3156	**Tate & Lyle** green - *76*	5	7
3157	**LMS** red - *76*	3	5
3160	**Ford** blue - *75-76*	4	6
3168	**Fyfes** yellow - *75-76*	4	6
3169	**Castrol GTX** grey - *75-76*	4	6
3170	**SR** brown - *75-76*	5	7
3515	**Explosives** (Australian) - brown - *78-83*	15	20
?	**CIE** brown - *made?*	NPG	NPG

W14. 20T BR Standard Brake Van

3152	**BR** B954521 brown - *76*	3	5
3153	**NE** 159486 grey - *76*	3	5
?	**CIE** grey - *made?*	NPG	NPG

W15. GWR Toad Brake Van

3166	**GW** 57740* light grey - *not made*	4	6
3166	**GW** 114756 light grey - *74-76*	4	6

* This appears to have been a Hornby model fitted with Continental couplings for the catalogue illustration.

Lima 0 (British)

HISTORY

It is probably no coincidence that the Lima's British outline 0 gauge range was launched in 1973 just as the Tri-ang Big Big system was disappearing from the shops. Indeed, it is understood that Rovex Ltd assisted Lima to get started in this market.

The British range was only a small part of a much larger international 0 gauge system made by Lima and which included 16.5mm track, lineside accessories and train sets. to 1:48 scale.

At present we have only limited information about the dates when the Lima 0 gauge models for the British market were available but it would seem that they arrived in 1973 and ended in the early 1980s. It would appear that the tools were brought out of the storeroom in 1991 to produce a batch of Class 33 locomotives and Mk1 coaches in Network SouthEast livery for a special order - returning then to the store. Six of the models again featured in the 1999/2000 Lima catalogue, these being the two LMS versions of the 0-6-0 Fowler loco, two LMS Mk1 coaches and two versions of the mineral wagon. We do not know what happened to the tooling after that and it is assumed that it is still with Lima.

We are keen to learn more about Lima's venture into the UK 0 gauge market and would like to hear from anyone who can add to the story.

LOCOMOTIVES

Although three types of locomotive were made for the British market, only two were based on British prototypes. One of these, the LMS 4F 0-6-0, was also shown in the catalogue in the early 1970s in SNCF green livery.

The locomotives had 12v DC pancake motors and ran on two rails. The motor itself is quite good, relative to the price, but the locos sometimes suffered from poor current collection and the plating wearing off the wheels after a lot of use. The 0 gauge track had a plastic sleeper web with 00 scale rail.

Cat.No.	Number, Company, Colour, Dates	£	£
L1.	**Class 4F 0-6-0**		
6533	**4547** LMS black - *75-00*	40	55
6533	**4547** BR black - *made?*	NPG	NPG
6534	**4683** LMS red - *75-00*	40	55

Class 4F [L1] (Lima)

L2. Diesel Shunter 0-4-0DS

This was a model made for the US market and is thought to be of a freelance or Continental design. Kits were available, from another source, with which to convert this model into a Sentinel shunter or a Wisbech and Upwell tram engine (Toby).

6546	**D2852** BRe blue - *73-80*	25	40
6546	**D9574** BRe blue - *made?*	NPG	NPG
6545	Esso - *73-?*	NPG	NPG

L3. Class 33 Diesel

Continental bogies.

6576	**D6514** BRc green - *77-78*	35	50
6576	**D6506** BRc green - *78-82*	35	50
6577	**D6524** BRe blue - *77-82*	35	50
?	**?** BR Railfreight Construct. grey - *91*	45	60

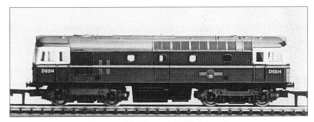

Class 33 diesel [L3] (Lima)

COACHES

Only two coach types were made - both BR Mk1s. The Network SouthEast versions of 1991 both had Thames route branding. They had Continental bogies.

Cat.No.	Company, Number, Colour, Dates	£	£
C1a.	**Mk1 Corridor Composite**		
6616	**LMS** 15865 maroon - *75-00*	20	25
6617	**BR(S)** S15865 green - *75-80*	20	25
6620	**GWR** 5015 choc+cream - *75-82*	20	25
6618	**BR** 15218 red+cream - *75-82*	25	30
6619	**BR** 15867 blue+grey - *75-82*	25	30
?	**BR** NSE ? blue+red+grey - *91*	25	30

Mk1 corridor composite [C1a[(Lima)

C1b. Mk1 Brake End

6645	**LMS** 5051 maroon - *76-00*	20	25
6647	**SR** S1297 green - *76-80*	25	30
6646	**GWR** 5103 choc+cream - *76-82*	20	25
6644	**BR** 34100 red+cream - *76-82*	25	30

			£	£
6654	**BR** 35028 blue+grey - *76-82*		25	30
?	**BR NSE** ? blue+red+grey - *91*		25	30

WAGONS

As with the H0 and N gauge ranges, Lima produced a small number of British wagons, in this case only two, and widened the range by using Continental wagons turned out in liveries that might be acceptable in the UK. It is possible that some of the Continental range of wagons produced for other markets found their way into the UK but these have not been included here as it is thought that they were not made for this purpose.

Cat.No.	Company, Number, Colour, Dates	£	£

Original Continental Style Wagons

W1. Continental LWB Mineral Wagon

6726	**NCB** 1879 grey - *76-82*	7	9
?	**BRe** grey - *77?*	7	9

W2. Continental Ferry Van

The NE version was described as a 'box van'.

6745	**BRe** brown - *75-82*	12	15
6751	**NE** 167349 brown - *77-80*	12	15

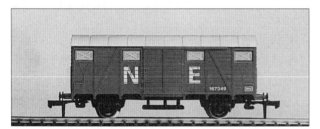

Continental ferry van [W2] (Lima)

W3. Continental Refrigerator Van

6710	**Schweppes** cream - *76-80*	12	15

Also available on the Continent as Spatenbrau, Ledererbrau, Carlsberg and Coca Cola.

W4. Continental Bogie Tanker

6764	**Esso** 521155? silver - *73-76?*	12	15
6765	**Shell** yellow+grey - *73-82*	12	15
6766	**BP** green+grey - *73-82*	12	15
6768	**Mobiloil** white - *73-82*	12	15
6770	**Texaco** red+grey - *77-82*	12	15

Continental bogie tanker [W4] (Lima)

W5. Freightliner Wagon + 3 x 20' Containers

6781	**Danzas** white, **K&N** blue, FFSS - *73?*	10	12
6782?	+ **ACL** red, **Sea Wheel** grey, **Carl Tidderman** light blue - *73?*	10	12
6783	**Sealand** white, **ACL** red, **Carl Tidderman** light blue - *73?-80*	10	12
6784	**Seatrain** white, **LEP European Container Services** brown, **Contrans** orange - *73?-80*	10	12

British Design Wagons

16T mineral wagon [W6] (Lima)

W6. 16T Mineral Wagon

6729	**North Thames Gas** 357260 brown - *75-80*	8	10
6730	**Kendall & Co**. 26 grey - *75-82*	7	9
6731	**Caxton** 32 lime green - *75-82*	7	9
6732	**BR** B54884 brown - *73-80*	8	10
6733	**Hall & Dean** 115 yellow - *75-82*	7	9
6737	**Oxford Gas** 18 lime green * - *77-80*	8	10
6738	**Dearne Valley** 61 blue * - *77-80*	8	10
6739	**GW** 122060 grey * - *77-00*	8	10
6754	**Clay Cross** 1791 brown * - *77-00*	7	9
6755	**Glasshoughton** 126 yellow * - *77-82*	7	9
6756	**Evans & Bevan** 1759 black * - *77-82*	7	9
?	**Royal Arsenal** 144 brown - *?*	NPG	NPG

* Pre-production models were 7-plank wagons but the actual production models were steel mineral wagons.

W7. GWR Toad Brake Van

6746	**GW** 114756 light grey - *75-82*	8	10

Lima had proposed a planked wagon but used the steel mineral wagon instead [W6] (Lima)

Lima 00

HISTORY

Lima has been one of a handful of model railway manufacturers that are truly international; producing models for many different overseas markets. They date from 1946 but did not entered the British market until 1973, first with an unsuccessful range of British H0 models before recognising that, if they were to sell to British modellers, they would need to make their products in the uniquely British 00 scale. This they did in 1976.

In the 1980s Lima made a serious bid for the modern image market and greatly improved the quality of their models. They recognised that modern image modellers were interested in the minor variations between different members of a class of locomotives. They employed batch production which meant that a limited number of each model were made before it was replaced by another version of it. As a result, the range in shops was constantly changing with new releases each month.

Lima's production for the British market has been almost exclusively diesel and electric locomotives and modern coaching stock, with collectors forming a major part of their market. At one time, Lima, more than any other manufacturer supplying the British market, were prepared to accept commissions, from retailers, to produce exclusive short runs of special editions. This resulted in a vast range of model variations over the last twenty years.

Milestones

1946 Lima formed.
1973 Lima enter the UK market.
1976 Lima change production for the British market to 00 scale.
1977 Deltic model appears.
1979 Last steam outline models launched.
1985 The Class 73 is released.
1987 The most prolific UK model, Lima's Class 47, is launched.
1994 The highly detailed Class 59 is released.
1999 Lima become the first manufacturer to market a model of the new Class 66.
2002 Lima part company with UK importer, Riko, and The Hobby Company replace them.
2003 Lima Group goes into liquidation.
2004 Hornby make a bid to take over the Lima Group.

Range Development

Lima modern image locomotives were introduced in the following years:

1977 Classes 33 and 55
1978 Class 09
1979 Classes 52 and 87
1980 Classes 42, 117 and GWR autocoach
1982 Class 43
1984 Class 50
1985 Class 20
1986 Classes 37 and 73
1987 Class 47
1988 Class 40
1989 Classes 26, 27 and 31
1990 Class 60
1992 Class 156
1994 Classes 59 and 92
1996 Class 373 (ex- Jouef)
1997 Class 101
1998 Class 121
1999 Classes 57 and 66
2001 Class 67

The models were made at Vicenza in Italy and, since 1983, were imported by Riko International Ltd based in Hemel Hempstead and the importer recommend what should be made. In 2000 the dealership changed to The Hobby Company Ltd but, after disagreements between the importer and Lima the two parted company in 2002. Lima indicated their intention to upgrade many of their models saying that they would be sold under the Rivarossi label while the remainder would be sold in Hobby Line packaging. However, on 12th July 2003 the Lima Group went into liquidation.

During 2004, Hornby made a bid for the Lima Group which, besides Lima, includes Rivarossi, Arnold, Pocher and Jouef. At the time of going to press the bid is being considered by an Italian court and there is a possibility that business could be concluded as early as the autumn and certainly by the New Year. It is understood that the purchase would include all the tooling, trademarks and other intellectual assets of the group but will not include the group's debts. It is Hornby's intention to transfer production to China.

Collectors Club

You may also wish to join the Lima Collectors Society who publish a bimonthly newsletter, called *Modelimage*, which keeps members informed of news of new products and reviews aspects of the Lima range. The Society also publishes an extensive list of Lima models which is available to members. Details of this organisation may be obtained from the chairman, Peter Baker, who may be contacted on Tel: 01782 519267.

Dates - Only single years are shown in the tables below. This is because most Lima models are produced in single batches and therefore production is not spread over several years.

Listing - The locos are listed in order of size starting with tank engines followed by tender locos and ending with diesels, electrics and multiple units. The coaches are listed in order of introduction of the real vehicles but with a special section for parcels vans which are a speciality of Lima. Wagons are listed in the order of: flats, open wagons, hoppers, tanks, vans, brake vans and bogie stock.

LOCOMOTIVES

Common abbreviations - The following abbreviations have been used in the tables below:
ccb = central codebox
scb = split codebox
disc = disc codes
hyp = half yellow end panels
syp = small yellow end panels
fyp = full yellow end panels
sno = fitted with snow ploughs

Cat.No.	Number, Company, Colour, Dates	£	£

L1. Freelance 0-4-0T
This was used in starter sets.

-	**148** Great Western green - *79*		10	NA
-	**41312** BRb black - *80*		10	NA

L2. Pannier 0-6-0PT

L205117	**9400** GWR green - *79*		25	35
L205118	**9420** BRb black - *79*		30	40
L204815	**9401** BRb black - *94*		30	40

GWR pannier tank [L2]

L3. Class J50 0-6-0

L205101	**8920** LNER dark shade of green, no steps to smokebox and works plate, plastic whistle - *76*		25	30
L205101	**8920** LNER lighter shade of green - *77*		25	30

Lima 00

L205102	**68920** BRb black - *77*	25	35
-	**8920** LMS red ex-Midland Express train set 102606 - *8*	12	NA
-	**8920** lined red, ex-set 152300 - *82*	12	NA
-	**8920** lined green, ex-set 152301 - *82*	12	NA
-	**8920** lined blue, ex-set 152400 - *82*	12	NA

Ex - GWR Prairie tank [L4]

L4. Prairie 2-6-2T

L205111	**4589** GWR green - *78*	25	35
L205110	**5574** BRb black, lined - *79*	30	40
L205015	**4581** GWR green - *93*	25	35
L205014	**5557** BRb lined black - *93*	30	40
L100000	**5549** BR black - *?*	45	60

L4A. Freelance american Style 0-4-0

Sold mainly in South Sfrica and Austrailia. Sloping back to tender.

-	Great Western , H0 couplings ex-set - *80*	NPG	NPG

L5. Mogul (Crab) 2-6-0

L205119	**13000** LMS maroon, no. on tender - *80*	30	45
L205120	**42700** BRb lined black - *80*	35	50
L204814	**42760** BRc black, Ltd Edn 850 - *94*	40	65
L205057	**2724** LMS unlined black - *94*	NPG	NPG

Ex - LMS crab 2-6-0 [L5]

L6. Class V2 2-6-0

This would have been a nice model with separate hand rails throughout. It was probably dropped because the company decided to concentrate on modern image models in future.

L205130MG	**4771 'Green Arrow'** LNER light green, planned for 1980 - *not made*	NA	NA
L205131MG	**60964 'The Durham Light Infantry'** BRb lined black, planned for 1980 - *not made*	NA	NA

L7. Class 6000 'King' 4-6-0

L205103	**6000 'King George V'** Great (crest) Western green, single boiler bands, crests separate - *78*	30	42
L205103	**6000 'King George V'** Great (crest) Western green, separate handrails, double boiler bands, crests joined - *78*	30	42
L205104	**6009 'King Charles II'** BRb bright blue, moulded handrails, thin lining - *78*	30	45
L205104	**6009 'King Charles II'** BRb blue, moulded handrails, thick lining - *78*	30	45
L205104	**6009 'King Charles II'** BRb blue, separate handrails, thick lining - *78*	40	55
L205176	**6026 'King John'** BRb green, separate handrails, double boiler bands - *90*	40	55
L205056	**6012 'King Edward VI'** Great (crests) Western green, separate handrails, bell, Ltd Edn 500 - *93*	55	70

L8. Princess Royal Class 4-6-2

This was announced to the model railway press around 1981 but not made.

L8A. Class 23 4-6-2 (ex-Tri-ang Hornby)

The TC Pacific models were supplied by Rovex ready made and were sold in LIma boxes with Lima couplings fitted.

L208100	**2355 'Hiawatha'** black Lima couplings in Lima packaging - *68*	90	150

L9. Freelance 0-4-0DS

This was used in starter sets.

-	**D2785** BRe blue - *79*	10	20

L10. Classes 08/09/10/11

From 1999, the 08 chassis had all of its six wheels driven.

L205108	**3004** BRc green bright con rods - *78*	25	30
L205109	**7120** LMS black bright con rods - *78*	25	30
L205151	**D3489 'Colonel Tomline'** Townsend Thoresen light green, chevron ends, yellow rods - *83*	28	35
L205297	**08331** GNER navy + red stripe - *00*	25	30
L205297	**08331** GNER black + red stripe, error 48 made - *00*	50	70
L205297/A	As above with RFS roundels - *00*	50	70
L204638	**08611** Virgin red - *99*	25	30
L205259	**08720** EWS maroon - *00*	25	30
L205200	**08874** Silverlink blue+green - *99*	25	30
L204658	**08887** Virgin Pit Stop black - *99*	25	30
L204677	**08899** Midland Mainline teal green - *99*	25	30
L149972	**08899** Midland Mainline teal green + coaches in a train pack - *99*	NA	50
L204701	**09007** Mainline blue - *96*	30	40
L204758	**09009 'Three Bridges CED'** EW&S maroon - *97*	32	45
L205090	**09012 'Dick Hardy'** I-C Executive - *89*	28	40
L205201	**09023** EWS maroon - *99*	30	40
L205107	**09026** BRe blue, chevron ends, bright con rods - *79*	25	30
L20?	**09026** BRe blue no chevron ends - *?*	25	NPG
-	**09026** NSE bright blue no con rods ex set L101806TW - *88*	15	20
L205225	**09026** NSE bright blue, bright rods - *88*	28	35
L205112	**09027** Railfreight red stripe grey, Eastfield motifs - *86*	25	35
-	**09027** BRe blue no rods or yellow ends, Eastfield motifs ex-set - *86*	35	NA
L205058	**09101** BRe Depart plain grey - *94*	30	40
L205123	Swedish livery brown - *83*	NPG	NPG
L205124	Swedish livery orange - *83*	NPG	NPG
L205129	**511** Dutch livery yellow+grey - *83*	NPG	NPG

Class 08 in LMS black [L10]

L11. Class 20

ccb - centre code boxes. disc - disc codes. light - sealed beam headlight. gr = grey roof. ocr = orange cant rail. ov = oval buffers. syp = small yellow panel.

L204905	**D8000** BRc green disc gr ocr ov - *01*	35	50
L204900	**D8001** BRc green disc gr ob - *01*	35	50
-	**D8020** BRc green disc gr, sold with	35	NA

	D8163 see below - *00*		
L205031	**D8020 + D8163** sold as pair - *00*	NA	80
L204827	**D8040** BRc green gr 1st with 5-pole motor sold with D8041 Sp Edn (MR&ME) 475 - *93*	35	50
L204828	**D8041** as above - *93*	35	50
-	above two sold together - *93*	NA	100
L205156	**D8138** BRc green, ccb gr syp - *85*	30	45
-	**D8163** BRc green gr 7D58 ccb paired with D8020 see L205031 above - *00*	35	NA
L205156	**D8170** BRc green planned for 1985 but D8138 made instead	NA	NA
L205066	**2014** RFS all over grey - *93*	30	40
L205069	**20001** Eddie Stobart Ltd green Ltd Edn 750 (Trafford MC) - *01*	40	65
L204707	**20042** Waterman black, disc - *96*	30	45
L205220	**20048** BRe blue, disc, Eastfield motifs Sp Edn 550 (Harburn) - *99*	30	50
L149779	as above + 3 Mk1 coaches in Sp Edn pack 250 (Harburn Hobbies) - *99*	NA	80
L204865	**20059** Rft red stripe grey, disc - *95*	30	40
L205240	**20064 'River Sheaf'** BRe green red solebars disc + Oleo buffers - *88*	30	45
L205067	**20066** BRe blue disc - *94*	30	40
L205241	**20088** Rft unspecified triple grey - *89*	30	45
L204821	**20092** BRe Central Services pink+grey dummy, *see below*** - 93*	35	NA
-	*****20092 + 20169** BRe Central Services pink+grey, sold as pair, Sp Edn 475 (Greenyard+Hatton) - *93*	NA	140
L205203	**20112** BRe blue Ltd Edn 850 - *92*	75	90
L204944	**20121** BRe blue disc - *02*	30	45
L204836	**20131 'Almon B Strowager'** BRT grey, ccb - *94*	30	40
L204982	**20164** BRe blue - *02*	NPG	55
L204822	**20169** BRe Central Services pink +grey, light, *see ***20092 - 93*	35	NA
L205158	**20171** BReLL blue * ccb, light grey roof - *85*	30	40
-	**20172 'Redmire'** BRe blue, grey cab roof, name on red solebar Thornaby motif - *00*	50	NA
-	**20173 'Wensleydale'** as above - *00*	50	NA
L149974	above two Sp Edn 300 (Beatties) - *00*	NA	125
L205157	**20183** BRe (on body side) blue, ccb, domino style headcodes - *85*	30	40
-	**20183** BRe blue, no detail ex-set L103807TW - *85*	65	80
L205068	**20187** BRT grey+green * ccb - *93*	30	40
L204881	**20188** Waterman black, ccb 3D94 - *96*	25	35
L205159	**20215** BReLL Rft red stripe grey - *85*	30	40
L204634	**20222** BRe blue, ccb, light, large numbers, Haymarket motifs - *98*	25	35
L204662	**20227 'Traction'** Railfreight red stripe grey Sp.Edn. 500 (Traction) - *98*	35	50
L204902	**20227 'Sir John Betjeman'** maroon Met. livery Class 20 Loco Society - *01*	35	50
L205263	**20901** DRS. blue Sp Edn 750 (Rail Express), disc - *00*	35	50
L205263	**20901** DRS. blue Sp Edn 750 (Rail Express), disc,'Kosovo Train for Life' headboards - *00*	50	70
L204249	**20903 'Allison'** Hunslet-Barclay grey disc - *00*	30	40
L205113	**20904** DRS. blue, red sole, disc - *01*	35	50
L204813	**20906 'Kilmarmock 400'** Hunslet- Barclay grey Ltd Edn 850 - *93*	50	65
L204914	**20906** DRS. blue, red sole, ccb - *01*	35	50

* Not authentic.

L12. Class 26

sno = snowploughs.

L204699	**D5300/26007** BRc green Sp Edn 550 (Harburn) etched plaques and shedplates, plastic headlights - *99*	30	40
L205075	**D5301 'Eastfield'** BRc green Ltd Edn 550 - *93*	65	80

L204878	**D5310** BRc green - *94*	25	35
L205242	**26001** Railfreight Coal grey - *90*	25	35
L205246	**26003** BRe blue Haymarket motif - *89*	25	35
L205008	**26004** BRe Dutch grey+yellow, Eastfield shedplates - *91*	25	35
L205245	**26004** BRe Railfreight red stripe grey - *90*	25	38
L204677	**26006** BReLL Rft red stripe grey - *99*	25	35
-	**26010** Rft grey ex-set L106306 - *90*	35	NA
L205244	**26027** BRe blue, discs sno - *90*	20	35
L205243	**26038** BRe Railfreight red stripe grey, Eastfield motif - *90*	30	40
L205173	**26040** BRe Dutch grey+yellow Eastfield motif - *00*	30	40

Class 20 in BR green [L11]

L13. Class 27

L205248	**D5394** BRc green, yellow half panels, headcode 1Z98 - *90*	25	35
L204671	**27001** BRe blue, Eastfield motif - *99*	25	35
L205252	**27037** BRe blue, Eastfield motif - *89*	30	40
L205247	**27102** BRe blue - *89*	30	40

Class 26 in 'Duch' livery [L12]

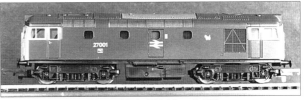

Class 27 in BR blue [L13]

L14. Class 31

L205239	**D5500** BRc green, discs, no yellow panels - *90*	30	40
L205093	**5518** BRe green Royal Train white roof - *00*	32	45
L204640	**D5551** BRc green Sp Edn 550 (MR&ME) - *98*	30	60
L204614	**D5578** BRc experimental blue, code ccb 7M68 - *98*	25	36
L204624	**D5579** BRc experimental 'golden ochre' - *98*	25	40
L204859	**D5583 'Stratford Major Depot'** BRc green, BR No.31165, yellow panel and white wrap windows - *94*	30	40

L205092	**D5679** BRc green - *89*	30	40
L205093	**D5830** BRc green, half yell panel - *89*	30	40
L205238	**31004** BRe blue, discs - *90*	30	40
L204868	**31105 'Bescot TMD'** Transrail triple grey - *96*	30	40
L204637	**31106 'The Black Countryman'** BRe Dutch grey+yellow see below - *98*	35	50
L204637	**31107 'John H. Carless VC'** BRe Dutch grey+yellow see below - *98*	35	50
-	above two locos sold as pair Sp Edn 300 (Langdale) - *98*	NA	100
L205109	**31107** BReLL Rft red stripe grey, headcode boxes removed - *01*	30	40
L204908	**31108** original Rft - *02*	NPG	55
L205282	**31110 'Traction'** BRc green 81A plates, small yellow panels, white stripes Sp Edn (Warner Group/Rails) - *00*	30	40
L204704	**31112** Transrail grey+yellow - *96*	30	40
L205072	**31116 'Rail 1981-1991'** BRe Dutch grey+yellow (sold in Scotland) - *91*	40	65
-	**31116 'Rail 1981-1991'** BRe Dutch grey+ yellow, with headcodes Sp Edn 500 (Rail) - *91*	30	55
L205114	**31116 'Rail Celebrity'** BRe Infrastruc yellow+grey Bescot motifs - *00*	30	40
L205172	**31019** BRe blue grey roof - *99*	30	40
L204967	**31130 'Caulder Hall Power Station'** BRe Coal Sector 2-tone grey Crewe Diesel motifs - *02*	NPG	55
L205232	**31160 'Phoenix'** BRe Railfreight Distribution grey, Tinsley plates - *90*	30	40
L204940	**31185** BRe Petroleum Sector - *02*	NPG	55
-	**31199** BReLL Rft Distribution grey - *?*	320	400
L205095	**31201 'Fina Energy'** BRe Rft Petroleum grey, Fina logo - *91*	30	40
L205031	**31206** BRe Rft red stripe grey - *91*	30	40
L205237	**31275** BRe Railfreight Coal grey, Canton shedplates - *89*	30	40
L205236	**31283** BRe blue, large numbers,	30	40
L205213	**31296 'Amlwch Freighter/Tren Nwyddau Amlwch'** BReLL Railfreight grey, yellow cabs - *90*	30	40
L205190	**31309 'Cricklewood'** BRe blue Sp Edn 500 (Beatties) - *99*	30	45
L205091	**31325** BRe blue - *89*	30	40
L205234	**31327 'Phillips Imperial'** Railfreight red stripe grey, large numbers - *89*	30	40
L205235	**31402** BRe blue - *89*	30	40
L204730	**31407** Mainline blue - *96*	30	40
L205255	**31410 'Granada Telethon'** BRe Regional Railways grey+blue - *00*	30	40
L204946	**31411** BRe blue, white stripe - *02*	30	45
L205032	**31413 'Severn Valley Railway'** BRe Severn Valley blue unofficial Provincial Services livery - *91*	30	50
L204845	**31421 'Wigan Pier'** BRe Regional Railways grey+blue - *96*	30	40
L205233	**31423** BRe I-C Mainline grey - *90*	60	80
L205069	**31439** BRe Regional Railways grey+blue Ltd Edn 850 - *93*	45	60
L204673	**31452** Fragonset Railways black - *99*	30	40
L205196	**31455 'Our Eli'** BRe Regional Railways grey+blue - *99*	30	40
L204980	**31467** BRe blue - *02*	NPG	50
L204661	**31466** EWS maroon - *98*	25	37
L204687	**31468** Fragonset Railways black - *99*	30	40
L205096	**31541** BRe Dutch grey+yellow, Immingham shedplates - *91*	30	40
L205094	**31568 'The Enginemans Fund'** BRe Departmental grey - *90*	30	40
L205094	**31601 'Bletchley Park Station X'** Fragonset Railways black - *00*	30	40
L205229	**31970** BRe Research Division red+grey - RTC Derby - *90*	30	40

Class 31 'Our Eli' in Regional Railways livery [L14]

L15.   Class 33

Body improved in 1986. sno = snowploughs.

L205115	**D6506** BRc green, big numbers, half yellow front - *78*	25	35
L205129	**D6506** BRc green, big numbers, no yellow panel - *88*	25	35
L205114	**D6524** BRe blue, yellow window frames - *77*	25	35
L205114	**D6524** BRe chromatic blue - *77*	25	35
	D6535 'Herefordshire Rail Tours' (see 33116)		
L205116	**215** CIE orange+black - *78*	NPG	NPG
?	IR orange+black Sp Edn (Murphy's Models) - *92*	25	40
L205221	**33008 'Eastleigh'** BRc green half yellow ends sno - *87*	25	47
L205126	**33008 'Eastleigh'** BRe green full yellow ends - *86*	25	35
L204911	**33021 'Eastleigh'** BRe Post Office red, Eastfield motif - *01*	25	35
L205114	**33024** BRe blue, yellow fronts - *81*	25	38
L205115	**33025** BReLL blue logo too small - *82*	30	40
-	**33025** BRe blue, small nos. ex-set - *82*	28	NA
L204660	**33025** EWS maroon - *98*	30	40
L205114	**33027 'Earl Mountbatten of Burma'** BRe blue, white cab roofs, red buffer beams - *83*	30	40
-	**33027 'Earl Mountbatten of Burma'** BRe blue, white cab roofs, black buff beam ex-set L103706V - *83*	28	NA
L204660	**33030** EWS maroon - *98*	25	45
-	**33033** Railfreight Construction grey, ex-set 104313 - *92*	28	NA
L205070SI	**33033** triple grey for Railwayana, no body markings - *89*	25	40
L205074	**33035** revised NSE bright blue, sno - *93*	25	35
L204610	**33046 'Merlin'** BRe grey+yellow - *98*	25	40
L205228	**33050 'Isle of Grain'** BRe Railfreight Construction grey - *89*	25	40
-	**33051 'Shakespeare Cliff'** Railfreight Construction grey ex-set L105111 - *89*	28	NA
L204756	**33051 'Shakespeare Cliff'** BRe grey+ yellow Sp Edn 500 (Rail Express) - *97*	40	55
L205142	**33052 'Ashford'** BRe blue sno - *01*	30	40
L205174	**33056 'The Burma Star'** BRe blue, red beam, white roof, large buffers - *87*	30	40
-	**33056 'The Burma Star'** BRe blue, red beam, white roof, small buffers ex-set L174MWG - *87*	28	NA
-	**33056 'The Burma Star'** BRe blue, black beam large buffers, white roof, ex-set L103407V- *87*	28	NA
-	**33056 'The Burma Star'** BRe blue, black beam small buffers, white roof ex-set - *87*	28	NA
L204705	**33063** BRe Mainline triple grey - *95*	25	42
L205030	**33065** BRe Dutch grey+yellow small numbers on body sides - *91*	25	42
L205116	**33105** BRe blue push-pull - *87*	30	40
L205073	**33109 'Captain Bill Smith RNR'** BRe Departmental plain grey - *94*	30	45
L205185	**33114 'Ashford 150'** Revised NSE bright blue, headboard, Ltd Edn 850 - *92*	70	100
L204841	**33116/D6535 'Hertfordshire Rail Tours'** BRe blue Sp Edn 500 (Hertfordshire Rail Tours Sales) - *98*	40	55
L205070	**33205** Railfreight Distribution grey, side body numbers small - *89*	30	45

L204986	**33207** DRS blue - *02*	NPG	55

Class 33 'Captain Bill Smith RNR' in department grey [L15]

L16. Class 37

sno = snowploughs fitted. syp = small yellow panels. scb = split codebox. ccb = central codebox. ib = improved body.

L204858	**D6607 'Ben Cruachan'** BRc green Sp Edn 500 (Harburn Hobbies) etched Eastfield Depot motifs + nameplates, syp, sno - *94*	90	150
L204644	**D6700** BRc green, small yellow panels, Sp Edn 500 (ModelRail) - *98*	35	50
L205222	**D6722** BRc green, no yellow ends - *87*	30	45
L205173	**D6755** BRc green, half yellow panel oversize nos. scb headcode 0F75 - *87*	30	45
L204834	**D6916 'Great Eastern'** BRc green Ltd Edn 1000 216 on ends, syp - *94*	50	65
L204772	**D6999** BRc green Sp Edn 550 (MR&ME) 300th diesel electric, 5T17 code in boxes - *97*	50	65
L205172	**37012 'Loch Rannoch'** BRe blue, white stripe, red buffer beams, silver handrails, sno, Eastfield motif, scb - *87*	45	50
-	**37012 'Loch Rannoch'** BRe blue, white stripe, black buffer beams sno Eastfield motif scb no end detail ex-set L106206- *87*	35	NA
L204717	**37013** Railfreight triple grey unspecified Sp Edn 500 (Geoffrey Allison) - *96*	40	55
L205198	**37013** Mainline blue, scb - *99*	30	45
L204866	**37023 'Stratford TMD Quality Approved'** Mainline blue, Stratford motif, split headcodes - *94*	35	50
L204879	**37025 'Inverness TMD'** BReLL blue (extended) Sp Edn 500 (Harburn Hobbies) etched nameplates yellow cab, Inverness motif, sno, scb - *95*	70	100
L20?	**37026 'Shap Fell'** Speedlink grey Sp Edn 500 (Collectable Models) - *01?*	NPG	NPG
L204693	**37027 'Loch Eil'** BReLL blue Sp Edn 550 (Geoffrey Allison) Eastfield motif, yellow cab, sno, scb - *99*	30	45
L204786	**37032 'Mirage'** Railfreight red stripe grey, Sp Edn 550 (Macclesfield Model Centre), unofficial name - *98*	35	47
L204968	**37042** BRe Mainline triple grey - *03*	NPG	50
L205189	**37043 'Loch Lomond'** BRe blue, Sp Edn 550 (Harburn Hobbies) etched metal nameplates small Eastfield motif - *99*	35	49
L205294	**37049** BRe blue, scb - *89*	30	45
-	**37051** Rft Metals grey, ex set L106307 - *92*	50	NA
L204613	**37057 'Viking'** EW&S maroon - *98*	28	37
-	**37063** Rft Distrib grey, ex-set L106307 - *89*	50	NA
L205076	**37069** BRe Dutch grey+yellow scb - *91*	30	45
L205190	**37081 'Loch Long'** BReLL blue, small Eastfield motif, 'computer' style numbers, sno, scb, yellow cabs - *87*	50	65
L205171	**37082** BReLL, Rft grey 8 - *87*	30	45
L205177	**(37093)** BR painted in Police car white livery for a TV advert, no number carried - *87*	45	85
L204760	**37095 'British Steel Teeside'** BRe blue, white cantrail stripe, Thornaby motif, scb - *97*	30	45

L205077	**37099 'Clydesbridge'** BRe grey Rft Metals, scb, Motherwell plates - *93*	30	45
L20?	**37100** Rft Metals grey, flush No.2 end Sp Edn (Moray's) - *cancelled*	NA	NA
L204680	**37111 'Loch Eil Outward Bound'** BReLL blue Eastfield motif Sp Edn 500 (Moray's) - *98*	30	45
L205091	**37112** BRe blue, scb, wrap round yellow ends, 1981 hybrid livery - *00*	30	45
L205286	**37113** BRe blue, scb, large Eastfield motif - *89*	30	45
L205288	**37114 'Dunrobin Castle'** BReLL blue, numbers and logo too small, Inverness motif, scb - *89*	55	80
L205128	**37114 'City of Worcester'** EW&S maroon, Inverness motif, scb - *01*	45	50
L204714	**37116 'Sister Dora'** Transrail on Rail blue Sp Edn 500 (Rail Express) etched plates enclosed - *96*	60	100
L205299	**37133** BRe Departmental grey - *91*	30	45
L205218	**37137 'Clyde Iron'** Railfreight Metals grey sno - *99*	30	40
L205289	**37140** BRe blue Stratford motif ccb - *89*	30	45
L204973	**37154** BRe Transrail triple grey - *02*	NPG	55
L205124	**37180 'Sir Dyfed/County of Dyfed'** Railfreight all-over grey, sno, ccb - *87*	35	50
L205018	**37184** Railfreight Petroleum grey, Immingham motif - *91*	30	45
L205019	**37185** Rft Distribution grey - *91*	30	45
L204948	**37188 'Jimmy Shand'** BReLL blue Sp Edn 500 (Harburn Hobbies) Eastfield motif - *02*	35	50
-	**37190** BReLL blue see ** below - *cancelled*	NA	NA
L204985	**37194 'British International Freight Association'** Mainline grey - *02*	NPG	50
L204700	**37201 'Saint Margaret'** Transrail on BRe Dutch grey+yellow - *96*	30	45
L205033	**37207 'William Cookworthy'** BRe blue, Cornish Railways on cab fronts with Cornish and BR flags - *00*	30	45
L204788	**37209 'Phantom'** BReLL blue Sp Edn 550 (Geoffrey Allison) sno - *98*	30	45
L208434	**37216 'Great Eastern'** green Ltd Edn 1000, D6916 - *94*	45	60
L204711	**37219** Mainline blue, number at wrong end one side - *96*	30	45
L205297	**37223** BRe Railfreight Coal grey, Canton motif - *90*	40	55
L205017	**37232 'The Institution of Railway Signal Engineers'** grey+yellow - *91*	35	50
L205079	**37251 'The Northern Lights'** InterCity Swallow grey - *93*	30	45
-	**37260 'Radio Highland'** BReLL blue Inverness motif (see ** below) - *cancelled*	35	NA
L20?	****above model + 37190 Sp Edn (Moray's) - *cancelled*	NA	NA
-	**37261 'Caithness'** BReLL blue see below - *00*	40	NA
—	**37262 'Dounreay'** BReLL blue see below - *00*	40	NA
L205262	above 2 models Ltd Edn 300 (Geoffrey Allison) - *00*	NA	100
L204663	**37275 'Oor Wullie'** BRe blue, Sp Edn 550 (Rails) - *98*	30	44
L204938	**37308** BRe blue, new body, Sp Edn 500 (Much Ado About Toys) - *02*	NPG	50
L205123	**37310 'British Steel Ravenscraig'** BReLL blue, dark roof, small logo Glasgow South motif, ccb - *87*	50	80
L205287	**37350/D6700** BRc green, small yellow panel - *89*	35	50
L205193	**37351** Transrail on grey+yellow scb - *99*	30	45
L205215	**37370** BReLL Railfreight red stripe grey, Glasgow South motif, sno - *99*	30	45

Code	Description		
L204960	37379 'Ipswich WRD Quality Approved' Mainline blue - 02	NPG	55
L205290	37401 'Mary Queen of Scots' InterCity Mainline grey, sno, ccb - 89	35	50
L204771	37401 'Mary Queen of Scots' BRe Railfreight Distribution triple grey Sp Edn 500 (Harburn Hobbies), sno, etched nameplates and arrows - 97	75	90
L204975	37401 'Mary Queen of Scots' EWS maroon - 02	NPG	55
L205178	37402 'Oor Wullie' BReLL blue, incorrect mould, no sealed beam headlight - 87	35	50
L204773	37402 'Bont-y-Bermo' Railfreight unspecified triple grey, Sp Edn 550 (Geoffrey Allison), sno - 97	30	45
L20?	37403 'Glendarroch' BRe triple grey unbranded, Eastfield motif, Rft Dist + Railfreight General decals, etched nameplates (Moray's) - cancelled	NA	NA
L205129	37404 'Ben Cruachan' InterCity Mainline grey Sp Edn 275 (Harburn) + metal etched nameplates sno - 00	50	150
L204812	37405 'Strathclyde Region' BReLL blue, small nos., small logo, large Eastfield motif, sno, ccb - 94	35	50
L205241	37405 'Strathclyde Region' InterCity Mainline grey Sp Edn 350 (Moray's) sold with 37417 - 00	35	50
L205219	37406 'The Saltire Society' Transrail on triple grey Sp Edn 550 (Harburn), sno, etched nameplates - 99	35	49
L204863	37407 'Blackpool Tower' Transrail, triple grey 407 on front end - 95	30	45
L204863	37407 'Blackpool Tower' Transrail, triple grey - 95	30	45
L204696	37407 'Loch Long' InterCity Mainline red stripe grey Sp Edn 500 (Morays) sno - 99	35	50
L204882	37408 'Loch Rannoch' BReLL blue, large Eastfield motif, sno - 95	30	70
L204882	37408 'Loch Rannoch' BReLL blue, large Eastfield motif, sno, no detail on front, ex-set - 95	45	NA
L204675	37409 'Loch Awe' BReLL blue Sp Edn 550 (Harburn) sno, Eastfield motif, etched nameplates, yellow cabs - 98	35	47
L204949	37410 'Aluminium 100' Transrail grey Sp Edn 500 (Harburn) - 02	35	50
L204762	37411 'Ty Hafan' EWS maroon, sno - 97	30	45
L20?	37412 'Loch Lomond' BReLL blue Sp Edn 500 (Collectable Models) - 01?	NPG	NPG
L204632	37413 'Scottish Railway Preservation Society' EWS maroon Sp Edn 700 (Harburn and SRPS), etched nameplates + SRPS Railtours headboard, ticket - 98	35	50
L204817	37414 'Cathays C&W Works 1846-1993' BRe Reg Rlys grey+blue Ltd Edn 850 - 93	100	130
L149442	37415/416/419/426 InterCity Mainline grey Sp Edn 300 (Rails) set of 4 models - 01	NA	180
-	37415 'Mt Etna' InterCity Mainline grey, Sp Edn see below*** - 01	40	NA
-	37416 'Mt Fuji' InterCity Mainline grey, Sp Edn see below *** - 01	40	NA
L149442	***37415/416/419/426 InterCity Mainline grey Sp Edn set 300 (Rails) - 01	NA	180
L205241	37417 'Highland Region' InterCity Mainline grey Sp Edn 350 (Moray's) sold with 37405 - 00	35	50
L205266	37417 'Rail Magazine' EWS maroon black and gold nameplates sno - 00	30	45
L204625	37418 'East Lancashire Railway' BRe Regional Railways grey+blue - 98	30	45
L204820	37418 'Pectinidae' Rft Petroleum grey Sp Edn 250 (Langdales) paired with 37421 - 99	35	50
L205027	37418 'An Comunn Gaidhealach' BReLL blue, Inverness motif + metal etched nameplates Sp Edn 550 (Harburn Hobbies) - 01	35	50
-	37419 InterCity Mainline grey ex-set L104311 - 92	65	NA
-	37419 'Mt Pinatubo' InterCity Mainline grey, Sp see above *** - 01	40	NA
L204641	37420 'The Scottish Hosteller' blue BReLL Sp Edn 550 (MR&ME) - 98	30	45
L204697	37420 'The Scottish Hosteller' BRe Regional Railways bright blue, etched nameplates and logo, sno, Sp Edn 1000 (Morays + Geoffrey Allison) - 99	35	50
L204731	37421 'The Kingsman' BRe Regional Railways grey+blue sno - 96	55	70
L204819	37421 'Strombidae' Railfreight Petroleum grey Sp Edn 250 (Langdales) paired with 37418 - 99	35	50
L204763	37422 'Robert F.Fairlie' BRe Regional Railways grey+blue, spelling mistake, sno - 97	30	45
L149932	37423 'Sir Murray Morrison...' Railfreight Distribution grey, sno, Sp Edn 330 (Langdales) paired with 37428 - 98	30	45
L204784	37424 'Isle of Mull' Mainline grey Sp Edn 550 (Harburn Hobbies) sno, etched nameplates - 98	35	50
L204782	37425 'Sir Robert McAlpine/ Concrete Bob' BRe Regional Railways grey+ blue Sp Edn 550 (Rails) sno - 97	50	65
L204897	37425 'Sir Robert McAlpine/ Concrete Bob' Raifreight Construction grey Sp Edn 500 (Rails) sno - 96	55	70
L204655	37425 'Sir Robert McAlpine/ Concrete Bob' BReLL blue Sp Edn 550 (Rails) sno yellow cab Eastfield motif - 98	30	45
L204612	37426 EWS maroon - 98	30	45
-	37426 'Mt Vesuvius' InterCity Mainline grey, Sp Edn see above *** - 01	40	NA
L204842	37427 'Highland Enterprise' BRe Regional Railways/ScotRail grey+blue, Sp Edn 500 (D&F) uncertificated - 94	70	100
L149932	37428 'David Lloyd George' Railfreight Petroleum grey, sno, Sp Edn 330 (Langdales) paired with 37423 - 98	30	45
L204659	37428 'Loch Awe' Royal Claret livery for the Royal Scotsman/GSWR train EWS motif Sp Edn 550 (Harburn Hobbies) sno - 98	50	70
L204887	37429 'Eisteddfod Genedlaethol' BRe Regional Railways grey+blue - 94	30	60
L205298	37430 'Cwmbran' InterCity Mainline grey, number wrong end one side - 92	50	80
L205176	37431 'County of Powys'/'Sir Powys' BReLL blue, red dragon motif, coat of arms, yellow cabs - 00	30	45
L204824	37431 'Bullidae' IC Mainline grey Petroleum train load logos sno Sp Edn 335 (Langdales) - 99	55	70
L205230	37501 'Teeside Steelmaster' BReLL British Steel blue, Thornaby motif, BSC logo - 90	50	65
L205231	37502 'British Steel Teeside' BReLL Railfreight red stripe grey, large nos. - 90	45	60
L204983	37505 'British Steel Workington' Transrail - 03	45	60
L205078	37506 'British Steel Skinningrove' BReLL Railfreight red stripe grey, Thornaby motif - 94	30	45
L204843	37510 InterCity Swallow grey - 95	30	60
L205293	37511 'Stockton Haulage' BRe Railfreight Metals grey, large numbers, Thornaby motif - 89	50	65
L204709	37517 'St. Aidens' Loadhaul black+	30	45

	orange - 96		
-	**37519** Railfreight red stripe grey, large nos, ex-set L107157 Thornaby motif - 89	55	NA
L204647	**37605** EPS triple grey Tunnel motifs - 98	55	70
L204684	**37607** DRS blue Ltd Edn 750 - 99	40	60
L204796	**37609** DRS blue - 98	50	70
L204605	**37610** DRS blue Sp Edn 550 (Rail Express) - 98	60	100
L204683	**37611** DRS blue - 99	50	70
L204737	**37671 'Tre Pol And Pen'** Rft Dist triple grey, St Blazey motif, sno - 97	60	100
L205285	**37673** Rft Dis gry St Blazey motif - 87	45	60
L204937	**37674 'Saint Blaise Church 1445- 1995'** Transrail grey, upgrade tool - 02	35	50
L205208	**37675 'William Cookworthy'** Railfreight red stripe grey Ltd Edn 850 - 92	50	65
L204754	**37682 'Hartlepool Pipe Mill'** EW&S maroon - 97	30	45
L205178	**37684 'Peak National Park'** BRe Rft Construction grey Buxton motif ib Sp Edn 500 (Geoffrey Allison + DPS) - 01	30	45
L205296	**37688 'Great Rocks'** BRe Railfreight Construction grey Buxton motif - 90	40	70
L204891	**37692 'The Lass O Ballochmyle'** BRe Rft Coal grey Sp Edn 500 (D&F Models) Eastfield motif - 95	70	100
L205025	**37693 'Sir William Arrol'** BRe Rft Coal grey, Eastfield motif, ib, etched nameplates, Sp Edn 550 (Harburn) - 00	35	50
L204979	**37697** original Railfreight - 02	NPG	55
L204765	**37698 'Coedbach'** Rft Coal grey - 97	30	45
L204735	**37702 'Taff Merthyr'** Railfreight Coal triple grey, Canton motif - 96	30	45
-	**37711 'Tremorfa Steel Works'** Railfreight Metals triple grey, see below - 01	40	NA
-	**37712 'The Cardiff Rod Mill'** Railfreight Metals triple grey see below - 01	40	NA
L204922	above two models Canton motifs Sp Edn 350 (Geoffrey Allison) - 01	NA	96
L204856	**37713** Loadhaul sticker attached black+ orange - 94	30	45
L204793	**37714** EWS maroon - 98	25	38
L204892	**37715 'British Petroleum'** BRe Mainline on Railfreight unspec triple grey Stewarts Lane BP logo - 95	30	45
L204964	**37715 'British Petroleum'** Railfreight Construction/Petroleum - 02	NPG	65
L204740	**37717 'Maltby Lilly Hall'** EW&S maroon - 97	30	45
L204886	**37718** Mainline blue, revised moulding, Stewarts Lane motif - 94	30	45
L204622	**37884 'Gartcosh'** Loadhaul black+orange - 98	22	34
L20?	**37887 'Castell Caerfilli/ Caerphilly Castle'** Railfreight Coal grey Sp Edn (Collectable Models) - 01	NPG	NPG
L20?	**37888 'Petrolea'** Railfreight Petroleum grey Sp Edn (Collectable Models) - 01	NPG	NPG
L205034	**37890 'The Railway Observer'** BRe Railfreight Petroleum triple grey Ripple Lane motif - 00	30	45
L205284	**37892 'Ripple Lane'** Railfreight Petroleum triple grey, Ripple Lane motif - 87	50	65
L204954	**37899** GIF light blue Spanish infrastructure livery - not released	NPG	NPG
L20?	**37901 'Mirlees Pioneer'** Railfreight Metals grey Sp Edn (Collectable Models) - 01?	NPG	NPG
L205285	**37905 'Vulcan Enterprise'** BRe Railfreight Metals triple grey Canton motif, 700 - 00	30	45
L205096	**37906 (Slug 6)** Transrail triple grey, only 300 made - 00	50	80
L204910	**37906** BReLL grey, Railfreight logos, wrap round yellow ends, red buffer beams - ?	NPG	NPG

L204910	**37906 (Slug 6)** Railfreight grey, Canton motif, 700 - 01	35	50
L204932	**37906 'Star of the East'** Transrail triple grey, new body shell - 01	35	50

* Not an authentic livery.

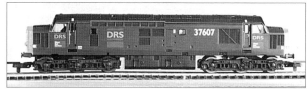

Class 37 in DRS livery [L16]

L17.   Class 40

scb = split codebox. ccb = central codebox. hyp - yellow half panels. fyp = full yellow panels.

L204939	**200** BRc blue - 02	30	45
L205064	**D205** BRc green no yellow panels, discs - 89	30	45
L205233	**D210 'Empress of Britain'** BRc green Sp Edn (Rails) - 99	30	40
L204728	**D233 'Empress of England'** BRc green, discs Sp Edn 550 (Rails) hyp - 97	40	55
L205060	**D261** BRc green, ccb 3E28 light grey roof, fyp - 88	30	45
L205065	**D334** BRc green scb, hyp - 89	30	45
L205201	**D335** BRc green scb - 88	30	45
L205062	**D354** BRc green ccb 1A75 hyp - 89	30	45
L204642	**337** BRc green scb - 98	30	45
L205189	**40001** BRe blue discs - 88	30	45
L204698	**40012 'Aureol'** BRe blue Sp Edn 500 (Moray's) - 99	35	50
L205063	**40052** BRe blue discs - 90	30	45
L205104	**40052** BRc green full yellow panels - 00	30	40
L205217	**40063** BRe blue ccb - 89	30	45
L205187	**40066** BRe blue ccb - 89	30	45
L205188	**40106 'Altantic Conveyor'** BRc revised green, discs fyp - 88	35	50
L205200	**40122/D200** BRc green, discs - 88	30	45
L205278	**40126** BRe blue scb - 89	30	45
L205202	**40140** BRe blue scb - 90	30	45
L205061	**40145** BRe blue ccb - 88	30	45
L204972	**40155** BRe blue red bufferbeam - 02	NPG	NPG
L204972	**40155** BRe blue blk bufferbeam - 03	NPG	NPG

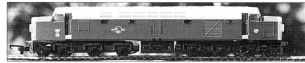

Class 40 in BR green [L17]

L18.   Classes 42 & 43 (Warships)

L205127	**D801 'Vanguard'** BRe blue, planned 1980 replaced by 'Dragon' - not made	NA	NA
L204894	**D807 'Caradoc'** BRe blue- 96	30	38
L204669	**D809 'Champion'** BRc maroon - 99	30	38
L149966	**D809 'Champion'** BRc maroon train pack with 3 coaches - 99	NA	70
-	**D814 'Dragon'** BRe blue ex-set L107307 - 80	35	NA
L205127	**814 'Dragon'** BRe blue, headcode 1A15 - 80	30	38
L204861	**D815 'Druid'** BRc maroon - 95	30	38
L204837	**D819 'Goliath'** BRc green Ltd Edn 1000, spelling error, red nameplates - 94	35	50
L205083	**828 'Magnificent'** BRe blue, headcodes 7C39, 1V13 - 93	30	38
L205128	**D838 'Pathfinder'** BRc maroon planned 1980 replaced by 'Rapid' - not made	NA	NA
L205128	**D838 'Rapid'** BRc maroon yellow half panels, headcode 1A15 - 80	30	45

Lima 00

L205135	**D843 'Sharpshooter'** BRc green headcode 1A15 - *80*	30	45

Class 42 'Champion' in BR maroon [L18]

L19. Class 43 HST Power & Dummy Cars

I-C = InterCity. ICs = InterCity Swallow.

L205253	**43024 + 43025** FGW green - *00*	NPG	NPG
L149909	**43043 'Leicestershire County Cricket Club'** + **43075** Midland Mainline teal green train pack - *98*	50	65
L205080	**43051 'Duke and Duchess of York'** ICs grey - *89*	25	35
L205082	**43051 'Duke and Duchess of York'** + **43072**ICs grey ex-set L106520 - *89*	50	NA
L205197 L205199	**43053 'County of Humberside'** + **43136** BRe I-C 125 exec grey ex L149811 set - *87*	50	NA
L149806	**43058 'Midland Pride'** + **43059** Midland Mainline teal green train pack - *98*	65	78
L14****	**43108 'Old Course St Andrews'** + **43105** ' pack 250 (Harburn) - *02*	65	85
L205160	**43113 'City of Newcastle Upon Tyne'** +	45	60
L205164	**43063** BRe I-C 125 blue L149751 train pack - *84*		
L205164	**43063** BRe I-C 125 blue, dummy - *84*	18	25
L205169	**43085 'City of Bradford'** BRe I-C 125 grey - *87*	25	35
L205198	**43091 'Edinburgh Military Tattoo'** BRe I-C 125 grey dummy - *87*	18	25
L149849	**43093 'Lady in Red'** + **43155** 'The Red Arrows' Virgin XC red train pack - *98*	65	NA
L149872	**43096 'The Great Racer'** + **43110** GNER navy, white lettering, train pack - *97*	60	75
L204681	**43100 'Blackpool Rock'** + **43101** 'The Irish Mail' Virgin red - *99*	35	50
-	**43105 'City of Inverness'** GNER navy blue *see ** below*	35	NA
-	**43108 'Old Course St Andrews'** GNER navy blue *see ** below*	35	NA
L149624	** pack containing 43105 and 43108 + 2 Mk3 coaches (41092+42179) Sp Edn 260 (Harburn Hobbies) - *02*	50	70
L149908	**43109 + 43167** GNER navy, pearl lettering, train pack - *98*	45	60
L205160	**43113 'City of Newcastle Upon Tyne'** (253042) BRe InterCity 125 blue- *84*	25	35
L205160	**43116 'City of Kingston Upon Hull'** + ? (253042) BRe InterCity 125 blue ex-107006 set of '84 - *made?*	NPG	NA
L149918	**43117 + 43118** GNER navy gold lettering, train pack - *98*	50	65
-	**43122 + 43178** Virgin red ex-set L106506 - *99*	45	60
L205184 L205180	**43125 + 43126(253028)** BRe I-C 125 executive grey - *85*	50	NA
L204733	**43129** ICs grey dummy - *96*	15	20
L149849	**43155 'The Red Arrows'** Virgin XC red - *98*	NPG	NPG
L205254	**43157 'HMS Penzance'** Virgin XC red - *99*	25	35
L149916	**43160 'Storm Force'** + **43090** Virgin red train pack - *98*	50	65
L205160 L205164	**W43167 + W43168** BRe I-C 125 blue ex L149751 train pack and L103416V set - *82*	50	NA
L205160	**W43167** BRe I-C blue 125 - *82*	25	35
L205164	**W43168** BRe I-C 125 blue dummy - *82*	18	25
L149975	**43172 + 43009** First Great Western green +	80	95

	2 Mk3 coaches - *00*		
-	**43177 'University of Exeter'** + **43139** ICs grey ex-set L106522 - *97*	65	NA
-	**43177 + 43139** ICs grey ex-set L106522- *98*	65	NA
L205081/ L205082	**43178 + 43072** ICs grey ex-set - *89*	40	NA
L204732	**43181 'Devonport Royal Dockyard'** ICs grey - *96*	35	40
L149871	**43185 'Great Western'** + **43168** GWT green train pack - *97*	65	NA
L205165/ L205168	orange+silver ex-Australian XPT L205165 pack, no numbers - *84*	35	NA

Class 43 in First Great western green [L19]

L20. Classes 45/46

This was shown as a proposed model in the 1989/90 catalogue but was dropped, possibly because there was already a model on the market and it was felt that it did not offer adequate variations in livery. ccb = central codeboxes. scb = split codeboxes.

L205203	**D100 'Sherwood Forester'** BRc green no yellow panels - *not made*	NA	NA
L205207	**45012** BRe blue ccb - *not made*	NA	NA
L205205	**45032** BRe blue scb - *not made*	NA	NA
L205204	**45054** BRe blue scb - *not made*	NA	NA
L205206	**46004** BRe blue+grey plated nose with lights - *not made*	NA	NA

L21. Class 47

sno = snowploughs fitted.

L205103	**D1111** BRc 2-tone green, - *02*	40	50
L204904	**D1524** BRc 2-tone green, headcodes 0F70 + 1E07 - *01*	30	40
L205215	**D1574** BRc 2-tone green, original as built livery - *89*	30	40
L204718	**D1664 'George Jackson Churchward'** BRc 2-tone green Sp Edn 500 (MR&ME) - *96*	50	90
L204775	**D1733** blue Sp Edn 240 (Langdales) headcode XP64, no red panels - *97*	70	85
L204775	**D1733** blue Sp Edn 280 (Langdales) headcode XP64, with red panels fitted after leaving the factory - *97*	60	80
L205049	**D1761** BRc 2-tone green, headcode 1S33 - *89*	35	50
L205219	**D1842** BRc 2-tone green, headcode 1M35 - *89*	35	50
L205192	**D1957** BRe blue - *99*	30	40
	D1962 (see 47833)		
L204835	**47004/D1524 'Old Oak Common T&RSMD'** BRc 2-tone green, headcode 0F70 - *95*	40	60
L205255	**47006** Rft Construction grey, sno - *90*	35	50
L149930	**47010 'Xancidae'** Railfreight Petroleum grey Sp Edn 200 (Macclesfield Model Centre) part of 4 pack - *98*	50	65
L205210	**47016 'Atlas'** BReLL Railfreight grey, '1546', yellow cabsides - *99*	30	45
L204710	**47033 'The Royal Logistics Corps'** Railfreight Distribution European grey, Tunnel motif - *96*	30	50
L205266	**47079** Railfreight Metals grey - *88*	30	40
L204600	**47114 'Freightliner Bulk'** Freightliner 2-tone green Sp Edn 550 (Rail Express) - *97*	50	75
L149930	**47125 'Tonnidae'** Railfreight Petroleum grey Sp Edn 200 (Macclesfield Model Centre) part of 4 pack - *98*	60	65
L204789	**47142 'Traction'** Railfreight red stripe grey Sp Edn 550 (Macclesfield Model Centre), unofficial name - *98*	35	50

Code	Description		
L204860	47145 'Merddin Emrys' Tinsley blue, Speedlink logo Ltd Edn 850 - 94	50	75
L204885	47157 Railfreight unspecified triple grey Sp Edn 500 (Geoffrey Allison) - 95	50	65
L205081	47163 BRe blue Stratford Union Jack Silver Jubilee finish - 01	30	45
L205210	47164 BRe blue Stratford Union Jack Silver Jubilee finish - 87	30	60
L205043	47190 'Pectinidae' Railfreight Petroleum grey, flush both ends - 89	30	40
L205298	47193 Freightliner green - 00	30	46
L204945	47207 'Bulmers of Hereford' BR Railfreight Distribution grey - 03	NPG	65
L205092	47210 'Blue Circle' BRe Railfreight Construction grey, Eastfield motif - 00	55	70
L205044	47213 'Marchwood Military Port' Railfreight Distribution (faded) triple grey Tinsley motifs - 03	NPG	65
L149930	47233 'Strombidae' Railfreight Petroleum grey Sp Edn 200 (Macclesfield Model Centre) part of 4 pack - 98	50	65
L204844	47241 Railfreight Distribution European grey, Tunnel motif, Tinsley shedplates - 95	30	40
L149930	47278 'Vasidae' Railfreight Petroleum grey, Sp Edn 200 (Macclesfield Model Centre) part of 4 pack - 98	50	65
L205045	47283 'Johnnie Walker' Railfreight Distribution grey- 89	30	45
L205048	47298 BRe blue- 89	30	40
L205035	47299 'Ariadne' BRe blue- 00	30	45
L205039	47301 BReLL Rft red stripe grey, large numbers, Thornaby motif - 89	35	50
L205260	47305 Chemical blue, yell stripe - 88	30	40
L204903	47306 'The Sapper' Railfreight European grey, blue roof, regimental badge, Tinsley motif - 01	35	50
L205257	47315 Departmental plain grey - 90	30	40
L205044	47317 'Willesden Yard' Railfreight Distribution grey- 89	30	45
L205075	47323 'Rover Group Quality Assured' Rft European grey, Tinsley motif Sp Edn 500 (Geoffrey Allison) - 01	30	40
L204962	47324 RES red+dark grey - 02	NPG	55
L20?	47325 'Red Rum' Railfreight grey, Sp Edn (Collectable Models) - 01	30	45
L204759	47348 'St Christopher's Railway Home' Railfreight Distribution European Channel Tunnel grey - 97	30	40
L205212	47363 'Billingham Enterprise' BReLL Railfreight grey, Thornaby motif - 87	30	40
L204832	47365 'Diamond Jubilee' Railfreight Distribution European grey, Tunnel motif, Tinsley shedplates - 95	30	40
L204633	47369 BRc 2-tone green with yellow cab - 98	25	35
L204889	47375 'Tinsley Traction Depot' Railfreight Distribution grey - 95	30	40
L204874	47376 'Freightliner 1995' triple grey Freightliner, Crewe Diesel motif - 95	30	40
L205033	47380 'Immingham' Railfreight Petroleum grey- 91	30	40
L205269	47401 'North Eastern' BRe blue - 89	30	40
L204666	47402 'Gateshead' BRe blue, yellow cab windows - 99	30	40
L204920	47423 ('Sceptre') BRe blue, NSE flashes - 01	30	40
L205216	47455 BReLL (extended), blue - 88	40	60
-	47461 'Charles Rennie Mackintosh' ScotRailblue+grey, Inverness motif, no front detail ex-set L107210 - 88	50	NA
L205264	47461 'Charles Rennie Mackintosh' ScotRail blue+grey, Inverness motif - 88	30	NA
L205209	47471 'Norman Tunna G.C.' I-C grey, yellow cabs + cab roofs, No.1 end flush - 99	35	40
L205036	47474 'Sir Rowland Hill' Parcels red - 90	30	50
L205254	47475 Provincial blue - 90	30	40
-	47475 'Restive' RES red, ex-set L104318 - 93	50	NA
-	47476 'Night Mail' Parcels red, ex-set L105114 - 91	50	NA
L205040	47484 'Isambard Kingdom Brunel' BRe Brunswick green, GWR 150, No.1 end flush - 89	40	60
L205218	47487 BRe blue - 87	30	40
L205214	47487 BRe InterCity executive grey, yellow doors, Stratford motif - 88	40	60
L204682	47488 Fragonset Railways, 2-tone green - 99	30	40
L205071	47489 'Crewe Diesel Depot' Parcels red - 91	35	50
-	47490 'Restive' RES red, as 47475 but incorrect number, should have been 'Resonant' ex-set L104318 - 93	40	NA
L20?	47492 'The Enterprising Scot' I-C ScotRail red stripe grey, Inverness motifs Sp Edn (Moray's) - cancelled	NA	NA
L205046	47508 'SS Great Britain' InterCity Mainline grey - 89	30	60
L204619	47513 'Severn' BReLL blue, grey roof, yellow cabs - 98	30	40
L204923	47517 'Andrew Carnegie' BReLL blue, blue roof, yellow cabs, Inverness motif - 01	35	50
L205042	47522 'Doncaster Enterprise' BRe Parcels, LNER green, flush both ends - 89	55	70
L204969	47528 'The Queen's Own Mercian Yeomanry' InterCity Mainline - 03	NPG	65
-	47530 Revised NSE bright blue ex-set L105112 - 90	50	NA
L205184	47535 'Saint Aidan' RES red, Crewe Diesel motif - 90	30	40
L205211	47541 'The Queen Mother' InterCity ScotRail red stripe grey+ Inverness motif, plinth, coat of arms, etched nameplates Sp Edn 550 (Harburn) - 00	60	77
-	47549 'Royal Mail' InterCity Executive grey, ex-set L107206- 91	50	NA
L204734	47555 'The Commonwealth Spirit' BRe blue, small logo, yellow cab windows - 96	30	40
L204774	47564 'Colossus' BReLL blue Sp Edn 550 (MR&ME) - 97	30	45
L204729	47565 'Responsive' RES red, headboard, Crewe Diesel motif - 96	30	40
L205259	47567 'Red Star' BRe blue - 88	35	50
L204947	47568 'Royal Engineers Postal & Courier Corps' BR InterCity Mainline grey - 02	35	50
-	47569 'The Gloucestershire Regiment' Parcels red, ex-set L105110 - 90	50	NA
L205220	47573 'The London Standard' BRe NSE bright blue, planned for 1987 but replaced by 47581 - not made	NA	NA
-	47576 'Kings Lynn' NSE bright blue, ex-set L107108 - 88	70	NA
L205038	47579 'James Nightall VC' BRe Revised NSE original blue, nameplates both at one end - 89	35	50
L205220	47581 'Great Eastern' BRe NSE btright blue, Stratford motifs - 87	30	60
L205209	47582 'County of Norfolk' NSE bright blue, Stratford motifs - 87	35	50
L205261	47583 'County of Herefordshire' NSE bright blue- 88	35	50
L205127	47583 'County of Hertfordshire' BReLL (extended), bright blue Sp Edn 500 (Langdale) - 00	30	45
L205084	47588 'Resurgent' BRe red RES, Leicester motifs - 89	35	50
-	47594 'Resourceful' BRe RES red, ex-set L104314 - 92	50	NA
L205047	47596 'Aldeburgh Festival' BRe blue,	35	50

Lima 00

	grey roof - *89*		
L205034	**47599** Railfreight Metals grey, wrong size symbols - *91*	35	50
L205268	**47609 'Fire Fly'** I-C executive grey - *89*	35	50
-	**47613 'North Star'** I-C executive grey, no details to front end, ex-set - *88*	55	NA
L205262	**47613 'North Star'** I-C executive grey - *88*	50	NA
L205041	**47620 'Windsor Castle'** InterCity Executive grey, flush No.2 end - *89*	30	60
L204962	**47624 'Saint Andrew'** RES red+grey Crewe Diesel motifs - *03*	NPG	65
L205205	**47625 'Resplendant'** RES red - *92*	35	50
L205213	**47628 'Sir Daniel Gooch'** Brunswick green, GWR 150 - *87*	30	60
L205206	**47635 'Jimmy Milne'** BReLL extend, blue, Inverness motif Ltd Edn 850 - *92*	50	65
L205258	**47637** InterCity ScotRail red stripe grey, Inverness motifs - *88*	65	80
L20?	**47641 'Fife Region'** BReLL blue, Eastfield motifs Sp Edn (Moray's) - *cancelled*	30	45
L204976	**47676 'Northamptonshire'** ICs - *02*	NPG	65
L204818	**47701 'Old Oak Common T&RSMD'** Revised NSE later blue, flush No.2 end - *94*	35	50
L204636	**47702 'County of Suffolk'** Virgin red Sp. Edn - *99*	35	50
L204898	**47703** Fragonset black - *98*	30	40
L204999	**47703 'Hermes'** Fragonset black - *03*	NPG	65
L205211	**47705 'Lothian'** ScotRail grey+blue, one side incorrect - *87*	30	60
L204703	**47705 'Guy Fawkes'** Waterman Railways black - *96*	30	40
L205267	**47709 'The Lord Provost'** ScotRail grey+ blue - *88*	30	60
L204880	**47710 'Lady Godiva'** Waterman Railways black - *95*	30	40
L204688	**47710** Fragonset Railways black with logos (also in pack 149971) - *99*	30	40
L149779	**47711 'Greyfriars Bobby'** BRe ScotRail grey+blue, yellow cab roof Sp Edn 300 (Harburn) ex-train pack - *95*	70	NA
L205037	**47711 'Greyfriars Bobby'** BRe ScotRail grey+blue, etched name + workplates, Scottie figurine Sp Edn 200 (Harburn Hobbies) - *95*	70	85
L204921	**47711 'County of Herefordshire'** NSE revised blue, Stratford motif, flush No.2 end - *01*	35	50
L205032	**47712 'Lady Diana Spencer'** BReLL blue, light grey roof, yellow cabs - *00*	40	70
L204959	**47712 'Lady Diana Spencer'** BRe Parcels red+grey Ltd Edn 1200 - *02*	NPG	65
L20?	**47713 'Tayside Region'** I-C ScotRail grey Sp Edn 350 (Moray's) sold with 47714 - *00*	35	50
L20?	**47714 'Grampian Region'** I-C ScotRail grey Sp Edn 350 (Moray's) sold with 47713 - *00*	35	50
L205037	**47716 'The Duke of Edinburgh's Award'** BRe ScotRail grey+blue, blue line, Haymarket motif - *88*	30	40
L204739	**47726 'Manchester Airport Progress'** RES red Sp Edn 500 (Langdale) - *96*	30	45
L204931	**47738 'Bristol Barton Hill'** RES maroon part of twin set with 67013 - *02*	NPG	NA
L149784	**47747 'Res Publica'** BRe RES red, ex-train pack - *95*	50	NA
L149808	**47749 'Atlantic College'** RES red, ex-train pack with NFX 92714, NOX 95133 + NJX 95138 - *97*	50	NA
L204690	**47758 'Regency Rail Cruises'** EWS maroon - *99*	30	40
L205258	**47760 'Ribblehead Viaduct'** EWS maroon - *00*	30	46
L204767	**47785 'Fiona Castle'** EWS maroon - *97*	30	45
L204792	**47786 'Roy Castle OBE'** EWS maroon - *98*	30	40

L204864	**47798 'Prince William'** RES royal dark purple, Crewe Diesel motif - *95*	30	40
L204794	**47798 'Prince William'** EWS Royal dark purple, new logos - *98*	30	40
L204888	**47799 'Prince Henry'** RES Royal dark purple, Crewe Diesel motif - *95*	30	40
L204795	**47799 'Prince Henry'** EWS Royal dark purple, new logos - *98*	30	40
L204853	**47803** Infrastructure yellow (transfers optional) Sp Edn 500 (Greenyards/ Hattons) - *93*	50	65
L204753	**47807** Porterbrook Leasing Co purple+white - *97*	45	60
L205085	**47809 'Finsbury Park'** ICs grey - *94*	70	80
L149949	**47810** ICs Porterbrook grey? Ltd Edn 200 (Macclesfield MC) ex 4-pack - *99*	35	50
L149949	**47811** ICs grey Ltd Edn part of 4-pack - *99*	35	50
L204825	**47811** First Great Western green - *00*	30	43
L204645	**47813 'SS Great Britain'** GWT green - *98*	25	35
L204761	**47814 'Totnes Castle'** Virgin red - *98*	30	40
L204727	**47817** Porterbrook purple+white - *96*	30	40
L204635	**47827** Virgin red - *99*	30	40
L204685	**47830** GWT green (also in 149970 sleeper pack) - *99*	30	40
L204685	**47830** Virgin red, issued in error, most recalled, reissued as 47827 - *99*	60	100
L205283	**47832** First Great Western revised green yellow stripe livery - *00*	30	40
-	**47833** ICs grey, ex-set L105108 - *93*	65	NA
L205089	**47833/D1962 'Captain Peter Manisty RN'** BRc 2-tone green Ltd Edn 850 - *93*	60	80
L205013	**47835 'Windsor Castle'** ICs grey, flush No.2 end Sp Edn 650 (Cheltenham Model Centre) - *93*	45	65
L205256	**47838** ICs grey, incorrect white skirting to body sides - *90*	35	50
L205256	as above, correct white skirting - *90*	35	50
L149960	**47840 'North Star'** ICs grey Ltd Edn part of 4-pack - *99*	35	50
L205202	**47841 'Institute of Mechanical Engineers'** ICs grey, Ltd Edn 500 (Macclesfield Model Centre) - *99*	30	45
L204621	**47844** Virgin red - *98*	30	40
L205171	**47846 'Thor'** GWT green - *99*	30	40
L205268	**47849 'Cadeirlan Bangor Cathedral'** Virgin red Ltd Edn 550 coat of arms over nameplate - *00*	30	45
L149960	**47853** InterCity Swallow grey, Ltd Edn, part of 4-pack - *99*	35	50
L20?	**47791 'VSOE'** RES red+grey Sp Edn (Collectable Models) - *01*	30	45
L204823	**47972 'Royal Army Ordnance Corps'** BRe RTC (Tech Services) red+grey Sp Edn 850 (Beatties) - *93*	50	65
L205035	**47976 'Aviemore Centre'** Dutch grey+ yellow - *91*	30	40
L205253	**97561 'Midland Counties Railway 150'** maroon, yellow cabs + lined border - *90*	40	50

Class 47 'The Sapper' in triple grey [L21]

L22. Class 50

The model used the bogies from the Class 55 which were to H0 scale. sno = snowploughs fitted

L205009	**D400** BRe blue Sp Edn 400 (Rail Magazine) headboard - *91*	110	140

L205009	**D400** BRe blue, headcode 1S57 - *92*	30	45
L205170	**50001 'Dreadnought'** BRe blue - *99*	30	45
L205265	**50003 'Tremeraire'** Revised NSE bright blue, these were 750 of 'Ark Royal' refinished in UK - *92*	55	80
L205140	**50007 'Sir Edward Elgar'** BRe Brunswick green, original mould - *85*	30	45
L205140	**50007 'Sir Edward Elgar'** BRe Brunswick green, modified mould - *91*	30	45
L205121	**50008 'Thunderer'** BRe blue, grey roof Ltd Edn 550 - *92*	85	120
L204811	**50009 'Conqueror'** BReLL blue - *94*	30	45
L205232	**50010 'Monarch'** BReLL blue, blue roof Sp Edn 550 (Traction magazine) - *99*	35	47
L205226	**50015 'Valiant'** BReLL blue - *87*	30	45
L205007	**50015 'Valiant'** BRe Dutch grey+yellow - *91*	30	45
L205135	**50017 'Royal Oak'** BRe NSE bt.blue - *86*	30	45
L205175	**50017** VSOE Northern Pullman maroon (LMS Royal Scot livery) - *00*	30	45
L204896	**50019 'Ramillies'** BRe blue, grey roof, Sp Edn 600 (Model Railway Enthusiast) - *94*	45	60
L205141	**50020 'Revenge'** BRe blue, original mould - *84*	30	45
L205279	**50021 'Rodney'** BReLL blue - *89*	30	45
L205131	**50023 'Howe'** BRe NSE bright blue - *86*	30	45
-	**50023 'Howe'** BRe NSE bright blue, ex-set L103408 no cab detail - *86*	35	NA
L205177	**50025 'Invincible'** BRe NSE bt.blue - *93*	30	45
L205291	**50027 'Lion'** NSE Revised bt.blue, sno - *01*	30	45
L205280	**50028 'Tiger'** BRe Revised NSE bright blue - *89*	30	45
-	**50030 'Repulse'** BRe Revised NSE bright blue ex-set L107208 - *89*	40	55
L205011	**50031 'Hood'** BReLL blue Sp Edn 650 (Cheltenham Model Centre) - *93*	60	75
-	**50033 'Glorious'** Revised NSE bright blue ex-set L104317 - *93*	45	NA
-	**50033 'Glorious'** Revised NSE bright blue ex-set L105179 - *00*	30	45
L205027	**50034 'Furious'** Revised NSE bt.blue - *91*	30	45
L205207	**50035 'Ark Royal'** Revised NSE bright blue Ltd Edn 850 - *92*	50	65
L204787	**50036 'Victorious'** BReLL blue, yellow cab, grey roof - *98*	30	40
L205227	**50038 'Formidable'** BReLL blue - *87*	30	45
L204961	**50040 'Leviathan'** BReLL blue Ltd Edn 1100 - *02*	30	45
-	**50041 'Bulwark'** Revised NSE bright blue ex-set L104312 - *92*	45	NA
-	**50042 'Triumph'** BReLL blue, black cab surrounds ex-set L106207 - *89*	100	120
L205142	**50043 'Eagle'** BReLL blue, original mould, light grey roof - *84*	30	40
L205142	**50043 'Eagle'** BReLL blue, revised mould - *84*	40	55
L205224	**50044 'Exeter'** NSE bright blue - *87*	30	45
L206920	**50046 'Ajax'** BReLL blue, black roof yellow cab, Ltd Edn 550 (MR&ME) - *99*	30	45
L204716	**50050 'Peco Golden Jubilee 1946- 1996'** BReLL blue Sp Edn 500 (Peco) - *96*	30	45
L205281	**50149 'Defiance'** BRe Railfreight General grey Laira motif (experimental motif) - *87*	30	45

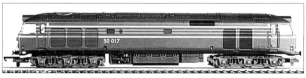

Class 50 in LMS Royal Scot livery [L22]

Class 52 in BR maroon [L23]

L23. Class 52

hyp = half yellow end panels. fyp = full yellow end panels.

L205130	**D1001 'Western Pathfinder'** BRc maroon - *01*	30	40
L205134	**D1003 'Western Pioneer'** BRc green, hyp, headcode 1A66 - *80*	30	40
L204800	**D1004 'Western Crusader'** BRc green, red nameplate, hyp, headcode 1V23 - *94*	30	45
L204846	**D1013 'Western Ranger'** BRe blue - *95*	30	40
L205010	**D1015 'Western Champion'** BRc golden ochre Sp Edn 500 (Cheltenham Model Centre) - *92*	70	120
L205121	**D1016 'Western Gladiator'** BRc maroon, headcode 1A66, hyp - *79*	30	40
L205126	**D1023 'Western Enterprise'** BRd sand, wrong name, headcode 1V86, fyp - *79*	30	40
L204776	**D1023 'Western Fusilier'** BRe blue Ltd Edn 550 (Langdale) - *98*	30	45
L204668	**D1043 'Western Duke'** BRe blue - *99*	30	40
L205122	**D1071 'Western Renown'** BRe blue, headcode 1A66 - *79*	30	40

L24. Class 55

hyp = half yellow end panels. fyp = full yellow ends. pcl = plated codeboxes with lights. This model had H0 scale bogies as the model was originally to have been made to this scale.

L204651	**D9000 'Royal Scots Greys'** BRc 2-tone green Sp Edn 550 (Geoffrey Allison) - *98*	35	50
L204781	**D9001 'St Paddy'** BRc 2-tone green Sp Edn 550 (Rails) - *97*	50	80
L205222	**D9002 'Kings Own Yorkshire Light Infantry'** BRc 2-tone green, no name on side, etched plates supplied Sp Edn 500 (Moray's) - *00*	35	50
L205105	**D9003 'Meld'** BRc 2-tone green, headcode 1S14 - *77*	30	40
L204951	**D9005 'The Prince of Wales's Own Regiment of Yorkshire'** BRc 2-tone green Ltd Edn 350 (Rails) - *02*	NPG	50
L205105	**D9008 'The Green Howards'** BRc 2-tone green, handrails not picked out, headcode 1A35 - *82*	30	40
L204657	**D9009 'Alycidon'** BRc 2-tone green, Sp Edn 550 (Rails/DPS) - *98*	30	45
L204952	**D9012 'Crepello'** BRc 2-tone green Ltd Edn 350 (Rails) - *02*	NPG	50
L204816	**D9013 'The Black Watch'** BRc 2-tone green, hyp, windows not picked out Sp Edn 650 (MR&ME) - *93*	60	75
L204656	**D9015 'Tulyar'** BRc 2-tone green, Sp Edn 550 (DPS/Rails) - *98*	30	45
L204607	**D9016 'Gordon Highlander'** BRc 2-tone green, Ltd Edn 850 - *98*	30	60
L205269	**D9018 'Ballymoss'** BRc 2-tone green, hyp - *00*	30	45
L204743	**D9019 'Royal Highland Fusilier'** BRc 2-tone green, hyp, steps not picked out Sp Edn 550 (MR&ME) - *97*	40	55
L204953	**D9020 'Nimbus'** BRc 2-tone green Ltd Edn 350 (Rails) - *02*	NPG	50
L201645	**9006 'Fife and Forfar Yeomanry'** BRe blue also chromatic blue, headcode 1G09 window bars painted on, bax numbered	35	85

'1645MW' & '5106MW' - 77

L205106	9006 'Fife and Forfar Yeomanry' BRe blue also chromatic blue, headcode 1G09 - 77	30	40
L205260	9016 'The Gordon Highlander' Porterbrook purple Ltd Edn 1200 - 00	35	60
L205299	55001 'St Paddy' BRe blue Ltd Edn 700 - 00	35	50
L204802	55002 'Kings Own Yorkshire Light Infantry' BRc 2-tone green, fyp, pcl Ltd Edn 500 - 94	40	60
L204801	55007 'Pinza' BRe blue, white cab surround, pcl - 93	30	60
L204869	55009 'Alycidon' BRe blue, silver grills and batteries - 94	30	60
L204936	55010 'The King's Own Scottish Borderer' BRe blue - 02	45	60
L204738	55015 'Tulyar' BRe blue Sp Edn 550 (DPS + Rails) - 96	45	60
L205191	55017 'The Durham Light Infantry' BRe blue, Ltd Edn 1000 - 99	30	45
L205230	55019 'Royal Highland Fusilier' BRe blue Sp Edn (DPS) - 00	30	45
L204702	55021 'Argyll and Sutherland Highlander' BRe blue, etched crests and nameplates + replica Argyll's badge Sp Edn 500 (Harburn Hobbies) - 96	35	60
L205106	55022 'Royal Scots Grey' BRe blue, handrails not picked out - 82	30	40

Class 55 'The Durham Light Infantry' in BR blue [L24]

L25.   Class 57

L204649	57001 'Freightliner Pioneer' Freightliner green Ltd Edn 750 (Rail Express) - 99	60	75
L204686	57002 'Freightliner Phoenix' Freightliner green - 99	30	50
L204686	57003 'Freightliner Evolution' green Freightliner - 99	30	50
L205250	57007 'Freightliner Bond' Freightliner green - 00	30	50

Class 57 'Freightliner Bond' in Freightliner livery [L25]

L26.   Class 59

L204838	59001 'Yeoman Endeavour' original Foster Yeoman silver+blue livery - 94	40	50
L204804	59002 'Yeoman Enterprise' original Foster Yeoman silver+blue livery - 94	40	55
L205029	59002 'Alan J Day' Mendip Rail green+ orange Sp Edn 750 (Rail Express) - 01	40	50
L204849	59003 'Yeoman Highlander' original Foster Yeoman silver+blue livery - 96	40	60
L204643	59003 'Yeoman Highlander' DB/ Yeoman silver+red+blue Sp Edn 500 (Beatties) - 98	45	70
L204850	59005 'Kenneth J Painter' original Foster Yeoman silver+blue livery - 95	40	55
L204646	59005 'Kenneth J Painter' revised Foster Yeoman silver+blue livery - 99	30	45
L204851	59101 'Village of Whatley' original ARC	40	55

L204667	59101 'Village of Whatley' revised ARC silver+yellow livery - 99	30	45
L204839	59102 'Village of Chantry' original ARC yellow livery - 94	40	55
L204803	59103 'Village of Mells' original ARC yellow livery - 94	40	55
L204665	59103 'Village of Mells' Hanson orange+ blue livery - 99	40	55
L204852	59104 'Village of Great Elm' original ARC yellow livery - 95	35	50
L205257	59104 'Village of Great Elm' Hanson orange+blue livery - 99	40	52
L204805	59201 'Vale of York' National Power blue - 94	45	60
L204664	59201 'Vale of York' EWS maroon - 99	35	50
L204674	59203 'Vale of Pickering' EWS maroon - 99	30	50
L205292	59206 'Pride of Ferrybridge' National Power blue - 00	40	52

Class 59 'Village of Great Elm' in Hanson livery [L26]

L27.   Class 60

hyp = half yellow end panel. OB = original body.

L204867	60000 Loadhaul black+orange Sp Edn 100 for Loadhaul personnel - 95	250	450
L205020	60001 'Steadfast' Railfreight Construction grey OB - 90	30	45
L204957	60001 'The Railway Observer' EWS maroon - 03	NPG	NPG
L205021	60002 'Capability Brown' Railfreight Petroleum grey OB, wrong side grill, Immingham motif - 90	30	45
L204764	60003 'Freight Transport Association' EWS maroon - 97	30	45
L205024	60003 'Christopher Wren' Railfreight Petroleum grey OB - 91	35	50
L205022	60004 'Lochnager' Rft Coal grey OB - 90	35	50
L204783	60006 'Scunthorpe Ironmaster' British Steel blue - 98	30	45
L204926	60006 'Scunthorpe Ironmaster' EWS Corus silver - 01	35	50
L205023	60008 'Moel Fammau' Railfreight Metals grey OB - 90	35	50
L204736	60008 'Gypsum Queen II' Loadhaul black+ orange - 97	50	70
L204715	60011 Mainline blue - 96	30	45
L204755	60012 EW&S maroon - 97	30	45
L204875	60015 'Bow Fell' Transrail on triple grey - 95	30	45
L204933	60016 'Rail Magazine' EWS maroon, yellow snow ploughs - 01	35	50
L204741	60019 EW&S maroon - 97	30	45
L204806	60032 'William Booth' BRe Railfreight Coal grey, Toton shedplates - 93	35	60
L204799	60033 'Tees Steel Express' British Steel blue - 98	35	50
L204918	60033 'Tees Steel Express' EWS Corus silver - 01	35	50
L204807	60039 'Glastonbury Tor' BRe Railfreight Construction grey, Stewarts Lane shed plates - 93	35	50
L204876	60040 'Brecon Beacons' BRe Mainline on 3-grey Railfreight, Stewarts Lane motif - 95	30	45
L205169	60044 'Ailsa Craig' Mainline blue - 99	30	45
L204808	60050 'Roseberry Topping' BRe Railfreight Metals grey, Thornaby shedplates - 94	30	45

L204857	60050 'Roseberry Topping' BRe Loadhaul on Railfreight grey - 95	30	45
L204854	60051 'Mary Somerville' Railfreight	30	45
L205025	60055 'Thomas Barnardo' Railfreight Coal grey - 91	35	50
L204867	60059 'Swinden Dalesman' Loadhaul black+orange - 95	30	45
L204768	60063 'James Murray' Transrail on triple grey - 97	30	45
L204909	60081 'Isambard Kingdom Brunel' GWR green, decals, lined, yhp, No.081 on front, Ltd Edn 1,000 - 01	45	70
L204620	60083 'Mountsorrel' EWS maroon - 99	30	40
L204924	60093 'Jack Stirk' Transrail on triple grey - 01	35	50
L205025	60098 'Charles Francis Brush' BRe Railfreight Construction grey Sp Edn 250 for Brush personnel - 93	230	320
L205026	60100 'Boar of Badenoch' BRe Railfreight Construction grey Ltd Edn 850 - 92	45	60

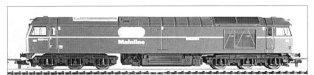

Class 60 'Alisa Craig' in Mainline livery [L27]

L28. Class 66

L204679	66001 EWS maroon - 99	35	75
L204691	66016 EWS maroon - 99	35	75
L205002	66068 EWS maroon - 02	35	75
L205197	66100 EWS maroon Ltd Edn - 99	40	75
L204906	66250 EWS maroon - 01	40	75
L205229	66501 Freightliner green Sp Edn 750 (Rail Express) - 99	45	75
L205227	66502 Freightliner green - 99	40	75
L205284	66504 Freightliner green Ltd Edn 700 - 00	40	75
L204901	66506 'Crewe Regeneration' Freightliner green, Railtrack - 01	40	75
L205059	66527 'Don Raider' Freightliner green, Railtrack - 03	40	75
L204917	66601 'The Hope Valley' Freightliner green - 01	40	75
L205122	66701 'Railtrack National Logistics' GBRf blue Sp Edn 750 (Rail Express) - 02	50	75
L204966	66703 GBRf blue - 03	40	75
L204943	66706 GBRf blue - 02	50	75

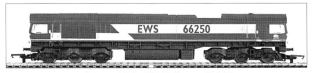

Class 66 in EWS livery [L28]

L29. Class 67

The model has a 5-pole motor, all wheel pickup and drive, precision helical gears, high rigidity ABS chassis construction with low set ballast, custom electronics control via PCB, scale starting acceleration control and dual directional lighting. The body is highly detailed with separately moulded handrails and super detail parts included. Glazing is flush and the couplings detachable.

L205261	67001 'Night Mail' EWS maroon - 02	40	70
L204963	67002 'Special Delivery' EWS mrn - 03	35	45
L204929	67003 EWS maroon - 02	40	70
L204942	67004 'Post Haste' EWS maroon - 03	35	45
L204931	67013 EWS maroon part of twin set with 47738 - 02	35	NA
L149619	67025 EWS maroon + 3 Super GUVs	NA	NPG

	(94123+94157+94208) - 02		
L205095	67030 EWS maroon - 03	35	45

Class 67 in EWS livery [L29]

L30. Class 73

L205276	E6001 BRc 2 tone green (SR EMU green with lime green bottom band) - 87	40	60
L205192	E6003 BRc Brunswick green - 87	50	70
L149929	E6003 'Sir Herbert Walker' BRc green Sp Edn 500 (Rails) paired with 73128 - 98	30	45
L205223	E6012 BRe in original blue with grey bottom band - 87	30	50
L205275	73001 BRe blue - 87	30	50
L205275	73001 BRe blue, grey roof - 87	30	50
L205274	73002 BReLL blue, large number - 89	30	50
L205273	73004 'The Bluebell Railway' BRe NSE bright blue, yellow cab roofs - 89	30	50
L205272	73005 'Watercress Line' BRe NSE bright blue, shown in 1989/90 catalogue - *not made*	NA	NA
L204618	73101 'Brighton Evening Argus' Pullman brown+cream - 98	30	75
L205186	73101 'The Royal Alex' Pullman brown+cream, commemorative edition first 3000* certificated - 92	35	75
L205270	73105 BReLL blue - 90	25	40
L205170	73108 BRe early blue, roof dark grey - 87	30	50
L205001	73109 'Battle of Britain 50th Anniversary' Revised NSE bright blue, Ltd Edn 550 - 92	100	130
L205001	73109 'Battle of Britain 50th Anniversary' Revised NSE bright blue original Ltd Edn body without lights and other detail - 92	NPG	250
L205090	73109 'Battle of Britain 50th Anniversary' SWT bright blue - 01	35	50
L205016			
L204862	73114 'Stewarts Lane Traction Maintenance Depot' Mainline blue, Stewarts Lane motif - 94	25	40
L204877	73118 triple grey EPS, code 73 - 94	25	40
L205193	73123 ' Gatwick Express' BReLL I-C executive grey, large numbers, full yellow ends, light grey roof - 87	30	40
L205193	I-C Executive grey full yellow ends, light grey roof no number or detail, 2 only - 87	NPG	150
L205191	73125 'Stewarts Lane 1860-1985' BReLL I-C executive grey, half yellow and half black cab ends - 86	30	40
-	73125 'Stewarts Lane 1860-1985' I-C executive grey, no running numbers, enlarged shed plate on cabside ex-set L103406 - 86	90	NA
L205012	73126 'Kent & East Sussex Railway' Revised NSE bright blue Sp Edn 650 (Signal Box) - 93	75	80
L204742	73128 EW&S maroon - 96	30	40
L149929	73128 'OVS Bullied' BRe Dutch grey+ yellow Stewarts Lane motif Sp Edn 500 (Rails) paired with E6003 - 98	30	45
L205178	73129 'City of Winchester' NSE bright blue without branding, city coat of arms - 00	30	45
L205277	73130 'City of Portsmouth' BRe Intercity Mainline grey - 89	30	40
L204757	73131 EW&S maroon - 97	30	45
L204648	73133 'Bluebell Railway' BRe Dutch grey+ yellow - 98	25	40
L205194	73134 'Woking Homes 1885-1985' BReLL InterCity black+grey, yellow cab roof - 99	30	45

L205169	**73136** BRe Departmental plain grey, code 20 - *91*	25	40
L205271	**73138 'Poste Haste'** BRe I-C Mainline grey, full yellow to front end only - *89*	30	40
L205169	**73142 'Broadlands'** BReLL blue - *86*	30	40
L205194	**73142 'Broadlands'** BReLL I-C Executive grey, dark roof, yellow cab roofs - *87*	30	40
L204847	**73212 'Airtour Suisse'** Gatwick Express grey - *94*	25	35
L204770	**73901** Merseyrail yellow Sp Edn 500 (Langdale) - *97*	40	55

* Certificate number 3,190 has been found!

Class 73 'Woking Homes 1885-1985' in Intercity livery [L30]

L31. Class 87

L204810	**87002 'Royal Sovereign'** ICs grey - *94*	30	45
L205195	**87003 'Patriot'** Virgin red - *99*	30	45
L205125	**87005 'City of London'** BRe blue - *79*	30	40
L205125	**87005 'City of London'** BRe I-C Executive grey - *87*	30	40
L204631	**87006 'George Reynolds'** Virgin red - *98*	30	35
L204798	**87009** Virgin red - *98*	30	40
L205195	**87009 'City of Birmingham'** BRe I-C Executive grey - *86*	30	40
L205130	**87012 'Couer de Lion'** BRe I-C Executive grey - *85*	30	40
L205185	**87018 'Lord Nelson'** BRe I-C Executive grey - *85*	30	40
L205175	**87019 'Sir Winston Churchill'** BRe blue - *84*	30	40
L204925	**87021 'Robert the Bruce'** BRe InterCity Executive grey - *01*	35	50
L205155	**87022 'Cock O' The North'** BReLL, non-authentic LL blue livery - *82*	30	40
L205179	**87031 'Hal O' The Wind'** InterCity Mainline grey - *90*	30	40
L204809	**87101 'Stephenson'** BRe Railfreight Distribution grey, Falcon shed plates - *93*	30	40

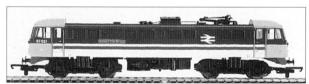

Class 87 'Robert the Bruce' in Intercity livery [L31]

L32. Class 90

This was shown as a proposed model in the 1989/90 catalogue but was dropped, possibly because Hornby had launched their model in 1988.

L205291	**90002** ICs grey - *not made*	NA	NA

L33. Class 91

This was shown as a proposed model in the 1989/90 catalogue but was dropped, possibly because Hornby had launched their model in 1988.

L205295	InterCity Swallow grey - *not made*	NA	NA

L34. Class 92

L204855	**92001 'Victor Hugo'** BRe Railfreight Distrib grey, Tunnel + Crewe Electric motifs, Commem. Edn. 3000 certificated - *94*	30	40
L204672	**92001 'Victor Hugo'** EWS maroon, Tunnel motif - *99*	30	45

L204893	**92003 'Beethoven'** BRe Railfreight EPS grey, Tunnel+Crewe Electric motifs - *95*	35	50
L204672	**92015 'DH Lawrence'** Railfreight Unspecified grey - *95*	30	40
L204871	**92017 'Shakespeare'** BRe Railfreight Unspecified grey, Tunnel motif - *95*	35	40
L204870	**92022 'Charles Dickins'** BRe Railfreight Distribution grey, Tunnel motif - *94*	35	40
L204873	**92023 'Ravel'** Railfreight SNCF grey, Tunnel + Crewe Electric motifs - *94*	35	50
L204708	**92030 'Ashford'** BRe Railfreight Distribution grey, Ltd Edn 850*, Tunnel + Crewe Electric motifs - *98*	30	40
L204984	**92031 'The Institute of Logistics and Transport'** EWS mrn Tunnel motifs - *03*	NPG	NPG
L204884	**92034 'Kipling'** Railfreight Unspecified grey - *96*	30	45
L204777	**92041 'Vaughan Williams'** Rft Unspecified grey Sp Edn 300 (Beatties) - *97*	75	90

* Both 300 and 850 appear on certificates.

Class 92 'Victor Hugo' in EWS tunnel livery [L34]

L35. Class 101

L149894	**51228/51506** BRe grey+blue Regional Railways - *97*	40	60
L149895	**M50321/M50303** BRc green, white stripe and whiskers - *97*	45	65
L149896	**53311/53322** NSE bright blue - *97*	40	60
L149897	**M50304/M50338** BRe blue - *97*	40	60
L149898	**51188/53268** BRe Regional Railways ScotRail grey+blue - *97*	40	60
L149899	**E51433/E51503** BRc green - *97*	45	60
L149814	**SC51800/SC51808** BRc green, destination Dundee - *98*	45	60
L149915	**E51425/59108/E51503** BRe blue+grey - *99*	35	55
L149927	**51177/59303/53269** BRe Regional Railways grey+blue - *99*	35	55
L149959	**51253/53171** Strathclyde PTE maroon 2-car set Sp Edn 300 (D&F) - *99*	50	85
L149973	**M53331/M59125/M53308** BRe, blue/ grey rework, destination Crewe - *00*	60	75
L149612	**E51206/E56364** BRc green, whiskers - *01*	45	60

Class 101 in BR green [L35]

L36. Class 117/2

Although these are listed as sets, cars could be purchased individually in most cases.

-	**117305 (51410/59520/51368)** BRc GWR brown+cream Sp Edn 300 (Model Railway Enthusiast magazine) - *94*	NA	140
L204829	**51410** BRc GWR brown+cream power car from above set - *94*	55	NA
L204830	**59520** BRc GWR brown+cream centre car from above set - *94*	20	NA
L204831	**51368** BRc GWR brown+cream dummy power car ex above set - *94*	20	NA
L149809	**W51342/W59518/W51340** BRc 1959 green livery 3-car pack, yellow half panels, headcode 1A20 - *84*	NA	65
L149851	as above pack - *93*	40	65

L205137	**W51342** BRc green motor brake 2nd powered - *80*	20	25
L205146	**W59518** BR green composite trailer - *82*	10	15
L205139	**W51340** BRc green motor brake 2nd non-powered - *80*	10	15
L149816	**W51334/W59493/W51332** BRe 1974 blue 3-car pack, headcode 2A71 - *85*	NA	60
L149852	as above pack - *93*	40	65
L205136	**W51334** BRe blue motor brake 2nd powered - *80*	20	25
L205145	**W59493** BR blue composite trailer - *82*	10	15
L205138	**W51332** BRe blue motor brake 2nd non-powered - *80*	10	15
L149810	**W51350/W59508/W51332** BRe 1981 blue+grey livery 3-car pack - *84*	NA	60
L149854	as above pack - *93*	40	65
L205147	**W51350** BRe blue+grey motor brake 2nd powered - *81*	20	25
L205148	**W59508** BR blue+grey composite trailer - *82*	10	15
L205149	**W51332** BRe blue+grey motor brake 2nd non-powered - *81*	10	15
L149815	**W51350/W59484/W51346** BRe white+blue refurbished livery 3-car pack - *85*	NA	60
L205152	**W51350** BRe white+blue motor brake 2nd powered - *82*	20	25
L205153	**W59484** BR white+blue composite trailer - *82*	10	15
L205154	**W51346** BRe white+blue motor brake 2nd non-powered - *82*	10	15
L149850	**117306 (51369/59521/51411)** BRe Regional Railways grey+blue 3-car pack - *93*	NA	60
L205086	**51369** BRe Regional Railways grey+blue motor brake 2nd powered - *91*	20	25
L205087	**59521** BRe Regional Railways grey+blue composite trailer - *91*	10	15
L205088	**51411** BRe Regional Railways grey+blue motor brake 2nd non-powered - *91*	10	15
L149853	**L424 (51362/59514/51404)** BRe NSE bright blue 3-car pack - *93*	NA	60
L205097	**51362** BRe NSE grey+blue motor brake 2nd powered - *92*	20	25
L205098	**59514** BR NSE grey+blue composite trailer - *92*	10	15
L205099	**51404** BRe NSE grey+blue motor brake 2nd non-powered - *92*	10	15

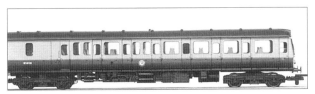

Class 117 [L36]

L37. Class 121/2 (Bubble Car) (see also table L26a for Class 960)

L205030	**W55020** BRc brown+cream, yellow front, white roof, 500 made - *00*	40	60
L204630	**W55025** BRc green, whiskers - *98*	30	45
L204617	**W55026** BRc green, small yellow warning panel, code 2T55 - *98*	30	45
L204611	**55027** NSE bright blue - *98*	30	40
L204623	**W55028** BRe blue+grey - *98*	30	40
L204912	**55029 'Marston Vale'** Silverlink blue+green - *01*	30	40
L204608	**W55035 (B135)** BRe blue, destination Bath - *98*	30	40
L205028	**55027 'Bletchly MD'** Silverlink blue+green - *00*	30	40

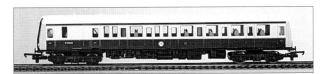

Class 121/2 in WR livery [L37]

L38. Class 156

L205053	**156470 (52470)** BRe Provincial blue, single car only - *92*	15	35
L204706	**156402 (52402+57402)** BRe 158 Class style grey Regional Railways Express, - *96*	40	55
L204935	**156407 (5740+/52407)** Central Trains green - *02*	45	60
L204895	**156420 (52420+57420)** BRe Regional Railways grey+blue, green stripe - *96*	40	55
L204791	**156433 'The Kilmarnock Edition' (52433+57433)** Strathclyde PTE carmine+cream, etched nameplates Sp Edn 300 (Harburn Hobbies) - *98*	75	125
L205050	**156443 (52443+57443)** BRe Provincial blue - *89*	35	55
L205050D	**156443** BRe Provincial blue, dummy car - *?*	NPG	NPG
L205119	**156447** ScotRail Whoosh grey etc. Sp Edn 400 (Harburn Hobbies) - *01*	30	60
L204676	**156454 'Whitby Endeavour' (52454 + 57454)** BRe Provincial blue - *99*	30	50
L204712	**156465 'Bonnie Prince Charlie' (52465+57465)** Provincial ScotRail blue, etched nameplates Sp Edn 500 (Harburn Hobbies) - *96*	40	65
L205051	**156480 (52480+57480)** BRe Provincial Blue - *89*	35	50
L205052	**156481 (52481+57481)** BRe Provincial Blue - *92*	35	50
L205036	**156490 (57491+52491)** Northern Spirit blue-green - *01*	40	55
L205054	**156501 (52501+57501)** BRe Strathclyde Transport orange+black - *89*	40	55
L205054D	**156501 (57501)** BRe Strathclyde Transp orange+black, dummy car only - *93*	25	30
L204840	**156502 (52502+57502)** BRe Strathclyde Transport orange+black Sp Edn 500 (D&F) uncertificated - *94*	60	75
L20?	**156510 (?+?)** carmine+cream Sp Edn (D&F Models) - *02*	60	75
L205055	**156512 (52512+57512)** BRe Strathclyde Transport orange+black Sp Edn 500 (Harburn) uncertificated - *92*	65	90
L204713	**156513 (52513+57513)** BRe Strathclyde Transport orange+black Sp Edn 400 (D&F Models) uncertificated - *96*	40	65
L204927	**156510 (52510+57510)** Strathclyde PT carmine+cream Sp Edn 400 (Harburn Hobbies) - *01*	50	66

Class 156 in Northern Spirit livery [L38]

L39. Class 373 (Eurostar)

-	**F5 (3211+3212)** Eurostar grey ex-set L106530, HO Ex-Jouef - *96*	40	50*

Lima 00

L40. Class 960 Sandite Unit (Bubble Car)

L204907	**ADB97723** Railtrack Clearing the Way brown - 01	35	50
L204928	**977858** Railtrack Clearing the Way maroon - 01	35	50

L41. GWR Railcars

L205132	**No.22** GWR (button) brown+cream, white roof - 80	30	55
L205133	**W22** maroon+cream 1948 numbering - 80	30	45
L204639	**No.29** Great()Western brown+cream - 98	25	40
L205150	**W30W** BRc green, whiskers - 83	30	40
L205267	**W32W** BRc green, white roof domes, whisker stripes - 00	30	40
L205267	**W32W** BRc green, white roof (error, approx. 10 exist) whisker stripes - 00	65	80
L205143	**No.34** GWR (button) brown+cream Express Parcels - 82	30	40
L204913	**W34** BRc maroon - 01	30	45
L205144	**W34** Express Parcels maroon - ?	30	40
L205144	**W34W** Express Parcels maroon - 82	30	40

GWR Railcar [L41]

COACHES

Lima coaches have been limited to only a few prototypes. These fall into two categories - BR standard coaching stock and non-passenger stock. The latter includes Syphons, CCTs and GUVs while the former are made up of Mk1s, Mk2s and Mk3s. In addition to these, there are centre cars for DMUs. As with Lima locomotives, the emphasis has been on extending the range of liveries that can be carried by each basic model.

Cat.No.	Company, Number, Colour, Dates	£	£

C1. Pullman

This was available for only one year with tension-lock couplings.

L309199	**Louisa** brown+cream - 77	6	10
L309200	**Golden Arrow** blue - 77	6	10

BR Mark 1 Stock

C2a. Mk1 Corridor 2nd (SK)

L305306	**NSE** 18711 early blue - 87	8	14
L305306	**NSE** 18711 late blue - 90	8	14
L305317	**Sealink** SC24850 - 87	8	14
L305326	**BR IC** M18753 grey - 86	8	12
L305361	**BR** M25308 blue+grey - 82	8	12
L305350	**BR** W18611 blue+grey - 99	8	12
L305362	**BR** W26070 brown+cream - 82	8	12
L305362	**BR** W26178 brown+cream - 82	8	12
L305363	**BR** W24437 red+cream - 82	8	12
L305363	**BR** W24490 red+cream - 82	8	12
L305364	**BR** M25623 maroon - 82	8	12
L305365	**BR** S25916 green - 82	8	12

BR Mk1 SK in BR blue and grey [C2a]

C2b. Mk1 Open 2nd (SO)

L305329	**BR** E4630 blue+grey - 95	NPG	NPG
L305330	**IC** swallow 4998 grey - 85	8	12
L305383	**BR** E4630 blue+grey - 87	8	12
L305384	**BR IC** M4479 grey - 87	8	12
	ScotRail West Highland green+cream		
L305444	Sc4243 Sp Edn 150 (Harburn Hobbies) - 99	15	18
L305445	Sc4610 Sp Edn 150 (Harburn Hobbies) - 99	15	18
-	Sc4419 Sp Edn 250 (Harburn Hobbies) ex-L149441 train pack - 01	15	NA
-	Sc4435 Sp Edn 250 (Harburn Hobbies) ex-L149441 train pack - 01	15	NA
-	Sc4900 Sp Edn 250 (Harburn Hobbies) ex-L149441 train pack - 01	15	NA

C2c. Mk1 Open 1st (FO)

-	**IC Mainline** grey ex-train pack Sp Edn (Harburn Hobbies) ex-Deerstalker train pack - 01	15	NA

C2d. Mk1 Corridor Composite (CK)

L305310	**BR** DE2513961 Eng. drab - 83	8	12
L305311	**BR** 15215 red+cream - 77	8	12
L305311	**BR** M34628 red+cream - 79	8	12
L305312	**LMS** 2257 maroon - 77	8	12
L305312	**BRc** M25264 maroon - 79	8	12
L305313	**GWR** 5014 brown+cream - 77	8	12
L305313	**BR** W24624 brown+cream - 79	8	12
L305314	**BR** S15865 green - 77	8	12
L305314	**BR** S33472 green - 79	8	12
L305315	**BR** W43671 blue+grey - 79	8	12
L305351	**BR** W45198 blue+grey - 99	8	12
L305318	**Sealink** Sc7997 - 87	8	14
L305346	**CIE** green - 78	15	30
L305347	**CIE** orange+black - 78	15	30

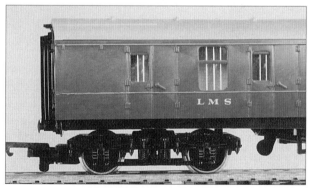

Mk1 corridor brake 2nd [C2e]

C2e. Mk1 Corridor Brake 2nd (BSK)

L305307	**NSE** 35193 early blue - 87	8	14
L305307	**NSE** 35193 late blue - 90	8	14
L305316	**Sealink** Sc35070 - 87	8	12
L305331	**BR** 34100 red+cream - 77	8	12
L305331	**BR** M34376 red+cream - 79	8	12
L305332	**LMS** 5051 maroon - 77	8	12
L305332	**BRc** M25290 maroon - 79	8	12
L305333	**GWR** 5103 brown+cream - 77	8	12
L305333	**BR** W24528 brown+cream - 79	8	12
L305334	**BR** S1297 green - 77	8	12
L305334	**BR** S33454 green - 79	8	12
L305335	**BR** W43281 blue+grey - 79	8	12
L305372	**BR IC** M35465 grey - 87	8	12
L305397	**BRT** KDB977167 silver grey Engineering Dept. Telecommunications - 94	8	12
	ScotRail West Highland green+cream		

| L305446 | Sc9312 Sp Edn 150 (Harburn Hobbies) - 99 | 15 | 18 |
| - | Sc21241 Sp Edn 250 (Harburn Hobbies) ex L149441 train pack - 01 | 15 | NA |

C2f. Mk1 Restaurant Buffet Refurbished (RBR)

L305320	**BR** InterCity IC1698 grey - 87	8	12
L305321	**BR** W1652 blue+grey - 77	8	12
L305321	**BR** W43212 blue+grey - 79	8	12
L305352	**BR** W? blue+grey - 99	8	12
L305322	**GWR** 9542 brown+cream - 77	8	12
L305322	**BR** W24760 brown+cream - 79	8	12
L305323	**LMS** 270 maroon - 77	8	12
L305323	**BRc** M25486 maroon - 79	8	12
L305324	**BR** S3056 green - 78	8	12
L305324	**BR** S33465 green - 79	8	12
L305325	**BR** M34642 red+cream - 79	8	12

Mk1 restaurant car in LMS maroon [C2f]

Mk1 Gangwayed Full Brake (BG) (found under 'PARCELS STOCK' after 'COACHES' section)

BR Mark 2 Stock

C3a. Mk2 Open Standard (SO)

L305302	**BR** W5449 blue+grey 2b - 77	8	12
L305386	**NSE** 5448 early blue 2b - 87	8	14
L305386	**NSE** 5448 late blue 2b - 89	8	14
-	**NSE** 5454 blue 2b ex-L104312 set - ?	8	NA
L305395	**Trans-Pennine** 5479 2b - 90	8	12
L305395	**Regional Railways** 5304 blue 2b Sp Edn (Signal Box) - 92	15	20
L305309	**BR IC** swallow livery 2e - *not made*	NA	NA
-	**ICs** 6025 grey 2e ex-L104311 set - ?	8	NA
L205264	**ScotRail** Sc5813 grey 2e ex-set - ?	8	NA
L305337	**BR IC** M5804 grey 2e - 87	8	15
L305305	**BR** M5940 blue+grey 2f - 85	8	12
L305306	**CIE** orange+black - 78	15	30
-	**IE** standard open wagon *(see C3i)*	-	-

C3b. Mk2a Tourist Open Standard (TSO)

L305423	**Virgin** 6157 [B] red+black - 98	8	13
L305424	**Virgin** 6064 [C] red+black - 98	8	13
L305425	**Virgin** 6067 [D] red+black - 98	8	13
L305426	**Virgin** 6170 [E] red+black - 98	8	13
L305427	**Virgin** 5976 [F] red+black - 98	8	13
-	**NIR** blue+grey open 2nd *(seeC3h)*		

Mk2a in Virgin trains livery [C3b]

C3c. Mk2 Corridor 1st (FK)

L305387	**NSE** 13442 early blue 2a - 87	NPG	NPG
L305387	**NSE** 13442 late blue 2a - 89	NPG	NPG
-	**NSE** 13482 blue ex-L104312 set - ?	8	NA
L305301	**BR** W13493 blue+grey 2b - 77	8	12
L305394	**Trans-Pennine** 13520 2c - 90	8	12

C3d. Mk2 Open 1st (FO)

L305329	**ScotRail** 3265 grey 2e - 86	8	12
L305336	**BR IC** M3229 grey 2e - 87	8	12
-	**ICs** 3228 grey 2e ex-L104311 set - ?	8	NA

| L305380 | **ScotRail** Revised Sc11008 grey - 87 | 8 | 12 |
| L305304 | **BR** M3310 blue+grey 2f - 85 | 8 | 12 |

C3e. Mk2 Brake Corridor 1st (BFK)

L305319	**BR IC** swallow livery - *not made*	NA	NA
L305388	**NSE** 17086 early blue 2a - 87	8	12
L305388	**NSE** 17086 late blue 2a - 89	8	12
L305303	**BR** W16084 blue+grey 2b - 77	8	12
L305388	**Regional Railways** 17123 blue 2c Sp Edn (Signal Box) - 89	15	20
L305607	**CIE** orange+black - ?	15	30
-	**NIR** blue+grey brake 2nd *(seeC3h)*	-	-

C3f. Mk2 Open Standard with Mini-Buffet (RMB)

| L305327 | **BR IC** 1883 grey - 86 | 8 | 12 |

C3g. Mk2c Micro-Buffet (TSOT)

| L305308 | **BR** E6524 blue+grey - 82 | 8 | 12 |
| L305327 | **BR IC** 1583 grey Restaurant/Buffet - ? | 8 | 12 |

C3h. Mk2a/b/c in Irish Liveries

The NIR coaches came in boxes branded Lima Jouef. The models are of the Lima Mk2b/c.

-	**NIR** 911 blue+grey brake/2nd open generator - 03	18	NA
-	**NIR** 924 blue+grey open 2nd - 03	18	NA
-	**NIR** 933 blue+grey open 2nd - 03	18	NA
LT600003	above 3 coaches in '80s Enterprise livery Sp Edn (Murphy Models) - 03	NA	80

C3i. Mk2e/f in Irish Liveries

The models came in boxes branded Lima Jouef.

-	**IE** 5209 standard open - 03	18	NA
-	**IE** 5232 standard open - 03	18	NA
-	**IE** 5233 standard open - 03	18	NA
LT600001	above 3 coaches of the Galway Line Sp Edn (Murphy Models) - 03	NA	80

BR Mark 3 Stock

C4a. Mk3 Trailer Standard Open (TSO) (HST Stock)

L305368	**BR IC** 42252 grey - 85	10	15
L305391	**BR ICs** 42191 grey - 89	10	15
-	**BR ICs** 42197 grey ex-L106522 set - 89	10	NA
L305402	**GNER** 42106 [B] navy blue - 98	10	15
L305437	**GNER** 42181 [C] navy blue - 98	10	15
L305438	**GNER** 42180 [D] navy blue - 98	10	15
L305439	**GNER** 42179 [E] navy blue - 98	10	15
L305460	**GNER** 42323 [?] navy blue - ?	10	15
-	**GNER** 42242 navy blue ex-L149872 train pack - 98	10	NA
-	**GNER** 42154 [B] navy blue ex-L149908 train pack - 98	10	NA
-	**GNER** 42150 [C] navy blue ex-L149908 train pack - 98	10	NA
-	**GNER** 42215 [E] navy blue ex-L149918 train pack - 98	10	NA
L305412	**Mid Mainline** 42228 [B] green+beige - 98	10	15
L305416	**Mid Mainline** 42227 [C] green+beige - 98	10	15
L305417	**Mid Mainline** 42229 [D] green+beige - 98	10	15
L305418	**Mid Mainline** 42194 [E] green+beige - 98	10	15
L305456	**Mid Mainline** 42337 [?] green+beige ?	10	15
-	**Mid Mainline** 42230 green+white ex-L149806 train pack - 98	10	NA
-	**Mid Mainline** 42157 [C] green+beige ex-L149909 train pack - 98	10	NA
L305404	**Virgin XC** 42189 [B] red+black - 98	10	15
L305420	**Virgin XC** 42188 [C] red+black - 98	10	15
L305421	**Virgin XC** 42187 [D] red+black - 98	10	15
L305422	**Virgin XC** 42326 [F] red+black - 98	10	15
-	**Virgin XC** 42239 red+black ex-L149859 train pack - 98	10	NA

L305429	**Virgin** 42317 [B] red+black - *99*	10	15
L305430	**Virgin** 42316 [C] red+black - *99*	10	15
L305431	**Virgin** 42315 [D] red+black - *99*	10	15
L305432	**Virgin** 42195 [F] red+black - *99*	10	15
-	**Virgin** 42314 [B] red+black ex-L149916 train pack - *?*	10	NA
L305414	**GWT** 42350 [D] green+ivory - *99*	10	15
L305441	**GWT** 42295 [E] green+ivory - *99*	10	15
-	**GWT** 42296 green+ivory ex-L149871 train pack - *98*	10	NA
-	**GWT** 42297 green+ivory ex-L149871 train pack - *98*	10	NA
L305449	**FGW** 43032 [B] green+ivory - *99*	10	15
L305478	**FGW** 42014 [C] - *99*	10	15
L305480	**FGW** 42068 [E] - *99*	10	15

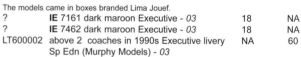

Mk3 in Midland Mainline livery [C4a]

C4b. Mk3a Open Second (SO)

L305328	**ScotRail** 12025 grey - *86*	10	15
L305366	**BR** M12004 blue+grey - *84*	10	15
L305379	**ScotRail** Revised 12024 grey - *87*	10	15
L305379/1	**ScotRail** Revised Sc12020 grey+blue Ltd Edn 200 (Harburn Hobbies) - *95*	15	20
L305379/2	**ScotRail** Revised Sc12030 grey+blue Sp Edn 200 (Harburn Hobbies) - *95*	15	20

C4c. Mk3 Open Composite (CO)

| L305385 | **ScotRail** 11907 grey - *87* | 10 | 15 |
| L305385/1 | **ScotRail** Sc11908 grey+blue Sp Edn 200 (Harburn Hobbies) - *95* | 15 | 20 |

C4d. Mk3 Trailer First Open (TFO) (HST Stock)

L305161	**BR** 41163 blue+grey - *82*	10	15
L305181	**BR IC** 41121 grey - *87*	10	15
L305392	**BR ICs** 41097 grey - *89*	10	15
-	**BR ICs** 41097 grey ex-L106522 set - *89*	10	NA
L305403	**GNER** 41092 [G] navy blue - *98*	10	15
L305440	**GNER** 41091 [H] navy blue - *98*	10	15
-	**GNER** 41092 navy blue ex-L149872 pack - *98*	10	NA
L305411	**Mid Mainline** 41069 [G] green+beige - *98*	10	15
L305419	**Mid Mainline** 41112 green+beige - *98*	10	15
L305454	**Mid Mainline** 42120 [?] green+beige - *?*	10	15
?	**Mid Mainline** 41041 [?] green+beige - *?*	10	15
-	**Mid Mainline** 41062 [G] green+white ex-L149806 train pack - *98*	10	NA
-	**Mid Mainline** 41079 [H] green+beige ex L149909 train pack - *98*	10	NA
L305405	**Virgin XC** 41095 [H] red+black - *98*	10	15
-	**Virgin XC** 41081 red+black ex-L149859 train pack - *98*	10	NA
L305434	**Virgin** 41107 [H] red+black - *99*	10	15
-	**Virgin** 41168 [H] red+black ex-L149916 train pack - *98*	10	NA
L305415	**GWT** 41143 [H] green+ivory - *99*	10	15
L305442	**GWT** 41144 [G] green+ivory - *99*	10	15
L305450	**FGW** 41032 [G] green+ivory - *99*	10	15
L305482	**FGW** 41094 [G] - *99*	10	15
L205166	**Australian** XPT silver+orange - *?*	10	15

C4e. Mk3 Pullman First Open (PFO)

L305374	**BR IC** 11076 'John Lennon' grey - *87*	18	20
L305375	**BR IC** 11091 grey - *87*	10	15
L305376	**BR IC** 11093 'L.S.Lowry' grey - *87*	18	20
L305377	**BR IC** 11091 'Sir Stanley Matthews' grey - *87*	18	20

| L305378 | **BR IC** 11085 'Sir John Barbirolli' grey - *87* | 18 | 20 |

C4f. Mk3 Trailer Guard Standard (TGS)(HST Stock)

L305162	**BR** 44080 blue+grey - *82*	20	25
L305182	**BR** 44028 IC grey - *87*	20	25
L305390	**BR ICs** 44071 grey - *89*	20	25
L305400	**GNER** 44058 [A] navy blue - *98*	20	25
-	**GNER** 44094 [A] navy blue ex-L149918 pack - *98*	20	NA
L305410	**Mid Mainline** 44073 [A] green+beige - *98*	20	25
L305428	**Virgin** 44090 [A] red+black - *99*	20	25
L305406	**Virgin XC** 44060 [A] red+black - *98*	20	25
L305408	**GWT** 44039 [A] green+ivory - *99*	20	25
L305448	**FGW** 44005 [A] green+ivory - *99*	20	25
L205167	**Australian** XPT silver+orange - *?*	20	25

C4g. Mk3 Trailer Restaurants (HST Stock)

L305163	**BR** 42258 blue+grey - *82*	10	15
L305433	**Virgin** 40418 [G] red+black (TRSB) - *98*	10	15
L305407	**Virgin XC** 40432 [G] red+black (TRSB) - *98*	10	15
L305393	**BR ICs** 40619 (TRFM) grey - *89*	10	15
L305183	**BR** 40322 IC grey (TRUB) - *87*	10	15
L305401	**GNER** 40704 [F] navy blue (TRFB) - *98*	10	15
L305413	**Midland Mainline** 40749 [F] green+ beige (TRFB) - *98*	10	15
L305409	**GWT** 40733 [F] green+ivory (TRFB) - *99*	10	15
L305447	**FGW** 40727 [F] green+ivory (TRFB) - *99*	10	15
L305481	**FGW** 40707 [F] (TRFB) - *99*	10	15

Mk3 trailer restaurant in GWT 'Fag Packet livery [C4g]

C4h. Mk3a Sleeper (SLE)

L305367	**BR** E10646 blue+grey - *84*	10	15
L305369	**BR IC** E10645 grey - *85*	10	15
L305443	**FGW** 10532 green+ivory - *99*	10	15
L305483	**FGW** 10588 - *99*	10	15
-	**IC** Mainline grey ex-train pack Sp Edn (Harburn Hobbies) - *01*	12	NA

C4i. Mk3 in Irish Liveries

The models came in boxes branded Lima Jouef.

?	**IE** 7161 dark maroon Executive - *03*	18	NA
?	**IE** 7462 dark maroon Executive - *03*	18	NA
LT600002	above 2 coaches in 1990s Executive livery Sp Edn (Murphy Models) - *03*	NA	60

Mk3 trailer 1st open [C4d]

C5. Class 101 Centre Car (TSL)

| L305381 | **ScotRail** 59539 grey+blue - *99* | 10 | 15 |

L305382	**BR** M59115 blue - *99*	10	15
L305398	**BR** E59523 green - *99*	10	15
L305399	**BR** Sc59553 green - *99*	10	15
-	**BR** 59108 blue+grey ex-L149915 train pack - *99*	10	NA
-	**Regional Railways** 59303 white+ blue ex-L149927 train pack - *99*	10	NA
-	**NSE** blue - *99*	10	15

C6. Class 117 Centre Car

L204830	**BRc** 59520 GWR brown+cream Ltd Edn 300 - *94*	20	NA
L205153	**BRe** W59484 white - *82-90*	10	15
L205145	**BRe** W59493 blue - *81-90*	10	15
L205146	**BRc** W59518 green - *81-95*	10	15
L205148	**BRe** W59508 blue+grey - *81-94*	10	15
L205098	**NSE** 59514 blue+white - *94-?*	10	15
L205087	**BR Reg Rlys** 59521 blue+grey - *94-?*	10	15

C7. Eurostar Cars

-	**EPS** 3211 grey ex-set L106530 - *?*	8	NA
-	**EPS** 3212 grey ex-set L106530 - *?*	8	NA

PARCELS STOCK

More than any other manufacturer, Lima have catered for parcels traffic and often found it hard to decide whether to classify the models as coaches or wagons. To avoid the confusion, we have included them all here under a new heading.

Cat.No.	Company, Number, Colour, Dates	£	£
P1.	**Bogie Parcel Van Siphon G**		
L305350	**BR** W2938W red - *81*	8	12
L305351	**GWR** 2792 dark brown - *78*	8	12
L305352	**GWR** Palethorpes 2766 brown - *78*	8	12
L305353	**BR** 2982 blue - *78*	8	12
L305354	**BR** ADW150426 blue Enparts - *79*	8	12

P2. LMS GUV Bogie Parcel Van

L305358	**LMS** 37762 maroon - *80*	8	12
L305359	**BR** M37794 red+cream - *80*	8	12
L305360	**BR** M37926 blue - *80*	8	12
L305370	**BR** DM395929 Engineering Dept. olive Air Compressor Van - *83*	8	12
L305371	**BR** M37776M maroon - *83*	8	12

P3. Mk1 Gangwayed Full Brake (BG)

L305340	**RES** 93134 red - *?*	10	12
L305341	**BR** B80855 blue - *77*	NPG	NPG
L305341	**BR** M80855 Express Parcels blue - *84*	8	12
L305342	**LMS** 30964 maroon - *77*	8	12
L305342	**BRc** M25742 lined maroon - *79*	8	12
L305343	**BR** M80855 blue+grey - *77*	NPG	NPG
L305343	**BR** W43462 blue+grey - *79*	8	12
L305344	**BR** M80855 red+cream - *77*	8	12
L305344	**BR** M34722 red+cream - *79*	8	12
L305345	**GWR** 4476 brown+cream - *77*	8	12
L305345	**BR** W24680 brown+cream - *79*	8	12
L305346	**Scotrail** 92128 - *87*	8	12
L305347	**Post Office** 80861 NDX red - *90*	8	12
L305348	**BR** S33456 green - *79*	8	12
L305349	**RES** 92355 NEX red - *93*	8	12
L305389	**NSE** 92236 late blue - *89*	8	12
L305373	**BR IC** M92001 grey - *87*	8	12
L305396	**Trans-Pennine** 92092 - *90*	8	12
-	**RES** 92714 red ex-L149808 pack - *99*	12	NA
-	**RES** 92750 red ex-L149784 pack - *?*	12	NA
-	**RES/Royal Mail** 92244 red NDX - *?*	12	NA
-	**IC Mainline** grey ex-train pack Sp Edn (Harburn Hobbies) - *01*	15	NA

Mk1 gangwayed full brake [P3]

P4. CCT/NOV Parcel Wagon

L305355	**Tartan Arrow** M94229 - *79*	6	10
L305356	**BR** M94291 blue - *79*	6	10
L305357	**BR** M94292 red - *79*	6	10

CCT parcel wagon [P4]

P5a. 57' GUV Bogie Parcel Van

L305610	**BR** 96102 Motorail Intercity grey - *90*	8	12
L305611	**BR** W96175 Motorail blue+grey - *90*	8	12
L305612	**NSE** 93852 Express Parcels late blue - *91*	8	12
L305613	**Post Office** 93395 NIX red - *91*	10	12
L305640	**BR RES** 93134 NJX red - *92*	10	12
L305656	**BR** 85117 Express Parcels blue+grey - *82*	8	12
L305657	**BR** W34674 maroon - *82*	8	12
L305657	**BR** W86470 lined maroon - *82*	8	12
L305658	**Theakstons** Brewer yellow - *82*	8	12
L305658	**Satlink Western** KDB977557 bright red+ yellow - *91*	8	12
L305658	**BR** yellow Engineering Dept Tool Van - *82*	8	12
-	**RES** 93143 red ex-L149784 pack - *?*	12	NA
-	**RES** 95133 red ex-L149808 pack - *99*	12	NA
-	**RES** 95138 red ex-L149808 pack - *99*	12	NA

57' GUV bogie parcel van in Satlink Western livery [P5a]

P5b. 57' NKA Super GUV

L305614	**RES** 94153 red+grey - *02*	12	17
L305619	**RES** 94212 EWS red - *01*	12	17
L305721	**RES** 94123 red - *02*	12	17
L305722	**RES** 94157 Royal Mail red - *02*	12	17
L305723	**RES** 94208 red - *01*	12	17
L305724	**RES** 94209 Royal Mail red - *01*	12	17
L305725	**RES** 94212 EWS red - *01*	12	17

WAGONS

In comparison with the locomotive range, the range of Lima wagons is limited to a few types which vary considerably according to the age of the model design. Early models were taken from Lima's Continental ranges and given liveries that might have been seen in Britain if the wagons had run there but models based on British prototypes gradually displaced the Continental ones. Some of these survived in the British range for many years.

Even early British wagon types, such as the 7-plank wagon and closed van were somewhat simplified but later models were more sophisticated and detailed. With Lima's concentration on modern image locomotives, understandably, the emphasis in recent years has been on modern wagons.

Cheap versions of some wagons, which incorporated body and chassis in one, were produced for starter sets but carried the same printing as the better wagons they were based on. They can be quickly recognised because the chassis is the same colour as the body (this does not include any black bodied wagons). If Lima wagons ever become targeted by collectors, these cheap versions, made exclusively for sets, are likely to become much sought after.

Cat.No.	Company, Number, Colour, Dates	£	£

Original Continental Style Wagons

W1. Continental 30' 4-Wheel Container Wagon

This was of Continental design and carried either one 40' H0 size container or two 20' ones. The wagon was black and those used in starter sets had no printing on them.

L302871	2104290324 + **Scotch Beef** grey - ?	5	10
L302870	2104290324 + 2 **Freightliner** red - 84	5	10
L302852	2104290324 + **Scotch Beef+LHB** blue+ orange - 77	5	10
L302871	2104290324 + **Freightliner** grey+red - 77	4	6
L302870	2104290324 + 2 x **ACL** grey - 80	5	10
L302874	wagon + 2 x **ACL** grey - 84	3	NA
L302682	wagon + 2 cars ex-starter sets - 84	3	NA

W2. Continental Twin Flat Bolster Wagons

L309039	brown + tubes - 77	6	10
L309038	brown + planks - 77	6	10

W3. Continental LWB Mineral Wagon

scc = chassis the same colour as the body.

L303173	**NCB** Cardiff 1879 light grey - 77	4	5
L303134	**NCB** Cardiff 1879 light grey scc - 77	4	5
L303175	**BRe** 100027 brown - 77	3	NA
L303318	**BR** brown scc ex-sets - 80	4	5
L303133	**BR** 100027 brown scc ex-sets - 84	3	NA
L303194	**Traffic Services** brown - ?	NPG	NPG

Continental LWB mineral wagon NCB [W3]

W4. Continental Twin Silo Wagon

L302805	**Blue Circle** Cement 7504 yellow - 77	4	5

W5. Continental 3-Cask Beer Wagon

L302822	**Watneys** P660513 red+brown - 77	4	5

W6. Continental Small Tank

L302713	**Shell** 557128 yellow - 77	4	5
L302715	**BP** green - 77	4	5
L302717	**Mobil** 57882 yellow LP-Gas - 79	4	5
L302718	**Gulf** white+red - 77	4	5
L302721	**Unigate** S252 white - 77	4	5
L302720	**ICI** Chemicals C1182 white - 77	4	5

L302720	**Amoco** AMOCO85600 white - 79	4	5
L305691	**Amoco** AMOCO85600 white - 85	4	5

Continental 3-cask beer wagon Watneys [W5]

W6A. Continental LWB Tank

Previously in the Lima H0 series

L302265?	**Mobiloil** red ex-sets - 80	4	NA
L302651	**Shell** yellow ex-sets - 80	4	NA
L302265?	**Texaco** red ex-sets - 80	4	NA
L302265?	**BP** dark green ex-sets - 80	4	NA

W7. Continental Ferry Van

L303155	**East Anglian Meat** E75 lime green - 77	7	10
L303165	**BR** 217021003910 brown - 77	4	6
L303162	**BR** 217021003910 brown * - 78	5	7
L302991	**NE** 167349 brown - 77	7	10

* This was a converter van having a Lima continental coupling on one end and a tension-lock coupling at the other end.

W8. Continental Refrigerator Van

St = with steps each end. scc = chassis the same colour as the body.

L303104	**Bell** white - ?	4	5
L303110	**Infrigo** blue - ?	4	5
L303142	**Coca Cola** white scc ex-sets - 84	3	NA
L303146	**Pepsi** white+red+blue scc ex-sets - 80	3	NA
L303118	**Schweppes** 2416S yellow - 77	4	5
L303144	**Schweppes** 2416S yellow scc ex-sets - 77	3	NA
L303114	**Grimsby Fish** N826421 St blue - 77	4	5
L303135	**Grimsby Fish** N826421 St blue scc - ex-sets 77	3	NA
L303545	**Heinz** 24516S St yellow - 79	4	5
L303145	**Heinz** 24516S yellow scc ex-sets - 84	3	NA

W9. Tierwag Type Car Carrier

L302681	brown ex-sets - 80	4	NA

W10. Continental Car Transporter

L309057	**British Leyland** 518098800213 black - 77	10	15
L305697	**British Leyland** 518098800213 black - 85	NPG	NPG
L309057	**Austin Rover** - 84?	NA	NA
L305696	**BR Motorail** 518098800213 blue - 87	10	15
L309053	**BR Motorail** 518098800213 blue - 77	10	15

W11. 26T Bogie Hopper

L302892	**ICI** Bulk Salt - *not made*	NA	NA
L302892	**NCB** 6783532 light grey - 82	6	10

W12. Continental Bogie Tanker

L302911	**Milk** 152D blue - 77	7	10
L302913	**Amoco** A1090 white - 77	6	8
L302916	**Texaco** red - 77	5	8
L302904	**Shellgas** yellow - 77	7	10
L302908	**Esso** 30000 red+white or silver - 79-82	6	8
L302909	**Total** PR82620 red - 79	7	10

W13. Bogie Refrigerator Van

L303204	**BR Railfreight** BRT yellow - 77	8	12
L303199	**BP** Offshore S42746 light blue - 77	8	12

W13A. Bogie Sliding Door Van

L303204	**BR Railfreight** BRT yellow - *77*	8	12
L303199	**Sundries** (Irish) yellow - *83*	8	12

W14. 35T Continental Breakdown Crane

This was an 8-wheel mobile crane with a bogie match truck which had a gantry to carry the weight of the jib.

L305698	**BRe** ADRC96708 yellow - *85*	7	10
L309059	**LNER** red - *77*	7	10
L309048	**BR** 654414 yellow - *?*	7	10

W15. 20-Wheel Articulated Heavy Carrier

L309067	**BSC** Foundry wagon white - *79*	10	15
L309056	**Phillips** transformer load grey - *77*	10	15
L309052	**Calf** Foundry wagon grey - *77*	10	15
L309068	**GEC** transformer load green - *79*	10	15

12T 7-plank wagon J.K. Harrison [W16]

British Design Wagons

W16. 12T 7-Plank Open Wagon

scc = chassis the same colour as the body.

L305674	**NBC** 423 black + coal - *83*	4	5
L305675	**BR** M3132 light grey + coal - *83*	4	5
L305672	**Royal Arsenal** 144 brown + coal - *83*	4	5
L305673	**Black & Decker** - *83*	4	5
L305676	**Raleigh Burner** 1117 blue + coal - *84*	4	5
L305679	**Ebbw Vale** 6117 black - *84*	4	5
L305690	**Austin Rover** 9191 grey + coal - *84*	4	5
L303365	**Austin Rover** 9191 grey scc ex-sets - *85*	3	NA
L305677	**Harrods** 45 brown + coal - *84*	4	5
L305678	**Courtaulds** 18 green + coal - *84*	4	5
L305614	**Oxford & District** 18 yellow-green - *77*	4	5
L305614	**Barrow & Barnsley** cream - *80*	4	5
L305615	**Dearne Valley** 61 bright blue - *77*	4	5
L305611	**Clay Cross** 1791 brown - *77*	4	5
L305613	**Evans & Bevan** 1759 black - *77*	4	5
L305612	**Black Park Colliery** 2021 maroon - *80*	4	5
L305612	**Glasshoughton** 126 yellow - *77*	4	5
L305616	**GWR** 122060 light grey - *77*	4	5
L305669	**Clarkes** 9 green + coal - *84*	4	5
L30?	**Clarkes** 9 green scc ex-sets - *94*	3	NA
L305670	**Pilkington Glass** 9 red + coal - *83*	4	5
L305671	**Prince of Wales** grey + coal - *83*	4	5
L305634	**Buxton** 24 grey - *79*	4	5
L305631	**JK Harrison & Co** maroon + coal - *79*	4	5
L305632	**PW Spencer** yellow - *79*	4	5
L30?	**PW Spencer** yellow scc ex-sets - *94*	3	NA
L305633	**Pinxton Collieries** Ltd 930 black - *79*	4	5
L303364	**SNCF** 7354 blue ex-starter sets - *84*	3	NA
L303362	**Australian** brown ex-starter sets - *84*	10	NA
L305617	**CIE** brown - *78*	10	NPG

W17. 50T Stone Hoppers

L305637	**BR** brown - *80*	6	8
L305636	**ARC Amey Roadstone** AR14228 cream - *80*	6	8
L305637	**ARC** (revised) AR14214 yellow - *86*	6	8
L305635	**Yeoman** PR14001 grey - *80*	6	8
L305638	**Yeoman** (revised) PR14019 grey - *87*	6	8

L305638	**Tilcon** 14099 light grey - *80*	6	8
L305639	**Tarmac** 14007 white - *81*	6	8
L305668	**BP Chemicals** PR8264 grey - *83*	6	8

12T 7-plank open wagon - Clay Cross [W16]

W18. 45T Grain Hopper

L305654	**Grainflow** BRT7780 green - *84*	7	10
L305653	**Bass Charringtons** 7 red - *83*	7	11
L305651	**Haig** 5834 blue - *82*	7	10
L305652	**Black and White** 6046 yellow - *82*	7	10
L305650	**Vat 69** 5835 pale blue - *82*	7	12

W19. PCA Depressed Centre Tank

L305603	**Castle** TRL9154 white - *89*	10	15
L305604	**Albright & Wilson** TRL10529 green - *89*	10	15
L305601	**Blue Circle** light grey - *89*	10	15
L305602	**Ketton** TRL9470 lime green - *89*	10	15
L305607	**Tiger** TRL10521 yellow - *89*	10	15
L305608	**Tiger** APG TRL10523 blue - *91*	10	15
L305605	**Lever Bros** TRL10537 purple - *89*	10	15
L305306	**BR** APCM9398 light grey - *89*	10	15

W20. 6-Wheel Tank

Based upon an ex-GWR vehicle but the brake gear was not representative of any of the grouping railways.

L305644	**CWS** W44520 very dark green - *81*	6	8
L305642	**IMS** 22 black - *80*	6	8
L305641	**St Ivels** W44520 white - *80*	6	8
L305640	**Corn Products Ltd** 37 black - *82*	6	8
L305643	**Express Dairies** black - *80*	7	10
L305643	**Express Dairies** white - *81*	6	8
L305643	**Express Dairies** W44520 blue - *83*	7	10
L305702	**BR** ADW2592 oil storage blue *02*	7	10
L305703	**United Dairies** W2009 white - *02*	7	10

W21. GWR Horse Box

L305625	**GWR** 546 brown - *79*	4	5
L305628	**Southern** green - *79*	4	5
L305626	**LMS** red - *79*	4	5

Horse box [W21]

W22. 20T Corrugated End Van

scc = chassis the same colour as the body.

L305607	**Birds Custard** deep blue - *80*	4	5
L383056	**Ever Ready** M3245 black - *83*	4	5
L305826	**Pearl** of Cyprus Services blue - *83*	4	5
L305688	**Stork Margarine** 100 yellow - *84*	4	5

L305689	**R White** 305689 white - *84*	4	5
L306608	**Castrol GTX** B785242 grey - *80*	4	5
L305604	**Lucas Batteries** M3245 black - *80*	4	5
L305605	**St Ivel** Unigate 68837 white - *77*	4	5
L305606	**GWR** 59701 light grey - *77*	4	5
L305601	**Typhoo** red - *77*	4	5
L305602	**Home Pride** BHP3228 white+blue - *77*	4	5
L305603	**Michelin** M3245 brown - *77*	4	5
L305687	**McCain** Beefeater yellow - *84*	4	5
L305681	**Ford** white - *83*	4	5
L305680	**BR** DE1240 tool van red - *83*	4	5
L305684	**Shredded Wheat** 714 yellow - *84*	4	5
L305686	**Walls** 469 brown - *84*	4	5
L305685	**Birds Eye** 441 white - *84*	4	5
L303375	**Birds Eye** 441 white scc ex-set - *85*	3	NA
L303373	explosives van brown scc ex-set - *84*	3	NA
L303374	**Lima** brown scc ex-sets - *84*	3	NA
L303157	**Castrol** light grey scc ex-sets - *84*	3	NA
L303372	light grey scc ex-sets - *84*	3	NA
L305605	**CIE** brown - *78*	10	NPG

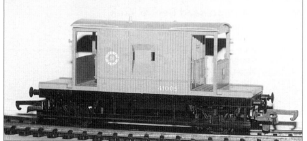

20T standard brake van in CIE livery [W23]

W23. 20T BR Standard Brake Van

L305622	**BRe Post Office** B954735 red - *91*	4	5
L305620	**BR** B954521 brown - *77*	4	5
L305621	**NE** 159486 grey - *77*	4	5
L305623	**Civil Link** DB950406 grey+yellow - *93*	4	5
L305622	**CIE** 41005 grey - *78*	10	NPG

W24. 30T Bogie Bolster Wagon

L305629	**GWR** 70897 grey + rails - *81*	6	8
L305631	**Civil Link** yellow + bogie load - *93*	6	8
L305630	**BR** brown + rails - *80*	6	8

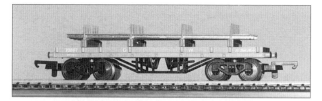

30T bogie bolster wagon with rails [W24]

W25. 102T PTA Bogie Ore Tippler

The model is based on the BREL built batch.

L305671	**Yeoman** PR26513 white - *89*	8	13
L305672	**Yeoman** PR26548 grey - *95*	8	13
L305670	**ARC** PR25735? yellow - *87*	8	13
L305663	**BSC** Iron Ore grey - *83*	8	13
L305664	**BSC** Iron Ore grey+red - *83*	8	13

W26a. Seacow Bogie Ballast Hopper

L305667	**BR** DB982881 grey+yellow - *84*	8	20
L305699	**BR Loadhaul** DB982878 - *95*	8	18
L305624	**EWS** DB980003 maroon - *99*	8	15
L305628	**EWS** 890064 maroon - *99*	8	15

L305629	**EWS** 892138 maroon - *99*	8	15
L305633	**EWS** 890004 maroon - *99*	8	15
L305642	**EWS** 890076 maroon - *99*	8	15
L305682	**EWS** 890016 maroon - *99*	8	15
L305683	**EWS** 890072 maroon - *99*	8	15
L305693	**EWS** 890067 maroon - *99*	8	15
L305694	**EWS** 890068 maroon - *99*	8	15
L305695	**EWS** 890069 maroon - *99*	8	15
L144967	**EWS** 892835 maroon ex-set - *99*	8	NA
L144967	**EWS** 891401 maroon ex-set - *99*	8	NA

W26b. Sealion Bogie Ballast Hopper

L305665	**BR** Eng DB982861 olive green - *84*	8	15
L305666	**BR** DB982924 brown - *84*	8	15

W27. 102T Procor Bogie Tank

L305643	**Shell** Ltd Edn (Langdale) - *?*	10	15
L305645	**Esso** PR78537 white - *83*	10	15
L305646	**Fina** black - *83*	10	15
L305647	**Phillips** white - *83*	10	15
L305649	**Total** PR82758 silver - *84*	10	15

W28. PDA Bogie Twin Tank Wagon

L305615	**Blue Circle** 20203 light grey - *91*	10	15
L305616	**Croxton & Garry** CG9526 white - *91*	10	15
L305617	**Lloyds & Scottish** 9736 light grey - *91*	10	15
L305618	**Derbyshire Stone** CG9536 white - *91*	10	15

W29. 82T Procor Bogie Pallet Van

L305659	**Neill & Brown** LS7020 blue - *83*	8	15
L305655	**Kemira** Fertilizers BRT7105 blue - *94*	8	15
L305662	**BR** LS7020 brown - *83*	8	15
L305661	**UKF** LS7008 white+brown - *83*	8	15
L305660	**Fisons** LS7020 white+green - *83*	8	15
L305660	**Fisons** LS7020 cream+green - *83*	8	15

BHA hooded steel carrier [W30]

W30. BHA Hooded Steel Carrier

L305681	**Tiphook** 962001 white - *91*	10	15
L305680	**Railfreight Metals** 962001 red - *90*	10	15

SETS

There have been many train sets over the years as well as some train packs. Special value is applied to these only where they contain models unique to them. To establish which these are, the locomotive list is worth studying. Other sets sell for between £25 and £50.

Lone Star 000

HISTORY

In 1940 Aubrey Robert Mills, known to his friends as Bob, worked in a lockup garage beneath the forecourt of The Bridge Filling Station in Green Lanes, Palmers Green, London, building a die-casting machine. He entered into a partnership with Sidney Ambridge and together they founded Die Casting Machine Tools Ltd (DCMT) to develop the business. Later the River Works at 152 Green Lanes, Palmers Green, became the home of DCMT. For a few years they found themselves involved in war work but, when peace came, they found good trade in supplying the blossoming array of new companies that formed to manufacture for the fast growing post-war market.

One of these new companies was founded by an ex-employee of DCMT, Rodney Smith and his partner Leslie Smith who pooled their demob money and bought one of the DCMT machines. The company they founded was Lesney and the product range the machine made for them was Matchbox Toys. Another famous ex-employee of DCMT was Jack Odell who worked for Lesney before setting up his own company Lledo to produce the Days Gone and Vanguard series of diecast vehicles.

With the war over, Ambridge and Mills made a lengthy visit to Frank Youssi's diecasting factory (Ambrit Industries) in Glendale, California in 1946 to study production there. It was not long before DCMT decided to go into manufacturing themselves and one of the first companies they did diecasting work for was Crescent Toys; a company also remembered for their model railway accessories. When they parted company with Crescent Toys in 1950 they decided to manufacture and market toys themselves.

The craze with children in the early '50s was the wild west films seen on television and a series particularly popular was 'Riders of the Range'. The writer remembers watching it, half hidden behind the sofa! DCMT cashed in on this craze and produced the first diecast toy revolver and the Lone Star range was born. Lone Star was hugely popular, partly through its links with the television programme but also through other links it developed with the Eagle boy's comic and a serial on Radio Luxembourg. The Company even launched its own Lone Star comic in 1953!

Lone Star's toy range became considerable and diverse in subject matter. In 1954/55 a new factory (now gone) was built for Lone Star production on Birchwood Industrial Estate at Hatfield and they tied up with the Harvey Toy Co. of Wood Green, London, who made, amongst other things, plastic soldier. By the end of the decade they had a range of 200 figures. Another factory in the DCMT group was AGM Industries the initial coming from the three principals - Ambridge, Gower and Mills. This factory (now gone) was in Holloways Lane, Welham Green, near Hatfield. Expansion of the toy business led to the Company moving to a new factory at Hatfield and a series of diecast cars called Road-masters followed. Next came the series for which they are best remembered by model train collectors.

While the idea of an N gauge system had been around for a long time, Lone Star were the first company to attempt producing a commercial range for the British market. It started as a push-along system, designed by Stuart Goss in 1957 and called Lone Star Locos. All items were to 000 scale with a track gauge of 8.25 mm (exactly half 00 gauge). Initially all parts, including the track

and buildings, were diecast and roughly based on real prototypes.

At the Harrogate and Brighton toy fairs in 1960, an electric range, known as Treble-O-Lectric, was launched which used many of the push-along castings fitted with plastic wheels to run on a finer scale 9 mm track and with tension-lock couplings. In order to fit a motor inside locomotives, two completely new models were tooled up and these were the Class 23 (Baby Deltic) and the Class 24 diesels.

1962 saw the introduction of an American range of locos and rolling stock which won DCMT a major contract to supply Montgomery Ward of Chicago. This company had a large mail order business and some 600 retail store outlets across North America. Blister packaging was also introduced in 1962. Vinyl was used the following year in the production of a series of buildings called Gulliver County and with these came a set of diecast 000 scale road vehicles. Encouraged by the good sales across the Atlantic, Canadian liveries followed in 1964.

In 1965 however, following an unsuccessful attempt to interest Lines Bros. (Tri-ang) in purchasing the railway system, production of Lone Star Locos and Treble-O-Lectric ceased.

In 1967, many of the passenger and goods stock items from the Treble-O-Lectric range were reissued in bubble-packs as Treble-0-Trains, using locomotives from the electric system, but without motors, and with a new plastic track produced for the series. In 1968, this system was renamed Impy Treble-0-Trains and new bubble-packs were produced.

Milestones
1940 DCMT formed by A.R.Mills and Sidney Ambridge.
1946 Mills and Ambridge visit Ambrit Industries in California.
1949 DCMT manufacturing for Crescent Toys.
1950 DCMT start their own toy range under the name Slikker Toys.
1955 Tie up with Harvey's hollow-cast figure business.
1956 Opening of additional factory at Hatfield.
1956 Road-masters car series introduced.
1957 Launch of Lone Star Locos.
1960 Introduction of Treble-O-Lectric
1962 American range.
1962 Arrival of blister packaging.
1963 Gulliver County launched.
1964 Canadian liveries.
1963 Impy cars launched.
1965 Production of Treble-0-Lectric and Lone Star Locos ceases
1967 New range of Treble-0-Trains launched.
1968 Push-along trains renamed 'Impy Treble-0-Trains'
1969 Tuf-Tots launched.
1970 Railway range removed from UK market and renamed 'Lone Star Model Trains'
c1973 Model trains withdrawn.
1978/79 Abortive plan to re-launch railway system.
1983 Lone Star/DCMT in liquidation.
1985 Trebl-0-Trains Ltd. dissolved
1988 Lone Star sold to Sohni-Esco Group.

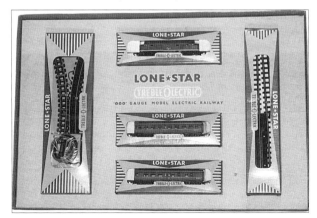

EL51 passenger set

Lone Star 000

In 1970 the train system was designated 'for export only', renamed Lone Star Model Trains, the term '000' finally dropped in favour of 'N Gauge' and the bubble-packs were replaced by boxes. It remained available for overseas sales until approximately 1973.

In 1979, Lone Star made plans to re-launch the model railway system. Contemporary subjects, such as the 125 High Speed train were mocked up but the system never reached production. Bob Mills had died in the 1960s but Sidney Ambridge died in 1980.

Meanwhile, the mid '60s had seen the launch of Lone Star's Impy series of small cars to compete with Matchbox and Huskey. Tuf-Tots, Roadmaster Majors, Kings of the Road and many other series followed. In 1988 Lone Star was taken over by Sohni-Esco of Germany and production at Hatfield came to an end. However, DCMT continued as an independent company still in the business of manufacturing diecasting machines.

Plastic copies of Lone Star 000 manufactured in Hong Kong may be found. Some were pirate copies made under the name 'Linda' and were imported into the UK in 1962 by Randall & Wood of Wood Green, London. Others were produced under the well known Hong Kong brand - 'Blue Box'. Later there were bubble-packed copies sold under the names 'Kelly' and 'HoHoHo' but it is not clear whether these are copies or from earlier tooling sold in the Far East.

GEM models reissued white metal copies of the Lone Star 000 Citroen and the articulated lorry while the Tuf-Tots were reissued as Mokes by Microlink of Swansea.

Some Impy/Treble-O-Trains goods stock was included in a Japanese N gauge set made by Loco-Mate in the early 70s.

Further Reading

A useful book called 'Lone Star: The Toy Company and its Model Cars' has been written by Andrew Ralston and published by Auto Review Publications (ISBN 1900482142). This provides a useful history of the Company but when it comes to describing the models it has a bias towards the car ranges rather than the railway.

A book called 'The Bumper Book of 'Lone Star' Diecast Models & Toys 1948-88', has been written by Geoffrey Ambridge whose father was one of the partners who started the whole thing. Geoffrey Ambridge also has a website for the book at www.lone-star-diecast-bk.com which is also a free forum for Loan Star collectors.

There were also two articles by Clive Gehle in the January and February 2000 issues of Model Railway Collector which were specifically about the Lone Star railway models.

Dutch collector, Donald Troost, has published a colour catalogue of the entire Lone Star 000 range and this is currently the definitive guide to the system and details may be obtained from DUTCHCOLL@cs.com.

Finally, for a more in depth study of the variations that occurred in the design of the Lone Star railway series, you are recommended to obtain a copy of Monty's Amateur Collectors Guide to Loan Star Trains. This is obtainable from S.Culverhouse, 17 Church Street, Clowne, Chesterfield S43 4JR.

THE MODELS

Numbering - As the various train series overlapped it is possible to find a particular model with more than one code number. For example, the signal box appeared as 33, 80, EL.152 and 92 and yet only the packaging changed. In order to keep it simple we have listed below the models as they were presented in series but be aware that if you have an unboxed item you may find it in more than one list.

Colours - Many of the models were produced in a variety of colours and some are rarer than others.

Prices - It is very difficult to give a realistic guide to these as dealers often have little idea of the rarity or otherwise of items they are selling. It is therefore possible to pick up unusual items at bargain prices but it is also possible to find relatively common pieces overpriced. A further consideration is that prices for mint boxed Canadian and US liveries are much higher in North America than they are in the UK. It is UK prices that we have included here.

Cat.No.	Details	£	£
1.	**'Lone Star Locos' in Boxes** (1957-60)		
1	0-6-0 Class 3F Tank Loco	5	8
2	2-6-2 Class 3 Tank Loco	5	8
3	Open Goods Wagon (2)	3	5
4	BR Midland Region Coach	3	5
5	Straight Track - metal (3)	2	4
6	Curved Track - metal (3)	2	4
7	0-6-0 Diesel Shunting Loco	4	7
8	4-6-2 Class A4 Gresley Loco	5	8
9	Tender for No.8	3	4
10	4-6-2 Class 8P Loco Princess Royal	5	8
11	Tender for No.10	3	4
12	US Diesel Loco	5	8
13	Brake Van	3	4
14	Cattle Wagon	3	4
15	UD Tank Wagon	3	4
16	BP Tank Wagon	3	4
17	Shell Tank Wagon	3	4
18	Goods Van (2)	5	6
19	BR Mk1 Composite Coach	4	5
20	Points - metal (1LH, 1RH)	4	5
21	Crossovers - metal (2)	3	4
22	Sleeper Built Buffer (3)	3	5
23	Re-railer Track - metal (3)	2	3
24	Station and Platform	7	10
25	Flat Wagon (3)	4	6
26	US Passenger Coach	4	5
27	Girder Bridge with Piers	6	8
28	Incline Piers (6)	3	5
29	Plastic Trees (3)	5	6
30	Telegraph Poles - plastic (12)	5	6
31	Fences and Gates - plastic (12+2)	5	6
32	Semaphore Signal	4	5
33	Signal Box	3	5
34	American flat car	3	5
35	American flat car with cars	17	20
36	American crane car	4	6
37	American tank car	4	6
38	American caboose	3	5
39	American box car	4	6
40	Level crossing	4	6
41	Automobiles (3)	21	25
42	Footbridge	5	8
GS1	Goods Train Set	NA	35
GS2	Mainline Express Set	NA	35
GS3	Mainline Goods Set	NA	35
GS4	American Diesel Set	NA	35

2-6-2 Class 4 tank [1]

2. 'Lone Star Locos' in Blister Packs (1962-65)

50	0-6-0 Class 3F Tank with Track	5	8
51	2-6-2 Class 3 Tank with Track	5	8
52	0-6-0 Diesel Shunter with Track	4	8
53	4-6-2 Class A4 Gresley Loco	5	8
54	4-6-2 Class Princess Royal	5	8
55	Tender for No.53 with 2 Straight Tracks	3	5
56	Tender for No.54 with 2 Straight Tracks	3	5
57	Midland Region Coach with Track	5	5
58	BR Mk1 Composite Coach	4	5
59	Brake Van with Flat Wagon	4	8
60	Cattle Wagon with Open Goods Wagon	5	8
61	UD Tanker with Straight Track	4	5
62	BP Tanker + Flat Wagon	4	6
63	Shell Tanker with Re-railer Track	4	5
64	Goods Van + Open Wagon	5	8
65	100T Breakdown Crane Wagon	4	5
66	US Diesel Loco	5	6
67	US Passenger Coach	4	5
68	Bogie Flat Wagon with Track	4	6
69	Bogie Tank Wagon	4	6
70	US Caboose	3	5
71	US Box Car	4	6
72	Straight Track (5)	4	5
73	Curved Track (5)	4	5
74	Points (1LH, 1RH) and Track (2)	5	6
75	Re-railer Track (4)	3	4
76	Crossover (1), Buffer (2) and Track (2)	4	6
77	Level Crossing with Re-railer Track	4	5
78	Girder Bridge with Piers	6	8
79	Incline Piers (6)	3	5
80	Signal Box with Signal	5	8
81	Signals (3)	6	10
82	Plastic Trees (5)	5	6
83	Telegraph Poles, Fences, Gates	6	8

Princess loco in blister pack [2]

3. 'Treble-O-Lectric' (1960-65)

Track and spare parts have been excluded from the following list. For set contents, see end of this section.

EL.50	Standard Goods Set	NA	55
EL.51	Standard Passenger Set	NA	55
EL.52	Goods Set with Accessories	NA	60
EL.53	Passenger Set with Accessories	NA	60
EL.54	Transcontinental Passenger Set	NA	65
EL.55	Transcontinental Goods Set	NA	65
EL.56	BR De-Luxe Scenic Set	NA	80
EL.60	D5000 Diesel Loco	10	12
EL.60A	D5000 Diesel Loco (non-motorised)	5	7
EL.61	D5900 Diesel Loco	10	12
EL.61A	D5900 Diesel Loco (non-motorised)	5	7
EL.62	US F7 Diesel Loco Union Pacific	12	25
EL.62A	US F7 Diesel Loco Union Pacific (non-motorised)	5	7
EL.63	US F7 Diesel Loco New Haven	15	30
EL.63A	US F7 Diesel Loco New Haven (non-motorised) USA & Canada only	20	25
EL.64	US F7 Diesel Loco Chesapeake & Ohio	15	30
EL.64A	US F7 Diesel Loco Chesapeake & Ohio (non-motorised) USA & Canada only	20	25
EL.65	US F7 Diesel Loco Kansas City Southern	15	30
EL.65A	US F7 Diesel Loco Kansas City Southern (non-motorised) USA & Canada only	20	25
EL.66	US 0-8-0 Baldwin Steam Loco + Tender Union Pacific	18	25
EL.66L	US 0-8-0 Baldwin Steam Loco + Tender Union Pacific with headlight	20	30
EL.67	F7 Diesel Loco Canadian Pacific	16	20
EL.67A	F7 Diesel Loco Canadian Pacific (non-motorised) USA & Canada only	20	25
EL.68	F7 Diesel Loco Canadian National	16	20
EL.68A	F7 Diesel Loco Canadian National (non-motorised) USA & Canada only	20	25
EL.70	Mk1 Composite Coach - maroon	4	5
EL.71	Mk1 Brake End Coach - maroon	4	5
EL.72	US Coach Union Pacific	4	6
EL.73	US Vista Dome Coach Union Pacific	4	6
EL.74	Mk1 Composite Coach - green	5	6
EL.75	Mk1 Brake End Coach - green	5	6
EL.76	US Coach New Haven	6	7
EL.77	US Vista Dome Coach New Haven	6	7
EL.78	US Coach Pullman	6	7
EL.79	US Vista Dome Coach Pullman	6	7
EL.80	Brake Van	2	3
EL.81	Shell Tank Wagon	3	4
EL.82	BP Tank Wagon	3	4
EL.83	UD Tank Wagon	3	4
EL.84	Cattle Wagon	3	4
EL.85	Open Goods Wagon	3	4
EL.86	Goods Van	3	4
EL.87	US Box Car Union Pacific	4	6
EL.88	100T Breakdown Crane Wagon	7	10
EL.89	Bogie Flat Wagon with Citroen DS19 and Land Rover	15	20
EL.90	Bogie Tank Wagon Mobilgas	7	9
EL.91	US Caboose Union Pacific	4	6
EL.92	US Box Car Boston & Maine	4	6
EL.93	US Box Car New Haven	4	6
EL.94	US Box Car Santa Fe	4	6
EL.95	Bogie Tank Wagon Texaco	7	9
EL.96	Bogie Flat Wagon with Austin Articulated Lorry	15	25
EL.97	US Caboose New Haven	4	6
EL.98	US Caboose Chesapeake & Ohio	4	6
EL.99	US Caboose Kansas City Southern	4	6
EL.100	Straight Track - nickel silver (9.2")	1	1
EL.101	Half Straight Track - nickel silver (2.6")	1	1
EL.102	Curved Track - nickel silver (12" radius)	1	1
EL.103	Half Curved Track - nickel silver (12" radius)	1	1
EL.104	Left Hand Point - nickel silver	3	4

Lone Star 000

EL.105	Right Hand Point - nickel silver	3	4
EL.106	Left Hand Diamond Crossing - nickel silver	3	4
EL.107	Right Hand Diamond Crossing - nickel silver	3	4
EL.108	Rerailer 9.2" with track - nickel silver	3	4
EL.109	Rerailer 4.6"	2	3
EL.110	Power Feed Terminal	1	2
EL.111	Uncoupler and Straight Track - nickel silver	1	2
EL.112	Uncoupler	1	2
EL.113	Power Feed Terminal Leads	1	2
EL.114	Point Operating Motor	4	5
EL.115	Electric Point Switch	2	2
EL.116	Left Hand Electric Point	7	10
EL.117	Right Hand Electric Point	7	10
EL.130	Canadian Pacific Coach	8	10
EL.131	Canadian Pacific Vista Dome Coach	8	10
EL.132	Canadian National Coach	8	10
EL.133	Canadian National Vista Dome Coach	8	10
EL.140	Box Car Canadian Pacific	8	10
EL.141	Caboose Canadian Pacific	8	10
EL.142	Refrigerated Box Car Canadian Pacific	8	10
EL.143	Caboose Canadian National	8	10
EL.150	Station and Platform	8	12
EL.151	Platform Extensions with Lamp Standards	10	12
EL.152	Signal Box	5	16
EL.153	Semaphore Signal - Home (2)	5	6
EL.154	Semaphore Signal - Distant (2)	5	6
EL.155	Rail Built Buffer (3)	2	3
EL.156	Girder Bridge with Piers	6	12
EL.157	Incline Piers (6)	3	7
EL.158S	Incline Tray - Straight (4)	8	10
EL.158C	Incline Tray - Curved (4)	8	10
EL.159	Telegraph Poles (28)	4	5
EL.160	Fences (24) and Gates (4)	4	5
EL.161	Trees (plastic) (3)	4	5
EL.162	Tunnel	5	10
EL.163	Footbridge	5	12
EL.164	Level Crossing with Barriers	4	8
EL.165	Loading Gauge (3) (not made)	-	-
EL.166	2-Colour Light Signals (3)	9	12
EL.167	Set of 12 Plastic Figures (unpainted)	10	12
EL.168	Set of Five Road Vehicles (Citroen DS19, Land Rover, Dennis Fire Engine, Austin Articulated Flat Lorry, AEC Regal IV Single Deck Bus)*	35	50
EL.169A	Bridge Girder (trade pack)	NPG	12
EL.169B	Bridge Pier (trade pack)	NPG	12
EL.170	Timber Yard Corner Piece	NPG	NPG
EL.171	Coal Yard Corner Piece	NPG	NPG
EL.172	Sand Quarry Corner Piece	NPG	NPG
EL.173	Farm Land Corner Piece	NPG	NPG
EL.174	Station Centre Section	NPG	NPG
EL.175	Level Crossing Centre Section	NPG	NPG
EL.176	Complete Set of 6 pieces - made?	NPG	NPG
EL.177	4-Piece Scenic Baseboard (36"x36")	20	25
EL.180	Fish Plates (12)	2	2
EL.181	Spare Band Drives (5)	4	4
EL.182	Battery Controller	5	6
EL.183	Track Clips (10)	4	5
EL.184	Variable Transformer Rectifier Controller	4	5
EL.185	Isolating Fish Plates (12)	3	3
EL.186A	Replacement Motor for Diesels	8	10
EL.186B	Replacement Motor for Baldwin	8	10
EL.187A	D5000 Chassis and Bogies (no wheels)	NPG	5
EL.187B	D5900 Chassis and Bogies (no wheels)	NPG	5
EL.187C	F7 Chassis and Bogies (no wheels)	NPG	5
EL.188A	British Coach Bogie and Wheels	NPG	4
EL.188B	US Coach Bogie and Wheels	NPG	4
EL.188C	US Goods Bogie and Wheels	NPG	4
EL.189	Brass Driving Wheels for Diesels (12)	NPG	5
EL.190A	British Coach Wheels (12)	NPG	5
EL.190B	US Coach Wheels (12)	NPG	5
EL.191A	British Goods Rolling Stock Wheels (12)	NPG	5
EL.191B	US Goods Rolling Stock Wheels (12)	NPG	5

EL.192	Track Fixing Screws (20)	NPG	4
EL.193	Carbon Brushes (2) and Springs (2)	NPG	5
EL.197	Transformer/Rectifier	5	10
EL.198	Controller	10	20
EL.199	Half Amp Cutout - not made	NA	NA

* This set of vehicle was at one time sold in a Gulliver County box.

F7 diesel - Kansas City Southern [3]

US 0-8-0 Baldwin [3] (Clive Gehle)

Canadian Pacific Caboose [3]

4. 'Treble-O-Trains' in Blister Packs (1966-68)

74	US Diesel Loco Union Pacific	10	12
75	D5900 Diesel Loco	10	12
76	US Baldwin 0-8-0 (tenderless)	10	15
77	BR Mk1 Composite Coach	4	5
78	US Passenger Coach	4	5
79	US Box Car New Haven	4	6
80	Bogie Tank Wagon Shell	4	5
81	Bogie Flat Wagon with Citroen DS19 and Land Rover	15	20
82	100T Breakdown Crane Wagon	7	10
83	US Caboose New Haven	4	6
84	Cattle Wagon and Brake Van	6	8
85	Curved Track - plastic (6)	4	6
86	Straight Track - plastic (6)	5	7
87	Trees (6)	5	6
88	Level Crossing with Barriers and Track	4	8
89	Figures, Telegraph Poles, Fences, Gates	10	12
90	Footbridge	5	10
91	0-6-0 Tank Loco with Open Goods Wagon	7	12
92	Signal Box with 2 Colour Light Signals	8	10
93	Crossovers - plastic	3	5
94A	Right Hand Point - plastic	4	5
94B	Left Hand Point - plastic	4	5

5. Impy 'Treble-O-Trains' in Blister Packs (1968-69)

With the exception of the five items listed below, this was an identical range to Treble-O-Trains in blister packs. They had the same catalogue numbers and values but different package design.

95	Princess Steam Locomotive	10	20

96	D5000 Diesel Locomotive	10	20
97	Vista Dome Coach	4	6
8020	Union Pacific Goods Set	NA	45
8030	Union Pacific Passenger Set	NA	45

Impy Treble-0-Trains [5]

6. Lone Star Model Trains

This was the same range shown in 4 and 5 above but packed in boxes with the new name and with a '7' added to the catalogue number.

7. 'Gulliver County' Buildings

These were vinyl moulded buildings, each a single moulding with features picked out with paint.

1320	Inn	10	18
1321	Church	10	18
1322	Fire Station	10	20
1323	Ranch Style Bungalow	10	18
1324	Shop with Car Park	10	18
1325	Garage Service Station	10	18
1326	Pair of Shops	10	18
1327	Two Storey House with Garage	10	18
1328	Thatched Cottage	10	18
1330	Town Square - not made	NA	NA
1331	Town Hall - not made	NA	NA
1332	Theatre - not made	NA	NA
1333	School - not made	NA	NA
1340	Twin Falls Station	10	18
	Scenic Village Set*	NPG	200

* The Scenic Village Set consisted of two pieces of hardboard painted green with roads marked out on them, one of each of the Gulliver County buildings, several of the N scale road vehicles, fences, telegraph poles and trees.

Garage [7] and Vehicles [3]

SETS

The Lone Star Locos sets were called 'Gift Sets' and were packaged in window boxes with card decking and trays. The five were made:

No.1 Goods Train Set - 2-6-2T, box van, UD tanker, Shell tanker, brake van, signal box and two signals.

No.2 Main Line Passenger Set - A4 loco and tender, 3 BR composite coaches and 2 signals.

No.3 Main Line Goods Set - Princess loco and tender, box van, goods truck, flat truck, brake van, signal box and 2 signals.

No.4 American Transcontinental Diesel Set - US diesel, 3 US passenger cars and 2 signals.

No.5 American Transcontinental Goods Set - US diesel, US box car, US tank car, US caboose and 2 signals.

The **Treble-0-Lectric** sets had the models still in their individual blue and yellow boxes which was slotted into spaces in the set box decking. The set box had no window but a lift-off lid. They had the following contents:

EL.50 BR Standard Goods Set - D5000 diesel, a brake van, cattle wagon, goods van and an oval of track.

EL.51 BR Standard Passenger Set - D5900 diesel with two coaches and an oval of track

EL.52 BR Goods & Accessories Set - D5000 diesel, brake van, Shell tanker, cattle wagon, open wagon, an oval of track, a point and siding, buffer stop, signal box, signal, station, fences & gates, trees and telegraph poles.

EL.53 BR Passenger & Accessories Set - This was the same as EL.52 but with the train from EL.51.

EL.54 Transcontinental Passenger Set - Union Pacific F7 diesel, 2 matching coaches and an oval of track. For USA and Canada only, sets were available in all liveries.

EL.55 Transcontinental Goods Set - Union Pacific diesel, Mobilgas tanker, UP box car, UP caboose and an oval of track. For USA and Canada only, sets were available in all liveries.

There was also a Baldwin Impy set comprising a tenderless push-along Baldwin, bogie Shell tanker, 100T crane and a US caboose. The box had no illustration on it but was labelled 'Durham Industries Inc.' with a New York address.

EL.56 BR De Luxe Scenic Set (2 Levels) - this had an elevated section in the middle and contained 4 vacuum-formed scenic sections which could be bought separately. It included over 90 pieces in all including a diesel passenger train and cost 9 guineas.

EL.57 BR De Luxe Scenic Set (Flat) - this had 4 scenic sections which together made a flat layout with roadways in the middle.

There was also a version exclusive to the USA that appeared in the Montgomery Ward catalogue, featuring a lake and mountain but this was made by Life-Like and not Lone Star.

For the Treble-0-Trains sets, in Impy packaging, the models were unboxed and laid in depressions in a vacuum-formed tray in a window set box. The contents of the Baldwin set were most strange consisting of a tender-less loco, bogie Shell tanker, 100 ton crane wagon, American box van, British brake van, signal box, 2 colour light signals, footbridge, level crossing and an oval of track.

214

Mainline

HISTORY

Palitoy was a division of the General Mills Corporation of America and had previously been in the model railway market when, in the early 1950s, they had made and marketed an S gauge train set. They already used the Kader Industrial Company in Hong Kong to manufacture toys for them and so it was natural for them to go to Kader when, in the mid 1970s, they decided to produce an 00 scale model railway system for the British market.

The new system was launched at the 1976 Harrogate Toy Fair followed by the Brighton Toy Fair. For their stand at Harrogate, Kader supplied the pre-production working chassis of the J72 and Palitoy provided cast resin shells for the bodies - they looked excellent! For the Brighton Fair a number of J72 pre-production models were running and attracted much attention. There were also pre-production wagons and coaches to be seen plus a pair of static 4MTs and a running Peak, all with cast resin shells.

Milestones
1976 Mainline Railways is launched by Palitoy.
1981 Release of the Manor Class model.
1981 Palitoy acquire Airfix assets.
1983 General Mills decide to pull out of toy production in Europe.
1983 Design Department closes in August
1985 Dapol acquire the intellectual assets of the Mainline range

The new system was called Mainline Railways and the excellent BR Standard 4MT 4-6-0, a Class 45 diesel and some Mk1 coaches quickly followed. The first steam locomotive was to have been a Standard Class 5 (later to be modelled by Bachmann) but, with the release of the Hornby Black 5, the marketing department at Palitoy mistakenly thought they were duplicating models and suggested the Class 4 instead. Models they considered as a subject for an 0-6-0 tank before choosing the J72 were an LNER J94, a Southern G6 and an LMS Jinty. The latter was dropped as Hornby retooled their own Jinty at about this time. Development and expansion carried on apace and 1981 saw the release of the model of a Manor Class locomotive which set the highest standards so far.

In 1981 Palitoy took over the rival Airfix GMR system and the Airfix models were gradually absorbed into the Mainline range.

Unlike Airfix, Palitoy did not own the tools with which its models were made. When Mainline models were ordered from Kader it was on the understanding that Kader retained ownership of the tools. When Palitoy acquired Airfix, it became owners of the Airfix tools and, at the advice of Palitoy (Far East) office, placed the ex-Airfix wagon tooling with Todco who were the third manufacturing company involved with Airfix tools after Sandakan and Cheong Tak. This was to lead to complications and misunderstandings later when the Mainline Railways assets were sold.

In 1983, General Mills decided to withdraw from toy development in Europe. This was not a sign of failure on the part of the Mainline range but rather a sweeping decision made many miles away on the other side of the Atlantic which affected various European toy ranges. The design department at Coalville was officially closed on August 31st 1983 and the research and development facility within the Company, for most product ranges, came to an end. The Company was acquired by Kenner Parker (later Kenner Parker Tonka) and subsequently the Palitoy name disappeared.

On the 17th of May 1985 the Mainline stock and intellectual assets were sold to Dapol.

Further Reading

A detailed listing of the Airfix and Mainline model railway systems was produced by the late Charles Manship in the 1980s but this is no longer available. However, there has been a series of articles by Graham Smith-Thompson, in *Model Railway Enthusiast* magazine, profiling the Airfix and Mainline ranges together with other systems that later used the tools. There were six parts devoted specifically to Mainline Railways published in the January-May and July 1999 issues of the magazine.

Couplings - There were three types of coupling used on Mainline stock. The first of these (type A) were based on a concept coupling drawn in Hong Kong to similar dimensions to the Hornby tension lock ones but with the arm in a sprung socket. This was redrawn by the designer at Palitoy and formed the coupling first seen on models when the system was launched. There were problems with the type A and before bulk production got underway it was redesigned (type B) and is the most common type found on Mainline stock. Type C couplings were made at the Todco factory and came after acquisition of the Airfix range. They had a gravity operated hook and were either push-fitted or screwed on. This design was later used by Dapol.

Catalogue Numbers - In some cases these were used for more than one item, as in the case of trade packs - e.g. 37067. Later numbers were often prefixed by a '9' when a new computer was installed at Palitoy. From that time, all products carried a six figure code and it is probable that the '9' prefix indicated that the item was from the Hobbies Division. Because a model is listed here with the '9' prefix it does not mean that it cannot be found boxed or listed in a catalogue without the prefix - and visa-versa. Brackets applied to catalogue numbers indicate that the number applied to more than a solo model, i.e. a train set or trade pack.

Dates - Those shown in the following lists are based on catalogue and price list appearances and are provided for guidance only. Where it is known that catalogue dates are misleading they have been altered accordingly.

Listing - The locos are listed in order of size starting with tank engines followed by tender locos and ending with diesels, electrics and multiple units. The coaches are listed with pre-Nationalisation stock first followed by vehicles of later years. Wagons are listed in the order of: flats, open wagons, hoppers, tanks, vans, brake vans and bogie stock.

LOCOMOTIVES

Samples on the Market - Far East manufacturers sent samples to their customers for approval before proceeding with full production. These samples often ended up in collections and today they command a good price. In some cases samples exist of Mainline models that did not reach the production stage and these are of even greater interest to collectors.

Smoke - Some models were advertised 'with smoke' in 1982 but mention of it was immediately dropped after this. It seems that the locomotives described were produced but without smoke generators fitted.

Cat.No.	Number, Company, Colour, Dates	£	£

L1. Class 14XX 0-4-2 Tank (ex-Airfix)

937096	**1403** GWR green - *not made*	NA	NA

937097	**1442** BRb black - *not made*	NA	NA

See Dapol D19.

L2. Class 57XX Pannier Tank 0-6-0PT

9/37084	**5764** GWR button green - *83*	250	260*
9/37084	**5764** Great Western green - *81-84*	22	30
9/37084	as above but green numberplates, and number missing from rear bufferbeam - *81*	90	100
9/37085	**5768** BRb black yellow spots - *81-84*	30	38
9/37085	as above but blue spots, error - *81*	120	130

* The highest recorded price at auction is £300.

L3. Class J72 0-6-0T

Rpsv = Ross pop safety valves.   esv = enclosed safety valves

37054	**581** LNER green lined Rpsv - *76-79*	20	28
37055	**68745** BRa black Rpsv - *76-79*	20	28
37070	**69001** BRb black esv - *80-81*	18	26
37067*	**69023** 'Joem' North Eastern green esv as preserved - *80*	20	28
937506	**LNER** black modified model - *not made*	NA	NA
937507	**BR/NER** green York Station Pilot - *not made*	NA	NA

* This catalogue number was also used for a trade pack of 6 mixed J72s.

Class J72 0-6-0 tank [L3]

L4. Class 66XX 0-6-2T

One of two Mainline models with blackened metalwork.

937038	**6697** GWR green - *83-84*	30	35
937038	As above but incorrectly with 'GWR' from the Collett Goods - *83-84*	150	160
937039	**6652** BRb black - *83-84*	30	35
937508	**?** BRc lined green only 8 samples made - *84*	300	NA

L5. Class N2 Tank 0-6-2T (ex-Airfix)

The completed models arrived too late to be sold by Airfix and, instead, were marketed by Palitoy. They carried the Airfix logo beneath the keeper plate.

9/54154	**9522** LNER lined green - *82-84*	22	30
9/54155	**69531** BRb lined black - *82-84*	22	30
954158	**4744** LNER lined black - *83-84*	28	38

L6. Class 61XX Prairie 2-6-2T (ex-Airfix)

Unlike the Airfix versions of this model, those made by Palitoy had flanged centre drivers.

937083	**6169** GWR green - *84*	27	35
937086	**6167** BRc lined green - *84*	27	35

L7. Class 2P 4-4-0

So late was this model, that some were released only in their polystyrene trays. A large quantity went to Dapol who released it in their own packaging.   It had the former 4F tender

937514	**635** LMS lined black - *84*	32	42
937515	**40568** BRb lined black - *84*	30	40

L8. Class 2251 'Collett Goods' 0-6-0

37058	**3205** GWR matt green sample 6 made - *78*	400	NA
37058	**3205** GWR semi-gloss green - *78-80*	NPG	NPG
37059	**2213** BRb black lined - *78-80*	30	35
37077	**3210** BRc green lined - *80*	32	40

37059 was demonstrated at the 1981 Harrogate Toy Fair with steam and whistle sound. This was to also be fitted to 37058.

L9. Class 2301 'Dean Goods' 0-6-0 (ex-Airfix)

The moulds for the plastic parts of this model were made for Airfix by Heller in France and taken over by Palitoy who shipped them out to Sanda Kan in Hong Kong to make. One of two Mainline models with blackened metalwork.

9/54156	**2516** GWR green - *82-84*	28	38
9/54156	as above but black - *82?*	250	260
9/54157	**2538** BRb black - *82-84*	28	38
9/54157	as above but blue green - *82*	250	260

L10. Class 4F 0-6-0 (ex-Airfix)

This was to have been a revised version from the Airfix tooling.

937512	**?** LMS black - *not made*	NA	NA
937513	**?** BR black - *not made*	NA	NA

L11. Class 43XX Mogul 2-6-0

BR fitted outside steam pipes to the Class 43XX and so the GWR models were assembled without them and the BR ones with them - however errors did occur.

9/37045	**4358** BRb lined green advertised with smoke - *82-84*	32	40
37090	**5322** Great Western green - *81-82*	32	40
37090	as above but with steam pipes fitted, 3 were found by quality control, later sold - *81*	250	260
9/37091	**5328** BRb black - *81-84*	37	45
937090	**4375** Great Western semi-gloss green, one of 3 examples, proposal dropped - *84*	NPG	NPG

L12. Class 78XX 'Manor' 4-6-0

9/37043	**7827** 'Lydham Manor' BRc green advertised with smoke - *82-84*	32	40
9/37078	**7819** 'Hinton Manor' GWR green - *80-84*	32	40
37079	**7812** 'Erlestoke Manor' BRb lined black - *80-81*	42	50
937100	**7808** 'Cookham Manor' GWR green - *83-84*	32	40
-	**7822** 'Foxcote Manor' * BR green** *not made*	NA	NA

* This was to be the power unit for the Cambrian Coast Express passenger set but production was cancelled. The pre-production sample was sold at auction in 1997 for £340. ** This was shown with Cambrian Coast headboard, 2 white lamps and whitened buffers.

GWR Manor Class 4-6-0 [L12]

L13. Modified Hall 4-6-0

Planned for 1984 but not made.

L14. Class 6P/7P 'Rebuilt Patriot' 4-6-0

37065	**5530** 'Sir Frank Ree' LMS black * - *80*	50	60
37082	same with steam sound - *80*	100	120
37082	**45530** 'Sir Frank Ree' BR black * with steam sound - *80*	80	100
37066	**45532** 'Illustrious' BRc green - *80-81*	35	42
37075	**45540** 'Sir Robert Turnbull' BRa experimental green - *80-81*	38	50
37076	**45536** 'Private W. Wood V.C.' BRa black - *80-81*	35	42
37082	same with steam sound * - *80*	70	100

* not in the catalogue.

L15. Class 5XP 'Jubilee' 4-6-0

Finer quality wheels with plastic centres called Dyna-Cast, made in Singapore, were proposed for the Jubilee but due to technical difficulties all models were released with Scot type wheels.   In 1981, the Jubilee received a re-profiled chimney with skirt mounting studs and improved wheels. Some had turned brass safety valves fitted. Ffst = Fowler flush sided 3500 gallon tender. Frt = Fowler riveted 3500 gallon tender. St = Stannier 4000 gallon tender

37061	**5690** 'Leander' LMS maroon St small nameplate - *79-80*	28	34
9/37061	same with correct size nameplate - *80-81*	30	36

9/37061	same with improved wheels - *81-83*	35	40
37095	same with Mk2 steam + whistle sound - *81*	58	70
37089	**45690 'Leander'** BRc green St - *81-82*	32	38
37062	**45691 'Orion'** BRc green St small nameplate - *79-80*	30	36
9/37062	same with correct size nameplate - *80-81*	32	38
9/37062	same with improved wheels - *81-83*	35	40
37081	same with Mk1 steam sound - *80-81*	37	42
37095	same with Mk2 steam + whistle sound - *81*	NPG	NPG
37074	**5687 'Neptune'** LMS black straw lining St small nameplateand other errors, 3 samples exist - *80*	400	410
37074	**5687 'Neptune'** LMS black straw lining St correct nameplate - *80-81*	30	38
37095	same with Mk2 steam + whistle sound - *81*	75	100
9/37046	**5719 'Glorious'** LMS maroon, fine wheels, Ffst advertised with smoke - *82-84*	40	48
37034	same with steam sound - *82*	NPG	NPG
37034	**45698 'Mars'** BRb green Frt advertised with smoke, fine wheels - *82*	35	42
9/37047	same with smoke and steam sound - *82-84*	45	50
936153	**45700 'Amethyst'** BRb black lined Ffst new cab glazing, turned brass safety valves, fine wheels - *83-84*	30	38

L16. Royal Scot Class (Parallel Boiler) 4-6-0
Differed from Rebuilt Scot only in the body shell used.

9/37092	**6127 'Old Contemptibles'** LMS maroon - *81-83*	32	40
9/37092	as above with improved finish - *83-84*	40	50
937509	as above without coal rails or smoke deflectors - *not made*	NA	NA
9/37093	**46137 'Prince of Wales's Volunteers, South Lancashire'** BRb green - *82-83*	32	40
9/37093	as above with improved finish - *83-84*	40	50

L17. Class 6P/7P 'Rebuilt Royal Scot' 4-6-0
All were fitted with the Stanier 4000 gallon tender.

37056	**6115 'Scots Guardsman'** LMS black lined straw - *77-79*	30	38
37057	**46100 'Royal Scot'** BRb green - *77-79*	33	40
37057	as above with semi-gloss livery and BRc, fine wheels, just 4 samples received - *81?*	400	NA
37060	**6100 'Royal Scot'** LMS maroon as preserved, bell on front, name on smokebox door - *80*	30	38
37080	as above but with Mk1 steam sound - *80*	40	60
37060	as above but all black cab fronts * about 2,000 used mainly in sets - *80*	38	45
937088	**46115 'Scots Guardsman'** BRc green new pattern matt silver cadmium plated fine scale driving wheels - *83-84*	35	42

* Due to a production fault, a batch was made with all black cab fronts instead of LMS maroon.

L18. Class B1 4-6-0
Pre-production models were made and finished as listed here ready for the 1984 catalogue which did not materialise.

937510	**1000 'Springbok'** LNER apple green - *not made*	NA	NA
937511	**61007 'Klipspringer'** BR lined black - *not made*	NA	NA

L19. Standard Class 4 4-6-0

37052	**75006** BRb black (small) lined - *76-80*	38	42
37053	**75001** BRc green lined, matt finish - *76-80*	38	42
37053	as above with semi-gloss livery, just 8 samples made - *84?*	400	NA
937052	**75033** BRc black lined, traction tyres fitted, sold in tray only - *83-84*	260	NA
937053	**75027*** BRc green lined, traction tyres fitted 3 samples made - *84?*	500	NA
?	BR with B1 tender, planned for 1985 -	NA	NA

not made

* Three samples were made and one of these was sold by auction in 1997 for £500.

L20. Class 03 Diesel Shunter 0-6-0DS

9/37036	**03382** BRe blue - *82-84*	18	29
9/37037	**D2179** BRc green - *82-84*	20	30

L21. Class 42 'Warship' Diesel Hydraulic B-B

9/37063	**827 'Kelly'** BRe blue - *79-84*	20	30
9/37064	**D824 'Highflyer'** BRc green - *79-84*	22	30
9/37073	**D823 'Hermes'** BRc maroon - *80-84*	25	32
37087	**D825 'Intrepid'** BRc green - *81-82*	25	32
37094	**827 'Kelly'** BRe blue, as 37063 but with diesel sound and klaxon - *81*	30	40
37094	**D824 'Highflyer'** BRc green, as 37064 but with diesel sound and klaxon - *81*	30	40

L22. Class 45 Diesel 1Co-Co1

-	unpainted grey plastic only 12 made and distributed to the trade for comments. Not all were returned - *76?*	400	NA
37050	**D49 'The Manchester Regiment'** BRc green early matt, later semi-gloss - *77-79*	25	35
37050	as above but grill surrounds painted the same grey as the roof, no BR decals, sample - *77*	200	210
37051	**45039 'The Manchester Regiment'** BRe blue early matt, later semi-gloss - *76-79*	22	32
37051	as above with split diecast motor block, no traction tyres, diecast wheels, no pick-ups on trailing bogie, 144 made - *76*	80	85
(37068)1	**45044 'Royal Inniskilling Fusilier'** BRe blue - *80*	22	NA
(37068)1	**D52 'The Lancashire Fusilier'** BRc green - *80*	22	NA
9/37040	**45048 'Royal Marines'** BRe blue split headcode boxes - *82-84*	34	45
9/37041	**D100 'Sherwood Forester'** BRc green split headcode boxes - *82-84*	45	65
(37048)2	**45048 'Royal Marines'** BRe blue split headcode boxes, as 37040 but with diesel sound and klaxon - *82-83*	45	65
(37048)2	**D100 'Sherwood Forester'** BRc green split headcode boxes, as 37041 but with diesel sound and klaxon - *82-83*	45	65

1 In 1980, retailers were offered packs of six Class 45s consisting of two each of these two plus two of Cat. No. 37051 (above). 2 Also sold together in a trade pack.

Class 45 diesel 1Co-Co1 [L22]

L23. Class 56 Diesel Co-Co

937035	**56079** blue - *83-84*	25	35
937044	**56084** BReLL blue - *83-84*	22	30

OTHER LOCOMOTIVES PLANNED

1985
SR Lord Nelson Class 4-6-0 [later modelled by Bachmann in 1992]
LMS 8F 2-8-0 (with both Stanier and Fowler tenders) [later modelled by Hornby in 1988]
GWR Class 28XX 2-8-0 [later modelled by Hornby in 1991]
LNER/BR Class A1 4-6-2 [later made by Bachmann in 2001]
LMS/BR Ivatt 2MT 2-6-2T [later made by Bachmann in 1995]
SR Class N 2-6-0 [later modelled by Bachmann in 1998]

1986
BR Class 25 [previously modelled by Hornby and later by Bachmann in

217

Mainline

2001]
LMS/BR Black 5 4-6-0 [previously modelled by Hornby]
SR/BR Class Q1 0-6-0 [later made by Hornby in 2003]
LNER/BR Class J94 0-6-0ST [modelled by Dapol in 1985]
GWR Class 8750 0-6-0PT [later modelled by Bachmann in 1999]

COACHES

The first coaches Palitoy produced were BR Mk1s and these were followed by some early LMS panelled stock. With the exception of livery changes, expansion of this range was slow until 1981 when a full brake and some Collett type coaches were announced. After that the coach range was greatly enlarged by the addition of the former Airfix models.

A pair of LNER Gresley coaches was developed but never got to the mould-making stage in the Far East.

Cat.No.	Company, Number, Colour, Dates	£	£

C1. GWR Suburban B Stock (ex-Airfix)

937320	**GWR** 6396 brown+cream - *83-84*	15	18
937320	**GWR** 6896 brown+cream - *83-84*	15	18
937321	**BR** W6447W lined maroon - *83-84*	12	18

C2. GWR Collett 60' Stock

937123	**GWR** 6507 brown+cream brake/composite - *83-84*	15	18
937124	**GWR** 1116 brown+cream all 3rd - *83-84*	15	18
937124	**GWR** (button) 1137 brown+cream all 3rd - *83-84*	15	18
937308	**BR** W7365W lined maroon brake/composite - *83-84*	15	18
937309	**BR** W1087W lined maroon all 3rd - *83-84*	15	18

C3. GWR Centenary Stock (ex-Airfix)

937314	**GWR** 6659 brown+cream Cornish Riviera Limited composite - *83*	8	14
937316	**GWR** 4575 brown+cream Cornish Riviera Limited brake 3rd - *83*	8	14

C4. GWR Auto Trailer (ex-Airfix)

937318	**GWR** 187 brown+cream twin coats of arms - *82-84*	12	18
937319	**BR** W176W red+cream 1956 livery - *83-84*	12	18
937319	**BR** W178W red+cream 1956 livery - *83-84*	12	18

C5a. 57' LMS Panelled Composite

37109	**LMS** 3621 maroon 1936 livery - *77-81*	10	15
37109	as above but mid grey roof - *?*	50	55
37111	**BR** M3621M red+cream 1948 livery - *78-81*	12	16
37115	**BR** M3542M lined maroon 1956 livery - *80-81*	14	18
37115	**BR** M3542M dull maroon with mid grey roof and gold and black lining - *80*	50	55
37115	**BR** M3542M semi-gloss maroon with mid grey roof and gold and black lining - *80*	50	55

C5b. 57' LMS Panelled Brake 3rd

37110	**LMS** 5327 dull maroon, silver-grey roof - *77-81*	10	15
37110	as above but mid grey roof - *?*	50	55
37112	**BR** M5371M red+cream 1948 livery - *78-81*	12	16
37116	**BR** M5335M semi-gloss maroon yellow lining and yellow-grey roof - *80-81*	14	18
37116	**BR** M5335M dull maroon with mid grey roof and gold and black lining - *80*	50	55
37116	**BR** M5335M semi-gloss maroon with mid grey roof and gold and black lining - *80*	50	55

C6. LMS 50' Parcels Van Type BG

937117	**BR** M31298 blue 1966/67 livery NFV - *83-84*	10	15
937118	**LMS** 30965 maroon - *83-84*	10	15

937304	**BR** M31262M blue+grey - *83-84*	10	15
937307	**BR** M31361 red - *83*	12	16
937347	**BR** lined maroon - *84*	15	18
937336	**BR** red+cream - *84*	15	18

LMS panelled coaches [C5] (Palitoy)

C7a. LMS Stanier Composite (ex-Airfix)

937326	**LMS** 3935 maroon 60' (A)* - *84*	12	20
937327	**BR** M3868M maroon 60' lined improved finish - *83-84*	10	18

*These resulted from a colour correction ordered by Airfix but were kept in store until old stocks were used up. They were inherited by Palitoy who boxed and sold them.

C7b. LMS Stanier Brake End (ex-Airfix)

937328	**LMS** 5542 maroon 57' (A)* - *84*	12	20
937329	**BR** M3868M maroon 57' lined improved finish - *83-84*	12	20

*see note for C7a.

C7c. LMS Stanier Vestibule 3rd/2nd (ex-Airfix)

Palitoy redesigned this Airfix proposal as a one piece moulding, to improve the appearance of the glazing and to fit a new 57' chassis. The conversion was later finished by Replica Railways who sold the model.

937348	**LMS** maroon 57' - *not made*	NA	NA
937349	**BR** maroon 57' - *not made*	NA	NA

C8. LMS 68' Dining Car (12-wheel) (ex-Airfix)

These were in the design stage when Airfix went into receivership and Mainline took up the project. It next fell into the hands of Dapol who actually produced the first batch of models. Their tools, thought to have been damaged in a factory fire, were later sold to Hornby who modified them and now make the model.

937345	**LMS** maroon - *not made*	NA	NA
937346	**BR** maroon - *not made*	NA	NA

C9. LMS 57' Suburban Stock (ex-Airfix)

937332	**LMS** maroon lavatory brake/3rd - *not made*	NA	NA
937334	**LMS** maroon lavatory composite - *not made*	NA	NA
937333	**BR** maroon lavatory brake/2nd - *not made*	NA	NA
937335	**BR** maroon lavatory composite - *not made*	NA	NA

C10. LNER Gresley Stock

These were planned for 1984 but not made.

C11a. Mk1 Corridor 2nd

cb = Commonwealth bogies

37101	**BR** W24720 red+cream - *76-80*	10	15
37103	**BR** M1709 blue+grey - *76-80*	9	13
37103	**BR** M25454 matt blue+grey, white line masked and sprayed - *76-?*	9	13
37103	as above but blue semi-gloss and white line printed - *?-80*	9	13

37105	**BRc** brown+cream - *77-80*		10	15
37107	**BRc** M25390 maroon - *77-80*		10	15
937107	**BRc** M25390 semi-gloss maroon cb* - *83*		10	15
937107	as above but yellow-grey roof - *83-84*		18	22
37121	**BRc** S25915 green - *81*		14	17

* This and the maroon brake end had the descriptions in the catalogue and on the boxes transposed.

C11b. Mk1 1st Open (FO)
cb = Commonwealth bogies

937305	**BR** M34571 blue+grey - *not made*		NA	NA
937341	**BRc** brown+cream open cb - *not made*		NA	NA
937339	**BRc** maroon cb - *not made*		NA	NA

C11c. Mk1 Corridor Brake 2nd (BSK)
cb = Commonwealth bogies, sb = standard bogies

37102	**BR** W34820 red+cream - *76-80*		10	15
37104	**BR** M34571 matt blue+grey, white line masked and sprayed - *76-?*		9	13
37104	as above but semi-gloss blue, white line printed - *?-80*		9	13
37106	**BRc** W34860 brown+cream - *77-81*		10	15
37108	**BRc** M35040 matt maroon - *77-81*		10	15
37108	as above but semi-gloss maroon paint sb - *83*		25	30
937108	**BRc** M35040 semi-gloss maroon cb* - *83*		15	18
937108	as above but yellow-grey roof sb - *83-84*		25	30
37122	**BRc** S34938 green - *81*		14	17

* This and the maroon composite had the descriptions in the catalogue and on the boxes transposed.

BR Mk1 brake end [C11c]

C11d. Mk1 Corridor Brake Composite (BCK)
cb = Commonwealth bogies

937306	**BRc** M1708 blue+grey - *not made*		NA	NA
937344	**BRc** brown+cream cb - *not made*		NA	NA
937342	**BRc** maroon cb - *not made*		NA	NA

C11e. Mk1 Buffet Restaurant Car
cb = Commonwealth bogies

937113	**BR** Inter-City W24716 blue+grey cb - *81-84*		9	13
937338	**BRc** brown+cream cb - *84*		10	15
937114	**BRc** M1713 maroon lined cb - *81-84*		10	15
937114	as above but 'Kitchen' in lower case, only 2 made - *81*		150	160
937337	**BRc** green - *84*		14	17

C12. Mk2D Stock (ex-Airfix)

937301	**BR** Inter-City E5690 blue+grey open 2nd brake - *83-84*		12	20
937302	**BR** Inter-City E3170 blue+grey open 1st - *not made*		NA	NA
937303	**BR** Inter-City E9479 blue+grey open 2nd - *83-84*		10	14

OTHER COACHES PLANNED

1985
SR/BR Bulleid brake 3rd, composite and semi-open 3rd [later made by Bachmann]
BR Mk1 SO coach [later made by Bachmann in 2000]
LMS 12-wheel 69' sleeping car

1986
LNER Gresley buffet car
SR utility van
BR Mk1 BG full brake [later made by Bachmann in 2000]
GWR Collett 1st [later made by Bachmann in 1990]

WAGONS

A large range of Mainline wagons was made the later ones coming from Airfix tooling. Typically Mainline were the small hopper, small tank wagon, cattle truck and the coke wagon. Many of the open wagons had private owner liveries and some later ones had loads. The latter are scarcer.

So as not to place all their eggs in one basket, most of the newly acquired Airfix tools went to a different Hong Kong company for production. This was the Todco Engineering Company.

Some Mainline wagons were reissued with Airfix style chassis. A new 10' chassis was tooled up from the acquired Airfix drawings and improved by the incorporation of such features as the small integral 'dummy' hooks on the buffer headstocks and separately attached vacuum-cylinder to the underside for 'fitted' wagons, with 3-hole disc wheels on shouldered steel axles. Screw attachment posts were added to the underside and the RCH type buffer shanks, which frequently broke on the Airfix wagons, were slightly thickened up. The chassis had fine in-line brake gear and steel shouldered axles with plastic wheels. The chassis became standard across the range and was later used by Replica Railways and Bachmann Branchline.

In 1984, a completely new, modern style hopper wagon, type HEA, was tooled up, but it did not attain production due to the termination of the range.

Cat.No.	Company, Number, Colour, Dates	£	£

W1a. Conflat (ex-Airfix) with AF Container
After the acquisition of the Airfix tools, those for this model were transferred to the Kader factory in Hong Kong so that they could be modified to take the Palitoy small AF container.

937384	**BR** + blue insulated AF container - *84*	5	8

W1b. Conflat (ex-Airfix) with BD Container
After the acquisition of the Airfix tools, those for this model were transferred to the Kader factory in Hong Kong so that they could be modified to take the Palitoy small AF container.

937352	**BR** B735833 red brown + **BR** maroon container - *83-84*	5	7
937352	**BR** W36507 red brown + **BR** maroon container - *84*	5	8
937355	**GW** 39005 dark grey + **GWR** Furniture container - *83-84*	5	7
937364	**GW** 39005 dark grey + **Pickfords** container - *83*	5	7
937393	**GW** 39324 dark grey + **C&G Ayers** 37 container - *84*	5	8

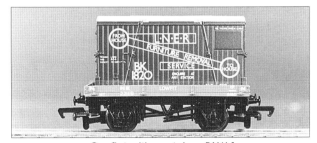

Conflat with container [W1b]

W2a. 1-Plank Open Wagon

37149	**BR** B450023 red brown Lowfit - *78-80*	4	6
37150	**NE** 221119 red brown Lowfit - *78-80*	4	6

Mainline

W2b. 1-Plank Open Wagon + AF Container

37401	**GW** 70001 dark grey Match Truck + GWR white container AF-2102 - *82*	5	7
937401	as above but new chassis - *83-84*	5	7

W2c. 1-Plank Open Wagon + BD Container

937402	**BR** B450000, B450023 red brown + **Bird's Eye** container - *82-84*	5	7
937368	**NE** 221119 red brown Lowfit + **LNER** container - *83-84*	5	7
937433	**LMS** 219215 grey + **LMS** container - *83*	5	9
937458	**NE** 221119 red brown Lowfit + **Frasers'** container - *83*	5	9

W3. 3-Plank Open Wagon

This model was based on inherited Airfix design work and had a new chassis largely based on the Airfix one.

937419	**LMS** 471419 grey - *82-84*	4	6
937420	**BR** M473453 red brown - *82-84*	4	6
937361	**J.Carter** & Sons 172 grey - *83-84*	5	7
937362	**E.Turner** & Sons 26 cream - *83-84*	5	7
937379	**NE** 535962 grey - *84*	5	8

W4. 5-Plank Open Wagon

37130	**LMS** 24361 grey - *77-80*	5	7
37131	**Ellis & Everard Ltd** 136 red+black - *76-80*	4	5
37132	**Warrener** 3 green - *76-80*	4	6
37170	**BR** M360 241 red brown - *79-81*	5	6
37176	**Wadworths** 66 black - *80-81*	5	7
937421	**Timpson** 5 blue grey - *82-83*	6	8

5-plank wagon - LMS [W4]

W5. 5-Plank Open Wagon (ex-Airfix)

937455	**Black Rock Quarries** 46 black - *83-84*	4	7
937455	as above but brown - *83-84*	100	120
937456	**BAC** 4253 red brown - *83-84*	4	6
937380	**NE** 214021 red brown - *84*	5	8
937389	**Webster** 341 dark brown - *84*	5	8
937382	**LMS** red brown - *84*	5	8

W6. 7-Plank Open Wagon

37126	**NE** HB4333 grey Loco - *77-80*	4	6
937126	**NE** HB333 grey Loco - *83-84*	5	7
37127	**Colman's** 25 yellow - *77-80*	4	6
37128	**Persil** 258 dark green - *77-80*	4	6
37129	**CWS** 1941 dark brown - *77-84*	4	6
37151	**Courtaulds** 18 green - *78-80*	4	6
37152	**BR** P99347 grey - *78-80*	4	7
37152	**BR** P99347 early BR grey ex-set - *81*	12	NA
37167	**S.J.Moreland** 1 red+black - *79-81*	4	7
37168	**Horlicks** 1 brown - *79-81*	4	7
37169	**Cambrian** 1078 black - *79-81*	4	7
937175	**Bass** 65 grey - *80-83*	4	6
937404	**Diamond** 34 red - *81-82*	4	7
937405	**GW** 06515 dark grey - *81-82*	4	7
937406	**Patent Nut & Bolt** Co. 658 dark brown - *81-82*	4	7
937428	**Emlyn** 813 grey - *82-83*	4	7
937457	**Perfection** 82 red - *83-84*	4	7
937386	**Parkinson** 107 dark blue - *84*	5	8

W7. 7-Plank Open Wagon (ex-Airfix)

937385	**David Jones** 650 red brown - *84*	5	8
937387	**Brentnall & Cleland** 3000 black - *84*	5	8

W8. 12T 9-Plank Coke Wagon

37157	**MOY** 1851 red brown - *78-80*	4	7
37158	**TCD** 171 dark brown - *78-80*	4	7
37163	**Coalite** 552 dark brown - *79-81*	4	7
937163	**Coalite** 552 dark brown new chassis - *83-84*	5	7
37164	**Bedwas** 621 light grey - *79-81*	4	7
37178	**CCC** 105 dark red - *80-81*	4	7
37179	**TWW** 1746 brown - *80-81*	4	7
37409	**Baldwin** 2030 black - *81-83*	4	7
37429	**Carpenter** 28 red - *82-83*	4	7
937363	**Arthur H.Stabler** 21 grey - *83-84*	4	7
937388	**Dinnington** 254 red brown - *84*	5	8

W9. NE 9-Plank 20T Mineral Wagon (ex-Airfix)

937446	**Charringtons** 257 brown - *83-84*	5	7
937394	**Gas Light & Coke** 794 grey - *84*	5	8

9-plank wagon [W9]

W10. 16T Steel Mineral Wagon

37133	**BR** B265451 grey - *76-80*	4	6
37133	as above but pale grey, early sample* - *75*	30	35
37133	the same but one stripe at wrong end* - *75*	35	40
37133	**BR** B265451 early BR grey ex-set - *81*	12	NA
37133	**BR** B118301 grey - *81?*	4	6
37144	**BR** B566728 red brown - *77-80*	4	6
37144	**BR** B595150 red brown - *77-80*	4	6
37145	**ICI** 776 dark blue Mond Division - *77-80*	4	6
37403	**BR** B118301 grey + ore load - *81*	5	8
937424	**BR** B595150 red brown + coal - *82,84*	5	8
937374	**BR** grey - *84*	5	8

* The chassis on these early examples did not have the Mainline logo on the underside and some had spoked wheels.

W11. GWR 20T Steel Mineral Wagon (ex-Airfix)

937437	**Blaenavon** 2441 brown - *83-84*	5	7
937438	**Glenhafod** 2277 black - *83-84*	5	7
937439	**Stewart & Lloyds** 3506 grey - *83-84*	5	7
937459	**Avon Tyres** 1 black - *83-84*	5	7
37390	**PJ&JP** 3619 black - *84*	5	8
37391	**SC** 25503 dark grey - *84*	5	8
37424	**BR** grey + coal - *84*	5	8
937377	**GW** PO Lease Hire - *84*	8	10

W12. 12T Hopper Wagon

37159	**BR** B433473 grey Ore Hop - *78-80*	4	6
37159	**BR** B433473 early BR grey, ex-set - *81*	12	NA
37160	**BISC** 776 dark grey iron ore - *78-80*	4	6
937160	**BISC** 776 dark grey iron ore new chassis - *83-84*	4	6
37161	**Sheepbridge** 8251 red brown - *79-80*	4	6
37162	**BR** B435975 red brown - *79-80*	4	6
37180	**Clay Cross** 72 red brown - *80*	5	8
37407	**Hoare Bros** 101 black - *81*	5	8
937408	**Cadbury Bournville** 156 blue - *81-83*	5	7
37422	**BR** B436398 grey Sand + sand load - *82, 84*	5	8

W13. NE 21T Hopper Wagon (ex-Airfix)

937351	**BR** E289595K grey - *83-84*	5	7
937357	**NE** 193258 grey - *83-84*	5	7
937441	**MOT** 1324 black - *83-84*	5	7
937441	as above but in bauxite brown - *83*	100	120
937443	**Charringtons** B421814K grey+orange - *83-84*	5	7
937444	**House Coal Concentration** B429816K red brown - *83-84*	5	7
937392	**Norman Jackson** 10 black - *84*	5	8

W14. HBA Hopper Wagon

937370	**BR** red brown - *84*	6	8
937372	**BR** Railfreight grey - *84*	6	8

W15. 12T Tank Wagon

37134	**Royal Daylight** 1534 black - *76-80*	5	7
37135	**BP** 5049 light grey, black solebar - *76-80*	4	6
937135	**BP** 5049 light grey, red solebar - *83-84*	5	7
37136	**United Molasses** 128 red-brown - *76-80*	5	7
37146	**National Benzole** 2003 black - *77-80*	5	7
37146	as above but name in white and 6-pointed star, early sample - *77*	50	55
37147	**Crossfield Chemicals** 49 dk.green - *77-80*	5	7
37153	**Esso** 3066 silver - *78-81*	5	7
37165	**Shell** 4492 silver - *79-81*	5	7
37166	**ICI** 895 dark blue - *79-81*	5	7
37166	as above but CC sympol missing from yellow square - *79*	45	50
37177	**Benzole By-Prod** 1 buff - *80-81*	5	7
937410	**Ronuk** 38 blue - *81-83*	5	7
37411	**National** 731 silver - *81-82*	5	7
937393	**LMS** Cresote 304592 grey - *84*	5	8
937396	**Shell Electrical Oils** SM2202 brown - *84*	5	8
937396	as above but yellow body with red lettering, original samples - *84*	45	50

12T tank wagon [W15]

W16. 20T Tank Wagon (ex-Airfix)

937453	**ICI** 499 dark blue - *83-84*	6	8
937395	**Crossfield** 15 dark green - *84*	6	8
937395	semi-gloss green planned but cancelled, only one made - *84*	NA	NA

W17. LMS Cattle Wagon

37143	**BR** M12093 red brown - *77-81*	4	6
37154	**LMS** grey - *78-80*	4	6

W18. GWR 12T Goods Fruit Van

37173	**BR** W134251 red brown - *80-81*	5	7
37174	**GW** 134149 dark grey *80-81*	5	7
937174	**GW** 134149 dark grey new chassis - *83-84*	6	8

W19. GWR 12T Mogo Van

These were vans with double end doors used for transporting motor cars.

37412	**BR** W105682 red brown Mogo - *81*	5	7
37413	**Shepherds Neame** 3 cream - *81-83*	5	7
37430	**GW** 126342 dark grey Mogo - *82-84*	4	6

W20. LMS 12T Single Vent Sliding Door Van

37137	**BR** B753722 red brown - *76-80*	4	7

37137	as above but oxide brown instead of bauxite, one of initial launch batch - *75*	35	40
37138	**Allsopp's** 4 cream - *76-80*	4	6
37148	**LMS** 511476 grey - *77-80*	4	7
937365	**ICI** 2300 maroon Salt fixed doors - *83-84*	5	8

LMS ventilated van with sliding doors [W20]

W21. LMS 12T Planked Single Vent Van (ex-Airfix)

937371	**LMS** 508587 grey - *83-84*	5	7
937375	**BR** B753722 red brown - *84*	6	8
937373	**BR** M501083? blue Cell truck - *84*	8	10

W22. GWR 12T Planked Double Vent Van

37414	**GW** 123507 dark grey - *81*	5	7
937414	**GW** 123507 dark grey, new chassis - *83-84*	5	7
937415	**BR** W141826 red brown - *82-84*	4	6
937431	**BR** W133971 grey - *82-84*	4	6

W23. SR 12T Box Van (ex-Airfix)

937449	**BR** S47002 brown - *83-84*	4	6

W24. GWR 20T Brake Van

37155	**BR** W68816 red brown - *78-80*	4	6
37156	**GW** 56684 dark grey Shrewsbury - *78-81*	4	6
937426	**GW** 56590 dark grey Oswestry - *82-84*	4	6
937427	**BR** W68855 light grey - *82-84*	5	7

W25. LMS 20T Brake Van (ex-Airfix)

937376	**BR** grey - *84*	4	7
937381	**LMS** brown - *84*	4	7

W26a. 16' LNER/Standard 20T Brake Van

37139	**BR** B951480 red brown - *76-81*	5	7
37139	as above but yellow-brown 2,000 made error used up in sets - *76*	10	NA
937366	**BR** B950880 grey - *83-84*	5	7
937369	**NE** 182922 brown - *83-84*	5	7

W26b. 10' Short Brake Van

37140	**NE** 178595 brown - *76*	4	6
37140	as above but chocolate brown, error, few made for launch at Harrogate, then used as rep samples - *75*	50	55
37140	**NE** 182030 brown - *76-80*	4	6
37142	**BR** E168064 light grey - *77-80*	4	6
37142	**BR** E168064 early BR grey ex-sets - *81*	12	15

W27. GWR Macaw B Bogie Bolster Wagon

37171	**BR** W84922 grey larger numbers - *81-82*	6	9
37171	same but underscale numbers - *80*	8	10
37416	**BR** W84922, W84921 grey + girder load - *81-83*	8	12
37416	same but underscale numbers - *81*	10	15
37172	**GW** 84773 dark grey - *80*	6	10
37172	**GW** 107291 dark grey - *81*	8	10
37172	same but underscale numbers - *80*	8	10

W28. GWR Macaw H Bogie Bolster Wagon (ex-Airfix)

937353	**BR** W107364 grey, Bogie Bolster A - *83-84*	6	9
937378	**GW** dark grey Macaw H - *84*	6	10

W29. GWR Crocodile H Well Wagon

37182	**BR** W41947 grey Weltrol WH - *80-83*	6	8
37181	**GW** 41973 dark grey - *80-81*	6	8
37181	as above but white printing missing on one side from lower deck side - *?*	20	25
37418	**GW** 41973 dark grey + marine boiler - *81-83*	9	12

W30. GWR Siphon G Bogie Milk Van (ex-Airfix)

937322	**GW** 1478 brown - *83-84*	10	15
937323	**BR** W1457 maroon - *82-84*	10	15
54307	**BR** W1452 maroon - *82-84*	10	15

W31. GWR Siphon H Bogie Milk Van (ex-Airfix)

937324	**GW** 1437 brown - *82-83*	10	15
937325	**BR** W1429 maroon - *83-84*	10	15

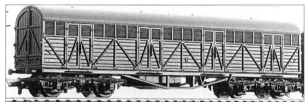

GWR Siphon H milk van [W31] (Palitoy)

OTHER WAGONS PLANNED

<u>1985</u>
BR Chevron type PCA tank wagon
Freightliner wagon and containers
SR 25T brake van [later made by Bachmann]

<u>1986</u>
LNER box van
GWR cattle wagon
TEA bogie tank wagon
bogie pallet van

ACCESSORIES

Palitoy accepted Peco's offer of their Setrack which was made by Garnet in Austria. Airfix, who used the same source, had chosen black sleeper bases and so, for Mainline, a brown moulded sleeper base were ordered. Both had steel rails. Due to continual production difficulties in Austria, none of the correct specification isolating points was ever delivered to Palitoy. Instead, Peco were compelled to supply their own UK-made ones from the Steamline range, with their nickel silver rails, for the assembly of Mainline train sets at the Coalville factory.

The only other accessories produced were power and circuit controllers, electronic steam sound with whistle and diesel sound with klaxon modules. There was also a series of card building kits, by Gilmour. Palitoy had planned to reintroduce some of the former Airfix plastic lineside kits in 1984 but this was abandoned.

SETS

Sets do not seem to have been too prominent and the Company were not encouraged along this line as they did not sell well. Over the years a total of 20 were made. At present these are not attracting enough attention from collectors to push the prices up and are best valued according to their contents.

Marklin H0 (British)

HISTORY

The German company Marklin are almost certainly the world's longest surviving manufacturers of model railways and in the first half of the 20th Century made 0 gauge (and larger) models for the British market. Many of these were marketed through Bassett-Lowke. Over the years they have manufactured models in all the leading gauges including Z gauge.

Just before the Second World War Marklin made their first attempt at breaking into the British 00/H0 market with a number of their German H0 locomotives and coaches produced in LMS and LNER liveries. However, the most interesting development was the production of an LMS Compound which did not look out of place on a Trix Twin layout and, today, is one of the most sought after Marklin models. These were not repeated after the war. The Compound and other models finished in British liveries before the Second World War are not included this time but we hope to add them to a future edition.

H0 scale remains their largest range and in the mid 1960s they attempted to widen their place in the British market by producing another model based on a British prototype. By now, however, British modellers were committed to 00 scale and were becoming increasingly aware of authenticity. A model of a British diesel hydraulic locomotive in the smaller H0 scale, however well engineered it was, looked too small alongside British 00 models and sales were not sufficiently good for Marklin to experiment further.

LOCOMOTIVE

The locomotive was in the Marklin Hamo range, the trademark having been introduced for 2-rail models. A review of the model appeared in the October 1967 issue of *Model Railway Constructor*.

Cat.No.	Number, Company, Colour, Dates	£	£

L1. Class 42 'Warship' Diesel-Hydraulic B-B

8373*	**D830 'Majestic'** green BRc - *67*	30	40

* Also sold under catalogue number 3073.

MasterModels

HISTORY

The 00 scale lineside accessories, which were to become MasterModels, were started by Don Bowles of Croydon. His first advertisement appeared in July 1950 and referred to 'realistic' models which were 'hand-built to scale and not diecast'. The illustration accompanying the advert showed six lineside accessories ranging from a telegraph pole to a water tower. Bowles advertised on a regular basis until February 1951 when B.J.Ward of Grand Buildings, Trafalgar Square, London, advertised that they were now the sole distributors of MasterModels. Don Bowles moved to Angel Hill, Tiverton in July 1951 and reverted to being a model railway retailer.

B.J.Ward was founded by Bertram (Bertie) John Ward and the Company's address was soon being given as 130 Westminster Bridge Road. From the time Ward became involved, a cottage industry gave way to mass production by die casting which was carried out by a company called Kenlow.

The MasterModels series was manufactured until 1962 and during that time more than 100 lineside accessories were introduced including, towards the end, some rather poor looking plastic figures.

Several items were dropped from the B J Ward catalogue by 1954 but a number of new models were introduced into the range as well. The range appeared to have reached its peak by 1956 and it seems likely that 1958 was the last year any new models were introduced; with the final release being in October of that year.

Milestones
1950 First MasterModels made by Don Bowles.
1951 Don Bowles hands over to B.J.Ward and a new numbering system introduced.
1952 Special value sets released.
1952 Bestseller Smith's bookstall released.
1954 Apparent end of Don Bowles influence.
1954 Tudor building series launched.
1954 Girder bridge released.
1956 Earliest known catalogue.
1957 Major changes to the range.
1958 Building papers.
1958 Last known catalogue and last diecast model introduced.
1962 The year the set of plastic figures is thought to have been released.
1962 MasterModels range peters out.

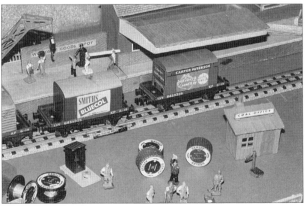

The models were initially sold in grey boxes and these were later replaced by the more familiar cream coloured ones. A few, especially when a special size of box was needed, came in plain brown cardboard boxes with a MasterModel label attached. Small translucent paper envelopes were sometimes used, each with a stapled MasterModel card. Box labels were usually off-white or cream but strange colours, such as bright blue do sometimes turn up.

MasterModels were advertised in the model railway press and in both the Gamages and Bradshaw's catalogues. The Company also produced their own sales leaflet and in 1956, 1957 and 1958 published their 'Catalogue and Handbook' which provided good detail of the range and their associated series.

Like all good model ranges, MasterModels had its imitators. A Japanese company called AHI Brand Toys produced 'Tru-Size Metal Miniature Figures and Animals in HO gauge' a series which definitely contained copies of the British range. They had a larger and thicker base than their MasterModels originals but were otherwise identical. As far as we know, two sets were made. One contained the No. 23 track repair party but with the flag waving figure replaced by a cable drum. The other set was a mixture of figures from sets 2, 3, 23 and 67.

Apart from MasterModels, B.J.Ward also marketed platform and building series that including Woodside, Rickwood, Clarewood (kits), Hailey and Dudley. Rick-wood and Clare-wood were named after his children. Hailey models were made at Goods Depot Sackville Road, Hove while Dudley models were apparently made by a couple of joiner/carpenters on Dudley Road in Eastbourne who did a bit of model making when things were slow.

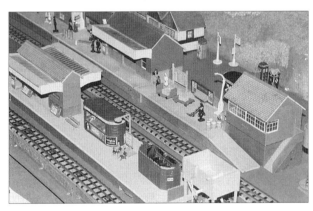

They also sold the 'Wardie' tunnels and road bridge and the 'K' Series garage accessories which were larger than 00 scale. The 'Gilco' sets, which B.J.Ward distributed, contained some of the 'Wardie' garage accessories, such as petrol pumps. Puck sponge rubber scenery (made by Grovewell Ltd), Kentoys (presumably made by Kenlow), the Wee World Series and the Anorma range of building kits were all advertised in the MasterModels catalogue and handbook.

Further Reading

Listing of MasterModels has been done by various people in the past including Bob Smith and Paul & Jennifer Brookes but the only published work we know to be available at present is *MasterModels - Listing of Models for Collectors'* by the latter. *Model Railway Enthusiast* magazine had a long running series called 'The MasterModels Gallery' which included coloured photographs of most of the range. This may be found in every issue of the magazine from June 1998 to March 2000.

Identifying MasterModels - There have been a number of makes of 00 scale figures available in Britain and it is not easy to identify

MasterModels

them as they rarely carry a maker's mark. The most common are MasterModels and Britains Lilliput. While Britains figures are quite smooth and nicely proportioned, those of MasterModels are a little more rugged. The MasterModels range included many lineside and platform accessories and some of the larger ones carry the tooled-in inscription "British Made".

No1 set railway staff

Some figures, such as the wheelbarrow and track repair workmen with tools, turn up in several sets while some castings, such as the telephone kiosk, turn up in a variety of disguises. Very early models were made in brass sheet by modeller Don Bowles and these are quite different from the later cast models and have a 'tinplate' feel about them. At the very end, B.J.Ward started using plastic mouldings instead of metal castings for some of its figures but these were quite crude and generally unattractive.

Colours - Colours of many of the items in the sets vary. The colour of the clothes worn by figures were changed from time to time. Seats, lamps, hoardings, signs etc. changed between light green, dark green, red brown, chocolate, grey and cream. We have not recorded these colours here as there is little evidence of when changes occurred and which colour combinations were brought together in sets. No doubt some colours are rarer than others but we have little information on this to offer you.

Packaging - Most items/sets sold in a cream coloured box. Early boxes were printed in black in an oval on a cream, yellow or blue (very rare) label. Later ones were printed in three colours with a 'Master 00 Gauge Models' logo. Some early models were sold in translucent paper envelopes.

Dates - The dates given in the following table are taken from when advertisements for the models appeared in the model railway press or in retailer's catalogues.

No. Column - An additional column has been provided to record the number of items in the box.

Tudor series buildings

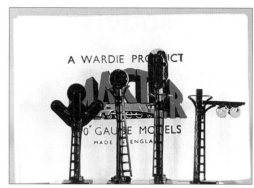

4 electric signals

MODELS

Cat.No.	Subject and Dates	£	£

1. Early Lettered Items and Sets

This untidy pattern of codes was used on early models some of which were later added to the numbered series above. DB = thought to be a Don Bowles design

Cat.No.	Subject and Dates	£	£
A	**Set of Track Signs** 3 bar type signs on two posts and base: 'Catch Points', 'Danger', 'Weigh Bridge' - *51-59*	10	15
B	**Set of Track Signs** 2 squarish signs on single posts: 'Passengers Must Not Cross the Line', 'Beware of the Trains' - *51-61*	6	10
BBS/1	**Bridge End Supports** 2 embankment ends for No.68 in numbered table below, made from wood and cardboard - *56*	NPG	15
BBS/2	**Bridge End Supports** 2 as above but for No.77 double girder bridge - *56*	NPG	15
BC4	**Track Signs** (4) B (above) and C (below) sets of signs combined - *55-60*	10	15
BR/1	**Dog & Partridge Inn** wood block building decorated with printed paper, sign Dog and Partridge Inn - *54*	20	35
BR/2	**Black Horse Inn** wood block building decorated with printed paper, sign Black Horse Inn - *54*	20	35
BR/3	**Tudor House** wood block building decorated with printed paper - *54*	20	35
BR/4	**Blue Anchor Inn** wood block building decorated with printed paper, sign Blue Anchor Inn - *54*	20	35
BR/7	**Transformer Station** these can vary considerably in appearance usually including a brick building, transformer, fence and notices - *53-57*	20	30
BR/8	**House** wood block building decorated with printed paper, also referred to as TS/5 - *54-57*	20	35
BR/9	**Barber Shop** wood block building decorated with printed paper, sign S.Todd.Barber., possibly the same as TS/4 - *54-55*	20	35
BR/10	**The Rising Sun** wood block building decorated with printed paper, sign Rising Sun, also referred to as TS/2 - *54-57*	20	35
BR/11	**The Bell Inn** wood block building decorated with printed paper, sign The Bell - *54-55*	20	35
BR/12	**The Coach Inn** wood block building decorated with printed paper, sign The Coach Inn, also referred to as TS/1 - *54-57*	20	35
BR/13	**The Smugglers Inn** wood block building decorated with printed paper, sign Ye Old Smugglers Inn, access to coaching yard beneath building - *54-56*	20	35
BR/14	**Hotel Royal** wood block building decorated	20	35

Code	Description		
	with printed paper - *54-56*		
BR/15	**Antique Shoppe** wood block building decorated with printed paper, also referred to as TS/3 - *54-56*	20	35
BR/16	**Corner Shop** wood block building decorated with printed paper - *54-56*	20	35
BR/17	**Manor House** wood block building decorated with printed paper - *54-55*	20	35
BS	**Buffer Stop** with Buffers earlier code for BS1 - *50*	4	8
BS1	**Buffer Stop** with Buffers DB, single casting, grey with red buffer beam - *51-57*	4	8
BS2	**Buffer Stop** with Lamp single casting with lamp but no buffers, grey with red buffer beam and lamp - *51-60*	4	8
BS3	**Buffer Stop** with Lamp and Buffers single casting with lamp and buffers, grey with red buffer beam - *52-57*	4	8
C	**Set of Track Signs** 2 squarish signs on single posts: 'British Railways - Do not Touch Conductor Rails', 'British Railways - Take Care When Crossing' - *51-57*	6	10
C1	**Imitation Coal** small bag of imitation coal - *52?*	NPG	8
C2	**Imitation Coal (double size)** large bag of imitation coal - *52-60*	NPG	10
D1	**Miniature Posters (00)** 50 in packet, including coloured posters and monochrome railway signs - *55-59*	NPG	5
D2	**Miniature Posters (00)** 25 in packet - *55-60*	NPG	5
D3	**Sheet of Miniature Posters (00)** 12 on a sheet by 'Posterstamps' - *55-58*	NPG	5
	Miniature Posters (00) sheet of 60 coloured posters and sheet of 20 monochrome railway signs - *?*	NPG	5
	Sheet of Miniature Posters (TT) two thirds size posters in 2 packet of 50 - *55*	NPG	8
DH/1	**Building Paper** Red Brick, 30"x22" - *58*	NPG	4
DH/2	**Building Paper** Stone, 30"x22" - *58*	NPG	4
DH/3	**Building Paper** Parquet, 30"x22" - *58*	NPG	4
DH/4	**Building Paper** Green Roman Tile, 30"x22" - *58*	NPG	4
DH/5	**Building Paper** Red Roman Tile, 30"x22" - *58*	NPG	4
DS	**Double Signal** earlier code for DS3 below - *50*	5	10
DS3	**Double Signal** (Home and Distant) DB, no further information - *52-53*	5	10
ES	**Electric Signal** no further information - *52*	8	15
F6	**6" Fencing with Base** (6) (see FB6 below) - *51*	12	15
F12	**12" Fencing** 9 post 3 rail flexible fencing made from wire with 5 lengthened posts for fixing into the baseboard - *51-57*	15	20
FB6	**6" Fencing** with bases six 6" lengths of 3 rail flexible fencing made from wire with bases on 3 of the 5 posts - *52*	12	15
H1	**Hoarding** (Small) small hoarding between 2 posts on a base with 1 coloured advert - *51-54*	3	5
H1/T3	**Small Hoarding/ Large Timetable** set combining H1 (above) and T3 (below) - *55-59*	8	12
H2	**Hoarding** large hoarding between 2 posts on a base with 2 coloured adverts - *51-61*	5	8
H2/T1	**Large Hoarding/ Small Timetable** set combining H2 (above) and T1 (below) - *55-61*	8	12
H3	**Hoarding (Warning Notice)** small hoarding between 2 posts on a base with notice: 'British Railways - Warning - Trespassers Will Be Persecuted - By Order' - *51-53*	3	5
H3/T4	**Warning Notice and Departures Board**	8	12

Code	Description		
	set combining H3 (above) and T4 (below) - *55-59*		
LA2	**Lamps with Advertisement Board** 2 modern street lamps with curved tops and an advert board on the standard, square bases, 'Keep Death off the Roads', 'Buy British, Buy Master Models' - *55-61*	8	12
LCG	**Level Crossing Gates** (2) (see 9 in numbered list below) - *51-52*	8	12
LDB	**Double Lamp** no further information - *51*	5	10
LG	**Loading Gauge** DB, (see 80 in numbered list below) - *50-51*	5	10
LSA	**Lamp with Advertisement Board** (2) (see LA2 above) - *51-55*	4	10
LSB	**Single Lamp** no further information - *50-51*	5	10
MP	**Miniature Posters** (see D1, D2, D3 above) - *55-60*	NPG	NPG
MS/1	**Office Building** 5 storey modern building with clock - *57*	20	35
MS/2	**Hospital Building** 2 storey modern building - *57*	20	35
MS/3	**Flats Building** 4 storey modern building - *?*	20	35
00	**Scale Scenic Background** (4) (see 98 in numbered list below) -*52-61*	10	15
00	**Bus and Coach Stops** (4) (see 94 in numbered series) - *53-61*	4	10
00	**Posters** (see D1, D2, D3 etc.) - *?*	NPG	NPG
00	**Telegraph Pole** made from steel wire with 2 or 3 arms - *54*	4	6
PL1	**New Universal Plus Point Lever** no further information - *?*	NPG	NPG
Q1	**Imitation Quarry Granite** no further information - *56-61*	NPG	10
RC1	**Rail Cleaner** no further information - *60-61*	NPG	NPG
SA	**Advertisement** small black brass hoarding with coloured advert: 'Chivers Jellies' - *51*	8	12
SG	**Grey Seat** small grey wrought-iron and plank seat - *51-53*	2	4
SG4	**4 Grey Seats** 4 of SG (above) - *55-59*	8	10
SM	**Green Seat** small green wrought-iron and plank seat - *51-53*	2	4
SM4	**4 Green Seats** 4 of SM (above) - *55-59*	8	10
SS	**Single Semaphore Signal** home or distant - *52*	4	6
SS1	**Single Semaphore Signal (Home)** DB, home - *50-53*	4	6
SS2	**Single Semaphore Signal (Distant)** DB, distant - *50-53*	4	6
?	**Signal Arms** upper and lower quadrant - *?*	5	8
ST	**Timetable & Seat** DB, brass sheet and bar seat, GWR timetable on back of seat, later replaced by No.39 - *51*	5	8
T	**Water Tower** DB, a water column of early design - *50*	20	30
T1	**Timetable (Small)** small hoarding between 2 posts on a base with a small timetable, sometimes with 'Arrivals' on label on reverse - *51-55*	3	5
T2	**Timetable** no further information - *51*	8	10
T3	**Timetable (Large)** large hoarding between 2 posts on a base with large timetable - *51-55*	4	8
T4	**Train Departure Board** large hoarding between 2 posts on a base with 2 small timetables, sometimes with 'Train Departures' on label on reverse - *51-55*	4	8
TD6	**Telegraph Pole** DB, double pole structure (joined by cross pieces) with 6 arms, no base, later coded TPD6, listed also as TPD - *50-52*	2	3
TH	**Water Tower** water column - *51*	12	18
TNL	**Water Tower** large water column with 2 moveable hoses and chains and a ladder -	18	25

51-52

Code	Description		
TNS	**Water Tower** small water column with 2 hoses and chains but no ladder - *51-52*	18	25
TP	**Telegraph Pole** DB, pole with 4 arms and no base, later coded TP4 - *50-52*	4	6
	Telegraph Pole, pole 3¾ " long with 2 arms - *58-61*	4	6
TP4	**Telegraph Pole** (see TP above) - *52-57*	4	6
TPB	**Telegraph Pole** DB, pole with 4 arms and a base, later called TPB4 - *50-52*	4	6
TPB4	**Telegraph Pole** (see TPB above) - *52-57*	4	6
TPD	**Telegraph Pole** (see TD6 above) - *50-52*	4	6
TPD6	**Telegraph Pole** (see TD6 above) - *52-57*	4	6
TS/1	**The Coach Inn** (see BR/12 above) - *55*	20	35
TS/2	**The Rising Sun** (see BR/10 above) - *55*	20	35
TS/3	**Antique Shoppe** (see BR/15 above) - *55*	20	35
TS/4	(**Tea Shoppe** possibly same as BR/9) - *55*	20	35
TS/5	**House** (see BR/8 above) - *55*	20	35
TT	**Posters** (see D1, D2, D3 etc.) - *?*	20	35
W	**Track Signs** 3 bar type signs on two posts and base: 'Whistle', 'Reduce Speed', '20 mph on Curve' - *51-57*	10	15
WB4	**Wagon Buffers** (Round) 4 brass wagon buffers - *50-53*	NPG	8
WC	**Water Crane** DB, water crane made from wire with hose and chain and a winding handle rising from the base, replaced by No.48 - *50-53*	10	15
WT	**Water Tower (see** WT1 below) - *52-53*	18	25
WT1	**Water Tower** water tank on girder frame, also listed as WT - *51-57*	18	25
WT2	**Water Tower** water tower on wooden block disguised as a building with brick paper, same casting as WT1 - *53-55*	25	30
WT2	**Water Tower** as above but with a lean-to attached to the building - *?*	25	30
	Imitation Grass Mat sheet 12"x22", suede finish - *58-60*	NPG	8

Waltons fruit kiosk [37]

2. Numbered Items and Sets

After a period of haphazard letter codes a straight forward numbering system was introduced for models in the MasterModels range and these are listed below

No.	Description		
1	**Track Accessories** (4) station nameboard (Waterloo, Crewe, Cardiff or Glasgow), telegraph pole, single lamp standard, level post (brown + white) - *51-54*	12	15
1	**Railway Staff** (5) porter with sack barrow, station master, porter with 3 cases, guard with flag, short porter with silver box - *51-57?*	10	15
1	**Railway Staff** (5) porter with sack barrow, porter with 2 cases, porter with 3 cases, guard with flag, guard holding a lamp up high - *57?-60*	10	15
2	**Railway Passengers** (5) lady with coat over her arm, small boy, golfer with clubs, man with rolled brolly, postman - *51-60*	10	15
3	**Assorted Figures** (5) man in top hat and tails, woman in evening dress and cape, boy or girl, woman with handbag, man (green) with brolly and rolled newspaper - *51-60*	10	15
4	**Seated Figures** (5) two soldiers, a Wren, man in suit, woman in coat - *51-60*	10	15
5	**Seated Figures** (4) nun, woman in coat, man in overcoat, lovers - *51-62*	10	15
6	**Double Seats** (2) single casting double sided seats - *51-60*	5	10
7	**Platform Accessories** (7) weighing machine, chocolate machine, hand trolley, 3 churns, cycle - *51-60*	12	15
7	**Platform Accessories** as above but with 4 churns - *55-59*	12	15
8	**Milk Churns** 12 cone shaped with flared top -*51-57*	12	15
8	**Milk Churns** 6 bottle shaped and 6 cone shaped without flare - *58-61*	12	15
9	**Pair of Level Crossing Gates** each mounted on a post with a green base, each with half red disc, originally coded LCG, (see also 76 below) - *52-61*	6	10
10	**Station Equipment** (4) round or oval pillar box, bus or coach stop, telephone kiosk, single or double street lamp - *52-60*	12	15
10	**Station Equipment** (4) round or oval pillar box, bus or coach stop, telephone kiosk, Castrol hoarding - *58-60*	12	15
11	**Gradient Posts** (6) brown posts and bases with white arms - *51-55*	18	20
11	**4 Sheep in Pen** grey wooden base, green and cream metal fence - *56-60*	20	25
12	**Electric Trolley + Trailer** + driver (plugs into trolley), 2 barrels, 2 crates, trolley + trailer usually blue - *52-59*	12	15
14	**W.H.Smith's Bookstall** green (shades), single casting with printed card for back of stall, other detail on printed labels - *52-62*	15	20
15	**Telephone Kiosks** (2) single casting, detail in wrap-round printed label - *52-55*	8	12
16	**Single Station Lamp Standards** (3) round base, cast-iron type standards, curved-over top with modern lamps - *52-57*	9	12
16	**Single Station Lamp Standards** (3) tall, small round base, concrete type standards, curved-over top with tiny modern lamps - *58-61*	9	12
17	**Steel Girders** 6 pieces of unpainted girder shaped metal, also coded 'FI' - *52*	15	20
18	**Cable Drums** (2) single casting, unlagged type, Henley - *52-58*	6	10
18	**Cable Drums** (2) one lagged + one unlagged type, Henley - *58-60*	6	10
19	**Tar Barrels** (6) crude castings, black with yellow ends - *52-57*	9	12
19	**Tar + Oil Barrels** (12) crude castings, 6 black + 6 grey - *58-61*	12	15
20	**Oil Barrels** (6) crude castings, grey with white ends - *52-57*	9	12
21	**Platform Gardens** (2) island beds, 1 rectangular + 1 diamond, single castings with 1 bush each - *52-57*	6	10
21/22	**Platform Gardens** 1 rectangular + 1 diamond + 2 semicircle - *58-59*	12	15
22	**Platform Gardens** 2 semicircle border beds, single castings with 2 bushes each - *52-57*	6	10
23	**Track Repair Party** (6) lookout with flags, man with shovel, man with sledge hammer, man with pickaxe, man and a wheelbarrow - *52-60*	12	15
24	**Police Boxes** (2) same casting as telephone kiosk but different wrap-round printed label, dark blue - *52-58*	10	15

25	**Placards** (3) each a casting with a printed label showing posters behind wire - *52-57*	12	15
26	**Sleeper Buffer** - buffer stops built from old railway sleepers filled with sand or ballast, single casting - *52-60*	4	6
27	**Scales with Light Luggage** (5 pieces) green, black and silver scales that turn up in other sets, 2 suitcases, golf bag, basket of fruit - *52-57*	15	20
28	**Signal Ladders** (6) stamped metal ladders mounted on a card and probably sold separately - *53-59*	12	18
29	**Glass Crates** (3) single castings, painted cream and wrapped round with printed wood effect label - *52-57*	12	15
30	**Corrugated Iron Sheets** (3) grey castings - *55-58*	9	12
31	**Enquiry Kiosks** (2) same casting as telephone kiosk but with different printed wrap-round label, green - *52-58*	10	15
32	**Lagged Cable Drums** (2) as in 18 above but both lagged, Henley - *53-57*	6	10
33	**Esso Oil Drums** (3) red with white Esso labels, early box has been found with deep blue label - *52-54*	6	10
33	**Esso Oil Drums** 3 green and 3 red with white Esso labels - *55-61*	12	15
34	**Watchman's Hut** open front covered seat and brazier with red foil fire, man with sledge hammer - *52-60*	6	10
35	**Cable Laying Party** (5) man with sledge hammer, man with pickaxe, man with wheelbarrow, Henley cable drum (either) - *52-62*	10	15
36	**Finley's Tobacco Kiosk** same as 14 above but brown and with different printed card and stuck-on labels (these vary) - *52-62*	15	20
37	**Walton's Fruit Kiosk** same as 14 above but black and with different printed card and stuck-on labels - *52-62*	15	20
38	**Sand Bin & Fire Buckets** sand bin with red label, red rack and 4 fire buckets, man with shovel - *52-61*	8	12
39	**Seat with Station Name** seat attached to a station nameboard (Westbay, Glasgow, Crewe, Masterhalt, Waterloo, Swansea, Edinburgh) - *52-57*	4	6
40	**'Permanent Way Cabin** 'timber' hut on metal base with barrel and plastic pipe from gutter, man with pickaxe or shovel - *53-60*	8	12
41	**Water Column** cylindrical tank on top of post with round base, ladder and plastic pipe - *53-60*	6	10
42	**Railway Container** Don't carry it...send it by Carter Paterson** - *53-61?*	6	10
42	**Railway Container** Smiths Bluecol the Safe Anti Freeze - *53-61?*	6	10
42	**Railway Container** yellow plank effect sometimes marked British Railways Furniture - *53?-61*	6	10
43	**Cycle Rack & 4 Cycles** rack (a grey cast slab with grooves in), 4 cast cycles in different colours - *52-57*	10	15
44	**Petrol Pumps** (2) Esso pumps red or blue with plastic pipes, bit too large for 00 - *52-57*	10	15
45	**Coal Office** same as 40 above but sign on roof and no base, water butt or workman - *53-60*	10	15
48	**Water Crane** very like Hornby Dublo water crane but marked 'MasterModels' on the base - *53-61*	6	10

49	**Level Crossing** two pairs of gates on a single cast metal roadway ramp base that goes under the track - *53-57*	18	25
49	**Level Crossing** two pairs of gates on separate cast metal roadway ramps that abut the track - *58-61*	22	30
50	**AA Box & Patrolman** traditional AA box (special casting), motorcycle and AA sidecar, AA patrolman to sit on bike - *53-60*	30	40
51	**Semaphore Ground Signals** (2) black ground signal with grey horizontal arm operated by sprung counter weight, dummy lights - *53-57*	10	15
51/2	**Ground Signal and Disc Shunt** Signal one from set 51 above and one from set 52 below - *58-59*	10	15
52	**Disc Shunt Signals** (2) black shunting signals with grey disc with black bar operated by sprung counter weight, dummy lights - *53-57*	10	15
53	**4 Aspect Searchlight Junction Signals** (2) black searchlight signal with ladder and dummy lights, red light with grey surround - *53-57*	10	15
54	**2 Arm Electric Banner Signals** (2) black banner signal with ladder and 2 round discs (grey with red or green stripe) on horizontal arm - *53-57*	10	15
55	**3 Aspect Colour Light Signals** (2) black colour light signals with ladder and dummy lights in a grey surround - *53-57*	10	15
56	**Aspect Searchlight Signals** (2) black searchlight signal with ladder and dummy green light with grey surround - *53-57*	10	15
57	**Crew Unloading Trucks** (7) 2 men carrying plank between them on their shoulders, man with box on head, man carrying box in front of him, man lifting something down, foreman in suit - *53-60*	12	15
58	**Track Ballast** packet of track ballast - *53-61*	NPG	10
59	**Tarpaulin Covers** (2) black fabric with strings and printed in white with cross and BR317521 - *53-61*	8	12
60	**Station Names** 12 names on gummed paper - *53-57*	NPG	15
61	**AA Boxes** 2 of the traditional AA box No.54 from 50 above - *53-61*	12	20
62	**Police Box with Patrolman** Police box from 24 above, motorbike without sidecar, police rider on bike (ex-AA man) - *53-61*	30	40
63	**Pillar Boxes** 2 oval pillar boxes - *53-57*	6	10
64	**Wicket Gate** kissing type gate set in a short length of fence - *53-60*	6	10
65	**Charrington's Coal Bunker** block of three coal bunkers with nameboard across the top, scales, man carrying sack on back - *54-60*	5	10
66	**Station Clocks** 2 double sided bracket clocks with crazed faces - *54-61*	6	10
67	**Street Personnel** (5) woman in coat, man having his shoes cleaned, policeman conducting traffic, news vendor - *54-57*	10	12
67/9	**Street Personnel** (8) sets 67 and 69 combined - *58-62*	16	18
68	**Girder Bridge for Single Track** grey or brown hogs back bridge in cast metal pieces - *54-62*	25	35
69	**Belisher Crossing** Set 2 Belisher beacons and a crossing attendant with a stop board - *54-57*	6	10
70	**Bus Shelter** single casting in shades of green with London Transport posters and map on printed paper - *55-60*	8	12

MasterModels

71	**Loading Crane** on Base grey crane that swivels on a pyramidal stepped base, working jib and hook cable - *55-62*	15	20	
72	**Gent's Toilet** 2 castings which together form an outdoors wrought-iron urinal block - *54-61*	10	15	
73	**Mine Workers** 5 black workmen with silver kneepads, a wheelbarrow - *55-57*	18	20	
74	**6" Paling Fences** supplied 6 or 12 to a box they were sold singly, green single casting fence with top rail and base - *55-60*	12	15	
75	**Station Name & Seat with Figures** double seat with nameboard and three seated figures: nun, man in coat, woman in coat - *55-59*	10	15	
76	**Level Crossing Gates** (Double Track) pair of long reach gates on posts each with square base (2 sets needed) - *55-61*	8	12	
77	**Girder Bridge** (Double Track) same as 68 but extended in width with a second floor section and girder sections to join them - *55-60*	30	40	
78	**Sitting Army Figures** (5) 2 WRAC, 2 soldiers with hats, 1 soldier without - *55-57*	15	10	
79	**Sitting Naval Figures** (5) 2 WRN, 3 sailors - *55-58*	10	15	
80	**Loading Gauge** white with white pedestal fixed to a black base strip, white gauge suspended on short wires, originally coded 'LG' - *52-61*	6	10	
81	**Massey Harris Tractor & Roller** red tractor with black wheels, blue or green driver, blue roller with grey wheels, originally coded K49 - *55-61*	35	50	
82	**Massey Harris Tractor & Rake** red tractor with black wheels, blue or green driver, blue rake with red wheels, originally coded K50 - *55-61*	35	50	
83	**Massey Harris Tractor & Hay Trailer** red tractor with black wheels, blue or green driver, green trailer with black wheels, originally K47 - *55-60*	35	50	
84	**Gantry Signal dummy** colour light signals on black gantry cast in two halves and riveted together *** - *56-62*	15	20	
85	**Service Personnel** (5) Wren, seated sailor, army officer, soldier with kit bag, military policeman - *57-62*	10	15	
86	**BR Personnel** (7) driver, fireman, porter and broom, coach window cleaner and ladder, Pullman car steward - *57-62*	14	18	
87	**Petrol Pumps on Stand** all red with Essolube or Shell X100 motor oil on sign between 2 Esso pumps, plastic pipes, originally coded K16 - *56-60*	8	12	
88	**Roadside Kiosks** (4) RAC, telephone, enquiries and police kiosks, castings are slightly different from earlier ones* - *58-61*	20	25	
89	**Footbridge** two sections of 6" paling fence (74 above) welded to cast floor section - *58-62*	8	12	
90	**Sheep** (6) from 11 above - *60*	12	18	
92	*Four Electric Signals* this consists of one each from 53, 54, 55 and 56 above - *56-59*	20	25	
94	**Bus and Coach Stops** (4) London Transport design, 2 single flag bus stops, single flag coach stop with timetable, double flag coach + bus stop, (see 00 or K14 in other tables) - *59-61*	12	15	
94	**Bus and Coach Stops** (4) London Transport design, 3 single flag bus stops, single flag coach stop - *?*	12	15	
95	**4 Road Signs** round double sided signs:	12	18	

	road up, no parking, open/closed, no entry, from K9, K20 and K21 - *55-58*			
96	**Left Luggage Office** long double fronted kiosk with door between, both signs say Left Luggage - *58-61*	20	30	
96	**Left Luggage Office** as above but both signs say Parcels Office - *58-61*	20	30	
96	**Left Luggage Office** as above but one sign says Left Luggage and the other Parcels Office - *58-61*	20	30	
98	**Scale Scenic Background** cardboard tube containing 4 sheets 20"x8", (see also '00' in lettered table above) - *61*	15	20	
97	**Oil Storage Tanks** 2 silver tanks mounted on a cradle, Shell Petroleum Products transfer on each tank - *58-62*	15	20	
5800	**Single Signal** - *?-61*	10	15	

* The police and enquiries boxes now have a light projection on top and the RAC and telephone boxes share a flat topped casting. ** Identical to one sold by Trix and possibly supplied by B.J.Ward. *** This appears to have been designed so that an alternative semaphore gantry could be made with the castings.

Signal gantry [84]

3. Presentation Sets

1	**Special Value Set** (8) buffer stop, timetable, hoarding, 4 track signs, seat - *52-54*	NPG	40	
2	**Special Value Set** (7) siding buffer, 2 track signs, 2 station lamps with adverts, timetable, seat - *52-54*	NPG	40	
3	**Special Value Set** (8) 2 timetables, 4 track signs, 2 hoardings - *52-54*	NPG	40	
	Plastic Set (11) double lamp standard, 2 Belisha beacons, policeman, red woman, telephone kiosk, motorcycle, motorcyclist, news vendor, pillar box, bus stop - *62?*	NPG	15	

The plastic set has been found with some parts in metal.

Parcels office [96]

Milbro 0
(Mills Brothers)

HISTORY

Mills Brothers (Engineers) Ltd was founded in 1919 by three brothers - William, Frank and Herbert Mills. They were based at 129 St. Mary's Road, Sheffield, and were later registered as Mills Brothers (Sheffield) Ltd; another address was Ellesmere Road, Sheffield. They used the trade mark 'Milbro' and had a London showroom at 2 Victoria Colonnade, Victoria House, Southampton Row from the mid 1930s to the 1950s. The Company manufactured good quality, true to scale, 0 gauge railway models of prototypical appearance. While 0 gauge was their main output, they also produced some models in gauge 1. Wooden sleepered track was one of their principal products.

During the second half of the 1920s and throughout the 1930s, their locomotives set a standard higher than that of Bassett-Lowke but, being a small firm with low production runs, limited range and higher prices, they made less of a mark in the history of railway modelling. As an example of the higher cost of their quality products, in 1936, the Milbro 6-8 volt DC 'Princess Royal' cost £22.10.0d (£22.50) while the Hornby 0 gauge 20 volt AC 'Princess Elizabeth', when it was released the following year, was priced just £5.5s.0d (£5.25)!

Robinson 4-6-2T [L3]

Early catalogues produced by Mills Brothers Ltd suggest that they started off by marketing models produced by the Leeds Model Company (LMC) and then used the LMC motors as the power unit for their own models. However, before long, Mills were producing a mechanism of their own which was built into the chassis side-frames which stretched the length of the locomotive. As many Milbro products did not carry their trade mark, identifying their locomotives can be problematical and expert advice is recommended.

Like the Leeds Model Company, Mills sold parts for the scratch builder and these can mislead collectors into thinking that a model was made by Mills. Ultimately, experience is needed for sound identification of a Mills product but a common fault to look for on scratch built models is parts out of position such as buffers too wide apart, wagon axle guards too near the buffer beams or wagon strapping poorly applied.

By the end of the 1940s Mills were selling only their track and parts for scratch builders. After the war this level continued although they also stocked other manufacturers' products such as Romford motors and Bilteezi sheets. The Company became defunct in the early 1960s.

LOCOMOTIVES

Cat.No.	Number, Company, Colour, Dates	£	£

L1. Standard Tank 4-4-2T (Freelance)

The freelance 4-4-2 tank locomotive was produced in the late 1930s. Called the 'Standard Electric Tank Locomotive', it was LNER in character with a straight footplate, fully enclosed cab with two windows each side and a variety of chimneys and domes according to the railway it represented. All versions were 3-rail electric.

	Number, Company, Colour, Dates	£	£
-	**201, 420, 501** LMS maroon green - *37-39*	330	450
-	**401** SR - *37-39*	380	500
-	**601** GWR green - *37-39*	350	450
-	**347, 456, 701** LNER green - *37-39*	350	450

L2. Standard Tank 0-6-2T (Freelance)

This was similar to the 4-4-2 tank locomotive (1 above), with a common cab and the same side tanks, but with a leading driver replacing the front bogie on the former. All versions were 3-rail electric.

	Number, Company, Colour, Dates	£	£
-	**420** LMS maroon - *38-40*	350	450
-	**?** LMS black - *38-40*	350	450
-	**458** LNER green - *38-40*	350	450
-	**?** LNER black green - *38-40*	330	450
-	**?** GWR - *38-40*	330	450
-	**?** SR green? - *38-40*	380	500

LMS Crab [L3]

L3. 'Scale' Models

The Company normally produced only electrically powered locomotives and built to special order including to its catalogue items which were as follows (the numbers, names and liveries are as shown in the catalogue but almost certainly these would be done according to the customer's choice).

	Number, Company, Colour, Dates	£	£
-	**7100** LMS black 0-6-0 Jinty Tank - *33-39*	280	330
-	**764** LMS maroon 4-4-0 700 Class Express - *31-39*	NPG	NPG
-	**1102** LMS maroon 4-4-0 Compound - *32-39*	NPG	NPG
-	**5363** 'Harrier' LMS black 4-4-0 George V Class - *33-34*	NPG	NPG
-	**13098, 13126** LMS maroon 2-6-0 Crab - *32-39*	NPG	NPG
-	**13126** LMS black 2-6-0 Crab - *32-39*	NPG	NPG
-	**2500** LMS black 2-6-4 Stanier Tank - *34-39*	1400	1600
-	**6100** 'Royal Scot' LMS maroon 4-6-0 Fowler tender - *32-39*	800	1500
-	**6200** 'Princess Royal' LMS maroon 4-6-2 Fowler tender - *35-39*	1600	2100
-	**6220** 'Coronation' LMS blue 4-6-2 streamlined - *c38*	2000	3000
-	**5945** 'Ingestre' LMS maroon 4-6-0 Claughton Class - *33-34*	NPG	NPG
-	**1448** LNER black 0-6-0 J39 - *37-39*	NPG	NPG
-	**8304** LNER green 0-6-0 J72 - *?*	120	170
-	**373** GC green Robinson 4-6-2T - *?*	750	950
-	LNER green Robinson ex-Great Central 4-6-2 Tank - *?*	NPG	NPG
-	**35** GNR green Stirling Single - *33-34*	NPG	NPG
-	**4472** 'Flying Scotsman' LNER lt.green 4-6-2 - *37-39*	NPG	NPG
-	**2509** 'Silver Link' LNER silver 4-6-2 A4 - *36-39*	2100	2700
-	**2001** 'Cock of the North' LNER lt.green 2-8-2 - *34-39*	NPG	NPG
-	**10000*** LNER lt.green 4-6-4 Hush-Hush Compound - *31-34*	NPG	NPG
-	**3232** GWR green 2-4-0 3232 Class - *32-34*	NPG	NPG
-	**6000** 'King George V' GWR green 4-6-0 - *35-39*	NPG	NPG

-	**901 'Winchester'** green SR, 4-4-0 Schools - 37-39	850	1300
-	**17** Met brown electric Bo-Bo - 30-34	NPG	NPG
-	**5068** SR green EMU motor coach - 30-34	NPG	NPG

* Referred to in early catalogues as 'The Flying Scotsman'.

Southern Schools 'Winchester' [L3]

COACHES

The Milbro coaches were particularly attractive and have become very collectable, being made of wood with glass windows. They were available in gauges 0 and 1, as corridor or non-corridor stock and in the liveries of the Big Four. One could also buy the wooden parts, in both scales, with which to build your own and this included dining and Pullman cars. Interiors, including seating, tables and electric lights, could also be supplied. In 1928 they introduced articulated sets with compensating bogies. These were available in twins or triplets.

The LNER teak coaches (teak was actually used in their construction) are everyone's favourites, some of these having nicely detailed interiors with antimacassars on the seats and lamps on the tables. The LNER coaches go especially well with other companies' LNER locomotives, such as Bassett-Lowke, whose contemporary tinplate LNER coaches were very inferior products compared with Milbro.

NB. If you do not find your Milbro coach listed here, there is a good chance that it was made or finished to special order.

Cat.No.	Company, Number, Colour, Dates	£	£

C1. Standard Wooden Corridor Coaches

These 16½" long coaches had bodies made entirely of seasoned hardwood and were constructed by an interlocking process. They had recessed wooden panels, real glass in the windows and could be supplied as either side or centre corridor stock according to the customer's requirements. The interiors had a mahogany finish and the coaches were fitted will Milbro brass bogies and cast iron wheels. Concertina connectors were fitted to dining saloons and corridor coaches.

-	**LMS** 3762 maroon corridor 1st/3rd - *c26-40*	170	200
-	**LMS** maroon corridor brake/3rd - *c26-40*	170	200
-	**LMS** maroon corridor brake van - *c26-40*	170	200
-	**LMS** 3762 maroon corr dining car - *c26-40*	170	200
-	**LMS** maroon corridor sleeping car - *34-40*	200	220
-	**LMS** maroon corridor kitchen car - *36-40*	200	220
-	**LMS** maroon corridor full brake van - *36-40*	170	200
-	**GWR** brown+cream corridor 1st/3rd - *c26-40*	170	200
-	**GWR** 3014 brown+cream corridor brake/3rd - *c26-40*	170	200
-	**GWR** brown+cream corridor brake van - *c26-40*	170	200
-	**GWR** brown+cream corr dining car - *c26-40*	170	200
-	**GWR** brown+cream corr sleeping car - *35-37*	170	200
-	**GWR** brown+cream corr kitchen car - *36-40*	170	200
-	**GWR** brown+cream corridor full brake - *36-40*	170	200
-	**SR** green corridor 1st/3rd - *28-40*	170	200
-	**SR** green corridor brake/3rd - *28-40*	170	200
-	**SR** green, corridor brake van - *28-40*	170	200
-	**SR** 1739 green, corridor dining car - *28-40*	170	200
-	**SR** green, corridor sleeping car - *35-37*	NPG	NPG
-	**SR** green corridor kitchen car - *36-40*	200	220
-	**SR** green corridor full brake - *36-40*	170	200
-	**LNER** 8173 teak corridor 1st/3rd - *28-40*	220	280

-	**LNER** 8052, 8173 teak corr all 1st - *28-40*	220	280
-	**LNER** 8061, 8173 teak corridor brake/3rd - *28-40*	220	280
-	**LNER** 6789, 8052 teak corr all 3rd - *28-40*	220	280
-	**LNER** teak corridor brake van - *28-40*	220	280
-	**LNER** 8032 teak corr restaurant car - *28-40*	220	280
-	**LNER** teak corridor sleeping car - *35-40*	250	300
-	**LNER** teak corridor kitchen car - *36-40*	250	300
-	**LNER** 8061 teak corridor full brake - *36-40*	250	300

LMS restaurant car [C1]

C2. Standard Wooden Non-Corridor Coaches

These 15" long coaches had bodies made entirely of seasoned hardwood and were constructed by an interlocking process. They had recessed wooden panels and real glass in the windows. The interiors had a mahogany finish and the coaches were fitted will Milbro brass bogies and cast iron wheels.

-	**LMS** maroon 1st/3rd - *c26-40*	140	170
-	**LMS** maroon brake/3rd - *c26-40*	140	170
-	**LMS** maroon full brake - *c26-40*	140	170
-	**SR** green 1st/3rd - *28-40*	170	200
-	**SR** green brake/3rd - *28-40*	170	200
-	**SR** green full brake - *28-40*	170	200
-	**LNER** teak 1st/3rd - *28-40*	140	170
-	**LNER** teak brake/3rd - *28-40*	140	170
-	**LNER** teak full brake - *28-40*	140	170
-	**GWR** brown+cream 1st/3rd - *c26-40*	140	170
-	**GWR** brown+cream brake/3rd - *c26-40*	140	170
-	**GWR** brown+cream full brake - *c26-40*	140	170

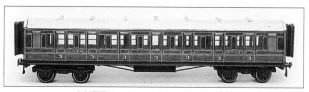

LNER teak corridor all 3rd [C1]

C3. Pullman Cars

These were also built in hardwood throughout and had a mahogany interior. They were lined and detailed in gold and fitted with Maunsell type cast iron wheels and compensated bogies. They were finished in brown and cream with white roofs.

-	**Pullman** 'Princess Helen' brown+cream parlour car - *c28-40*	220	270
-	**Pullman** 'Bessborough' brown+cream parlour car - *c28-40*	220	270
-	**Pullman** 'Pullman Lady' brown+cream parlour car - *c28-40*	220	270
-	**Pullman** brown+cream brake end - *c28-40*	220	270

Pullman car [C3]

C4. Unpainted Wooden Coach Bodies

These were the bodies of the coaches listed in tables C1 and C2 which could be bought without fittings and unpainted.

-	corridor coach - c26-40	NPG	NPG
-	dining car - c26-40	NPG	NPG
-	non-corridor coach - c26-40	NPG	NPG
-	Pullman car - c28-40	NPG	NPG

C5. 6-Wheeled Suburban Stock

-	**LMS** maroon - 28-40	70	90
-	**GWR** brown+cream - 28-40	70	90
-	**LNER** 6173 teak - 28-40	70	90
-	**SR** green - 28-40	70	90

C6. 4-Wheeled Suburban Stock

-	**LMS** maroon - 28-40	45	70
-	**GWR** brown+cream - 28-40	45	70
-	**LNER** teak - 28-40	45	70
-	**SR** green - 28-40	45	70

C7. Triplet Articulated Sets

These were built to the same specification as the coaches in tables C1 and C2 but consisted of three shorter coaches joined in a triple articulated set by shared compensating bogies.

-	**LMS** maroon - 28-40	170	200
-	**GWR** brown+cream - 28-40	170	200
-	**LNER** teak - 28-40	170	200
-	**SR** green - 28-40	170	200

C8. Twin Articulated Sets

These were built to the same specification as the coaches in tables C1 and C2 but consisted of two shorter coaches joined in a twin articulated set by shared compensating bogies.

-	**LMS** maroon - 28-40	140	170
-	**GWR** brown+cream - 28-40	140	170
-	**LNER** teak - 28-40	140	170
-	**SR** green - 28-40	140	170

C9. Mail Vans

These were built to the same specification as the coaches in tables C1 and C2 but were more modern vehicles.

-	**LMS**, Royal Mail maroon - 38-40	170	200
-	**GWR**, Royal Mail brown+cream - 38-40	170	200
-	**LNER**, Royal Mail teak - 38-40	170	200

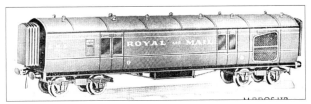

Mail van [C9] (Mills Brothers)

C10. Buffet Cars

These were built to the same specification as the coaches in tables C1 and C2 but were more modern vehicles.

-	**LMS** 1239? maroon Buffet Car - 38-40	200	220
-	**LNER** teak Buffet Car - 38-40	200	220

C11. Coronation Scot

-	**LMS** ? blue 1st brake - c38	200	220
-	**LMS** ? blue 3rd brake - c38	200	220
-	**LMS** ? blue 1st dining car - c38	200	220
-	**LMS** 1468 blue 3rd dining car - c38	200	220
-	**LMS** ? blue kitchen car - c38	200	220

WAGONS

There was a wide range of wooden wagons available, in gauges 0, 1 and 2½. They were made of embossed wood, to represent planking, with embossed metal strapping, corner plates etc. nailed and glued on. Van roofs were fitted with ventilators and brake vans had chimneys, handrails and footboards. Axle boxes were screwed onto the solebars and buffers, in brass, were screwed onto the buffer beams (sprung buffers and axle boxes were used in some larger gauge models). Couplings were of pressed steel or sprung stamped out nickel plated brass and the wheels cast iron although solid brass wheels were available at an additional cost. The wagons were initially finished with enamel paint but by the 1930s a matt finish was being applied.

The wagons were both produced in quantities or made to order but examples of what could be bought were illustrated in the catalogues and it is on the basis of the catalogues that the following tables have been prepared. As customers could have the wagons made in any livery and, presumably, with any running number, other versions are bound to be found. Nearly all were also available in kit form.

Cat.No.	Company, Number, Colour, Dates	£	£

Flat and Open Wagons

W1. Single Bolster Timber Wagons

These could be used singly or in pairs to transport long loads. The bolster swivelled and it came with chains fitted. Also available as a kit.

-	**MR** grey - ?	15	25
-	**LMS** grey - 30-40	15	25
-	**GW** dark grey - 30-40	15	25
-	**NE** 2573 grey - 30-40	15	25
-	**NE** 32573 black - 30-40	15	25
-	**SR** brown - 30-40	15	25

W2. Carriage Wagons

Fitted with Maunsell carriage type cast iron wheels and carriage type axle guards, it had side rails with 2 cross ties but open ends. Also available as a kit.

-	**MR** 3501? grey? - 28?-30?	NPG	NPG
-	**GN** brown? - 28?-30?	25	35
-	**GC** grey? - 28?-30?	25	35
-	**LNWR** grey? - 28?-30?	25	35
-	**LMS** grey? - 28?-40	15	25
-	**GW** dark grey - 28?-40	15	25
-	**NE** grey? - 28?-40	15	25
-	**SR** brown - 28?-40	15	25
-	**SR** light green, yellow lining 2573 - 28?-40	100	120

Carriage wagon [W2]

W3. 3-Plank Double Bolster Wagon

Fitted with chains.

-	**GW** 5204 dark grey - 30-40	25	35

W4. 10T 3-Plank Open Wagon

This was referred to in the Milbro catalogues as an 'Engineering Department ballast and low sided wagon'.

-	**MR** grey? - ?-31?	25	35
-	**GN** brown? - ?-31?	25	35
-	**GC** grey? - ?-31?	25	35
-	**LNWR** grey? - ?-31?	25	35
-	**LMS** grey - ?-40	15	25
-	**GW** dark grey - ?-40	15	25

-	**NE** brown - *?-40*	15	25
-	**SR** 2573 brown - *?-40*	15	25

W5. 4-Plank Open Fish Wagon
This was a dropside wagon inscribed 'Fish'.

-	**NE** 32573 brown? Fish - *32-40*	25	35

W6. Lithographed 12T Open Wagon
From 1930 the catalogues contained a short range of open wagons, made in wood but with litho paper finishes on sides and ends. They had diecast wheels, brass buffers, single or 3-link couplings and cast axle boxes on a steel back plate. When first introduced, it had been intended to extend the range but nothing came of this. The trademark 'Milbro' was carried on the end paper

-	**LMS** 56705 brown? 7-plank - *30-40*	25	35
-	**GW** 109451 dark grey 5-plank - *29-40*	25	35
-	**NE** 19107 brown? 6-plank - *30-40*	25	35
-	**SR** 15117 brown 7-plank - *30-40*	25	35

W7. 12T Standard 6-Plank Open Wagon

-	**LMS** 2573 grey? - *30-40*	20	25
-	**GW** dark grey - *30-40*	20	25
-	**NE** grey - *30-40*	20	25
-	**SR** brown - *30-40*	20	25
-	**Eveson** 6504 - *36-40*	70	90
-	**Wagon Repairs** Ltd 1574 black - *36-40*	70	90
-	**OXO** Beef in Brief 25742 black - *36-40*	70	90
-	orange **Virol** School Children Need It 7960 - *36-40*	70	90
-	**William Younger's** Scotch Ale 51367 maroon - *36-40*	70	90
-	**Bass** Great Stuff This 987 green - *36-40*	70	90
-	**Hamleys** red - *36-40*	25	30

12T Standard 6-plank open wagon Eveson [W7]
(Mills Brothers)

W8. 20T 6-Plank Tube Wagon

-	**LMS** 2573 grey? Tube Wagon - *30-40*	25	35
-	**GW** dark grey - *30-40*	25	35
-	**NE** grey - *30-40*	25	35
-	**SR** brown - *30-40*	25	35

W9. 10T 7-Plank Open Wagon
Also available as a kit.

-	**MR** grey? - *?-40*	25	35
-	**GN** brown? - *?-40*	25	35
-	**GC** grey? - *?-40*	25	35
-	**LNWR** grey? - *?-40*	25	35
-	**LMS** 39817 grey - *?-40*	15	25
-	**GW** 39817 dark grey - *?-40*	15	25
-	**NE** grey? - *?-40*	15	25
-	**SR** 3987 brown - *?-40*	15	25

W10. 8T 10-Plank Coke Wagon

-	**LMS** grey? - *30-40*	25	35
-	**GW** dark grey - *30-40*	25	35
-	**NE** 5204 grey - *30-40*	25	35
-	**SR** brown - *30-40*	25	35

Tank Wagons

W11. Square Tar Tank Wagon
This was lettered in white, had metal strapping and tie bars.

-	**LMS** 5204 black Tar - *29?-40*	35	45

W12. Tar & Oil Tank Wagons
The model was illustrated in the catalogue carrying the 'GN' insignia on its solebars. It is not known what other railway company's initials can be found on this model. Also available as a kit.

-	**GN** 3955? black Tar - *?-35*	35	45
-	**Pratt's Spirit** 46213 silver- *31-35*	120	140
-	**Royal Daylight** 46213 black - *31-35*	120	140
-	**Esso** 1960? black, white letters - *36-40*	120	10
-	**Esso** 2373? black, white letters - *36-40*	120	140
-	**Esso**, cream, blue/red letters - *36-40*	120	140

Royal Daylight tank wagon [W12]

Vans

W13. Lime Wagon
This was the traditional 5-plank wagon and pitched roof type. Also available as a kit.

-	Lime - *40*	25	35

W14. Cattle Wagon
Also available as a kit.

-	**MR** grey? - *?-31?*	25	35
-	**GN** brown? - *?-31?*	25	35
-	**GC** 30121 grey? - *?-31?*	25	35
-	**LNWR** grey? - *?-31?*	25	35
-	**LMS** grey - *?-40*	15	25
-	**GW** dark grey - *?-40*	15	25
-	**NE** grey? - *?-40*	15	25
-	**SR** 25742 brown - *?-40*	15	25

W15. Gunpowder Van
The van had white lettering and black metal strapping.

-	**LMS** 431 red Gun Powder Van - *c28-40*	45	70
-	**NE** red Gun Powder Van - *c28-40*	45	70

W16. Horse Box
These were constructed in the same way as Milbro coaches of the period and had glass in the windows.

-	**LMS** maroon - *c29-40*	170	220
-	**SR** green - *c29-40*	170	220

W17. Fish Van

-	**NE** 2573 brown Fish - *32-40*	35	45

W18. Cement Van

-	**Earle's Cement** 2573 yellow - *36-40*	120	140

W19. Ventilated Van

-	**OXO** 2045 black Beef in Brief - *36-40*	120	140
-	**Gaymer's Cider** 46213 yellow - *36-40*	120	140
-	**Bovril** 2573 blue - *36-40*	120	140
-	**Virol** 2573, 7960 orange - *36-40*	120	140
-	**Stephen's** 98014, 39317 blue - *36-40*	120	140

-	**Bass** 2134 green - *36-40*	120	140
-	**Player's** Please 13625 blue - *36-40*	120	140

Ventilated van - Virol [W19] (Mills Brothers)

W20. All-Metal Goods Rolling Stock

In 1930, Milbro started manufacturing in metal, models of steel prototype wagons. The only example they illustrated in their catalogues was the LNER box van. The models were all built to the customer's specification.

-	**NE** box van - *30-40*	25	35

W21. Box Van

Also available as a kit.

-	**MR** 1321 grey? - *?-31?*	25	35
-	**GN** brown? - *?-31?*	25	35
-	**GC** grey? - *?-31?*	25	35
-	**LNWR** grey? - *?-31?*	25	35
-	**LMS** grey - *?-40*	15	25
-	**GW** dark grey - *?-40*	15	25
-	**NE** 79607 grey? - *?-40*	15	25
-	**SR** brown - *?-40*	15	25

W22. Refrigerator & Banana Van

-	**NE** white black letters Refrigerator Van - *c28-40*	35	45

W23. Meat Van

-	**LMS** 39817, 46213 grey? Meat - *33-40*	45	80

W24. Fruit Van

-	**NE** 25742 brown Fruit - *33-40*	35	45

W25. Goods Brake Vans

The Midland Railway and LNER models were also available in kit form in the 1920s.

-	**MR** grey? 10T veranda one end and platform at other - *?-30*	35	45
-	**LMS** 2573 grey 10T veranda one end and platform at other - *?-40*	20	30
-	**GN** brown? 10T - *?-30*	35	45
-	**LNWR** grey? 10T - *?-30*	35	45
-	**LMS** 9061 grey 20T 6-wheel - *31-40*	35	45
-	**GW** 46213, 9061 dark grey 10T 1 veranda - *?-40*	25	35
-	**NE** 13987 grey? 10T 2 verandas and duckets - *?-40*	25	35
-	**SR** 46213 brown 10T 2 verandas - *?-40*	25	35

W26. 6-Wheel Milk Vans

-	**LMS** 1239 maroon - *c29-40*	70	90
-	**GW** 1794 brown - *c29-40*	70	90
-	**LNER** - *c29-40*	70	90
-	**SR** green? - *c29-40*	70	90

Bogie Wagons

W27. 30T Bogie Bolster Wagon

Fitted with brass compensating bogies and two bolsters with chains.

-	**NE** 5756 brown? - *32-40*	90	120
-	**NE** 9061 grey+timber load - *32-40*	90	120

W28. Bogie Carriage Wagon

This was like a a long bogie version of the Carriage Wagon in table W2, made to go with passenger stock. In 1930, the title of the wagon in the catalogue was extended with '...or Theatrical Property Wagon'.

-	1367 - *28?-40*	90	120

W29. Bar & Rail Bogie Bolster Wagon

This was a bogie bolster wagon with 6 bolsters, their pins linked across in pairs by fine chains. It was fitted with brass compensating bogies. Also available as a kit.

-	**LMS** 12314, 79607 Steel Bars - *30-40*	90	120
-	**NE** - *30-40*	90	120

W30. 30T Bogie Plate Wagon

This model seems to have been based on a drawing in the April 1929 issue of *Model Railway News* which had the same running number. It had 3 planks.

-	**LMS** grey? - *32-40*	90	120
-	**GW** dark grey - *32-40*	90	120
-	**NE** 139422 grey Plate - *32-40*	90	120
-	**SR** brown - *32-40*	90	120

W31. 50T Bogie Brick Wagon

This model was fitted with a diamond frame, brass bogies and cast iron wheels. This seems to have been based on a drawing in the April 1929 issue of *Model Railway News* which had the same running number. This has 6 planks.

-	**NE** 451001 brown? Brick - *32-40*	90	120

W32. High Capacity Bogie Wagon

Also available as a kit.

-	**MR** 37410? grey - *?*	NPG	NPG
-	**LMS** 32573? grey - *30-40*	90	120
-	**GW** dark grey - *30-40*	90	120
-	**NE** grey? - *30-40*	90	120
-	**SR** 720 brown - *30-40*	90	120

W33. Bogie Oil Tank Wagon

This was fitted with compensating bogies, cast iron wheels and tensioning wires.

-	Oil 840? black - *28?-*	140	170
-	**Pratts** silver? - *30-35?*	170	220
-	**Esso** 2360 cream blue/red letters - *36?-40*	170	220

W34. High Capacity Box Wagons

This was fitted with 4 sliding doors, compensating brass bogies and cast iron wheels.

-	**MR** grey? - *?-31?*	140	170
-	**GN** brown? - *?-31?*	140	170
-	**GC** grey? - *?-31?*	140	170
-	**LNWR** 720 dark grey - *?-31?*	140	170
-	**LMS** 2070 grey - *?-40*	140	170
-	**GW** 51367 dark grey - *?-40*	140	170
-	**NE** grey? - *?-40*	140	170
-	**SR** 13989 brown - *?-40*	140	180

ACCESSORIES

There was an interesting range of buildings and accessories all of which were made of wood including stations, low overbridges, tunnel mouths, signal cabins and platelayers huts. It seems that some of these, at least, were made for Milbro by outside manufacturers such as Hailey. Other accessories included buffer stops, level crossings, loading gauges, field sign posts, coal stacks, turntables and gradient posts. These were also made in both scales.

Minitrix (British)
including Hornby Minitrix

HISTORY

Minitrix Electric first appeared in Germany in 1964 although the Minitrix name had previously been used on a push-along range of trains since 1959. The Wrexham based British Trix company, by then part of the Courtaulds Group, marketed Minitrix in the UK from 1965. It was decided that there was a market for models based on British prototypes and permission to go ahead with these was given by Trix. The plastic parts for the new British range were tooled and made in the Trix factory in Wrexham.

In 1967, British Trix was sold to Trix in Germany and a company called Thernglade Ltd was established to take over production in the UK. Ernst Rozsa, who had been with the British Trix company since 1961, was made a Director of Thernglade and was responsible for Minitrix development at that time. Now in financial difficulty themselves, in 1971 the German owners decided to pull out of train production in the UK and production ceased in November that year. As the Minitrix market had been expanding quite nicely in Britain, the Minitrix tooling and stocks were moved to Germany for further use.

Class A4 [L6]

In 1972, the German Trix company merged with George Adam Mangold Gmbh to form Trix-Mangold Gmbh and they invited Rovex, the former Tri-ang company and now part of Dunbee Combex Marx (DCM), to market their British range of Minitrix models in the UK. These were sold under the name Hornby Minitrix and the agreement ran from January 1st 1973.

Rovex had been making the Tri-ang Hornby 00 system and had been skirting around the perimeter of N gauge without wishing to commit themselves to manufacturing an N gauge range as well. As a stopgap they had marketed the Lima N gauge system during the 1960s through their subsidiary G&R Wrenn. Wrenn had become an independent company again with the break-up of the Tri-ang empire in 1971 and the agreement Rovex had with Lima was at an end. This left Rovex (whose 00 system was now called Hornby Railways) free to transfer their loyalty to another N gauge brand and the result was a very satisfactory partnership with Trix-Mangold that lasted until the end of 1986.

The British Minitrix models were now well marketed and with help from Rovex (later known as Hornby Hobbies Ltd) the range was steadily expanded. Rovex found it a good and trouble free system and they got on well with the manufacturers. They had a quality inspector who had previously worked for Rolls Royce and when the first Minitrix locomotives arrived he started unpacking them to test them. Surprised that the man should think this necessary, he was sent over to Nuremberg, to the Trix factory, to see how well they were tested there.

Trix had produced a model of a Warship diesel for the British market but Rovex said if they were going to handle Minitrix sales in the UK they wanted more steam locomotives. The model of the Britannia was already in production by 1971 and therefore not suggested by Rovex but, instead, they found locomotives that suited the Minitrix chassis and supplied drawings so that Trix could make them. Trix always needed some persuasion to make new models of British outline locomotives because of the high cost involved and the small size of the market. The use of existing German chassis meant compromise but helped to convince the Germans that the models were worth doing.

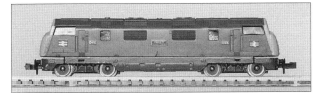

Class 42 Warship [L10]

The series of N scale lineside buildings were not made in Germany. They were based on Hornby 00 scale railway buildings and were made in Hong Kong probably from drawings prepared at Margate. It is possible that the DCM owned Louis Marx Inc. factory in Hong Kong, known as the ELM Tooling Company, produced them. The white plasticard mock-ups of these models have survived at Margate.

Hornby Minitrix was never big business and they were made in fairly small quantities but it ticked over nicely for several years. In their peak year Rovex sold £150,000 worth of Minitrix. £75,000 of that would probably have gone to Minitrix to tool up another loco. The models had superb pulling power and were always seen as the quality end of the N gauge market.

Despite being sold as Hornby Minitrix in the UK, some of the British models were included in the German catalogue, just as 'Minitrix'.

On 1st January 1987, Euro Models & Toys became the importers of the whole of the Minitrix range and the name 'Hornby' was dropped from the packaging. Although the range continued to expand, rising prices and the fast expansion of the Graham Farish range took their toll. Principal casualties were the low volume British models and from 1990 these were available only on occasions when batches had recently passed through the factory. The shortage of new models had the effect of driving up the price of second-hand ones.

HAA MGR hopper [W9]

From 1995, distribution of Minitrix in Britain was in the hands of Bachmann, while the models were available. Trix were in financial difficulty again and on 1st January 1997 Trix-Mangold was taken over by Marklin. At this point, Gaugemaster became the importer

Minitrix (British)

but it was not until the Summer of 2000 that Bachmann cleared the last of their stock. This, strangely enough, coincided with their purchase of Graham Farish. With Bachmann upgrading the Graham Farish N gauge range, the future of the British Minitrix range does not look good!

Catalogue Numbers - Some models have appeared under several different catalogue numbers which causes confusion. Trix, British Trix and Rovex/Hornby Hobbies all had their own numbers for the same model. Alternative catalogue numbers are shown in brackets ().

Further Reading

For a more in depth study of the variations that occurred in the design of the Minitrix range for the British market and the types of packaging used, you are recommended to obtain a copy of Monty's Amateur Collectors Guide to British Minitrix. This is very well written and is the result of an extensive study of the subject. It is obtainable from S.Culverhouse, 17 Church Street, Clowne, Chesterfield S43 4JR.

LOCOMOTIVES

All Minitrix locomotives used existing chassis from the German models; even those made in the UK. This made it necessary to make many compromises with the locomotive bodies.

Cat.No.	Number, Company, Colour, Dates £	£	

L1. Fowler Class 2F (Dock Tank) 0-6-0T

This model was solely made in Germany and may also be found in an East German livery.

N201	**47160** BRc black (12052) - *73*	30	40

L2. Class J63 0-6-0T

A white metal body kit made in the UK, subsequently marketed by Beaver as kit N452 and fitted to the German T3 locomotive chassis. The Minitrix instructions suggested that it be finished as shown in this table. W&H also advertised the German T3 finished in LNER green livery.

2991	**E8210** LNER black - *67*	NA	60

L3. Ivatt Class 2MT 2-6-2T

N205	**41234** BRc black (12040) - *74*	45	55

Ivatt Class 2MT [L4]

L4. Ivatt Class 2MT 2-6-0

N213	**46406** BRc green (12038) - *82*	55	65
12038	**46402** BRc green - *85*	75	85
N202	**46400** BRc black (12039) - *73*	45	55

L5. Class A3 4-6-2

Class A3 [L5]

N215	**60101 'Cicero'** BR green - *not made*	NA	NA
N216	**4472 'Flying Scotsman'** LNER green - *not made*	NA	NA

N218	**2500 'Windsor Lad'** LNER green - *not made*	NA	NA
12950	**4472 'Flying Scotsman'** LNER light green - *88*	85	95
12949	**60103 'Flying Scotsman'** BR green - *88*	90	100

L6. Class A4 4-6-2

N214	**4498 'Sir Nigel Gresley'** LNER blue (12946) - *83*	85	95
N211	**60022 'Mallard'** BRc green (12947) - *80*	100	110

L7. Britannia Class 4-6-2

The model was originally advertised under the catalogue number '2906' but, by the time it was assembled in the UK and released, it had changed to '2037'.

2037	**70000 'Britannia'** BRc green (12037, N203) - *71*	70	80
N217	**70036 'Boadicea'** BRc green (12042) - *85*	85	95

Britannia Class [L7]

L8. Class 9F 2-10-0

N209	**92220 'Evening Star'** BRc green (12041) - *79*	80	90
N207	**92018** BRc black (12058) - *75*	75	85

L9. Class 27 Diesel Bo-Bo

2902	**D5370** BRe blue - *67*	60	70
2901	**D5379** BRc green (N204, 12940) - *67*	40	50
N212	**27014** BRe blue (12969) - *80*	45	55

Class 27 diesel [L9]

L10. Class 42 'Warship' Diesel B-B

The Warship chassis came in three versions. The original one, assembled in the UK and used between 1970 and 1972 in the UK and Germany, had a completely cast base. The 2nd style, used from 1974 (on the introduction of N206), was made in Germany and had a full length insert base. The 3rd style, made from 1979 (on the introduction of N208) had a revised rigid chassis with bogie frame detail.

2035	**D805 'Benbow'** BRc green - *70*	60	70
2905	**D815 'Druid'** BRe blue - *70*	60	70
2904	**D816 'Eclipse'** BRc green - *70*	60	70
2905	**D816 'Eclipse'** BRe blue - *71*	65	75
2034	**D823 'Hermes'** BRe blue (N206, 12942) - *70*	40	50
N208	**D825 'Intrepid'** BRc green (12943) - *79*	45	55
2036	**D838 'Rapid'** BRc maroon - *71*	110	120
2906	**D866 'Zebra'** BRc maroon - *71*	85	100
2904	**D866 'Zebra'** BRc green (2035) - *71*	65	75
2905	**D866 'Zebra'** BRe blue (2034) - *72*	65	75

L11. Class 47 Diesel Co-Co

N210	**47170 'County of Norfolk'** BReLL blue (12966) - *82*	55	65
N220	**47378** BReLL Rft grey - *not made*	NA	NA
12024	**47378** BReLL Rft grey - *87*	60	70
N221	**47487** BR IC grey - *not made*	NA	NA
12025	**47487** BR IC grey - *87*	60	70
N219	**47541 'The Queen Mother'** BRe blue (12958) - *85*	55	65

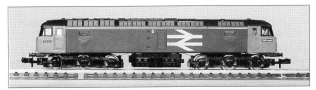

Class 47 [L11]

COACHES

The first Minitrix coaches for the British market were suggested by Sydney Pritchard, head of Peco, and the earliest ones were sold in Peco packaging during 1967 and 1968. These were the BR Mk1s. Numbers appeared on the coaches from the start as indicated in the following tables but sometimes numbers turn up on the wrong coach.

The first two Mk1 coaches (2921 and 2929) were described as having a moulded chassis and superstructure, nylon bogies, turned metal wheels, provision for interior lighting and printed sides. They were five and three eighths inches in length over the buffers.

The Mini Coachbuilder kits were available in 1970 and numbered 3921-3928. They were UK made and unmade kits are very rare.

Cat.No.	Company, Number, Colour, Dates	£	£

C1a. Gresley Corridor 3rd

13014	LNER 4237 teak - 88	17	22
13116	BR E12451E maroon - 91	25	30

C1b. Gresley Brake Composite

13013	LNER 4173 teak - 88	17	22
13115	BR E10076E maroon - 91	25	30

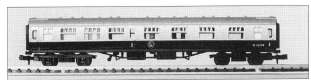

Mk1 corridor composite [C2a]

C2a. Mk1 Corridor Composite CK

2921	BRc M16171 maroon (13005, N305) - 67	8	11
-	above as a Mini Coachbuilder kit - 70	NPG	NPG
2923	BRc W16198 brown+cream (13004, N301) - 67	8	11
-	above as a Mini Coachbuilder kit - 70	NPG	NPG
2925	BRc S15900 green - 67	12	15
-	above as a Mini Coachbuilder kit - 70	NPG	NPG
2927	BR M16171 blue+grey (13003, N303) - 67	7	10
-	above as a Mini Coachbuilder kit - 70	NPG	NPG
2933	BR S15900 blue - 70	14	17
2934	BR W16198 blue+grey (13003, N303) - 70	7	10
2941	LMS 1671 maroon - 72	12	15
2943	GWR 2018 brown+cream - 72	12	15
13065	BR M4330 red+cream - 87	12	15

C2b. Mk1 Corridor 2nd SK

Mk1 brake composite [C2c]

2925/2	BRc S15902 green (2931) - 68	14	17
2927/2	BR M16171 blue+grey (2932) - 68	12	15
2929	BRc M16752 maroon - 68	12	15
2930	BRc ? brown+cream- 68	22	27

C2c. Mk1 Brake Composite BCK

2922	BRc M21240 maroon (13008, N308) - 67	8	11
-	above as a Mini Coachbuilder kit - 70	NPG	NPG
2924	BRc W21194 brown+cream (13007, N302, N307) - 67	8	11
-	above as a Mini Coachbuilder kit - 70	NPG	NPG
2926	BRc S2301 green - 67	12	15
-	above as a Mini Coachbuilder kit - 70	NPG	NPG
2928	BR M21240 blue+grey (13006, N306) - 67	7	10
-	above as a Mini Coachbuilder kit - 70	NPG	NPG
2935	BR ? blue+grey - 70	22	27
2936	BR S2301 blue - 70	14	17
13066	BR M26546 red+cream - 87	12	15
2942	LMS 5540 maroon - 72	12	15
2944	GWR 3146 brown+cream- 72	12	15

C2d. Mk1 Brake 2nd BSK

2922/2	BRc M21240 maroon - 68	12	15
2926/2	BRc S2301 green - 68	14	17
2928/2	BR M21240 blue+grey - 68	12	15

C2e. Mk1 Full Brake BG

2937	BR or BRc 80555 maroon - 71	12	15
2938	BR 81304 blue+grey - 71	15	18

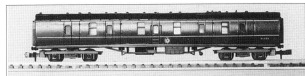

Mk1 full brake [C2e]

C2f. Mk1 Sleeping Car SLE

2939	BRc maroon - not made	NA	NA
2940	BR blue+grey - not made	NA	NA

WAGONS

The first wagons issued were models of BP tanks using 15' wheelbase chassis. These moulds passed to Peco who altered the moulds to carry their own name. The rest of the early wagons were based on items from the British Trix 00 range. They used a common 10' wheelbase chassis and some were sold in pairs. A few wagons were actually from the German range but produced in British liveries.

Cat.No.	Company, Number, Colour, Dates	£	£

Continental Style Wagons

W1. LWB Barrel Wagon

The barrels and mounting plate can be a combination of red, blue, yellow or grey.

N504	BRe B740387 brown + 5 barrels (13573) - 73	5	7

W2. Side-Tipping Hoppers (pair)

Standard German item.

N524	both red+green - 84	7	10

W3. LWB Van (CovAB)

N505	BRe 200424 brown (13574) - 73	4	7

W4. Car Transporter

The cars were various colours. Standard German item.

N510	DB 869014 brown + 4 cars - 73	6	9

W5. Bogie Ballast Hopper

N506	**BRe** B413161 grey (13575) - *73*	6	9

W6. Bogie Covered Wagon

Standard German item.

N509	**Ford** 0554178 blue - *73*	6	9

British Style Wagons

8-plank wagons [W7]

W7. 8-Plank Open Wagon

3208	**LMS** 299471 brown - *72*	9	12
3209	**GWR** 109432 grey - *72*	9	12
3210	**SR** 36327 grey - *72*	9	12
3211	**LNER** 87365 brown - *72*	9	12
3259	**A.J.Salter** 122 red-brown - *not made*	NA	NA
3268	**Isaac Wilkinson Ltd**. 35 red - *71*	15	20
3271	**Chubb** 101 red-brown - *71*	8	11
3272	**Wm Gordon Jameson's** 51 yellow (13577, N507) - *71*	4	7
3273	**Roberts Jenks** 100 black (13580, N508) - *71*	4	7
3274	**Sutton Manor** 1075 grey - *71*	8	11
3275	**Nicholsons' Brewers** 1 black - *71*	8	11
N523	**Arnolds Sands** red-brown (13284) - *84*	4	7
N514	**Sheepbridge** 8234 brown (13578) - *80*	4	7
N515	**E Foster & Co** 2009 grey (13579) - *80*	4	7
N522	**Scarwood** light grey (13581) - *84*	4	7
N511	**Ilkeston & Heanor** Water Board 14 blue (13583) - *74*	4	7
N512	**Millom Co-op** green (13584) - *74*	4	7
13633	**British Steel** 20 blue* - *91*	5	10
13832	**Lilleshall** 1641 red-brown - *92*	5	8
13833	**F.S.Brightmore** 113 grey - *92*	5	7
13834	**Shrewsbury** 16 grey - *92*	5	8

* Often found in a 13833 box.

W8. 16T Mineral Wagon

3206	**BR** B239021 grey (N513, 13571) - *79*	5	8
3207	**BR** B586537 brown (N502, 13576) - *71*	4	7

16T mineral wagon [W8]

W9. HAA MGR Hoppers

Prices of these were around the £18-£20 mark until Bachmann released their models in the Graham Farish range.

N517	**BR** B351540 aluminium+brown (13277) - *82*	6	9
N529	**BR** Rft B352556 aluminium+red - *not made*	NA	NA
13632	**BR** Rft B352556 aluminium+red - *87*	7	10
13637	**BR** Coal 351556 - *91*	7	10

W10. 10' Tank Wagon

N516	**Shell BP** A5066 silver (13272) - *82*	6	9
N518	**Esso** 1800 silver (13273) - *83*	6	9
N519	**National Benzole** P93 buff (13274) - *83*	6	9
13634	**Duracell** black+copper - *91*	5	8

W11. 15' Modern Tank Wagon (Peco)

These tanks were designed, tooled up and produced by Trix but the tooling was later taken over by Peco who tooled a replacement chassis which could also be used on other wagons.

2955	**BP** 1350, 9675, 9682, 9689 white - *67*	15	20
2956	**BP** green - *67*	15	20
2957	**BP** 9682 silver - *67*	15	20
2958	**BP** 9689 black - *67*	15	20

15' modern tank wagon [W11]

W12. Ventilated Van

Planned but not made in the UK.

3213	**BR** grey - *not made*	NA	NA
3214	**BR** brown - *not made*	NA	NA
N503	**BR** B852193 grey VAN - *not made*	NA	NA
N503	**BR** B852193 grey shock van (13572) - *73*	4	7
13572	**BR** B852193 brown shock van - *?*	10	13
N525	**BR** Rft 230002 grey+red - *not made*	NA	NA
13631	**BR** Rft 230002 grey+red - *87*	6	9

W13. BR Standard Brake Van

Planned but not made in the UK.

3221	**BR** brown - *not made*	NA	NA
N501	**BR** B952698 brown (13570) - *73*	5	8
N526	**BR** Rft B954817 grey+red - *not made*	NA	NA
13630	**BR** Rft B954817 grey+red - *87*	6	9
13636	**BR** Sector B972163 - *91*	6	9

W14. Bogie Container Wagon

13635	black + **P&O** blue, **Metal Box** grey, **Royal Mail Parcels** red - *91*	11	14

Bogie container wagon [W14]

Peco N

HISTORY

Peco is the trademark of the Pritchard Patent Product Company which was established in April 1946 by Mr and Mrs S.C.Pritchard. It started operations in a small cottage in Devon at Branscombe with just one employee. Over the years that followed, Peco became the leading company in the production of model railway track.

In need of more room, the company moved to a church hall in Sidmouth in 1947 and later acquired a separate office in town. They also acquired premises for a workshop in a yard off what was then Sidmouth railway station. The next move came in January 1951 when a head office, showroom and stores were established in Seaton (this showroom was the birthplace of the writer's own interest in railway modelling, as opposed to toy trains, following a visit there at the age of 12 while on holiday in Devon!).

Although track has always been the best known Peco product, and is today sold all over the world, the company has repeatedly looked for gaps in the market and set about filling them. So it was, in the mid 1960s, that the need for British outline N gauge models was realised and, initially in association with Trix, the company became involved in the production of N gauge wagons. The first of these were made in the production unit in Seaton.

By the late 1960s, the Peco business had grown to such an extent that a new factory was required. After some difficulty in obtaining planning permission to build in this beautiful part of South Devon, a site in Beer, the next village along the coast, was purchased from Axminster Rural District Council in 1970. Here a brand new factory and exhibition complex was built to the company's own specification and opened for production the following year. It is here that Peco products are made today.

Dates - The listing of Peco products has not been an easy task and while we have a good idea when models first appeared there is little or no evidence of when production ceased. Only dates of introduction are given, therefore.

LOCOMOTIVE

The model was produced in conjunction with Rivarossi who sold it outside the UK.

White metal locomotive body kits, thought to have been made by Wills, were also available from 1973 for fitting to Arnold chassis. These included a Hymek, Class 4 diesel (made by Anbrico), a Fairburn 2-6-2 tank, an 0-6-0 dock tank, Peckett 0-4-0ST, 0-4-0T and a Manning Wardell type 0-4-0ST. Painting and detailing was left to the modeller. Briefly, a complete kit for a Collett 0-6-0 was available.

Cat.No.	Number, Company, Colour, Dates	£	£

L1. LMS Jubilee Class 4-6-0 (Rivarossi)

NL22 was supplied unnamed and with a sheet of transfers for all six names and numbers. 'Silver Jubilee' also had its transfers provided and this and NL22 also had an alternative double chimney supplied in the box.

NL21	**5713 'Renown'** LMS black - *69*	60	75
NL22	**5593 'Kolhapur'** LMS maroon - *85*	70	85
NL22	**5690 'Leander'** LMS maroon - *85*	70	85
NL22	**5691 'Orion'** LMS maroon - *85*	70	85
NL22	**5696 'Bahamas'** LMS maroon - *85*	70	85
NL22	**5729 'Furious'** LMS maroon - *85*	70	85
NL22	**5738 'Sampson'** LMS maroon - *85*	70	85
?	**5572 'Silver Jubilee'** LMS black - *77*	75	90

COACHES

Coaches were initially produced in conjunction with Minitrix who also sold them. They were made in the Trix factory at Wrexham but Peco sold them as 'Wonderful Coaches'.

Cat.No.	Company, Number, Colour, Dates	£	£

C1a. Mk1 Corridor Composite CK (Minitrix)

NR50	**BRc** M16171 maroon - *67*	10	15
NR60	**BRc** W16198 brown+cream - *67*	10	15
NR70	**BRc** S15900 green - *67*	10	15
NR80	**BR** M16171 blue+grey - *67*	10	15

C1b. Mk1 Brake Composite BCK (Minitrix)

NR51	**BRc** M21240 maroon - *67*	10	15
NR61	**BRc** W21194 brown+cream - *67*	10	15
NR61	**BRc** W21060 brown+cream - *68*	NPG	NPG
NR71	**BRc** S2301 green - *67*	10	15
NR81	**BR** M21240 blue+grey - *67*	10	15

C1c. Mk1 All 2nd SK (Minitrix)

NR52	**BRc** M16752 maroon - *68*	10	15
NR62	**BRc** ? brown+cream - *68*	10	15
NR72	**BRc** S15902 green - *68*	10	15
NR82	**BR** M16171 blue+grey - *68*	10	15

WAGONS

The first wagon was the modern tank wagon which was produced initially in conjunction with Minitrix and jointly sold by them. It was designed, tooled and made in the Trix factory. This arrangement did not last long.

The ready to run wagons were introduced as 'Wonderful Wagons' and were on either a 10' or a 15' wheelbase chassis. Peco also made wagon kits of the standard range as well as some additional subjects. These included an SR brake van and on a 9' chassis a pig iron wagon, tippler wagon and a mineral wagon. The catalogue numbers of kits were prefixed with 'KNR' and the kit built models had no printing on them and so needed finishing. A good range of wagon chassis could be bought separately.

From 1973, loads for wagons were also available separately, if required, and eventually included the full container range (as listed below in table W2a), coal, planks, bricks, barrels, crates and sand. The plastic mouldings for open wagon loads were made in such a way that they could be cut in half so that one and a half loads could be used in the long wheelbase wagons. Coal rails were also available for the open wagons.

Cat.No.	Company, Number, Colour, Dates	£	£

W1. Lowmac

This was to be a 22' wheelbase vehicle, proposed and illustrated in the catalogue in 1983.

NR-35B	**BR** B904662 brown - *not made*	NA	NA

Lowmac [W1] (Peco)

W2. Conflats & Containers

NR-20	**GWR** grey + **GWR** Furniture BK-1869 brown - *81*	4	6
NR-21	**LMS** B73570 light grey + **LMS** Furniture K1 maroon - *81*	4	6
NR-22	**BR** B73570 brown + **BR** Furniture BK1872 brown - *83*	4	6
NR-P30	grey + **Raleigh Cycles** green - *81*	4	6
NR-P31	grey + **Lyons Tea** blue - *81*	4	6
NR-P32	grey + **LEP** red - *83*	4	6

Conflat + LEP container [W2] (Peco)

W2a. Containers Only

These were sold in pairs of different designs e.g. GWR + LMS, BR + LEP, Raleigh + Lyons (recommended value - £5 per pack).

NR-207	**GWR** Furniture BK-1869 brown - *82*	2	NA
NR-207	**LMS** Furniture K1 maroon - *82*	2	NA
NR-208	**BR** Furniture BK1872 red-brown - *83*	2	NA
NR-208	**LEP** red - *83*	2	NA
NR-209	**Raleigh Cycles** green - *82*	2	NA
NR-209	**Lyons Tea** blue - *82*	2	NA

W3. Bolster Wagon

Sold in pairs (at £7 per pair).

NR-39M	**LMS** 14555 light grey - *82*	3	NA
NR-39E	**NE** 231331 brown - *73*	3	NA

W4a. Plate Wagon (lwb)

NR-5W	**GW** 32637 dark grey - *74*	3	4
NR-5B	**BR** grey - *68*	3	4
NR-12R	**BR** Railfreight 200278 red - *82*	3	4

W4b. Double Bolster Wagon (lwb)

NR-4M	**LMS** 14565? light grey - *made?*	NPG	NPG
NR-4E	**NE** 231331 brown - *74*	3	4

W5a. 5-Plank Open Wagon

NR-40W	**GW** 109458 dark grey - *75?*	3	5
NW-40BW	**GW** dark grey weathered* - *81*	NPG	NPG
NR-40M	**LMS** 345699 light grey - *71*	3	5
NR-40E	**LNER** 625484? red-brown - *99*	3	5
NR-40S	**SR** 5095 dark brown - *71*	3	5
NW-40BS	**SR** dark brown weathered* - *81*	NPG	NPG
NR-P80	**Garswood** blue - *72*	4	6
NR-P81	**Mendip Mountain** 238 grey - *75?*	4	6
NR-P82	**A Gresley** 7 red-brown - *72*	3	5
NR-P83	**Charles Dunsdon** 21 dark green - *72*	3	5
NR-P84	**Hopton Wood** 2 grey+red - *97*	3	5
NR-P85	**Cranmore Granite** 367 light grey - *98*	3	5
NR-P86	**Constable Hart** 127 dark grey - *98*	3	5
NR-P87	**Cumberland Granite** 22 dk.grey - *99*	3	5
NR-P88	**John Allbutt** 1 grey - *99*	3	5
NR-P89	**E A Stevenson** 10 blue - *96*	3	5
NR-P111	**Dowlow Lime** 141 red-brown** - *00?*	3	4

* Proposed weathered and repaired wagons which were included in a late supplement to the 1981 catalogue. **This was originally sold with a roof but the Dowlow family told Peco that they generally ran without a roof as it was more trouble than it was worth. Thus, Peco produced it without a roof (see Lime Wagon below for earlier version).

5-plank wagon [W5a] (Peco)

W5b. 5-Plank China Clay Hoods

-	**BR** brown + hood blue Sp Edn (Mevagissey) - *01*	4	6

W5c. Lime Wagon (5-plank with roof)

NR-P111	**Dowlow Lime** 141 red-brown* - *75?*	3	4
NR-P112	**Crawshay Bros**. 136 cream - *73*	3	4
NR-P113	**SLB** 702 grey - *75?*	3	4

*This were originally sold in this form but the Dowlow family told Peco that they generally ran without a roof as it was more trouble than it was worth. Thus, Peco produced it without a roof (see 5-Plank Wagon above for later version).

W6. 6-plank Tube Wagon (lwb)

NR-7W	**GW** 94856 dark grey - *74*	3	4
NR-7B	**BR** red-brown - *68*	3	4
NR-7R	**BR** Railfreight red - *82*	3	4

W7a. 7-Plank Coal Open Wagon

NR-41W	**GW** 29617 dark grey - *77*	3	4
NW-41BW	**GW** 24572 grey weathered* - *81*	NPG	NPG
NR-41M	**LMS** 313159 light grey - *81?*	3	4
NW-41BM	**LMS** light grey weathered* - *81*	NPG	NPG
NR-41E	**LNER** 803436? grey - *99*	3	4
NR-41S	**SR** 5095 dark brown - *71*	3	4
NR-41S	**SR** (no number) dark brown - *?*	4	5
NR-P90	**Ward & Sons** 12 red-brown - *75?*	4	5
NR-P91	**Parkend** 330 black - *73*	3	4
NR-P92	**Kingsbury** 710 green - *75?*	4	5
NR-P93	**Hood & Sons** 3 green - *77*	4	5
NR-P94	**Norchard** 13 black - *92*	3	4
NR-P95	**Lydney Coal Co**. 9 green-grey - *92*	3	4
NR-P96	**Princess Royal** 250 bright red - *92*	3	4
NR-P97	**Peco Golden Jubilee** 1946-1996 blue+ gold Ltd Edn (Peco) - *96*	5	6
NR-P98	**Ammanford Colliery** 48 brown - *96*	3	4
NR-P99	**Crigglestone Collieries** 222 red - *96*	3	4
NR-P105	**Edward Eastwood** 2 green - *97*	3	4
NR-P106	**Bradford & Sons** 3 brown Sp Edn 500+ (Howe & Davies***) - *00*	4	5
NR-P107	**Tredegar** 5100 red - *99*	3	4
NR-P108	**Chatterley Whitfield** 1822 grey** - *99*	3	5
NR-P114	**ICI** Lime Ltd 9395 grey - *97*	3	4
-	**Edinburgh Collieries Company Ltd** 558 grey Sp Edn (Harburn) - *97*	4	5
-	**Glasgow Iron & Steel Co**. 963 red-brown Sp Edn (Harburn) - *97*	4	5
-	**Fife Coal** brown Sp Edn (Harburn) - *02*	4	5
-	**White & Beeny** 304 black - *97*	3	4
-	**Burgess & Penfold** 5 grey Sp Edn (Scale Rail) - *96*	4	5

* Proposed weathered and repaired wagons which were included in a late supplement to the 1981 catalogue. ** Shown as a 5-plank wagon in the 2000 catalogue. *** initially sold only through Pecorama at Beer, Devon.

W7b. Salt Wagon (7-plank with roof)

NR-P120	**Saxa Salt** 251 yellow - *73*	3	4
NR-P121	**Shaka Salt** 166 bright blue - *75?*	3	4

Salt wagon [7b] (Peco)

W8a. 9-Plank Wagon with High Bar (lwb)

NR-10S	**SR** 6241 dark brown - *75?*	3	4
NR-10B	**BR** brown - *68*	3	4

W8b. OBA 9-Plank Wagon (lwb)

NR-11R	**BR** Railfreight 110264 red+grey OBA no bar - *82*	3	4

W9. Butterley Steel Type Coal Wagon

NR-44E	**NE** 131450 brown - *71*	3	4
NR-44W	**GW** 23301 dark grey - *75?*	3	4
NR-44B	**BR** B288543 grey - *84*	3	4
NR-P100	**Charringtons** 7190 orange-red - *75?*	3	4
NR-P101	**Denaby** 950 black - *75?*	4	5

W10. HAA MGR Hopper Wagon

NR-300	**BR** B350397 silver - *TBA*	NPG	NPG

W11. Bulk Grain Wagon

NR-11AC	**Abbot's Choice** - blue (NR-P67) - *69*	4	5
NR-11WH	**White Horse** blue (NR-P69) - *69*	4	5
NR-11JH	**Haig** blue (NR-P68) - *69*	4	5
NR-P64	**Grant's** blue - *95*	4	5
NR-P65	**Dewar's** blue - *?*	4	5
NR-66	**Grain** 7586 red-brown - *90?*	4	5
NR-P70	**The Malsters Association of Great Britain** yellow - *79*	4	5

Bulk grain wagon [W11] (Peco)

W12a. 14T Small Tank Wagon (Fuel)

NR-P160	**Shell/BP** black - *81*	4	5
NR-P161	**Esso** ? silver - *81*	5	6
NR-P161	**Esso** 3061? silver - *03*	6	7
NR-P162	**Shell/BP** - *not made*	NA	NA
NR-P162	**National Benzole** 256 buff - *84*	4	5
NR-P163	**Royal Daylight** red - *8*	4	5
NR-?	**Berry Wiggins** silver Sp Edn (N Gauge Society 35th Anniversary) - *02*	5	6

W12b. Small Tank Wagon (Milk)

With ladders either side.

NR-P167	**United Dairies** white Milk - *82**	4	5
NR-P168	**Express Dairies** dark blue or black Milk - *82**	4	5

* These were originally listed in 1981 as NR-162 and NR-163 respectively.

W13a. 15' Modern Tanker (end ladders) (ex-Minitrix)

These tanks were designed, tooled up and produced by Trix but the tooling was later taken over by Peco who tooled a replacement chassis which could also be used on other wagons.

NR1	**BP** 9675 white (NR-P50) - *67*	5	7
NR-P50	**BP** 9678 white - *81*	4	6
NR2	**BP** 1354 silver grey (NR-P51) - *67*	5	7
NR3	**BP** 1336 green (NR-P52) - *67*	5	7
NR-P52	**BP** 9685 green - *81*	4	6
NR4	**BP** 9678 black (NR-P53) - *67*	5	7
NR-P53	**BP** 9685 black - *81*	4	6
NR-P74	**Rugby Cement** PR9435 grey - *83*	4	6
NR-P75	**Albright & Wilson** MD22 light blue - *83*	4	6
NR-P76	**Fina** 2 silver - *03*	6	8

15' modern tanker [W13a] (Peco)

W13b. 15' Modern Tanker (side ladders)

NR-P71	**ICI Mond Div** ICI M70801 dark grey - *82*	4	6

W13c. 15' Modern Tanker (no ladders)

NR-P79	**Mobil LP Gas** 57882 white - *83*	4	6

W14. Cattle Wagon

NR-45W	**GW** 13865 dark grey - *77*	3	4
NR-45M	**LMS** 294528 light grey - *71*	3	4
NR-45E	**LNER** red-brown - *99*	3	4
NR-45S	**SR** 53710 dark brown - *75?*	3	4
NR-?	**BR** brown - *made?*	NPG	NPG

W15. Pallet Van (lwb)

NR-8B	**BR** brown - *68*	4	5
NR-8A	**Army** 41000 dull green (NR-P54) - *68*	3	4
NR-8F	**Ford** blue - *69*	4	5
NR-P55	**Ford** dark blue revised livery - *76*	3	4
NR-P56	**Izal** B782357 bright green - *79*	3	4

W16. Twin Ventilated Box Van

NR-43W	**GW** 100418 dark grey - *71*	3	4
NR-43M	**LMS** 291859 light grey - *77*	3	4
NR-43E	**NE** 15216 brown - *71*	3	4
NR-43B	**BR** W11275 brown - *84*	3	4
NR-P130	**Worthington** 3 red-brown - *72*	3	4
NR-P131	**Bass** 13 dark grey - *75*	3	4

W17. Fish/Parcels Van (lwb)

NR-6	**BR** E8700? white Fish (NR-6B) - *68*	3	4
NR-9	**BR** E87641 light blue Express Parcels (NR-9B) - *68*	3	4
NR-12R	**BR** Railfreight 200278? red+grey - *82*	3	4

Fish/parcels van [W17] (Peco)

W18. Refrigerator Box Van

NR-42E	**NE** 151275 white - *71*	3	4
NR-42S	**SR** 50680 cream Banana Van - *73*	3	4
NR-42R	**BR Rft** 712307? red+grey VEA - *83*	3	4
NR-P140	**Fyffes Bananas** yellow - *74*	3	4
NR-P141	**Colman's Mustard** yellow - *73*	3	4

W19. LNER 10ft Brake Van

NR-49E	**NE** 157691 brown - *72*	3	4
NR-49E	**NE** 178595 brown - *not made?*	3	4

W20. LMS 10ft Brake Van

NR-48M	**LMS** 1675, 1875 grey - *72*	3	4

W21. MR 10ft Brake Van

Verandah one end and open platform the other.

NR-47	**MR** M521 grey - *77*	3	4

W22. 20T BR(ER) Brake Van (lwb)

NR-28E	**NE** 157691 brown - *73*	4	5
NR-28B	**BR** B952116 brown - *73*	4	5
NR-28R	**BR Rft** B954673 red+grey - *91*	4	5

W23. Freightliner Container Flat

This was illustrated in April 1968 but no further information about it has been found.

NR-?	**BR** flat with 3 20' BRe Freightliner containers - *made?*	NPG	NPG

If you are really serious about buying or selling trains or toys, there is only one place to visit . . .

Sandown Park

Europe's No.1 Toy Collectors Fair

Sandown Exhibition Centre, Sandown Park Racecourse, Esher, Surrey

10:30am - 4:00pm

2005
Sandown Dates

Saturday 5th March
Saturday 28th May
Saturday 6th August
Saturday 29th October

(2006 dates available later)

The finest 500 Stalls in Britain!

Meet all the country's Top Dealers and Collectors and see the best of everything in Collectable Toys and Trains.

Sandown Park is only 5 miles from Junction 10 of the M25.
Free Parking is available for 6,000 cars.
Regular trains run from Waterloo to Esher.

Adults £4-50   Seniors £4-00   Children £2-00

Call us for a free detailed calendar of events on 01604 770025 or 01858 468459

BARRY POTTER
····· *Fairs* ·····

Full details also available on our website: **www.barrypotterfairs.com**

Playcraft

HISTORY

Although never developed into a major British range, the appearance of this 12 volt 2-rail system in the market in 1961 sent shivers down the spines of Britain's major model railway manufacturers at the time. The reason: its price! Advertised as 'Build that Big Layout for a Small Price', Playcraft was the cheapest mass-produced electric railway system yet seen.

Throughout the 1950s, the competitive British market, led by Tri-ang Railways, offered comprehensive model railway systems at very attractive prices, but from 1961 the new Playcraft range cut the cost of 'getting started' even further. Sold mainly through F.W.Woolworths, Mettoy were clearly interested in the beginner's market and offered starter sets at £1 each. As a result, two of the major players at the time responded with cheap starter sets of their own and Playcraft's expansion of British models was contained.

The Playcraft trademark was owned by Mettoy of Northampton, who also owned Corgi Cars and distributed Aurora plastic kits in the UK. Playcraft was first used on a re-badged version of the Aurora model highways systems, but was quickly applied to the new railway range and the Aurora kits. Most of the railway models were made in France by Jouef, although elements were also produced by Brawa, Pola, Aurora and at the Mettoy plant at Forest Fach. To give maximum flexibility, the range was scaled at 3.5mm/ft, HO scale. Some British outline wagons were nearer to 4mm/ft, as were the British designed accessories such as the excellent Signals Kit. It is also true that many of the models were based on French and other Continental prototypes.

Playcraft Railways was launched at the 1961 Toy Fair with the first sets being available by the following Christmas. Throughout their life a mixture of Playcraft Railways and Jouef boxes were used. Larger sets such as the Kangarou and Cockerill crane used standard Jouef packaging with English instructions on a card insert. Production of the British models continued quite actively up until the end of 1968 after which there seems to have been a general run-down so that, by the end of the decade, only models of French prototypes were being offered.

This, however, was not the end of the British range. In the early 1970s a hideous clockwork version of the Class 29 diesel, fitted to a rigid 4-wheel chassis was produced. Partnered with SNCF day cars re-branded as BR Buffet and Composite coaches, it was sold as a Starter Set. Similar treatment befell the SNCF BB66150 diesel, this time matched with bright red ex-SNCF coaching stock. The 1976 Jouef catalogue shows the Class 29 (D6100) but now fitted with Continental couplings. This was a re-tooled version using a later Jouef M20 motor driving one bogie only, catalogued 8911. All exterior detail is on raised mouldings, including numbers and BR arrows. Re-branded ex-SNCF day cars were matched

Milestones
1961 Launch by Mettoy of Jouef models under the Playcraft label at Toy Fair.
1961 First sets available for Christmas.
1961 Class 29 released.
1963 Playcraft sets with track-mats are advertised.
1963 Diesel shunter released.
1963 TPO released.
1967 Release of the Kangourou.
1968 The year of the last catalogue.
1969 Last UK price list.
1970 Only French models available.
c1975 A late batch of Class 29 diesels is available

with it, given correct BR Mk1 numbers for a Buffet, brake 2nd and Composite!

Further Reading

We know of no books specifically about the Playcraft range but there was a series of articles in *Model Railway Collector: Volume 7 Nos. 3 and 4* (March and April 2000).

Couplings - Playcraft models may be found with three types of coupling. The earliest type, known as 'Lanal', were original Jouef couplings, similar to a type used by Tri-ang. From around 1963/64, the Peco design, used for Hornby-Dublo and Trix models, were fitted to Playcraft stock. After 1968, stock began to appear with European lifting bar couplings as fitted to Jouef items. Despite this, Jouef were using Lanal couplings on starter sets as late as the 1980s.

Numbering - Early models were numbered with a 'PR' prefix which, by 1964, had been reduced to just 'P'. For simplicity, we have dropped the 'R' and given all the models a 'P' prefix.

Dates - These are the dates that the models first appeared in British catalogues.

Listing - The locos are listed in order of size starting with tank engines followed by tender locos and ending with diesels, electrics and multiple units. The coaches are listed with pre-Nationalisation stock first followed by vehicles of later years. Wagons are listed in the order of: flats, open wagons, hoppers, tanks, vans, brake vans and bogie stock.

LOCOMOTIVES

Cat.No.	Number, Company, Colour, Dates	£	£

L1. 0-4-0 Tank (Continental)

Early models has silver wheels and later ones had red ones.

P535	**708** BRc green clockwork - *61*	5	10
P535	**708** BRc green electric - *61*	7	15
P535	**708** BRc black clockwork - *61*	5	10
P831	**708** BRc black electric - *61*	7	15
-	**708** BRe red clockwork from a set - *69*	10	NA

L2. 0-4-0 Diesel Shunter

P838	**D2705** green no decals hazard stripes - *64*	25	30
P8381	**D2705** BRe blue hazard stripes - *68*	35	40
P536	**D2705** green clockwork no decals - *64*	12	22

0-4-0 diesel shunter [L2]

Playcraft

L3. Class 29 Diesel Bo-Bo

Cat.No.	Description	£	£
P837	**D6100** BRc green - *61*	10	30
P8371	**D6100** BRe blue - *68*	12	35
-	**D6100** BRe blue from sets clockwork with 4 wheels only - *70*	10	NA
J8911	**D6100** BRe blue raised detail 4-wheel drive in new chassis Sp Edn (Tonbridge Wells Model Shop) - *75*	15	NA

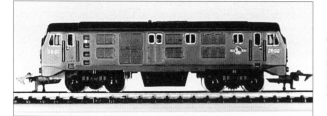

Class 29 diesel [L3]

L4. Continental Locos sold as Playcraft

cc = closed cab. oc = open cab.

Cat.No.	Description	£	£
P828	**SNCF** 2-8-0 green - *68*	20	40
P828	**SNCF** 2-8-0 black - *68*	20	40
P829	**SNCF** 0-8-0 tank green cc - *67*	20	35
P829	**SNCF** 0-8-0 tank black cc - *67*	20	35
P830	**SNCF** 0-8-0 tank green oc - *67*	20	35
P830	**SNCF** 0-8-0 tank black oc - *67*	20	35
P836	**Nord** Type 231C green Pacific - *63*	20	35
P836	**Nord** Type 231C black Pacific - *63*	20	35
P836	**Nord** Type 231C brown Pacific tender drive - *63*	40	55
P840	**SNCF** 0-4-0 diesel shunter - *65*	15	25
P841	**SNCF** BB67001 Class diesel - *65*	12	28
P842	**SNCF** BB13001 Class electric - *65*	20	45
P843	**TEE** CC40101 electric - *65*	20	40
P852	**SNCF** Panoramic rail car - *66*	15	35
P853	**SNCF** BB 66150 Class diesel - *66*	15	30
P854	**SNCF** CC 7107 Class electric - *66*	20	40
P855	**Dutch** 1308 electric - *67*	60	70
P856	**SNCF** CC70000 Class diesel-elec - *67*	15	35
P761	**Budd** stainless steel 2-car EMU - *67*	15	35

COACHES

The British coaches were rather short for Mk1s but a special feature was the early fitting of interiors. These were correctly a light timber colour and the restaurant car even had its kitchen detailed with printed self-adhesive stickers. Thus, the interiors were much better than those of Tri-ang Hornby, the main competitor at the time. The four British Mk1s were issued in blue and grey livery during 1967 together with teak versions. By October 1963, a Royal Mail travelling post office set was being offered; the coach from the set also being available separately as well as a non-operating version.

There were several Continental coaches sold in Playcraft packaging. These initial models had Lanal couplings but soon changed to the Peco type. The demand for the Continental stock in Britain is quite low, although the rare ones command premium prices. The 1969 price list shows two 'vintage' SNCF coaches. These would be rare if ever released in Playcraft boxes.

Cat.No.	Company, Number, Colour, Dates	£	£

C1. Travelling Post Office

The model may be found with black or brown nets.

Cat.No.	Description	£	£
P454	**Royal Mail** operating TPO set red - *63*	10	15
P459	**Royal Mail** non-operating coach red - *63*	8	12

Travelling Post Office [C1]

C2a. BR Mk1 Composite

Cat.No.	Description	£	£
P337	**BR** green - *62*	5	7
P347	**BR** brown+cream - *61*	5	7
P457	**BR** maroon - *61*	4	6
P4571	**BR** blue+grey - *67*	10	15
?	teak - *67*	15	20

C2b. BR Mk1 2nd Class Open

Cat.No.	Description	£	£
P336	**BR** green - *62*	5	7
P346	**BR** brown+cream - *61*	5	7
P456	**BR** maroon - *61*	4	6
P4561	**BR** blue+grey - *67*	10	15
?	teak - *67*	15	20

C2c. BR Mk1 2nd Brake Corridor

Cat.No.	Description	£	£
P338	**BR** green - *62*	5	7
P348	**BR** brown+cream - *61*	5	7
P458	**BR** maroon - *61*	4	6
P4581	**BR** blue+grey - *67*	10	15
?	teak - *67*	15	20

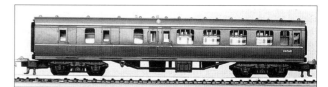

Mk1 brake 2nd corridor coach [C2c]

C2d. BR Mk1 Restaurant Kitchen Car

Cat.No.	Description	£	£
P335	**BR** green - *62*	5	7
P345	**BR** brown+cream - *61*	5	7
P455	**BR** maroon - *61*	4	6
P4551	**BR** blue+grey - *67*	10	15
?	teak - *67*	15	20

C3. Continental Coaches sold as Playcraft

Cat.No.	Description	£	£
P451	**SNCF** 1st class stainless steel - *63*	5	7
P452	**SNCF** standard 1st green - *63*	5	7
P453	**SNCF** standard composite green - *62*	5	7
P460	**Wagon-Lits** luggage van blue - *63*	8	12
P467	heating generator van blue - *68*	15	20
P850	**SNCF** post office van brown - *63*	7	10
P860	**Wagon-Lits** dining car blue - *62*	7	10
P861	**Wagon-Lits** 1st class Pullman car - *62*	7	10
P862	**Wagon-Lits** 3933 sleeping car blue - *63*	7	10
P863	**Wagon-Lits** Channel ferry sleeper - *63*	7	10
P864	**TEE** passenger coach - *64*	7	10
P865	**TEE** luggage/generator car - *64*	7	10
P8651	**TEE** luggage/generator car + lights - *64*	15	20
P866	**Budd** EMU centre car - *67*	8	12
P868	**Wagon-Lits** dining car red - *68*	15	20
P4500	**STM** green vintage double deck French suburban - *69*	20	30
P4501	**STM** green vintage French suburban - *69*	20	30

WAGONS

Although we tend to think of certain Playcraft wagons as being British, they were, in fact, based largely on French vehicles. The bogie wagons ran on American type diamond bogies typical of the TP stock supplied to France by the USA after the last war. An attractive feature of those wagons that were supposed to represent British prototypes was the use of British Railways names for them such as 'Boplate', 'Weltrol' and 'Walrus' which were on printed data panel labels but later printed directly onto the side of the wagon.

The Continental wagons have limited appeal in Britain although the Kangourou set has tempted a number of British Railways stalwarts!

Cat.No.	Company, Number, Colour, Dates	£	£

W1. Open Goods Wagon
This wagon had the name 'Tube' moulded into it. With brake gear.

P631	**BR** B731490 grey - *64*	4	6
P631	**BR** B731490 bright yellow - *?*	10	12

W2. Coal Wagon with Load
Without brake gear.

P632	**BR** B731490 maroon + black load - *62*	5	7
P632	**BR** B731490 maroon + grey load - *62*	6	8

W3. 24.5T Open Mineral Wagon

P633	**BR** B280650 grey - *64*	4	6
P633	**BR** B280650 brown - *?*	10	12
P633	**BR** B280650 yellow - *?*	10	12

W4. Drop-Side Goods Wagon

P634	grey + ballast - *62*	6	8

W5. 13T Drop-Side Wagon
These were also marked SNCF as crane riding wagons and were sold two to a set.

P644	**BR** B468400 or.brown + 3 tubes - *64*	5	7
P645	**BR** B468400 choc-brown with lugs + 2 maroon BR containers - *64*	7	9
P646	**BR** B468400 brown with lugs - *64*	4	6
P646	**BR** B468400 olive green with lugs - *64*	4	6

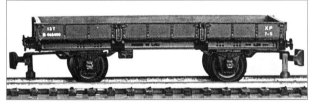

13T drop-side wagon [W5]

W6. European Open Goods Wagon

P623	**SNCF** green - *65*	8	10
P623	**SNCF** brown - *69*	8	10

W7. Twin Silo Bulk Cement Wagon

P642	**Blue Circle** B24 grey - *64*	4	6

W8. Cereal Hopper

P647	**Algeco** SNCF 502134 grey - *65*	5	8

W9. Twin Barrel Wagon

P643	E762100 Wines from France red - *64*	5	7
P643	E762100 Wines light maroon - *?*	8	10

Cereal Hopper [W8]

W10. Small Tank

P640	**Shell BP** 1608 silver - *made?*	NPG	NPG
P640	**Shell BP** 6010 silver - *64*	5	7
P636	**Solonia** - *?*	10	20
P637	**Butagaz** - *?*	10	20
J639	**Primagaz** - *69*	10	20

Small tank wagon - Shell [W10]

W11. Goods Van with Sliding Doors

P635	maroon - *62*	4	6
P635	dark brown - *c67*	4	6
P635	bright green - *62?*	10	12

W12. French Mineral Water/Beer Van

P625	**Evian/Badoit** SNCF 506013 silv - *65*	6	8
P625	**Evian/Evian** SNCF 506013 silver - *?*	15	20
P626	**Kronenbourg** SNCF 506015 red - *65*	6	8
P627	**Heineken** Nederland NS280785 - *67*	12	15

French beer van [W12]

Playcraft

W13. European Goods Van

P624	**SNCF** 337557 brown - *67*	8	10
P6241	**SNCF** 337557 brown with lights - *67*	10	12

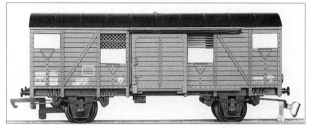

European goods converter van [W13]

W14. European Goods Wagon with Sliding Roof

P622	**SNCF** grey - *65*	8	10

W15. BR 20T Standard Brake Van

P630	**BR** B951718 brown - *62*	4	6
P630	**BR** B951718 green ex sets - *?*	10	12

Standard brake van [W15]

W16. 30T Bogie Bolster Wagon

P655	**BR** B922768 dark grey + 3 logs - *62*	5	7
P659	**BR** B922768 dark grey + 3 cars - *63*	6	10

W17. 35T Weltrol Well Wagon

P658	grey - *62*	4	6
P658.2	grey + brown transformer - *64*	5	7

W18. 12.5T Tierwag Car Carrier

P654	**BR** B909204 grey + 6 cars - *64*	6	10
P654	**BR** B909204 black + 6 cars - *62*	6	10
P654	**BR** B909204 blue grey + 6 cars - *67*	6	10

W19. French STVA Artic Car Transporter

P6571	**SNCF** 2087 grey + 8 cars - *67*	15	20

W20. French Kangourou Road Rail

P664	**SNCF** CIMT Algeco + CIMT Segi wagons + Calberson and Bailly trailers + Lorraine tractor - *67*	35	50
P665	Kangourou wagon + semi-trailer - *67*	10	15

W21. 42T Bogie 3-Plank Open Wagon Boplate

P652	**BR** B947147 dark grey - *62*	5	7

W22. 50T Bogie Open Wagon

P650	**BR** E451023 green - *62*	5	7
P650	maroon - *c65?*	5	7

W23. 40T Walrus Bogie Hopper Wagon

P657	**BR** DB992500 brown non-operating - *62*	4	6
P657	**BR** DB992500 grey non-operating - *62*	4	6

P660	**BR** DB992500 operating set - *64*	10	12
P661	**BR** DB992500 brown operating - *64*	4	6
P661	**BR** DB992500 grey operating - *64*	4	6
P661	**BR** Tare 25-3 brown operating - *c67?*	4	6
P661	**BR** Tare 25-3 grey operating - *c67?*	4	6

W24. Short Bogie Tanker

P651	**Shell** 1608 silver - *62*	5	7

Short bogie tanker [W24]

W25. Long Wheelbase Bogie Tanker

P6511	**Butagaz** 00744756 silver - *69*	15	25

W26. Long Wheelbase Bogie Cattle Van

P6531	**SNCF** 1900144 brown - *69*	15	25

W27. 10T Bogie Goods Van with Sliding Doors

P653	green - *62*	5	7
P653	**BR** 86512 green GUV - *c69?*	5	7
P653	brown - *64*	5	7

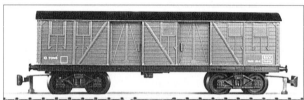

Bogie goods van [W27]

W28. 7T Bogie Refrigerator Van

P656	**BR** GUV 86512 white - *62*	5	7
P656	**Stef** white - *64*	6	8

W29. 85T Cockerill Large Crane

P663	**SNCF** 559 grey Operating set - *66*	20	30

ACCESSORIES

There was a good range of accessories with the goods depot and engine shed being particularly popular. The shed was very similar to that offered in the Hornby Dublo range, but was bright red, and also had an extension set. Curiously it was described as having operating smoke vents! The girder bridge set was modelled on the Great Central Railway overbridge at Rugby and designed in the UK.

SETS

There was quite a large range of train sets which took the names of famous stations and goods depots according to whether they were passenger or freight sets. In nice condition the more common sets (Clapham, Stratford, Broad Street and Snowhill) sell for between £25 and £40. The sought after sets are, of course, the London-Paris Night Ferry in its original picture box, the operating crane train set and, interestingly, some of the later starter sets with vehicles in odd colours. Expect to pay around £70 for an early Night Ferry set with a black Nord Pacific. The prestigious Lakeside sets in good boxed condition can command a price of £200 or more.

Replica

HISTORY

When General Mills decided to cease toy production in Europe, Dapol acquired the stock, intellectual assets and the former Airfix tooling from Palitoy. The tools for Palitoy's own Mainline Railways belonged to Kader of Hong Kong, their manufacturer.

Godfrey Hayes of Railwayania sold Mainline models and spares and ran a sideline of repaints, transfers and detailing components under the name of Replica Railways. Discovering that the Mainline tools belonged to Kader, Hayes approached them in 1984 with a view to taking over the distribution of models made by them. In May 1985 Hayes was invited to Hong Kong to discuss the project

A production plan was worked out and in the autumn of 1985, the first sample wagons arrived. Advertisements were placed in the model railway press to launch the new range. Dapol, who owned the intellectual assets of the Mainline system were unhappy with the arrangement and a court case followed. Replica, however, weathered the storm, and more wagons and some coaches were available by Christmas. A steady stream of models appeared over the next few years.

Godfrey Hayes set very high quality standards and every item brought in from the Far East was unpacked and inspected. After testing for running qualities and finish the models were repackaged in the green Replica boxes and rejects were returned to Kader.

In 1987, Kader took over the American toy company of Bachmann, for whom they were a primary manufacturer and this effectively signalled the end of the Replica range. In order to expand into Europe, Kader formed Bachmann Industries Europe and the former Mainline range became the core of their products for the British market. Kader could not manufacture for their new European company while at the same time produce models for a rival and so further access to the Mainline tools was denied Replica.

Further Reading

There has been a series of articles by Graham Smith-Thompson, in *Model Railway Collector* magazine (formerly *Model Railway Enthusiast*), profiling the Airfix and Mainline ranges and other systems that later used the tools. There were three parts devoted specifically to Replica Railways published in the December 1999 and January and February 2000 issues of the magazine.

Dates - As there were only two Replica catalogues, we have depended on press advertising to determine when models reached the shops. A single date has been given because Replica models were produced in batches. Generally there was only an initial batch of models which, when sold-out, was not repeated.

Listing - The locos are listed in order of size starting with tank

	Milestones
	1984 Hayes approaches Kader regarding use of the Mainline tools.
	1985 Hayes goes to Hong Kong to visit Kader and work out a production plan.
	1987 First catalogue released.
	1987 B1 model is released.
	1987 Kader buys Bachmann.
	1989 Bachmann Industries Europe Ltd is formed.
	1990 The Modified Hall is released.
	1990 Bachmann Branchlines launched in UK initially using former Mainline tools which are no longer available to Replica Railways.

engines followed by tender locos and ending with diesels. The coaches are listed with pre-Nationalisation stock first followed by vehicles of later years. Wagons are listed in the order of: timber open wagons, steel open wagons, hoppers, tanks, vans and brake vans.

Numbers - the running numbers were usually changed when a new batch of models was made.

LOCOMOTIVES

Cat.No.	Number, Company, Colour, Dates	£	£

L1. Class 57XX Pannier Tank 0-6-0PT (ex-Mainline)
11001	**7768** GWR shirt button logo green - *86*	27	38
11002	**7843, 8743** BRc black - *88*	27	38
11003	**7752** G W R green - *88*	27	38

L2. GWR Collett Goods 0-6-0
(ex-Mainline with Manor tender)
11041	**2244** G W R green - *89*	30	40
11042	**2203** BRb black - *89*	30	40

Collett goods 0-6-0 [L2]

L3. GWR Modified Hall Class 4-6-0 (Mainline/Replica)
Production had reached the test-shot stage when Replica took it over. It was much improved by Replica and the tender completely retooled.
11151	**6976 'Graythwaite Hall'** G()W green - *90*	43	48
11152	**7911 'Lady Margaret Hall'** BRc green - *90*	43	48
11153	**6998 'Burton Agnes Hall'** G()W green as preserved - *90*	43	48

L4. Class B1 4-6-0 (partly ex-Mainline)
This was in an advanced stage of tooling when Mainline collapsed and so the Replica models were the first to be produced from these tools. The resulting model reflected original Mainline quality and style rather than later production under the Bachmann name.
11011	**61026 'Ourebi'** BRb black - *87*	44	50
11011U	**BRb** black, as 11011, unnamed, unnumbered - *?*	NPG	NPG
11012	**1000 'Springbok'** LNER green - *87*	44	50
11013	**1059** LNER lined black - *90*	42	50
11014	**61132** BRb lined black - *90*	42	50
11014A	**61264** BR lined black Sp Edn 300 (Steam World Magazine) - *93*	70	100

L5. BR Standard Class 4 4-6-0 (ex-Mainline)
This has a separate chimney moulding and finer printing than the Mainline model. It also had a completely redesigned chassis with a can motor.
11031	**75019** BRb black lined Ltd Edn 750 - *90*	75	100
11032	**75024** BRc green lined Ltd Edn 24 only - *90*	200	250
11032A	**75027** BR black? lined 2 mockups done then dropped - *92?*	NPG	400
11033	**75037** BRc black lined Ltd Edn 750 - *90*	75	100

L6. Class 03 Diesel Shunter 0-6-0DS (ex-Mainline)
11021	**D2083** BRc green - *87*	26	36
11022	**03189** BRe blue - *87*	26	36

L7. Class 45/1 Diesel-Electric 1Co-Co1 (ex-Mainline)
Manufacture of the Replica model reflected original Mainline quality and style rather than later production under the Bachmann label.
11501	**45128** BRe blue - *89*	27	38
11501U	as 11501, unnamed, unnumbered - *?*	NPG	NPG
11502	**45106** BRc green - *89*	27	38

Replica

Class 03 diesel [L6] (Replica Railways)

COACHES

Initially these reflected Mainline types but with different liveries and Commonwealth bogies on Mk1s. There were reruns of Collett and LMS 57' and 50' types but all had different fleet/stock numbers. New types produced included Mk1 corridor composite brakes, first opens and full brakes in various liveries. Most were developments of existing Mainline tools but the full brake was an entirely Replica model. The prices vary but the higher quality of Replica coaches is respected and they generally sell at higher prices than those from the Airfix and Mainline ranges. The appearance of the 'Bachmann' name on the underneath of the model can cause confusion.

Cat.No.	Company, Number, Colour, Dates	£	£

Collett Stock

C1a. Collett 60ft Corridor Brake Composite
(ex-Mainline)

12041	**GWR** 6356, 6544 brown+cream 1st/3d brake - *89?*	12	18
12042	**BR** W6487W maroon 1st/3rd - *91?*	12	20
12043	**BR** W6543? red+cream 1st/2nd - *91?*	12	18

C1b. Collett 60ft Corridor 3rd (2nd) (ex-Mainline)

12051	**GWR** 1087, 1116, 1137 brown+cream all 3rd - *87?*	12	18
12052	**BR** W1098W maroon all 2nd - *89*	12	20
12053	**BR** W1139 red+cream all 3rd - *89*	12	18
12053	**BR** W1087W maroon all 3rd - *89*	12	18

Collett corridor 3rd [C1b]

LMS Stock

C2a. 57ft 1920s Corridor Composite (ex-Mainline)
Although ex-Mainline, the roof was retooled to take separate vents. They also had rubber corridor connectors in place of the plastic ones.

| 12201 | **LMS** 3621 maroon silver roof - *89* | 12 | 18 |
| 12202 | **BR** 3621 maroon 1st/2nd, grey roof - *89* | 12 | 18 |

C2b. 57ft 1920s Corridor Brake End (ex-Mainline)
Although ex-Mainline, the roof was retooled to take separate vents. They also had rubber corridor connectors in place of the plastic ones.

| 12211 | **LMS** 5270 maroon 3rd brake, silver roof - *89* | 12 | 18 |
| 12212 | **BR** M5314M maroon 2nd brake, grey roof - *89* | 12 | 18 |

C3a. Stanier 1930s Vestibule 3rd
(Mixed Parentage)
Designed by Airfix and redrawn by Palitoy and tooled by Kader but not produced. Replica redrew the roof and Kader made it for them.

| 12221 | **LMS** 9174 maroon all 3rd, silver roof - *90?* | 15 | 20 |

C3b. Stanier 1930s Open 2nd

| 12222 | **BR** M9088M maroon 2nd, grey roof - *90?* | 12 | 18 |

C4. LMS 50' Parcel Van (ex-Mainline)

12251	**LMS** 31239 maroon - *89*	10	15
12252	**BR** M31293M maroon - *89*	10	15
12253	**BR** M31262M? red+cream - *89*	10	15

Mk1 Stock

C5a. BR Mk1 Corridor 2nd (SK) (ex-Mainline)

12111	**BR** S25942 green - *86?*	12	18
12112	**BR** I-C M18753 Executive grey - *86?*	12	18
12113	**BR** 18955 NSE blue - *87?*	12	18

C5b. BR Mk1 Brake Composite (BCK)
(Mixed Parentage)
Developed by Palitoy for Mainline but not made. Altered by Replica and made for them by Kader. Replica purchased the tooling from Kader.

12141	**BR** S21263 green - *90?*	15	20
12142	**BR** IC 21266? Executive grey - *90?*	15	20
12144	**BR** W21243 brown+cream - *90?*	15	20
12145	**BR** M21268 blue+grey - *90*	15	20
12146	**BR** E21086 maroon - *90?*	15	20
12147	**BR** M21076 red+cream - *90*	15	20

Mk1 brake composite [C5b] (Replica Railways)

C5c. BR Mk1 1st Open (FO) (Mixed Parentage)
Developed by Palitoy for Mainline but not made. Altered by Replica and made for them by Kader. Replica purchased the tooling from Kader.

12131	**BR** S3067 green - *90?*	15	20
12132	**BR** IC 3114 Executive grey - *90?*	15	20
12134	**BR** W3101 brown+cream - *90?*	15	20
12135	**BR** M3119 blue grey - *90?*	15	20
12136	**BR** Sc3102 maroon - *90?*	15	20
12137	**BR** M3024 crimson+cream - *90?*	15	20

C5d. BR Mk1 Brake 2nd (BSK) (ex-Mainline)

12121	**BR** S34642 green - *86?*	12	18
12122	**BR** I-C M35454 Executive grey - *86?*	12	18
12123	**BR** NSE 35193, 35464 blue - *87?*	12	18

C5e. BR Mk1 Buffet Restaurant Car (RB)
(ex-Mainline)

12101	**BR** S1717 green - *86*	12	18
12102	**BR** I-C E1868 Executive grey - *86?*	12	18
12102A	**BR** IC Charter 1659 grey - *90?*	12	18
12104	**BR** W1732 brown+cream - *89?*	12	18
12106	**BRc** M1646, M1714 maroon - *90?*	12	18
12106	**BR** M1676 maroon - *90?*	12	18

C5f. BR Mk1 57' Full Brake (BG)
Designed by Replica and tooled by Kader, tools owned by Replica.

| 12161 | **BR** green - *94* | 15 | 20 |
| 12162 | **BR IC** Executive grey - *94* | 15 | 20 |

12163	**BR NSE** blue - *94*	15	20
12164	**BR** brown+cream - *94*	15	20
12165	**BR** blue+grey - *94*	15	20
12166	**BR** M80855 maroon - *94*	15	20
12167	**BR** W21243 brown+cream - *94*	15	20
12167	**BR** M80725 red+cream - *94*	15	20
12168	**BR** Blue - *94*	15	20
12169	**BR ScotRail** grey+blue - *94*	15	20
12170	**BR Post Office** 92207 red - *94*	15	20
12171	**BR Provincial Services** 92317 blue+buff - *94*	15	20
12172	**BR RES** red+dark grey - *94*	15	20
12173	**BR** E80654 red - *94*	15	20

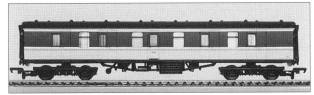

Mk1 57' full brake [C5f]

C6. PCV
Also available in kit form.

15001	**PO** 94303, 94338, 94322, 94332 supplied as transfers red + black - *03*	20	27
15002	**RES** (blue flash) supplied as transfers red + black - *03*	20	27

WAGONS
Without a catalogue or check list, these are going to cause confusion in future years when they turn up unboxed. Chassis are to Airfix style with brakes in-line with the wheels.

Cat.No.	Company, Number, Colour, Dates	£	£
W1.	**1-Plank Wagon** (ex-Mainline)		
13051	**LMS** grey + B container - *not made*	NA	NA
13052	**LNER** brown + B container - *not made*	NA	NA
13053	**LNER** brown + B container **Frasers** - *not made*	NA	NA
13101	**LMS** 210401 grey + brown container **Pimm & Son** - *90?*	6	8
13102	**LNER** 203175 brown + brown container H. **Timson & Sons** - *90?*	6	8
13103	**LNER** 221104 brown + maroon container **William Whiteley** - *90?*	6	8
W2.	**3-Plank Wagon** (ex-Mainline)		
13301	**Bath & Corsham** 14 light grey - *89*	5	7
13302	**W. Neave & Son** 6 grey - *89*	5	7
13303	**Trimsaran** 51 dark red - *89*	5	7

7-plank wagon [W3]

W3. 7-Plank Wagon (ex-Mainline)
13201	**GWR** 6515 grey - *85?*	4	6
13202	**Patent Nut and Bolt** 658 brown - *85?*	5	7
13203	**Diamond** 34 red - *85?*	5	7
13204	**C & G Ayres** 530 green+yellow - *87*	5	7
13205	**F & E Poole** 200 light blue - *87*	6	8
13206	**Bognor Coal & Transport** 4 red - *87*	6	8
13207	**Lambert & Cox** 19 red-brown - *88*	5	7
13208	**Renwick Wilton** 658 black - *88*	5	7
13209	**Hugh Wood** 50 grey - *88*	6	8
13210	**Llewellyn Brothers** 203 brown - *90*	5	7
13211	**Thomas Lockwood** 108 grey - *90*	5	7
13212	**Stanton** 9988 orange - *90*	5	7

W4. 9-Plank Coke Wagon (ex-Mainline)
13351	**Abbott** 3606 black - *89*	5	7
13352	**Suncole** 5050 black - *89*	5	7
13353	**Smokeless Fuels** 232 black - *89*	5	7

9-plank coke wagon [W4]

W5. 16T Steel Mineral Wagon (ex-Mainline)
13401	**BR** M621988 grey - *89*	4	6
13402	**BR** B569425 MCV brown - *89*	4	6

W6. 24T Hopper Wagon (ex-Mainline)
13411	**BR** B436872 1960s grey Iron Ore - *89*	5	7
13412	**BR** B437398 1970s grey Ore Hop - *89*	5	7

W7. 46T HEA/HBA Hopper Wagon (ex-Mainline)
14101	**BR** 360364 bauxite - *86*	6	8
14102	**BRe Railfreight** 360694 red+grey - *86*	6	8
14103	**Railfreight** revised livery - *86*	6	8
14103B	**Railfreight** - *88?*	6	8
14103C	**Railfreight (Coal)** 360711 black+yellow - *90?*	6	8
14103D	**Railfreight Distribution** 361579 black+ yellow - *90?*	6	8

W8. 12T Tank Wagon (ex-Mainline)
13801	**Shell Electrical Oils** 3102 yellow - *88*	6	8
13801	**Shell Electrical Oils** 2443 yellow - *88*	6	8
13802	**Esso Petroleum** 3060 silver - *88*	6	8

W9. 12T Fruit Van (ex-Mainline)
13601	**GWR** 134287 dark grey - *89*	6	8
13602	**BR** W134281 brown - *89*	6	8

W10. 12T Ventilated Van (ex-Mainline)
13611	**GWR** 134065 dark grey - *89*	6	8
13612	**BR** 142051 brown - *89*	6	8

W11. GWR 20T Toad Brake Van (ex-Mainline)
13551	**GWR** 58759 dark grey Worcester - *89*	6	8

W12. BR 20T Standard Brake Van (ex-Mainline)
13501	**BR Railfreight** B954978 grey+red - *87?*	5	7
13502	**BR** DB951968 Depart grey+yellow - *87?*	5	7
13503	**BR** B954603 brown+yellow air-piped - *87?*	5	7
13504	**BR Railfreight** B954835 grey+red air-piped yellow flash - *87?*	5	7

Rivarossi H0 (British)

HISTORY

Rivarossi were an Italian company which later became part of the Lima Group. They had a good reputation for the quality of their models which found a large market in America.

Along with a number of other Continental manufacturers, Rivarossi decided, in 1977, to attempt to break into the British market. Failing to understand the importance of the scale difference between 00 and H0, they produced their launch models in the Continental H0 scale. The British market was almost completely 00 and so the models appeared too small alongside their British equivalents. Had they chosen 00 scale from the outset, they could have caused quite an upset. Instead, they withdrew and their stock of British H0 models took many years to clear. Some were still in their catalogue in 1988.

LOCOMOTIVES

This was announced at the 1977 Nuremberg Fair but did not arrive until two years later.

It was made to mixed scales. The height and width were 1:80 scale and the length was 1:84 scale. However, the diameter of the wheels was 1:87 scale

Cat.No.	Company, Number, Colour, Dates	£	£

L1. Royal Scot Class 4-6-0
These were parallel boiler Scots. Only 'Hector' had smoke deflectors.

1348	**6100 'Royal Scot'** maroon LMS - *78-80?*	30	50
1350	**6140 'Hector'** maroon LMS - *79?-80?*	40	60

COACHES

The coaches announced at the 1977 Nuremberg Fair were of a later Stanier design, looking like Hornby Dublo coaches, but the coaches that arrived in 1979 were earlier Reid panelled stock. All were stated to be used in the Royal Scot train formation.

The 1st class coach was identified as being of 1928 build and we know that only 16 of that seating arrangement were made and not all were identical to the model.

The coaches came with two clip-in corridor end boards and replacement plug-in tension-lock couplings.

Cat.No.	Number, Company, Colour, Dates	£	£

C1. Corridor Vestibule 1st

2932	**LMS** 15604 maroon - *79-80?*	NPG	NPG
2933	**LMS** 15933 maroon - *79-80?*	15	25

C2. Brake Corridor 3rd

2934	**16100** maroon LMS - *79-80?*	15	25

C3. Corridor 3rd

2935	**LMS** 14299 maroon - *79-80?*	15	25
2936	**LMS** 14520 maroon - *79-80?*	15	25

SETS

Only one set was made and this is a hard item to find. It consequently fetches as much as £230 in unused condition. The set contained 'Royal Scot and four LMS coaches.

Rovex Tri-ang Hornby

This section includes the model railway range started by **Rovex** in 1950, renamed **Tri-ang Railways** in 1952, again renamed in 1965 as **Tri-ang Hornby**, becoming **Hornby Railways** in 1972 and finally just **Hornby** around 1997. While the name changed several times, it remained one continuous system being made first at Richmond, then at Margate and now in China. It does not include Hornby Trains (0 gauge) or Hornby Dublo both of which were made in Liverpool by Meccano Ltd until train production there ceased in 1964.

HISTORY

Rovex Plastics Ltd was founded in 1946 by Alexander Venetzian who made toys for Marks & Spencer's. Venetzian was asked to produce an electric train set based on the LMS express locomotive 'Princess Elizabeth'. Needing more space for this project the Company was moved from Chelsea to a disused brewery in Richmond. The train set was delivered in time for Christmas 1950 but financial limitations prevented further development.

Meanwhile, the giant toy manufacturer Lines Bros. Ltd, who traded under the name 'Tri-ang', was wanting to get into the post war model railway market. In 1951, Rovex Plastics Ltd. became a wholly owned member of the Lines Bros. Group. The trains would now be called Tri-ang Railways and the Company renamed Rovex Scale Models Ltd. To aid development of the system, a brand new factory was built at Margate, in Kent, and production moved there in the Summer of 1954.

Demand from the public for new models was so great that in 1951 Rovex bought the tools of a goods train set made by Pyramid Toys Ltd. which they were selling under the name Trackmaster. This gave them an 0-6-2 tank engine, with a diecast body, and two wagons.

By farming out work to outside designers and tool makers progress was made. The Jinty 0-6-0T and a range of station buildings came in 1952 and a guards van and other wagons in 1953.

Almost immediately there was pressure on the young firm to produce for the export market and the first of a range of Transcontinental models, primarily for North America, was released in 1954.

Under constant pressure, the system expanded fast. 1955 saw the first real Tri-ang Railways retail catalogue which soon became the best in the UK. By 1956 there were 10

locomotives available and a good range of rolling stock and lineside buildings etc. As if the existing pressure was not enough, in 1957 Rovex were pressed by Lines Bros. to start a TT gauge model railway system. A completely new 00 track system called Series 3 also arrived that year.

At around this time, in order to overcome trade tariffs, Lines Bros. Ltd. were expanding toy production overseas and Tri-ang Railways was soon being made in South Africa, Australia and New Zealand; in each case for local markets but creating interesting variations for future collectors.

1962 was a high water mark in the development of Tri-ang Railways. That year another new track system called Super 4 was introduced and along with it an extensive new series of station buildings.

There were now 25 locomotives to choose from (including two historical subjects), an extensive range of British and Transcontinental rolling stock, new scale length coaches had just been added, there was a catenary system, locos had Magnadhesion and smoke and the famous railway artist, Terence Cuneo, had been engaged to show how you could 'weather' your Tri-ang models.

Much of this growth was at the expense of other manufacturers and the two main rival systems, Trix and Hornby-Dublo, were feeling the draught. The former had already changed hands twice and in 1964, Meccano Ltd, the manufacturers of Hornby-Dublo, invited Lines Bros. Ltd to buy them out. Meccano Ltd. joined the Lines Bros. Group.

By this time, production of Hornby-Dublo had already ceased but there were large stocks to clear. Under public pressure it was agreed to retain the Hornby name by renaming Tri-ang Railways, 'Tri-ang Hornby'. This was presented at the time as an amalgamation of the two systems but the only additions this brought to the Tri-ang system were the E3000 (after extensive modification) and, for a brief period, the terminus station kit.

It is interesting to note that Lines Bros. were also invited to buy both Trix and Lone Star Treble-0-Lectric! On both occasions they declined.

Another subsidiary of Lines Bros., G&R Wrenn Ltd., put in a bid for the Hornby-Dublo tools and these were used to launch Tri-ang Wrenn in 1967. They also took over remaining stocks of Hornby-Dublo and Tri-ang Railways TT. Lines Bros. Ltd were under pressure to get into N gauge but chose instead to import the Lima system which they marketed through G&R Wrenn Ltd.

The Tri-ang Hornby period will be best remembered for the change to blue liveries for modern stock, the introduction of pre-

Milestones
1946 Venetzian founds Rovex Plastics Ltd.
1949 Pyramid Toys launch Trackmaster set.
1950 First Rovex train set in an M&S store.
1951 Lines Bros. buy Rovex Plastics Ltd.
1951 Trackmaster tools purchased by Lines.
1952 Tri-ang Railways launched in May.
1953 Renamed Rovex Scale Models Ltd.
1954 Move to purpose-built factory in Margate.
1954 Launch of Transcontinental Series.
1955 Production starts up in South Africa.
1956 First New Zealand made models in shops.
1956 Polystyrene replaces cellulose acetate.
1957 Australian production starts at Moldex Ltd.
1957 Launch of Tri-ang TT.
1959 Tension-lock couplings introduced.
1961 Tri-ang factory opens in Calais.
1961 Walter Lines retires.
1962 Major expansion of range including introduction of Super 4 track.
1963 Rovex absorb Real Estate kits and re-launch as Model-Land.
1964 Lines Bros. take-over Meccano Ltd.
1964 Lines turn down LoneStar buyout invite.
1965 Tri-ang Railways becomes Tri-ang Hornby.
1966 Lines Bros. turn down Trix buyout invite.
1966 Tri-ang Big Big 0 gauge trains launched.
1966 Rovex absorb Frog kit production.
1967 First models made for ATT of USA.
1967 Internal mergers form Rovex Industries Ltd.
1967 Rovex absorb Minic Motorway.
1969 Name changed again to Rovex Tri-ang Ltd.
1970 Finer scale adopted for track and wheels.
1971 Lines Bros. in receivership.
1972 Rovex bought by Dunbee-Combex-Marx.
1972 Tri-ang Hornby becomes Hornby Railways
1972 Death of Walter Lines.
1974 Tampo printing starts at Margate.
1976 Rovex International formed to export.
1976 Hornby Hobbies name first used.
1976 Hornby face Airfix/Mainline challenge.
1977 Frog and Big Big tools sent to Russia.
1979 H&M purchased and later absorbed.
1979 Hornby live-steam 'Rocket' in shops.
1980 DCM liquidates. Rovex in receivership.
1980 Paint finish adopted throughout range.
1980 Renamed Hornby Hobbies Ltd.
1981 Management buyout by Wiltminster Ltd.
1986 Hornby Group plc floatation.
1995 First model made by Sandakan in China.
1996 Hornby buy tools from Dapol Ltd.
1997 First former Aifix/Dapol model in shops.
1997 Hornby Collectors Club formed.
1998 Hornby Collectors Centres established.
1999 Last model made in the Margate factory.
2000 Hornby plc. invite buyers; later withdrawn.
2000 Rebuilt Merchant Navy released.
2001 Hogwarts Express released.
2003 Hornby announce record profits.
2003 Live Steam arrives
2004 Special 50th Edition Catalogue released.

Rovex Tri-ang Hornby

Nationalisation liveries for steam locomotives, the disappearance of the Transcontinental range, the appearance of Battle Space and the introduction of exhaust noise. Memorable locomotives of this period include E3000, Hymek, Class 37, M7, Hall, 'Flying Scotsman', Coronation and, of course, 'Evening Star'. Around 1970 Tri-ang Hornby went 'finescale' with a new track system and re-profiled wheels.

In 1967, Rovex Scale Models Ltd. had become the core of Rovex Industries Ltd. which was called the 'model division' and included Minic Ltd., Minimodels Ltd., Spot-On Ltd., Pedigree Dolls Ltd. and IMA Ltd. (Frog). It also had under its wing G&R Wrenn Ltd which was not a fully owned company. The division was renamed Rovex Tri-ang Ltd. in 1969.

Amongst other things, losses overseas saw the giant Lines Bros. Group in trouble. At their peak they had 40 companies world-wide. In 1971 the crash came when Lines Bros. Ltd called in the Receiver. The Group was broken up and sold off. The profitable Rovex Tri-ang Ltd was for a brief period called Pocket Money Toys Ltd and then sold as Rovex Ltd, with its factories at Margate and Canterbury, to Dunbee Combex Marx Ltd. (DCM). At this point it parted company with G&R Wrenn which had bought itself free and renamed its system Wrenn Railways. The name Tri-ang had been sold with one of the other companies and so a new name was required for the Tri-ang Hornby system. 'Hornby Railways' was chosen and this took effect from January 1972.

The 1970s saw new challenges come from Airfix and Palitoy who both launched model railway systems that offered finer scale models. This and pressure from Lima forced Rovex Ltd to raise its standards. There was steady development of new locomotives (over 20 in all) including the A4, Footballer, King, Patriot and Duchess. New diesels included the HST which was to become a major money spinner. There was also a new range of regional coaches as well as BR Mk3s and these would serve the system for many years.

In 1980 DCM were in trouble and the ball was in the air once again. Hornby Hobbies Ltd., as it was now called, became an independent company through a management buyout, with the help of venture capital. On 29 October 1986, Hornby Group plc was floated on the Unlisted Securities Market and became a public company. By now both the GMR (Airfix) and Mainline (Palitoy) systems had ceased to be produced and this led to a new player, Dapol, entering the field and Lima getting a stronger toehold.

Changes taking place on British Railways brought new liveries thus offering more subjects to model. The demand for higher standards of modelling lead to a number of models being retooled and a search for ways to improve printing on models. In 1996, Hornby Hobbies purchased a number of tools from Dapol including several formerly used for the Airfix GMR system.

During 2004, Hornby made a bid for the Lima Group which, besides Lima, includes Rivarossi, Arnold, Pocher and Jouef. At the time of going to press the bid is being considered by an Italian court and there is a possibility that business could be concluded as early as the autumn of 2004 and certainly by the New Year. It is understood that the purchase would include all the tooling, trademarks and other intellectual assets of the group but will not include the group's debts. It is Hornby's intention to transfer production to China.

Today, the privatised railways have brought a further rash of new liveries. Hornby Hobbies now has its models made by Sanda Kan in China and is gradually upgrading its range. Competition comes from Bachmann, using upgraded Mainline tools as well as new quality tooling, and from Heljan of Denmark who only recently entered the UK 00 model diesel market.

2004 also saw Hornby's friendly purchase of Spain's leading model railway manufacturer, Electrotren, and a start made on transferring its production to China. If the Lima deal goes through, Hornby will own the leading model railway companies in Britain, Italy, Spain and France as well as companies in Germany and an important export business to America. It will also move from being a model maker solely in 00 gauge to one also producing H0 and N gauge.

Hornby Hobbies recognises the important collectors' market and have established the Hornby Collectors Club and a chain of Collectors Centres. Now called just 'Hornby', it justifiably retains the position it has held for the last 40 years as Britain's leading model railway system.

Further Reading

If you are interested in further study of this model railway system, we recommend that you read 'The Rovex Story' by Pat Hammond. So far, three volumes have been published by New Cavendish Books. These are 'Volume 1 - Tri-ang Railways' (ISBN 0904568571), which covers the story from 1950 to 1965, 'Volume 2 - Tri-ang Hornby' (ISBN 1872727581) which covers the period 1965 to 1971 and 'Volume 3 - Hornby Railways' (ISBN 1904562000) which takes the story from 1972 up to 1996. A briefer history of the Hornby name from 1920 to the present day will be found in Ian Harrison's book 'Hornby - The Official Illustrated History' published by Harper Collins (ISBN 000715173X)

Collectors Clubs

We would also like to recommend the Tri-ang Society which caters for collectors of a wide range of Tri-ang toy products. The Society has a quarterly newsletter, called Tri-ang Telegraph, which contains a number of original articles by well known collectors. Details of the Tri-ang Society may be obtained from the Miles Rowland on Tel: 0161 9765059. Tri-ang Railways and Tri-ang Hornby are also usually well covered in the magazine of the Train Collectors Society (details at the front of the book).

As indicated above, Hornby Hobbies sponsor their own Collectors Club which publishes a full colour bimonthly magazine, called The Hornby Collector, which includes news of latest releases and regular profiles of models from the past. Further information about this organisation may be obtained from Fiona Baulard-Cato on Tel: 01223 208308 or from the Hornby Website at: http://www.hornby.com

Overseas Models - Many Tri-ang models were made in Australia, New Zealand and South Africa for local distribution but only British made models are listed here.

'R' Numbers - These are catalogue numbers. The additional ones are for the tender (steam engines) or dummy unit (multiple units) when sold separately. In the early 1970s, with the introduction of computers, it became necessary to bring 'R' numbers up to three digits and this was done by adding one or two noughts before those numbers less than '100'. Thus, R52 became R052.

'R' Numbers in Brackets - These are used where the correct part number for a model from a train set or pack is not known. The

number in the brackets is that for the set or pack from which the model comes.

Dates - Wherever possible, in this chapter, with models made after 1971, we have given you the years in which we understand that the models were actually made and it should be remembered that models often appeared in the catalogue after production had ceased in order to clear slow moving stock. Where production dates were unavailable (post 1999) we have provided the years the model appeared in the catalogue. By this time it was usual for only one batch to be made and if, for example, the dates given are 01-03 then the models would almost certainly have been made in 2001 but remained in the catalogue until 2003 to clear stocks.

Listing - The locos are listed in order of size starting with tank engines followed by tender locos and ending with diesels, electrics and multiple units. The coaches are listed with pre-Nationalisation stock first followed by vehicles of later years. Wagons are listed in the order of: flats, planked open wagons, steel sided wagons, hoppers, grain and bulk powder carriers, tankers, vans, brake vans and bogie stock.

Packaging - The very early Tri-ang Railways was sold in dark red boxes and these are popular with collectors adding about 30%-50% to the value of boxed items.

Couplings - Couplings provide a useful way of dating stock. The original rolling stock consisted of a pair of coaches made by Rovex Plastics Ltd for the Princess Elizabeth train set and some 7-plank open wagons and closed vans acquired from Trackmaster. These both had their own type of non-universal hook and loop couplings (a hook at one end and a loop at the other). The first Tri-ang couplings were a universal automatic coupler which had a large triangular hook and a bar (MkIIa). A vertical bar attached to the hook could be forced up by a ramp set in the track to effect an automatic uncoupling. In 1954 a skid-like lump was put on the bottom of this vertical bar to add weight to the hook to stop it sticking. This altered design is known as the MkIIb. In 1959 this coupling was replaced by the tension-lock coupling (MkIII) which had the bar fixed at both ends and a finer hook which actually gripped the bar of the adjoining coupling. This became the standard British design, adopted by other manufacturers, but during its production in the Margate factory it underwent evolution resulting in a number of minor variations which can be used to date rolling stock.

Rolling Stock Wheels - These changed over the years roughly according to the following order: split plastic sleeve axle with open axle boxes (1952-63), plastic wheels on steel pin-point axles (1963-1974) and all plastic axles and wheels (1974-present day). White rims first appeared in 1971 and have been used at various times, on certain items. Metal tyres (originally known as Silver Seal wheels) were introduced in 1974 and became standard for many years. Models, when transferred to the

Silver Seal range were given a new 'R' number although only the wheels were different (when considering these as another variation, bear in mind that wheels are easily exchanged). There is currently a move back to steel axles and metal wheels.

LOCOMOTIVES

'Noise' - refers to a tender fitted device which created a 'chuff-chuff'' sound.

Code 3 Models - There are a number of excellently renumbered and renamed Hornby models which have been done for shops, in batches, professionally, outside the factory. These normally have etched metal nameplates but have not been included in this section.

Loco Search by Running Number
In order to help you find your locomotive we have listed below, in the left column, the numbers that appear on the side of models (running numbers) and, in the right column, the number of the table(s) in which you will find the model.

Loco Search							
06003	L60	7	L3	101	L14		
06005	L60	7	L2	101	L52		
06008	L60	7	L2	102	L14		
08096	L61b	7	L5	103	L50c		
08201	L61b	7	LP6	103	L14		
08500	L61b	7	LP7	104	L14		
08523	L61b	8	L4	105	L3		
08531	L61b	8	L9	112	L2		
08568	L61b	8	L3	123	L24		
08633	L61b	8	L2	156	L16		
08642	L61b	8	L9	157	L16		
08661	L61b	C8	L34A	196	L16		
08673	L61b	8	L60	205	L2		
08810	L61b	8	LP7	222	L29		
08828	L61b	9	L4	245	L7		
08830	L61b	9	L5	249	L7		
08896	L61b	9	L3	254	LP6		
08933	L61b	11	L13	256	LP6		
08938	L61b	13	L13	270	L2		
09	L5	17	L61b	300	L55a		
1	L61b	21	L3	302	L60		
1	L3	21C101	L52a	303	L52		
1	L51a	21C110	L52b	313	L2		
1	LP6	21C119	L52a	328	L7		
1	LP7	21C123	L525b	359	L29		
2	L3	21C151	L52a	501	LT7		
2	L11	21C155	L52	503	LT7		
2	LP8	21C157	L52a	579	L27		
3	L58	21C164	L52a	627	L2		
3	L2	21C164	L52b	634	L27		
3	L13	21C165	L52a	644	L27		
3	L41b	21C166	L52a	645	L27		
4	L3	21C170	L52a	690	L26		
4	L2	23	L3	709	L3		
4	L60	23	L5	748	L5		
4	LP7	27	L4	795	L45		
4	LP8	34	L3	900	L31		
4	L5	36	L3	903	L31		
4	L50b	40	L5	905	L31		
5	L58	43	L5	907	L31		
5	L8	44	L27	914	L31		
5	L5	45	L3	921	L31		
5	LP7	45	L27	926	L31		
5	LP8	49	L16	928	L31		
5	L4	60	L34	930	L31		
6	L3	61	L50b	934	L31		
6	L2	83	L13	936	L31		
6	L60	94	L50c	1000	L28		
6	LP7	99	L3	1004	L39		
7	L4	100	L16	1006	L39		
		101	L42	1010	L39		

Dating Models by Couplings

IIa - old Tri-ang large hook and bar type 52-54.

IIb - as IIa but skid at bottom of uncoupling bar 54-58.

IIIa - modern tension lock coupling with black stud hinge and hole at back of coupling 58-62?

IIIb - as IIIa but no hole 59-62.

IIIc - as IIIb but eyelet instead of stud 62-69.

IIId - as IIIc but larger hook 67-79.

IIIe - re-profiled hook to effect closer coupling 79-85

IIIf - plastic coupling bar with profiled hook 86-95

IIIg - as IIIf but hook stem straight again 95-

Note that on some later models, the plastic coupling bar is an extension of the chassis or bogie moulding.

The most recent models from Hornby have a new small coupling some of which are clipped into a NEM socket

1015	L39	2865	L56	5071	L38	6237	L49a	25555	L36	37424	L66
1020	L39	2866	L44	5073	L38	6241	L49	27000	L73	37518	L66
1022	L39	2869	L56	5074	L38	6242	L48b	27002	L73	37677	L66
1026	L39	2918	L37	5097	L38	6244	L49a	27006	L73	37688	L66
1029	L39	2920	L37	5112	L41a	6245	L49a	30027	L7	37885	L66
1203	L5	2927	L37	5138	L41a	6253	L49a	30111	L7	37937	L66
1226	L11	2937	L37	5156	L41a	6818	L35a	30902	L31	40610	L27
1241	L11	3000	LT4	5158	L41a	6862	L35a	30908	L31	40634	L27
1247	L11	3015	L86b	5241	L41b	6869	L35a	30911	L31	41043	L28
1404	LT3	3016	L86b	5379	L41b	6922	L36	30912	L31	42202	L64
1410	L6	3021	L86b	5514	L42	7005	LT4	30925	L31	42305	L21a
1419	L6	3022	L86b	5533	L42	7005	L38	30927	L31	42308	L21a
1421	L6	3046	L23	5539	L42	7025	L38	30935	L31	42310	L21a
1427	L6	3111	L11	5541	L42	7028	L38	31018	LT7	42319	L21a
1432	L6	3211	L86a	5771	LP4	7178	L4	31027	LT7	42322	L21b
1444	L6	3212	L86a	5934	L36	7321	LP3	31110	L64a	42355	L21b
1445	L6	3219	L86b	5955	L36	7476	L43	31270	L64a	42356	L21b
1458	L6	3306	L86b	5972	L38	7503	LT6	31757	L30	42363	L21a
1470	L6	3400	LT7	6000	L40b	7553	LT4	32635	L13	43002	L67
1472	L6	3403	LT7	6002	L40c	7606	L10	32636	L13	43003	L67
1520	L61a	3775	L33	6005	L40b	7675	L55b	32640	L13	43010	L67
1542	LT1	3821	L25	6006	L40b	7744	LP3	32670	L13	43011	L67
1730	L18	3824	L25	6008	L40b	8006	L16	33009	L34A	43046	L67
1757	L30	3825	L25	6009	L40b	8027	L55a	33037	L34A	43050	L67
1760	L50c	3828	L25	6010	L40b	8035	L55a	34029	L52a	43051	L67
1763	L18	3830	L25	6013	L40b	8042	L55b	34037	L52b	43058	L67
1863	LP3	3973	L61b	6014	L40b	8118	L55a	34041	L52b	43059	L67
1863	LP5	3975	L11	6018	L40b	8193	L55a	34051	L52a	43063	L67
2021	L10	3980	L11	6024	L40a	8233	L55a	34051	L52b	43065	L67
2300	L21a	4008	LT3	6026	L40b	8400	L20	34054	L52a	43066	L67
2301	L21a	4086	L38	6027	L40b	8453	L55b	34061	L52b	43072	L67
2305	L21b	4093	L38	6028	L40c	8473	L12	34067	L52b	43080	L67
2309	L21a	4097	L38	6029	L40c	8474	L12	34070	L52b	43086	L67
2311	L21b	4098	L38	6042	LP3	8477	L12	34074	L52b	43090	L67
2312	L21a	4418	L34	6105	L19	8479	L12	34076	L52a	43092	L67
2322	L32	4466	L51a	6113	L19	8481	L12	34081	L52b	43093	L67
2335	LT1	4468	L51a	6119	L19	8504	L43	34083	L52b	43102	L67
2341	L21b	4468	L51d	6121	L19	8509	L43	34085	L52a	43117	L67
2345	L21a	4468	L51b	6124	L63	8510	L55b	34091	L52b	43118	L67
2468	L32	4468	L51c	6132	L19	8537	L43	35005	L53	43124	L67
2500	L50e	4469	L51a	6134	L19	8544	L43	35012	L53	43128	L67
2505	L50c	4472	L50a	6142	L63	8546	L43	35016	L53	43141	L67
2509	L51a	4472	L50b	6147	L19	8572	L43	35020	L53	43142	L67
2509	L51c	4472	L50c	6150	L19	8578	L43	35021	L53	43154	L67
2510	L51b	4472	L50d	6156	L19	8579	L43	35022	L53	43193	L67
2511	L51b	4476	L50b	6167	L19	8733	L9	35023	L53	43620	L33
2512	L51a	4482	L51a	6200	L46	8751	L9	35025	L53	43775	L33
2526	L32	4485	L51a	6200	L47a	8773	L9	35027	L53	44313	L34
2571	LP3	4495	L51c	6201	L46	9003	LT7	35028	L53	44331	L34
2579	L32	4498	L51a	6201	L47a	9828	L12	35029	L53	44447	L34
2606	L5	4657	L41a	6201	L47b	9832	L12	37042	L66	44523	L34
2730	L8	4718	LP4	6204	L46	11232	L1	37047	L66	44781	L41c
2744	L8	4744	L18	6206	L47a	11250	L1	37063	L66	44808	L41b
2747	L8	4749	L18	6207	L47b	13002	L61a	37071	L66	44871	L41b
2751	L50c	4753	L18	6208	L47a	13005	L61a	37072	L66	44932	L41b
2753	L29	4830	LT2	6210	L46	13012	L61b	37073	L66	45021	L41a
2759	L8	4901	L51d	6210	L47a	14010	L24	37130	L66	45156	L41a
2761	L8	4902	L51a	6211	L47a	16020	L2	37166	L66	45158	L41a
2771	L8	4902	L51c	6212	L46	16023	L2	37167	L66	45192	L41a
2776	L8	4903	L51	6220	L49	16030	L2	37174	L66	45253	L41c
2783	L8	4916	L36	6221	L49a	16031	L2	37187	L66	45292	L41b
2788	L8	4930	L36	6221	L49b	16032	L2	37198	L66	45422	L41b
2799	L8	4983	L36	6222	L49	16440	L20	37202	L66	44454	L34
2821	L56	5000	L41c	6223	L49b	25033	L62	37203	L66	44666	L41c
2844	L56	5004	L38	6224	L49a	25052	L62	37207	L66	44668	L41c
2848	L44	5007	LT4	6225	L49b	25054	L62	37216	L66	44762	L41c
2857	L44	5007	LT5	6228	L49	25056	L62	37248	L66	44781	L41c
2857	L56	5029	L38	6229	L49b	25071	L62	37293	L66	44908	L41c
2859	L44	5038	L38	6230	L49b	25078	L62	37298	L66	44924	L34
2859	L56	5042	L38	6233	L48a	25218	L62	37371	L66	45253	L41c
2861	L56	5053	L38	6233	L48b	25241	L62	37405	L66	45455	L41c
2862	L44	5055	L41c	6234	L48a	25247	L62	37410	L66	45515	L42
2864	L44	5069	L38	6235	L49b	25550	L4	37416	L66	45519	L42

45537	L42	47586	L68	56109	L70	61651	L44	86242	L75	92203	L57c
46200	L46	47606	L10	56113	L70	61654	L44	86243	L75	92207	L57b
46201	L46	47613	L68	56118	L70	61656	L44	86245	L75	92212	L57b
46201	L47a	47620	L68	56119	L70	61661	L44	86246	L75	92215	L57a
46201	L47b	47711	L68	56123	L70	61662	L44	86255	L75	92220	L57
46203	L47b	47712	L68	56127	L70	61663	L44	86261	L75	92222	L57b
46204	L47a	47716	L68	56131	L70	61652	L44	86401	L75	92231	L57b
46205	L46	47722	L68	57317	L83	61663	L44	86405	L75	92239	L57c
46208	L47a	47741	L68	57325	L83	61664	L44	86414	L75	92239	L57a
46209	L47a	47805	L68	57344	L83	61665	L44	86417	L75	92241	L57b
46210	L47a	47807	L68	58001	L71	61672	L44	86417	L75	92099	L57
46212	L47b	47808	L68	58002	L71	62700	L29	86419	L75	142013	L82
46221	L48a	47814	L68	58005	L71	62750	L29	86419	L75	142015	L82
46224	L48a	47816	L68	58006	L71	62758	L29	86426	L75	142020	L82
46225	L48a	47822	L68	58007	L71	64875	L87	86431	L75	142023	L82
46225	L48b	47839	L68	58008	L71	64899	L87	86504	L75	142048	L82
46226	L48a	47841	L68	58021	L71	64899	L87	86602	L75	142065	L82
46228	L48b	47845	L68	58023	L71	68049	L16	86631	L75	142069	L82
46230	L48a	47853	L68	58024	L71	68062	L16	90001	L76	142074	L82
46231	L48a	47854	L68	58025	L71	68071	L16	90012	L76	155317	L83
46232	L48a	48119	L55b	58027	L71	68074	L16	90014	L76	155325	L83
46236	L48a	48141	L55a	58030	L71	68075	L16	90015	L76	155344	L83
46237	L48a	48142	LT4	58033	L71	68080	L16	90018	L76	253001	L67
46239	L48a	48154	L55b	58034	L71	68450	L12	90020	L76	253005	L67
46239	L48b	48278	L55a	58037	L71	68463	L12	90024	L76	253028	L67
46244	L48b	48705	L55a	58039	L71	68472	L12	90028	L76	253036	L67
46245	L48b	48758	L55a	58041	L71	68474	L12	90029	L76	370001	L85
46247	L48a	48773	L55b	58042	L71	68478	L12	90030	L76	370002	L85
46247	L48a	48774	L55a	58044	L71	68846	L11	90033	L76	466016	L87
46248	L48a	50002	L68A	58046	L71	69506	L18	90034	L76	466020	L87
46250	L48a	50007	L68A	58047	L71	69522	L18	90037	L76	466035	L87
46251	L48a	50018	L68A	58048	L71	69546	L18	90039	L76	919799	L77
46251	L48b	50031	L68A	58050	L71	69561	L17	90040	L76	A5	L60
46252	L48a	50035	L68A	58051	L71	70000	L54	90042	L76	D261	LP7
46255	L48a	50037	L68A	60006	L51a	70004	L13b	90128	L76	D1008	L69
46400	L35	50045	L68A	60007	L51b	70006	L54	90130	L76	D1013	L69
46521	L35	51218	L1	60008	L51c	70010	L54a	90131	L76	D1035	L69
47079	L68	51222	L78	60009	L51b	70012	L54b	90135	L76	D1039	L69
47085	L68	51231	L1	60010	L51a	70013	L54a	91001	L77	D1058	L69
47120	L68	51232	L1	60012	L51b	70014	L54	91001	L77	D1062	L69
47124	L68	51235	L78	60014	L51b	70018	L54c	91003	L77	D1670	L68
47156	L68	52317	L83	60017	L51b	70021	L54b	91003	L77	D1738	L68
47170	L68	52325	L83	60019	L51	70023	L54b	91004	L77	D2412	L60
47207	L68	52344	L83	60020	L51a	70025	L54c	91008	L77	D2424	L60
47231	L68	55554	L82	60021	L51a	70028	L54b	91009	L77	D2428	L60
47234	L68	55556	L82	60022	L51a	70030	L54	91010	L77	D2907	L59
47237	L68	55564	L82	60024	L51b	70032	L54b	91011	L77	D3010	L61b
47270	L68	55589	L82	60026	L51a	70034	L54b	91014	L77	D3035	L61a
47285	L68	55604	L82	60028	L51a	70038	L54b	91019	L77	D5177	L62
47301	L68	55606	L82	60029	L51a	70040	L54c	91022	L77	D5200	L62
47311	L68	55614	L82	60030	L51b	70042	L54b	91025	L77	D5206	L62
47345	L68	55639	L82	60031	L51b	70046	L54b	91026	L77	D5512	L64a
47353	L68	55715	L82	60031	L51d	70047	L54a	91031	L77	D5572	L64
47376	L68	55761	L82	60034	L51b	70050	L54b	91129	L77	D5578	L64
47378	L68	55742	L82	60046	L50c	70052	L54b	92000	L57	D6103	L63
47406	L68	55770	L82	60048	L50c	70054	L54c	92001	L57b	D6110	L63
47409	L68	56010	L2	60052	L50b	78327	L87	92001	L78	D6119	L63
47421	L68	56025	L2	60061	L50b	78351	L87	92009	L78	D6129	L63
47432	L68	56038	L2	60071	L50b	82004	L20	92020	L78	D6130	L63
47458	L20	56047	L70	60075	L50b	86102	L75	92022	L78	D6137	L63
47473	L68	56048	L70	60077	L50e	86210	L75	92026	L78	D6713	L66
47480	L20	56049	L70	60080	L50b	86213	L75	92031	L78	D6721	L66
47483	L68	56058	L70	60085	L50c	86218	L75	92045	L78	D6736	L66
47487	L68	56059	L70	60092	L50c	86219	L75	92099	L57c	D6796	L66
47501	L68	56066	L70	60103	L50b	86220	L75	92108	L57c	D6830	L66
47541	L68	56068	L70	60106	L50c	86225	L75	92134	L57c	D7046	L65
47549	L20	56088	L70	60110	L50c	86227	L75	92139	L57c	D7063	L65
47556	L20	56098	L70	61520	L43	86228	L75	92151	L57c	D7067	L65
47568	L68	56099	L70	61553	L43	86233	L75	92156	L57c	D7093	L65
47573	L68	56100	L70	61565	L43	86235	L75	92158	L57c	D7097	L65
47576	L68	56101	L70	61572	L43	86236	L75	92166	L57a	D7568	L62
47579	L68	56105	L70	61649	L44	86237	L75	92183	L57a	D7571	L62
47583	L68	56107	L70	61650	L44	86241	L75	92200	L57a	D7581	L62

D7596	L62	E51834	L81	L90	L9
D7596	L62	E51840	L81	M79079	L79
D7597	L62	E51844	L81	M79628	L79
DC230	L76	E51846	L81	M79629	L79
E112	L50c	E52066	L81	M79632	L79
E1664	L44	E52073	L81	S1052S	L84
E3001	L74	E52078	L81	S1057S	L84
E27000	L73	E52080	L81	T336	LT4
E51812	L81	E52085	L81	TR20071	L58
E51815	L81	E59695	L81	W2	L13
E51816	L81	E59707	L81	W11	L13
E51819	L81	E59708	L81	W12	L13
E51824	L81	E59814	L81	W60095	L80
E51827	L81	E59816	L81	W60745	L80
E51829	L81	GM12	LT10	W60747	L80
E51832	L81	H2000	L2		

Cat.No.	Number, Company, Colour, Dates	£	£

Tank Locomotives

L1. Class 0F L&Y Pug 0-4-0ST (ex-Dapol)

R2065	**11232** LMS plain black - *98-99*	25	30
R2065A	**11250** LMS plain black - *00-02*	25	32
R2093A	**51218** BRb plain black - *99*	25	30
R2093B	**51222** BRb plain black - *99*	25	30
R2093C	**51235** BRb plain black - *00-02*	25	32
R2335	**51231** BRb plain black weathered - *03*	25	35
R2335A	**51232** BRb plain black weathered - *03*	25	35

L2. Class 0F Caledonian Pug 0-4-0ST

R057	**270** CR blue - *80-81*	15	25
R2361	**270** CR dark blue Sp Edn (HRCC) - *03*	15	25
R255	**8 'Loch Ness'** HR blue - *88-93*	15	22
R072	**6 'Ben-Y-Gloe'** HR blue - *94-00*	15	22
R161	**3** William Mansfield blue - *86-87*	20	NA
R214	**7** Powergen light blue - *94-97*	15	20
R782	**56025 'Smokey Joe'** BR black - *83-05*	12	26
R150	**627** LYR black - *86-92*	18	25
R300	**16023** LMS black - *92-98*	15	20
R770	**16032** LMS black Sp Edn 480 (Beatties) - *83*	30	45
R266	**16020 'Monty'** LMS black - *90*	22	28
R337	**16030** LMS black - *95-98*	17	22
R2049	**56038** BRa black Sp Edn (HCC) - *97*	18	30
X?	**56010** BRc black in R1017 set - *99-02*	15	NA
R159	**313 'Robbie Burns'** MR maroon ex-set - *86-87*	18	NA
R152	**16031** LMS maroon ex-set - *90-94*	20	NA
R2150	**H2000** maroon Ltd Edn (Millennium Collectors Edition) - *00*	15	25
R779	**7 'Desmond'** red - *81-83*	18	25
R?	**1 'Hornby USM Debut December 1986'** red Sp Edn 34? (Hornby Share Launch Debut) - *86*	120	NPG
R752	**205** Stewart & Lloyds brown - *83-85*	20	28
R750	**205** Stewart & Lloyds brown Sp Edn 260 (Grattans) - *83*	NPG	NPG
R174	**4** Huntley & Palmer brown - *85*	25	30
R162	**112** NCB yellow - *84*	20	28

Class of Caledonian Pug [L2]

L3. Class 101 Holden Tank 0-4-0T

A blue 'Forest of Pendle MRS' Holden 0-4-0T is Code 3, the transfers having been put on an R796 tank by the Society. 150 were made. pf = paint finish. npf = non-paint finish.

R077	**101** Great Western green, npf - *78-80*	10	18
R099	**99** CIE green, npf - *79*	40	NA
R2130	**9** CIE green - *99-02*	18	22
R333	**101** Great Western green, pf - *80-81*	15	25
R173	**101** (GWR 150) 1985 green - *85*	25	35
R794	**4** H.A.R.Wood green - *91-92*	20	25
R758	**6 'Northern Nellie'** blue -*83*	20	25
R796	**2** Crewe & District blue - *91-92*	20	25
R759	**7 'Southern Connie'** yellow - *84*	18	25
R759?	**7 'Connie'** yellow - *84*	20	25
R155	**21** Colman's yellow, npf - *84-85*	18	NA
R155	**21** Colman's yellow, pf - *84-85*	25	NA
R760	**8 'Polly'** red - *83*	18	25
R336	**36 'Roger'** red - *82-84*	20	NA
R766	**1 'Super S'** red - *84-85*	20	NA
R2129	**105** red - *99-02*	15	22
R781	**34 'Terry'** orange - *83*	15	22
R163	**45** Ford white - *84-85*	20	30
R153	**1** Tolgus Tin Co. grey - *86-88*	20	25
R795	**6** Lion Works black - *91-92*	25	28
R854	**23 'Sentinel'** maroon - *96-98*	15	25
R2263	Lynne & Co. Collieries blue - *02-04*	15	26
R2304	**101** GWR green Sp Edn (HCC) - *02*	25	30
(R1035)	**709** LSWR light brown ex-R1035 set - *03-04*	18	NA
R2430	**Hornby** red - *04*	18	25

Industrial tank [L4]

L4. Industrial Tank 0-4-0T (Freelance)

R355B	**6, 7 'Nellie'** blue - *60-68*	20	48
R355	**6, 7, 9 'Connie'** blue - *60-62?*	35	65
R?	BRb black - *61-62*	40	60
R?	BRc black - *c65*	40	60
R?	black (no decals) - *?*	20	NA
R355B	**6 'Connie'** deeper blue ex-set - *72-73*	35	NA
R355B	**7 'Nellie'** deeper blue - *71-72*	30	60
R255	**7178** blue with gold or yellow lining - *76-78*	20	40
R255	**7178** blue with white lining - *76*	60	NPG
R355Y	**6 or 8 'Connie'** yellow - *63-65*	50	80
R?	**7 'Nellie'** yellow - *?*	65	NPG
R355R	**6 or 9 'Polly'** red - *63-70*	25	55
R455	**25550** red, chrome dome - *73-75*	25	40
R455	**25550** red, no chrome dome - *73-75*	30	45
R355G	**27** shades of green - *70-72*	20	60

L5. Class D 0-4-0T

R531	**40 'King George V'** red - *91-92*	12	18
R863	**43 'Queen Mary'** red - *92-97*	10	NA
R058	**Hornby** red - *93-97*	10	NA
R153	**5** ER red - *94-99*	15	20
R069	**23** Hensall Sand blue - *93*	15	20
R063	British Toy & Hobby Association 50th Anniversary blue Sp Edn 300 - *94*	45	60
R2058	**7** BRb blue - *98*	20	25
R2131	**1203** CR blue - *99-02*	15	20

R068	**5** NCB grey - *93-94*	15	20
R066	Hornby grey - *93*	20	NA
R856	**9** BRa green - *96-97*	10	NA
R368	**40 'King George V '** green - *95-96*	12	18
R066	Hornby yellow - *93-98*	10	15
R2245	**4** BRa black, Hornby Club model - *01*	18	35
X?	**2606** LNER black ex-R1030 set - *02-03*	15	NA
R2264	**09** Southern black - *02-04*	15	26
R2189	**LMS** maroon ex-R1031+R1027 sets - *02-04*	15	25

Class D 0-4-0T [L5]

More 0-4-0 tanks will be found under 'PLAY LOCOMOTIVES' later on in this section.

L6.   Class 14XX 0-4-2T (ex-Airfix)

Some Hornby Class 14XXs have been renumbered after leaving the factory. These may be listed in the Code 3 section at the back of the book.

R2026	**1458** GWR green - *97-98*	25	35
R2026A	**1472** GWR green - *98*	25	35
R2026B	**1427** GWR green - *00-01*	30	42
R2026C	**1444** GWR green - *00-01*	30	42
R2026D	**1410** GWR green - *03*	30	42
R2095A	**1421** BRc green - *99-01*	30	42
R2095B	**1470** BRc green - *99-01*	30	42
R2095C	**1445** BRc green - *01-02*	30	42
R2173	**1432** BRc green, train pack with 2 coaches Ltd + Sp Edn 1,250 - *00*	NA	60
(R2173)	**1432** BRc green - *00*	40	NA
R2381	**1419** BRb plain green - *04*	NPG	46

L7.   Class M7 Tank 0-4-4T

npf = non-painted finish

R754	**30027** BRc black, npf, fire glow - *67-70*	50	75
R862	**30111** BRc black - *87-88*	50	75
R868	**328** SR bright green, npf, fire glow - *69-70*	35	65
R868	**328** Southern bright green, npf - *71*	35	65
R868	**245** Southern dark green, npf - *72-75*	35	65
R103	**249** Southern olive - *85-86*	55	80

L8.   Class 2721 0-6-0PT (open cab)

Versions of this model made from 2001 onwards had much improved detail.

R59	**2744** Great Western green - *81-84*	20	28
R165	**2783** Great Western green - *89-96*	20	28
R760	**2776** Great Western green - *96-98*	20	28
R760A	**2783** Great Western green - *99*	25	30
R760B	**2730** Great Western green - *00*	25	30
R2198	**2771** GWR green - *01*	30	35
R2198A	**2759** GWR green - *02*	NPG	38
R2328	**2799** GWR green - *03*	25	36
R2328A	**2759** GWR green - *04*	NPG	36
(R1037)	**2761** GWR green, ex-R1037 set - *03-04*	25	NA
R2006	**2788** Great Western green ex-R1000 set - *96-02*	20	NA
R158	**2747** Great Western black - *85-88*	35	50
R073	**5** red with a coat of arms - *93*	25	35

L9.   Class 57XX Pannier Tank 0-6-0PT

npf = non-painted finish.

R51S/R051	**8751** GWR green gloss, npf, smoke - *71-74*	18	30
R041	**8751** GWR green, npf, no smoke - *75-80*	18	30
R300	**8773** GWR green - *80-81*	22	35
R048	**L90** London Transport ex-set red - *78*	30	NA
R382	**8** GWR bright green with face - *see Thomas section*	-	-

L10a.   Class 3F 'Jinty' Tank 0-6-0T (1952 model)

This model was also made in New Zealand and Australia from a different body tool. This usually has a lamp mounted on the smokebox.   s-tw = see-through wheels (gaps between spokes)

R52	BRa unlined black - *53*	100	150
R52	**47606** BRb unlined black - *53-57*	10	30
R52	**47606** BRb lined black - *57-59*	20	45
R52	**47606** BRc lined black - *59-64*	15	40
R52/R52S	**47606** BRc lined black s-tw, - *64-74*	20	40
R52/R52S	**47606** BRc lined black, cream logos, s-tw - *72*	30	50
R757	**2021** LMS lined black s-tw, - *73*	25	NA
R52RS/ R52AS	**7606** LMS maroon, s-tw, with smoke unit - *70-73*	25	35
R452	**7606** LMS maroon, s-tw - *73-74*	25	35
R377S	GN&SR brown, s-tw, ex-Ltd Edn RS615 Railway Children set - *70-72*	60	NA
R558S	Battle Space khaki, s-tw - *66-67*	50	NA

Original model of a class 3F 'Jinty' 0-6-0T [L10a]

L10b.   Class 3F 'Jinty' Tank 0-6-0T (1978 model)

With cab interior. npf = non-paint finish

R052	**16440** LMS maroon npf - *78-79*	25	30
R301	**16440** LMS maroon - *80-89*	30	35
R058	**47458** BRc black - *78-79*	25	30
R302	**47480** BRc black - *80-86*	30	35
R053	**47556** BRc black - *88-91*	35	40
R130	**8400** LNER green - *88-89*	30	NA

L11.   Class J13/J52 0-6-0ST

R396	**1247** GNR green - *81-82*	30	45
R2186A	**1241** GNR green - *00-03*	28	33
R2186B	**1226** GNR green - *00-03*	28	33
R861	**3980** LNER black - *87-88*	35	55
R504	**3111** LNER black - *92-93*	35	50
R186	**68846** BRc black - *92-94*	30	45
R2274	**68846** BRc black - *02-03*	35	45
R2400	**3975** LNER plain black - *04*	28	38
R2401	**No.2** BRb plain weathered black - *04*	30	38

L12.   Class J83 0-6-0T

R252	**8477** LNER gloss green no lines - *76-77*	18	25
R252	**8477** LNER matt green no lines - *77-78*	18	25
R316	**8473** LNER green no red lining - *94-98*	25	35
R2164A	**8481** LNER green - *00-02*	22	30
R2164B	**8477** LNER green - *00-02*	22	30
X?	**8474** LNER green ex-R1030 - *02-03*	25	NA
R2325	**9832** LNER lined black - *03*	25	35
R2325A	**9828** LNER lined black - *04*	25	35
R722	**68472** BRa green - *95-96*	23	NA
R2155A	**68474** BRb black - *00-01*	22	30
R2155B	**68463** BRb black - *00-01*	22	30
R2155C	**68478** BRb black - *01-02*	22	30

R2324	**68450** BR weathered black - *03*	28	35
R2384	**68474** BRb lined black - *04*	25	35

L13.   Class A1X 'Terrier' Tank 0-6-0T (ex-Dapol)

R2063	**W2 'Freshwater'** SR green - *98*	35	45
R2100A	**W11** SR green - *99-01*	30	40
R2100B	**W12** SR green - *00-02*	30	40
R2407	**13 'Carisbrooke'** SR malachite - *04*	NPG	45
R2165A	**32670** BRc black - *00-03*	32	40
R2165B	**32636** BRc black - *00-04*	32	45
R2165C	**32640** BRc black - *01*	32	42
R2177	**54 'Waddon'** LBSC pale brown Ltd Edn 1000 (HCC) - *00*	35	45
R2190	**83 'Earlswood'** LBSC pale brown - *01*	35	42
R2406	**32635 'Brighton Works'** BR pale brown - *04*	35	45
R2216	**3 'Bodiam'** Kent & East Sussex Railway dark blue - *01-02*	35	42

L14.   Class E2 Tank 0-6-0T

npf = non paint finish

R353	**100** LBSC brown npf - *79*	30	45
R315	**100** LBSC brown - *80*	30	45
R261	**104, (101, 102, 103)** Southern olive, alternative number transfers - *82-84*	40	50
R157	**103** Southern black - *85*	50	60

L15.   Class S Saddle Tank 0-6-0ST (Freelance)

R153	**748** BRb black - *56-58*	30	50
R151	**748** BRb black c/w - *57-58*	35	75
R153	**748** BRc black - *59-61*	25	50
R255	TR black+green c/w - *59-58*	30	75

Class S saddle tank [L15]

L16.   Class J94 'Austerity' 0-6-0ST (ex-Dapol)

Fitted with a type 7 motor. Some Hornby Class J94s have been renumbered/named after leaving the factory. These may be listed in the Code 3 section at the back of the book.

R2062	**8006** LNER black - *98*	35	45
R2094A	**68049** BRc black - *99*	35	45
R2094B	**68062** BRc black - *99*	35	45
R2094C	**68080** BRc black - *00-02*	35	45
R2145	**68075** BRb black Sp Edn 500 (HCC) - *00*	35	45
R2326	**68074** BRb black - *03-04*	35	45
R2380	**68071** BRb plain black weathered - *04*	NPG	45
R2151	**157** LMR blue Sp Edn (HCC) - *99-00*	35	45
R2151A	**196** LMR blue - *01-02*	35	45
R2251B	**156 'McMurdo'** LMR blue - *02-03*	35	45
R2096	**'Harry'** NCB red - *99-01*	35	45
R2212	**'Whiston'** NCB Bold Colliery green - *01*	35	45
R2281	**'Joseph'** NCB light green - *02-04*	35	45
R2327	**'Peter'** NCB light green - *03*	35	45
R2399	**49** NCB bright green - *04*	35	45

L17.   Class N2 Tank 0-6-2T (ex-Trackmaster)

The original Trackmaster model was sold in its own packaging by Pyramid Toys.

-	**69561** BRa black Trackmaster - *49-51*	35	95
R51	**69561** BRa black - *51-53*	45	110
R51	**69561** BRb black - *53-54*	55	125

L18.   Class N2 Tank 0-6-2T (ex-Airfix)

5-pole motor. W = weathered.

R2178A	**69546** BRc lined black - *00-01*	35	45
R2178B	**69506** BRc lined black - *00-02*	35	45
R2214A	**1763** GNR green - *01-03*	35	45
R2214B	**1730** GNR green - *01-04*	35	45
R2251	**4744** LNER W lined black - *02-04*	35	45
R2251	**4749** LNER W lined black - *not made*	NA	NA
R2269	**4753** LNER lined black - *02-04*	35	45
(R1029)	**69522** BRb lined black from R1029 set - *02-03*	35	NA

L19.   Class 61XX Prairie Tank 2-6-2T (ex-Airfix)

Some Hornby Class 61XXs have been re-sprayed and renumbered after leaving the factory. These may be listed in the Code 3 section at the back of the book.

R2098	**6113** Great Western green - *99*	35	45
R2098A	**6147** Great Western green - *00-01*	35	45
R2098B	**6105** Great Western green - *02*	35	46
R2098C	**?** Great Western green - *02-03*	35	46
R2098D	**6121** Great Western green - *03*	35	46
R2098E	**6119** Great Western green - *04*	NPG	54
R2143	**6150** Great Western green Ltd Edn 1000 - *99*	40	46
R2213A	**6156** BRb black - *01*	40	50
R2213B	**6134** BRb black - *01-03*	40	50
R2357A	**6167** BRc lined green - *03-04*	35	50
R2357B	**6132** BRc lined green - *04*	NPG	50

L20.   Class 3 Standard Tank 2-6-2T

s-tw = see-through wheels (gaps between spokes)

R59	**82004** BRb lined black - *56-58*	30	75
R59	**82004** BRc black - *59*	30	75
R59	**82004** BRc green - *60*	30	75
R59	**82004** BRc green, s-tw - *61-66, 69-72*	25	65
R59	**82004** BRc green, nickel tyres, s-tw - *72*	50	100

L21a.   Class 4P Tank 2-6-4T (1980 model)

The chassis was modified in 1992.

R055	**2300** LMS maroon - *80-81*	30	40
R505	**2312** LMS maroon - *92-95*	35	40
R261	**2301** LMS maroon - *94-95*	30	40
R299	**2309** LMS maroon - *96-98*	30	40
R088	**2345** LMS lined black - *84-85*	50	65
R062	**42308** BRc lined black + alt. nos. **42305, 42310, 42319** - *82-84*	35	50
R239	**42363** BRb lined black - *92-95*	35	45

Class 4P 2-6-4 tank [L21a]

L21b.   Class 4P Tank 2-6-4T (2002 model)

Super detailed model with a new chassis and 5-pole motor. W = weathered

R2224	**2305** LMS maroon - *not made*	NA	NA
R2224	**2311** LMS maroon - *03-04*	45	60
R2223	**42356** BRb black - *not made*	NA	NA
R2223	**42355** BRb lined black - *03-04*	45	60
R2287	**42322** BRb lined black weathered - *03-04*	45	60
R2397	**2341** LMS plain black - *04*	NPG	64
R2398	**42322** BRa plain black - *04*	NPG	64

Tender Locomotives

L22.   'Rocket' 0-2-2

The locomotive comes with two crew in period costume. These are sometimes missing and, if so, this greatly reduces the value of the model.

R651S+ R652	**'Rocket'** L&MR yellow + smoke - *63*	45	130

R346	**'Rocket'** L&MR yellow + smoke + 1 coach - *64-66*	60	135
R651+ R652	**'Rocket'** L&MR yellow no smoke + 3 coaches - *68-69*	65	150
R796	**'Rocket'** L&MR yellow + 3 coaches train pack - *82-84*	NA	150
R?	**'Rocket'** L&MR yellow ex-train pack nickel tyres - *82-84*	60	NA
R771	**'Rocket'** L&MR yellow + 3 coaches train pack (made for France) - *83-84*	NA	200

L23. Dean Single 4-2-2

R354+ R37	**3046 'Lord of the Isles'** Great() Western matt green - *61-65,67*	25	85
R354	**3046 'Lord of the Isles'** Great() Western gloss green - *70-74*	30	85
R795	**3046 'Lord of the Isles'** Great() Western green, tampo printed splasher, + 3 coaches - *81-82*	NA	135
R049	**3046 'Lord of the Isles'** Great() Western green, tampo printed splashers, ex-R795 pack - *81-82*	65	NA

L24. 'Caledonian Single' 4-2-2

R553+ R554	**123** CR matt blue - *63-66*	55	100
R553	**123** CR gloss blue - *71-74*	60	85
R763	**14010** LMS maroon - *83*	40	65
R765	**14010** LMS maroon Sp Edn 400 (Grattans) - *83*	40	90

L25. Class 38XX 'Churchward County' 4-4-0
Great()Western green

R392	**3821 'County of Bedford'** - *81-84*	45	60
R390	**3830 'County of Oxford'** - *84-85*	45	65
R584	**3825 'County of Denbigh'** - *91*	40	55
R298	**3828 'County of Hereford'** Ltd Edn 2000 - *91*	50	70
R125	**3824 'County of Cornwall'** - *94-95*	40	55

L26. Class 2P 4-4-0 (ex-Tri-ang L1)

R450	**690** LMS lined black - *73-74*	25	45

'Tri-ang Southern L1 model converted into an LMS 2P [L26]

L27. Class 2P 4-4-0 (ex-Mainline)

R2099A	**579** LMS lined black - *99-01*	40	54
R2099B	**645** LMS lined black - *99*	40	40
R2099C	**644** LMS lined black - *00-04*	40	54
R2183A	**40610** BRa lined black - *00-04*	40	54
R2183B	**40634** BRa lined black - *00-04*	40	54
R2172	**634** LMS black + 3 coaches train pack Sp Edn 1250 (Kays) - *00*	45	80
R2217	**44** S&DJR very dark blue - *01*	45	57
R2217A	**46** S&DJR very dark blue - *02-04*	NPG	60

L28. Class 4P Compound 4-4-0

R376	**1000** LMS maroon - *81-82*	40	60
R755	LMS Sp Edn 300 - *82*	NPG	NPG
R355	**1000** MR maroon - *83-85*	40	60
R175	**41043** BRa black - *86-87*	40	68

L29. Class D49/1 'Shire/Hunt' 4-4-0
LNER green

R378	**2753 'Cheshire'** - *81-82*	45	60
R859	**359 'The Fitzwilliam'** - *88-89*	40	55
R123	**222 'The Berkeley'** - *94-95*	40	55

BR black

R259	**62700 'Yorkshire'** BRb - *82-84*	55	70
R860	**62750 'The Pytchley'** BRb - *88-89*	45	60
R2021	**62758 'The Cattistock'** BRc - *97-98*	45	60

L30. Class L1 4-4-0

R350+R36	**31757** BRc green - *60-67*	55	80
R350	**1757** Southern dark green - *71-72*	45	75

L31. Class V 'Schools' 4-4-0

Many Hornby Schools have been renumbered/renamed after leaving the factory. These may be listed in the Code 3 section at the back of the book. RD = presentation pack with Royal Dalton plate.

Southern

R380	**928 'Stowe'** malachite - *81-82*	50	70
R583	**921 'Shrewsbury'** malachite - *91-92*	40	60
R648	**905 'Tonbridge'** malachite RD Ltd Edn 3000 - *96*	60	90
R2018	**930 'Radley'** malachite - *97-98*	45	60
R2124	**907 'Dulwich'** malachite - *99-00*	45	60
R2144	**914 'Eastbourne'** malachite Sp Edn 1000 (Collectors Centre) - *00*	45	60
R683	**926 'Repton'** olive - *83-84*	55	70
R817	**900 'Eton'** olive, sometimes without smoke deflectors - *86-87*	45	60
R057	**903 'Charterhouse'** olive - *89-90*	40	60
R533	**934 'St. Lawrence'** olive Ltd Edn 2000 - *92*	55	70
R132	**936 'Cranleigh'** olive - *94-95*	40	60

British Railways

R257	**30911 'Dover'** BRc green - *82-83*	70	110
R317	**30908 'Westminster'** BRc green - *96*	45	60
R2082	**30902 'Wellington'** BRc green + 3 coaches pack Sp Edn 1500 (Kays) - *98*	70	100
R2181	**30935 'Sevenoaks'** BRc green - *00-01*	60	75
R084	**30927 'Clifton'** BRb black - *84-85*	65	90
R2039	**30925 'Cheltenham'** BRb black Sp Edn 1000 (Cheltenham MC) - *97*	40	55
R2079	**30912 'Downside'** BRc black + 3 Pullman train pack Ltd Edn 2000 - *98*	90	120

The pre-production model of Schools Class 'Stowe' [L31]

L32. Class 2301 'Dean Goods' 0-6-0 (ex-Airfix)

R2064	**2468** Great Western green - *98-00*	35	45
R2064A	**2322** Great Western green - *99*	35	45
R2064B	**2526** Great Western green Ltd Edn 500 (HCC) - *99*	50	60
R2064C	**2579** Great Western green - *00-01*	38	50
R2210	**2579** BRb lined black - *01*	40	50
R2275	**2322** BRb plain black - *02-04*	NPG	50

L33. Class 3F (Deeley/Johnson) 0-6-0

R251+ R33	**43775** BRc black - *58-66*	40	75
R661S	**43775** BRc weathered black - *65*	80	NA
R251	**43620** BRc maroon - *not made*	NA	NA
R251	**3775** MR maroon - *66-67*	40	70

L34. Class 4F Fowler 0-6-0 (ex-Airfix)

R2066	**44331** BRc black - *98*	30	35
R2135M	**44313** BRc black, yellow stripe - *99-00*	35	40
R2138	**44523** BRb black + 6 wagons train pack Sp Edn 1000 (A.B.Gee) - *99*	40	70
R2148	**60** S&DJR dark blue Ltd Edn 1000 (Collectors Centres) - *00*	45	60
R2193	**4418** LMS plain black - *01*	40	45
R2276	**44447** BRb plain black - *02-04*	NPG	50
R2276A	**44454** BRb plain black - *03-04*	NPG	50
R2396	**44924** BRa plain black - *04*	NPG	50

L34A. Class Q1 0-6-0

R2343	**C8** SR plain black - *03-04*	NPG	60
R2343A	**?** SR plain black - *04*	NPG	60
R2344	**33009** BRc plain black - *not made*	NA	NA
R2344	**33009** BRc weathered black - *03-04*	NPG	60
R2344A	**?** BRc weathered black - *04*	NPG	60
R2355	**33037** BRb weathered black - *not made*	NA	NA
R2355	**33037** BRb plain black - *03-04*	NPG	60
R2355A	**?** BRb plain black - *04*	NPG	60

L35. Class 2 'Ivatt' 2-6-0

R857	**46400** BRc black - *75-77*	30	45
R852	**46521** BRc green - *78-79*	30	50

L35A. Class 68XX 'Grange' 4-6-0

DCC ready, NEM coupling pockets, 5-pole skew drive.

R2402	**6818** GWR green - *04*	NPG	90
R2403	**6862** BRb green - *04*	NPG	90
R2404	**6869** BRc green weathered - *04*	NPG	90

L36. Class 49XX 'Hall' 4-6-0

R759	**4983 'Albert Hall'** BRc green - *66-69*	35	60
R759G, R759N, R759A	**4983 'Albert Hall'** Great()Western gloss green, alternative names, with or without noise or nickel wheels - *70-72*	25	50
-	**4916 'Crumlin Hall', 6922 'Burton' Hall', 5955 'Garth Hall'** alt names for R759G, R759N + R759A - *70-72*	45	NA
R759	**4983 'Albert Hall'** Great()Western gloss green + sound - *73-76*	25	45
R759	**4983 'Albert Hall'** Great()Western wax green + sound - *77*	25	45
R761	**5934 'Kneller Hall'** Great()Western green - *78-79*	28	45
R313	**4930 'Hagley Hall'** Great()Western green - *80-83*	30	50
R765	**25555 'Lord Westwood'** red - *73-75*	25	55
R?	**25555 'Lord White'** red - *not made*	NA	NA

Class 49XX Hall 'Lord Westwood' [L36]

L37. Class 29XX 'Saint' 4-6-0

Adapted from the Tri-ang Hornby Hall

The Tri-ang Hornby Hall Class model was converted into a saint Class [L37]

R380	**2937 'Clevedon Court'** BRb black - *88-91*	40	50
R830	**2920 'Saint David'** Great()Western green - *86-87*	40	55
R141	**2918 'Saint Catherine'** Great()Western green - *94-95*	45	60
R2019	**2927 'Saint Patrick'** G()W green - *97-98*	40	55

L38. Class 4073 'Castle' 4-6-0 (ex-Dapol)

Unless otherwise indicated, all models had the Hawksworth tender. Some Hornby Castles have been renumbered/renamed after leaving the factory. These may be listed in the Code 3 section at the back of the book. st = step sided tender, dc = double chimney. hb = headboard.

R2024	**5042 'Winchester Castle'** BRb green train pack with 3 coaches - *97-98*	70	90
R2086	**5053 'Earl Cairns'** BRb green - *98-01*	50	60
R2088	**5097 'Sarum Castle'** BRa green Sp Edn 1000 (Beatties) - *98*	60	80
R2090	**5004 'Llanstephen Castle'** BRb green train pack with 3 coaches Ltd Edn 2000 - *99*	70	90
R2133M	**7025 'Sudeley Castle'** BRb green train pack with 3 coaches Sp Edn 1000 (Kays) - *99*	80	100
R2141	**5069 'Isambard Kingdom Brunel'** BRb green Sp Edn 1000 (A.B.Gee) - *99*	60	80
R2196M	**5029 'Nunney Castle'** GWR button grn, st, train pack with 3 coaches Sp Edn 1500 - *01*	60	80
R2232	**4097 'Kenilworth Castle'** Great () Western green, st - *01-02*	60	80
R2280	**5073 'Blenheim'** BRc green, dc, st - *02*	NPG	80
R2317	**4093 'Dunster Castle'** Great()Western green st - *03*	NPG	82
R2318	**5071 'Spitfire'** BRc green dc st - *03*	NPG	85
R2364M	**5038 'Morlais Castle'** BRb green, hb, st Torbay Express Ltd Edn 1500 train pack with 3 brown+cream Mk1s - *03*	NA	120
R2389	**4086 'Builth Castle'** Great () Western green st - *03-04*	NPG	85
(R1048)	**7028 'Cadbury Castle'** BRc green ex-R1048 set - *04*	NPG	NA
R2424	**5074 'Hampden'** BRc green st dc - *04*	NPG	85
R?	**7005 'Sir Edward Elgar'** BR green + coaches Sp Edn 1,000 (Hereford Models) - *04*	NA	120
	'Hogwarts Express'		
R2284	**5972 'Hogwarts Castle'** red, hb, st in Pilosopher's Stone packaging - *01-02*	60	70
R2337	**5972 'Hogwarts Castle'** as above but Chamber of Secrets packaging - *03*	NPG	70
R2378	**5972 'Hogwarts Castle'** as above but Prisoner of Azkaban packaging - *04*	NPG	70
R2301	**5972 'Hogwarts Castle'** red as above but gold plated metal, st - *01*	120	220

L39. Class 1000 'County' 4-6-0 (ex-Dapol)

dc = double chimney

R2025	**1004 'County of Somerset'** G()W green train pack with 3 coaches - *97-98*	70	110
R2085	**1029 'County of Worcester'** G()W green - *98*	55	70
R2166	**1006 'County of Cornwall'** BRc green + 3 coaches train pack Ltd Edn 2000 - *00*	70	100
R2211	**1020 'County of Monmouth'** BRc green, dc - *01*	60	80
R2097	**1015 'County of Gloucester'** BRb black - *99-00*	55	70
R2174	**1022 'County of Northampton'** BRb black Sp Edn 1500 (Kays) - *00*	55	75
R2391	**1010 'County of Carnarvon'** G()W green - *04*	NPG	85
R2392	**1026 'County of Salop'** BRc green dc - *04*	NPG	85

L40a. 'King' Class 6000 4-6-0 (1978 model)

On this model, the boiler was not undercut.

R78	**6024 'King Edward I'** Great()Western green, npf - *78-80*	25	40

L40b. 'King' Class 6000 4-6-0 (1980 model)

The boiler was now undercut. Some Hornby Kings have been renumbered/renamed after leaving the factory. These may be listed in the Code 3 section at the back of the book. npf = non paint finish. dc = double chimney. RD = presentation pack with Royal Dalton plate.

Great (crest) Western green

R349	6013 **'King Henry VIII'** - 80-83	30	40
R070	6000 **'King George V'** ex-set - 85	35	NA
R292	6027 **'King Richard I'** - 88-91	40	55
R82	6008 **'King James II'** - 93-94	40	55
R650	6018 **'King Henry VI'** RD Ltd Edn 3000 - 96	45	60
R2022	6006 **'King George I'** - 97-98	40	55
R2119	6014 **'King Henry VII'** - 97-01	40	55
R303	6005 **'King George II'** BRc green, dc - 95-96	40	55
R845	6010 **'King Charles I'** BRc green ex-set, dc - 96-98	45	NA
R2077	6026 **'King John'** BRc green + 3 coaches train pack - 98	70	90
R2084M	6009 **'King Charles II'** BRa green train pack Sp Edn 1500 (Kays) - 98	45	100
R737	6000 **'King George V'** BRb blue, bell on front - 96-97	45	55

L40c. 'King' Class 6000 4-6-0 (2002 model)

This is the Super Detail model tooled-up in China but the motor is still in the tender. All have had blackened metalwork. dc = double chimney.

R2233	6029 **'King Stephen'** green Great () Western - 03	70	83
R2234	6002 **'King William IV'** green BRc, dc - 03-04	70	83
R2309	6028 **'King George VI'** blue BRb Ltd Edn 1000 (Collectors Centres) - 03	70	83
R2390	6028 **'King Henry II'** green Great () Western - 04	70	85

L41a. 'Black 5' Class 4-6-0 (1973 model)

Body has top feed but no dome. ovg = old valve gear (from Britannia).

R859	45192 BRc black, ovg, + alternative numbers and names - 73-75	25	50
-	45158 **'Glasgow Yeomanry'**, 45156 **'Ayrshire Yeomanry'** alternative numbers and names for R859 - 73-75	30	NA
R068	45021 BRc black Ltd Edn 2500 - 84	40	60
R061	5112 LMS black, ovg, + alternative numbers and names - 76	25	42
-	5158 **'Glasgow Yeomanry'**, 5156 **'Ayrshire Yeomanry'** alternative numbers and names for R061 - 76	30	NA
R840	5112 LMS black, + alternative numbers and names - 77-78	30	40
-	5158 **'Glasgow Yeomanry'**, 5156 **'Ayrshire Yeomanry'** alternative numbers and names for R840 - 77-78	35	NA
R320	5138 LMS black - 81-84	30	40
R842	4657 LMS maroon - 78-79	30	45

L41b. 'Black 5' Class 4-6-0 (1987 model)

New body with dome.

R314	44808, 44871,44932 BRc black - 90-91	30	40
R292	45422 BRc black - 96-97	35	45
R2081	45292 BRa lined black Ltd Edn 1500 (Littlewoods) - 98	45	70
R347	44932 BRc green Sp Edn 1500 (Kays) - 92	40	55
R858	5241 LMS black - 87-89	35	45
R2083M	5379 LMS black Sp Edn 1500 (Kays) - 98	50	70
R9049	3 green with face - see Thomas section	-	-

Black 5 special edition model [L41b]

L41c. 'Black 5' Class 4-6-0 (2002 model)

Retooled super detail model. DCC ready and 5-pole motor.

R2257	5055 LMS lined black - 02	55	75
R2323	5000 LMS lined black, NRM series - 03	65	75
R2258	44781 BRc black - not made	NA	NA
R2258	44781 BRc black - 02	55	75
R2360	44762 BRc weathered black - 02	55	75
R2250	45253 BRb weathered black - not made	NA	NA
R2250	45253 BRb lined black - 02	55	75
R2358	44908 BRb black - 02	55	75
R2321	45455 BRc plain black - 03-04	65	86
R2322	44668 BRb lined black - 03-04	65	86
R2382	44666 BRc lined black weathered - 04	NPG	86

L42. 'Patriot' Class 4-6-0

From 2000 this model had blackened metalwork.

R357	5541 **'Duke of Sutherland'** LMS maroon, non paint finish - 79	32	40
R311	5541 **'Duke of Sutherland'** LMS mrn - 80	35	45
R308	5533 **'Lord Rathmore'** LMS mrn - 95-97	35	50
R2182A	5539 **'E.C.Trench'** LMS maroon - 00-02	40	60
R2182B	5514 **'Holyhead'** LMS maroon - 00-02	40	60
R324	45519 **'Lady Godiva'** BRa black - 83	50	65
R578	45537 **'Private Sykes VC'** BRb green - 91	50	70
R2208	45515 **'Caernarvon'** BRc green - 01-02	45	65

L43. Class B12 4-6-0

smoke = smoke generator fitted. N = chuff-chuff sound fitted.

R150	61572 BRc black - 63-69	25	40
R150S	61572 BRc black, smoke - 64-69	30	45
R150SF	61572 BRc black, smoke Acho couplings - 67-70	70	150
R359S	61572 BRc black, smoke, kit - 68-69	NA	120
R150NS	61572 BRc black, smoke + N - 70-71	30	50
R2102A	61520 BRb lined black + N - 99	37	45
R2102B	61553 BRb lined black + N - 99	37	45
R2320	61520 BRb lined black + N - 03-04	NPG	55
R2134M	61565 BRc black + 3 coaches, Sp Edn 1500 (Kays) train pack - 99	80	100
R150	7476 NE black + N - 76-78	30	45
R150	8504 LNER matt green - ?	NPG	NPG
R866	8509 LNER matt green - ?	30	55
R866S	8509 LNER gloss green, smoke - 70	30	55
R359S	8509 LNER gloss green, smoke, kit - 70-71	NA	140
R866NS/ R866AS	8509 LNER green, smoke + N - 71-74	25	40
R866	8509 LNER matt green + N - 78-79	25	40
R284	8579 LNER fully lined green + N - 96-00	30	40
R?	8572 LNER fully lined green + N - ?	30	40
R2156A	8537 LNER fully lined green + N - 00-02	40	50
R2156B	8578 LNER fully lined green + N - 00-03	40	50
R2156C	8546 LNER fully lined green + N - 01-02	40	50
(R1032)	8544 LNER fully lined green + N Sp Edn (Woolworth) ex-set - 03	40	NA

Class B12 0-6-0 [L43]

L44. Class B17/4 4-6-0

R053	2862 **'Manchester United'** LNER green + sheet alt. names - 80-81	30	55
	2864 **'Liverpool'**, 2848 **'Arsenal'**, 2866 **'Nottingham Forest'** alternative names for R053 - 80-81	40	NA
R188	2848 **'Arsenal'** LNER green - 92	30	50
X3558	2862 **'Manchester United'** LNER green,	40	NA

X3607	green cylinders Sp Ed 1500 (Kays) - *97*		
R2056	**2857 'Doncaster Rovers'** LNER green - *98*	35	55
R2185	**2859 'Norwich City'** LNER green - *00-04*	55	70
R060	**61656 'Leeds United'** BRb green + sheet alt. names - *82-83*	45	70
	61663 'Everton', 61665 'Leicester City', 61672 'West Ham United' alternative names for R060 - *82-85*	40	NA
R133	**61663 'Everton'** BRc green - *94-95*	35	50
R315	**61662 'Manchester United'** BRc green - *96-97*	35	50
R2038A	**61650 'Grimsby Town'** BRb green Sp Edn 250 (Rails) - *97*	75	100
R2038B	**61654 'Sunderland'** BRb green Sp Edn 250 (Rails) - *97*	75	100
R2038C	**61651 'Derby County'** BRb green Sp Edn 250 (Rails) - *97*	75	100
R2038D	**61649 'Sheffield United'** BRb green Sp Edn 250 (Rails) - *97*	75	100
R2014	**61664 'Liverpool'** BRc green Ltd Edn 1000 - *97*	45	55
R2209	**61652 'Darlington'** BRb green - *01*	60	80
R2044	**E1664 'Liverpool'** BRa black + 3 coaches train pack Sp Edn 1500 (Kays) - *97*	55	80
R2273	**61663 'Everton'** BRc green - *02-04*	NPG	80
R2319	**61661 'Sheffield Wednesday'** BRa light green - *03-04*	NPG	80

L45. Class N15 'King Arthur' 4-6-0

R154	**795 'Sir Dinadan'** Southern gloss green - *76-77*	40	65
R154	**795 'Sir Dinadan'** Southern matt green - *78*	45	70

Class N15 King Arthur 'Sir Dinadan' [L45]

L46. 'Princess' Class (Short) 4-6-2

This model was also made in New Zealand and Australia using the earliest tools. gold = gold BRb logo on tender.

	46201 'Princess Elizabeth'		
R50+R30	BRb black, gold, roller pickups - *50*	2000	N/A
R50+R30	BRb black, gold, plunger pickups - *50-52*	20	50
R50+R30	BRb black, gold - *52-55*	15	50
R50+R30	BRb black, transfer logo - *55*	30	65
R50+R30	BRb black, transfers + lining - *55-58*	20	45
R50+R30	BRb black, transfer logo, red letters on black nameplate - *58*	80	95
R53+R31	BRb olive green, gold - *53*	30	50
R53+R31	BRb olive green, transfer logo - *54*	45	65
R53+R31	BRb olive green, transfers + lining - *54-56*	30	50
R53+R31	BRb green, transfers + lining - *56-57*	20	45
R53+R31	BRc green, transfers + lining, lacquered finish - *58-61*	25	60
R386	BRc green, CKD kit - *62-69*	N/A	180
	46205 'Princess Victoria'		
R50+R30	BRc black, transfers + lining - *59-62*	20	35
R050	BRb black, gold, mail order model - *74*	25	65
R053	BRb green, gold, mail order model - *74*	25	65
R048	BRb maroon, gold, mail order - *74*	100	NPG
-	BRb blue, gold - *not made*	NA	NA
R258+R34	**46200 'The Princess Royal'** BRc maroon, t+l - *59-64,69*	25	65
-	**46213 'Princess'** BRc blue - *not made*	NA	NA
R258	**6201 'Princess Elizabeth'** LMS maroon - *70-74*	25	35
R258NS			
	6204 'Princess Louise', 6210 'Lady	40	NA

	Patricia', 6212 'Duchess of Kent' alternative names for R258 - *70-72*		
R386	**6201 'Princess Elizabeth'** LMS maroon kit- *70?*	25	300
R386?	**6201 'The Princess Royal'** LMS maroon kit - *70*	NA	300
R260	details unknown Sp Edn 200 - *73*	NPG	NPG

L47a. 'Princess' Class 4-6-2 (1984 model)

This original scale model was a great improvement on the original Rovex Princess but was limited to dome-less examples thus preventing its use for Princesses in BR maroon livery. Some Hornby Princesses have been renumbered/renamed after leaving the factory. These may be listed in the Code 3 section at the back of the book.

R832	**6201 'Princess Elizabeth'** LMS maroon, maroon tender chassis - *86-87*	40	55
R084	**6201 'Princess Elizabeth'** LMS maroon, black tender chassis - *93-94*	40	55
R080	**46201 'Princess Elizabeth'** BRb green - *84-85*	40	60
R050	**6200 'The Princess Royal'** LMS maroon, Fowler tender - *84-85*	45	60
R2033	**6208 'Princess Helena Victoria'** LMS maroon + 3 coaches Ltd Edn 3000 train pack - *97*	70	90
R138	**46208 'Princess Helena Victoria'** BRb blue - *94-95*	45	60
R2052	**6211 'Queen Maud'** LMS maroon Sp Edn 1000 (A.B.Gee) - *98*	50	75
R2051	**6206 'Princess Marie Louise'** LMS black Sp Edn 1000 (A.B.Gee) - *98*	50	75
R2070	**46204 'Princess Louise'** BRb green Sp Edn 1000 (A.B.Gee) - *98*	50	75
R037	**46210 'Lady Patricia'** BRb blue - *89-91*	55	80
R375	**6210 'Lady Patricia'** LMS maroon Sp Edn 1000 (Kays) - *90*	55	75
R196	**46209 'Princess Beatrice'** BRb green - *92-93*	45	65

2nd version of a Princess 'The Princess Royal' [L47a]

L47b. 'Princess' Class 4-6-2 (2001 model)

This was the Super Detail model tooled-up in China and using the chassis from the scale length Coronation of 2000. A changeable mould allowed both domed and dome-less examples to be modelled. It is fitted with a loco mounted 5-pole motor.

R2225	**6207 'Princess Arthur of Connaught'** LMS maroon - *01-02*	65	85
R2226	**46203 'Princess Margaret Rose'** BRb green, domed boiler - *01-02*	65	85
R2215	**6201 'Princess Elizabeth'** maroon LMS gold plated Ltd Edn 5000 - *02*	75	100
R2313	**6204 'Princess Louise'** LMS mrn - *03-04*	70	89
R2314	**46212 'Duchess of Kent'** BRc green - *03*	70	89
(R1045)	**6201 'Princess Elizabeth'** LMS maroon ex-R1045 Sp Edn (M&S) - *03*	75	NA
R2426	**46201 'Princess Elizabeth'** BRb black Ltd Edn 2004 - *04*	NPG	90

L48a. 'Duchess' Class 4-6-2 (1977 model)

Many Hornby Duchesses have been renumbered/renamed after leaving the factory. These may be listed in the Code 3 section at the back of the book. npf = non paint finish. RD = presentation pack with Royal Dalton plate.

R066	**6233 'Duchess of Sutherland'** LMS maroon, npf - *77-80*	30	50
R305	**6234 'Duchess of Abercorn'** LMS maroon - *80-81*	45	70
R459	**6253 'City of St Albans'** LMS black RD Ltd Edn 3,000 - *96*	50	90

R372	**46231 'Duchess of Atholl'** BRb blue Sp Edn 1,500 (Kays) - *92*	65	90
R262	**46231 'Duchess of Atholl'** BRb green - *82-84*	40	65
	46232 'Duchess of Montrose', 46230 'Duchess of Buccleugh' alternative names and numbers for R262 - *82-84*	35	NA
R102	**46250 'City of Lichfield'** BRc green Sp Edn 2000 (Kays) - *91*	60	90
R221	**46252 'City of Leicester'** BRc green - *92-93*	40	75
R2015	**46255 'City of Hereford'** BRb green - *97*	40	75
R2112	**46237 'City of Bristol'** BRc green + 3 coaches, train pack - *99*	70	100
X?	**46236 'City of Bradford'** BRc green first with dark metalwork R1004 set - *99*	50	NA
R2176M	**46221 'Queen Elizabeth'** BRc green train pack with 3 coaches, Sp Edn 1500 (Kays) - *00-01*	60	110
R?	**'Queen Elizabeth'** gold plated metalwork - *02* NPG		150
R577	**46251 'City of Nottingham'** BRc maroon - *91-94*	45	60
R194	**46247 'City of Liverpool'** BRc maroon Sp Edn 1500 (Kays) - *94*	55	80
R2041	**46247 'City of Liverpool'** BRc maroon, red nameplates Sp Edn 1000 (Hattons) - *97*	45	70
R134	**46226 'Duchess of Norfolk'** BRc maroon - *94-95*	60	90
R2023	**46225 'Duchess of Gloucester'** BRc maroon - *97-98*	50	70
R2078	**46248 'City of Leeds'** BRc maroon + 3 coaches train pack - *98*	70	90
R208	**46239 'City of Chester'** BRb blue ex-R775 set - *94-95*	80	NA

L48b. 'Duchess' Class 4-6-2 (2002 model)

This was the completely retooled Super Detail model released in 2002 based on the fine detailed chassis from the Coronation Class model of 2001. It has a loco mounted 5-pole motor. SST = sloping smokebox top. HB = head board

R2230	**6230 'Duchess of Buccleuch'** LMS maroon - *02-03*	NPG	75
R2231	**46228 'Duchess of Rutland'** BRb green, SST - *02-04*	60	75
R2262	**46245 'City of London'** BRc maroon Sp Edn 1,000 (Collector Centres) - *02*	60	75
R2303M	**46224 'Princess Alexandra'** BRb blue SST HB + 3 coaches train pack Ltd Edn 1,500 (Mail Order) - *02*	NA	120
R2306	**46244 'King George V1'** BRb green + 3 Mk1s Ltd Edn 2,000 train pack - *03-04*	NA	120
R2311	**6242 'City of Glasgow'** LMS black SST - *03-04*	70	89
R2312	**46239 'City of Chester'** BRc green, red nameplates - *03-04*	70	89
R2383	**46251 'City of Nottingham'** BRc maroon - *04* NPG		90
R2370	**6233 'Duchess of Sutherland'** LMS maroon + 3 royal coaches - *04*	NPG	115
R2386	**46225 'Duchess of Gloucester'** BRb blue SST - *04*	NPG	90

'City of Nottingham' weathered [L48b]

L49a. 'Coronation' Class 4-6-2 (1970 model)

LMS 6220 'Coronation'

R864	gloss blue - *70-72*	30	75
-	**6221 'Queen Elizabeth', 6222 'Queen Mary', 6224 'Princess Alexandra'** alternative	35	NA

names for R864 - *70-72*

R685	matt blue - *83-85, 92-94*	40	60
R175	matt blue? Special 325 (B/P) - *94*	NA	70
R752	matt blue? Special 30 (QVC) - *94*	NA	120
	LMS 6244 'King George VI'		
R871	gloss maroon - *71-74*	35	65
	6228 'Duchess of Rutland', 6221 'Queen Elizabeth', 6241 'City of Edinburgh' alternative names for R871 - *71-72*	35	NA
R767	matt maroon Sp Edn 500 (Beatties) - *83*	55	80
R834	**6222 'Queen Mary'** LMS matt blue - *85-86*	50	80
R072	**6237 'City of Bristol'** LMS matt maroon - *85-86*	70	90
-	**6237 'The Stock Exchange'** LMS matt maroon, Sp Edn for Hornby USM Debut December 1986 - *86*	1000	1200
R2092	**6245 'City of London'** LMS matt black, Ltd Edn 1000 - *98*	60	90
	LMS 6221 'Queen Elizabeth'		
R2050	black listed for 1999 - *not made*	NA	NA
R2068	blue listed for 1999 - *not made*	NA	NA
R2087	maroon listed for 1999 - *not made*	NA	NA

Original Coronation model 'King George VI' [L49a]

L49b. 'Coronation' Class 4-6-2 (2001 scale length model)

This was a completely new model introduced in 2001. It has a loco mounted 5-pole motor. Some Hornby Coronations have been renumbered/renamed after leaving the factory. These may be listed in the Code 3 section at the back of the book.

R2179	**6229 'Duchess of Hamilton'** LMS maroon - *not made*	NA	NA
R2179	**6229 'Duchess of Gloucester'** LMS maroon - *01*	50	80
R2205	**6225 'City of Birmingham'** LMS maroon - *01-04*	65	80
R2206	**6220 'Coronation'** LMS blue - *01-02*	65	80
X?	**6220 'Coronation'** LMS maroon in R2199M train pack - *01*	65	NA
R2270	**6241 'City of Edinburgh'** LMS black - *02-04*	65	80
R2271	**6223 'Princess Alice'** LMS blue - *02-04*	65	80
R2285	**6221 'Queen Elizabeth'** LMS blue Sp Edn 500 (HCC) - *02*	70	84
(2371M)	**6224 'Princess Alexandra'** LMS blue ex-R2371M Coronation Scot train pack - *04*	70	84

L50a. Class A3 4-6-2 (1968 model)

This was the original Tri-ang Hornby model with the body as a single moulding and a banjo dome. ct = corridor tender. nct = non-corridor tender. npf = non-paint finish. N = chuff-chuff sound from tender. fsw = fine scale wheels

	LNER 4472 'Flying Scotsman'		
R855	light green, ct, npf - *68-70*	18	35
R855N	light green, N, ct, npf - *71-77*	20	35
R845	light green improv lining, ct, fsw, npf - *78-79*	30	40
R322	light green, ct, fsw, crew - *80*	30	40
	BRc 60103 'Flying Scotsman'		
R850	green, nct, npf, red nameplate - *68*	30	45
R850	green, nct, npf, black.nameplate - *69-70*	25	40
R850	green, ct, npf - *69-70*	30	45

L50b. Class A1/A3 4-6-2 (1981 model)

The model was virtually completely redesigned in time for release in 1981. this gave it wire handrails, daylight under the boiler, reshaped cab and (from 1993) a choice of domes, tenders, chimneys and the option of smoke deflectors. GN = Great Northern style tender (with rails round top). ct = corridor tender. nct = non-corridor tender. gsd = German smoke deflectors. rd = early round dome (all others have a banjo dome). dc = double chimney

Rovex Tri-ang Hornby

LNER 4472 'Flying Scotsman'

R398	light green, ct, rd - 81-04	22	40
R398	light green, ct, rd, silver hinges + handles - 96-02	25	45
R387	light green, simplified lining**, rd - 82-84	20	85
R074	light green, GN, rd - 93-94	30	55
R075	light green, 2 tenders (both green), rd, Ltd Edn 2800* - 93	60	150
R114	light green, 2 tenders (both green), rd, Sp Edn 2000 (GUS)* - 93	60	150
R098	light green, 2 tenders (one blue/grey) Ltd Edn 5000 - 95	50	90

60103 'Flying Scotsman'

R078	BRc green, nct, gsd, dc - 93-96	35	60
R080	BRc green, nct, gsd, dc, Sp Edn 200 (BCA) - 93	NA	120
R2020	BRb green, nct - 97-98	40	75
R375	**61 'Pretty Polly'** LNER light green, GN, Sp Edn 1000 (Beatties) - 95	45	80
R059	**60061 'Pretty Polly'** BRc green, GN, gsd, dc, Sp Edn 1000 (Beatties) - 94	70	95
R129	**60061 'Pretty Polly'** BRb blue, GN, Sp Edn 1000 (Beatties) - 95	50	75
R042	**4476 'Royal Lancer'** LNER light green, ct, rd - 89-90	30	55
R295	**60080 'Dick Turpin'** BRb green, GN - 95-97	40	65
R146	**60052 'Prince Palatine'** BRb blue, GN - 94-95	35	60
R140	**60071 'Tranquil'** BRa dark blue, GN, Sp Edn 1000 (Littlewoods) - 96	55	75
R2036	**60075 'St Frusquin'** BRa dark blue, GN, Sp Edn 1500 (Kays) - 97	40	65
R383	**4** blue with face - see Thomas section	-	-

* These were the same product but the GUS version had an extra outer protective box. They shared a number sequence for the certificates. ** The loco had no gold printing on the buffer beam, no boiler band next to the cab and no pen-line handrails on cab or tender. It was mostly used in the R547 and R548 train sets.

L50c. Class A1/A3 4-6-2 (1998 model)

This was the Super Detail version tooled-up in China and can be identified by a join-line along each side of the boiler and a finely detailed chassis. It came with a separate front coupling and dust shield and doors for the cab. brake rods and brake pipes were already fitted. Wheels and rods were of a finer profile. Many Hornby A3s have been renumbered/renamed after leaving the factory. These may be listed in the Code 3 section at the back of the book. GN = Great Northern style tender (with rails round top). ct = corridor tender. nct = non-corridor tender. gsd = German smoke deflectors. rd = early round dome (all others have a banjo dome). dc = double chimney. hb = headboard. From late 2002, the A3 models (identifiable in having a grey gear fitted to the rear of the driven tender wheels) had 5-pole armatures.

R2146	**103 'Flying Scotsman'** LNER light green, rd, nct, gold metalwork, Ltd Edn 2000 - 99-00	80	155
R2147	**4472 'Flying Scotsman'** LNER light green, dc, ct, Ltd Edn 500 (HCC) - 00	60	80
R2261	**4472 'Flying Scotsman'** LNER light green, ct, Pegler Edition - 02-03	NPG	85
R2103	**2505 'Cameronian'** LNER light green, GN - 99-00	45	70
R2168	**E112 'St Simon'** BRa light green, GN, train pack with 3 Pullman cars - 00	50	100
R2191	**94 'Colorado'** LNER light green, GN, Ltd Edn 500 (HCC) - 01	60	80
R2054	**60103 'Flying Scotsman'** BRc green, nct, dc - 98-01	60	80
R2126	**60046 'Diamond Jubilee'** BRc green, nct, dc, Ltd Edn 500 - 99	80	100
R2140	**60048 'Doncaster'** BRb green, GN, Sp Edn 1000 (A.B.Gee) - 99	60	80
R2152	**60085 'Manna'** BRc green, GN, gsd, nct, dc - 00	60	80
R2201	**60110 'Robert the Devil'** BRb blue, GN - 01	65	85
R2195M	**60106 'Flying Fox'** BRc green, GN, Sp Edn 1500 train pack with 3 coaches - 01	80	100
X?	**1760 'Hamleys Express'** red ex-set Sp Edn (Hamleys) - 02	70	NA

A later development of the Flying Scotsman model 'Humorist' [L50c]

R2265	**2751 'Humourist'** LNER green, GN, dc, rd - 02-03	NPG	85
R2363M	**60092 'Fairway'** BRa green hb + 3 Gresley coaches Ltd Edn 1500 The Northumbrian train pack - 03	NA	120
R2365M	**60051 'Blink Bonny'** BR + 3 Pullman cars Sp Edn 1500 The Queen of Scots MO train pack - 04	NA	120

L50d. Class A1 4-6-2 (2004 loco drive model)

This is a super detailed model released in 2004 with the motor in the loco. It came DCC ready, 5-pole motor and was fitted with NEM coupling sockets.

R2405	**4472 'Flying Scotsman'** LNER green - 04	NPG	95

L50e. Class A3 4-6-2 (2004 loco drive model)

This is a super detailed model released in 2004 with the motor in the loco. It came DCC ready, 5-pole motor and was fitted with NEM coupling sockets.

R2341	**2500 'Windsor Lad'** LNER green - 04	NPG	95
R2342	**60077 'The White Knight'** BRc green - 04	NPG	95

L51a. Class A4 4-6-2 (1979 model)

This is the original model before it went out to China for detailing. Many Hornby A4s have been renumbered/renamed after leaving the factory. These may be listed in the Code 3 section at the back of the book. ct = corridor tender. nct = non-corridor tender. v = with valances down over the wheels (all others non-valanced). pq = with plaque. npf = non-paint finish. dc = double chimney. RD = presentation pack with Royal Dalton plate.

R077	**4468 'Mallard'** LNER blue ct pq v dc - 84-85, 91-92	40	50
R327	**4468 'Mallard'** LNER blue ct v dc - 88-89	35	45
R304	**4468 'Mallard'** LNER blue nct pq v dc - 93-98	40	55
R376	**60022 'Mallard'** BRa blue ct pq dc Sp Edn 1000 (Kays) - 90	80	120
R350	**60022 'Mallard'** BRc green ct pq dc npf - 79-81	40	50
R309	**60022 'Mallard'** BRc green ct pq dc - 80-83, 89-93	30	40
(R1040)	**60022 'Mallard'** BRb exp. blue ex-R1040 Toys-R-Us train set - 03	80	NA
R328	**4469 'Sir Ralph Wedgewood'** LNER blue nct v Ltd Edn 3000 - 94	50	80
R341	**4466 'Sir Ralph Wedgewood'** NE black nct Ltd Edn 3000 - 94	60	80
R353	**60006 'Sir Ralph Wedgewood'** BRc green nct dc Ltd Edn 3000 - 94	50	80
	above 3 locos in wooden box - 94	NA	250
R099	**2512 'Silver Fox'** LNER silver ct v - 85-89	60	85
R312	**2509 'Silver Link'** LNER silver ct v - 90-94	55	75
R313	**4482 'Golden Eagle'** LNER green ct v - 90-91	45	70
R372	**4902 'Seagull'** LNER blue ct v dc - 81-82	45	60
R888	**4498 'Sir Nigel Gresley'** LNER blue ct v - 87-89	50	70
R528	**4498 'Sir Nigel Gresley'** LNER blue ct Ltd Edn 2000 - 92	60	95
R304	**4469 'Gadwall'** LNER blue nct v Sp Edn 1500 (Kays) - 95	70	90
R099	**4466 'Herring Gull'** LNER black nct Sp Edn 985 (Littlewoods) - 95	120	180
R649	**1 'Sir Ronald Matthews'** LNER blue nct RD Ltd Edn 3000 - 96	50	80
R294	**60028 'Walter K. Whigham'** BRa deep blue ct - 95	40	60
R2037	**60029 'Woodcock'** BRa deep blue ct Sp	70	90

	Edn 1000 (Beatties) - 97		
R2040	**60026 'Miles Beevor'** BRa? deep blue? Sp Edn (BCA) - *not made*	NA	NA
R204	**60019 'Bittern'** BRb green nct ex-R770 set - *94-95*	45	NA
R144	**60010 'Dominion of Canada'** BRc green ct dc - *94-95*	40	60
R286	**60009 'Union of South Africa'** BRc green planned for 1996 - *not made*	NA	NA
R286	**60021 'Wild Swan'** BRc green ct dc Ltd Edn 1000 - *96-97*	40	65
R2032	**60020 'Guillemot'** BRc green nct + 3 coaches train pack - *97*	NA	100

Class A4 'Kingfisher' [L51b]

L51b. Class A4 4-6-2 (1998 model)

This was the Super Detail model tooled-up in China with a much finer chassis. Many Hornby A4s have been renumbered/renamed after leaving the factory. These may be listed in the Code 3 section at the back of the book. ct = corridor tender. nct = non-corridor tender. v = with valances down over the wheels (all others non-valanced). pq = with plaque. dc = double chimney. sc = single chimney

R2246	**2510 'Quicksilver'** LNER grey ct v Sp Edn (Collectors Centres) - *01*	60	80
(R2278M)	**2511 'Silver King'** LNER grey ct v Sp Edn ex-mail order train pack - *02*	NPG	110
R2059	**4468 'Mallard'** LNER blue nct v dc Ltd Edn box 1500 - *98*	50	80
R2059	**4468 'Mallard'** LNER blue nct v dc - *99-03*	50	80
R2127	**4903 'Peregrine'** LNER blue nct v dc Ltd Edn 500 - *98-99*	90	130
R2154	**4485 'Kestrel'** LNER blue ct v sc - *00-01*	60	80
R2167	**60034 'Lord Farringdon'** BRa garter blue ct dc + 3 coaches train pack Ltd Edn 2000 - *00*	60	110
R2149	**60007 'Sir Nigel Gresley'** BRa garter blue ct Ltd Edn 500 (HCC) - *00*	60	80
R2089	**60014 'Silver Link'** BRb green ct + 3 coaches train pack Ltd Edn 2000 - *99*	70	90
R2136	**60012 'Commonwealth of Australia'** BRb green ct etched brass nameplate Sp Edn 500 - *99*	100	160
R2101	**60030 'Golden Fleece'** BRc green ct dc - *99*	60	75
(R1024)	**60031 'Golden Plover'** BRc green ct dc - *01-02*	75	NA
R2203	**60024 'Kingfisher'** BRc green ct dc - *01*	65	75
R2302	**60009 'Union of South Africa'** BRc* green ct dc Ltd Edn 500 (HCC) - *02*	NPG	80
R2247	**60019 'Bittern'** BRc green Sp Edn 500 - *02*	NPG	85
R2266	**60017 'Silver Fox'** BRc green - *02*	NPG	85

* The model carried a special emblem on one side only.

Live Steam A4 locomotive [L51c]

L51c. Class A4 4-6-2 (2003 live steam model)

This is the Live Steam model launched in 2003, with a boiler in the tender which generates steam to drive the cylinders and operate the whistle. The body is made with a special heat-resistant plastic.

(R1041)	**4468 'Mallard'** LNER blue - *03-04*	275	NA
R2259	**4902 'Seagull'** LNER blue - *04*	NPG	325

R2277	**60008 'Dwight D Eisenhower'** BRb green - *04*	NPG	325
R2367	**2509 'Silver Link'** LNER silver grey - *04*	NPG	325
R2368	**4495 'Golden Fleece'** NE black - *04*	NPG	325

L51d. Class A4 4-6-2 (2004 loco drive model)

This is a super detailed model released in 2004 with the motor in the loco. It came DCC ready, 5-pole motor and was fitted with NEM coupling sockets.

R2338	**4901 'Charles H Newton'** NE black - *04*	NPG	95
R2340	**60031 'Golden Plover'** BRc green - *04*	NPG	95
R2339	**4468 'Mallard'** LNER blue - *04*	NPG	95

L52a. Battle of Britain/West Country Class 4-6-2 (1961 model)

R356+ R38	**34051 'Winston Churchill'** BRc green - *61-69*	45	75
R356+ R38	**34051 'Winston Churchill'** BRc green in Tri-ang Railways box - *61-69*	45	115
R074	**34076 '41 Squadron'** BRb green - *85-86*	80	110
R310	**34054 'Lord Beaverbrook'** BRc green - *95-97*	45	60
R646	**34085 '501 Squadron'** BRb green Golden Arrow Sp Edn 1000 (Beatties) - *96*	120	160
R869S	**21C151 'Winston Churchill'** SR bright green with black shading - *69*	80	NPG
R869S	**21C151 'Winston Churchill'** SR bright gloss green, red shading - *69-72*	55	85
	21C157 'Biggin Hill', 21C164 'Fighter Command', 21C165 'Hurricane' alternative names for R869S - *69-72*	40	NA
R374	**21C166 'Spitfire'** Southern matt malachite green - *81-83*	50	70
	21C155 'Fighter Pilot', 21C165 'Hurricane', 21C170 'Manston' alternative names for R374 - *81-83*	50	NA
R866	**21C155 'Fighter Pilot'** Southern matt malachite green - *87?*	50	60
R866	**21C155 'Fighter Pilot'** SR malachite green, Golden Arrow - *88-89*	45	55
R320	**21C101 'Exeter'** Southern matt malachite green Ltd Edn 4000 - *95*	50	80
R265	**21C119 'Bideford'** Southern matt malachite green - *96-97*	45	55

West Country Class 'Bideford' [L52a]

L52b. Battle of Britain/West Country Class 4-6-2 (2001 model)

Completely new model released in 2001 with a 5-pole motor. ht = high tender, lt = low tender, ssd = short smoke deflectors. wc = wide cab, nc = narrow cab

R2219	**21C110 'Sidmouth'** Southern malachite green - *not made*	NA	NA
R2219	**21C123 'Blackmore Vale'** Southern malachite green, ht, ssd, nc - *01-04*	65	75
R2220	**34081 '92 Squadron'** BRa malachite, ht, wc - *01-04*	65	75
R2218	**34041 'Wilton'** BRc green, lt, nc - *01-04*	65	75
R2221	**34067 'Tangmere'** BRb green, wc - *01-04*	65	75
R2282	**34091 'Weymouth'** BRc green, lt, wc - *02*	65	75
R2283	**21C155 'Fighter Pilot'** Southern malachite green, ht nc - *02-04*	65	752
R2279M	**34057 'Biggin Hill'** BRa green, ht, nc, + 3 Pullmans Ltd Edn 1500 (mail order) - *02*	NA	120
R2260	**34070 'Manston'** BRc green, lt, nc, Sp Edn 500 (HCC) - *02*	NPG	84
R2286	**21C164 'Fighter Command'** SR grey, nc, ht,	NPG	100

	Sp Edn 1000 (Much Ado) - *02*		
R2315	**34037 'Clovelly'** BR malachite green, no tender decals, ht, nc - *03*	NPG	95
R2316	**34061 '73 Squadron'** BRb green, ht - *03*	NPG	95
R2385	**34051 'Winston Churchill'** BRc green, lt, nc, NRM series - *04*	NPG	*
R2369	**34074** BRa malachite green, ht, wc, Golden Arrow + 3 Pullman cars - *04*	NA	130
R2388	**34083 '605 Squadron'** BRb green, ht, wc - *04*	NA	130

L53. Merchant Navy Class (Rebuilt) 4-6-2

This model has a loco mounted 5-pole motor. Some Hornby Merchant Navies have been renumbered/renamed after leaving the factory. These may be listed in the Code 3 section at the back of the book. hb - headboard. 5100 = 5100 gallon tender.

R2169	**35028 'Clan Line'** BRc green, bulbous smokebox door - *00*	60	75
R2169	**35028 'Clan Line'** BRc green, flatter smokebox door - *01-02*	60	75
R2170	**35023 'Holland-Afrika Line'** BRb green - *00*	65	80
R2171	**35005 'Canadian Pacific'** BRb blue - *00-03*	65	80
R2194	**35022 'Holland-America Line'** BRc green, Atlantic Coast Express hb + 3 SR Mk1s train pack - *01*	NA	140
R2204	**35020 'Bibby Line'** BRc green - *01-04*	70	85
R2267	**35025 'Brocklebank Line'** BRb green - *02-04*	70	85
R2268	**35027 'Port Line'** BRc green - *02-03*	70	85
R2294	**35029 'Ellerman Lines'** BRc green, NRM series - *02*	75	90
R2300	**35021 'New Zealand Line'** BRb hb green + 3 Pullman cars Bournemouth Belle train pack - *02*	NA	130
R2310	**35016 'Elders Fyffes'** BRc green 5100 - *03-04*	80	95
(R1038)	**35012 'United States Lines'** BR green 5100 ex-R1038 set - *03-04*	75	NA

Merchant Navy 'Elders Fyffes' [L53]

L54a. Britannia Class 7P6F 4-6-2 (1960 model)

This model was loco driven until 1973 after which the motor was in the tender. From 1971 the models had sticker nameplates. nsd = no smoke deflectors. ul = no lining on loco or tender.

R259+ R35	**70000 'Britannia'** BRc green, metal nameplates - *60-70*	25	75
R259SF	**70000 'Britannia'** BRc green, Acho couplings - *67-70*	90	180
R259NS	**70000 'Britannia'** BRc green - *71-72*	35	60
	70006 'Robert Burns', 70013 'Oliver Cromwell', 70010 'Owen Glendower' alternative names for R259NS - *71-72*	55	NA
R056	**70047 'Iron Duke'** * BRc green, ul, nsd - *75-76*	35	NA
R056	**70047 'Iron Duke'** * BRb green, ul, nsd - *75?*	120	NA
R056	**70014 'Iron Duke'** * BRc green, ul, nsd - *75-76*	40	NA
R056	**70014 'Iron Duke'** * BRc green, ul, smoke deflectors (c50 made) - *76?*	120	NA
R057	mail order model for sets for '75 - *not made*	NA	NA
R552	**70013 'Oliver Cromwell'** BRc green - *73-75*	35	50
R063	**70000 'Britannia'** BRc green - *76-79*	35	50

* Cheap mail order model

L54b. Britannia Class 7P6F 4-6-2 (1981 model)

This model was tender driven and had wire handrails. After 'Morning Star', the models were fitted with the 9F slide bars and valve gear. The nameplates were printed directly onto the smoke deflector. Many Hornby Britannias have been renumbered/renamed after leaving the factory. These may be listed in the Code 3 section at the back of the book.

R033	**70021 'Morning Star'** BRc green - *81-82*	45	65
-	**70028 'Royal Star', 70034 'Thomas Hardy', 70038 'Robin Hood'** alternative names for R033 - *81-82*	50	NA
R329	**70004 'William Shakespear'** BRc green - *90-91*	40	55
R190	**70000 'Britannia'** BRb green - *92*	35	65
R507	**70000 'Britannia'** BRb green Ltd Edn 2000, Royal Duties (white cab roof) - *92*	50	85
R378	**70032 'Tennyson'** BRc green Sp Edn 2000 (Kays) - *91*	75	110
R242	**70006 'Robert Burns'** BRb green Sp Edn 2000 (Kays) - *96*	45	90
R2031	**70023 'Venus'** BRb green, train pack with 3 coaches Ltd Edn 3000 - *97*	70	110
R2010	**70042 'Lord Roberts'** BRb green Ltd Edn 1000 - *98*	45	85
R2091	**70028 'Royal Star'** BRb green - *99*	70	95
X?	**70012 'John of Gaunt'** BRc green, ex-R1021 Kays set - *99*	55	NA
R2104	**70050 'Firth of Clyde'** BRc green, late tender - *99*	40	75
R2142	**70038 'Robin Hood'** BRb green Sp Edn 1000 (A.B.Gee) - *99*	50	70
R2192	**70046 'ANZAC'** BRc green, late tender Ltd Edn 1000 (Collectors Centres) - *00*	50	70
R2175	**70052 'Firth of Tay'** BRc green, late tender Sp Edn 1500 (Kays) - *00*	45	65

L54c. Britannia Class 7P6F 4-6-2 (2000 model)

This is the Super Detail model which is similar to the 1981 model (above) but has a finely detailed chassis and later style smoke deflectors with cut-out handholds instead of handrails on some of the models. Some models were fitted with the high sided BR1D tender fitted to the last 10 members of the class. hb = headboard.

R2180	**70040 'Clive of India'** BRc green - *00-01*	50	75
R2207	**70000 'Britannia'** BRb green - *01-02*	50	75
R2272	**70025 'Western Star'** BRc green - *02-03*	50	75
R2329M	**70054 'Dornoch Firth'** BRc green weathered BR1D hb + 3 coaches Ltd Edn 1500 Thames-Clyde train pack - *03*	NA	120
R2387	**70018 'Flying Dutchman'** BRb green - *04*	NPG	95

L55a. Class 8F 2-8-0 (1988 model)

Tender drive.

R315	**8193** LMS black (also R325) - *88-91*	40	60
R325	**8027** LMS black - *90-91*	50	70
R325	**8118** LMS black - *90-91*	50	70
R325	**8233** LMS black - *90-91*	50	70
R297	**8035** LMS black - *96-97*	40	60
R322	**48758** BRb black - *89*	40	60
R324	**48774** BRb black - *90-91*	50	70
R324	**48141** BRb black - *90-91*	50	70
R324	**48278** BRb black - *90-91*	50	70
R2055	**48705** BRc black - *98*	45	65
R2043	**300** WD grey Sp Edn 500 (Much Ado About Toys) - *97*	130	160

Class 8F [L55a]

L55b. Class 8F/O6 2-8-0 (2002 model)

The model has a 5-pole loco mounted motor

R2227	**7675** LNER plain black - *03-04*	60	75
R2228	**8510** LMS plain black - *03-04*	60	75

R2229	**48154** BRb plain black - *03*	60	75
R2249	**8042** LMS weathered plain black - *03-04*	60	75
R2393	**48773** BRc plain black - *04*	NPG	85
R2394	**8453** LMS plain black - *04*	NPG	85
R2395	**48119** BRb weathered plain black - *04*	NPG	85

L56.   Class 2800 2-8-0

R532	**2859** Great Western green - *91-93*	55	70
R2053	**2844** GWR (button) green - *98*	45	65
R2153A	**2821** GWR green - *00-01*	60	80
R2153B	**2869** GWR green - *00-01*	60	80
R143	**2857** BRc plain black - *94-96*	50	65
R2202	**2861** BRb plain black - *01*	60	80
R2202A	**2865** BRb plain black - *02-04*	NPG	85

L57a.   Class 9F 2-10-0 (1971 model)

This was the original Evening Star model which can be easily identified by its handrails being part of the body moulding. When originally designed only the handrails on the back edge of the cab had daylight behind them but this left them prone to breaking and so the gap was soon filled in. npf = non-paint finish.

92220 'Evening Star'

R861	BRc gloss green, npf, separate cab handrails - *71*	40	70
R861	BRc gloss green, npf, - *71-74*	30	55
R065	BRc matt green, npf, - *77-79*	30	50
R303	BRc green - *80-82*	30	45
R301	BRb green Sp Edn (NRM) - *?*	35	100
R330	BRc green, Sp Edn 125 (NRM) - *83*	30	70
R264	**92166?** BRb black - *72*	30	50
R550	**92166** BRb black - *73*	30	50
R264	**92200** BRc black alt nos. - *82-83*	30	50
-	**92183 , 92215 and 92239** alternative numbers for R264 - *82-83*	35	NA

L57b.   Class 9F 2-10-0 (1988 model)

This was similar to the last model but now had wire handrails.

R373	**92220 'Evening Star'** BRc green - *88-91*	35	55
R330	**92207, 92231, 92222** BRc black - *90-91*	40	55
R864	**92241** BRc black - *96*	40	55
R2016	**92001** BRc black - *97*	40	55
R2057	**92212** BRc black - *98*	40	55

L57c.   Class 9F 2-10-0 (1999 model)

This third model had a much improved chassis, blackened metalwork and a choice of tenders. It was the Super Detail model and the tooling work was done in China. lt = large tender.

R2187	**92220 'Evening Star'** BRc green - *00-01*	60	75
R2105A	**92108** BRc black, lt - *99*	55	70
R2105B	**92139** BRc black, lt - *99*	55	70
R2105C	**92158** BRc black, lt - *00-01*	60	75
R2105D	**92156** BRc black, lt - *02-04*	60	75
R2137	**92203 'Black Prince'** BRc black Sp Edn 500 - *99*	50	85
R2139	**92099** BRc black + 5 vans train pack Sp Edn 1000 (A.B.Gee) - *00*	NA	120
R2244	**92099** BRc black ex-R2139 Sp Edn train pack repackaged - *00*	70	90
R2200	**92151** BRc weathered black, lt - *01*	55	75
R2200A	**92134** BRc weathered black, lt - *01-03*	60	75
R2248	**92239** BRc weathered black - *02-04*	60	75

Class 9F 2-10-0 'Black Prince' [L57c]

Diesel Locomotives

L58.   Dock Shunter/Yard Switcher (Freelance)

Some bodies were printed in New Zealand and these include ones with 'TR' but no shield.

R253	**5** Dock Authority black, early coupling - *57-61*	20	65
R253	**3** Dock Authority black - *72-78*	20	35
R253	**3 or 5** Dock Authority red - *62-71*	20	35
R353	Tri-ang Railways yellow, no buffers - *60-62*	25	48
R353	**TR20071** TR yellow, no buffers - *?*	25	48
R353	**TR20071** TR red, no buffers - *63-65*	20	NA
R655	TR red, no buffers - *64*	35	NA

L59.   North British Diesel Shunter 0-4-0DS

R557	BRc blue c/w - *62-65*	15	75
R557?	BRc green c/w - *68?*	95	125
R756	BRc red c/w - *66*	30	NA
R?	Battle Space red - *66-67*	35	NA
R654	BRc blue - *64-65*	25	NA
R557?	violet c/w - *68?*	40	NA
R?	black c/w - *65*	40	NA
R559	**D2907** BRc green - *63-67*	25	75

L60.   Class 06 Diesel Shunter 0-4-0DS

R061	Hornby Railways yellow - *93*	15	25
R234	**A5** Robert Horne cream - *95-97*	20	30
R2188	**D2412** BRc green Sp Edn (HCClub) - *00*	25	35
R136	**D2424** BRc green - *95*	25	35
R875	**D2428** BRc green - *88-91*	25	35
R799	**4** CEGB grey - *91-92*	22	30
R051	**6** Redland green - *93-94*	25	35
R2009	**8** ECC green - *97-98*	22	30
R801	**302** Tilbury Refineries yellow - *91-94*	22	30
R2184	**06003** Rft Distribution grey - *00-01*	22	27
R874	**06005** BRe blue - *88-91*	20	35
R2003	**06008** BRe grey Set R1003 - *97-98*	28	NA
R2375	Virgin red+silver Sp Edn (HCC) - *04*	NPG	NPG

Class 06 diesel shunter [L60]

L61a.   Class 08 Diesel Shunter 0-6-0DS (1956 model)

This model was also made in New Zealand and Australia with a different body tool. This has a higher cab roof.

R256	TR black c/w - *57?*	80	100
R256	TR maroon c/w - *57-58*	40	75
R316	VR blue, made for Australia - *74-75*	60	80
R152	**D3035** BRe blue - *69-75*	25	35
R1520	**1520** bright blue made for Canada - *71*	60	95
R152	**13002** BRb black - *56*	50	65
R152	**13002** BRb green - *59?*	75	100
R152	**13005** BRb black - *56-58*	20	40
R154	**13005** BRb black c/w - *57-58*	80	100
R152	**13005** BRb olive - *56?*	50	65
R152	**13035** BRb green - *58-68*	25	40
R317	black with face - *see Thomas section*	-	-
R9066	green+yellow with face - *see Thomas*	-	-
R9067	green+yellow with face - *see Thomas*	-	-

L61b. Class 08 Diesel Shunter 0-6-0DS
(1976 model)

arc = automatic rear coupling. ladders = metal ladders up sides of radiator

R165	NSWR maroon (Australia) arc, ladders - 77-78	40	65
-	Dinosafari buff ex-T1500 set - 00-02	25	NA
-	Battle Zone dark green ex-T1501 set - 00-02	25	NA
R339	**17** WD green, arc, ladders - 82-84	25	50
R2334	**3973 'Concorde'** LMS (BRML) lined dark maroon - 03	25	40
R354	**D3010** BRc green paint finish, arc, ladders - 80-81	25	37
R156	**13012** BRc green, arc, ladders - 76-79	20	25
R2157B	**08096** BRc green - 00-03	30	37
R780	**08201** BRe blue, arc, ladders - 81-88	25	30
R780	**08201** BRe blue, red wheels, ladders - 87-88	20	25
R2123	**08500 'Thomas 1'** York Wagon Depot maroon - 99-01	25	30
R2007	**08523** Mainline blue ex-R1002 set - 97-98	25	NA
R2157A	**08531** BRc green - 00-02	30	37
R2425	**08568** St Rollox black+white - 04	NPG	41
R050	**08633 'The Sorter'** Express Parcels red+ black - 93-94	30	45
R2008	**08661 'Europa'** Rft Dist grey - 97-98	30	38
R054	**08673 'Piccadilly'** BRe grey - 88-92	30	38
R2239	**08810** Anglia blue - 01-02	30	38
R2163	**08828** EWS maroon - 00-02	30	38
R2256	**08830** BRe blue weathered - 02	NPG	35
R2111	**08896 'Stephen Dent'** EWS maroon - 99	25	30
R272	**08933** BRe Railfreight grey - 95-96	25	38
R803	**08938** ED grey, ladders - 86-88	25	38
R2333	**08642** BRML Eastleigh Works lined black - 03	25	40

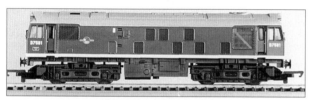

Class 25 diesel [L62]

L62. Class 25 Diesel Bo-Bo

npf = non paint finish. wbl = with blue line. wgl = with grey line

R878	- BRc green, wbl, D5177, D5200, D5206, D7568, D7597 alt. number transfers - 87-88	NA	40
-	**D5177** (transfers) BRc green, wbl see R878 above - 87-88	25	30
-	**D5200** (transfers) BRc green, wbl see R878 above - 87-88	25	30
-	**D5206** (transfers) BRc green, wbl see R878 above - 87-88	25	30
R253	**D5206** BRc green, wbl - 95-96	30	40
-	**D7568** (transfers) BRc green, wbl see R878 above - 87-88	25	30
R327	**D7571** BRc green, wbl - 80-81	20	30
R2121A	**D7581** BRc green, wgl - 00-02	35	40
R072	**D7596** BRc green, wbl, npf - 77-79	20	30
R2121	**D7596** BRc green, wgl - 99	35	40
-	**D7597** (transfers) BRc green, wbl see R878 above - 87-88	25	30
R877	- BRe blue, 25218, 25071, 25078, 25052, 25054 alt. number transfers - 87-89	NA	40
-	**25052** (transfers) BRe blue see R877 above - 87-88	25	30
-	**25054** (transfers) BRe blue see R877 above - 87-88	25	30
-	**25071** (transfers) BRe blue see R877 above - 87-88	25	30
-	**25078** (transfers) BRe blue see R877 above - 87-88	25	30
R2237B	**25033** BRe blue - 01	32	38
R2237A	**25056** BRe blue - 01	32	38
-	**25218** (transfers) BRe blue see R877 above - 87-88	25	30
R326	**25241** BRe blue - 80-84	20	30
R068	**25247** BRe blue - 77-79	20	30

L63. Class 29 Diesel Bo-Bo

npf = non paint finish.

R084	**6124** BRe blue - 78-80	15	25
R337	**6142** BRe blue - 80-82	20	27
R318	**6142** BRe blue, chip fitted Sp Edn (Beatties) - 82	NPG	NPG
R338	**D6103** BRc green - 80-81	22	30
R080	**D6110** BRc green, npf - 78-79	20	35
R2122A	**D6119** BRc 2-tone green - 00-01	30	38
R2238A	**D6129** BRe blue - 01	32	37
R2122	**D6130** BRc 2-tone green - 99	30	48
R2238B	**D6137** BRe blue - 01	32	37

Class 29 diesel [L63]

L64a. Class 31 Diesel (Brush Type 2) A1A-A1A

R357(G)	**D5572** BRc dull green - 63-67	15	25
R357	**D5572** BRe electric blue - 68	20	30
R357	**D5572** BRe rail blue - 69-71	15	25
R357	**D5572** BRc gloss green - 72-76	15	25
R357(G)	**D5578** BRc dull green - 63-67	55	70
R357	**D5578** BRc exp. blue, pale blue window surrounds - 62	50	95
R357B	**D5578** BRc exp. blue, with white lines and roof - 65-66	30	65
R307	**42202** NSWR maroon (Australia) - 74-76	50	85

L64b. Class 31 (Brush Type 2) A1A-A1A (1964 model)

R2420	**D5512** BRc green - 04	NPG	85
R2413	**31270** BRe blue - 04	NPG	85
R2421	**31110** Civil Engineers grey - 04	NPG	85

L65. Class 35 Hymek Diesel Hydraulic B-B

Two different motor bogies were used. npf = non-painted finish. W = weathered.

R768	CIE orange - 77, 81	45	85
R2410	**D7046** BRc green - 04	NPG	54
R758	**D7063** BRc green, npf - 67	15	45
R074	**D7063** BRc green, npf - 77-78	15	35
R758	**D7063** BRe electric blue, npf - 68	12	35
R396	**D7063** BRe electric blue, npf, kit - 68	NA	200
R758	**D7063** BRe blue, npf - 70-76	10	25
R396	**D7063** BRe blue, npf, kit - 69-70	NA	120
R2423	**D7067** BRe blue W - 04	NPG	54
R122	**D7093** BRe blue, white window frames - 94-96	25	45
R335	**D7097** BRc green - 79-82	25	35

L66. Class 37 Diesel (English Electric Type 3) Co-Co

Two different motor bogies were used. scb = split code box on cab front. npf = non-painted finish. W = weathered.

R9064	**D261** green with face on one end -see Thomas series	30	41
R284	**D6713, D6721, D6796** BRc green, scb, alternative numbers - 88-90	NA	40
-	**D6721** (transfers) BRc green, scb see R284 above - 88-90	20	30
-	**D6713** (transfers) BRc green, scb see	20	30

	R284 above - *88-90*		
R347	D6736 BRc green, scb - *86-87*	20	30
-	D6796 (transfers) BRc green, scb see R284 above - *88-90*	20	30
R751	D6830 BRc green, npf - *66-67*	15	50
R751	D6830 BRe blue, npf R751A - *68-76*	12	22
R2128	Eddie Stobart green Sp Edn 1000 (Eddie Stobart Club/Trafford Model Centre) - *99*	40	80
X?	37001 'Norman Bell' Eddie Stobart Ltd. green Sp Edn 1000 (Eddie Stobart Club/Trafford Model Centre) ex-R1026 set - *02*	40	NA
R2027	37042 EWS maroon, scb - *97-98*	35	NA
R2255	37057+37042 (dummy) EWS W maroon pair - *02*	55	70
R348	37063 BReLL Rft grey, scb - *86-89*	25	40
R359	37071 BReLL bright blue - *82-85*	18	NA
R365	37072 BReLL bright green - *84*	18	30
R369	37073 BRe blue - *80-83*	18	30
R751	37130 BRe blue, npf - *77-79*	15	25
R285	37166, 37187, 37202 BRe blue, alternative numbers - *88-90*	NA	35
-	37166 (transfers) BRe blue see R285 above - *88-90*	20	30
R2255A	37174+37298 (dummy) EWS W maroon pair - *03-04*	55	75
-	37187 (transfers) BRe blue see R285 above - *88-90*	20	30
R2012C	37198 Mainline blue - *97*	30	45
-	37202 (transfers) BRe blue see R285 above - *88-90*	20	30
R2012B	37203 Mainline blue - *97*	30	45
R402	37207 'William Cookworthy' BRe blue - *84-86*	20	35
R2412	37216+37248 'Midland Railway Centre' (dummy) Mainline W blue pair - *04*	NPG	75
-	37248 (see 37216)	-	-
-	37298 (see 37174)	-	-
R2012A	37371 Mainline blue - *97*	30	45
R2255	37405+37416 EWS W maroon coupled pair - *not made*	NA	NA
R2409	37410 'Aluminium 100' grey Transrail - *04*	NPG	54
R2060C	37415 EW&S maroon - *98*	30	40
R327	37424 BR Transrail grey - *96-97*	25	40
R2060A	37427 EW&S maroon - *98*	30	40
R286	37518, 37677, 37688 BReLL Rft grey, alternative numbers - *88-89*	NA	45
-	37518 (transfers) BReLL Rft grey see R286 above - *88-89*	20	30
-	37677 (transfers) BReLL Rft grey see R286 above - *88-89*	20	30
-	37688 (transfers) BReLL Rft grey see R286 above - *88-89*	20	30
R2060B	37688 EW&S maroon - *98*	30	40
R243	37885 BRe Rft Metals grey - *95*	25	45
R871	37xxx BRe blue, number choice - *96*	20	40

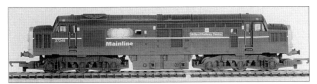

Class 37 'Midland Railway Centre' [L66]

L67. Class 43 'HST 125'

neb = no exhaust baffle on cab roof

R069/070	253 001(W43002/W43003) BRe I-C 125 blue 2-car, neb - *78-80*	20	35
R332(R370/371)	253 005 (43010/43011) BRe I-C 125 blue 3-car, neb - *80-84*	20	45
R401(R708/709)	253 028 BRe I-C 125 grey 3-car, neb, + sheet of numbers - *83-91*	25	45

R2115	43002/43124 Great Western green+ivory 4-car pack - *99-01*	40	60
R2299	43042/43029 FGW purple 4-car pack - *02-04*	NPG	85
R336(R706/707)	43046/43080/ 43066/43050 InterCity Swallow dark grey 3-car pack - *90-97*	25	40
R?	43051 'Armada 400'/43072 ICs grey Sp Edn 3-car pack - *88-89?*	100	130
R2046	43058 'Midland Pride'/43059 Mid. Mainline blue/green 4-car pack - *97-98*	40	60
R2045	43063 'Maiden Voyager'/43093 'Lady in Red' Virgin red 4-car pack, also in R1023 set - *97-04*	40	60
R2298	43068 'The Red Arrows'/43062 Virgin red 4-car pack - *02-03*	65	85
R2298A	43065/43080 Virgin red 4-car pack - *04*	NPG	90
R397(R797/798)	43072/43051 InterCity Swallow grey, 3-car pack - *88-91*	30	45
R2114	43092 'Institution of Mechanical Engineers 150th Anniversary 1847-1997'/43090 Virgin red 4-car pack - *99-01*	40	60
(R901)	43102/43086 ICs dark grey from 4-car set - *96-97*	50	NA
R2000	43117/43118 GNER navy blue 4-car pack - *97-98*	40	60
R2296	253036(W43142/W43141) BRe Inter-City 125 blue 4-car - *02-04*	65	85
R897(R3392/R3393)	43154 'Intercity'/43193 ICs dark grey from 2-car set, Ltd Edn. 5000 - *96*	35	NA
R2116	GNER navy blue 4-car pack - *99-00*	40	60
R696(R741/742)	Intercity XPT silver 3-car pack*, neb - *83-84*	70	100
R2347	? Virgin West Coast red+black 4-car - *03*	NPG	85

* Examples may be found with either a power car and 2 coaches or with one of the coaches replaced by a dummy power car.

L68. Class 47 Diesel Co-Co

npf = not with a paint finish. W = weathered.

R245	BRe Rft Distribution grey, choice of names/ numbers - *89-90,96*	NA	50
R287	BRe blue choice of names/ numbers - *88-89*	NA	50
R219	BRe NSE bright blue, choice of numbers /names - *89-93*	NA	50
R288	BRe InterCity grey, choice of names/ numbers - *88-90*	NA	50
R060	D1520 BRc green npf - *76*	15	35
R073	D1670 'Mammoth' BRc green npf - *79-80*	18	40
R328	D1670 'Mammoth' BRc green - *80-81*	20	35
R863	D1738 BRc gloss green npf - *75*	25	35
R342	47079 BRe Rft Construc grey - *90-92*	30	NA
R416	47085 'REPTA 1893-1993' Railfreight Distribution grey - *94?*	30	35
R2254	47120 BReLL W blue - *02*	35	50
-	47124 BRe blue see R287 above - *88-89*	25	30
R416	47156 'REPTA 1893-1993' Railfreight Distribution grey - *94?*	40	50
R307	47170 'County of Norfolk' BReLL blue - *82-83*	25	35
-	47207 'Bulmers of Hereford' BRe Rft Distribution grey see R245 above - *89-90,96*	20	NA
-	47231 'The Silcock Express' BRe Rft Distribution grey see R245 above - *89-90,96*	20	NA
R116	47234 Rft Distribution grey - *94*	28	45
R2353	47237 DRS dark blue - *not made*	NA	NA
R2013	47270 Freightliner grey - *97*	25	30
R2013	47301 Freightliner grey - *97*	25	30
-	47311 'Warrington Yard' BRe Rft Dist grey, see R245 above - *89-90,96*	20	NA
R2080	47345 Freightliner grey train pack with 3 wagons - *98*	50	75
-	47353 BRe blue see R287 above - *88-89*	25	30
R2013	47376 'Freightliner 1995' Freightliner grey - *97*	25	30
R898	47378 BReLL Rft Gen. grey - *87-88*	25	40

269

R354	47406 'Rail Riders' BRe blue - 85	30	40
-	47409 BRe blue see R287 above - 88-89	25	30
R075	47421 BRe blue npf - 77-78	15	25
R2254A	47432 BReLL W blue - 03-04	30	54
R2254B	47473 BReLL W blue - 04	NPG	54
R769	47480 'Robin Hood' BRe blue Sp Edn 480 (Beatties) - 83	35	60
R802	47487 BRe InterCity grey - 86-87	30	40
R2353	47501 DRS dark blue - 04	NPG	54
R319	47541 'The Queen Mother' BRe blue - 83-85	30	40
R329	47541 'The Queen Mother' BRe blue Sp Edn 187 (Grattans) - 83	NA	50
-	47549 'Royal Mail' BRe InterCity grey see R288 above - 88-89	20	NA
R404	47568 BRe blue - 84-87	25	30
R876	47573 'The London Standard' BRe NSE bright blue - 87-88	30	40
-	47576 'King's Lynn' BRe NSE bright blue see R219 above - 89-93	20	NA
-	47579 'James Nightingale GC' BRe NSE bright blue see R219 above - 89-93	20	NA
-	47583 'County of Hereford' BRe NSE bright blue see R219 above - 89-93	20	NA
R587	47586 'Northamptonshire' InterCity Swallow grey - 91-92	30	35
-	47613 'North Star' BRe InterCity grey see R288 above- 88-90	20	NA
-	47620 'Windsor Castle' BRe InterCity grey see R288 above- 88-90	20	NA
R886	47711 'Greyfrier's Bobby' BRe ScotRail grey - 87-88	30	45
R316	47712 'Lady Diana Spencer' BReLL blue - 81	30	35
R887	47716 'The Duke of Edinburgh's Award' BRe ScotRail grey - 87-88	30	45
R2289C	47722 'The Queen Mother' Virgin red+ black - 03	35	52
R2289D	47741 'Resilient' Virgin red+black - 03	35	52
R2289E	47805 'Pride of Toton' Virgin red+black - 04	NPG	54
R2289A	47807 'Lion of Vienna' Virgin red+black - 02	35	50
R717	47808 BRe Parcels red - 95-96	35	NA
R2061B	47814 'Totnes Castle' Virgin red+black - 98	35	40
R2352	47816 'Bristol Bath Road' FGW green gold stripe- 04	NPG	54
X3857	47822 'Pride of Shrewsbury' Virgin red+ black R1022 set (Kays) - 99-00	35	NA
R2351	47839 Riviera Trains navy blue - 04	NPG	54
R2289B	47841 'Spirit of Chester' Virgin red+black - 02	35	50
R2061A	47844 Virgin red+black - 98	35	40
R2061C	47845 'County of Kent' Virgin red+black - 98	35	40
R2422	47853 'Express' D1733 Riviera Trains BRe light blue - 04	NPG	54
R2289G	47854 'Womens Royal Voluntary Service' Virgin red+black - 04	NPG	54

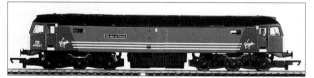

Virgin Trains Class 47 'Lion of Vienna' [L68]

L68A. Class 50 Diesel Co-Co

DCC ready, drive to both bogies and pickuW = weathered.

R2429	50002 'Superb' NSE Revised bright blue W - 04	NPG	85
R2408	50007 'Sir Edward Elgar' BR heritage green - 04	NPG	85
R2348	50018 'Resolution' BRe blue - 03-04	70	85
R2374	50031 "Hood" BReLL blue Ltd Edn	NPG	85
	(Hornby Collector Centres) - 04		
R2349	50035 'Ark Royal' BReLL blue - 03-04	70	85
R2428	50037 'Illustrious' BRe blue - 04	NPG	85
R2350	50045 'Achilles' NSE Revised bright blue W - 03-04	70	85

L69. Class 52 'Western' Diesel Hydraulic C-C

npf = non paint finish

R778	D1008 'Western Harrier' BRe blue - 81-82	30	40
R2158	D1013 'Western Ranger' BRe blue - 00-03	30	40
R319	D1035 'Western Yeoman' BRc green - 92-93	30	40
-R101	D1039 'Western King' BRc maroon - 94-95	30	40
R348	D1058 'Western Nobleman' BRe blue - 96-97	30	40
R352	D1062 'Western Courier' BRc maroon, npf - 79	20	30
R368	D1062 'Western Courier' BRc maroon - 80-81	25	35

L70. Class 56 Diesel Co-Co (ex-Mainline)

Some Hornby Class 56s have been renumbered/named after leaving the factory. These may be listed in the Code 3 section at the back of the book. W = weathered.

R2288B	56038 EW&S maroon - 02	35	50
R2106A	56047 Transrail Dutch grey+yellow - 00-01	30	50
R2235C	56048 BReLL blue - 02	35	50
R2106	56049 Transrail Dutch grey+yellow - 99	30	50
R2075	56058 EW&S maroon+yellow - 98	30	45
R2288D	56058 EW&S maroon+yellow - 04	NPG	54
R2288A	56059 EWS maroon+yellow - 02	35	50
R2107D	56066 BRe Transrail grey - 00-01	30	50
R2288A	56068 EW&S maroon+yellow - not made	NA	NA
R2288C	56088 EW&S maroon+yellow - 03	35	52
R2235E	56098 BReLL blue - 03-04	35	54
R2235D	56099 BReLL blue - 02	35	50
R2074	56100 Loadhaul black - 98, 00	30	50
R2235A	56101 BReLL blue - 01	30	50
R2075A	56105 EW&S maroon Ltd Edn 500 - 98	50	70
R2253A	56105 BReLL W blue - 03	35	52
R2416	56107 Loadhaul black+orange - 04	NPG	54
R2074B	56109 Loadhaul black - 98, 00-01	30	50
R2235B	56113 BReLL blue - 01	30	50
R2074A	56118 Loadhaul black Ltd Edn 500 - 98	50	70
R2107A	56119 BRe Transrail grey - 99	30	50
R2107C	56123 'Drax Power Station' BRe Transrail grey - 99	30	50
R2253	56123 BReLL weathered blue - 02	35	50
R2107B	56127 BRe Transrail grey - 99	30	50
R2235G	56131 'Ellington Colliery' BReLL blue - 04	NPG	54

L71. Class 58 Diesel Co-Co

W = weathered.

R250	58001 Rft red stripe - 84-87	20	30
R2336	58002 'Daw Mill Colliery' + 58005 ''Iron Bridge Power Station' (dummy) Mainline blue W - 03-04	50	75
-	58005 ''Iron Bridge Power Station' (see above)	-	-
R332	58006 Rft Coal grey - 90-91	30	47
R250	58007 BRe grey, number both ends - 82	30	40
R250	58007 Rft red stripe number one end - 83	25	35
R2071	58008 Mainline blue - not made	NA	NA
R2011B	58021 'Hither Green Depot' Mainline blue - 97	40	50
R2011A	58023 'Peterborough Depot' Mainline blue - 97-98	35	45
R2411	58024 EW&S + 58037 'Worksop Depot' EWS maroon+yellow pair W - 04	NPG	75
R332	58025 Rft Coal grey - 90-91	30	47
R250?	58027 Rft red stripe - 83?	40	50
R2125A	58030 EWS maroon+yellow - 99	35	45
R2346	58033 EW&S early maroon - 03-04	35	54
R283	58034 'Bassetlaw' Rft red stripe - 88-89	35	50

R2034	58037 EWS maroon+yellow - *97-98*	35	45
-	58037 **'Worksop Depot'** EWS maroon W - *see 58024*	-	-
R2125B	58039 EWS maroon+yellow - *99*	35	45
R2252A	58041 **'Ratcliffe Power Station'** Rft Coal grey W - *03-04*	35	54
R2011C	58042 **'Petrolea'** Mainline blue - *97*	40	50
R332	58044 Rft Coal grey - *90-91*	30	47
R2345	58046 **'Thornaby Colliery'** Rft Coal grey - *03-04*	35	54
R252B	58047 **'Manton Colliery'** Rft Coal grey - *04*	NPG	54
R2125C	58047 EWS maroon+yellow - *00, 02*	30	40
R262	58048 Rft red stripe ex-R887 set - *94*	30	NA
R2072	58048 EW&S maroon - *not made*	NA	NA
R705	58050 **'Toton Traction Depot'** Rft Coal grey - *89*	30	45
R2252	58050 Rft Coal grey W - *02*	30	45
R358	58050 **'Toton Traction Depot'** Mainline blue - *96*	40	55

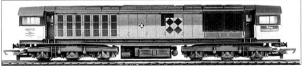

Class 58 diesel [L71]

Electric Locomotives

L72. Steeple Cab Electric 0-4-0 (Freelance)

R254	BRc green - *59-64*	35	75
R254	TR green - *61-63*	65	75
R252	TR maroon dummy pantograph - *59-62*	40	75

L73. Class EM2 Electric Co-Co

R351	27000 **'Electra'** BRc green - *61-65*	55	120
R388	27000 **'Electra'**, 27002 **'Aurora'**, 27006 **'Pandora'** BRc green CKD kit with choice of names - *65*	NA	120
R351	27000 **'Electra'** BRc electric blue - *66-68*	50	135
R388	27000 **'Electra'**, 27002 **'Aurora'**, 27006 **'Pandora'** BRc electric blue CKD kit with choice of names - *66-67*	NA	250
R388	27000 **'Electra'**, 27002 **'Aurora'**, 27006 **'Pandora'** BR electric blue kit with name choice - *68*	NA	240
R351	27000 **'Electra'** BRe rail blue - *69-71*	60	120
R388	27000 **'Electra'**, 27002 **'Aurora'**, 27006 **'Pandora'** BRe rail blue, kit with name choice - *69-70*	NA	240
R351	E27000 **'Electra'** BRe rail blue - *71*	75	120

Class EM2 electric [L73]

L74. Class 81 (AL1) Electric

R753	E3001 BRd electric blue with 2 pantographs - *66*	120	160
R753	E3001 BRd electric blue with 1 pantograph - *67*	90	130
R753	E3001 BRe electric blue with 1 pantograph - *68*	70	100
R753	E3001 BRe rail blue with 1 pantograph - *69-70*	60	85

L75. Class 86/2 Electric

Some have non-functioning pantographs.

R289	BRe I-C grey alternative names - *88*	NA	50
R289	86102 **'Robert A Riddles'** BRe I-C grey Sp Edn 950 (IWPA) - *89*	50	75
R289	86213 **'Lancashire Witch'** BRe I-C grey Sp Edn? - *89?*	55	75
R301	86210 **'C.I.T 75th Anniv'** BRe RES red Sp Edn 1000 (CIT) - *96*	35	45
R2120	86218 **'NHS 50'** Anglia blue - *99*	32	40
R360	86219 **'Phoenix'** BRe blue - *81-83*	30	35
R2160A	86220 **'The RoundTabler'** Anglia blue - *04*	NPG	54
R2290B	86225 **'Hardwick'** Virgin red+blk - *02*	35	50
R2362	86227 **'Golden Jubilee'** Anglia blue, Union Jacks - *03*	35	47
-	86228 **'Vulcan Heritage'** BRe I-C grey - *see R289 at top*	35	NA
R2414	86233 **'Alstom Heritage'** E3172 BRd electric blue - *04*	NPG	54
R2415	86235 **'Novelty'** ICs grey - *04*	NPG	54
R2160	86235 **'Crown Point'** Anglia blue - *00-02*	35	45
R2290C	86236 **'Josiah Wedgwood'** Virgin red+black - *03*	NPG	47
R2243	86237 **'University of East Anglia'** Anglia blue - *not made*	NA	NA
R2331	86241 **'Glenfiddich'** RES red - *03*	NPG	47
R2290A	86242 **'James Kennedy'** Virgin red+black - *02*	NPG	50
R367	86243 **'The Boy's Brigade'** BRe blue - *83-84*	35	55
R2242	86245 **'Caledonian'** Virgin blue - *01*	35	45
R800	86246 **'Royal Anglian Regiment'** BRe I-C grey - *86-87*	30	35
-	86255 **'Penrith Beacon'** BRe I-C grey - *see R289 at top*	35	NA
R2159	86261 **'The Rail Charter Partnership'** EWS maroon - *00-02*	35	45
R2159A	86401 **'Hertfordshire Rail Tours'** EWS maroon+yellow - *03*	35	47
R368	86401 BRe NSE bright blue - *88-89*	35	50
R333	86405 I-C grey - *90-91*	30	45
R388	86414 **'Frank Hornby'** BRe I-C grey Ltd Edn 1750 - *88-89*	35	45
R322	86417 BRe RES red - *96-97*	35	50
-	86417 **'The Kingsman'** BRe I-C grey - *see R289 at top*	35	NA
R333	86419 I-C grey - *90-91*	30	45
R589	86419 **'Post Haste'** BRe Parcels red - *91-92*	30	50
R2204	86426 EWS maroon - *01*	35	45
R333	86431 I-C grey - *90-91*	30	45
R335	86504 **'Halley's Comet'** BRe Rft General grey - *90-91*	30	45
R2241B	86602 Freightliner green - *01*	35	50
R2241A	86631 Freightliner green - *00-01*	35	50

Class 86 electric 'Phoenix' [L75]

L76. Class 90 Electric

R242	90001 Intercity Swallow grey - *88-90*	35	45
R2048	90002 **'Mission Impossible'** Virgin red+blk Sp Edn 525 (Model Rail) - *97*	60	85
R2067	90012 **'British Transport Police'** Virgin red+black - *98*	35	45
R2109A	90014 Virgin red+black - *99-00*	35	45
R2109B	90015 **'The International Brigade Spain 1936-1939'** Virgin red+black - *99-00*	35	45

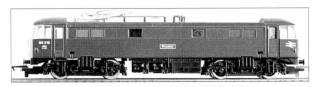

R062	**90018** BRe RES red - *93-94*	45	55
R595	**90020** BRe Parcels red, dummy pantograph - *91-93*	45	NA
R2110	**90020 'Sir Michael Heron'** EWS maroon - *99-00*	35	45
R2236	**90024** GNER navy blue - *01*	38	50
R471	**90028** BRe I-C grey dummy pant - *92*	50	60
R2230	**90029 'FrachtVerbindungen'** BR/DB red - *03*NPG		52
R593	**90030** BRe grey - *91*	40	50
R593	**90033** BRe grey - *91*	40	50
R593	**90034** BRe grey - *91*	40	50
R2291A	**90037** Railfreight grey - *02-04*	40	52
R586	**90037** BRe Railfreight Distribution grey - *91*	40	50
R2291B	**90039** Railfreight grey - *02-04*	40	52
R586	**90040** BRe Railfreight Distribution grey - *91*	40	50
R586	**90042** BRe Railfreight Distribution grey - *91*	40	50
R847	**90?** BRe Railfreight Distribution grey Sp Edn 30 (QVC) - *94*	NA	NPG
R2292	**90128 'Vrachtverbinding'** BR/SNCB blue - *02*	40	50
R2358	**90130 'Fretconnection'** Sibic SNCF grey+ yellow - *04*	NPG	54
R270	**90131** Rft Distribution grey - *95-96*	35	45
R2005	**90135** Rft Distribution grey - *97*	35	45
R?	**DC230 ST 'Connectivity'** red+black Sp Edn 60 (Xerox) metalic nameplates* - *98*	120	150

* Possibly a Code 3 model. It was given as prizes on a series of training courses run by the Xerox Corporation and had numbered certificates.

L77. Class 91 Electric

ICs = InterCity Swallow grey livery

R240	**91001** ICs - *90-91*	30	40
R585	**91001 'Swallow'** ICs - *91-94*	45	60
R356	**91003 'The Scotsman'** ICs - *94*	40	50
R736	**91003 'The Scotsman'?** ICs Sp Edn 30 (QVC) - *94*	NA	NPG
X?	**91003** GNER navy blue ex-set - *98*	35	45
R585	**91004 'The Red Arrows'** ICs - *91-94*	45	60
R240	**91008** ICs - *90-91*	30	40
R293	**91009 'Saint Nicholas'** ICs - *95*	40	50
R240	**91010** ICs - *90-91*	30	40
R585	**91011 'Terence Cuneo'** ICs - *91-94*	45	60
R269	**91014** ICs, dummy pant - *94-99*	30	NA
R2002	**91019 'Scottish Enterprise'** (X3554) navy blue GNER 4-car pack - *97-00*	50	75
R2002A	**91023** GNER navy 4-car pack - *02-04*	NPG	100
R2002A	**91019 'Scottish Enterprise'** navy blue GNER 4-car pack - *02-04*	50	75
R2069	**91022 'Robert Adley'** ICs - *98-99*	35	45
R392	**91025 'BBC Radio One FM'** ICs - *93*	45	60
R392	**91025 'BBC Radio 1 FM'** ICs - *93*	45	60
R367	**91031 'Henry Royce'** ICs - *96*	35	45
R392	**919799 'BBC Radio One FM'** ICs Sp Edn 71 (BBC Radio 1) - *92*	90	120
R2427	**91129 'Queen Elizabeth II'** navy blue GNER Mallard 4-car pack - *04*	NPG	90

Class 91 electric 'BBC Radio One FM' [L77]

L78. Class 92 Electric

Many have non-functioning pantographs.

R2354A	**92001 'Victor Hugo'** EWS Tunnel maroon+ yellow - *03-04*	35	54
R289	**92009 'Elgar'** BRe Tunnel Railfreight Distribution grey - *95-96*	35	NA
R374	**92020 'Milton'** EPS Tunnel grey - *96*	45	60

R855	**92022 'Charles Dickens'** BRe Rft Dist Tunnel grey ex-R825 set - *96-98*	35	NA
R2004	**92026 'Britten'** BRe Tunnel grey - *97-98*	40	55
R2354B	**92031 'The Institute of Logistics and Transport'** EWS Tunnel maroon+ yellow - *03-04*	35	55
R2035	**92045 'Chaucer'** EPS Tunnel grey - *97*	45	60

Multiple Units

L79. Class 101 DMU

R157+ R158	**M79079/M79632** BRc green from 66 with yellow panels 2-car - *62-67*	25	65
R157	**M79079/M79632** BRc green illuminated headcode 2-car - *74-78*	35	45
R157C	**M79079/M79632** BRe blue with yellow panel 2-car - *70-71*	50	75
R157+ R158	**M79628/M79629** BRb grn 2-car - *58*	30	70
R157+ R158	**M79628/M79629** BRc green 2-car - *59-61*	20	60

L80. 'Blue Pullman' DMU

Up until 1969 the white window panel in the sides of the cars was a separate moulding and the glazing was flush. For the new livery of 1969 the body tool was modified and the window panel was painted on. The glazing was now no longer flush. The 1974 model has the white window band painted through to the end of the side of the car.

R555+ R556	BR Pullman blue+white, crest on front - *63-67*	25	65
R555+ R556	BR Pullman blue+white, yellow front - *68*	35	60
R555+ R556	BR Pullman blue+white, yellow front, Rail blue - *68*	50	80
R538	BR Pullman blue+white crest on sides - *74*	40	NA
R555C	**W60095/W60747** BR Pullman grey+blue - *69-72*	30	65
R555C	**W60095/W60745** BR Pullman grey+blue - *?*	40	75

Blue Pullman DMU [L80]

L81. Class 110 DMU

alt. nos. = a sheet with two sets of alternative numbers is provided in the pack. dest. = a choice of three destination blinds is provided.

R403	**E51815/E59814/E52078** BRe 3-car set, alt. nos., dest. blue+grey - *84*	40	60
R698	**E51816/E59707/E51832** BRe white 3-car set, alt. nos., 2 sets of dest. - *82-83*	35	50
R267	**E51819/E51846** BRe blue 2-car set, alt. nos., dest. - *89-91*	30	40
R687	**E51824/E59708/E51844** BRc green 3-car set, 2 sets of dest. - *83-84*	40	55
R2073	**E51827/E59808/E52080** BRe blue+grey 3-car set, dest. - *98*	40	60
R369	**E51829/E59695/E51812** BRc green 3-car set, dest. - *92-97*	40	55

R369A	**E51840/E59701/E51815** BRc green 3-car set, dest. - *98*	35	50
R2297A	**E51841/E59710/E51819** BRc green 3-car set - *02-03*	45	65
R2297B	**E51834/E59703/E51827** BRc green 3-car set - *03-04*	40	60
R2073A	**E52066/E59696/E52085** BRe blue+grey 3-car set, dest. - *99-00*	40	60
R377	**E52073/E59816/E51846** BRe white 3-car set, dest. - *96-97*	35	50

L82. Class 142 'Pacer' DMU

R297	**142013 (55554/55604)** BRe Manchester PTE orange - *89*	45	65
R326	**142015 (55556/55606)** BRe Western England brown+cream - *92-93*	50	70
R?	**142020 (55589/55639)** BRe Reg Rlys Tyne & Wear PTE yellow - *95-96*	40	NA
R103	**142023 (55564/55614)** BRe Regional Railways grey - *94-95*	35	55
R867	**142048 (55589/55639)** BRe Provincial Sector blue - *87-92*	28	45
X?	**142065 (55715/55761)** Northern Spirit blue Sp Edn (Kays) - *99*	30	NA
R451	**142069 (55719/55765)** BRe Regional Railways MPTE grey - *96-97*	35	55
R2161	**142074 (55724/55770)** Northern Spirit blue - *00-02*	40	55

L83. Class 155 Super Sprinter DMU
(ex-Dapol model)

R2162B	**155317(57317/52317)** Provincial grey+ blue 2-car set - *00-04*	45	60
R2162A	**155325(57325/52325)** Provincial grey+blue 2-car set - *00-04*	45	60
R2108	**155344(57344/52344)** Metro maroon 2-car set - *99-04*	45	60

L84. Class 4SUB EMU
Most of the British sets are a blue-green but those produced towards the end were a yellow-green. Tools went to New Zealand in 1965 where a similar but slightly different model was made.

R156+ R225	**S1052S/S1057S** BRb green 2-car - *57-58*	55	110
R156+ R225	**S1052S/S1057S** BRc green 2-car - *59-62*	45	110
R156+ R225	**S1052S/S1057S** BRc yellow-green 2-car - *62-64*	75	130

Class 4SUB EMU [L84]

L85. Class 370 APT

R543	**370 001/2 'City of Derby'** BRe I-C APT grey, all yell front, 5-car set - *80*	100	NA
R794	**370 001/2 'City of Derby'** BRe I-C APT grey, yell + black front, 5-car train pack - *81-84*	100	140

L86a. Class 373 'Eurostar' (Jouef)
(H0 scale model)

R543	**3211/3212** Eurostar grey (Jouef on under side) - *95-96*	30	50

L86b. Class 373 Eurostar (Hornby)

Eur3015X	**3015** Eurostar grey power car - *96-98*	18	NA
Eur3016X	**3016** Eurostar grey dummy car - *96-98*	12	NA
R665	**3015/3016** Eurostar grey train pack - *96-98*	NA	50
Eur3019X	**3019** Eurostar grey power car - *96-97*	18	NA

Eur3020X	**3020** Eurostar grey dummy car - *96-97*	12	NA
R?	**3019/3020** Eurostar grey train pack - *96-97*	NA	50
Eur3021X	**3021** Eurostar grey power car - *96-97*	18	NA
Eur3022X	**3022** Eurostar grey dummy car - *96-97*	12	NA
-	**3021/3022** Eurostar grey ex-set - *96-97*	35	NA
R665A	Eurostar grey train pack - *99*	35	50
(R1013)	**3219/?** Eurostar grey ex-set - *99-04*	35	NA
R2379	Eurostar grey 6-car train pack - *04*	60	80
R2197	**3301/3302** GNER navy + 2 coaches train pack - *01-03*	60	80
R2197A	**3306 'Golden Jubilee' /3305** GNER navy + 2 coaches train pack - *04*	NPG	120

L87. Class 466 'Networker' EMU

R2001A	**466016 (64875/78327)** NSE white Kent 1 Link Networker - *99-0*	45	65
R2001	**466040 (64899/78351)** NSE white Kent Link Networker - *97-98*	50	70
R2307A	**466020 (78331/64879)** Connex white - *03-04*	NPG	80
R2307B	**466035 (78346/64894)** Connex white - *03-04*	NPG	80

BATTLE SPACE

LB1. Turbo Car
The electic motor drove a fan at the rear of the vehicle which propelled it.

R752	red with yellow plastic spike - *67*	35	65
R752	red with yellow plastic spike - *68-70*	25	45

PLAY LOCOMOTIVES

LP1. Top Tank 0-4-0T

R657	black also R659, R659 - *63-67*	3	8
R660	bright blue - *66?*	4	10
R660	mid blue - *66?*	8	15
R660	yellow - *67*	4	10
R660	dark green - *68*	5	12

Top Tank 0-4-0T [LP1]

0-4-0 Diesel Shunter
(see L59. North British Shunter 0-4-0DS)

LP2. Barclay 0-4-0DS

R858	blue - *69-71?*	25	NA
R858	red - *?*	35	NA

LP3. Continental Tank 0-4-0T
c/w = clockwork.

R852	**7744** blue - *68-74*	12	NA
R852	**7744** black - *?68*	10	15
R852T	**7744** black NMRA couplings - *?68*	10	15
R852CN	**Chugga** yellow - *69-71*	40	80
R854	red c/w - *69?-79*	5	NA
R854	**1863** red c/w - *71?*	25	NA
R854	maroon c/w - *69?-79*	8	NA
R854	green c/w - *71*	10	NA
R852?	blue with red chassis electric - *?*	10	NA

R854	**7321** bright green c/w - *71-72*	12	NA
R854	**7321** dark green c/w - *?*	8	NA
R854	**7321** red c/w - *?*	10	NA
R854	**7321** black c/w - *73-82*	10	15
R854T	NMRA couplings - *?*	30	60
R762	black sold in a temporary box - *73*	15	20
R755	**6042** black, can motor - *73-75*	10	NA
R854	**'Timmy'** red c/w - *83-87*	12	NA
T121	**'Peter'** yell c/w - *83-85*	12	NA
T118	**'Adam', 'Michael', 'Simon', 'Robert'** red c/w - *84-90?*	12	NA
T118	**'Edward', 'Douglas'** blue c/w - *84-90?*	12	NA
T118	**'Henry'** green c/w - *84-90?*	12	NA
T118	**'Ivor'** red c/w - *91-?*	14	NA
T774	**'Postman Pat'** 1 red c/w T107 set - *84-87*	20	NA
?	**'Mr Puffer'** light blue c/w - *?*	20	NA
T868	**2571** red c/w - *88-94*	7	10
T113	**'Pound Puppies'** yellow c/w ex-T113 set - *?-87*	20	NA

Continental 0-4-0T [LP3]

LP4. Swedish Diesel 0-4-0

R853	blue - *69*	25	NA
R853	**5771** yellow - *69-71*	20	NA
R853	**4718** red - *69-71*	20	NA

LP5. Wild West 0-4-0

R873	**1863** red ex-Wild West set - *71-72*	80	NA*
-	grey loco only no markings - *?*	20	NA

* the set sells for about £150.

LP6. International Tank 0-4-0T

R254	**254** black - *75-76*	15	20
R256	**256** black - *76-77*	12	17
R256	**256** red - *77*	12	17
R257	**256** green - *76*	15	20
R256	**7 'Bulldog'** green - *83*	20	25
R164	**1 'Iron Horse'** grey - *84-85*	20	25

International 0-4-0T [LP6]

LP7. Thomas the Tank Engine and Friends

R251	**1** (Thomas) blue 0-6-0T push along - *88-92 95-?*	5	NA
R352	**1** (Thomas) blue 0-4-0T c/w - *86-98*	8	13

R9005	**1** (Thomas) blue 0-4-0T c/w - *98-99*	8	13
R354	**1** (Thomas) blue 0-4-0T elec - *95-98*	10	NA
R9034	**1** (Thomas) blue 0-6-0T c/w - *99-02*	5	8
R350	**6** (Percy) green 0-4-0ST elec - *85-04*	15	21
R810	**6** (Percy) green 0-4-0ST c/w - *87-98*	8	13
R9004	**6** (Percy) green 0-4-0ST c/w - *98-99*	8	13
R9035	**6** (Percy) green 0-4-0ST c/w - *99-02*	5	8
R351	**1** (Thomas) blue 0-6-0T elec - *85-04*	20	30
R383	**4** (Gordon) blue 4-6-2 elec - *86-92, 95-04*	35	70
R382	**8** (Duck) green 0-6-0PT elec - *86-91, 95-04*	25	30
R317	(Devious Diesel) black 0-6-0DS elec - *87-88*	25	40
R9050	(Devious Diesel) blk 0-6-0DS elec - *02-04*	NPG	31
R852	**5** (James) red 2-6-0 elec - *88-04*	30	60
R90	(Bertie the Bus) maroon battery - *88-92, 95-98*	15	NA
R9024	**'Bill'** yellow 0-4-0ST c/w - *99*	4	6
R9025	**7** (Toby) Tram c/w brown - *99*	4	6
R9026	**'Ben'** yellow 0-4-0ST c/w - *99*	4	6
R9047	**'Bill'** yellow 0-4-0ST elec - *01-04*	15	21
R9046	**7** (Toby) brown Tram elec - *01-04*	15	21
R9048	**'Ben'** yellow 0-4-0ST elec- *01-04*	15	21
R9049	**3** (Henry) green 4-6-0 elec - *02-04*	NPG	60
R9064	**D261** (Diesel) green - *03-04*	30	42
R9066	Sodor Ironworks green+yellow, face with open mouth (Bert) - *03-04*	22	31
R9067	Sodor Ironworks green+yellow, face with closed mouth ('Arry) - *03-04*	22	31

LP8. Push-Along Models 0-4-0T

T123	**Gordon** blue push along - *84*	3	NA
T123	**Percy** green push along - *84*	3	NA
T123	**Thomas** blue push along - *84*	3	NA
T123	**James** red push along - *84*	3	NA
T119	**4 'Dixie'** red push along - *83-85*	3	NA
T120	**2 'Pixie'** blue push along - *83-87*	3	NA
T116	**'My First Train'** red push along - *87-91*	5	NA
T106	**5 'Postman Pat'** red push along - *84*	5	NA

TRANSCONTINENTAL (produced with overseas markets in mind)

LT1. Class 23 TC Pacific (Hiawatha) 4-6-2

The model was also sent out to Australia and New Zealand for finishing and sale in local packaging. 8wt = 8 wheel tender. 6wt = A3 6 wheel tender.

R54+R32	**2335** black 8wt - *54-61*	20	50
R54+R32	**2335 'Hiawatha'** black 8wt - *62-69*	30	60
R54+R32	**2335 'Hiawatha'** blk 8wt no. in yell - *?*	40	70
R54S	**2335 'Hiawatha'** blk 8wt + smoke - *68*	40	60
R54S	**2335 'Hiawatha'** blk Acho c'plgs - *68*	50	100
R54S+ R32L	**2335 'Hiawatha'** black Lima couplings - *68*	90	150
R?	**2335 'Hiawatha'** black 6wt - *70?*	40	60
various	**1542** black 6wt - *70-73*	30	65
various	**2335** Canadian Pacific black - *69-73*	70	120

LT2. Class Wab Baltic Tank 4-6-4T

The tank was fitted with lamps front and back but these are sometimes missing on used models. The model was also made in Australia, New Zealand and South Africa.

R56	**4830** Tri-ang Railways black - *55-60*	20	70
R56	**4830** Tri-ang Railways maroon - *61*	100	200
R56	**4830** TR shield logo maroon - *61*	120	180

LT3. Class F7 A+B Units (Single Ended Diesel)

The model was also sent out to Australia and New Zealand for finishing and sale in local packaging. TR = Tri-ang Railways. TC = Transcontinental. TA = TransAustralia. CN = Canadian National. CP (and CPRail) = Canadian Pacific.

R55	**4008** (A unit) TR silver+red, silver cabs - *55-57*	15	40
R57	**4008** (dummy A unit) TR silver+red, silver cabs - *55-57*	10	30
R56	**4008** (B unit) TR silver+red no cabs - *56-60*	15	40
R56	**4008** (B unit) TR silver+red, no cabs, number both ends - *56*	30	50
R56	**4009** (B unit) TR silv+red no cabs - *?*	50	90

R55	**4008** (A unit) TR silver+red, red cabs - *58-61*	12	40
R57	**4008** (dummy A unit) TR silver+red, red cabs - *58-61*	8	30
R55	**4008** (A unit) TC silver+red - *62-64*	20	55
R55	**4008** (A unit) TC silv+red 2 m'tors - *63*	50	90
R55	**4008** (A unit) TA silver+red - *66-66,70*	90	120
R0551	**4008** (A unit) CN black+red - *65-66, 69-73*	12	40
R0552*	**4008** (A unit) CP grey+maroon - *67-69*	80	120
R0553*	**1404** (A unit) CPRail red - *70-73*	20	30
R0550*	**1404** (A unit) TC red - *72-73*	15	NA

* Also found with other 'R' numbers

LT4. RS2 Switcher Bo-Bo

TR = Tri-ang Railways. CN = Canadian National. CPRail = Canadian Pacific. NSWR = New South Wales Railway. VR = Victorian Railways.

R155	**5007** TR maroon - *57*	80	200
R155	**5007** TR green - *57*	80	250
R155	**5007** TR yellow - *57*	70	170
R155	**5007** TR yellow, dazzle stripes - *58-60*	15	45
R155	**7005** TR yellow, dazzle stripes - *61*	20	50
R155	**7005** Transcontinental yellow - *62-64*	20	50
R1550	**7005** TransAustralia yellow - *65-67*	50	100
R1551	**3000** CN black - *65-72*	25	50
R1552	**3000** Canadian Pacific grey - *69*	100	150
R1553	**7553** CPRail red - *71-73*	20	50
R308	**48142** NSWR maroon - *made?*	NPG	NPG
R308	**34051** NSWR maroon - *74-76*	55	85
R763	**T336** VR blue - *76*	45	75

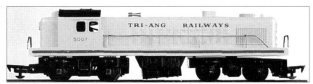

Transcontinental Bo-Bo switcher [LT4]

LT5. B-60 'Double Ended Diesel'

The model was also made in Australia and New Zealand and in different liveries. TR = Tri-ang Railways.

R159	**5007** TR blue+yellow - *58-61*	10	30
R250	**5007** TR blue+yell dummy unit - *58-61*	10	30
R159	**5007** TR shield blue+yellow - *62-69*	15	40
R159	**5007** TR shield grn-blue+yell - *68, 70*	30	50
R159	**5007** TR or VR on front bt.blue+yell, no name or shield on sides - *71-78*	35	60
R?	**5007** TR green+yellow - *60?*	90	150

LT6. TC Electric Loco

(same body tool as 'Double Ended Diesel')

R257	**7503** Tri-ang Railways grn+org - *59-60*	50	120
R257	**7503** Tri-ang Railways 2 -tone grn - *61*	90	160
R257	**7503** TR shield 2 -tone green - *62-64*	75	150

Yard Switcher (see L58. Dock Dhunter 0-4-0DS)

LT7. Budd RDC-2

TC = Transcontinental.

R352	**31018** TC silv+red - *61-67*	50	110
R232	**31018** TC silv+red, dummy - *61-67*	90	150
R232	**31027** TC silv+red, dummy - *61-67*	90	150
R352CN	**101** CN silv+blk - *65-71*	40	110
R232CN	**101** CN silv+blk, dummy - *65-71*	40	80
R829	**303** Northern Pacific silver - *68*	45	110
R825	**303** Northern Pacific silv dummy - *68*	45	80
R830	**3400, 3403** Santa Fe silver - *68*	45	110
R826	**3400, 3403** Santa Fe silv dummy - *68*	45	80
R831	**9003** C&O silver - *68*	45	110
R827	**9003** C&O silver, dummy - *68*	45	80
R832	**501, 503** Reading Lines silver - *68*	45	110
R828	**501, 503** Reading Lines silv d'my - *68*	45	80
R352A	**31018** TransAustralia silv+red - *65-67*	90	165

LT8. Davy Crockett 2-6-0

R358/R233	**1863 'Davy Crockett'** red+yellow (also R358S) TTR - *62-65*	40	125
R358SL	**1863 'Davy Crockett'** red+yellow Lima couplings, TTR - *62-65*	90	150

'Davey Crockett' [LT8]

LT9. Continental Prairie 2-6-2T

R653	black single dome - *63-65*	50	125
R653	black+red double dome - *69*	70	140

NSWR Suburban Electric

(made only in Australia and so not included here)

LT10 S Class GM Co-Co

VR = Victorian Railways

R317	**S311** VR blue+yel - *77-78*	35	65
R317	**'Sir Ferdinand Muller'** VR blue+yellow - *77-78*	60	75
R317	**'Sir Charles Gavin Duffy'** VR blue+yellow - *77-78*	60	75
R318	**GM12** commonwealth Railways maroon - *77-78*	50	70

COACHES

Standard British Passenger Stock

Tri-ang, Railways, Tri-ang Hornby and Hornby Railways coaches are always plastic and marked on the underside with 'Tri-ang', 'Tri-ang Hornby', 'Hornby Railways' or 'Hornby'. On some, the name 'Tri-ang' has been erased on the mould but the words 'Built in Britain' remain.

Coach Finder

6" coaches - C1
7" coaches - C2
9" coaches - C4, C5 & C6
TPOs - C3, C22, CT2
Suburban coaches - C5 & C16
Pullman cars - C6, C7, C8 & C9
DMU centre cars - C9, C10 & C11
Ex-Airfix GWR coaches - C16, C17 & C18
Clerestory coaches - C14 & C15
Caledonian coaches - C20
Collett coaches - C19
Maunsell coaches - C26 & C27
Stanier coaches - C22 & C23
Gresley coaches - C24 & C24A
Thompson coaches - C25
Rocket coaches - C12
4-wheel coaches - C13
12-wheel diner - C23
Mk1 coaches - C28
Mk2 coaches - C29 & C30
Mk3 coaches -C31 & C32
Mk4 coaches - C33
DVT - C34
Eurostar stock - C35
Coach Packs - C36
Play coaches - CP1
Transcontinental cars - CT1, CT2, CT3 & CT4

Rovex Tri-ang Hornby

LMS 6" coaches showing end variations [C1]

Cat.No.	Company, Number, Colour, Date	£	£

Tri-ang Short Coaches of the 1950s

C1. LMS 6" Coach

Rovex	**LMS** 7573, 27424 maroon, hook+loop couplings - *50-52*	8	15
R20	**LMS** 7573, 27424 maroon' Tri-ang transfers on underside - *52*	15	20
R20	**LMS** 7573, 27424 maroon, hook+bar coupling (Mk2) - *52?-56*	4	10

C2. BR 7" Coach + Primary Coach

R21	**BR** M7071 red+cream Tri-ang transfers on underside - *52*	10	15
R21	**BR** M7071 red+cream - *52-56*	5	8
R22	**BR** S17035 green - *53-56*	8	15
R230	no number maroon Primary - *59-62*	4	10
R231	no number green Primary - *59-61*	4	10

C3. 7" Travelling Post Office (1955 model)
(see also CT2 below)

The car was sold as part of an operating accessory which included pick-up and put-down trackside apparatus. The 'R' number and values refer to the complete set.

R23	**Royal Mail** M30224 brown, transfers - *55*	40	50
R23	**Royal Mail** M30224 maroon, transfers - *55-56*	10	18
R23	**Royal Mail** M30224 maroon - *57-68*	5	16
R402M	**Royal Mail** M30224 blue+grey - *69-72*	7	18

N.B. The ''boxed'' value is for the set is given, i.e. the coach with the lineside accessories.

C4a. BR 9" Composite

The tools for the composite were later used in New Zealand for green coaches. Models with closed axle boxes sometimes sell for more than those with open axle boxes.

R29	**BR** M24001 red+cream - *56-57*	8	11
R29	**BR** M24001, 24010 maroon+cream - *58-62*	7	10
R221	**BR** S15033, S15034 blue-green - *57-61*	10	12
R221	**BR** S15034 yellow-green - *61-62*	15	17
R321	**BR** M24001, 24010 maroon - *59-61*	8	10
R330	**BR** W15771 dark brown+cream - *60-62*	12	15
R720	**BR** red+cream also R724 - *63-67*	5	NA
R?	red with or without buffers - *66?*	5	NA

C4b. BR 9" Brake

The tools for body of the brake 3rd were later used in New Zealand for green coaches. Models with closed axle boxes sometimes sell for more than those with open axle boxes.

R28	**BR** M34000 red+cream - *56-57*	8	11
R28	**BR** M34000, 34002 maroon+cream - *58-62*	7	10
R220	**BR** S34243, S34245 blue-green - *57-61*	10	12
R220	**BR** S34245 yellow-green - *61-62*	15	17
R320	**BR** M34001, 34002 maroon - *59-61*	8	10
R329	**BR** W34302 dark brown+cream - *60-62*	12	15

C4c. BR 9" Restaurant Car

The tools for the restaurant car were later used in New Zealand for green coaches. Models with closed axle boxes sometimes sell for more than those with open axle boxes. O = orange curtains. B = blue curtains.

R224	**BR** M2001, 2401 maroon+cream O or B - *57-62*	8	15
R229	**BR** S1007 blue-green O or B - *58-61*	12	15
R229	**BR** S1007 yellow-green O - *61-62*	15	17
R322	**BR** M2001, 2401 maroon O - *59-61*	8	15
R331	**BR** W301 dark brown+cream O - *60-62*	12	18

C5a. BR 9" Suburban Composite
ca - closed axle boxes.

R121	**BR** M14006, 41007 maroon - *56-61*	10	12
R121	**BR** 41007 maroon ca - *61-62,67*	12	14
R223	**BR** S3152S, S3155S, S3153S* blue-green - *57-61*	10	15
R223	**BR** S3153S yell-green ca - *61-6,67*	15	18

* large or small numbers may be found.

C5b. BR 9" Suburban Brake

The tools for the brake 3rd were later used in New Zealand for green coaches. ca - closed axle boxes.

R120	**BR** M43171, 53171 maroon - *56-61*	10	12
R120	**BR** 53171 maroon ca - *61-62,67*	12	14
R222	**BR** S4717S, S4718S* blue-green - *57-61*	10	12
R222	**BR** S4718S yellow-green ca - *61-63,67*	15	18

* large or small numbers may be found.

Utility Van - see SR 9" Utility/Luggage Van under 'Pre-Nationalisation Stock'

Pullman Cars

C6a. 9" Pullman Saloon + Continental Sleeper
(1958 model)

The 9" Pullman cars sometimes had plain brass lampshades and sometimes they were painted pink. At one stage lampshades were reduced to a narrow spike. A rarer version has a cream coloured roof and late models had white rim wheels. The Golden Arrow stickers were supplied in a separate packet in 1962 together with a locomotive headboard.

R228	**Pullman** 'Anne', 'Jane'*, 'Ruth' or 'Mary' dark brown+cream - *58-73*	8	15
R228	as above with white wheel rims - *70*	10	15
R228	as above with deep cream roof - *?*	13	18
R228	with Golden Arrow stickers - *62-63*	18	20
R625	Continental Sleeping Car blue - *63-65*	20	40

* An example of 'Jane' has been found with blue (instead of pink) lampshades and is considered to be very rare.

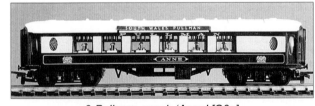

9 Pullman coach 'Anne' [C6a]

C6b. 9" Pullmans Brake Car (1960 model)

See note with 6a (above) re-lampshades, roof colour and Golden Arrow stickers.

R328	**Pullman** 'Car No.79' dark brown+cream - *60-73*	8	14
R328	with white wheel rims - *70*	10	15
R328	with deep cream roof - *?*	13	15
R328	with Golden Arrow stickers - *62-63*	18	20

C7a. Pullman Parlour Car (1975 model)

npf = non-paint finish i.e. the main body colour is provided by the colour of the plastic. SS = Silver Seal (metal rimmed) wheels.

Dark Brown & Yellow or Cream

R229	**Pullman** npf 'Lucille' SS - *75-76*	8	13
R229	**Pullman** 'Lucille', 'Agatha', 'Ursula', 'Sheila' transfers detailed arms SS npf - *77-79*	10	15
R223	**Pullman** 'Lucille', 'Agatha,' Ursula', 'Sheila' crude arms SS - *80-81*	10	15
R223	**Pullman** 'Lucille', 'Agatha,' Ursula', 'Sheila' crude arms, white rims - *82-93*	10	15
R223	**Pullman** 'Lucille', 'Agatha,' Ursula', 'Sheila' design change - *94-01*	10	15
R469	**Pullman** Orient Express 8 names choice white roof - *84-87*	10	15
R491	**Pullman** Orient Express 'Cygnus' white roof - *84-85*	12	18
R492	**Pullman** Orient Express 'Persius', white roof - *84-85*	12	18
R493	**Pullman** Orient Express 'Phoenix', white roof - *84-85*	12	18
R586	**Pullman** Orient Express 'Phoenix', 'Persius' or 'Cygnus' in grey box - *84*	NA	45
R241	**Pullman** 'Ansonia' ex-Tees Tyne Pullman set - *94-96*	12	NA
R217	**Pullman** 'Rosemary' ex-Tees Tyne Pullman set - *94-96*	12	NA
R4037	**Pullman** 'Adrian' ex-R2079 The Kentish Belle pack - *98*	12	NA
R4038	**Pullman** 'Lydia' ex-R2079 The Kentish Belle pack - *98*	12	NA
(R2168)	**Pullman** 'Zena' ex-Yorkshire Pullman pack - *00*	12	NA
(R2168)	**Pullman** 'Eunice' ex-Yorkshire Pullman pack - *00*	12	NA
(R1024)	**Pullman** 'Juana' ex-Queen of Scots set - *01-02*	12	NA
(R1024)	**Pullman** 'Sheila' ex-Queen of Scots set - *01-02*	12	NA
(R2279M)	**Pullman** 'Coral' ex-Thanet Belle MO pack - *02*	12	NA
(R2279M)	**Pullman** 'Maid of Kent' ex-Thanet Belle MO pack - *02*	12	NA
(R1048)	**Pullman** 'Aurelia' ex-Western Pullman set - *04*	12	NA
(R1048)	**Pullman** 'Chloria' ex-Western Pullman set - *04*	12	NA

Blue & grey

R230	**Golden Arrow** S309S large number SS - *75-76*	18	25
R230	**Golden Arrow** S309S small number SS - *76-78*	15	20

C7b. Pullman Brake Car (1980 model)
SS = Silver Seal (metal rimmed) wheels.
Dark Brown & Yellow or Cream

R233	**Pullman** 77, 78, 79, 80 SS - *80-01*	10	15
R233	**Pullman** 77, 78, 79, 80 white rim wheels - *82-98*	10	15
R236	**Pullman** 'Car No.77' ex-Tees Tyne Pullman set - *94-95*	12	NA
R4039	**Pullman** 'Car No.68' ex-R2079 The Kentish Belle pack - *98*	12	NA
R2168	**Pullman** 'Car No.65' ex-Yorkshire Pullman pack - *00*	12	NA
R1024	**Pullman** 'Car No.78' Queen of Scots ex-set - *01-02*	12	NA
(R2279M)	**Pullman** Third Class 'Car No.11' ex-Thanet Belle pack - *02*	12	NA
(R1048)	**Pullman** 'Car No.54' ex-Western Pullman set - *04*	12	NA
(R1048)	**Pullman** 'Car No.27' ex-Western Pullman set - *04*	12	NA

C8a. Pullman 1st Parlour Car (2003 Model)
M = matchboard sides. S = smooth sides.
Dark Brown & Cream

R4143	**Pullman** 'Leona' M - *03*	20	25
R4143A	**Pullman** 'Niobe' M - *03-04*	20	25
(R2300)	**Pullman** 'Rosemary' S ex-Bournemouth Belle train pack - *03*	20	NA
R4162	**Pullman** 'Minerva' S - *03-04*	20	25
(R1038)	**Pullman** 'Cygnus' S ex-Orient Express set - *03-04*	20	NA
(R1038)	**Pullman** 'Ibis' S ex-Orient Express set - *03-04*	20	NA
(R2369)	**Pullman** 'Niobe' M ex-Golden Arrow train pack - *04*	20	NA
(R4196)	**Pullman** 'Onyx' M ex-Golden Arrow coach pack - *04*	20	NA

C8b. Pullman 3rd/2nd Parlour Car (2003 Model)
M = matchboard sides. S = smooth sides.
Dark Brown & Cream

R4144	**Pullman** Car No.35 M - *03*	20	25
R4144A	**Pullman** Car No.34 M - *03-04*	20	25
(R4169)	**Pullman** Car No.66 S ex-Bournemouth Belle coach pack - *03*	20	NA
R4163	**Pullman** Car No.64 S - *03-04*	20	25

C8c. Pullman 1st Kitchen Car (2003 Model)
M = matchboard sides. S = smooth sides.
Dark Brown & Cream

R4145	**Pullman** 'Minerva' - *not made*	NA	NA
R4145	**Pullman** 'Cynthia'' M - *03*	20	25
R4145A	**Pullman** 'Sappho' M - *03-04*	20	25
(R4169)	**Pullman** 'Fingall' S ex-Bournemouth Belle coach pack - *03*	20	NA
R4164	**Pullman** 'Argus' S - *03-04*	20	25
(R1038)	**Pullman** 'Minerva' S ex-Orient Express set - *03-04*	20	NA
(R2369)	**Pullman** 'Cecilia' M ex-Golden Arrow train pack - *04*	20	NA
(R2369)	**Pullman** 'Minerva' M ex-Golden Arrow train pack - *04*	20	NA
(R4196)	**Pullman** 'Adrian' M ex-Golden Arrow coach pack - *04*	20	NA
(R4196)	**Pullman** 'Zenobia' M ex-Golden Arrow coach pack - *04*	20	NA
(R4196)	**Pullman** 'Rosmond' M ex-Queen of Scots train pack - *04*	20	NA

C8d. Pullman 3rd/2nd Kitchen Car (2003 Model)
M = matchboard sides. S = smooth sides.
Dark Brown & Cream

R4146	**Pullman** Car No.59 - *not made*	NA	NA
R4146	**Pullman** Car No.171 M - *03*	20	25
R4146A	**Pullman** Car No.166 M - *03-04*	20	25
(R2300)	**Pullman** Car No.169 S ex-Bournemouth Belle train pack - *03*	20	NA
R4165	**Pullman** Car No.167 S - *03-04*	20	25

C8e. Pullman Brake 3rd/2nd Car (2003 Model)
M = matchboard sides. S = smooth sides.
Dark Brown & Cream

R4150	**Pullman** Car No.54 - *not made*	NA	NA
R4150	**Pullman** Car No.65 M - *03*	20	25
R4150A	**Pullman** Car No.161 M - *03-04*	20	25
(R2300)	**Pullman** Car No.62 S ex-Bournemouth Belle train pack - *03*	20	NA
(R4169)	**Pullman** Car No.63 S ex-Bournemouth Belle coach pack - *03*	20	NA
R4166	**Pullman** Car No.248 S - *03-04*	20	25

DMU Centre Cars

C9. Blue Pullman DMU Centre Car

R426	**Pullman** W60745 (or none) blue+white crests on window panel - *63-68*	18	40
R426	**Pullman** W60745 grey+blue - *69-70*	15	35

| R426 | **Pullman** W60745 blue+white crest below window panel ex-R538 set- *74* | 16 | NA |

C10. Class 101 DMU Centre Car

| R334 | **BR** M59120 green - *61-67* | 15 | 20 |
| R334 | **BR** M59120 small number green - *77* | 15 | 20 |

Class 101 DMU centre car [C10]

C11. Class 110 DMU Centre Car (Trailer 2nd)

R699	**BR** E59707 white 2nd - *82-83*	15	20
X3320	**BR** E59816 white 2nd ex-R377 pack - *96*	15	NA
R688	**BR** E59708 green 2nd - *84-85*	18	20
R688	**BR** E59695 green 2nd - *92-98*	15	17
X?	**BR** E59710 green ex-R2297A - *02-03*	15	NA
X?	**BR** E59703 green ex-R2297B - *03-04*	15	NA
R428	**BR** E59814 blue+grey 2nd - *84-85*	12	15
X3655	**BR** E59808 blue+grey 2nd ex-R2073 pack - *98-99*	12	NA
X3655A	**BR** E59696 blue+grey 2nd ex-R2073A pack - *00*	12	NA

Pre-Nationalisation Stock

C12. 'Rocket' Coach

The coaches were produced with a choice of 3 names, in equal quantities, 'Times', 'Dispatch', 'Experience'.

R621	**Liverpool Manchester** yellow 'Railway Company' - *63-65*	12	25
R621	**Liverpool Manchester** yellow - *64-66*	12	25
R?	**Liverpool Manchester** yell. ex-R795 pack, few sold solo, metal tyres - *82*	15	35

SR 4-wheel coach [C13]

C13. 4 Wheeled Coach

R212	12 blue SS yellow line - *76-78*	5	10
R199	12 blue white rims gold line - *86-87*	5	10
X?	12 bright blue ex-R1016 set - *99-01*	5	NA
R213	**GWR** 12 dark brown+yellow SS - *78-81*	5	8
R213	**GWR** 12 dk.brown+yellow white rims - *82-83*	5	8
R213	**GWR** 12 dark brown+yellow + crest - *?*	10	20
R446	**GWR** 12 dk.brown+yellow white rims - *87-?*	5	8
R446	**GWR** 12 dk.brown+yellow fine printing -*?-04*	5	8
R219	**CR** 12 maroon+white - *80-82*	7	12
R468	**LMS** 12 maroon - *84-04*	6	8
R296	**BR** 12 yellow track cleaner - *82-04*	10	12
R110	**'Annie'** teak white rims - *85-04*	6	8
R112	**'Clarabel'** teak white rims - *85-04*	6	8
R252	**'Annie'** teak motorised ex-Thomas set - *88-?*	7	NA
R498	**LNER** 12 teak ex-set - *87-88*	8	NA
X?	**LNER** 137 teak ex-R1030 set - *02-03*	8	NA

X?	**LNER** 138 teak ex-R1030 set - *02-03*	8	NA
R176	12 blue+red brake van chassis - *93-96*	5	7
R176	12 red+blue brake van chassis - *93-96*	5	NA
R095w	**HR** 12 red ex-Toys-R-Us set - *94*	7	NA
R4121	**SR** 100 malachite green - *00-01*	6	9
R4135	**SR** 350 olive green - *01-04*	6	8
-	maroon ex-R1031 set - *02-03*	6	NA
-	green with red roof ex-R1046 set - *04*	6	NA

C14a. GWR Clerestory All 3rd (short)

R379	maroon+white ex-R795 Railway Children set - *71-72*	45	NA
R024	**LNER** 61456 teak composite - *72-73*	18	20
R391	**LNER** 2247 teak composite - *88-95*	12	15
R332	**LNER** 4103 teak ex-Woolworths set - *03*	12	NA
R384	**LMS** 4863 maroon composite - *86-89*	12	20
R?	bright red white roof ex-set - *73?*	20	NA
	Dark Brown + Cream Coaches		
R332	**GWR** 5017 - *61-70*	10	15
R332	**GWR** 5017 white wheel rims - *71-72*	12	17
R332	**GWR** 5017 with crests ex-pack - *71-72*	20	25
R24	**GWR** 5017 paint finish ex-R795 pack - *81*	15	NA

C14b. GWR Clerestory Brake 3rd (short)

R620	**BR** 20 black Engineer's Dept. - *63-65*	15	20
R620	**BR** 20 dark green Engineer's Dept. - *66-67*	12	20
R025	**LNER** 62420 teak - *72-73*	18	22
R449	**LNER** 1475 teak - *88-95*	12	15
R333	**LNER** 3857 teak ex-Woolworths set - *03*	12	NA
R385	**LMS** 6438 maroon - *86-89, 94-95*	12	20
R761	bright red, white roof, no buffers ex-R505 set - *73*	8	NA
	Dark Brown + Cream Coaches		
R333	**GWR** 2316 - *61-70*	10	15
R333	**GWR** 2316 white wheel rims - *71-72*	12	17
R333	**GWR** 2316 with crests - *72*	20	25
R025	**GWR** 2316 paint finish ex-R795 pack - *81*	15	NA

C15a. GWR Clerestory Comp or All 3rd (scale)

R122	**GWR** 1602 dark brown+yellow - *82-85*	12	15
R435	**GWR** 3162 dark brown+cream - *85-87*	14	18
R484	**GWR** 3162 dark brown+cream - *92-96*	14	17
R4119A	**GWR** 945 cream+dark brown - *00-01*	12	15
R4119B	**GWR** 950 cream+dark brown - *00-01*	12	15
R4119C	**GWR** 947* cream+dark brown - *02*	12	15
R4119C	**GWR** 948** cream+dark brown - *02-03*	12	15
R4119D	**GWR** 951* cream+dark brown - *02*	12	15
R4119D	**GWR** 954** cream+dark brown - *02-03*	12	15
R4198	**GWR** 3162 cream+dark brown - *04*	NPG	18
R452	**MR** 2913 maroon - *84-85*	15	18

* As per 2002 catalogue.   ** As per Oct/Nov 2002 'The Hornby Collector' magazine.

C15b. GWR Clerestory Brake 3rd (scale)

R123	**GWR** 3371 dark brown+yellow - *82-85*	12	15
R436	**GWR** 3371 dark brown+cream - *85-87*	15	18
R488	**GWR** 3371 dark brown+cream - *92-96*	14	17
R4120A	**GWR** 3380 cream+dark brown - *00-01*	12	15
R4120B	**GWR** 3375 cream+dark brown - *00-01*	12	15
R4120C	**GWR** 3371 cream+dark brown - *02-03*	12	17
R4199	**GWR** 3321 cream+dark brown - *04*	NPG	18
R453	**MR** 1490 maroon - *84-85*	15	18

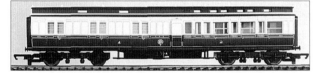

Scale GWR Clerestory brake 3rd [C15b]

C16. GWR Suburban B Brake (ex-Airfix)

These are made from Airfix tooling purchased from Dapol in 1996.

R4030A	**GWR** 6904 dark brown+cream - *97-98*	10	13
R4030B	**GWR** 6900 dark brown+cream - *97*	10	13
R4030C	**GWR** 6762 dark brown+cream - *00-03*	10	13
R4030D	**GWR** 6763 dark brown+cream - *00-04*	10	13
R4099A	**BR** W6381W maroon - *99-02*	12	15
R4099B	**BR** W6382W maroon - *99-03*	12	15

C17. GWR Autocoach (ex-Airfix)

These are made from Airfix tooling purchased from Dapol in 1996.

R4025	**GWR** 190 dark brown+cream - *97-98*	12	15
R4025A	**GWR** 189 dark brown+cream - *00-01*	12	15
R4025B	**GWR** 192 dark brown+cream - *00-02*	12	15
R4186	**GWR** button 189 dark brown+cream - *03*	12	15
R4100A	**BR** W188W maroon - *99*	12	15
R4100B	**BR** W196W maroon - *99*	12	15
R4100C	**BR** W187W maroon - *02-04*	12	18
R4100D	**BR** W000W maroon - *02-04*	12	18
X?	**BR** W194W maroon ex-R2172M pack - *00*	13	NA
X?	**BR** W195W maroon ex-R2172M pack - *00*	13	NA
R4187	**BR** W195W red+cream - *03*	12	15
R4187A	**BR** W192W red+cream - *04*	12	18

C18a. GWR Centenary Composite (ex-Airfix)

These are made from Airfix tooling purchased from Dapol in 1996.

GWR Paddington-Swansea Cars			
R4026	6658 dark brown+cream - *97-99, 02-03*	12	15
R4026A	6859 dark brown+cream - *04*	12	18
R4035	6659 dk.brn+cream ex-R2025 pack - *97-98*	16	NA
R4034	6660 dk.brown+crm ex-R2025 pack - *97-98*	16	NA
R4126	6661 dark brown+cream - *01*	12	15
BR Paddington-Weston Cars			
R4028	W6660W red+cream - *97-98*	12	15
R4031	W6658W red+cream ex-R2024 pack - *97-98*	16	NA
R4032	W6661W red+cream ex-R2024 pack - *97-98*	16	NA

C18b. GWR Centenary Brake (ex-Airfix)

These are made from Airfix tooling purchased from Dapol in 1996.

GWR Paddington-Swansea Cars			
R4027	4576 dark brown+cream - *97-00*	12	15
R4036	4577 dk.brn+cream ex-R2025 pack - *97-98*	12	NA
R4139	4576 dark brown+cream - *01-04*	12	18
R4139A	4580 dark brown+cream - *02-04*	12	18
BR Paddington-Weston Cars			
R4029	W4578W red+cream - *97-98*	12	15
R4033	W4580W red+cream ex-R2024 pack - *97-98*	16	NA

While the other 'Regional' Coaches were produced in BR liveries the Collettes were not. This is a pre-production sample suggesting that they were considering the idea [C19a]

C19a. GWR Collett Composite

npf = non-paint finish i.e. the main body colour is provided by the colour of the plastic. Until 1979 the coaches had BR bogies and then, from 1979, Collett ones were fitted.

R121	**Gordon's** green+yellow - *86-03*	10	13
R091	**James's** red+white - *89-91, 02-03*	12	14
R9051	**James's** red+white - *02-04*	12	14
Dark Brown & Cream Coaches			
R429	**GWR** 6024 shiney BR bogies npf - *77-78*	10	12
R456	**GWR** 6024 satin finish - *79-80*	10	12
R159	**GWR** 6050 crest - *94-97*	10	12
R4065	**GWR** 6099 crest - *98-99*	10	15

R4065A	**GWR** 6068 crest - *00-02*	10	15
R4065B	**GWR** 6030 crest - *03*	12	15
R4065C	**GWR** 6105 crest - *04*	12	18
X3733	**GWR** 6105 black roof ex-R2084 pack - *98*	12	NA
X3734	**GWR** 6181 black roof ex-R2084 pack - *98*	12	NA
X?	**GWR** 6201 Paddington Aberystwyth + Pwllheli ex-R2196M Sp Edn 1500 - *01*	12	NA
X?	**GWR** 6203 Paddington Aberystwyth and Pwllheli ex-R2196M Sp Edn 1500 - *01*	12	NA

C19b. GWR Collett Brake End

npf = non-paint finish i.e. the main body colour is provided by the colour of the plastic. Until 1979 the coaches had BR bogies and then, from 1979, Collett ones were fitted.

R120	**Gordon's** green+yellow - *86-04*	10	13
R094	**James's** red+white - *89-91*	12	14
R9052	**James's** red+white - *02-04*	12	14
Dark Brown & Cream Coaches			
R430	**GWR** 4913 shiney BR bogies npf - *77-78*	10	12
R457	**GWR** 4913 satin finish - *79-80*	10	12
R161	**GWR** 4913 crest - *94-97*	10	12
R4066	**GWR** 4944 crest - *98-99*	10	15
R4066A	**GWR** 4930 crest - *00-01*	10	15
R4066B	**GWR** 4940 crest - *02-03*	NPG	16
R4066C	**GWR** 4932 crest - *04*	NPG	18
X3735	**GWR** 4924 black roof ex-R2084 pack - *98*	12	NA
X?	**GWR** 4920 Paddington Aberystwyth + Pwllheli ex-R2196M Sp Edn 1500 - *01*	12	NA

C19c. GWR Collett Restaurant Car

Based on a design of 1925 of which only four were made. Until 1979 the coaches had BR bogies and then, from 1979, Collett ones were fitted.

R454	**GWR** (button) 9578 dark brown+cream shiney dark BR bogies - *78*	10	15
R458	as above but satin finish - *79-80*	10	15
R157	**GWR** 9578 dark brown+cream crest - *94-96*	10	15
R4151	**GWR** 9578 dark brown+cream crest - *02-03*	12	17
R4151A	**GWR** 9579 dark brown+cream crest - *04*	NPG	18

C20a. Caledonian Composite

R427	**CR** 7511 mroon+white, roof white - *62-67*	15	20
R427	as above with roof grey - *72-73*	14	18
R747	**LMS** 2643 maroon - *71-73*	8	10
R749	**SR** S1750 olive green - *71-73*	12	15
R26	**GWR** dark brown+cream - *72-73*	15	20

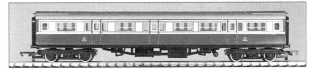

Caledonian coach [C20a]

C20b. Caledonian Brake

R428	**CR** 7501 maroon+white, roof white - *62-67*	15	20
R428	as above with roof grey - *72-73*	14	18
R748	**LMS** 2640 maroon - *71-73*	8	10
R750	**SR** S1774 olive green - *71-73*	12	15
R27	**GWR** 8176, 8178 dark brown+cream - *72-73*	15	20

C21a. LMS Stanier Composite

npf = non-paint finish i.e. the main body colour is provided by the colour of the plastic. Unless otherwise stared the maroon coaches has silver roofs.

maroon			
R433	**LMS** 3934 npf - *77-79*	7	10
R474	**LMS** 4120 LMS - *80-85*	7	10
R474	**LMS** 4120 L M S - *86-97*	7	10
R4041	**LMS** 4069 ex-R2033 pack - *97*	10	NA
R4040	**LMS** 4075 ex-R2033 pack - *97*	10	NA
R4061	**LMS** 4183 - *98-99*	10	NA
R4061A	**LMS** 4113 - *00-01*	10	12
X?	**LMS** 4028 ex-R2167 pack - *00*	10	NA
X?	**LMS** 4024 ex-R2167 pack - *00*	10	NA

X?	**LMS** 4114 ex-R2172M pack - *00*	10	NA
X?	**LMS** 4115 ex-R2172M pack - *00*	10	NA
R4130A	**LMS** 4000 grey roof - *01-02*	10	12
R4130B	**LMS** 4001 grey roof - *01-03*	10	12
R4130C	**LMS** 4020 grey roof - *02-03*	12	17
R4130D	**LMS** 3954 grey roof - *04*	12	18
R429	**BR** M4316 - *91-93*	12	15
X?	**BR** M15387 ex-R2176M pack Euston Keswick Windermere - *00-01*	15	NA

red & cream

R437	**BR** M4329 - *77-79*	8	10
R421	**BR** M4329 - *80-83*	8	10
R442	**BR** M4330 - *85-97*	8	10
R355	**BR** ex-R775 set - *94*	10	NA
X?	**BR** M4070M The Royal Scot ex-R2303M pack - *02*	10	NA
X?	**BR** M4071M London Glasgow ex-R2303M pack - *02*	10	NA

LNER Silver Jubilee Coaches

R872w	1582 silver Gresley bogies ex-set - *92-93*	18	NA
(R2278M)	1586 G 3rd silver BR bogies ex-pack - *02*	18	NA
X?	1582 B 1st silver BR bogies ex-R4168 coach pack - *02*	18	NA

The Coronation Scot Coaches

R422	**LMS** 1070 blue - *84-87, 92-96*	15	18
R4128A	**LMS** 1069 blue - *01, 04*	12	18
R4128B	**LMS** 1070 blue - *01-02*	10	15
R4128C	**LMS** 1071 blue - *02-03*	12	17
X?	**LMS** 3934 maroon ex-R2199M pack - *01*	10	NA
X?	**LMS** 3935 maroon ex-R2199M pack - *01*	10	NA
R4141	**LMS** 3936 maroon - *01*	10	15
R4141A	**LMS** 3937 maroon - *02*	10	15

C21b. LMS Stanier Brake End

npf = non-paint finish i.e. the main body colour is provided by the colour of the plastic.

Maroon

R434	**LMS** 5644 npf - *77-79*	7	10
R475	**LMS** 5714 LMS - *80-81*	7	10
R475	**LMS** 5714 LMS - *82-85*	7	10
R475	**LMS** 5714 L M S - *86-97*	7	10
R4042	**LMS** 5708 ex-R2033 pack - *97*	10	NA
R4060	**LMS** 5200 - *98-99*	10	12
R4060A	**LMS** 5215 - *00-01*	10	12
X?	**LMS** 5619 ex-R2167 pack - *00*	10	NA
X?	**LMS** 5220 ex-R2172M pack - *00*	10	NA
R4129A	**LMS** 5205 grey roof - *01-02*	10	12
R4129B	**LMS** 5206 grey roof - *01-03*	10	12
R4129C	**LMS** 5214 grey roof - *02-03*	12	17
R4129D	**LMS** 5456 grey roof - *04*	12	18
R447	**BR** M5750 - *91-93*	12	15
X?	**BR** M34285 ex-R2176M pack Euston Keswick Windermere - *00-01*	15	NA
X?	**BR** M34358 ex-R2176M pack Euston Keswick Windermere - *00-01*	15	NA

Red & Cream

R438	**BR** M26545 - *77-79*	8	10
R424	**BR** M26545 - *80-83*	8	10
R443	**BR** M26546 - *85-97*	8	10
R357	**BR** ex-R775 set - *94*	10	NA
X?	**BR** M5709 ex-R1004 set - *97*	10	NA
X?	**BR** M5218M The Royal Scot ex-R2303M pack - *02*	10	NA
R592	**Royal Mail** 80868 bright red - *90-93*	12	15

Silver Jubilee Coaches

R873w	**LNER** 1587 Gresley bogies ex-set - *92-93*	18	NA
X?	**LNER** 1581 [A] 1st BR bogies ex-train pack - *02*	18	NA
X?	**LNER** 1587 [F] 3rd BR bogies ex-R4168 coach pack - *02*	18	NA

The Coronation Scot Coaches

R423	**LMS** 5792 blue - *84-87, 92-96*	15	18
R4127A	**LMS** 5812 blue - *01*	10	15
R4127B	**LMS** 5814 blue - *01*	10	15
R4127C	**LMS** 5792 blue - *02-03*	12	17
R4218	**LMS** 5052 blue - *04*	NPG	18
X?	**LMS** 5447 maroon ex-R2199M - *01*	10	NA
R4142	**LMS** 5448 maroon - *01*	10	15
R4142A	**LMS** 5449 maroon - *02*	10	15

C22. Travelling Post Office (1978 model)

npf = non-paint finish i.e. the main roof colour is provided by the colour of the plastic.
SS = metal wheel tyres (Silver Seal).

Maroon

R413	**LMS** 30250 TPO set, SS, npf - *78-79*	12	16
R412	**LMS** 30250 TPO set, wt rims - *83-85*	12	16
R461	**LMS** 30250 TPO set ex-R542 set - *80*	12	NA
R164	**LMS** 30249 TPO set - *94-99*	12	16
R4155	**LMS** 30246 TPO set - *02-04*	20	30
R597w	**BR** M30250M ex-R758 set - *91-93*	16	NA

Blue & Grey

R416	**BR** M80328 SS - *80-82*	16	20
R416	**BR** M80328 white rims - *80-82*	16	20

Dark Brown & Cream

R440	**GWR** 848 TPO set - *85-87*	20	25
R4108	**GWR** 848 TPO set - *00-02*	20	25
R416	**Royal Mail** NSX80363 bright-red TPO set - *88-93*	14	18

C23. LMS 12-Wheel Diner (ex-Dapol)

Maroon

R4095	**LMS** 235 Dining Car - *99-00*	12	15
R4095A	**LMS** 228 Dining Car - *01-02*	12	15
R4095B	**LMS** 230 Dining Car - *02-04*	13	18
R4131A	**BR** M230M Rest Car - *01-02*	12	15
R4131B	**BR** M239M Rest Car - *02-04*	13	18
X?	**BR** M229M ex-R4177 coach pack - *03*	14	NA

Red + Cream

R4188	**BR** M234M Rest Car - *03*	13	17
R4188A	**BR** M235M Rest Car - *03-04*	13	18

Detail on part of the LMS 12-wheel diner [C23]

C24a. LNER Gresley Composite (1977 model)

npf = non-paint finish i.e. the main roof colour is provided by the colour of the plastic.
BlkE = black coach ends (the rest have teak ends). Until 1979 the coaches had BR bogies and then, from 1979, Gresley ones were fitted.

Teak

R435	**LNER** 22357 BlkE BR bogie npf - *77-78*	7	10
R435	**LNER** 22357 BlkE npf - *79*	10	12
R477	**LNER** 22357 - *80-97*	10	13
R477	**LNER** 22357 - *99-02*	10	NA
X?	**LNER** 22356 ex-R1039 set - *03-04*	10	NA
X?*	**LNER** 22357 ex-R1039 set - *03-04*	10	NA
R?	**LNER** 22352? - *99-02*	10	NA
R4062	**LNER** 22287 - *98-99*	10	13
R4062A	**LNER** 24386 - *00*	10	13
R4062B	**LNER** 32441 - *01*	10	15
R4062C	**LNER** 32275 - *02-03*	NPG	16
R4047	**LNER** 24337 ex-Kays pack - *97*	12	NA
R4046	**LNER** 24367 ex-Kays pack - *97*	12	NA

Maroon

R483	**BR** E11002E - *83-85*	12	14
R400	**BR** E11029E - *92-97*	12	14
R4055	**BR** E18271E - *98-99*	12	14
R4055A	**BR** E18249E - *00-02*	12	14
R4055B	**BR** E18207E - *02-03*	12	16
X3905	**BR** E11000E ex-R2134M pack - *99*	12	NA

Red + Cream

R409	**BR** E18276 - *88-93*	12	14
R4043	**BR** E18299 ex-Kays pack - *97*	12	NA
R4044	**BR** E18301 ex-Kays - *97*	12	NA
R4189	**BR** E18236E - *03-08*	12	18
X?	**BR** E18274E ex-R2363M pack - *03*	12	NA
X?	**BR** E18269E ex-R2363M pack - *03*	12	NA
X?	**BR** E18281E ex-R1040 Toys-R-Us set - *03*	12	NA

*This version had blackened metal wheels.

C24b. LNER Gresley Brake End (1977 model)

npf = non-paint finish i.e. the main roof colour is provided by the colour of the plastic.
BlkE = black coach ends (the rest have teak ends). Until 1979 the coaches had BR bogies and then, from 1979, Gresley ones were fitted.

Teak

R436	**LNER** 4237 BlkE BR bogies npf - *77-78*	7	10
R436	**LNER** 4237 BlkE - *79*	10	12
R478	**LNER** 4237 - *80-91*	10	13
R4063	**LNER** 5547 - *98-99*	10	13
R4063A	**LNER** 7913 - *00-01*	10	13
R4063B	**LNER** 5550 - *02-03*	12	16
R478 *	**LNER** 4237 ex-R1001 set - *97-02*	10	NA
R?	**LNER** 1076 ex-Kays pack - *97*	12	NA
X?	**LNER** 4236 ex-R1039 set - *03-04*	10	NA
X?**	**LNER** 4237 ex-R1039 set - *03-04*	10	NA
R4048	**LNER** 32557 ex-Kays pack - *97*	12	NA

Maroon

R484	**BR** E16769E - *83-85*	12	14
R448	**BR** E10076E - *92-97*	12	14
R4054	**BR** E10073E - *98-01*	12	14
R4054A	**BR** E10108E - *00-02*	12	14
X?	**BR** E10065E ex-R1021M set - *99*	12	NA
X3906	**BR** E10058E ex-R2134M pack - *99*	12	NA
X3907	**BR** E10064E ex-R2134M pack - *99*	12	NA

Red + Cream

R410	**BR** E10066 - *88-93*	12	14
R4045	**BR** E10098 ex-Kays - *97*	12	NA
R4190	**BR** E10066 - *03-04*	12	18
X?	**BR** E10066E ex-R2363M pack - *03*	12	NA
X?	**BR** E10097E ex-R1040 Toys-R-Us set - *03*	12	NA
X?	**BR** DB10074 red ex-R1029 set -*02-03*	15	NA

* See also catalogue picture. **This version had blackened metal wheels.

The LNER Gresley type brake end [C24b]

C24c. LNER Gresley Sleeping Car (1978 model)

npf = non-paint finish i.e. the main roof colour is provided by the colour of the plastic.
BkE = black coach ends (the rest have teak ends).

Teak

R448	**LNER** 1316 BkE BR bogies npf - *78*	7	10
R448	**LNER** 1316 BkE npf - *79*	8	10
R479	**LNER** 1316 - *82-85*	10	13
R413	**LNER** 1316 - *88-90*	10	13
R430	**LNER** 1237 - *96-97*	10	13
R4064	**LNER** 1147 - *98-99*	10	13
R4064A	**LNER** 1261 - *00-03*	10	13
R485	**BR** E1237E maroon - *82-83*	15	18
R419	**BR** E1237 red+cream - *88-91*	14	16
R4191	**BR** E1209E red+cream - *03-04*	12	18

C24Aa. LNER Gresley 1st (2004 model)

R4171	**LNER** ? teak - *04*	NPG	25
R4179	**LNER** ? red+cream - *04*	NPG	25

C24Ab. LNER Gresley 3rd (2004 model)

R4172	**LNER** ? teak - *04*	NPG	25
R4180	**LNER** ? red+cream - *04*	NPG	25

C24Ac. LNER Gresley Brake (2004 model)

R4170	**LNER** ? teak - *04*	NPG	25
R4178	**LNER** ? red+cream - *04*	NPG	25

C24Ad. LNER Gresley Buffet Car (2004 model)

R4173	**LNER** ? teak - *04*	NPG	25
R4181	**LNER** ? red+cream - *04*	NPG	25

C24Ae. LNER Gresley 1st Sleeper (2004 model)

R4174	**LNER** ? teak - *04*	NPG	25
R4182	**LNER** ? red+cream - *04*	NPG	25

C25a. LNER Thompson Full 3rd

R745	**LNER** 1010 teak white rims - *70-75*	7	12
R937	**LNER** 1010 teak steel rimmed wheels- *76-77*	7	12

C25b. LNER Thompson Brake End

R746	**LNER** 1870 teak white rims - *70-75*	7	12
R938	**LNER** 1870 teak steel rimmed wheels- *76-77*	7	12
R740	**BR** bright red Breakdown Train Unit (Riding) - *71-73*	15	20

The LNER Thompson brake as crew coach [C25b]

C26a. SR Maunsell Composite

npf = non-paint finish i.e. the main body colour is provided by the colour of the plastic.

R431	**SR** 1384 dark green npf - *77-79*	7	10
R441	**SR** 1384 dark green npf - *80-81*	7	10
R441	**SR** 1384 olive green - *84-90*	8	12
R162	**SR** 5544 olive green - *94-97*	10	15
R4059	**SR** 5523 olive green - *98-01*	10	15
R486	**SR** 5117 malachite green - *81-83*	8	12
R424	**SR** 5585 malachite green - *91-93*	8	12
R4009	**SR** 5530 malachite green - *97-98*	10	15
R4009A	**SR** 5540 malachite green - *99-01*	10	15
R4009B	**SR** ? malachite green - *?*	10	15
R4009C	**SR** 5505 malachite green - *00-02*	10	15
R4009D	**SR** 5512 malachite green - *02-03*	12	16
R4009E	**SR** 5508 malachite green - *04*	NPG	18
R437	**BR** S5162S green - *85-86*	15	20
R4125A	**BR** S5505S green - *01-02*	15	20
R4125B	**BR** S5520S green - *01-02*	10	14
R4125C	**BR** S5515S green - *03-04*	12	18
R4125D	**BR** S5516S green - *03-04*	12	18
R4125E	**BR** S3571S green - *04*	12	18

C26b. SR Maunsell Brake End

npf = non-paint finish i.e. the main body colour is provided by the colour of the plastic.

R432	**SR** 1405 dark green npf - *77-79*	7	10
R445	**SR** 1405 dark green npf - *80*	7	10
R445	**SR** 1405 olive green - *84-90*	8	12
R163	**SR** 3562 olive green - *94-97*	10	15
R4058	**SR** 3566 olive green - *98-00*	10	15
R487	**SR** 6564 malachite green - *81-83*	8	12
R425	**SR** 6564 malachite green - *91-93*	8	12
R4008	**SR** 3572 malachite green - *97-98*	10	15
R4008A	**SR** 3570 malachite green - *99-01*	10	15
R4008B	**SR** 3566 malachite green - *99-01*	10	15

R4008C	**SR** 3582 malachite green - *00-02*	10	15
R4008D	**SR** 3563 malachite green - *03*	10	15
R4008E	**SR** 3575 malachite green - *03-04*	10	18
R438	**BR** S?S green - *85-86*	15	20
R4124A	**BR** S3579S green - *01*	10	14
R4124B	**BR** S3568S green - *01*	10	14
R4124C	**BR** S3569S green - *03*	10	14
R4124D	**BR** S?S green - *03*	10	14

C27. SR 9" Utility Van/Luggage Van

Green utility vans were also finished in New Zealand for use there.

R227	**BR** S2357S maroon - *58-61*	12	15
R227	**BR** S2355S maroon - *?*	15	18
R226	**BR** S2355S blue-green - *58-61*	12	15
R226	**BR** S2357S blue-green - *?*	15	18
R226	**BR** S2355S yellow-green - *62-63*	15	20
R226	**BR** S2357S yellow-green - *67*	15	20
R226	**BR** S2355S, S2357S electric-blue light grey roof - *68*	20	25
R226	**BR** S2355S rail-blue, dark grey roof - *69-70*	18	22
R4122	**BR** S2390S blue - *00-03*	10	12
R726	**BR** red+green from RS61 set - *64-65*	50	NA
R178	**SR** 2300 malachite-green - *94-96*	10	12
R4057	**SR** 2330 malachite-green - *98-00*	10	12
R4057A	**SR** 2315 malachite-green - *02-04*	10	18
R4057B	**SR** 2299 malachite-green - *04*	NPG	18
R174	**SR** 2355 olive-green - *94-96*	10	12
R4056	**SR** 2281 olive-green - *98-00*	10	12

SR 9' utility/luggage van [C27]

BR Mk1 Coaching Stock

C28a. BR Mk1 Composite

npf = non-paint finish i.e. the main body colour is provided by the colour of the plastic. Hogwarts Express coaches were first issued with 'Philosopher's Stone' packaging but 'CS Box' refers to 'Chamber of Secrets' packaging, 'PA box' 'Prisoner of Askaban' packaging. W = weathered. SS= Silver Seal steel rimmed wheels.

Maroon

R422	**LMS** 2257 3rd npf - *69-75*	7	10
R935	**LMS** 2257 3rd npf SS- *76-77*	8	11
R422	**BR** 15918 npf - *62-69*	7	12
R382	**BR** 15917, 15918, 15863, 15865 kit of 2 npf - *62-66*	NA	80
R4005	**BR** E15692 - *97-99*	12	15
R4019	**BR** E15700 ex-R2032 pack - *97*	12	NA
R4020	**BR** E15770 ex-R2032 pack - *97*	12	NA
(R1007)	**BR** E15398 ex-set - *97?*	12	15
R4092	**BR** M15350 ex-R2078 pack - *98*	14	NA
R409W	**BR** M15443 ex-R2078 pack - *98*	14	NA
X3849	**BR** M15050 ex-R2112 pack - *99*	14	NA
X3850	**BR** M15181 ex-R2112 pack - *99*	14	NA
(R1021M)	**BR** E15399 ex-set - *99*	14	NA
(R1021M)	**BR** E15398 ex-set - *99*	14	NA
(R2176M)	**BR** M15287 ex-pack - *00*	14	NA
R4133A	**BR** M15311 - *01-02*	12	15
R4133B	**BR** M15821 - *02-03*	12	17
R4133C	**BR** M15824 - *04*	12	19
R4201	**BR** M15625 W - *04*	12	18
X?	**BR** E16008 Marylebone Rugby Sheffield Sp Edn 1500 - *01*	14	NA
X?	**BR** E16009 Marylebone Rugby Sheffield Sp Edn 1500 - *01*	14	NA
(R2306)	**BR** M15993 ex-train pack - *03-04*	14	NA
(R2306)	**BR** M15986 ex-train pack - *03-04*	14	NA
(R4177)	**BR** M16005 ex-coach pack - *03*	14	NA

(R2329M)	**BR** M15987 W ex-pack - *03*	12	NA
(R2329M)	**BR** M15917 W ex-pack - *03*	12	NA
X4148	**Hogwarts** 99716 ex-R1025 set - *01*	12	NA
R4148A	**Hogwarts** 99716 - *02*	12	17
R4175A	as above but CS box - *03*	12	18
R4219A	as above but PA box - *04*	12	18
R4148B	**Hogwarts** 99718 - *02*	12	17
R4175B	as above but CS box - *03*	12	17
R4219B	as above but PA box - *04*	12	18

Red & Cream

R626	**BR** 15918, 15865 npf - *63-65*	8	15
R445	**BR** E15769 - *96-97*	12	15
R4017	**BR** W15100 ex-R2031 pack - *97*	12	NA
R4018	**BR** W15597 ex-R2031 pack - *97*	12	NA
R4068	**BR** E15695 - *98-99*	12	15
(R2090)	**BR** W15059 ex-pack - *99*	14	NA
(R2090)	**BR** W15064 ex-pack - *99*	14	NA
X3843	**BR** E15406 ex-R2089 pack - *99*	14	NA
X3842	**BR** E15400 ex-R2089 pack - *99*	14	NA
(R2133M)	**BR** W15583 ex-pack -*99*	14	NA
(R2133M)	**BR** W15584 ex-pack - *99*	14	NA
R4206	**BR** E15331 - *04*	12	18

Bright Red & Yellow

R626	**BR** M15210 lines npf - *72*	7	12
R626	**BR** 15210 lines npf - *73-75*	7	12
R890	**BR** M15210 no lines* npf - *72*	7	12
R890	**BR** 15210 no lines* npf - *74*	7	12
R928	**BR** 15210 no lines* SS npf - *76-77*	7	12

Green

R622	**SR** 5015 yellow-green grey roof npf - *69-70*	12	15
R622	**SR** 5015 yellow-green white roof npf - *71*	12	15
R622	**SR** 5015 dark green npf - *74*	10	12
R933	**SR** 5015 dark green SS npf - *76-77*	10	12
R933	**SR** 5740 dark green SS npf - *76-77*	15	17
R622	**BR** S15873 npf - *63-69*	8	15
R4007	**BR** S15042 - *97-98*	12	15
R4115	**BR** S15021 - *00-01*	12	15
R4115A	**BR** S15035 - *02-03*	12	17
R4115B	**BR** S15049 - *04*	NPG	18
X3730	**BR** S15043 rake 885 ex-R2082 pack -*98*	14	NA
(R2194)	**BR** S15915 ex-pack - *01*	18	NA
(R2194)	**BR** S15567 ex-pack - *01*	18	NA
(R4140)	**BR** S15568 ex-coach pack - *01*	18	NA

Dark Brown & Cream

R743	**GWR** 5015 npf - *69-71, 74-75*	10	15
R931	**GWR** 5015 SS npf - *76-77*	10	15
R438	**BR** W15533 - *96-97*	12	15
R848	**BR** W15861 ex-R826 set - *96-98*	12	NA
R858	**BR** W15771 ex-R826 set - *96-98*	12	NA
R4051	**BR** W15542 - *98-99*	12	15
R4089	**BR** W15425 ex-R2077 pack - *98*	14	NA
R4090	**BR** W15428 ex-R2077 pack - *98*	14	NA
(R2166)	**BR** W15584 ex-pack - *00*	14	NA
(R2166)	**BR** W15583 ex-pack - *00*	14	NA
(R2364M)	**BR** W15059 ex-pack - *00*	14	NA
(R2364M)	**BR** W15063 ex-pack - *00*	14	NA
R4209	**BR** W15334 - *04*	12	18

Blue & Grey

R727	**BR** 15865 electric blue npf - *65-68*	10	15
R730	**BR** 15865 electric blue ex-kit npf - *67-68*	NA	50
R727	**BR** 15865 npf - *69-71*	7	12
R730	**BR** 15865 ex-kit npf - *69*	NA	50
R4110	**BR** W15599 - *00-01*	12	15
R4110A	**BR** W16201 - *02-04*	12	18

*Mail order models had no black line above and below window band.

BR Mk1 composite coach [C28a]

C28b. BR Mk1 Brake

npf = non-paint finish i.e. the main body colour is provided by the colour of the plastic. Hogwarts Express coaches were first issued with 'Philosopher's Stone' packaging but 'CS Box' refers to 'Chamber of Secrets' packaging 'PA box' = 'Prisoner of Azkaban' packaging. W = weathered. SS = Silver Seal (metal rimmed) wheels

Maroon

R423	**LMS** 5051 npf - *69-75*	7	10
R936	**LMS** 5051 SS npf - *76-77*	8	11
R423	**BR** 35115 npf - *62-69*	7	12
R383	**BR** 35115, 35116, 35024, 35025 kit of 2 npf - *62-66*	NA	80
R4004	**BR** E34007 - *97-99*	12	15
R4021	**BR** E34225 ex-R2032 - *97*	12	NA
(R1007)	**BR** E34160 ex-set - *97?*	12	15
R4094W	**BR** M34100 ex-R2078 - *98*	14	NA
X3851	**BR** M34389 ex-R2112 - *99*	14	NA
(R2176M)	**BR** M34285 ex-pack - *00*	14	NA
(R2176M)	**BR** M34358 ex-pack - *00*	14	NA
R4132A	**BR** M34288 - *01-02*	12	15
R4132B	**BR** M34106 - *02-04*	12	18
X?	**BR** E34413 Marylebone Rugby Sheffield Sp Edn 1500 - *01*	14	NA
(R2306)	**BR** M35099 ex-train pack - *03-04*	14	NA
(R4177)	**BR** M35110 ex-coach pack - *03*	14	NA
(R2329M)	**BR** M34286 W ex-pack - *03*	12	NA
R4200	**BR** M34399 W - *04*	12	NA
(R1025)	**Hogwarts** 99723 ex- set - *01*	12	NA
R4149A	**Hogwarts** 99723 - *02*	12	17
R4176A	as above but CS box - *03*	12	18
R4220A	as above but PA box - *04*	12	18
R4149B	**Hogwarts** 99312 - *02*	12	17
R4176B	as above but CS box - *03*	12	17
R4220B	as above but PA box - *04*	12	18

Red & Cream

R627	**BR** 35115, 35024 npf - *63-65*	8	15
R450	**BR** E34600 - *96-97*	12	15
R4022	**BR** W34154 ex-R2031 pack - *97*	12	NA
R4069	**BR** E34010 - *98-99*	12	15
(R2090)	**BR** W34302 ex-pack - *99*	14	NA
X3844	**BR** E34232 ex-R2089 pack - *99*	14	NA
(R2133M)	**BR** W34301 ex-pack - *99*	14	NA
R4205	**BR** E34412 - *04*	12	18

Bright Red & Yellow

R891	**BR** M34100 no lines* npf - *72*	7	12
R891	**BR** 34100 no lines* npf - *74*	7	12
R627	**BR** 34100 no lines* npf - *73-75*	7	12
R929	**BR** 34100 lines SS npf - *76-77*	7	12

Green

R623	**SR** 4351 yellow-green grey roof npf - *69-70*	12	15
R623	**SR** 4351 yell-green white roof npf - *71*	12	15
R623	**SR** 4351 dark green npf - *74*	10	12
R934	**SR** 4351 dark green SS npf - *76-77*	10	12
R623	**BR** S34936 npf - *63-69*	8	15
R4006	**BR** S34269 - *97-98*	12	15
R4114	**BR** S34284 - *00-02*	12	15
R4114A	**BR** S34158 - *03-04*	12	18
X3729	**BR** S34271 rake 885 ex-R2082 pk - *98*	14	NA
X3728	**BR** S34272 rake 885 ex-R2082 pk - *98*	14	NA
(R2194)	**BR** S34641 ex-pack - *01*	18	NA
(R4140)	**BR** S34642 ex-coach pack - *01*	18	NA

Dark Brown & Cream

R744	**GWR** 5104 npf - *69-71, 74-75*	10	15
R932	**GWR** 5104 SS npf - *76-77*	10	15
R437	**BR** W34149 - *96-97*	12	15
R850	**BR** W34154 ex-R826 set - *96-98*	12	NA
R4050	**BR** W34151 - *98-99*	12	15
R4091	**BR** W34300 ex-R2077 pack - *98*	14	NA
(R2166)	**BR** W34315 ex-pack - *00*	14	NA
(R2364M)	**BR** W34312 ex-pack - *00*	14	NA
R4208	**BR** W34800 - *04*	12	18

Blue & Grey

R728	**BR** 35024 electric blue npf - *65-68*	10	15
R731	**BR** 35024 electric blue ex-kit npf - *67-68*	NA	50
R728	**BR** 35024 npf - *69-71*	7	12
R731	**BR** 35024 ex-kit npf - *69*	NA	50
R4109	**BR** W34809 - *00-01*	12	15
R4109A	**BR** W34917 - *02-04*	12	18
R4109B	**BR** ? - *03-04*	12	18

*Mail order models had no black line above and below window band.

C28c. BR Mk1 Buffet

npf = non-paint finish i.e. the main body colour is provided by the colour of the plastic. rwe = raised window frames (from 1974 onwards) unpainted (mail order). chrm = chrome raised window frames. alum = aluminium raised window frames. SS = Silver Seal (metal rimmed) wheels

Maroon

R424	**BR** 1807 npf - *62-67*	7	15
R384	**BR** 1805, 1807, 1823, 1825 kit of 2 npf - *62-65*	NA	80
R441	**BR** E1821 - *96-97*	12	15
R4067	**BR** E1853 - *98-99*	12	15
R4203	**BR** M1817 W - *04*	12	18

Red & Cream

R628	**BR** 1825 npf - *63-65*	8	15

Bright Red & Yellow

R628	**BR** 1805 line npf - *72-74*	7	10
R892	**BR** 1805 no line* npf - *74*	7	10

Green

R624	**BR** S1851 npf - *63-67*	8	15
R4072	**BR** S1849 - *98-99*	12	15
R4117	**BR** S1852 - *00-01*	12	15
R4117A	**BR** S1850 - *02-03*	12	17
R4117B	**BR** S1857 - *04*	12	18
(R4140)	**BR** S1850 ex-coach pack - *01*	12	NA

Dark Brown & Cream

R455	**BR** W1814 - *96-97*	12	15
R4052	**BR** W1816 - *98-99*	12	15
R4211	**BR** W1813 - *04*	12	18

Blue & Grey

R729	**BR** 1825 electric blue npf - *67-68*	10	15
R732	**BR** 1825 electric blue ex-kit npf - *67-68*	NA	50
R729	**BR** 1825 npf - *69-71*	7	12
R732	**BR** 1825 ex-kit npf - *69*	NA	50
R844	**BR** 1805 npf chrm - *74-75*	7	10
R897	**BR** 1805 npf rwe * - *74*	7	10
R897	**BR** 1807 npf rwe - *74?*	12	15
R923	**BR** 1805 npf chrm SS - *76-78*	7	10
R923	**BR** 1805 npf alum - *79*	7	10
R419	**BR** 1805 paint finish - *80-82*	7	10
R4112	**BR** W1849 - *00-02*	12	15

Grey & Beige

R4138A	**BR IC (Anglia)** 1850 - *01-03*	12	15

*Mail order models had no black line above and below window band.

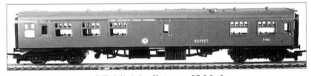

BR Mk1 buffet car [C28c]

C28d. BR Mk1 Sleeping Car

npf = non-paint finish i.e. the main body colour is provided by the colour of the plastic. chrome = chrome raised window frames. alum = aluminium raised window frames.

Maroon

R339	**BR** 2510 npf - *61-67*	8	15
R381	**BR** 2510, 2511 mrn kit of 2 npf - *62-65*	NA	80
R339	**BR** 80658 npf - *61-67*	18	20
R461	**BR** E2510 - *96-97*	12	15
R4070	**BR** E2121 - *98-99*	12	15
R433	**BR** W2105 - *96-97*	12	15
R4049	**BR** W2005 - *98-99*	12	15
R4210	**BR** W2104 - *04*	12	18
R4134A	**BR** M2003 - *01-02*	12	15
R4134B	**BR** M2064 - *02-04*	12	18
R4202	**BR** M2008 W - *04*	12	18

Blue & Grey

R339	**BR** 2510 electric blue npf - *68*	10	15
R339	**BR** 2510 npf - *69-72*	7	12
R339	**BR** 2510 rail chrome npf - *74-75*	7	12
R924	**BR I-C** 2510 chrome npf - *76-78*	7	10
R924	**BR I-C** 2510 alum npf - *79*	7	10
R420	**BR I-C** 2510 paint finish alum - *80-82*	7	10
R4113	**BR** W2574 - *00-02*	12	15

C28e.   BR Mk1 Full Parcels Brake

npf = non-paint finish i.e. the main body colour is provided by the colour of the plastic.

Maroon

R425	**BR** 80531, 80657 npf - *62-67*	8	14
R387	**BR** 80531, 80532, 80657, 80658 CKD kit of 2 npf - *62-65*	NA	80
(R1007)	**BR** E80617 ex-set - *97?*	14	NA
R4204	**BR** M80532 W - *04*	12	18

Red & Cream

R440	**BR** E80533 - *96-97*	12	15
R4073	**BR** E80535 - *98-99*	12	15
R4207	**BR** E80532 - *04*	12	18

Green

R4071	**BR** S81510 - *98-99*	12	15
R4116	**BR** S81542 - *00-02*	12	15
R4116A	**BR** S81292 green - *03-04*	12	15

Dark Brown & Cream

R436	**BR** W81021 - *96-97*	12	15
R4053	**BR** W81259 - *98-99*	12	15
R4212	**BR** W80705 - *04*	12	18

Blue & Grey

R425	**BR** 80657 electric blue npf - *68*	10	15
R425	**BR** 80657 npf - *69-71*	7	15
R4111	**BR** W80660 - *00-03*	12	15

BR Mk1 full brake [C28e]

BR Mk2 Coaching Stock

C29a.   BR Mk2 Open Coach

npf = non-paint finish i.e. the main body colour is provided by the colour of the plastic.
MO = mail order. chrome = chrome window frames. alum = aluminium window frames.
plain = plain window frames. SS = Silver Seal (metal rimmed) wheels.

Blue & Grey

R722	**BR** M5120 interior lights npf - *68-72*	10	15
R724	**BR** M5120 IC chrome npf - *73-75*	7	10
R895	**BR** M5120 IC plain MO npf - *74*	7	10
R921	**BR** M5120 IC chrome SS npf - *76-78*	7	10
R968	**BR** M? IC plain MO npf - *c78*	7	10
R921	**BR** M5120 IC alum SS npf - *79*	7	10
R417	**BR** M5232 IC alum SS - *80-83*	8	12
X3299	**BR** E5305 ex-Flying Scotsman coach pack - *95-96*	25	40
X3296	**BR** E5293 ex-Flying Scotsman coach pack - *95-96*	25	40

Miscellaneous Liveries

R432	**Regional Railways** 5267 - *96-97*	15	20
R428	**Regional Railways** 5221 ScotRail - *96*	12	15
R395	**Regional Railways** 5157 ScotRail - *96*	12	15
R720	**CIE** orange+black SS - *76*	30	40
R439	**NSE** 5381 bright blue - *87-91*	18	22
R4153	**NSE** 5261 blue W - *04*	12	18

C29b.   BR Mk2 Brake

npf = non-paint finish i.e. the main body colour is provided by the colour of the plastic.
MO = mail order. chrome = chrome window frames. alum = aluminium window frames.
SS = Silver Seal (metal rimmed) wheels. W = weathered.

Blue & Grey

R723	**BR** M14052 brake 1st npf with lights - *68-72*	10	15
R726	**BR** M14052 IC chrome frames npf - *73-75*	7	10
R896	**BR** M14052 IC plain frames MO npf - *74*	7	10
R922	**BR** M14052 IC chrome npf SS - *76-78*	7	10
R929	**BR** M14052 IC chrome npf SS - *76-78*	7	10
R969	**BR** M9439 IC plain frames MO npf SS - *c78*	7	10
R969	**BR** W5449 IC plain frames MO npf - *c78*	8	12
R922	**BR** M14052 IC alum paint npf SS - *79*	7	10
R418	**BR** M9439 IC alum paint frames SS - *80-83*	8	12
X3297	**BR** E14090 blue+grey ex-Flying Scotsman coach pack - *95-96*	25	40

Deep Purple

R459	**Royal Train** 2905 sleeper/power car - *84-85*	15	25
X?	**Royal Train** 2921 royal household couchette ex-R1045 M&S set Sp Edn + R2370 train pack - *03-04*	20	NA
X?	**Royal Train** 2920 royal household couchette ex-R4197 coach pack - *04*	20	NA

Miscellaneous Liveries

R431	**Regional Railways** 17118 1st - *96-97*	15	20
R435	**ScotRail** 17099 brake 1st - *96*	12	15
R721	**CIE** orange+black SS - *76*	30	40
R098	**QPV** ADB975468 yellow breakdown crew coach - *87-90*	15	20
R444	**NSE** 17086 bright blue brake 1st - *87-90*	18	22
R4153	**NSE** 17057 blue W - *04*	12	18

C30a.   BR Mk2d Coaches (ex-Airfix)

These are made from Airfix tooling purchased from Dapol in 1996.

Red & Black

R4086	**Virgin** 5744 standard - *98*	10	13
(R1022)	**Virgin** 6165 standard ex-set - *99*	14	NA
R4086A	**Virgin** 6149 standard - *99-01*	10	13
R4086B	**Virgin** 6059 [E] standard - *02*	12	17
R4086C	**Virgin** 5948 [E] standard - *03*	12	17
R4086D	**Virgin** 5955 [E] standard - *04*	12	18
R4088	**Virgin** 3293 1st - *98-01*	10	13
R4088A	**Virgin** 3345 1st - *99-01*	10	13
R4088B	**Virgin** 3397 [C] 1st - *not made*	NA	NA
R4088B	**Virgin** 3350 [D] 1st - *02-03*	12	17
R4088B	**Virgin** 3345 [D] 1st - *02-03*	12	17
R4088C	**Virgin** 3382 [F] 1st - *03*	12	17
R4088C	**Virgin** 3362 [D] 1st - *04*	12	17

Light Blue

R4137A	**Anglia** 3368 1st - *01*	12	15
R4137B	**Anglia** 3358 1st - *02-03*	12	15
R4137C	**Anglia** 3290 1st [K] - *03-04*	12	18
R4136A	**Anglia** 6800 high density standard - *01*	12	17
R4136B	**Anglia** 5836 high density standard - *02-04*	12	18

Blue & Grey

R4215	**BR** W3172 1st - *04*	12	18
R4216	**BR** W5619 standard - *04*	12	18

BR Mk2d coach [C30a]

C30b.   BR Mk2d Brake (ex-Airfix)

These are made from Airfix tooling purchased from Dapol in 1996.

Red & Black

R4087	**Virgin** 9496 - *98*	10	13
R4087A	**Virgin** 9523 - *99-00*	10	13
R4087B	**Virgin** 9538 [A] - *02*	12	17
R4087C	**Virgin** 9525 [A] - *03*	12	17
R4087D	**Virgin** 9513 [A] - *04*	12	18
(R1022)	**Virgin** 9531 ex-set - *99*	12	NA

BR Mk3 Coaching Stock

C31a. BR Mk3 Open (7 windows) (1977 model)

Window strip with raised window frames was printed with the window surrounds. *A sheet of number transfers was provided.

R439	I-C * blue+grey Mk2 bogies 2nd - 77-79	7	12
R439	I-C * blue+grey 2nd - 78-79	7	12
R428	I-C * blue+grey 1st - 79	7	12
R426	I-C * blue+grey 2nd - 80-85	7	12
R425	I-C * blue+grey 1st - 80-84	7	12
R489	I-C 125 42251 stone/grey 2nd - 84	10	14
R488	I-C 125 41121 stone/grey 1st - 84	10	14
R743	XPT trailer silver - 83	15	NA

*These contained six pairs of numbers on a sheet. For 2nd class HST stock there were W42003, W42004 and W42005 and for loco hauled stock there were M12004, M12005 and M12006. For 1st class HST stock there were W41003, W41004 and W41005 and for loco hauled stock there were M11007, M11008 and M11009.

C31b. BR Mk3 Queen's Saloon

This was the same as 31c below but had double doors at one end of each side.

R451	Royal Train 2904 deep purple - 84-85	10	20

C31c. BR Mk3 Open (8 windows) (1984 model)

The window strip was a clear plastic strip, without raised window frames, onto which window surrounds were printed. Thus, different window arrangements, such as those on the Duke's Saloon, can appear on what was structurally a standard coach design.

R455	Royal Train 2903 deep purple Duke's Saloon - 84-85	10	20
R454	Hover Speed blue+red - 86-87	15	18
R426	Dept M&EE ADB975814 red+blue Test Coach 10- 91-92	15	18
R431	I-C *blue+grey open 1st - 85-88	8	12
R432	I-C *blue+grey open 2nd - 85-88	8	12
	Inter-City Beige & Grey		
R433	I-C 125 41121 - 1st - 85-87	7	12
R433	as above but beige and dark grey	7	12
R434	I-C 125 42251 - 2nd - 85-87	7	12
R434	as above but beige and dark grey	7	12
	INTERCITY Beige & Dark Grey/Black		
R395	IC 41*** choice of numbers 41098, 41098 or 41117 - 1st - 88-89	7	12
R420	IC 42*** choice of numbers 42191, 42192 or 42193 - 2nd - 88-91	7	12
R704	IC 42*** choice of numbers 42191, 42192 and 42193 2nd - 90-98	8	12
R719	IC 41*** choice of numbers 41097, 41098 and 41117 1st - 91-92	8	12
X3397	IC 42220 Tourist ex-R897 set -96	9	NA
X3394	IC 42230 Tour ex-R897 set - 96	9	NA
X3407	IC 42090 Tour R901 set - 96-97	10	NA
X3412	IC 42095 Tour R901 set - 96-97	10	NA
	ScotRail Blue		
R895	11909 grey composite - 88-89	12	15
R896	12030 grey tourist - 88-89	12	15
	Navy Blue		
R4010	GNER 41097 1st - 97	8	10
X3552	GNER 42191 tourist ex-R2000 set - 97-98	10	12
X3553	GNER 42192 tourist ex-R2000 set - 97-98	10	12
R4011	GNER 42158 2nd - 97	8	10
R4077	GNER 41098 [H] 1st - 98	10	15
R4078	GNER 42092 [F] 2nd - 98	10	15
	Red+Black		
X3604	Virgin 42090 [E] R2045 pk - 97	10	NA
X3605	Virgin 42103 [F] R2045 pk - 97	10	NA
R4081	Virgin 42116 [D] 2nd - 98	9	15
R4080	Virgin 41081 [H] 1st - 98	9	15
	Jade		
X3605	MM 42121 [B] Tour R2046 pack 97	10	NA
X3604	MM 42120 [C] Tour R2046 pack -97	10	NA
R4084	MM 42119 [D] 2nd - 98	9	15
R4083	MM 41061 [G] 1st - 98	9	15

* A sheet of number transfers was provided. For 2nd class HST stock there were W42003, W42004 and W42005 and for loco hauled stock there were M12004, M12005 and M12006.

Original BR Mk3 coach in virgin livery [C31c]

C31d. BR Mk3a Brake (1977 model)

R467	Inter-City 125 blue+grey - not made	NA	NA

C31e. BR Mk3 Buffet Car (1980 model)

This was basically the same model as the open coach (31c) but with different windows printed onto the window strip and a different roof moulding.

R427	BR W40307 blue+grey Restaurant Buffet 125 - 80-81	8	10
R427	BR 40307 blue+grey Restaurant Buffet 125 - 82-87	8	10
R490	BR 40322 beige+grey Restaurant Buffet 125 - 84-87	8	12
R430	INTERCITY 40***, choice of nos. 40097, 40098 or 40117 beige+grey Mk3 - 88-89	7	12
R713	INTERCITY 40***, choice of nos. 40097, 40098 or 40117 beige+black - 90-92	9	12
X3395	INTERCITY 40754 beige+black ex-R897 set - 96	9	NA
R4012	GNER 40750 navy blue Mk3a - 97	8	10
R4079	GNER 40740 [G] navy blue Mk3a - 98	10	15
R4082	Virgin 40401 [G] red+black Mk3a - 98	9	15
R4085	Midland Mainline 40729 [F] jade Mk3a - 98	9	15

C32a. BR Mk3 Open Car (Full Length)

	Navy Blue		
R4105	GNER 42104 [E] standard - 99-00	12	15
(R2116)	GNER 42171 [C] stand ex-pack - 99	14	NA
(R2116)	GNER 42172 [D] stand ex-pack - 99	14	NA
R4104	GNER 41088 [G] 1st - 99-00	12	15
	Red & Black		
(R2114)	Virgin 42230 [E] stand ex-pack - 99-01	14	NA
(R2114)	Virgin 42237 [D] stand ex-pack - 99-01	14	NA
(R1023)	Virgin ? standard ex-set - 99-04	12	NA
(R1023)	Virgin ? standard ex-set - 99-04	12	NA
R4097	Virgin 12083 [F] standard - 99-01	12	15
R4097A	Virgin 42239 [F] standard - 00-03	12	17
R4097B	Virgin 12154 [F] standard - 03-04	12	18
(R2298)	Virgin 42217 [D] stand ex-pack - 02-03	14	NA
(R2298)	Virgin 42216 [E] stand ex-pack - 02-03	14	NA
(R2298A)	Virgin 42109 [D] stand ex-pack - 04	14	NA
(R2298A)	Virgin 42108 [E] stand ex-pack - 04	14	NA
R4096	Virgin 11011 [H] 1st - 99-01	12	15
R4096A	Virgin 41168 [H] 1st - 00	12	15
R4096B	Virgin 11042 [H] 1st - 02-03	12	17
R4096C	Virgin 11026 [H] 1st - 03-03	12	18
	Ivory & Green		
(R2115)	GWT 42081 [C] standard ex-pack - 99	14	NA
(R2115)	GWT 42082 [D] standard ex-pack - 99	14	NA
R4102	GWT 42089 [E] standard - 99-03	12	15
R4102A	GWT 42083 standard - 00	12	15
R4101	GWT 41003 [G] 1st - 99-01	12	15
R4101A	GWT 41004 1st - 00	12	15
	Purple		
R4160A	FGW 41005 [G] 1st - 02-03	12	17
R4160B	FGW 41004 [H] 1st - 02	12	17
R4160C	FGW 41055 open 1st [G] - 04	12	18
R4161A	FGW 42083 [E] standard - 02-04	12	18
R4161B	FGW 42071 [D] standard - 02-04	12	18
R4161B	FGW 42118 standard - 02-03	12	17
(R2299)	FGW 42069 [C] stand ex-pack - 02-04	14	NA
(R2299)	FGW 42070 [B] stand ex-pack - 02-04	14	NA
	White & Blue		
R4213	MM ? 1st - 04	12	18
R4214	MM ? standard - 04	12	18

Rovex Tri-ang Hornby

Inter-City Blue & Grey

R4158A	**BR** W42285 2nd - *02-03*	12	17
R4157A	**BR** W41137 1st - *02-04*	12	18
(R2296)	**BR** W42283 2nd ex-pack - *02-04*	14	NA
(R2296)	**BR** W42284 2nd ex-pack - *02-04*	14	NA

Deep Purple

X?	**Royal Train** 2903 Queen's parlour car ex-R1045 set Sp Edn (M&S) + R2370 Royal set - *03-04*	20	NA
X?	**Royal Train** 2904 Duke's parlour car ex-R1045 set Sp Edn (M&S) + R2370 Royal set - *03-04*	20	NA
(R4197)	**Royal Train** 2918 Royal Household car ex-coach pack - *03-04*	20	NA
(R4197)	**Royal Train** 2919 Royal Household car ex-coach pack - *03-04*	20	NA

C32b. BR Mk3 Buffet Car (Full Length)

R4106	**GNER** 40706 [F] navy - *99-00*	12	15
R4098	**Virgin** 10217 [G] red+black - *99*	12	15
R4098A	**Virgin** 10219 [?] red+black 10253 [?] red+black - *00-01*	12	15
R4098B	**Virgin** 10253 [G] red+black - *02*	NPG	17
R4098C	**Virgin** 10205 [G] red+black - *03*	12	17
R4098D	**Virgin** 10220 [G] red+black - *03-04*	12	18
R4103	**GWT** 40703 [F] ivory+green - *99*	12	15
R4103A	**GWT** 40707 [F] ivory+green - *00-01*	12	15
R4183A	**FGW** 40703 [F] purple - *03*	12	17
R4183B	**FGW** 40712 [F] purple - *03*	12	17
R4183B	**FGW** 41005 [G] purple - *03-04*	12	18
R4159A	**BR** W40330 blue+grey - *02-04*	12	18

Scale model of BR Mk3 buffet car [C32b]

BR Mk4 Coaching Stock

C33a. BR Mk4 Tourist Open

R407	**IC** 12401 beige+black - *90-96*	10	14
R407	**IC** 12406 beige+black - *90-96*	10	14
R407	**IC** 12414 beige+black - *90-96*	10	14
R452	**IC** 12410 beige+black ex-R696 set - *91-96*	12	NA
R453	**IC** 12408 beige+black ex-R696 set - *91-96*	12	NA
R4002	**GNER** 12514 or 12574? navy blue - *97*	12	15
X3556	**GNER** 12405 navy ex-R2002 pack - *97-00*	14	NA
X3557	**GNER** 12406 navy ex-R2002 pack - *97-00*	14	NA
(R1012)	**GNER** 12488 navy blue ex-set - *98-99*	14	NA
(R1012)	**GNER** 12487 navy blue ex-set - *98-99*	14	NA
(R2002A)	**GNER** M12452 [D] navy ex-pack - *02-04*	14	NA
(R2002A)	**GNER** M12453 [C] navy ex-pack - *02-04*	14	NA
R4075	**GNER** 12330 [F] navy blue - *98-00*	12	15
R4075A	**GNER** 12308 [F] navy blue - *02-04*	12	16
R4075B	**GNER** 12315 navy blue - *02-04*	12	16

C33b. BR Mk4 Open 1st

R405	**IC** 11203 beige+black - *90-96*	10	14
R405	**IC** 11208 beige+black - *90-96*	10	14
R405	**IC** 11214 beige+black - *90-96*	10	14
R4001	**GNER** 11229 navy blue - *97*	12	15
R4074	**GNER** 11262 [H] navy blue - *98-00*	12	15
R4074A	**GNER** 11239 [H] navy blue - *02-04*	12	18
R4074B	**GNER** 11206 navy blue - *02-04*	12	18

C33c. BR Mk4 Catering Car

R408	**IC** 10303 beige+black - *90-96*	10	14
R408	**IC** 10305 beige+black - *90-96*	10	14
R408	**IC** 10308 beige+black - *90-96*	10	14

R4003	**GNER** 10304 navy blue - *97*	12	15
R4076	**GNER** 10333 [G] navy blue - *98-00*	12	15
R4076A	**GNER** 10322 [G] navy blue - *02-04*	12	16
R4076B	**GNER** 10308 navy blue - *02-04*	12	16

C34. BR Driving Van Trailer (DVT)

R472	**ICs** 82205? beige+black - *91-97?*	15	NA
R268	**ICs** 82201 beige+black - *91-97*	15	18
R268	**ICs** 82207 beige+black - *93-97*	15	18
R268	**ICs** 82204 beige+black - *93-97*	15	18
X3555	**GNER** 82204 navy ex-R2002 pack - *97-00*	12	NA
X?	**GNER** 82230 navy blue ex-R2002A - *02-03*	12	NA
X3708	**GNER** navy blue ex-R1012 set - *98*	12	NA
R4147A	**Virgin** 82110 red+black - *02-03*	NPG	17
R4147B	**Virgin** 82141 red+black - *02-04*	NPG	17

C35. Eurostar Passenger Saloon

Eur3021/1X	373021 grey ex-set R816 - *96-97*	8	NA
Eur3022/1X	373022 grey ex-set R816 - *96-97*	8	NA
Eur3015/1X	373015 grey ex-pack R665 - *97*	8	NA
Eur3016/1X	373016 ex-pack R665 - *97*	8	NA
R4013	373015, 373016 grey 2 x sals - *97-98*	16	20
Eur3219/1X	grey ex-R1013 set - *98-04*	8	NA
Eur2220/1X	grey ex-R1013 set - *98-04*	8	NA
R4013A	373003, 373004 grey 2 x sals - *99-00*	16	20
R4013B	grey 2x centre saloons - *00*	16	17
(R2379)	grey ? 2x saloons ex-pack - *04*	20	NA
(R2379)	grey ? 2x saloons ex-pack - *04*	20	NA
(R2197)	**GNER** 373301/1 navy ex-pack - *01-03*	10	NA
(R2197)	**GNER** 373302/1 navy ex-pack - *01-03*	10	NA
(R2197A)	**GNER** 373305/1 navy blue ex-pack - *04*	10	NA
(R2197A)	**GNER** 373306/1 navy blue ex-pack - *04*	10	NA
R4152A	**GNER** 373303/9+373304/9 navy blue 2 x sals - *02-04*	25	30
R4152B	**GNER** navy 2 x centre saloons - *02-04*	25	33

COACH PACKS

C36. Various

R4140	**BR** 3 green Mk1s for ACE - *01*	NA	45
R4168	**LNER** 3 silver Staniers - *02*	NA	45
R4169	**Pullman** The Thanet Belle - *not made*	NA	NA
R4169	**Pullman** The Bournemouth Belle - *03*	NA	67
R4177	**BR** 2 maroon Mk1s + ex-LMS restaurant car for The Caledonian - *03*	NA	45
R4197	**Royal Train** 3 cars - *04*	NA	50
R4196	**Pullman** Golden Arrow - *04*	NA	80

STARTER SET COACHES

CP1. 4 Wheel Starter Set Coach

R733	yellow + end verandas - *69-71*	4	NA

Coach from starter sets [CP1]

TRANSCONTINENTAL PASSENGER STOCK

In addition to the British range of coaches there were two series of Transcontinental passenger cars plus, an American style mail car and an old time coach. The coaches in the first series were shorter and toy-like and all carried the inscription 'Tri-ang Railways' The second series consisted of four attractive models which were available from 1962. Early examples of the second series also carried the inscription 'Tri-ang Railways' but that was soon changed to 'Transcontinental'. This same distinction also applies to the Mail car where the earlier wording is most common.

The blue used for Victorian Railways stock was a muddy dark blue but in 1970, the stock of this colour plastic ran out and some VR stock was made in rail blue much to the consternation of the Australian factory.

The series was principally made for Canada where Canadian liveries were later used but it was also sold in Australia where 'TransAustralia' versions were also available. In the late '60s they were exported to America and sold by ATT. These had American railroad names and were made in the UK but packaged in the States. The American range also turn up in Australia where residue stock was sent when the stores were cleared.

CT1.   First Series Passenger Cars

The name and other printed detail was originally applied by transfers but this gave way to heat printing at quite an early stage. TR = Tri-ang Railways

	TR All Silver Cars		
R24	10724, 20425 passenger car - *54-57*	6	10
R25	20425, 10724 vista dome top seating area yellow, dark blue and red - *54-57*	8	12
R25	20425, 10724 vista dome top seating area white, light blue and red - *54-57*	8	12
R25	20425, 10724 vista dome top seating area green, red and yellow - *56-57*	6	10
R125	20537 observation car - *57*	10	15
R130	baggage car - *57*	10	15
	TR Silver & Red Cars		
R24	10724, 20425 passenger car - *58-61*	5	10
R25	20425, 10724 vista dome - *58-61*	5	10
R125	20537 observation car- *58-61*	5	10
R130	baggage car- *58-61*	5	10
R324	diner - *60-61*	10	15
	TR Blue Cars		
R131	10724 passenger car blue roof - *58-60*	5	10
R131	10724 passenger car grey roof - *60-61*	5	10
R132	20425 vista dome blue roof - *58-60*	5	10
R132	20425 vista dome grey roof - *60-61*	5	10
R133	20537 observation car blue roof - *58-60*	5	10
R133	20537 observation car grey roof - *60-61*	5	10
R134	baggage car blue roof - *58-60*	5	10
R134	baggage car grey roof - *60-61*	5	10
R325	diner grey roof - *60-61*	10	15

CT2.   Mail Car

The car was sold as part of an operating accessory which included pickup and put-down trackside apparatus. The 'R' number and values refer to the complete set. The name and other printed detail was originally applied by transfers but this gave way to heat printing at quite an early stage. As the transferred version commands a higher price if the transfers are in good condition, it is listed separately here. TR = Tri-ang Railways. TC = Transcontinetal

R119	**TR** 3609 maroon Mail Express transfers - *56-57*	15	20
R119	**TR** 3609 maroon Mail Express heat printing -*58-61*	10	15
R400	**TC** 3609, 3606 red Mail Express - *62-63*	15	20
R401	**TC** 3606, 3609 blue Mail Express - *62-63*	15	20
R?	**Mail** red ex-RS101A Overlander set - *72*	10	NA
R401	**BR Royal Mail** M30224 blue+grey - *74-77*	10	25
R725	**Battle Space** Command Car D-778 khaki green + commandos- *67-71*	20	50

Transcontinental mail car [CT2]

CT3.   Second Series Passenger Cars

The colour of under frames on these passenger cars varied between black, grey and silver. Initially, the silver was self coloured plastic but this never looked good. Consequently the factory resorted to spraying the coaches silver and these are the ones described below as 'bright silver'. Those in American liveries were fitted with NMRA couplings and sold in ATT boxes or sets but the few sent to Australia had normal tension lock couplings and Tri-ang Hornby boxes. TR = Tri-ang Railways. TC = Transcontinental. TA = TransAustralia. CN = Canadian National. CP = Canadian Pacific. CPRail = Canadian Pacific.

	Green Tri-ang Railways		
R335	70831 passenger car - *62*	35	50
R336	91119 observation car - *62*	35	50
R337	baggage/kitchen car - *62*	35	50
R338	diner - *62*	35	50
	Green Transcontinental		
R335	70831 passenger car - *62-63*	20	45
R336	91119 observation car - *62-63*	20	45
R337	baggage/kitchen car - *62-63*	20	45
R338	diner - *62-63*	20	45
	Blue Transcontinental		
R444	70831 passenger car - *62-66*	10	18
R445	91119 observation car - *62-66*	10	18
R446	baggage/kitchen car - *62-66*	10	18
R447	diner - *62-66*	10	18
	Silver & Red Transcontinental		
R440	70831 passenger car - *62-63*	15	23
R441	91119 observation car - *62-63*	15	30
R442	baggage/kitchen car - *62-63*	15	30
R443	diner - *62-63*	15	25
	Bright Silver & Red Transcontinental		
R4400	70831 pass car silver roof - *70-73*	12	NA
R4410	91119 observation car silver roof - *70-73*	12	NA
R4430	70831 diner silver roof - *70-73*	12	NA
	White & Green Ambulance		
R248	**R.A.M.C** (ex-baggage car) - *63-67,71*	10	30
R248	**R.A.M.C** (ex-baggage car), crosses on sides heat printed* - *?*	12	30
	Blue TransAustralia		
R444A	70831, 31027, 61116 passenger car - *62-64, 68-70*	20	30
R445A	91119 observation car - *62-64, 69-70*	20	30
R446A	baggage/kitchen car - *62-64*	20	30
R447A	diner - *62-64*	20	30
R444A	70831 rail blue passenger car - *70*	30	40
R445A	91119 rail blue observation car - *70*	30	40
	Silver & Red TransAustralia		
R440A	70831, 31027, 31018 passenger car - *62-67,70*	25	35
R441A	9119 observation car - *62-64,70*	25	35
R442A	baggage/kitchen car - *62-64*	25	35
R443A	diner - *62-64,70*	25	35
	Silver NSWR		
R440	passenger car First - *74-78*	18	30
R442	baggage car - *74-78*	18	30
R443	dining car - *74-78*	18	30
	Blue VR		
R444	passenger car First - *76-78*	18	30
R446	baggage car - *76-78*	18	30
R447	dining car - *76-78*	18	30
	Silver & Black Canadian National		
R444CN	300, 303 passenger car - *65-69*	18	25
R445CN	304 observation car - *65-69*	18	25
R446CN	304 baggage/kitchen car - *65-69*	18	25
R447CN	303, 300 diner - *65-69*	18	25
	Bright Silver & Blk Canadian National		
R4441	73831, 91119 passenger car - *70-71*	20	25
R4451	91119, 73831 observation car - *70-71*	20	25
R4461	baggage/kitchen car - *70-71*	20	25
R4471	diner - *70-71*	20	25
	Grey & Maroon Canadian Pacific		
R444CP	7752 passenger car yellow lining - *67*	25	30
R444CP	7752 passenger car - *68*	23	30
R445CP	7420 observation car yellow lining - *67*	25	30
R445CP	7420 observation car - *68*	23	30

R446CP	7914 baggage/kitchen car yellow lining - 67	25	30
R446CP	7914 baggage/kitchen car - 68	23	30
R447CP	7525 diner yellow lining - 67	25	30
R447CP	7525 diner - 68	23	30
Silver & Red CPRail			
R4403	passenger car Danff - 70	20	25
R4403	passenger car Banff - 71	20	25
R4413	observation car Danff - 70	20	25
R4413	observation car Banff - 71	20	25
R4423	baggage/kitchen car Danff - 70	20	25
R4423	baggage/kitchen car Banff - 71	20	25
R4433	diner Danff - 70	20	25
R4433	diner Banff - 71	20	25
Silver & Maroon Pennsyvania			
R803	7752, 1580 passenger car - 67	30	45
R807	7525 diner - 67	30	45
R811	3101 baggage/kitchen car - 67	30	45
R815	3102 observation car - 67	30	45
Silver Burlington			
R804	3100 passenger car - 67	30	35
R808	diner - 67	30	35
R812	3101 baggage/kitchen car - 67	30	35
R816	3102 observation car - 67	30	35
Silver Santa Fe			
R805	3100 passenger car - 67	30	35
R809	diner - 67	30	35
R813	3101 baggage/kitchen car - 67	30	35
R817	3102 observation car - 67	30	35
Silver & Blue Baltimore and Ohio			
R806	3100 passenger car - 67	30	35
R810	diner - 67	30	35
R814	3101 baggage/kitchen car - 67	30	35
R818	3102 observation car - 67	30	35

*These were usually stickers.

2nd series TC passenger car [CT3]

CT4. Old Time Coach

R448	Smoking Car 257 yellow black lining - 62-65	15	25
R448	Smoking Car 257 yellow no lining - ?	18	25
R802	**Central Pacific** 257 yellow - 67	30	35
R801	**Pullman** 250 green - 67	30	35
R378	teak from Railway Children set - 72	23	NA

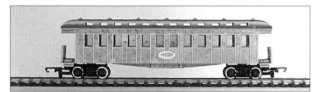

Old time coach from the Railway Childern set [CT4]

WAGONS

If the range of coaches was large, that of wagons is huge. Like coaches, the range is divided here into Standard British Goods Stock, Starter Set Wagons and Transcontinental Freight Stock but we have also included the Battle Space and Military Wagons in a subsection of their own.

British Goods Wagons: The tools for the first two wagons were bought from Pyramid Toys who had made wagons with cellulose acetate bodies and metal chassis from 1949 until 1951 and sold them under the name 'Trackmaster'. These were purchased in 1951 along with tools for their 0-6-2 tank which was also absorbed into the Tri-ang range.

Some strange colours may be found among Trackmaster wagons due to sunlight discoloration of the brown pigments, turning them to lime green!

Cat.No.	Company, Number, Colour, Date	£	£

W0a. Trackmaster Open Wagon

These were wagons made by Pyramid Toys before they sold their tools to Tri-ang. The wagons were either used in the Trackmaster train set or were sold singly in cream coloured boxes with a picture of the wagon on them. Later the open wagons were available with a coal load moulding and the boxes stamped 'COAL' and later still they were available with Hornby Dublo couplings in which case the box was stamped 'HD'. They are inscribed 'Trackmaster' underneath.

	GW Blue Grey Wagons		
-	10836 open - 49-51	7	12
-	10836 open HD couplings - 51	12	18
-	10836 open + coal - 50-51	8	15
-	10836 open + coal HD couplings - 51	13	20
	NE Brown Wagons		
-	83610 open - 49-51	7	12
-	83610 open H D couplings - 51	12	18
-	83610 open + coal - 50-51	8	15
-	83610 open + coal HD couplings - 51	13	20
-	86301 open - ?	25	30

W0b. Trackmaster Closed Van

These were wagons made by Pyramid Toys before they sold their tools to Tri-ang. The wagons were either used in the Trackmaster train set or were sold singly in cream coloured boxes with a picture of the wagon on them. Later they were available with Hornby Dublo couplings in which case the box was stamped 'HD'. They are inscribed 'Trackmaster' underneath.

-	**GW** 62134 blue-grey - 49-51	7	12
-	**GW** 62134 blue-gry HD couplings - 51	12	18
-	**GW** 62314 blue-grey - ?	25	30
-	**NE** 86203 brown - 49-51	7	12
-	**NE** 86203 brown HD couplings - 51	12	18

The development of wheels on Rovex/Tri-ang/Hornby wagons followed that of the coaches and the wagons, too, are usually well marked with the manufacturer's name, except for those from the late 1960s. Early wagons had diecast chassis (the 10' chassis having been developed from the Trackmaster one) which underwent constant development and, consequently, provided a rich assortment of variations to collect.

Chassis were metal until 1963, after which nearly all were plastic. Exceptions were made where extra weight was required as in the case of cranes and the unloading hopper wagon. A few wagon bogies remained metal until quite late for the same reason e.g. the rocket launcher and helicopter car. As chassis types do not usually affect value, we have not detailed them here unless relevant to do so.

Other changes that help to identify wagons, and especially early ones, are the colour of plastic used and the running number carried. Many different colours and shades of plastic were used in the 1950s as small batches of unspecified colours of plastic granules could be bought cheaply. In those days it did not seem to matter whether a van was red or white or a well wagon bright orange or blue. Initially, the plastic used was Cellulose-Acetate which had a glossy finish and warped slightly. Around 1956 Rovex changed to using Polystyrene which was more rigid and showed no signs of warping.

Running numbers were applied by heat printing (much akin to branding with a hot iron) and the heat printing tool sometimes

Bonhams 1793

AUCTIONEERS & VALUERS

Bassett-Lowke close-up

Toys and Trains at Auction

Bonhams hold four sales a year devoted to Toys and Trains at both our central London Knightsbridge salesroom and in the heart of England at our Midlands Knowle salesroom, offering for sale trains and models by famous manufacturers such as: Hornby '0' and Dublo, Bassett-Lowke, Marklin, Bing, Tri-ang and many others.

Catlogue sales
01666 502 200

Catalogues can be viewed on-line three weeks prior to sales at www.bonhams.com

For further information concerning buying or selling in our auctions, please call:

Leigh Gotch (London Office)
020 7313 3137
l.gotch@bonhams.com

Kegan Harrison (Knowle Office)
01564 776151
keganharrison@bonhams.com

www.bonhams.com

Freelance
4-4-0 in
SR livery

[table L14]

D10
Director Class
'Prince George'

[table L15]

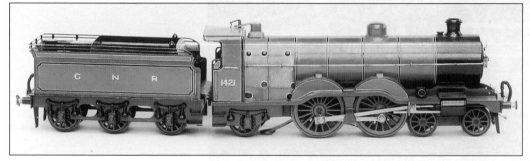

GNR
Atlantic

[table L24]

Robinson
D2
'City of
London'

[table L16]

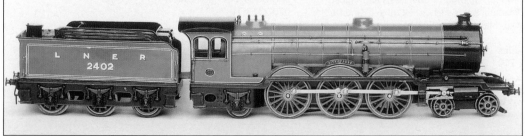

Raven Class
A2
'City of York'

[table L23]

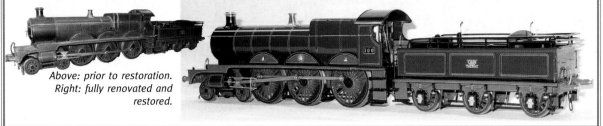

59539

ScotRail livery on a Class 101 (L305381)   [table L35]

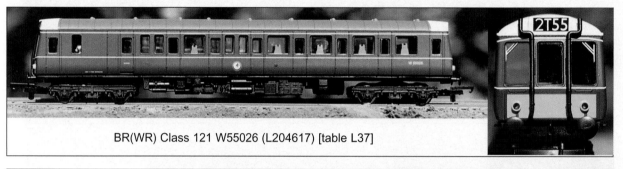

BR(WR) Class 121 W55026 (L204617) [table L37]

Virgin Class 87
87003
'Patriot'
(L205195)

[table L31]

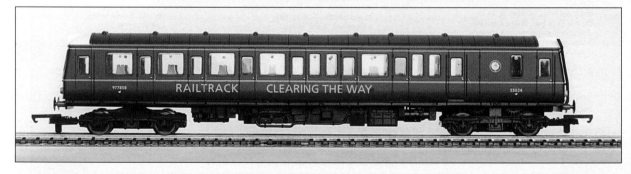

Railtrack Class 960 Sandite Unit (L204928)   [table L40]

GWR Railcar 29 (L204639)   [table L41]

EWS Class 92 92001 'Victor Hugo' (L204672)
[table L34]

NSE Class 73 73129 'City of Winchester'
(L205178)   [table L30]

EWS Class 67 67003 (L204926)   [table L29]

Freightliner Class 66 66506 'Crewe Regeneration'
(L204901)   [table L28]

Hanson Class 59 59103 'Village of Mells' (L204665)
[table L26]

BR Engineering Class 26 26040 (L205173)   [L12]

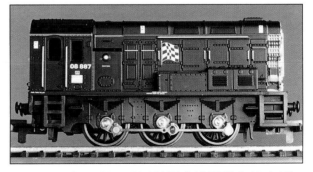

Virgin Pit Stop Class 08 08887 (L204658) [table L10]

Lima

Porterbrook Class 55 9016 'Gordon Highlander' (L205260)   [table L24]

DRS Class 20 20904 (L205113)   [table L11]

EWS Class 37 37417 'Rail Magazine' (L205299)   [L16]

Railfreight Construction Class 33 33050 'Isle of Grain' (L205228)   [table L15]

BR Class 50 50001 'Dreadnought' (L205170) [table L22]

GWT Class 47 47846 'Thor' (L205171) [table L21]

Virgin Class 43 43100 'Blackpool Rock' (L204681) [table L19]

Mainline Class 60 60044 'Ailsa Craig' (L205169)   [table L27]

No.1 Goods Train set with standard tank loco

Plastic train set from Hong Hong which includes a copy of the Lone Star tank wagon

EL51 set with D5900

Impy set with tender-less Baldwin

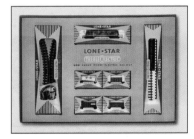

EL 50 Goods set with D5000

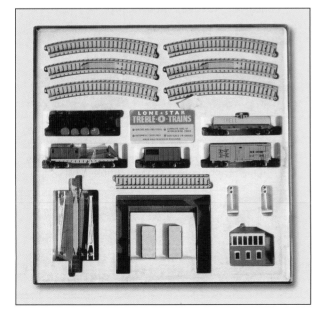

Impy set with tender-less Baldwin

No.2 Main Line Passenger set with A4 loco

LMS Rebuilt Patriot 5530 'Sir Frank Ree'
(37065)   [table L14]

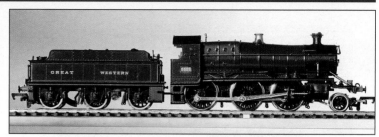

GWR Class 43XX 5322 (37090) pre-production sample
[table L11]

BR Rebuilt Royal Scot 46100 'Royal Scot'
(37057)   [table L17]

GWR Class 57XX 5764 pre-production sample (37084)
[table L2]

GWR Manor Class 7808 'Cookham Manor'
(937100)   [table L12]

BR Royal Scot Class 46137 'Prince of Wales Volunteers South
Lancashire' (37093)   [table L16]

LNER Class N2 9522 (954154)
[table L5]

BR Standard 4 75001 pre-production sample in gloss
finish (not made) (37053)   [table L19]

BR Rebuilt Patriot 37075 'Sir Robert Turnbull' pre-prod.
sample with grey edge to footplate (37075) [table L14]

LMS Jubilee Class 5690 'Leander' (37061)
[table L15]

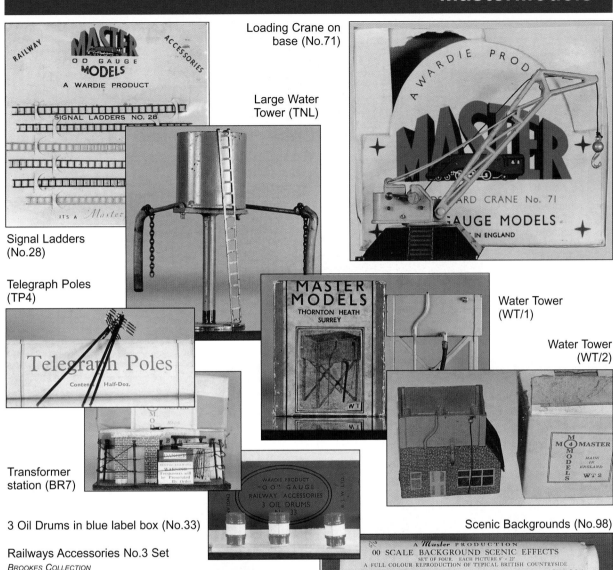

Loading Crane on base (No.71)

Large Water Tower (TNL)

Signal Ladders (No.28)

Telegraph Poles (TP4)

Water Tower (WT/1)

Water Tower (WT/2)

Transformer station (BR7)

3 Oil Drums in blue label box (No.33)

Railways Accessories No.3 Set

BROOKES COLLECTION

Scenic Backgrounds (No.98)

Single Girder Bridge (No.68)

LMS Crab
13126

[table L3]

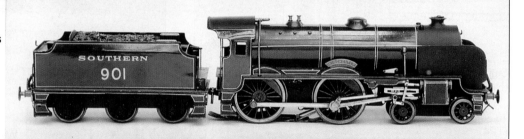

SR Schools Class
901
'Winchester'

[table L3]

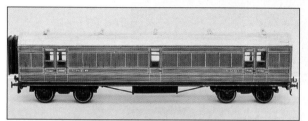

LNER full brake 8061   [table C1]

LMS dining car 3762   [table C1]

Stephen's Inks van 39817   [table W19]

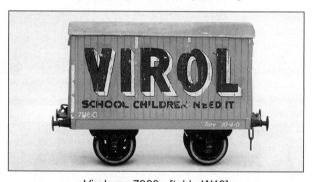

Virol van 7960   [table W19]

Pratts tank wagon   [table W12]

Royal Daylight tank wagon   [table W12]

BR Ivatt 2MT 2-6-2T 41234 (N205)   [table L3]

BR 2F dock tank 47160 (N201)   [table L1]

BR Class 27 27014 (N212)   [table L9]

BR Ivatt 2MT 2-6-0 46406   [table L4]

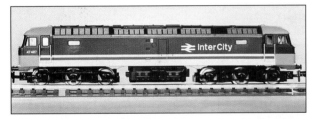

InterCity Class 47 47487 (12025)   [table L11]

BR Class 9F 92018 (N207)   [table L8]

BR 70000 'Britannia' (2037)   [table L7]

LNER Class A4 4472 'Flying Scotsman' (12950)
[table L5]

LNER Class A4 4498 'Sir Nigel Gresley' (N214)   [table L6]

BR Mk1 BG 81304 (2938)
[table C2e]

GWR Mk1 corridor brake 3146
(2944) [table C2c]

LMS Mk1 composite 1671 (2941)
[table C2a]

BR(LMR) Mk1 SK M16752 (2929)
[table C2b]

BR(ER) Gresley brake composite E10076E
(13116) [table C1b]

LNER Gresley all 3rd 4237 (13014)
[table C1a]

BR(SR) Mk1 BCK S2301 (2926)
[table C2c]

BR(LMR) Mk1 CK M16171 (N303)
[table C2a]

BR(LMR) Mk2 CK M4330 (13065)
[table C2a]

PO 8-Plank Wm.Gordon Jameson's (N507)
[table W7]

SR 8-Plank 36327 (3210)
[table W7]

PO 8-Plank British Steel 20 (13633)
[table W7]

PO 8-Plank Ilkestone & Heanor 14 (N511)
[table W7]

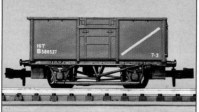

BR mineral wagon B586537 (N502)
[table W8]

Small tank Shell/BP (N518)
[table W10]

Small tank National Benzole (N519)
[table W10]

Small tank Duracell (13634)
[table W10]

Railfreight van 230002 (13631)
[table W12]

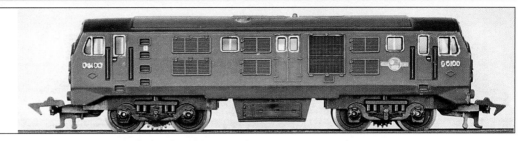

BR Class 29
D6100
(P837)

[table L3]

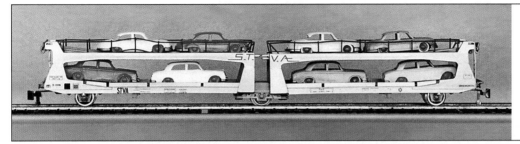

STVA
articulated
car transporter
(P6571)

[table W19]

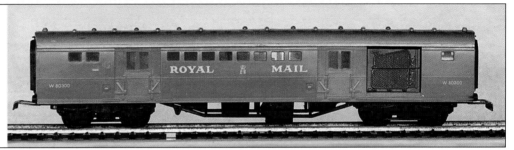

BR
Royal Mail TPO
(P454)

[table C1]

Wine wagon E762100 (P643)   [table W9]

Blue Circle twin silo cement wagon (P642)   [table W7]

Algeco cereal hopper (P647)   [table W8]

Shell/BP small tank wagon (P640)   [table W10]

Replica

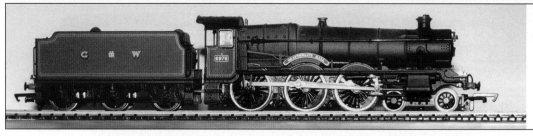

GWR
Hall Class
6976
'Graythwaite
Hall'
(11151)

[table L3]

GWR
Collett Goods
2244
(11041)

[table L2]

BR(LMR) Mk1 RB M1676 (12106) [table C5e]

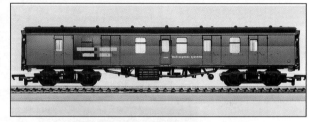

RES Mk1 BG (12172) [table C5f]

PO 7-plank F & E Poole 200 (13205) [table W3]

PO 3-plank Bath & Corsham Freestone Quarries 14
(13301) [table W2]

PO 9-plank coke wagon Abbott 3606 (13351) [table W4]

LMS 1-plank + container William Whiteley (13103) [W1]

Dock Authority shunter (R253)
[table L58]

BR 0-6-0ST 748 (R153)
[table L15]

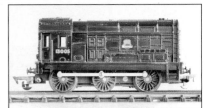

BR 0-6-0DS 13005 (R152)
[table L61a]

BR Class N2 0-6-2T 69561 (R51)   [table L17]

BR Class 3F 0-6-0 43775 (R251)
[table L33]

BR 0-6-0T Jinty (R52)   [table L10a]

BR Class 3MT 2-6-2T 82004 (R59)   [table L20]

BR Class B12
4-6-0
61572
(R150)

[table L43]

BR
46201
'Princess
Elizabeth'
(R50)

[table L46]

Tri-ang Hornby

CR
Caledonian
Single 123
(R553)

[table L24]

LNER
Class A3
4472
'Flying
Scotsman'
(R855)

[table L50a]

BR
Class AL1
E3001
(R753)

[table L74]

BR
Class 37
37073
(R369)

[table L66]

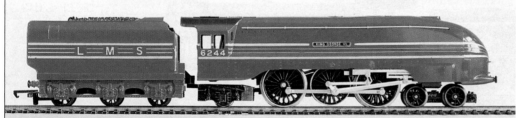

LMS
Coronation
6244
'King George VI'
(R871)

[table L49a]

BR
Class 9F
92220
'Evening Star'
(R861)

[table L57a]

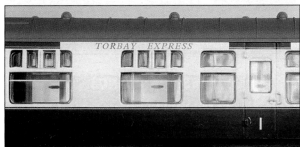

PO 7-plank Tredegar 5100 weathered (R6156)
[table W19]

PO 5-plank ICI (Lime) Ltd 3034 weathered
(R6156)   [table W14]

PO 9-plank The Gas Light & Coke Co. 766
(R6048)   [table W23]

Lion Emulsions small tank wagon (R6052)
[table W49]

Unbranded Vee tank 9205 weathered
(R6153)   [table W42]

Shell 20T tank wagon (R6170)
[table W50]

SR 8-Plank 36327 (3210)
[table W7]

Loadhaul HEA 361878 weathered
(R6152)   [table W34]

SR Conflat 39153 + container K599
(R6182)   [table W5]

LMS brake van 730450 (R6079)
[table W71]

PO large mineral wagon West Midlands Joint Electricity Authority
(R6127)   [table W29]

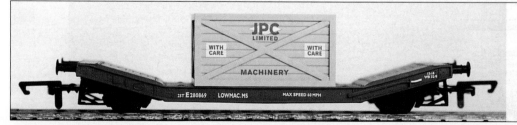

BR(ER)
Lowmac + JPC crate

[table W1]

BR Duchess 46224 'Princess Alexandra'
(R2303M)   [table L48b]

BR Rebuilt Merchant Navy 35027 'Port Line'
(R2268)   [table L53]

BR 60034 'Lord Faringdon' (R2167)
[table L51b]

Hamleys A3 1760 'Hamleys Express'   [table L50c]

LMS Class 8F 8042 (R2249)
[table L55b]

LNER A4 **Live Steam** '4468 'Mallard' (R1041)
[table L51c]

NSE Class 50 50045 'Achilles'
weathered (R2350)   [table L68a]

LMS Coronation 6225 'Duchess of
Gloucester' (R2179)   [table L49b]

SR Class Q1 0-6-0 C8 (R2343)
[table L35A]

BR
Jinty tanks
47607 and 4171
(T90)

[table L1]

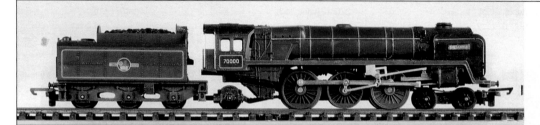

BR
70000
'Britannia'
(T97)

[table L5]

BR
Brush Type 2
D5501
(T96)

[table L7]

BR
Class 61XX
6157
(T99)

[table L2]

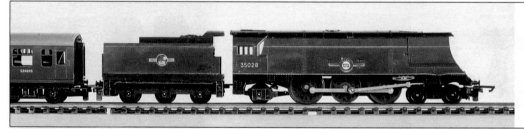

BR
Merchant Navy
35028
'Clan Line'
(T93)

[table L4]

Kay's
gold
Merchant Navy
'Clan Line'
(T43)

[table L4]

Pullman car
'Eagle'
(T185)

[table C6]

BR(SR)
utility van
S227S
(T135)

[table C4]

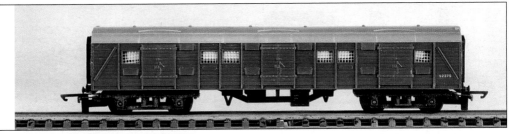

BR
Mk1 sleeping car
2510
(T86)

[table C3]

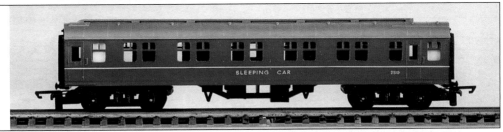

BR
low sided
steel wagon and
cattle wagon with
Peco chassis

[table W3 + W10]

Small tank wagons
BP/Shell and
Shell 5056
(T73)

[table W9a]

BR
bogie bolster with
timber load
B940050
(T277)

[table W17]

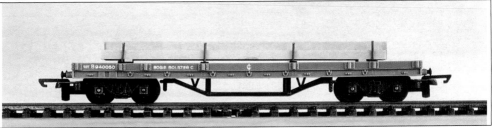

Green Standard Class V [table L19]

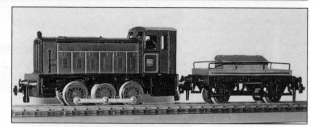

Ruston Hornsby 0-6-0DS [table L20]

Class E2 0-6-0 tank [table L16]

Green Class EM1 'Triton' [table L22]

Green Collett Class 5600 [table L17]

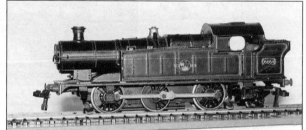

Black Collett Class 5600 [table L17]

Trans-Pennine DMU [table L30]

Class AL1 E3001 [table L29]

BR Class A2 'A.H.Peppercorn' [table L24]

LNER Class A2 'A.H.Peppercorn' [table L24]

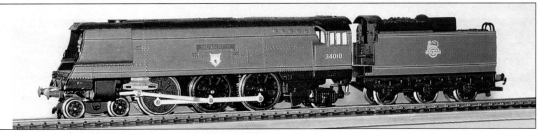

BR
WC CLass
34010
'Sidmouth'
(W2291)

[table L11]

WD
Class 8F
302
(W2281)

[table L13]

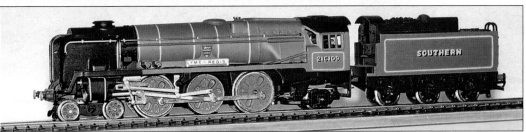

SR
Rebuilt WC
21C109
'Lyme Regis'
(W2237)

[table L12]

BR
Duchess
46245
'City of
London'
(W2226)

[table L8]

BR
Merchant Navy
35026
'Lamport and
Holt Line'
(W2267)

[table L11]

LNER A4
4489
'Woodcock'
(W2283)

[table L10]

A selection of MasterModels from
the Brookes Collection

broke or got misplaced. The result was changing running numbers on wagons and occasionally numbers used on the wrong wagon. It was not until the mid 1970s that tampo printing was introduced to the factory and much more intricate detail could be carried on rolling stock.

Over the years there have been about 100 wagon types and in the case of the 7-plank open wagon there have been over 100 variations (many not worth listing here)!

Flat Wagons

W1. Lowmac MS (ex-Airfix)

R6075	**BR** B904685 grey + **Blaney** crate - *99-00*	5	6
(R1037)	**BR** E280996 brown + **DWS** crate red ex-set - *03-04*	6	NA
R6130	**BR** E260864 brown + **ESG** Machinery crate - *01-02*	5	6
R6130A	**BR** E260855 brown + **ESG** Machinery crate - *03-04*	5	7
(R1036)	**BR** E280869 brown + **JPC** Limited machinery crate ex-set - *03-04*	6	NA
R6240	**BR** E662048 brown + **EJB** Castings crate - *04*	5	7
(R6176)	crate - **Blaney** Machine Tools	1	NA
(R6176)	crate - **ESG** Machinery	1	NA
(R6176)	crate - **AMR** Pyrotechnics	1	NA
(R6176)	crate - **NDS** Engineering	1	NA
R6176	above set of 4 crates - *02-04*	NA	7
(T1500)	buff ex-set - *00-02*	5	NA
(T1501)	dark green ex-set - *00-02*	5	NA

Lowmac MS [W1]

W2a. Bolster Wagon (1st Type)

This had a flat floor with holes in it into which bolsters or loads could be plugged. The bolsters were squeeze fitted two per wagon and were black plastic mouldings each with two bright metal pins protruding from beneath.

R17	**BR** 58698 grey - *53*	10	12
R17	**BR** 43726 grey '10T' - *53*	7	9
R17	**BR** 43726 grey '1OT' - *53-54*	7	9
R17	**BR** 43726 grey '1' in '1OT' inverted - *54-55*	7	9
R17	**BR** 3726 grey '1' in '1OT' inverted - *55*	8	10
R17	**BR** 3726 grey - *55*	8	10
R17	**BR** 7893 grey - *55-56*	7	9
R17	**BR** 7893 orange-brown - *56*	15	17
R17	**BR** M59015 grey (11.5 mm) - *56-58*	5	7
R17	**BR** M59015 grey (9 mm) - *59-61*	5	7
R17	**BR** M59015 light grey (9 mm) - *61*	7	9
R17	**BR** M59034 grey (11 mm) - *59*	5	7
R17	**BR** M59034 grey (10 mm) - *59-61*	5	7

W2b. Cable Drum Wagon (1st Type)

This used the 1st type bolster wagon (above) without the bolsters but with two plastic cable drums which plugged into the wagon base. Values quoted are for the more common wagon variations. Early drums were open with thick plastic tube wound on (type 1). These were replaced by open drums with a moulding to represent finer cable (type 2) and these, in turn, were replaced by closed drums (type 3). Cable and drums both varied in colour as indicated in this table. As drums could easily be swapped around it is impossible to say which version of the bolster wagon was used in each case. There were four colours for the cables on the types 1 and 2 drums - red, yellow, green or silver and a white cable has been found on a J&P type 1 drum.

R18	**Pirelli General** type 1 black - *53-55*	9	11
R18	**Johnson & Philips** type 1 black - *53-55*	10	12

R18	**Johnson & Philips** type 1 black - *53-55*	15	20
R18	**Liverpool Cables** type 1 black - *53-55*	10	12
R18	**Pirelli General** type 2 black - *56-57*	7	9
R18	**Johnson & Philips** type 2 black - *56-57*	8	10
R18	**Liverpool Cables** type 2 black - *56-57*	8	10
R18	**Pirelli General** type 3 green - *58-61*	5	7
R18	**Pirelli General** type 3 maroon - *58-61*	6	8
R18	**Pirelli General** type 3 brown - *58-61*	7	9
R18	**Johnson & Philips** type 3 green - *58-60*	6	8
R18	**Johnson & Philips** type 3 maroon- *58-60*	7	9
R18	**Johnson & Philips** type 3 brown - *58-60*	8	10
R18	**Liverpool Cables** type 3 green - *58-61*	6	8
R18	**Liverpool Cables** type 3 maroon - *58-61*	7	9
R18	**Liverpool Cables** type 3 brown - *58-61*	8	10
R18	**J&P Cables** type 3 green - *60-61*	7	9
R18	**J&P Cables** type 3 maroon - *60-61*	8	10
R18	**J&P Cables** type 3 brown - *60-61*	9	11

Cable drum wagon [W2b]

W2c. Tarpaulin Wagon

This used the bogie bolster wagon (above) with a single moulding of a tarpaulined load replacing the two bolsters. The loads were supplied by Minic Ltd who used it with some of their Push-and-Go vehicles. As loads could easily be swapped around it is impossible to say which version of the bolster wagon was used in each case. Values quoted are for the more common wagon variations. Sometimes the moulding was heat printed each side with 'Tri-ang' in silver and sometime the silver has disappeared leaving only the impression. Others had no printing on them.

R19	grey tarpaulin - *53-59*	4	8
R19	dark green tarpaulin - *53-59*	6	8
R19	violet-grey tarpaulin - *53-59*	4	8
R19	grey-green tarpaulin - *53-59*	4	8
R19	red-brown tarpaulin - *53-59*	6	8
R19	red tarpaulin - *53-59*	8	10

W3a. Bolster Wagon (2nd Type) and Car Loads

This had a flat floor with a central bolster moulded into it which had two black pins protruding from it.

R17	**BR** B913011 light grey - *62*	8	10
R17	**BR** B913011 red-brown '3' with flat top - *62-63*	4	6
R17	**BR** B913011 red-brown '3' with round top - *63-65*	4	6
R17	**BR** B913011 orange-brown - *?*	12	14
R17	**BR** 17351 red-brown - *63-64?*	10	12
R17	**BR** B913011 red-brown Minix car, no pins (also R17C) - *66-73*	10	15
R676	**BR** B913011 green - *71-74*	6	8
R17CNP	red-brown no printing ex-starter sets, Minix car - *c68*	8	12
R17CNP	green no printing ex-starter sets, Minix car - *c68*	8	12

W3b. Cable Drum Wagon (2nd Type)

This used the 2nd type bolster wagon (above) without the pins but with two plastic cable drums which had flat bottoms and were held to the wagon with rubber bands hooked over the buffers.

R18	**Pirelli General** B913011 green - *62-71*	6	8
R18	**Pirelli General** B913011 brown - *62-71*	7	9
R18	**J & P** B913011 green - *62-71*	6	8
R18	**J & P** B913011 brown - *62-71*	7	9
R18	**AEI** B913011 green - *62-71*	7	9
R18	**AEI** B913011 brown - *62-71*	7	9

W3c. Flat Wagon with Container

This model, which used the 2nd type bolster wagon without the bolster pins, was based on actual containers in this livery used for transporting Tri-ang products from their factories. The inscription 'Return to Wimbledon SR' suggests the Merton factory in particular.

R561NP	blue-black container no printing ex-starter sets - c68	10	NA
R561NP	orange container no printing ex-starter sets - c68	10	NA
R?	**Lyons Maid** Ice Cream white cont'r - c68	30	NA
R574	**Kellogg's Rice Krispies** BK8900 blue-black container - 68	25	NA
	Tri-ang Toys Pedigree Prams		
R561	BK8900B blue-black - 62-64?	8	10
R561	BK8900 blue-black - 65?-68?	6	8
R561	BK8900 black - ?	12	14
R561	BK890B blue-black - 69?-71	8	10

W4. Conflat A

R017	**BR** Conflat A B727734 brown + **Freightliner** container 09L91 - 82-83	10	12

Conflat A & container [W4]

W5. Conflat and Container (ex-Airfix)

R6014	**GW** 39326 dark grey + **GWR** container BC-1710 dark brown - 97-99	6	8
R6013	**LMS** N300465 pale grey + **LMS** container K37 maroon - 97-99	6	8
R6241	**LMS** 4757 dark grey + **LMS** container K1 maroon - 04	5	7
R6082	**GW** 39026 dark grey + **GWR** container BK-1835 dark brown - 99-00	5	6
R6131	**GW** 39030 dark grey + **GWR** container K-1704 dark brown - 01-03	5	6
(R1037)	**GW** 39238 dark grey + **GWR** container BK-1924 dark brown ex-set - 03	5	NA
R6036	**Book Club** 20 Years Sp Edn 2000 - 99	7	10
R6136	2001 dark grey + **Hornby** 2001 container BK01 blue - 01	5	6
R6182	**SR** 39153 dark brown + SR container K599 green - 02	NPG	7
R6182A	**SR** 39149 dark brown + SR container K596 green - 03-04	NPG	7
(R6175)	container - **LMS** K37 maroon - 02-03	2	NA
(R6175)	container - **GWR** BC1710 dark brown - 02-03	2	NA
(R6175)	container - **GWR** BK1835 dark brown - 02-03	2	NA
R6175	set of above 3 containers - 02-04	NPG	7

W6. Conflat L with 3 Containers

This was based on the BR 11T Conflat L which was designed with locating brackets on the floor of the wagon to take three L type containers. The model containers were produced carrying one of two numbers - L17253B or L17429B. The containers vary considerably in the shade of grey plastic used to mould them.

R340	**BR** B734259 red-brown Conflat L + 3 containers - 62-72	5	7
R340	**BR** B734259 orange-brown Conflat L + 3 containers - ?	10	12

W7. Shunter's Truck

The model had side rails and used the short break van's chassis. SS = Silver Seal wheels. The shunters truck came with a grey plastic uncoupler.

R028	**Severn Tunnel** Junc. grey - 73-75	5	7
R208	**Severn Tunnel** Junc grey SS - 76-78	5	7

R005	red flat with car - 82-83, 87-94	6	12

W8. Plate Wagon (Winkle)

The large load fills the wagon whereas the small load fills only three quarters of the wagon.

R19	**BR** ED931972 dark green + large load - 72-73	7	10
R19	**BR** ED931972 dark green + small load - ?	8	12

W9. Girder Flat

R133	red + boat load - 74	15	25
R182	red + load of 4 black L type containers - 74	8	10
R131	red + load of 4 wheel sets - 74-75	5	7
R224	red + load of 4 wheel sets SS - 76	5	7

W10. Bogie Steel AB

R236	**BR** 400105 brown - 79	5	6
R225	**BR** 400105 brown paint finish - 80-81	9	11
R246	**BR Rft** 400105 grey+red - 81-83, 87-94	4	5
R427	**BR Rft** 400044 grey+red - 96-98	5	6
R6023	**BR** 400044 grey+yellow Engineer's - 97-98	6	NA
R6209	**BR Rft** 40386 grey+red + 5 pipes - 03	5	7
R6209A	**BR Rft** 40127 grey+red + 5 pipes - 04	6	8
R6210	**BR Rft** 40223 grey+yellow + 12 rails - 03	5	7
R6210A	**BR Rft** 40119 grey+red + 12 rails - 04	6	8
(R1046)	with a load of Christmas trees ex R1046 set - 04	8	NA

Planked Open Wagons

W11. 3-Plank Wagon

Originally introduced as a 'First' CAD designed wagon in 1995 but then absorbed into the general range.

R041	**E.Turner & Son** 26 cream - 95	5	6
R151	**The Patent Victoria Stone Co** 3 pale blue - 95-97	5	6
R403	**Trimsaran**. 51 red - 96-97	5	6
R6008	**Royal Dockyard Chatham** 7 grey - 97-99	4	5
R6111	**William Neave** 6 grey - 00-01	4	5
R6133	**S.J.** 32 light rey - 01-03	4	5
R6167	**Cammel Laird** 630 red - 02	4	5
R6167A	**Cammel Laird** 631 red - 03	4	5
X?	**Robert McAlpine** 112 blue - 02	5	NA
X?	**Babcock & Wilcox** 334 grey - 02	5	NA
R6190	above two models Sp Edn 500 (Harburn Hobbies) - 02	NA	12
R6197	**Ceiriog Granite Co.** 195 brown - 03	4	6
R6230	**Easter Iron Mines** 4 brown - 04	NPG	6
R6231	**Imperial Chemical Industries Buxton Lime Firms** 48 grey - 04	4	6

W12. 4-Plank Wagon

Originally introduced as a 'First' CAD designed wagon in 1995 but then absorbed into the general range.

R040	**Tildsey** 42 buff - 95	5	6
R087	**H.Hotson** 25 red - 95	5	6
R131	**Clee Hill Granite** 331 grey - 95	5	6
R6232	as above numbered 350 - 04	4	6
R399	**Bold Venture** 24 grey - 96-97	5	6
R6009	**Hensall Sand** 2 red+white - 97-99	4	5
R6112	**Mark Williams** 9 brown - 00-01	4	5
(R6219)	as above W ex-wagon set - 03-04	5	NA
R6134	**Tarslag** 605 grey - 01-03	4	5
R6168	**Teign Valley Granite** 735 red - 02	4	5
R6168A	as above now numbered 736 - 03	4	5
R6168B	as above now numbered 737 - 04	4	5
(R6191)	**John Nicolson** 15 brown	5	NA
(R6191)	**William Mitchell** 37 red	5	NA
R6191	above two models Sp Edn 500 (Harburn Hobbies) - 02	NA	12
R6198	**Dutton Massey** 41 black - 03-04	4	6
R6233	**The Harts Hill Iron Co** 6 brown - 04	4	6

4-plank wagon [W12]

W13. 5-Plank Wagon

R104	**A.W.Day** green 320 - *73-74*	5	7
R210	**General Refractories** 85 pale grey heat printed (thinner lettering) - *73-74*	5	7
R210	as above but tampo printed - *74-76*	5	7
R163	**M.Spiers** 3 pale grey - *74*	5	7
R012	**A. Bodell** 1 pale grey Sp Edn 19,000 (W.H.Smith) - *81*	5	7
R091	**J.R.Wood** 98 orange planned in 1975 - not made	NA	NA
R241	**C&A** (Australia) grey - *77*	10	12
R241	as above but black - *78*	10	12
R096	**Bestwood** 655 black - *77-79*	3	5
R097	**Arnold Sands** red-brown - *77-79*	3	5
R717	as above with paint finish - *80-81*	5	6
R?	ditto unpainted orange-brown body - *?*	5	NA
R?	as above with no letter shading - *?*	5	NA
R?	as above but black body - *84-85*	8	NA
R?	ditto but grey body with shading - *?*	8	NA
R120	**SLNC** 145 maroon (Ireland) - *79*	12	NA
R119	**CIE** 11895 pale grey (Ireland) - *79*	12	NA
R716	**Scarwood** 13 grey, black moulding - *80-?*	3	5
R716	as above but grey moulding - *?-88*	6	7
R716?	**Scarwood** No.13 grey - *99-02*	4	NA
R004	**Colgate** red - *82*	5	8
R116	**Amos Benbow** 29 pale blue - *83*	5	7
R222	**Jif** yellow - *83-87*	3	6
R107	dark brown with face ex-Thomas Series - *85-04*	4	6
R024	**Crook & Greenway** No.2 blue - *88-98*	4	5
R014	**Lucas** bright green - *92-94*	5	6
R011	**Hornby Railways** 1992 bright red Ltd Edn 3000 - *92*	6	10
R038	**Pounsbery** 1 green - *93-96*	4	5
R008	**BR** DM401274 brown Engineer's - *93, 97-98*	4	5
R149	**Hunting** 7 red - *94-99*	5	6
R686	**Burgess & Penfold** 55 grey Sp Edn 1000 (Scale Rail) - *96*	7	10
(R6006)	**Cumberland** 22 black	5	NA
(R6006)	**Cumberland** 30 black	5	NA
(R6006)	**Cumberland** 38 black	5	NA
R6006	set of above 3 wagons - *97*	NA	15
R6018	**GW** 81791 dark grey - *97-01*	4	NA
R6030	**Aberdeen** 34 maroon Sp End 1500 (Harburn Hobbies) - *97*	6	10
(R6039)	**Spencer** 22 red	5	NA
(R6039)	**Spencer** 23 red	5	NA
(R6039)	**Spencer** 24 red	5	NA
R6039	set of above 3 wagons - *98*	NA	15
R6065	**Morningside** 270 brown Sp Edn 1200 (Harburn Hobbies) - *98*	6	10
R6066	**Hamilton Palace** 201 maroon Sp Edn 1160 (Harburn Hobbies) - *98*	6	10
R6089	**Hornby Roadshow** 1999 red Ltd Edn 670 - *99*	4	10
R6118	**Hornby Roadshow** 2000 red Ltd Edn 1000 ** - *00*	4	10
R6149	**Hornby Roadshow** 2001 red Ltd Edn 1000 - *01*	4	10

(R6149)	**Martin** * 25 grey - *99*	5	NA
(R6149)	**Martin** 26 grey - *99*	5	NA
(R6149)	**Martin** 27 grey - *99*	5	NA
R6087	set of above 3 wagons - *99*	NA	15
(R6115)	**Nathl. Atrill** 20 maroon - *00-01*	4	NA
(R6115)	**Nathl. Atrill** 24 maroon - *00-01*	4	NA
(R6115)	**Nathl. Atrill** 25 maroon - *00-01*	4	NA
R6115	set of above 3 wagons - *00-01*	NA	15
R61**	**Wilsden** 420 dark grey Sp Edn (The Model Railway Club) - *00*	5	6

* This was also used in the R6117 Three Assorted Plank Wagons pack in 2001. ** This wagon may be found moulded from either black or light grey plastic.

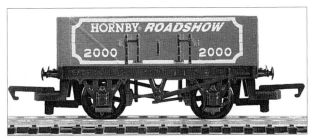

Original 5-plank wagon [W13]

W14. 5-Plank Wagon (ex-Airfix)

W = weathered.

R6053	**John Allbutt** 1 dark grey - *98-99*	4	5
R6060	**ICI (Lime) Ltd** 3034 dark grey - *98-99*	4	5
(R6156)	as above W ex-wagon set - *02-03*	5	NA
R6072	**Pontithel Chemical** 7 maroon - *99-02*	4	5
(R6219)	as above W ex-wagon set - *03-04*	5	NA
R6073	**Candy & Co.** 111 light grey - *99-00*	4	5
R6121	**James Durnford** 37 black - *01*	4	5
R6128	**Lillishall Limestone** 1750 brown - *01*	4	5
R6162	**Lyle & Son** 35 light grey - *02*	4	5
R6162A	**Lyle & Son** 36 light grey - *03*	4	6
(R1030)	**William Lawson** 2 red ex-set - *02-03*	5	NA
(R1030)	**Wm Barnard** 23 grey ex-train set - *03-04*	5	NA
R6199	**Derby Co-operative** 62 black - *03*	4	6
R6234	**Somerset Trading Co.** 56 red - *04*	4	6
R6235	**Crook & Greenway** 2 blue - *04*	4	6

Ex-Airfix 5-plank wagon [W14]

W15. 6-Plank Wagon

Originally introduced as a 'First' CAD designed wagon in 1995 but then absorbed into the general range.

R128	**Grassmoor** 359 dark grey - *95*	5	6
R106	**Edwin W Badland** 57 dark maroon - *95*	5	6
R454	**Henry Heaven** 1 brown - *96-97*	5	6
R6010	**Richard Weale** 17 red - *97-99*	4	5
X?	as above weathered ex-R6156 wagon set - *02-03*	5	NA
R6113	**Thomas Meakins** 48 red - *00-01*	4	5
R6135	**South Wales & Cannock Chase** 774 red - *01-03*	4	5
R6169	**Parkinson** 39 dark blue - *02*	4	5
R6169A	**Parkinson** 36 dark blue - *03*	4	5

R6189	**Hornby Roadshow** 2002 red Ltd Edn 1,000 - *02*	4	5
(R1036)	**Evans & Bevan** 482 black ex-set - *03-04*	4	NA
R6200	**Sneyd** 833 teak* - *03*	4	6
R6237	**S.J.Moreland** 1 blue+red - *04*	4	6
R6236	**Spiers** 347 yellow - *04*	4	6

*The body of this wagon was made with the same teak effect plastic used for moulding LNER coach bodies.

W16a. 7-Plank Wagon (1st Type) (ex- Trackmaster)

This was a simple 7-plank wooden type open wagon (designed by Pyramid Toys for their Trackmaster set) to which loads were later added to extend the range (see 1a and 1b below). The Trackmaster inscription on the underside of the wagon was replaced with 'TRI-ANG MADE IN ENGLAND'. A replacement body was tooled up in 1954 which was almost identical to the Trackmaster one but was inscribed 'Tri-ang R10/R13 MADE IN ENGLAND'. ** If any of those marked thus have mark IIa couplings (as described in introduction) add £1-£2 to the value. SS = Silver Seal wheels.

R10	**GW** (thick or thin letters) 10836 brn - *52-54*	5	7
R10	**GW** (thick or thin letters) 10836 blue-grey - *52-54*	5	7
R10	**GW** (thick or thin letters) 10836 wht - *52-54*	8	10
R10	**NE** 83610 brown - *52-53*	5	7
R10	**NE** 83610 blue-grey - *52-53*	5	7
R10	**NE** 83610 white - *52-53*	8	10
R10	**NE** (thin) 83670 brown - *53*	7	9
R10	**NE** (thin) 83670 blue-grey - *53*	7	9
R10	**NE** (thin) 83670 red - *53*	9	11
R10	**NE** (thick) ** 83670 brown -*54-55*	4	6
R10	**NE** (thick) ** 83670 blue-grey - *54-55*	4	6
R10	**NE** (thick) ** 83670 white - *54-55*	6	8
R10	**NE** (thick) ** 83670 red - *54-55*	5	7
R10	**NE** (thick) ** 83670 grey-green - *54-55*	4	6
R10	**NE** (thick) ** 83670 light grey - *54-55*	8	10
R10	**NE** (thick) ** 83670 orange - *54-55*	15	17
R10	**NE** (thick) ** 83670 silver - *54-55*	18	20
R10	**NE** 22132 brown - *54*	3	5
R10	**NE** 22132 blue-grey - *54*	3	5
R10	**NE** 22132 red - *54*	4	6
R10	**NE** 22132 white - *54*	5	7
R10	**NE** 22132 grey-green - *54*	3	5
R10	**NE** 22132 grey - *54*	6	8
R10	**NE** 76853 brown - *54*	4	6
R10	**NE** 76853 blue-grey - *54*	4	6
R10	**NE** 76853 grey-green - *54*	4	6
R10	**NE** 32075 brown - *55-56*	3	5
R10	**NE** 32075 blue-grey - *55-56*	3	5
R10	**NE** 32075 grey-green - *55-56*	3	5
R10	**NE** 32075 mid-green - *55-56*	5	7
R10	**NE** 3207 dark-grey - *55*	10	12
R10	**NE** 47205 grey - *55-57*	3	5
R10	**NE** 47205 brown - *55-57*	3	5
R10	**NE** 47205 grey-green - *55-57*	3	5
R10	**NE** 47205 translucent-grey - *55-57*	10	12
R10	**BR** M2313 grey - *58*	8	10
R10	**BR** M2313 brown - *58*	8	10
R10	**BR** M2313 dark green - *58*	7	9
R10	**BR** M2313 maroon - *58*	12	14
	W1005 number 10.5 mm long		
R10	**BR** W1005 brown (shades) - *57-60*	4	6
R10	**BR** W1005 grey - *57-60*	3	5
R10	**BR** W1005 dark green - *57-60*	3	5
R10	**BR** W1005 yellow-brown - *57-60*	6	8
R10	**BR** W1005 maroon - *57-60*	10	12
	W1005 number 9.5 mm long		
R10	**BR** W1005 grey - *60*	6	8
R10	**BR** W1005 green - *60*	6	8
R10	**BR** W1005* pale brown - *60*	10	12
	W1005 number 8 mm long		
R10	**BR** W1005 grey - *60*	6	8
R10	**BR** W1005 brown - *60*	6	8
R10	**BR** W1005 dark green - *60*	6	8
	W1005 number 7 mm long		
R10	**BR** W1005 grey (shades) - *61-70*	4	6
R10	**BR** W1005 dark green - *61-70*	4	6

R10	**BR** W1005 pale grey - *61-70*	5	7
R10	**BR** W1005 green - *61-70*	4	6
R10	**BR** W1005 dung-brown - *62*	10	12
R10	**BR** W1005 maroon - *?*	10	12
R577	black converter wagon with Hornby Dublo coupling one end - *66-70*	10	15
R10NP	various colours*** not printed ex-starter sets - *60-72*	3	NA
R10A	**SR** 12530 dark brown - *71-73*	4	6
R10A	**SR** 12530 bright red - *74*	6	8
R10A	**SR** 12530 bright blue - *74*	7	9
R10A	**SR** 12530 grey - *73*	20	NPG
R100	**Northern United** P284063 dark brown - *73*	150	NPG
R100	**Lancashire Coke Co. Ltd** 322 red - *73-74*	5	7
R312	**C&A**, black (Australia) - *74-75*	10	15
R009	**Ocean** 921 dark brown - *75*	5	7
R204	**Ocean** 921 dark brown SS - *76*	5	7
R009	**Ocean** 921 maroon - *75*	7	9
R090	**Princess Royal** 250 maroon - *75*	5	7
R209	**Princess Royal** 250 maroon SS - *76*	5	7
R010	**Pugh******380 red Sp Edn 120,000 - *79*	5	7
R010	**Pugh** 380 red bottom edge of sides black Sp Edn - *79*	15	17

* Also known as Caramac brown. *** Colours known to exist include blue, maroon, orange brown, red and green. **** The lettering was usually white but often turned out light grey.

Original 7-plank open wagon [W16a]

W16b.   Coal Truck (ex-Trackmaster)

This was R13 and used the R10 open wagon with a single plastic moulding to give the effect of it being full of coal. As the moulding was loose, it tended to move round from wagon to wagon and so it is difficult to say in which versions of the open wagon they were originally used. Three different mouldings were used over the years, the earliest one being from the Trackmaster tools. For the coal wagon add £1 to the value of the open wagon according to which version has been used. The coal truck was available between 1952 and 1961.

W16c.   Open Wagon with Planks or Drums

During 1960 and 1961 the open wagon was available with either a plank or drum load, in both cases these were represented by a single buff coloured plastic moulding. The wagon with oil drums was R245 and that with planks was R246. For either wagon add £2 to the value of the open wagon according to which version has been used.

W17.   7-Plank Drop Door Wagon

This looked like the open wagon (table W16a) but had a drop-down door either side.

R112	**NE** 83670 light grey - *54-55*	6	8
R112	**NE** 83670 blue-grey - *54-55*	10	12
R112	**NE** 22132 grey - *54*	8	10
R112	**NE** 22132 dark red - *54*	6	8
R112	**NE** 22132 grey-green - *54*	10	12
R112	**NE** 22132 bright red - *54*	10	12
R112	**NE** 22132 SR-green - *54*	12	14
R112	**NE** 76853 grey - *54*	10	12
R112	**NE** 32075 grey - *55-56*	8	10
R112	**NE** 32075 grey-green - *55-56*	6	8
R112	**NE** 32075 brown - *55-56*	12	14
R112	**NE** 47205 grey - *56*	8	10
R112	**NE** 47205 maroon - *56-57*	6	8
R112	**BR** M2313 (10 mm) red - *56-60*	6	8
R112	**BR** M2313 (10 mm) dark red - *56-60*	5	7
R112	**BR** M2313 (10 mm) grey - *56-60*	8	10
R112	**BR** M2313 (6 mm) dark red - *60-70*	5	7

R112A	**LMS** 12527 maroon - *71*	8	10
R112A	**LMS** 12527 bright red - *71-72*	5	7
R112A	**LMS** 12527 orange-brown - *72*	8	10

W18a. 7-Plank Wagon (2nd Type)

This was very like the body of the 1st type of open wagon listed in table W16a but had woodgrain effect on the planking.

R139	**Wm.Shaw** 137 red - *84-86*	5	7
R094	**Pilkington** 1489 red Ltd Sp Edn 17,700 (W.H.Smith) - *81*	4	5
R208	**Texas Homecare** white - *85-86*	4	5
R206	**Chance & Hunt** 142 orange-brown - *85-00*	4	5
R118	**Emlyn** 813 dark green - *86-96*	5	6
R469	**Emlyn** 813 red ex-train sets - *90-95*	4	5
R142	**Evans & Bevan** 388 black - *89-96*	4	5
R031	**Spiers** 347 yellow - *92-96*	5	6
R036	**DCA** 4981 brown - *93-98*	4	5
R156	**Edinburgh** 558 grey Sp Edn 1000 (Harburn Hobbies) - *94*	9	11
R155	**Tudhope** 40 black - *94-95*	5	6
R028	**Beatties** yellow Sp Edn 1960 (Beatties) - *95*	8	10
R135	**Glasgow** 962 brown Sp Edn 1500 (Harburn Hobbies) - *96*	8	10
X?	**Charles Stott** 78 brown - *97*	4	NA
X?	**Charles Stott** 81 brown - *97*	4	NA
X?	**Charles Stott** 87 brown - *97*	4	NA
R6005	**Charles Stott** above 3 wagons - *97*	NA	15
R6031	**C.Murrell** 10 red Sp Edn 500 (Jane's Trains) - *97*	10	12
X?	**W.E.Wise** 18 black - *98*	4	NA
X?	**W.E.Wise** 19 black - *98*	4	NA
X?	**W.E.Wise** 21 black - *98*	4	NA
R6038	**W.E.Wise** set of above 3 wagons - *98*	NA	15
X?	**Rumbelow** ** 10 red - *99*	4	NA
X?	**Rumbelow** 11 red - *99*	4	NA
X?	**Rumbelow** 12 red - *99*	4	NA
R6086	**Rumbelow** above 3 wagons - *99*	NA	15
X?	**Kilkenny** yellow ex-R1020 set - *99*	8	NA
X?	**7 Up** green ex-R1015 set - *99-02*	4	NA
X?	**Cowham & Shearer** 25 red - *00-01*	4	5
X?	**Cowham & Shearer** 26 red - *00-01*	4	5
X?	**Cowham & Shearer** 27 red - *00-01*	4	5
R6116	**Cowham & Shearer** above 3 - *00-01*	NA	15
R9056	**Sodor Scrap Co,** grey blue - *02-04*	4	6
R9068	**S.C.Ruffey** grey + brown - *03-04*	4	6
(R1046)	with a load parcels ex R1046 set - *04*	6	NA

** This was also used in the R6117 Three Assorted Plank Wagons pack in 2001.

2nd type 7-plank wagon [W18a]

W18b. Sheet Rail Wagon (7-Plank)

W = weathered

R240	**GW** 102971 grey - *79-81*	8	10
R016	**Perfection** 82 red - *82-83*	7	9
R6211	**Chance & Hunt** 158 red W + tarpaulin - *03*	4	7
R6211A	**Chance & Hunt** 161 red W + tarpaulin - *04*	4	7

W19. 7-Plank Wagon (ex-Airfix)

W = weathered

R6047	**Wemyss** 1997 grey - *98-99*	5	6
R6059	**Tredegar** 5100 red - *98-99*	5	6

(R6156)	as above W ex-wagon set - *02-03*	5	NA
R6067	**Gedling** 598 red - *99-00*	4	5
R6068	**Berthlwyd** 385 dark green - *99-00*	4	5
(R6219)	as above W ex-wagon set - *03-4*	5	NA
R6129	**Llewellyn Brothers** 203 dark brown - *01*	4	5
R6164	**Blidworth** 2323 grey - *02*	NPG	5
X?	**Forth & Clyde** 249 red - *02*	5	NA
X?	**Bannockburn** 656 grey - *02*	5	NA
R6192	above two models Sp Edn 500 (Harburn Hobbies) - *02*	NA	12
R6238	**I.W.Baldwin & Co** 15 black - *04*	4	6

A.B.Gee ex-R2138 Sp Edn 1000*

(R2138)	**BR** M609546 grey - *99*	5	NA
(R2138)	**BR** M609580 grey - *99*	5	NA
(R2138)	**BR** M609585 grey - *99*	5	NA
(R2138)	**BR** M609600 grey - *99*	5	NA
(R2138)	**BR** M609601 grey - *99*	5	NA
R6201	**T Threadgold** 1915 red - *03*	4	6

* These were specially made for the A.B.Gee commissioned Colliery train pack (R2138) in 1999 and 1000 were made.

Ex-Airfix 7-plank wagon [W19]

W20. Coke Wagon (7-Plank)

This was similar to a 5-plank wagon but had its sides extended upwards with open bars.

R781	**N.E.R** 52220 dark grey - *71-73*	6	8
R781	as above but rail blue - *?*	7	9
R781	as above but grey - *73*	8	10
R101	**Plean Colliery** 4 grey heat print - *73-?*	5	7
R101	as above but tampo printed - *?-79*	8	10
R719	**Roberts Davy** 25 grey - *80*	7	9
R719	as above but dark blue-grey - *80-81*	6	8
R006	**Barrow** 1225 white - *82*	7	9
R203	**Arther H Stabler** 21 grey - *95-00*	5	8
(R6007)	**Dinnington** 250 brown	5	NA
(R6007)	**Dinnington** 254 brown	5	NA
(R6007)	**Dinnington** 258 brown	5	NA
R6007	**Dinnington** above 3 boxed set - *97*	NA	18
(R6037)	**TWW** 1690 brown	5	NA
(R6037)	**TWW** 1692 brown	5	NA
(R6037)	**TWW** 1694 brown	5	NA
R6037	**TWW** above 3 in boxed set - *98*	NA	18
R6063	**Miller** 19 grey Sp Edn 1200 (Harburn Hobbies) - *98*	6	10
(R6151)	**Gilbert*** 211 grey weathered	5	NA
(R6151)	**Gilbert*** 212 grey weathered	5	NA
(R6151)	**Gilbert*** 213 grey weathered	5	NA
R6151	above 3 in boxed set - *02-04*	NA	16
(R6151A)	**Gilbert*** 218 grey weathered	5	NA
(R6151A)	**Gilbert*** 219 grey weathered	5	NA
(R6151A)	**Gilbert*** 220 grey weathered	5	NA
R6151A	above 3 in boxed set - *03-04*	NA	16

* This appeared to have been misspelled 'Cilbert'. The models were based on wagons belonging to H. Gilbert of Birmingham.

W21. 8-Plank End-Tipping Wagon

This wagon was introduced with the R515 and R528 operating tipper and conveyor sets but its value as a model in its own right was recognised in 1995 and it was released from then on in various guises without the tipping lever attached.

R032	**Hargreaves** 455 grey tipping lever - *82-84*	5	7
R199	**Great Mountain** 980 brown - *95-01*	4	5
R003	**Fife** 963 brown Sp Edn 2000 (Harburn Hobbies) - *95*	10	12

R6028	**Newbattle** 319 black Sp Edn 1500 (Harburn Hobbies) - *97*	9	11
X?	**Ammanford** 15 brown * - *99*	4	NA
X?	**Ammanford** 16 brown - *99*	4	NA
X?	**Ammanford** 18 brown - *99*	4	NA
R6088	set of above 3 wagons - *99*	NA	15
X?	**Airedale** 3434 black - *00-01*	4	NA
X?	**Airedale** 3438 black - *00-01*	4	NA
X?	**Airedale** 3440 black - *00-01*	4	NA
R6114	set of above 3 wagons - *00-01*	NA	15
R6212	**Adler & Allan** 107 red - *03*	4	6
R6212A	**Adler & Allan** 108 red - *04*	4	6
R6239	**McKay** 477 red - *04*	4	6

* This was also used in the R6117 Three Assorted Plank Wagons pack in 2001.

W21A. 8-Plank LWB Open Wagon

This wagon was introduced to the Thomas and Friends Series as the Troublesome Truck.

R9053	Troublesome Truck 1 - grey with face - *02-04*	3	4
R9054	Troublesome Truck 2 - grey with face - *02-04*	3	4

W22. Mixed Wagon Sets of Three

In 1998, in order to clear old stocks of the 'First' Series of 9' wagons, Hornby introduced an assorted pack of three (R6035). This contained 6-plank, 4-plank and 3-plank wagons and 280 packs were assembled. This exercise was repeated in 2001 but with surplus wagons from triple wagon sets of two years earlier.

R6002	**Hotson + Turner + Badland** in original boxes with outer sleeve Sp Edn 1500 (Toys R Us) - *98?*	NA	18
R6035	3x 9' wheel base wagons (various) Sp Edn 240 - *98*	NA	18
R6113	3x 10' wheel base wagons (mix) - *01*	NA	18
R6156	**Tredegar + ICI (Lime) Ltd + Richard Weale** weathered - *02-03*	NA	15
R6219	**Berthlwyd + Pontithel Chemical Co + Mark Williams** weathered - *03*	NA	15

W23. Large 9-Plank Wagon (ex-Airfix)

W = weathered

R6058	**NE** 30987 grey Loco - *98-99*	5	6
R6048	**The Gas Light & Coke** 766 grey - *98-99*	4	5
R6108	**BR** E30991 grey - *00-01*	4	5
R6108A	**BR** E30996 grey - *02*	NPG	5
R6108B	**BR** E30995 grey - *03-04*	NPG	5
(R6218)	**BR** E61004 grey W	5	NA
(R6218)	**BR** E61005 grey W	5	NA
(R6218)	**BR** E61006 grey W	5	NA
R6218	above 3 wagons in a sleeve - *03-04*	NPG	16
R6177	**Hornby** 2002 grey - *02*	NPG	5

W24. OAA/OBA Open Wagon

R235	**BRe Rft** 110003 brown - *79-81,87*	6	7
R248	**BRe Rft** 110264 grey+red Speedlink Distribution - *81-85, 87-90*	4	6
R209	**BRe Rft** 110264 grey+red Speedlink Distribution + dice Sp Edn 3200 - *83*	20	35
R067	**BR Rft** 100005 dark grey OAA - *90-96*	5	6
R035	**Hornby Railways** 1993 red Ltd Edn 3600 - *93*	8	10
R401	**Rft** Distribution 100027 grey OAA - *96-97*	6	7

Steel Open Wagons

W25. Drop Side Wagon

This was a low-sided steel type 13T wagon with both long sides hinged so that they could be dropped down. It was based broadly on LMS design. For 1966 the body moulding was altered t o provide door stops to reduce the danger of the doors breaking off.

R113	**BR** B712 (2.7 mm high) grey - *54*	10	12
R113	**BR** B712 (2.7 mm high) maroon - *54*	6	8
R113	**BR** B712 (2.7 mm high) grey-green - *54*	15	17
R113	**BR** B712 (2 mm high) maroon - *54-56*	6	8
R113	**BR** B712 (2 mm high) grey-green - *54-56*	13	15

R113	**BR** B712 (2 mm high) bright red - *54-56*	12	14
R113	**BR** B712 (2 mm high) orng-brown - *54-56*	15	17
R113	**BR** 8051 grey - *54*	20	22
R113	**BR** B4593 maroon flat top '3' - *57-65*	6	8
R113	**BR** B4593 grey flat topped '3' - *57-65*	8	10
R113	**BR** B4593 pale brown* - *60*	10	12
R113	**BR** B4593 dung-brown flat top '3' - *62*	12	14
R113	**BR** B4593 maroon round top '3' - *66-73*	6	8
R113	**BR** B4593 grey round top '3' - *66-73*	8	10
R113	**BR** B4596 - *?*	NPG	NPG
R113	**BR** B4597 maroon - *68-71*	6	8
R113	**BR** B4597 bright red - *68?*	10	12
R113NP	maroon no printing ex-starter sets - *c68*	8	NA
R113NP	bright red no printing ex-starter sets - *c68*	8	NA

* Also known as Caramac brown.

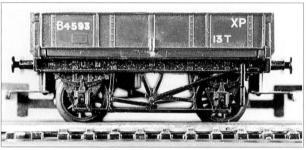

Drop-side wagon [W25]

W26. Small Mineral Wagon

This was based on an all steel wagon with side and one end door and was initially offered with or without a coal load which was a black moulded plastic insert (R244). For these add £1 unboxed and £4 mint boxed. SS = Silver Seal wheels.

R243	**BR** B75201 pale green-grey - *60-72*	5	7
R243	**BR** B75201 pale green-grey stripes on wrong sides - *60-61*	7	10
R243	**BR** B75201 pale grey - *72-75*	5	7
R243	**BR** B75201 v.pale grey - *72*	12	14
R217	**BR** B75201slate-grey SS - *76-78*	5	7
R244	**Beatties** yellow four addresses Sp Edn 3000 (Beatties) - *73*	10	NPG
R243NP	yellow no printing ex-starter sets - *c68*	8	NA
R243NP	bright blue no printing ex-starter sets - *c68*	8	NA

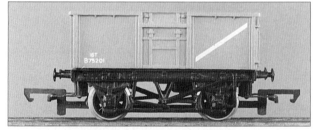

Small mineral wagon [W26]

W27. Tippler Mineral Wagon

W = weathered.

R239	**BR** B385760 brown Stone - *79-86*	4	5
R6085	**BR** B385640 brown Stone - *99-00*	4	5
R6085A	**BR** B386639 brown Stone - *01*	4	5
R6085B	**BR** B385726 brown Stone - *02*	4	5
R6085C	**BR** B386447 brown Stone - *03-04*	4	5
(R6155)	**BR** B385641 brown Stone W	5	NA
(R6155)	**BR** B385642 brown Stone W	5	NA
(R6155)	**BR** B385643 brown Stone W	5	NA
R6155	set of above 3 wagons - *02*	NA	15
(R6155)	**BR** B386001 brown Stone W	5	NA
(R6155)	**BR** B386002 brown Stone W	5	NA

(R6155)	**BR** B386003 brown Stone W	5	NA
R6155	set of above 3 wagons - *03*	NA	15
R079	**BR** B388469 brown MSV - *87-01*	4	5
R6022	**BR** B433698 red+yellow ZKV - *97-02*	5	NA
R6107	**BR** DB389035 grey+yellow ZKV - *00-01*	4	5
R6107A	**BR** DB389040 grey+yellow ZKV - *02-04*	NPG	5
R081	**BR** B437000 grey Iron Ore - *90-93*	5	6
R388	**BR** B388639 grey Iron Ore - *96-98*	4	5
R6000	**BR** B436192 grey Iron Ore - *97-98*	4	5
R?	**GW** 102971 grey - *79?*	6	NA
R009	**B&Q** B388404 white - *92-96*	4	6
R501	**Lion** 221 black Ltd Edn 2560 - *91*	7	9
R6061	**Hornby** 1999 grey Ltd Edn 2500 - *99*	5	8

W28. Large Mineral Wagon

SS = Silver Seal wheels. nls = no letter shading   tp = tampo printed.

R22	**Wm Cory** 8008 mrn transfer* - *72-74*	7	8
R22	**Wm Cory** 8008 maroon tp - *74*	6	7
R102	**NCB** 3471 black - *73-78*	4	5
R310	**Miller** (Australia) orange-brown - *74-75*	9	11
R386	**Miller** (Australia) orange-brown SS - *76-78*	9	11
R093	**Norstand** 480 blue - *75*	4	5
R220	**Norstand** 480 blue SS - *76-79*	4	5
R136	**Bolsover** 6390 maroon - *78-79*	4	5
R136	**Bolsover** 6390 maroon painted grey inside - *78-79*	5	6
R136	**Bolsover** 6390 maroon nls - *78-79*	6	NA
R136	**Bolsover** 6390 maroon dark blue-grey moulding paint finish - *80-81*	4	5
R136	**Bolsover** 6390 maroon grey moulding paint finish - *80-81*	4	5
R?	**Bolsover** 6390 dark blue-grey nls - *84-85*	6	NA
R?	**Bolsover** 6390 rail-blue - *83-87*	6	NA
R?	**Bolsover** 6390 rail-blue nls - *83-87*	5	NA
R?	**Bolsover** 6390 black - *?*	6	NA
R?	**Bolsover** 6390 black nls - *?*	6	NA
R730	**SC** 25506 light olive-grey - *80-81*	6	7
R730	**SC** 25506 olive-grey - *86-92*	5	6
R?	**SC** 25506 red nls - *82*	8	9
R021	**Black & Reoch** 22 red - *82-84*	5	6
R021	**Black & Reoch** 22 red nls - *82-84*	5	NA
R?	**Black & Reoch** 22 rail-blue - *?*	6	7
R211	**British Steel** 20 blue - *85-00*	3	5
R100	Station Master red+yellow - *93-96*	4	NA
R085	Station Master blue+yellow - *93-96*	4	NA
R088	Station Master yellow+red - *93-96*	4	NA
R102	Station Master box of 3 above - *93-96*	NA	12
R379	**Hornby Railways** 1996 red Ltd Edn 3000 - *96*	6	10
R6163	**Glenhafod** 2277 black - *02-03*	4	5
(R1031)	grey ex-starter set - *02*	4	NA
(R1031)	brown ex-starter set - *02*	4	NA

* The transfers on these were particularly vulnerable and ones in good condition are not easy to find.

W29. 21T Steel Mineral Wagon (ex-Airfix)

R6051	**Charringtons** 7301 red - *98-99*	5	6
R6057	**Cilely** 12 black - *98-01*	4	5
R6070	**BR** P339290K grey - *99-00*	4	5
R6071	**Richard Thomas** 23301 black - *99-00*	4	5
R6127	**West Midlands** 16 black - *01*	4	5
R6161	**BR** B310312K brown - *02*	4	5
R6161A	**BR** B310824K brown - *03*	4	5
R6161B	**BR** B310796K brown - *04*	4	6
(R1036)	**BR** B310799K brown ex-set - *03-04*	4	NA

W29a. Coalfish Box Open MHA

W = weathered.

R6216	**EWS** 394119 maroon - *03-04*	NPG	8
(R6225)	**BR** 394120 maroon W ex-wagon set	7	NA
(R6225)	**BR** 394121 maroon W ex-wagon set	7	NA
(R6225)	**BR** 394122 maroon W ex-wagon set	7	NA
R6225	set of above 3 wagons - *03-04*	NA	30

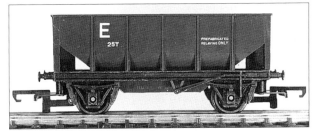

Engineer's wagon [W30]

Hopper Wagons

W30. Ore Hopper & Engineer's Wagon

This was the early grain wagon without the top section fitted. Most were fitted with a working trapdoor triggered by a lever on the side but, for a while, they had a solid base.

R214	**BR** B1402 pale green-grey no black panel - *58-59*	10	12
R214	**BR** B1402 pale green-grey - *60-63*	6	8
R347	**BR** black Engineer's thick 'E' - *63*	12	14
R347	**BR** black Engineer's - *63-65*	6	8
R347	**BR** dark green Engineer's - *66*	6	8
R347	**BR** dark green Engineer's no mechanism - *67-68*	6	8
R214	**Consett Iron** 1441 maroon - *75*	7	9
R232	**Consett Iron** 1441 dark green - *76-79*	6	8
R732	**Consett Iron** 1441 dark green paint finish - *80-82*	15	17

W31. Large Hopper Wagon

This 35T wagon employed the bottom half of the large bulk grain wagon.

R214	**BR** B35000 pale grey - *69-72*	8	10
R103	**Roberts** 1100 black - *73-74*	8	10

W32. 20T Hopper (ex-Airfix)

R6016	**BR** B413161K grey - *97-01*	4	5
R6017	**NE** 194720 dark grey - *97-00*	4	5
R6124	**BR** E252543K grey - *01*	4	5
R6124A	**BR** B414551K grey - *02*	4	6
R6124B	**BR** B414145K grey - *03-04*	4	6
R6125	**NE** 193254 dark grey - *01*	4	5
R6125A	**NE** 194720 dark grey - *02-03*	4	6
R6125B	**NE** 193259 dark grey - *03-04*	4	6
(R1030)	**NE** 193265 dark grey ex-set - *02-03*	4	NA

W33. PGA Aggregate Hopper

W = weathered

R015	**Yeoman** PR14069 blue+silver - *88-96*	6	8
R019	**Tilbury** TRB14521 red+white - *88-89*	7	9
R026	**Redland** REDA14502 dull-green - *90-91*	8	10
R013	**Tarmac** TAMC14865 white+drab - *88-89*	7	9
R002	**Tarmac Quarry Products** TAM14869 dark green - *91-93*	8	10
R6217	**Tarmac Quarry Products** TAMC14863 very dark brown - *03-04*	8	10
R004	**BIS** BIS7987 white - *91*	8	10
(R6154)	**RMC** PR14376 red W	7	NA
(R6154)	**RMC** PR14377 red W	7	NA
(R6154)	**RMC** PR14378 red W	7	NA
R6154	set of above 3 wagons - *02*	NA	18
(R6154A)	**RMC** PR14365 red W	7	NA
(R6154A)	**RMC** PR14366 red W	7	NA
(R6154A)	**RMC** PR14367 red W	7	NA
R6154A	set of above 3 wagons - *03*	NA	19
(R6254)	**Redland** REDA14502 buff W	7	NA
(R6254)	**Redland** REDA14503 buff W	7	NA
(R6254)	**Redland** REDA14504 buff W	7	NA
R6254	set of above 3 wagons - *04*	NA	19

W34. HEA Hopper (ex-Dapol)

W = weathered

R6049	**Loadhaul** 361874 black+orange - *98*	5	6
R6083	**Loadhaul** 361876 black+orange - *99-02*	5	6
R6083A	**Loadhaul** 360695 black+orange - *03-04*	5	7
(R6152)	**Loadhaul** 361878 black+orange W	5	NA
(R6152)	**Loadhaul** 361879 black+orange W	5	NA
(R6152)	**Loadhaul** 361880 black+orange W	5	NA
R6152	set of above 3 wagons - *02*	NA	19
(R6152A)	**Loadhaul** 360696 black+orange W	5	NA
(R6152A)	**Loadhaul** 360697 black+orange W	5	NA
(R6152A)	**Loadhaul** 360698 black+orange W	5	NA
R6152A	set of above 3 wagons - *03-04*	NA	20
(R6152B)	**Loadhaul** 36**** black+orange W	5	NA
(R6152B)	**Loadhaul** 36**** black+orange W	5	NA
(R6152B)	**Loadhaul** 36**** black+orange W	5	NA
R6152B	set of above 3 wagons - *04*	NA	20
R6050	**EWS** 361870 maroon - *98*	5	6
R6084	**EWS** 361866 maroon - *99-00*	4	6

W35a. HAA Merry-Go-Round Hopper

W = weathered

R238	**BR** 351540 silver+brown - *80-81*	6	8
R249	**BR Rft** 352556 silver+red - *81-03*	4	6
R039	**BR Rft** 351923 silver+yellow Coal - *88-90*	6	8
R033	**BR Rft** 350897 silver+yellow Coal (small) - *90-03*	4	6
R6041	**EW&S** 353397 maroon - *98-04*	4	6
(R6150)	**EW&S** 353390 maroon W	5	NA
(R6150)	**EW&S** 353391 maroon W	5	NA
(R6150)	**EW&S** 353392 maroon W	5	NA
R6150	set of above 3 wagons - *02*	NA	18
(R6150A)	**EW&S** 352487 maroon W	5	NA
(R6150A)	**EW&S** 352488 maroon W	5	NA
(R6150A)	**EW&S** 352489 maroon W	5	NA
R6150A	set of above 3 wagons - *03-04*	NA	18

W35aa. HAA 32.5t MGR Hopper (2003 model)

W = weathered.

R6213	**BR** 355760 silver+red - *03-04*	6	8
(R6222)	**BR** 355761 silver+red W ex-wagon set	7	NA
(R6222)	**BR** 355762 silver+red W ex-wagon set	7	NA
(R6222)	**BR** 355763 silver+red W ex-wagon set	7	NA
R6222	set of above 3 wagons - *03-04*	NA	30

W35b. HBA MGR with Hood

R6157	**BR** 350001 silver+red - *02*	5	6
R6157A	**BR** 350002 silver+red - *03-04*	5	6

W35ba. HBA 32.5t MGR + Hood (2003 model)

W = weathered.

R6215	**BR** 368300 silver+red - *03-04*	NPG	8
(R6224)	**BR** 368301 silver+red W ex-wagon set	7	NA
(R6224)	**BR** 368302 silver+red W ex-wagon set	7	NA
(R6224)	**BR** 368303 silver+red W ex-wagon set	7	NA
R6224	set of above 3 wagons - *03-04*	NA	30

Bulk Grain & Powder Wagons

W36. CDA Hopper Clay Hopper

This was basically the HAA merry-go-round hopper wagon with a lid on it.

R052	**ECC** 353224 silver+blue - *88-92,97*	5	7
R6106	**ECC** 375007 silver+blue - *00-03*	4	6

W36a. CDA China Clay Hopper (2003 model)

W = weathered.

R6214	**ECC** 375048 silver+blue - *03-04*	NPG	8
(R6223)	**BR** 375409 silver+blue W ex-wagon set	7	NA
(R6223)	**BR** 375050 silver+blue W ex-wagon set	7	NA
(R6223)	**BR** 375051 silver+blue W ex-wagon set	7	NA
R6223	set of above 3 wagons - *03-04*	NA	30

W37. Grain Wagon

Most were fitted with a working trapdoor triggered by a leaver on the side and the wagon had two sliding hatches in the roof.

R215	**BR** B85040 green - *58-59*	12	14
R215	**BR** B85040 pale green-grey - *60-66*	6	10
R215	**BR** B85040 pale green-grey no mechanism - *67-68*	6	10

W38. Trix/Tri-ang BRT Bulk Grain Wagon

These 35T BRT bulk grain vans were made, or part made, by Liliput for Trix and supplied by Trix to Rovex with Tri-ang couplings fitted. They were packaged in Tri-ang Hornby boxes. Due to production difficulties, few were supplied and some came as bodies only which Rovex fitted to their China Clay wagon chassis. The body of the Trix wagon was smaller than that of the Tri-ang Hornby model (below) which Rovex were forced to produce to meet mounting orders.

R647	**Dewers** blue - *68*	15	18
R648	**Johnny Walker** blue - *68*	15	18
R649	**Vat 69** blue - *68*	15	18
R650	**Haig** blue - *68*	15	18
R650	**Haig** blue (Trix body on Tri-ang chassis) - *68*	20	30

Trix body on a Tri-ang Hornby chassis - a rare combination [W38]

W39. Tri-ang BRT Bulk Grain Wagon

This slightly larger model was tooled-up when it was clear that Trix would be unable to meet their commitment to supply sufficient of their own model to meet the orders Rovex were receiving.

R648	**Johnny Walker** 5833 blue BRT - *69-73*	12	14
R649	**Vat 69** 5820 blue BRT - *69-71*	12	14
R238	**Heygates Grain** 12 white - *86-87*	10	12
R023	**BRT** 7799 blue - *89-95*	10	12

W40. Cement Wagon

SS = Silver Seal wheels.

R564	**Blue Circle** LA211 light grey - *66-71*	7	9
R564	**Blue Circle** yellow - *72-75*	5	7
R237	**Blue Circle** yellow SS - *76*	5	7
R309	**Readymix** (Australia) pale grey - *74-75*	15	20
R385	**Readymix** (Australia) pale grey SS - *76*	15	20

W41. Prestwin Silo Wagon

R125	**BR** B873001 brown Prestwin - *78-79*	5	6
R723	**BR** B873001 brown Prestwin, paint finish - *80-82*	7	8
R011	**Fisons** B872001 white - *82-85*	7	8
R095	**Bulk Powder** B873740 buff - *89-90*	8	9

W42. PCA Presflo (Vee Tank) (ex-Dapol)

W = weathered

R6026	**Lever Bros** TRL10522 purple - *97-00*	5	7
R6027	**Ketton Cement** TLG9462 yellow - *97-99*	5	7
R6090	**Hornby Collector** black Sp Edn 7700 (HCC) - *99*	6	7
R6126	**Alcan** BAHS10800 grey - *01*	4	6
R6160	**BR** 9202 grey - *02-04*	6	7
R6160A	**BR** 9288 grey - *03*	6	7
(R6153)	**BR** 9203 grey W	6	NA
(R6153)	**BR** 9204 grey W	6	NA
(R6153)	**BR** 9205 grey W	6	NA
R6153	set of above 3 wagons - *02*	NA	19

(R6153A)	**BR** 9198 grey W	6	NA
(R6153A)	**BR** 9199 grey W	6	NA
(R6153A)	**BR** 9200 grey W	6	NA
R6153A	set of above 3 wagons - 03	NA	20
(R6153B)	**BR** 9113 grey W	6	NA
(R6153B)	**BR** 9114 grey W	6	NA
(R6153B)	**BR** 9115 grey W	6	NA
R6153B	set of above 3 wagons - 04	NA	20
(R6253)	**Blue Circle** 9343 grey	6	NA
(R6253)	**Blue Circle** 9344 grey	6	NA
(R6253)	**Blue Circle** 9345 grey	6	NA
R6253	set of above 3 wagons - 04	NA	20

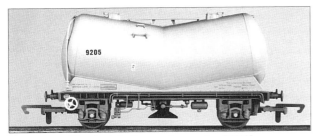

Vee tank bulk powder carrier [W42]

W43. Lime Wagon

This model used the 5-plank wagon body and had the pitched section added on top. tp = tampo printed.

R211	**Minera Lime** 125 brown - 73-75	4	7
R211	**Minera Lime** 125 brown tp - 76-78	5	8
R6243	**Whitecliff Lime** Co 6 white - 04	NPG	6

Bulk Liquid Tank Wagons

W44. Slurry Tank Wagon

R668	**Bowater's** 1025 pale blue broad blue ladder + gantry - 69	15	17
R668	**Bowater's** 1025 pale blue narrow blue ladder + gantry - 70-73	9	13
R668	**Bowater's** 1025 pale blue narrow white ladder + gantry - 72	12	12

W45a. Small Tanker (1st Type)

This had the barrel made in three sections which plugged together and the tank cap was part of the centre moulding. Red solebars were usual on the silver tanker and black on the black and yellow ones but this did not always apply. tf = transfers.

R12	**Shell + BP** (opposite sides) silver tf - 54-57	6	8
R12	**Shell + BP** (opposite sides) grey tf - ?	10	12
R210	**Shell BP** black tf - 56-57	6	12
R211	**Shell Lubricating Oil** yellow tf - 56-57	6	8

W45b. Small Tanker (1st Type) with ladders

This was the same design as that in table W45a (above) but had a ladder each side.

R15	**UD** white, red heat printing - 54-57	7	9

W46a. Small Tanker (2nd Type)

This improved tank wagon had the barrel and one end as a single moulding and the other end and the cap added afterwards. When the Shell BP joint marketing company tanks no longer had Shell on one side and BP on the other, Tri-ang had both a Shell and a BP tank running simultaneously in their range but they shared the same 'R' number. The running number on these were sometimes swapped over. The solebars were usually red on the silver tanker but may be found unpainted (i.e. black). On the black and yellow tankers they are usually black. hp = heat printed. tf = transfers. st = stickers.

R12	**Shell + BP** tf (on op sides) silver - 57	12	14
R12	**Shell + BP** hp (on op sides) silver - 57-61	5	7
R12	**Shell** 2 tf each side 5056 silver - 62-66	5	7
R12	**Shell** 2 tf each side 5057 silver - 62-66	10	12
R12	**Shell** 2 small tf each side 5056 silver - ?	15	17
BP 2	tf each side 5057 silver - 62-71	5	7
R12	**Shell** 2 st each side 5056 silver - 67-71	5	7
R12	**Shell** 2 st each side 5057 silver - 67-71	7	9
R12NP	silver no print ex-starter sets - c68	8	NA

R12	**Shell** 2 st each side 5056 grey - 67-71	5	7
R210	**Shell** BP tf both sides black - 57	12	14
R210	**Shell** BP hp both sides black - 58-65	5	10
R211	**Shell Lubricating Oil** tf yellow - 57	12	14
R211	**Shell Lubricating Oil** hp yellow - 58-68	5	7
R211NP	no printing ex-starter sets yellow - c68	8	NA

W46b. Small Tanker (2nd Type) with ladders

This was the same style of tank in table W46a above but had a ladder each side. hp = heat printed. tp = tampo printed.

R15	**UD** white, red + black transfers - 57	12	14
R15	**UD** white, hp in red (narrow 'U') - 58	10	12
R15	**UD** white, hp in red - 59-73	5	7
R15NP	white no print ex-starter sets - c68	8	NA
R015	**UD** white hp in red + black - 74	12	14
R015	**UD** 101 white tp in red + black - 74-75	5	7
R108	**Esso** silver - 74-75	7	9
R311	**Peters Milk** white - 74-75	12	14

W47a. Small Tanker (3rd Type) with cross stays

This was similar to the 2nd type (table W46a) but has had a retooled cradle and the tank had more lines of rivets. The cap was also smaller but the most noticeable difference was the stays that crossed in the middle of each side.

R008	**Esso** (stickers) silver - 74-79	4	5
R713	**Esso** (printed) silver paint finish - 80-81	6	8
R096	**Esso** (in red) white - 84-96	4	NA
R096	**Esso** (in blue) white - 84-91	4	NA
R096	**Esso** (in blue) pale grey - ?	9	NA
R140	**Duracell** gold+black - 84-90	7	9
R203	**Trimite** black - 85-88	7	9
R343w	**Regent** 15 red - 90-96	7	NA
R6019	**Shell** 3 light grey+red - 97-02	4	NA
R6032	**Scottish Oil Agency** 24 red Sp Edn 1 400 (Harburn Hobbies) - 97	8	10
R6064	**Crichton's Oil Company Ltd** 47 black Sp Edn 1200 (Harburn Hobbies) - 98	8	10
X?	**Burmah** red+ white - 99	8	NA
X?	**Pepsi** dark blue - 99-02	5	NA
R086	**Hornby Railways** 1995 red Ltd Edn 3300 - 95	6	8
R105	**Tidmouth Milk** (in blue) white - 85-04	4	5
R105	**Tidmouth Milk** (in red) white - 85-96	4	5
R305	**Tar** black - 89-94	4	5
R9006	**Tar** black - 99-04	4	5
R9055	**Sodor Fuel** yellow - 02-04	4	5

3rd type small tank wagon [W47a]

W47b. Small Tanker (3rd Type) with ladders

This was the same style of tank in table W47a (above) but had a ladder each side instead of the cross stays. SS = Silver Seal wheels.

R007	**United Dairies** white - 76-78	4	5
R311	**Peters Milk** (Australia) white - 74-75	12	14
R387	**Peters Milk** (Aust) white SS - 76-78	12	14
R003	**Polo** green - 82-84	6	8
R096	**Esso** (red) white - not made	NA	NA

W48. Small Tank Wagon (4th Type)
This was a much more detailed model with wire stays, ladders and gantry.

R245	**Shell BP** 4497 silver - *80*	6	8
R221	**National Benzol** P93 buff - *81-83*	7	9
R014	**Esso** 1800 silver - *82-83*	6	8
R127	**Castrol** 65 green - *87-04*	4	5
R129	**Redline** 245 blue - *87-90*	6	7
R025	**Regent** 101 silver - *88-90*	5	7
R6029	**Anglo-Scottish Chemical Co Ltd** 266 black Sp Edn 1480 (Harburn Hobbies) - *97*	9	11

W49. 14T Tank Wagon (ex-Dapol)
This was a copy of the Mainline 12T tank wagon and tooled in China.

R6052	**Lion Emulsion** C.15 black - *98-99*	4	5
R6069	**Shell Electrical Oils** SM3000 red-brown - *99-00*	4	5
R6109	**Royal Daylight** 27258 orange-brown - *00-01*	4	5
R6165	**Berry Wiggins** 116 silver - *02*	NPG	6
-	**McEwan's** 707107 buff - *02*	5	NA
-	**McEwan's** 707108 buff - *02*	5	NA
R6193	above two models Sp Edn 500 (Harburn Hobbies) - *02*	NA	13
R6207	**Esso** 1634 buff Dalkeith - *03*	5	7
R6207A	**Esso** 1635 buff Dalkeith - *04*	5	7

W50. 20T Tank Wagon (ex-Airfix)

R6011	**The Yorkshire Tar Distillers** 597 black - *97-99*	6	7
R6012	**United Oil Importers** silver - *97-99*	6	7
R6122	**The Distillers Company** 226 buff - *01*	5	6
R6170	**Shell** Motor Spirit 1719 silver - *02*	NPG	6
R6208	**ICI** 308 silver Methanol - *03*	5	7
R6208A	**ICI** 309 silver Methanol - *04*	5	8

W51. Monobloc Tank Wagon
These are 115mm long modern looking tanks with a gantry along the top and usually two ladders at the end although on some versions of the model these were left off. SS = Silver Seal wheels. tp = tampo printed. hp = heat printed.

R020	**Shell** 500 grey 2 logos stickers* hp - *73-79*	3	5
R715	**Shell** 500 grey painted + 2 logos printed - *80-81*	5	6
R720	**Shell** 500 yellow painted + 2 logos printed - *83-93*	5	NA
R181	**Esso** 500 silver sticker - *74*	6	NA
R315	**CIG** white (Australia) - *74-75*	12	14
R391	**CIG** white (Australia) SS - *76-78*	12	14
R132	**Shell** yellow 'Shell' + logo hp - *74*	3	5
R132	**Shell** yellow 'Shell' + logo tp - *75*	3	5
R227	**Shell** yellow 'Shell' + logo SS - *76-79*	3	5
R184	**Texaco** 500 red - *75*	3	5
R231	**Texaco** 500 red SS - *76-82, 86-91*	3	5
R731	**Gulf** 731 grey+orange - *80-81`*	5	6
R023	**Pfizer** green - *82*	6	8
R026	**Albright & Wilson** MD22 pale blue - *82-83*	6	8
R115	**Fina** No.4 silver - *83-84*	6	8
R133	**Milk Marketing Board** MMB4028 chrome - *83-84*	6	10
R210	**Think Tanker** chrome Sp Edn 2200 - *83*	15	20
R143	**Carlsberg** white - *84*	5	8
R218	**BP Chemicals** CU2 grey - *86-97*	5	6
R071	**Duckhams QXR** dark blue - *87-88*	5	8
R111	**National Benzol** 2020 black - *89-91*	5	6
R119	**Shell Oils** SUKO65911 grey TTA - *91-98*	5	6
R6025	**Shell Oils** SUKO65905 grey TTA - *97*	7	NA
R032	**Shell Petrol** SUKO67149 grey TTA - *92-96*	5	6
R6021	**Shell Petrol** SUKO67129 grey TTA - *97-98*	6	NA
R001	**BP** BPO60194 green TTA - *92-97*	5	6
R503	**Norris Fertilizer** 010 green Ltd Edn 2500 - *92-97*	7	10
R148	**ICI Petrochemicals** ICIA54360 white TTA black gantry - *94-97*	4	8
R148	**ICI Petrochemicals** ICIA54360 white TTA white gantry - *97-01*	4	8

R212	**Vedette & Sentinal** yellow Sp Edn 1000 - *84* 15	NA
R200	**Texaco** Station Master red - *93-96*	3	NA
R6001	**Hornby Railways** 1997 red Ltd Edn 2500 - *97* 6	10
R6034	**Beatties** 97 black Sp Edn 1000 - *97*	6	10
R6043	**BRT** 57650 grey - *98*	6	7
R6044	**Shell** SUKO65537 black TTA - *98-04*	4	5
R6081	**Water** 56963 - *99-00*	5	8
R6194	**Virgin Trains** 2002 silver+red Sp Edn 500 (Virgin for Warley Show) - *02*	NPG	10
R6255	**RMC** RC10045 orange PCA - *04*	NPG	7

* These stickers vary in colour, the three most common being: bright red and yellow, dark red and lemon, dark red and white.

Monobroc tank wagon [W51]

Vans

W52. 12T LMS Large Cattle/SR Sheep Wagon
Probably based on an LMS design, this was the longest surviving item of rolling stock in the range having originally been tooled up in 1955 and was still in production in the mid 1990s. The body was a single moulding with the exception of the roof which started white, changed to grey and returned to white in later years (some late models have a brown coloured roof). hp = heat printed. tp = tampo printed.

R122	**LMS** brown - *not made*	NA	NA
R122	**BR** M3712 orange-brown cream roof - *56*	12	14
R122	**BR** M3712 orange-brown grey roof - *56-71*	5	7
R122	**BR** M3713 orange-brown - *59-71*	5	7
R122	**BR** M3713 dung-brown - *62*	10	12
R122	**BR** M3712 orange-brown white roof - *72*	7	9
R122	**BR** M3712 black - *72*	10	12
R122	**BR** M3712 dark brown - *72*	10	12
R106	**SR** 51915 black - *72?*	10	12
R106	**SR** 51915 dark brown hp or tp - *72-81*	5	7
R097	**SR** 51915 buff - *84-85*	9	NA
R104	51915 buff ex-Thomas - *86-90*	7	9
R?	**SR** 51915 grey - *82*	12	NA
R022	**GW** 38901 grey - *82-84*	8	10
R215	**Harvey Bros.** 12563 dark green - *86-89,96*	7	9
R470w	**LMS** 23716 grey - *90-93*	8	NA

Cattle wagon [W52]

W53. GWR Horse Box
Based on a GWR design.

R123	**BR** M3713 grey - *not made*	NA	NA
R123	**BR** M3713 red - *56*	10	12
R123	**BR** M2313 red - *56*	10	12
R123	**BR** B542 ddark red nos. in white - *58-60*	7	9
R123	**BR** B542 maroon nos. in yellow - *60-61*	5	7
R123	**BR** B547 maroon - *62-70*	5	7
R123	**BR** B547 maroon white roof - *71*	15	17

R123A	**GW** 505 brown - *72-74*	5	7
R094	**Lord Derby Stables** brown - *not made*	NA	NA
R578	**BR** B547 maroon converter wagon *HD* coupling one end - *67-68*	10	15

W54a. Closed Van (ex-Trackmaster)

This was a planked van designed by Pyramid Toys for their Trackmaster set but the tools were bought from them to speed up the expansion of the Tri-ang Railways range. The body mould was also used as an Insulfish and an Express Parcels van (see W54b and W54c) below. The body was retooled around 1954 when the inscription on the base was changed (see notes at head of table W16a above). Roofs were more commonly plain early on but later rain strips were usual. Roofs could be grey or white (sometimes discoloured to cream).

R11	**NE** 86203 brown - *52*	6	8
R11	**NE** 86203 blue-grey - *52*	6	8
R11	**GW** 62134 blue-grey - *52*	6	8
R11	**GW** 62134 brown - *52*	6	8
R11	**GW** 62134 white - *52*	9	11
R11	**GW** 43726 blue-grey - *52-53*	6	8
R11	**GW** 43726 brown - *52-53*	6	8
R11	**GW** 43726 white - *52-53*	9	11
R11	**GW** 43726 red - *52-53*	8	10
R11	**GW** 43720 blue-grey - *53-54*	6	8
R11	**GW** 43720 brown - *53-54*	6	8
R11	**GW** 43720 grey-green - *53-54*	7	9
R11	**GW** 43720 red - *53-54*	8	10
R11	**GW** 10528 blue-grey - *54*	8	10
R11	**GW** 10528 brown - *54*	8	10
R11	**GW** 10528 grey-green - *54*	9	11
R11	**GW** 10528 orange - *54*	15	17
R11	**GW** 87204 blue-grey - *54-55*	6	8
R11	**GW** 87204 brown - *54-55*	6	8
R11	**GW** 87204 grey-green - *54-55*	6	8
R11	**GW** 73628 blue-grey - *55-56*	6	8
R11	**GW** 73628 brown - *55-56*	6	8
R11	**GW** 73628 grey-green - *55-56*	6	8
R11	**GW** 73628 grey - *55-56*	8	10
R11	**GW** 73628 khaki - *55-56*	13	15
R11	**BR** N4301 blue-grey - *57*	10	12
R11	**BR** N4301 brown - *57*	10	12
R11	**BR** N4301 grey - *57*	10	12
	W8755 number 10 mm long		
R11	**BR** W8755 brown - *57-60*	6	8
R11	**BR** W8755 grey - *57-60*	6	8
R11	**BR** W8755 dark green - *57-60*	6	8
R11	**BR** W8755 light grey - *57-60*	8	10
R11	**BR** W8755** pale brown - *60*	10	12
	W8755 number 7 mm long		
R11	**BR** W8755 grey - *60-?*	6	8
R11	**BR** W8755 green - *60-68*	5	7
R11	**BR** W8755 dark brown - *?*	10	12
R11	**BR** W8755 dark green - *?*	8	10
R11	**BR** W8755 black - *?*	10	12
R11	**BR** W8755 dung-brown - *62*	10	12
R11NP	various colours*** no printing ex-starter sets - *65-72*	5	NA

**Also called Caramac brown. ***Colours known to exist include blue, vermilion & khaki.

W54b. Insulfish Van

This was a variation using the same body and roof tools as the closed van (above). All early vans were supposed to be white but are frequently cream, either due to discoloration by sunlight or through use of a cream coloured plastic when white was not available. Both grey and white roofs may be found and they may be plain or with rain strips. As roofs have become swapped over during the years it is hard to say what came with what. 'White' plastics were sometimes cream.

R14	**BR** 14280 (small digits) white - *52-54*	7	9
R14	**BR** 14280 (larger digits) white - *53-54*	6	8
R14	**BR** 61745 white - *55*	10	12
R14	**BR** 28174 white - *54-57*	6	8
R14	**BR** N6307 (10.5 mm) white - *57-58*	8	10
R14	**BR** N6301 (10 mm) white - *58-60*	5	7
R14	**BR** N6301 (7 mm) white - *61-65*	5	7
R14	**BR** N6301 (7 mm) pale blue* - *66-73*	4	6
R14	**BR** N6307 (7 mm) pale blue* - *72-73*	4	6
R14NP	pale blue* no printing, ex-starter sets - *64-67*	5	NA

R14NP	pale blue no printing, NMRA couplings for export - *68*	15	NA

*Two shades of the pale blue body may be found, the warmer shade being the later of the two.

W54c. SPV Express Parcels Van

This used the tools of the Closed Van. It had a grey roof and sometimes was sold with the roof from the Hull & Barnsley van (see table W55).

R780	**BRe** E12080 rail-blue - *71-73*	6	9

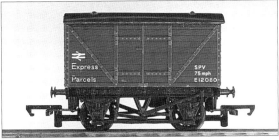

Express parcels van [W54c]

W55. Hull & Barnsley Van

Hornby never professed to the model being based on a Hull & Barnsley Railway design but it clearly was. The van had distinctive panelled sides and large roof ventilators. SS = Silver Seal wheels. tp = tampo printed.

R21	**NE** 7901 white Refrigerator - *72*	6	7
R013	**Fine Fish** E81010 pale blue - *73-75*	4	5
R206	**Fine Fish** E81010 pale blue SS - *76*	4	5
R206	**Fine Fish** E81010 pale blue tp* - *76-77*	6	7
R162	**Prime Pork** E71011 green - *74-75*	4	5
R216	**Prime Pork** E71011 green SS - *76*	4	5
R216	**Prime Pork** E71011 green tp* - *76-79,82*	4	5
R105	**Birds Eye** 14901 rail-blue - *74-79*	4	6
R130	**Lyons Maid** white - *74*	9	11
R135	**Smiths** white - *78-79*	4	5
R725	**Smiths** white paint finish - *80-81*	6	7
R725	**Smiths** pale grey - *?*	8	9
R728	**Weetabix** yellow - *80-81*	6	7
R728	**Weetabix** yellow with advert characters - *86-89*	5	NA
R722	**Kit-Kat** red - *80-81*	6	8
R001	**KP Nuts** dark blue - *82-83*	5	7
R002	**Birds** yellow - *82*	7	9
R132	**Baxters** blue - *83-84*	5	8
R134	**Callard & Bowser** white - *83*	8	10
R149	**Prima** yellow - *84*	7	8
R146	**OXO** blue - *84*	7	8
R042	**Railmail** light grey Sp Edn 5000 - *81*	8	10
R043	**Taylor & Mckenna** orng Sp Edn 5000 - *81*	7	9
R040	**Eastbourne Models** wht Sp Edn 4950 - *81*	7	9
R038	**Redgates** yellow Sp Edn 3500 - *81*	7	9
R111	**Yorkshire Pudding** yellow Edn 2500 - *82*	7	9
R?	**GW** 102971 rail-blue ex-set - *?*	7	8
R?	**GW** 102971 electric-blue ex-set - *?*	8	9
R502	**SR** 50643 buff Banana Ltd Edn 2500 - *91*	8	10
R108	dark brown Thomas with face - *85-90*	5	7
R205	**Van Houten's** Cocoa dark brown - *95-96*	5	10

* Tampo printed wagons have the printing crossing the door frames unbroken.

Hull & Barnsley van [W55]

W56. 12T Ventilated Van with Sliding Doors

Based on one of only 6 vans of this type built at Derby in 1962 the van had two doors each side that could be opened. SS = Silver Seal wheels.

R11A	**BR** B784287 brown, grey roof - *68-75*	6	8
R11A	**BR** B784287 brown, pale grey roof - *68-75*	6	8
R205	**BR** B784287 brown SS - *76-78*	6	8

W57. 12T VEA/Vanwide Ventilated Van

R242	**BR** E784690 brown, brown roof - *79-80*	7	8
R242	**BR** E784690 brown, white roof - *81-82*	5	6
R117	**BRe Rft** 230062 grey+red VEA red moulding - *83-85*	5	7
R117	**BRe Rft** 230062 grey+red VEA grey moulding - *87-94*	6	8
R243	**Rest Assured** cream - *86-87*	7	9
R063	**Yellow Pages** yellow - *87-88*	8	10
R?	**Mighty White** white - *88-91*	9	NA
R034	**BR Rft** 230069 dark grey VEA yellow ends - *90-92*	7	9
R115	**BRe** ADB778246 grey+light blue Rail Stores - *91-92*	7	9
R010	**BR** B783396 brown Vanfit - *93-94*	7	9
R045	**BR** DW107897 bright red Tool Van, Eastleigh black roof - *93-98*	6	8
R147	**Hornby Railways** 1994 bright red Ltd Edn 3160 - *94*	6	8
R213	**BR** B882356 brown Banana - *95-98*	6	7
R6099	**Pendle Forest** MRS 35 bright red Sp Edn 500 (Pendle Forest MRS) - *99*	5	7
(R1020)	**CIE** 2004 brown ex-set - *99*	8	NA
(R1015)	**Tango** black+orange ex-set - *99-02*	4	NA
R6178	**BR** B784837 red-brown R.Silcocks - *02-04*	5	7
R6179	**BR Rft** 230377 olive grey+yellow - *02-03*	5	7

W58. 12T BR Ventilated Van (ex-Dapol)

This van was designed and tooled by Dapol and a better scale model.

R6003	**BR** B763295 grey - *97-98*	5	6
R6003	**BR** B762430 grey - *99*	4	5
R6147A	**BR** B759180 brown Sp Edn 250* - *00*	5	9
R6147B	**BR** B759186 brown Sp Edn 250* - *00*	5	9
R6147C	**BR** B760429 brown Sp Edn 250* - *00*	5	9
R6147D	**BR** B763281 brown Sp Edn 250* - *00*	5	9
R6147E	**BR** B764100 brown Sp Edn 250* - *00*	5	9
R6186A	**BR** B777327? red-brown - *02*	5	6
(R1029)	**BR** DB756126 red ex-set - *02-03*	6	NA
(R1035)	**Welsh Tin Plate & Metal Stamping Co. Ltd** 4 brown-red ex-set - *03-04*	6	NA

* These originally appeared in the A.B.Gee commissioned train pack of which 1000 were made. The last 250 packs were broken up, the wagons individually boxed by Hornby and the entire stock sold to the Trafford Model Centre in Manchester.

W59. 12T GWR Mogo Van (ex-Dapol)

This van was a copy of the Mainline Mogo van and tooled in China.

R6056	**GW** 126336 dark grey - *98-99*	5	6
R6080	**GW** 124000 dark grey - *99-00*	4	5

W60. 10T BR Meat Van (ex-Dapol)

Based on 100 vans built at Wolverton Works in 1952.

R6185A	**BR** B870006 red-brown - *02*	NPG	6
R6185B	**BR** red-brown - *02-03*	5	6

W61. 8T LNER Refrigerator Van

Although mainly used by Hornby for fictitious private owner liveries, it was based on an LNER design of 1926 which had a 9' wheelbase.

R009	**Golden Shred** red - *82-84*	5	8
R015	**Canterbury Lamb** buff - *82*	6	8
R114	**Wimpy** 151275 red - *83-85*	5	8
R147	**NE** 151275 white - *84-87*	5	7
R147	**NE** 151275 white paint finish - *?*	6	8
R6180	**NE** 151276 white - *02-03*	5	7
R6181	**NE** 439848 white - *02-03*	5	7
R241	**Yorkshire Dales Railway** dark brown Sp Edn 1000 (YDR) - *85*	5	10

R214	**Gamleys** white Sp Edn 2000 - *84*	6	10
R722	**Kit Kat** red - *85?*	7	NA
R200	**ETC*** 314 white - *85-86*	7	8
R201	**Terry's** 254 grey - *85-86*	6	8
-	**Pendle Forest** blue Sp Edn 50 - *85*	30	35
-	**Pendle Forest** white Sp Edn 100 - *89*	20	25

* ETC stands for E.T.Carfrae - Tom Carfrae was the designer at Hornby!

LNER refrigerator van - 2 rare special issues [W61]

W62. Long Wheel Base Van

R109	**Cadburys** 476 white+purple - *74-75*	6	10
R134	**Heinz** emerald-green - *74*	7	10
R183	**Kelloggs** white outlined in red - *74*	5	8
R317	**Australian** markings (1975) - *not made*	NA	NA
R222	**Kelloggs** white - *76*	4	6
R222	**Kelloggs** blue large head small eye - *77*	3	5
R222	**Kelloggs** blue small head large eye - *77*	3	5
R?	**Rollei Cameras*** silver - *77*	NPG	NPG
R137	**McVities** blue - *78-79*	3	6
R727	**McVities** blue paint finish - *80-81*	4	6
R121	**CIE** 2007 white Insulated Container - *79*	30	NA
R138	**Silver Spoon** blue - *84*	8	12
R145	**Red Arrows** light blue design different on either side - *84-91*	5	8
R202	**Reconafork** pale grey Ransoms - *85-86*	5	8
R217	**Anglian** cream - *86-87*	5	9
R056	**Astra Fireworks** yellow - *87-88*	5	9
R596w	**Red Star Parcels** yellow - *91-95*	6	NA
R008	**Yellow Pages** yellow - *86*	10	12
R021	**Harvester Restaurants** yellow - *92-93*	5	8
R321	**Cox Brothers** Circus red - *94-96*	5	12
-	**Police** white - *not made*	NA	NA
-	**Coca Cola** red - *?*	NPG	NPG

* Very little is known about this wagon other than it was seen in an exhibition in 1977. It may have been a Code 3 model.

W63a. 45T VDA/ZRA Long Wheelbase Van

Many of these larger vans were built for BR in the 1970s.

R234	**BRe Railfreight** 210304 brown - *80-81*	8	10
R247	**BRe Railfreight** 210218 grey+red, red moulding - *81-83*	8	10
R247	**BRe Railfreight** 210218 grey+red, grey moulding - *87-94*	6	8
R237	**BRe Railfreight** 210218 grey+red Speedlink Distribution on roof Sp Edn 4000 - *83*	15	25
R016	**BR Railfreight** 200706 light grey yellow - *89*	8	9
R017	**BR Rft** 200659 dark grey+yellow - *90-94*	6	8
R156	**BR** DC200514 grey+yellow - *94-95*	6	8
R404	**BR** Rft 200895 light grey+yellow - *96-97*	6	7
R6042	**EWS** 200896 maroon - *98*	5	6
R6042A	**EWS** 210238 maroon - *01*	5	6
R6042B	**EWS** 200991 maroon - *02*	5	7
R6042C	**EWS** 200731 maroon - *03-04*	5	7
R6074	**BRe Civilink** 200660 grey+yellow - *99-00*	5	7
R6188	**BRe Civilink** grey+yellow - *02*	5	7
R6138	**Transrail Enterprise** 210195 grey - *01*	5	7
R6260	**Virgin Trains** 2004 Rail Bicentenary red+white Sp Edn 500 (Virgin) - *04*	6	8

W63b. PVA/PVB/ZRA Curtain-Sided Van

Although curtain sided vans were made, this model involves a lot of compromise.

R141	**Campbells** BRT6117 red - *84-85*	9	11
R216	**Procor** PR6915 blue - *86-88*	7	9
R097	**Caib** PR6917 red+white - *91-92*	8	10
R043	**Railiner** TRL6950 yellow - *93-96*	7	9
R6187	**Railiner** TRL? yellow - *02*	NPG	9
R6046	**Hornby** 1998 white Ltd Edn 2500 - *98*	7	9
R6101	**Eddie Stobart** green Sp Edn 1000 (Trafford Model Centre) - *00*	15	18
R6137	**EWS** DC201008 maroon ZRA - *01*	4	6

W64. VIX Ferry Van

Based on a Pressed Steel Co. Ltd design used on the Harwich-Zeebrugge Ferry. The model was fitted with a pair of 2-wheel bogies and had sliding doors. Early models (probably up to the end of 1974) had their bogies linked by a rubber band under tension. When the model was re-released in 1978 the bogies had flexible plastic projections, trapped in hoops, to self-centre the wheels.

R738	**BR** GB787102 maroon rubber band tensioned bogies - *70-72*	10	15
R738	**BR** GB787102 maroon plastic tensioned bogies - *78-79*	10	15
R740	**BR** GB787102 maroon paint finish - *80-81*	18	22
R6159	**BRe** 240157-5 brown - *02*	NPG	15
R6159A	**BRe** 2380-393/5 brown - *03*	NPG	15
R741A	**Transfesa** 0286184.3 bright blue - *72-74*	12	17
R742	**Interfrigo** 0286184.3 white - *72-73*	11	16
R787	**Ford** blue+white - *73*	15	NA
R786	**Fyffes** white+yellow - *73*	15	NA
R027	**BRe** Speedlink 2380 393.5 grey+red Railfreight International - *82-83, 87-90*	15	18

Ferry van - Interfrigo [W64]

W65. Six-Wheeled Van

Based on two vans built by the GWR at Swindon in 1936. pf = paint finish

R670	**Palethorpes** maroon - *76-79*	6	8
R733	**Palethorpes** maroon pf - *80-82*	9	11
R6158	**GWR** Palethorpes 280 brown - *02-04*	6	8
R671	**LMS** 3855 white Insulated Milk - *76-79*	6	8
R734	**LMS** 3855 white Insulated Milk pf - *80-81*	9	11
R6242	**LMS** 38553 maroon Insulated Milk pf - *80-81*	NPG	8
R6259	**Hornby** 2004 red - *04*	NPG	8

6-wheeled van - Palethorpes [W65]

Brake Vans

W66. Short Brake Van (1st Type)

This was the first wagon to be designed by Rovex and used the former Trackmaster chassis. It had a veranda at each end and was used in many sets as well as being sold solo. Initially it had stamped metal running boards which hooked over the chassis but later a special chassis casting, incorporating the boards, was made. Likewise, it had its own plastic chassis when these were introduced in the early '60s.

R16	**NE** 16083 light grey - *53*	9	11
R16	**NE** 16083 brown - *53*	8	10
R16	**NE** (thin) 129085 light grey - *53*	5	7
R16	**NE** (thin) 129085 brown - *53*	5	7
R16	**NE** (thin) 129085 grey - *53*	6	8
R16	**NE** (thin) 129085 red - *53*	8	10
R16	**NE** 129085 brown - *53-54*	7	9
R16	**NE** 129085 grey - *53-54*	7	9
R16	**NE** 129803 - *54*	8	10
R16	**NE** 129083 light grey - *54*	8	10
R16	**NE** 748936 light grey - *54*	6	8
R16	**NE** 748936 pale blue-grey - *54*	6	8
R16	**NE** 748936 brown - *54*	5	7
R16	**NE** 748936 red - *54*	8	10
R16	**NE** 138224 light grey - *54-55*	6	8
R16	**NE** 138224 brown - *54-55*	5	7
R16	**NE** 573684 light grey - *54-56*	6	8
R16	**NE** 573684 brown - *54-56*	5	7
R16	**NE** 650432 light grey - *56*	8	10
R16	**NE** 650432 brown - *56*	7	9
R16	**NE** 13326 light grey - *?*	10	12
R16	**NE** 73684 grey - *56-57*	6	8
R16	**NE** 73684 brown - *56-57*	6	8
R16	**BR** N53612 brown - *57*	7	9
R16	**BR** N53612 grey - *57*	7	9
R16	**BR** M73031 (12 mm) grey - *57-62*	4	6
R16	**BR** M73031 (12 mm) brown - *57-62*	4	6
R16	**BR** M73031 (12 mm) blue-grey - *57-62*	6	8
R16	**BR** M73031 (7 mm) brown - *62-67*	4	6
R16NP	brown no printing, for starter sets - *60-72*	5	6

W67. GWR Brake Van (1st Type)

Original 1956 body.

R124	**BR** W.6297 (10 mm) or-brown, wht roof - *56*	12	14
R124	**BR** W.6297 (10 mm) or-brown - *56-60*	7	9
R124	**BR** W6297 (8 mm) orange-brown - *60-70*	5	7
R124	**BR** W6297 (8 mm) dung-brown - *62*	10	12
R124A	**GW** GW57740 light grey - *71-74*	5	7
R124	**GW** GW57740 light grey LMS roof with rain strips - *74-75*	6	8

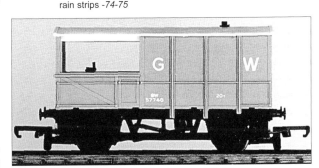

GWR toad brake van [W67]

W68. GWR Brake Van (2nd Type)

New 1976 body with more accurate profile being narrower than the type 1 brake van. It was also fitted with a red light at the back, with or without a means of lighting it.

R018	**GW** 114925 light grey 20Tons Saltney - *76*	9	11
R018	**GW** 114925 light grey 20T Saltney - *77-79*	7	9
R714	**GW** 114925 dark grey 20T Saltney paint finish - *80-02*	8	10
R402	**GW** 114775 dark grey Neath - *96-00*	7	9
R6020w	**GW** 56261 dark grey Reading - *97-98*	9	NA

W69. GWR Brake Van (ex-Airfix)

R6077	**GW** 114775 dark grey Worcester - *99-03*	5	7
R6077A	**GW** 56683 dark grey Worcester - *04*	5	7
(R1037)	**GW** 114763 dark grey Worcester ex-set - *03-04*	5	7
R6076	**BR** B950572 grey - *99-00*	5	7

R6146	**BR** W68870 brown Tavistock Junc - *01*	5	7
R6146A	**BR** W17441 brown Tavistock Junc - *02*	5	7
R6220	**BR** W114854 brown - *03*	5	7
R6257	**BR** W17274 brown Birkenhead - *04*	5	7
R6195	**Hornby** 2003 yellow Ltd Edn 3000 - *03*	5	7

W70.   LMS Brake Van

R107	**LMS** 730386 brown, working light silver handrails - *74-76*	8	10
R098	**LMS** 730386 brown thin 'S' white handrails - *77-79*	4	5
R718	**LMS** 730386 brown paint finish - *80-96*	7	8
R201	yellow Station Master model - *93-96*	3	5

W71.   LMS Brake Van (ex-Airfix)

R6079	**LMS** 730670 light grey - *99-00*	5	7
R6079A	**LMS** 730450 light grey - *02-03*	5	7
R6079B	**LMS** 723484 light grey - *03-04*	5	7
R6078	**BR** DM730767 dark olive - *99-00*	5	7
X?	**BR** M730708 grey - *99*	5	7
R6145	**BR** M730708 brown - *01-02*	5	7
R6145A	**BR** M730106 brown - *03-04*	5	7

W72.   LBSC Brake Van

R019	**LBSC** 43 grey unglazed - *80-82*	10	12
R029	**SR** (large) 55918 dark brown unglazed - *82-90*	9	11
R6144	**SR** (small) 55920 dark brown - *01*	5	7
R6144A	**SR** (small) 55925 dark brown - *02-03*	5	7
R6144B	**SR** (small) 55910 dark brown - *04*	5	7

W73a.   Short Brake Van (2nd Type)

R215	**NE** 178595 grey (also R114) - *73-76*	4	6
R215	**NE** 178595 grey larger digits - *76-79*	4	6
R215	**NE** 178595 grey tampo printed - *?*	7	9

W73b.   BR(ER) Brake Van (1st Type)

This was made to fit the chassis of the Western Region brake van (which was 2' too short to be correct) but the body was also used to make a short brake van using a 10' chassis (see below). The roof was initially grey but, for a while, a white one was fitted. The original version was catalogued as R636, R16A, R16 and R218 the last being when Silver Seal (SS) wheels were fitted.

R636	**BR** B952698 brown, grey roof - *67*	5	9
R16A	**BR** B952698 brown, grey roof - *67-72*	5	7
R016	**BR** B952698 brown, white roof - *73-75*	5	7
R218	**BR** B952698 brown, grey roof SS - *76-79*	5	7
R729	**BR** B952698 brown paint finish - *80-82*	7	9
X?	**BR** B952564 brown ex-R1017 set - *99-02*	8	NA
X?	**BR** B808733 brown ex-R1030 set - *02-03*	8	NA
	ex-Thomas Series		
R109	**BR** B952698 brown paint finish - *85-96*	7	9
R109	**BR** B952564 brown paint finish - *?*	7	9
R109	**BR** B952566 brown paint finish - *97-04*	7	9
	Made for Australia		
R313	**NSWR** maroon - *74-75*	10	12
R389	**NSWR** maroon SS - *76-78*	10	12
R314	**VR** blue - *74-75*	12	14
R390	**VR** blue SS - *76*	12	14

BR standard brake van [W73b]

W74.   BR(ER) Brake Van (2nd Type)

R030	**BR** brown - *82-84*	5	7
R031	**NE** 157838 grey - *82-84*	5	7
R048	**BR Rft** B954817 CAR grey+red - *87-92*	5	7
R089	**BR** Service Department B872163 grey+yellow ZTR - *89-90*	6	8
R049	**BR Rft** B954603 CAR dark grey - *90-91*	6	8
R264	**BR** Engineer's DB950436 grey+yellow ZTV - *94-96*	5	6
R6062	**BR** B457516? brown - *98*	5	6
R6148	**BR** B950866 brown Sp Edn 250 boxed (Trafford Model Centre) - *00*	5	10
R6119	**BR** B952005 brown - *01-03*	4	6
R6119A	**BR** B952008 brown - *04*	4	7
(R1036)	**BR** B952016 brown ex-set - *03-04*	5	NA
R6206	**BR Railfreight** B954779 grey+red W - *03*	5	7
R6206A	**BR Railfreight** B954720 grey+red - *04*	5	7

Mobile Cranes

W75.   Small Mobile Crane

This has a specially made heavy diecast chassis and was based on a Cowans Sheldon 10T crane used in railway yards. It used the 2nd type bolster wagon as a match truck. The hook was diecast and the chain brass.

R127	No.127 brown - *62-70*	9	11
R385	No.127 brown CKD kit - *66-71*	NA	30
R127	No.127 red - *71-79*	10	12
R142	yellow no markings - *84*	10	12
R6004	No.101 yellow Eng Dept Crane - *97-04*	10	15

W76.   Large Breakdown Crane

Based on a design by Cowans Sheldon Co. Ltd it represented a 75T mobile rail-crane and came with three trucks. Two of these were short and were both spacers and the third was a jib runner. Early versions of the model used an integral low sided wagon from the starter sets as the jib runner but for later versions the plate wagon was used, modified to provide a cradle in the centre of the wagon.

R739	**BR** DB966111 red Stratford District original jib runner* - *71-81*	18	25
R749	**BRe** DB966111 yellow Stratford District original jib runner* - *82-84*	22	30
R749	**BRe** DB966111 yellow Stratford District new jib runner* - *88-94*	24	30
R306	drab from Thomas Series - *89*	30	35
R197	**BR** DB966111 red Stratford District, Cowans Sheldon - *95-99*	20	25
R6104	**BR** DB966111 + DB998617 red weathered Stratford District, - *00-02*	22	30
X?	**BR** DB966111 + DB998617 red Stratford District ex-R1029 set - *00-02*	22	NA
R6183	**BRb** black DS1580 Ransomes Rapier weathered - *02-04*	NPG	35
R6204	**BRe** ADB141 + ADB998538 weathered yellow Eastleigh - *03-04*	24	35

* The jib runner was originally a former integral type flat wagon from a late 60s starter sets but, from 1988, the Winkle plate wagon was converted and used.

Large breakdown crane [W76]

Bogie Wagons

W77a.   Bogie Bolster Wagon (1st Type)

The body started as a rather crude moulding but over the years, detail was added. It was also used as a flat bed for other wagons the most famous of which was the rocket launcher. The earliest examples had the bogies from the ex-Rovex 6" LMS coach.

R110	**BR** 129085 grey Rovex bogies - *53-54*	10	12
R110	**BR** 129085 grey TC bogies - *54*	8	10
R110	**BR** 129803 grey Rovex bogies - *53-54*	10	12

R110	BR 129803 grey TC bogies - 54	8	10
R110	BR 129083 grey Rovex bogies - 53-54	15	17
R110	BR 129083 grey TC bogies - 54	10	12
R110	BR 708924 grey number on either end of wagon - 55	7	9
R110	BR M13127 grey - 56-59	7	9
R110	BR M13127 blue-grey - ?	10	12
R110	BR M13127 orange - ?	20	22
R110	BR M13127 orange-brown - ?	20	22
R110	BR M13071 (12 mm) grey - 59-60	6	8
R110	BR M13071(7 mm) grey - 60-61	6	8
R110	BR M13071 (7 mm) light grey log - 60-61	6	8

W77b. Bogie Bolster (1st Type) with Log Load

This used the bogie bolster wagon (above) with a log set between the bolster pins.

R212	BR M13127 grey - 57-59	15	20
R212	BR M13071(12 mm) grey - 59-60	15	20
R212	BR M13071(7 mm) grey - 60-61	15	20

Rocket Launcher - see Battle Space at end of section (table B1 below)

W78. Bogie Bolster (2nd Type) and Loads

This was more delicate looking and much more realistic being made from completely new tools. The bolsters were now part of the body moulding. The underframe was particularly vulnerable to damage.

R110	BR B940052 grey, pins - 61-66	10	12
R563	BR B940052 salmon + 3 Minix Ford vans - 67-72	22	30
R565	BR B940052 salmon + 2 Freightliner containers - 67-69	15	NA
R579	BR B940052 light grey black printing + 2 cti containers - ?	20	NPG
R569	BR B940052 salmon + 3 Minix cars - 68	18	NA
R1210	BR B940052 light grey pins reversed to hold steel rail load (Canada) - 71	15	25
R110NP	salmon no printing + 3 Minix cars ex-starter sets - c68	15	NA
R023	BR DB996821 black Engineer's Salmon + track load - 72-73	15	20
R244	brown BCV planned for 1986 - not made	NA	NA

2nd type Bogie bolster wagon [W78]

W79. Macaw H Bogie Bolster (ex-Airfix)

R6015	GW 107285 dark grey Macaw H - 97-00	5	6
R6123	BR W107259 grey Bogie Bolster A - 01-02	5	6
R6123A	BR W107363 grey Bogie Bolster A - 03	5	7
R6123B	BR W107293 grey Bogie Bolster A - 04	5	7

W80a. Well Wagon (see also table WT12 and the Battle Space Section)

The model consisted of a single plastic moulding slung between two standard issue diamond bogies. Later the basic model was a popular subject for spin-offs both as a load carrier and also as a flatbed to which structures could be fitted. It was also used in the Transcontinental range (included in this table) and these models usually had the metal buffers missing. During its long life, the body moulding tool was modified on a number of occasions. Early examples had no fixing pegs underneath. These were added in 1957. The number R213 was added beneath soon afterwards.

R118	BR 41913 brown - 60-63	10	12
	41917 number 13 mm long		
R118	BR dark blue - 55-56	8	10
R118	BR grey-green - 55-56	7	9
R118	BR orange - 55-56	7	9
	41917 number 10 mm long		
R118	BR dark blue 56-59	8	10
R118	BR grey-green 56-59	6	8

R118	BR orange 56-59	6	8
R118	BR grey 56-59	5	7
	41917 number 8.5 mm long		
R118	BR grey 59-67	5	7
R118	BR green 59-67	4	6
R118	BR brown 59-67	6	8

Well wagon [W80a]

W80b. Well Wagon with Crane Load (see also table WT12)

This used the standard well wagon with a mobile crane from the Minic Push-and-Go range.

R213	41917 blue, red+white + crane - 57-61	30	40
R213	41917 white+red + crane - 57-61	30	40
R213	41917 buff+green + crane - 57-61	30	40

Well Wagon with Tank (see table B2)

W81. Trestrol Wagon

This consisted of a single moulded body slung between two six-wheel bogies. The wagon, in khaki or green, was used as the basis of a number of military or Battle Space wagons which are listed towards the end of this section.

R242	BR B901600 grey Trestrol E C on right, number in centre - 61	10	12
R242	BR B901600 pale green-grey Trestrol E C in centre, number on right - 62	8	10
R242	BR B901600 pale green-grey Trestrol E C in centre, number on left - 62-63	8	10
R242	BR B901600 pale green-grey Trestrol E C in centre, number on right (3 black panels) - 64	10	12
R242	BR B901600 grey Trestrol E C in centre, number on right (3 black panels) - 64	12	14
R242	BR B901600 pale green-grey Trestrol E C in centre, number on right (2 black panels) - 65	10	12
R242	BR B901600 grey Trestrol E C in centre, number on right (2 black panels) - 65	10	12
R242	BR B901600 dark blue-grey Trestrol E C in centre, number on left + girder load - 72-73	15	25

W82a. Liner Train Container Wagon (3 x 20')

The long flat liner train wagon that carried the containers was sometimes rail blue and sometimes black. It is difficult to be accurate as to which colour was used with which containers. Where they were known to be blue they are marked with a 'B'. ATT = ones made for American Train & Track and boxed by them in their own packaging.

R633	+ 3 x Freightliner 05B41, 05B71, 05B17 pale grey+red - 67-69	15	20
R633	+ 3 x Freightliner Limited ,05B41, 05B71, 05B17 pale grey+red B - 71-74	15	20
R633	+ 3 x Freightliner Limited pale grey + red, no numbers B - 77-81	15	20
R632	+ 3 x open containers pale grey - 69-73	15	20
R635	+ 3 x BP Chemicals tanks white+green BP transfers B - 69?	25	30
R635	+ 3 x BP Chemicals tanks white+green BP stickers B - 69-72	15	20
R637	+ 3 x Harold Wood tanks yellow+buff B - 69-72	18	25
R678	+ Freightliner Limited + open + BP Chemicals B - 70-71	15	20
R6331	+ 3 x Canadian National (Canadian) 05B17 pale grey - 68	28	38
R6331	+ 3 x Canadien National (Canadian) pale grey - 68	25	35
R6331	+ 3 x Canadien National (Canadian) silver - 70	20	30
R7340	+ 3 x cti (export) red - 69-71	18	25
R820	+ 3 x Santa Fe (ATT) silver - 68	30	38
R821	+ 3 x Flexi-Van (ATT) silver - 68	30	38

R839	+ 3 x **ACT** (Australia) white+blue - *70-72*	18	NA
R035	+ 3 x **Freightliner** 09L91 white+red - *82-83*	15	17
R204	+ **Royal Mail Lines** 10082 red + **Scan Dutch** 203241 white + **OCL** 261830 blue B - *85-87*	15	17
R010	+ 3 x **Business Pages** GBX430 yellow B - *86*	20	NA
R010	+ 3 x **Business Pages** GBX430 yellow or white mix B - *86*	20	NA
R010	+ 3 x **Business Pages** GBX430 white B - *86*	20	NA
R020	+ **P&O** 086155 dark blue + **Royal Mail Parcels** 300216 red + **MB** 151470 dark blue B - *88-91*	15	17
R022	+ 3 x **Freightliner** 82L04 red+yellow B - *92-94*	15	17
X3716	+ **P&P** 086155 dark blue + **Hamburg Sud** 522400 red + **CGM** 222020 white - *98*	15	NA
R6141	+ **Seaco** SCZU718063[1] blue + **CGM** CGMU222020 [2] white + **Hamburg Sud** 522400 red - *01*	12	15
R6142	+ **P&O** 035756 blue + **MOL** 2880955 white + **Med Tainer Line** SCKU293417 [7] yellow - *01*	12	15
R6172	+ **CMA CGM** 113815[7] dark blue + **Uniglory** 852416[0] red + **UASC** 302792[8] very dark green - *02-04*	NPG	17
(R6174)	**Seaco** SCZU718063[1] blue	2	NA
(R6174)	**CGM** CGMU222020 [2] white	2	NA
(R6174)	**MedTainer Line** SCKU293417[7] yellow	2	NA
R6174	set of 3 above containers - *02-04*	NA	5
X?	3 x **Eddie Stobart** containers ex-R1026 set RF438, RF439, RF440 green - *01*	20	NA
R6203	+ **NSCSA** NSAU207785[7] turquoise + **Cronos** CRXU252411[3] brown + **Contship** CSQU308474[7] black - *03-04*	12	17

Liner train container wagon [W82a]

W82b. Liner Train Container Wagon (2 x 30')

The long flat liner train wagon that carried the containers was sometimes rail blue and sometimes black. It is difficult to be accurate as to which colour was used with which containers. Where they were known to be blue they are marked with a 'B'.

R634	+ **Pickfords** dark blue + **Containerway** red B - *69-72*	15	20
R719	+ **Sainsbury's** grey + **Ford** white B - *69-72*	15	20
R677	+ **Fyffes** yellow + **Manchester Liners** red B - *69-71*	15	25
R7352	+ 2 x **Canadian Pacific** yellow B - *69-71*	25	35
R7360	+ 2 x **Canadian Pacific** Sea yellow B - *69-71*	25	35
R7370	+ 2 x **Manchester Liners** red B - *69-71*	18	25
R7353	+ 2 x **CP Ships** grey B - *not made*	NA	NA
R036	+ **CP Ships** green + IFF IFF8010 silver B - *82-84*	15	17
R006	+ **Hapag-Lloyd** 406189 orange + **Evergreen** 120842 green B - *91*	16	18
R030	+ 2 x **Fletcher** blue B - *92-94*	15	17
R387	+ **Haulmark** 425528 dark blue + **Maersk** 2365746 silver - *96-98*	10	12
X3350	+ 2 x **Haulmark** 425528 dark blue - *96-97*	12	NA
X3348	+ 2 x **Maersk** 2365746 silver - *96-97*	12	NA
X3349	+ 2 x **ECL** dark grey - *96-97*	12	NA
X3463	+ 2 x **Ferryline** light blue - *97*	12	NA
X3462	+ **Ferryline** light blue + **Maersk** 23657 46 silver - *98*	12	NA
X3712	+ **Hyundai** 426091 red + **MSco** 381276 yellow - *98*	15	NA
X3714	+ **Hanjin** 717359 dark blue + **Yang Ming** grey - *98*	15	NA
R6100	+ 2 x **Eddie Stobart** green Sp Edn 1400	20	25

	(Trafford Model Centre) - *99*		
X?	+ 2 x **Eddie Stobart** RF538, RF916 green ex-R1026 Sp Edn set - *01*	20	NA
X?	+ 2 x **Eddie Stobart** RF539, RF917 green ex-R1026 set - *01*	20	NA
X?	+ 2 x **Eddie Stobart** RF540, RF918 green ex-R1026 set - *01*	20	NA
R6139	+ **Hyundai** HDCU426091[8] red + **IFF** IFFU890478[4] blue - *01*	12	15
R6140	+ **IBC** IBCU560570[9] red + **Yang Ming** 4471607 grey - *01*	12	15
R6171	+ **Waterfront** 970127[9] red + **Linea Mexicana** 232731[3] dark blue - *02*	NPG	17
-	**Tartan Arrow** red+white sold with container depot - *70-74*	8	NA
(R6173)	**IFF** IFFU890478[4] blue	3	NA
(R6173)	**IBC** IBCU550570[9] red	3	NA
R6173	set of above 2 containers - *02-04*	NA	5
R6202	+ **Evergreen** EMCU519644[4] white + **Di Gregorio** IRNU400318[8] orange - *03-04*	12	17

Liner train wagon [W82b]

W83. Bogie Carflat

R126	**BR** orange plain deck + 3 Triumph 2000 - *77-81*	15	18
R124	**BR** vermilion painted deck + 3 Triumph 2000 - *82-85*	15	18
R124	**BR** vermilion painted deck no railings + 3 Triumph 2000 - *86-89*	15	18
R124	**BR** vermilion painted deck + 3 Triumph 2000 - *90*	15	18
R126	**BR** vermilion painted deck + 3 Ford Sierras - *91-00*	12	14
R6143	**BR** B748698 yellow Carflat + 3 Ford Sierras - *01-04*	10	12

W84. Tierwag Car Transporter (Car-a-Belle)

The wagon had a lifting lower deck and a flap at each end of the upper deck which could be let down to bridge the gap between wagons. It came with six Minix cars (mixed).

R342	pale green-grey No Hump Shunting - *65-?*	25	28
R342	pale green-grey No Hump Shunting, Acho couplings (France) - *67*	25	28
R342	pale grey No Hump Shunting - *?-74*	25	28
R3421	**Canadian National** CN700184 black - *65-71*	30	35
R3423	**CPRail** black - *70-73*	30	35
R373	as above but different 'R' number - *73*	30	35

Tierwag car carrier [W84]

W85. Motorail Cartic Car Transporter

The model was sold in a large end flap-box along with the Minix cars still in their normal individual packaging. The prototype was a four wagon articulated unit but Rovex did not model the two shorter inner wagons. The Tri-ang Hornby model therefore consisted of two identical wagons, a separate bogie to join them and the cars.

R666	**BRe** blue Motorail + 16 mixed cars - *70*	50	270*
R666	**BRe** blue Motorail + 12 mixed cars - *71-73*	40	200*
R666	**Silcock Express** 90510 orange + 16 Alpine cars PJA - *89-90*	30	40

| R018 | **Silcock Express** 90510 orange + 12 Sierra cars PJA - *91* | 30 | 40 |

*These figures take account of the fact that the boxed cars themselves sell for at least £5 each and sometimes quite a bit more.

W86. 50T Bogie Brick Wagon

The 50T brick wagon was based on a GNR design and body and chassis were moulded as one. Initially it was offered with or without a load which was a salmon coloured moulded insert representing individually stacked bricks - obviously before the days of bulk handling!

R219	**BR** E451004 brown narrow 'R' and larger number digits - *59*	12	14
R219	**BR** E451004 brown - *60-67*	8	10
R219	**BR** E451004 brown + brick load - *59-61*	10	12
R219	**London Brick** red - *70-73*	7	9
R219	**London Brick** red chassis not painted - *70-73*	9	11
R2193	**CPRail** CP342826 red - *71*	25	30
R219NP	red no printing ex-starter sets - *c68*	6	NA
R219NP	salmon no printing ex-starter sets - *c68*	6	NA
R219NP	brown no printing ex-starter sets - *c68*	6	NA
R219NP	**M-T Express** (Canada) black - *67*	30	NA

W87. Bogie Caustic Liquor Tank Wagon

R247	**ICI** 357 red - *62-67*	10	12
R2470	**ICI** 357 blue (Export) - *70*	20	22
R349	**Murgatroyd's** T227 white - *63-70*	10	12
R349	**Murgatroyd's** T227 white+cream - *?*	20	22
R349	**Murgatroyd's** T227 cream - *?*	12	14
R3490	**Polysar** (Canada) white+blue - *70-71*	30	35
R3490	**Polysar** (Canada) white+rail-blue - *70-71*	35	40

Bogie caustic liquor tank wagon [W87]

W88. 100T Bogie Tank Wagon

R669	**Shell** 2309 pale grey - *70-72*	12	18
R669	**Shell** 2309 white - *72*	20	25
R6693	**CPRail** CP382920 off white - *not made*	NA	NA
R667	**BOC** 0005 white Liquid Oxygen - *72-74*	12	18
R669	**Shell BP** 2264 grey - *82-83*	12	15
R144	**Jet Conoco** grey - *84-85*	12	15
R236	**Gulf** GL815 dark blue - *86-87*	15	18
R028	**Esso** 20027 grey+red - *88-89*	12	15
R007	**BP** BPO87566 green - *91*	15	18
R216	**BP** BPO87460 grey - *95-96*	12	15
R6246	**BP** BPO7457 grey - *04*	NPG	15
R6045	**Murco** PR85300 red+blue - *98-99*	12	15
R6166	**Murco** MURCO30827 grey - *02-03*	NPG	17
R6110	**Elf** ELF82307 pale grey - *01*	12	15
R6103	**Hornby** 2000 HH2000 chrome - *00*	10	20
R6132	**Fina** pale grey - *01*	12	14

W89. 14T Siphon G (ex-Airfix)

GWR milk van with corridor connections built in 1926.

| R6055 | **GW** 1359 dark brown - *98* | 12 | 15 |
| R6055A | **GW** 1447 dark brown - *99-00* | 12 | 15 |

W90. 14T Siphon H (ex-Airfix)

GWR milk van with end doors and built in 1919.

| R6054 | **BR** W1422 maroon - *98* | 12 | 15 |
| R6054A | **BR** W1428 maroon - *99-01* | 12 | 15 |

100T Bogie tanker - Hornby 2000 [W88]

STARTER SET WAGONS

These are mainly of little value but some starter sets contained unique container wagons which are now much sought after. These include, Tri-ang Toys, Scalextric, Frog and Coca Cola. With the exception of the two Primary Series vehicles, they were sold only in sets. Wagons from the standard British and Transcontinental ranges were also used in an non-printed form and these will be found within the appropriate tables of those sections (i.e. non-printed 7-plank open wagons will be found in table W1 above and non-printed vans in table W2 etc.).

WP1. Primary Truck

Based on a Continental steel open wagon, the model had an integral chassis and was used in 'Primary' train sets in the late 1950s and early 1960s.

| R217 | grey - *59-62* | 4 | 14 |
| R217 | pale grey - *59-62* | 5 | 15 |

WP2. Primary Van

Based on a Continental van, the model had an integral chassis and was used in 'Primary' train sets in the late 1950s and early 1960s.

| R218 | blue-green - *59-62* | 4 | 14 |
| R218 | yellow-green - *59-62* | 5 | 15 |

WP3. Canadian Rocket Launcher

This was sold in starter sets in Canada and consisted of the rocket firing turret from the Battle Space range fitted to a standard 10' chassis.

| R570CN? | khaki green + 4 Red Eye rockets - *65* | 15 | NA |

WP4. Canadian Radar Tracking Car

We have not seen an example of this but believe that it consists of the radar tracking turret mounted on a small wagon chassis.

| R567CN? | ? - *c65* | 30 | NA |

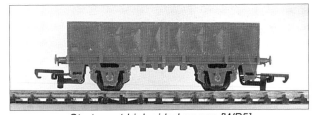

Starter set high sided wagon [WP5]

WP5. Integral High-Sided Wagon

Single body/chassis moulding with just wheels and couplings attached. It was produced in vast quantities and was also listed at times as R710NP. Playtrains wheels were large flangless wheels for use with the Playtrains track. MkIII = standard MkIII tension-lock couplings. Integ = couplings integral with the body/chassis moulding with a hook at one end and a loop at the other.

| R710 | MkIII red - *69-71* | 2 | NA |
| R710 | MkIII maroon - *69-71* | 3 | NA |

R710	MkIII blue - *69-71*	2	NA
R710	MkIII violet-blue - *69-71*	4	NA
R710T	NMRA couplings for ATT (US) - *69*	15	NA
R710	MkIII red, bulge * - *71-72?*	3	NA
R710	Integ red, pin-point wheels - *73-?*	3	NA
R710	Integ light blue, pin-point wheels - *73-?*	3	NA
R710	Integ blue - *73-98*	2	NA
R710	Integ red - *73-98*	2	NA
R710	Integ green - *73-98*	3	NA
R710	Integ yellow - *73-98*	3	NA
R710	Integ blue Playtrains wheels - *86-98*	2	NA
R710	Integ red Playtrains wheels - *86-98*	2	NA
R710	Integ yellow Playtrains wheels - *86-98*	2	NA
R710	Integ green Playtrains wheels - *86-98*	2	NA

* Presumably Rovex experienced complaints of the coupling boss in the moulding breaking off and strengthened it by putting a bulge in the wall above it. These were also fitted with the fine scale wheels.

WP6. Integral Low-Sided Wagon

Single body/chassis moulding with just wheels and couplings attached. It was also listed at times as R712NP. Playtrains wheels were large flangless wheels for use with the Playtrains track. MkIII = standard MkIII tension-lock couplings. Integ = couplings integral with the body/chassis moulding with a hook at one end and a loop at the other.

R712	MkIII yellow - *69-71*	2	NA
R712	MkIII translucent pale lemon - *69?*	5	NA
R712	MkIII dark green - *69?*	3	NA
R712	MkIII blue - *69-71*	2	NA
R712T	NMRA couplings, dark green? for ATT (US) - *69*	15	NA
R713CN	MkIII dark green + Minix car+caravan for Canada - *69*	10	NA
R888	MkIII + Minix Ford van - *70*	6	NA
R878	MkIII + Minix car + caravan - *71*	10	NA
R877	MkIII + 20' **Frog Kits** container - *71*	35	NA
R887	MkIII blue + Minix car - *71-72*	6	NA
R876	MkIII + 20' **Tri-ang Toys** container - *71-72*	40	NA
R712	MkIII bulge * lemon-yellow - *71-72?*	5	NA
R712	MkIII bulge * blue - *71-72?*	3	NA
R712	MkIII bulge * black - *71-72?*	7	NA
R712	MkIII bulge * red - *71-72?*	7	NA
R712	Integ yellow - *83-84*	4	NA
R712	Integral blue - *83-84*	4	NA
R712	Integral yellow, Playtrains wheels - *86-94*	2	NA
R712	Integral red, Playtrains wheels - *90-98*	3	NA

* Presumably Rovex experienced complaints of the coupling boss in the moulding breaking off and strengthened it by putting a bulge in the wall above it. These were also fitted with the fine scale wheels.

Integral low-sided wagon + container [WP6]

WP7. Integral Tank Wagon

Single body/chassis moulding with just wheels and couplings attached. It was also listed at times as R712NP. Integral = couplings integral with the body/chassis moulding with a hook at one end and a loop at the other.

R711	MkIII couplings yellow no printing - *69-71*	4	NA
R711T	NMRA couplings yellow for ATT (US) - *69*	15	NA
R711	Integral **Shell** yellow heat printed - *73-77*	2	NA
R711	Integral **Shell** yellow tampo printed - *78-91*	2	NA
R711	Integral **Tidmouth Milk** white - *86-98*	3	NA

WP8. Integral Long Low-Sided Wagon

Single body/chassis moulding with just wheels and couplings attached. It had sides but these were lower than those of the Integral Low-Sides Wagon (table WP6) but the wagon was longer and designed to take the 30' container. Colours seen include red, yellow, blue and violet blue.

R880	MkIII couplings 30' + **Tri-ang Toys** container - *70*	40	NA
R875	MkIII couplings + 30' **Coca-Cola** container red+white - *71-72*	45	NA
R875	MkIII couplings + 30' **Coca-Cola** container red+yellow+blue - *71-72*	45	NA
R?	MkIII couplings + 30' **Scalextric** container - *?*	45	NA

Starter set long flat wagon and container [WP8]

WP9. Integral Long Flat Wagon

Single body/chassis moulding with just wheels and couplings attached. It was long and had no sides but had four pegs to hold a 30' container in place. The only examples we have seen were yellow and were illustrations in the 1970 Trade Catalogue and it is possible that the model described in table WP8 (above) was released instead.

R879	MkIII couplings yellow + 30' **Coca-Cola** container - *70*	NPG	NA
R880	MkIII couplings yellow + 30' **Tri-ang Toys** container - *70*	NPG	NA
R881	MkIII couplings yellow + Minix car+ caravan - *70*	NPG	NA
R889	MkIII couplings yellow + Minix car - *70*	NPG	NA

BATTLE SPACE & OTHER MILITARY WAGONS

The Battle Space series was available during the second half of the 1960s and consisted of a range of standard models adapted for military purposes and turned out in a khaki green coloured plastic. It had been preceded by a rocket launching wagon and tank transporter in the late 1950s and some green Nato wagons in the mid 1960s.

The Battle Space range was quite large and for the first two years proved to be popular. After that, it experienced a lingering death until all the initial stocks had cleared the storeroom in the early 1970s. It was during its death throws that, what is today, the rarest wagon was made - the Q Car.

Two of the vehicles were based on Transcontinental passenger stock (Command Car and Ambulance Car) and these are listed above under their respective coach model type headings (tables CT2 and CT3).

Packaging - The range of packaging used for the comparatively small Battle Space series was surprisingly large. While a few were sold in standard Tri-ang Hornby boxes, most had specially designed Battle Space wrappings which ranged from simple end flap boxes to elaborate display trays. The latter are particularly sought after, especially if they still have their outer sleeve and this type of box can add £5 to the prices quoted below.

'K' Suffixes - While most of the Battle Space range were given 'K' suffixes to their 'R' number, these were sometimes dropped.

B1. Rocket Launcher

The model was based on the bogie bolster wagon (table W77a above) to which a rocket launcher from the Minic 000 Push-and-Go Series was fixed. The rubber tipped plastic rockets were fired by hand when a lever was used to release tension in a coil spring. The wagons originally had bolsters but these were later dropped. R = rocket. L = launcher.

R216	M13127 grey, clear R yellow L - 57	25	30
R216	M13127 grey, silver R yellow L - 58	25	30
R216	M13071 grey, red R yellow L - 58-62	12	20
R216	M13071 grey, red R blue L - 63-65	12	20
R216K	khaki, red R khaki L + 7 men - 66-71	25	35
-	as above without men	15	NA
R216F	M13071 grey, red R blue L Acho couplings (France) - 65	35	50
R216F	khaki, red R khaki L Acho couplings - 67-68	40	55

Rocket launcher [B1]

B2. Well Wagon + Tank

This used the standard grey, green or brown well wagon (table W80a) with a green Conqueror tank from the Minic Push-and-Go range.

R241	41917 green, grey or brown, green tank - 60-63	30	40
R241	41913 green, grey or brown, green tank - 60-63	30	40

B3. Helicopter Car

Based on a Lionel design, the wagon used the Transcontinental flat car to which were added a clockwork spring mechanism below the body and a spun mounting block above. When the spring was released the block spun, turning the bottom of the helicopter rotor shaft. This in turn suddenly rotated the rotor arms of the BR1 helicopter which lifted vertically into the air under its own power. H = helicopter.

R128	**NATO** TR7301 grey, red H - 62-63	15	25
R128	**NATO** TR7301 green, red H - 63-65	15	25
R128F	**NATO** TR7301 green, red H Acho couplings - 65	35	50
R128K	khaki, red H + men - 66	25	35
-	as above without men	15	NA
R128F	khaki, red H Acho couplings (France) - 67-68	35	50
R128K	khaki, yellow H + men - 66-68,70	25	35
-	as above without men	15	NA
R128K	khaki, maroon H + men - 69	25	35
-	as above without men	15	NA
R128K	khaki, green H + men - 71	25	35
-	as above without men	15	NA
R128	yellow, red H - not made	NA	NA
R128	white, yellow H - 82	30	NA
R165	helicopter only - 62	12	40

B4. Bomb Transporter

The model utilised the Trestrol wagon (table W81) and the Red Arrow Bomb from the Minic Maximus range: indeed, some examples of the bomb were heat stamped 'Tri-ang Minic' in silver. The nose of the bomb had an anvil for firing caps.

R239	**NATO** TR7190 green + red bomb - 62-65	30	40
R239K	khaki + red bomb + men - 66-71	35	45
-	as above without men	25	NA

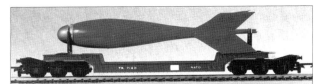

Bomb transporter [B4]

B5. Anti-Aircraft Searchlight Wagon

This was another wagon that used the Trestrol as its base. The superstructure was tooled up specially for the model.

R341	**NATO** TR7192 green, searchlight - 63-65	20	30
R341K	khaki, searchlight + men - 66-71	25	35
-	as above without men	15	NA

B6. Exploding Car

This was based on a design by Lionel. The sides and roof were carefully balanced and would stand the normal vibrations of movement but if hit by a rocket, the van would disintegrate.

R249	9841 red 'Warheads' - 63-65	12	20
R249F	9841 red 'Warheads' Acho cpls - 65	30	35
R249K	9841 khaki 'Warheads' + men - 66-71	25	35
-	as above without men	15	NA
R249F	9841 khaki 'Warheads' Acho cpls (France) - 67-68	35	50
R?	455 red 'Rockets' - 82	15	NA

B7. 4 Rocket Launcher

This was another wagon that used the Trestrol as its base. The superstructure was tooled up specially for the model but was used on other models. The four Red-eye missiles were plastic with metal tips and each was forced down onto one of the four turret mounted firing pins and this tensioned a spring ready for firing. Replica missiles are available.

R343	**NATO** TR191 green + 4 red tipped missiles - 63	20	30
R343	**NATO** TR191 green + 4 black tipped missiles - 63-65	20	30
R343	khaki + 4 black tipped missiles + men - 66-71	25	35
-	as above without men	15	NA

B8. Plane Launching Car

This was another wagon that used the Trestrol as its base. The ramp superstructure was tooled up specially for the model. The plane was the least realistic item in the whole series as it had to fly when fired by an elastic band.

R562	**NATO** green + plane - 66	35	45
R562	khaki + plane + men - 66-71	30	40

B9. Satellite Launching Car

This was one of two wagons that supplied the 'space' side of Battle Space. It was based on the Transcontinental flat car, using the launch mechanism from the helicopter car and superstructure from the searchlight car. Only the satellite was new - and the colour scheme!

R566	red+blue + satellite + men - 66-71	25	45
-	as above without men	15	NA

B10. Radar Tracking Car

This was a 4-wheel vehicle which used a metal brake van chassis and a superstructure borrowed from the searchlight car. The radar scanner turned by means of a drum beneath the model which was revolved by a rubber band driving off the wheel axles. A domed light also flashed as it moved along.

R567	blue + men - 66-71	25	35
-	as above without men	15	NA

B11. Assault Tank Transporter

This model used the well wagon and the tank with a new turret that carried twin Red-eye missile firing mechanisms. Two missiles were provided with it.

R568	khaki + khaki twin missile tank + men - 66-71	35	45
R?	sand + sand twin missile tank - 82	10	NA
R673	assault tank on its own + 2 missiles + men - 67-71	30	40
-	as above without men	20	NA

B12. POW Car

Based on the Transcontinental stock car.

R630	334 khaki + men - 67-71	25	40
-	as above without men	15	NA

B13. Sniper Car

This is a slightly modified giraffe car from the Transcontinental range.

R639	D-459 khaki + men + actuating rails + trigger - 67-71	30	45
-	as above without men	20	NA

B14. Tank Recovery Car (see also WT16)

This was another well wagon but this time with the small crane fixed to its base and a bolster from the early bolster wagon fitted at one end.

R631	901 khaki + men - *67-71*	30	40
-	as above without men	20	NA

B15. 'Q' Car

2,700 of these 'Q' Cars were made in 1968 and it used the body of exploding car to conceal the turret of the assault tank with its two Red-eye missiles.

R571	G-10 khaki + men + 2 missiles - *68*	150	200
-	as above without men 1	40	NA

'Q' car [B15]

B16. Twin Missile Site

The main part was made of expanded polystyrene painted green onto which had been fitted the turret of the assault tank with its two Red-eye missiles.

R670	green + men + 2 missiles - *67-71*	55	70
-	as above without men	45	NA

B17. Multiple Missile Site

Very similar to B16 (above) but fitted with the turret of the 4 rocket launcher with its 4 Red-eye missiles.

R671	green + men + 4 missiles - *67-71*	55	70
-	as above without men	45	NA

B18. Honest John Pad

The launcher was from the rocket launcher car and the rocket is thought to have been supplied by Meccano Ltd.

R672	5261 grey + men + Honest John rocket - *67-71*	45	60
-	as above without men	35	NA

TRANSCONTINENTAL FREIGHT STOCK

The TC range contained some very attractive freight cars produced principally for the Canadian market. They started to arrive in 1954 and throughout the rest of the 1950s they carried the road name 'Tri-ang Railways'. In the early 1960s this was changed to 'Transcontinental' and by the middle of the decade, overseas customers were demanding (and got) authentic road names. The greatest number of these were Canadian but Australian and American ones added to the variety. More than any other British manufacturer of a model railway system, Tri-ang catered for the overseas market.

'R' Number Changes - Many of those freight cars made for the Canadian market appeared under several different 'R' numbers although the model itself did not change during this time. Initially they had suffixes to the standard model's number and then they were given a four figure number and finally, when the new computer would not handle this, they were given a completely new three figure 'R' number. It is not feasible for us to record all these changes here.

WT1. Short Box Car

R114	TR TR22831 brown, white lettering - *?*	20	25
R114	TR TR22831 yellow, transfers - *54-56?*	9	12
R114	TR TR22831 orange, transfers - *54-56?*	9	12
R114	TR TR22831 yellow, heat print - *56?-59*	5	8
R114	TR TR22831 orange, heat print - *56?-59*	5	8
R114	TR TR22831 yellow, modified - *59-60*	6	9

WT2. Caboose

hs = heat stamped.

R115	TR 7482 red transfers - *54-55?*	9	12
R115	TR 7482 maroon transfers - *c55-56*	8	11
R115	TR 7482 maroon hs - *56?-61*	5	8
R115TR	TR shield TR7482 maroon - *62-68*	4	8
R1150	TR shield TR2742 maroon - *69-70*	4	8
R115CN	CN CN79184 soft-orange - *65-66*	12	18
R115CN	CN CN79184 bight orange - *67-68*	12	18
R115NP	M-T (sticker) orange - *67*	20	NA
R1151	CN 7482 orange - *68-69*	15	20
R1151	CN 7482 maroon - *69-71*	10	15
R1151	CN 7482 maroon shortened steps (also R270) - *72-73*	10	15
R1152	CP 346346 orange-brown - *69-71*	15	20
R115NP	yellow no print ex-starter sets (boxed as R1150) - *71*	12	18
R1153	CPRail CP35644 yellow - *70-72*	12	18
R1153	CPRail CP35644 yellow shortened steps - *72-74*	12	18

Canadian Pacific caboose [WT2]

WT3. Gondola

ED = 'Express Delivery'. tf = transfers. hp = heat printed.

R116	TR TR3576 translucent-blue tf - *54-55*	9	12
R116	TR TR3576 VR-blue tf - *54-55*	8	11
R116	TR TR3576 green tf - *54-55*	8	11
R116	TR TR3576 red tf - *54-55*	12	15
R116	TR TR3576 VR-blue hp - *55-59*	5	8
R116	TR TR3576 green hp - *55-59*	5	8
R116	TR ED TR3576 VR-blue - *59-61*	6	9
R116	TR ED TR3576 green - *59-61*	6	9
R116	TR ED TR3576 dull-red - *59-61*	10	13
R116	ED TR shield TR3576 VR-blue - *61-63*	7	10
R116	ED TR shield TR3576 green - *61-63*	7	10
R1161	CN CN141101 brown (also R116CN) - *66-74*	12	18
R1160	Rock Island Line pale grey - *70-74*	10	15

WT4. Hopper Car

These were fitted with an automatic unloading device. A trigger would release a trapdoor in the bottom of the hopper.

R111	TR 174421 orange - *55-61*	8	12
R111	TR 174421 dark green - *55-61*	10	15
R111	TR 174421 red - *55-61*	8	12
R111	TR shield TR174421 red - *62-66*	9	13
R1111	CN CN98103 orange-brown (also R111CN) - *67*	15	20
R1111	CN CN98103 orange-brown base plated over - *68-74*	12	18

CN hopper car [WT4]

WT5. Oil Tanker

tf= transfers. hp = heat printed.

R117	**Shell** SCCX333 dull-red tf - *55-58*	12	17
R117	**Shell** SCCX333 yellow tf - *55-58*	9	14
R117	**Shell** SCCX333 grey-green tf - *55-58*	15	20
R117	**Shell** SCCX333 blue tf - *55-58*	9	14
R117	**Shell** SCCX333 blue hp - *58-62*	7	12
R117	**Shell** SCCX333 VR-blue square logos hp - *62-66*	8	12
R1170	**Shell** yellow square logos tf (also R323) - *69-73*	8	12
R1170	**BP** yellow square logos tf (also R323) - *69-73*	8	12
R1171	**CN** CGTX20044 blue - *68*	20	NPG
R1171	**CN** CGTX20044 black logos always to the right (also R117CN) - *65-73*	6	9
R1171	**CN** CGTX20044 black logos both the same end - *72-73*	8	12

WT6. Stock Car

R126	**TR** shield (white) TR742 green - *57*	20	25
R126	**TR** shield (white) TR742 blue - *57*	20	25
R126	**TR** shield (white) TR742 maroon - *57*	20	25
R126	**TR** shield (white) TR742 brown - *57-78*	15	20
R126	**TR** shield (red) TR742 yellow - *58-61*	8	12
R126	**TR** narrow shield (red) TR2742 yellow - *62-71*	7	10
R126	**TC** TC1260 yellow - *70*	12	15
R1261	**CN** CN172350 orange-brown (also R126CN) - *65-68*	15	20
R1261	**CN** CN172350 orange-brown (also R271) - *69-74*	15	20
R1262	**CP** CP503588 yellow (also R126CP) - *69-71*	15	20

Canadian National stock car [WT6]

WT7. Refrigerator Car

R129	**TR** shield TR2690 white letters in blue * - *?*	9	12
R129	**TR** shield TR2690 white letters in black * - *57-61*	7	10
R129	**TR** shield (slim) TR2690 white letters in black * - *62-73*	7	10
R1291	**CN** CN211429 silver (also R129CN and R272) - *66-68, 71-74*	10	15
R1291	**CN** CN211429 white - *69-70*	12	17
R1292	**CP** - *70*	NPG	NPG
R1290	**C&O** C&O5500 white - *69-74*	12	17
R1293	**CPRail** CP288138 silver (also R273) - *70-74*	13	18
R1353	**CPRail** CP81030 green newsprint car (also R276) - *70*	15	20
R1330	**Eat More Beef** white beef car - *73-74*	12	15
R1350	white newsprint car names of newspapers (also 275) - *73*	12	15

* Roof and underframe grey or black.

WT8. Long Box Car

R136CN	**CN** CN523976 brown - *65-68*	15	20
R1361	**CN** CN523976 vermilion (also R277) - *69-74*	15	20
R1362	**CP** CP258599 brown (also R136CP) - *69-73*	15	20
R1363	**CPRail** CP202199 red (also R278) - *70*	15	25
R1363	**CPRail** CP202199 maroon (also R278) - *71-72*	15	20
R1343	**CPRail** CP35644 yellow (also R274) - *71-73*	15	20
R1353	**CPRail** CP81030 green - *71-74*	15	20
	TR Speedy Service		
R136	TR2703 brown - *58-?*	12	15

R136	TR2703 grey - *58-?*	14	17
R136	TR2703 grey - *58-?*	14	17
R136	TR2703 pink - *58-66*	10	13

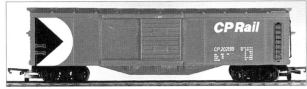

CP Rail long box car [WT8]

WT9. Cement Car

These were fitted with an automatic unloading device. A trigger would release a trapdoor in the bottom of the hopper.

R137	**TR** TR2127 grey - *58-61*	12	15
R137	**TR** TR2127 pale green-grey - *?*	15	18
R137	**TR** TR2127 pale blue - *c60?*	20	25
R137	**TR** shield (slim) TR2127 grey - *62-68*	15	18
R1371	**CN** (also R137CN) CN11 3000 grey - *66-67*	25	30
R1371	**CN** CN11 3000 grey base plated over - *68-69*	25	30
R1370	**Wabash** WAB31627 grey - *69*	12	15
R1370	**Wabash** WAB31627 grey - *71-74*	12	15

WT10. Snow Plough

R138	**TR** TR53437 green+black - *58-68*	15	20
R138CN	**CN** brown - *66-68*	20	30
R1381	**CN** green+grey (also R279) - *69-73*	20	30

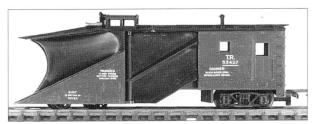

Snow plough [WT10]

WT11. Pickle Car

R139	**Westwood Pickles** TR63551 yellow+ cream - *59-69*	12	20
R139	**Westwood Pickles** TR63551 white+red, grey roof - *59-69*	12	20
R139	**Westwood Pickles** TR63551 white+red white roof - *?*	20	25
R1390	**Heinz Pickles** green - *70-73*	30	40

WT12a. Depressed Centre Car (see also table W80a)

This was the well wagon from the British range but with the buffers missing.

R236	**TR** TR2132 dark green - *61-63*	8	10
R236	**TR** TR2132 VR-blue - *61-63*	8	10
R236	**TR** TR2371 VR-blue - *61-63*	8	10
R236	**TR** TR2371 blue - *61-63*	8	10
R236	**TR** TR1371 VR-blue - *61-63*	8	10
R236	**TR** TR1371 light blue - *61-63*	10	12
R236	**TR** TR1371 grey-green - *61-63*	8	10
R236	**TR** TR2313 dark green - *61-63*	8	10

WT12b. Depressed Centre Car + Avro Delta Plane

The metallic coloured plane was from the Minic Push-and-Go Series and consisted of a body and two separate wings parcelled together with rubber bands. The model was used in the RSX military set sold in Canada.

R?	**TR** + Avro Delta (Canada) - *58*	20	NA

WT12c. Depressed Centre Car + Low-Loader + Dozer

The load was from the Minic Push-and-Go Series. Colours of the load varied according to what was supplied.

R237	**TR** green + mechanical horse + low-loader + dozer various colours - *60-61*	25	50

WT12d. Depressed Centre Car + Cable Drums

The large size cable drums used on this model were from the Mechanical Horse and Cable Drum Trailer in the Minic Push-and-Go Series. The drums were usually moulded in a cream coloured plastic but blue ones may be found.

R238	**British Insulated Callenders Cables** blue - *60-61*	18	35
R238	**BICC** blue - *60-61*	18	35

WT13. Flat Car

The flat car had 10 iron retaining pins that came in a cellophane packet in the box and are almost always missing! Without them the model is of little value. The model (minus pins) was used as the basis for a number of other freight cars, the most successful of which was the pulp wood car.

R234	**TR** TR3471 grey 10 metal retaining pins - *60-63*	20	25
R234CN	**CN** CN655309 brown 10 metal retaining pins - *67-68*	25	30
R1200, R1201	**CN** CN655309 black 10 metal retaining pins + 3 logs - *71-73*	30	35
R1200, R1201	**CN** CN655309 grey 10 metal retaining pins + 3 logs - *71-73*	30	35

WT14. Pulp Wood Car

This was based on the flat car (table WT13) but with bulkheads added and a load of logs, the latter being a single hollow moulding.

R235	**TR** TR3471 grey - *60-66*	10	15
R235	**TR** TR4415 grey - *60-70*	8	13
R2351	**CN** CN655309 brown (also R235CN) - *66-72*	15	20
R2351	**CN** CN655309 black - *68*	17	22
(R822)	**Northern Pacific** 621381 black (US) ATT boxes - *68-70*	20	28
(R823)	**Southern** 43271 black (US) ATT boxes - *68-70*	20	28
(R824)	**L&N** 25780 black (US) ATT boxes - *68-70*	20	28
(R822)	**Northern Pacific** 621381 black (US) Model Power boxes - *70-72*	20	25
(R823)	**Southern** 43271 black (US) Model Power boxes - *70-72*	20	25
(R824)	**L&N** 25780 black (US) Model Power boxes - *70-72*	20	25
R235CP	**CP** CP520047 black - *69-70*	20	30
R2353	**CPRail** CP304318 vermilion - *71-72*	20	25
R2350	**TC** TC2350 vermilion - *71-72*	12	27
R2354	**International Logging** 2350 vermilion - *72-73*	15	20
R2354	**International Logging** 2350 vermilion Acho couplings - *?*	NPG	50

WT15. Track Cleaning Car

This model used the body of the short box car when that was replaced by a more accurate model. The doors were no longer sliding but fixed in place and it contained a felt pad which was impregnated with Carbon Tetrachloride (until 1965) which was supplied in plastic capsules (6 to a box - RT528).

R344	TR9372 black - *61-65*	4	6
R344*	TR9372 dark green - *66-70*	4	6
R344	TR9372 red - *72-76*	4	6
R3441	**CN** dark green (also R344CN) - *69-70*	25	30
R344NP	**M-T Express** orange-brown (Canada) - *67*	25	NA

* When Carbon Tetrachloride could no longer be used, remaining stocks of the wagon were sold abroad numbered R344E.

WT16. Crane Car (see also B14)

This was physically identical to the Tank Recovery Car (table B14) in the Battle Space Series, consisting as it did of the well wagon (without buffers) and the small moblie crane.

R560	**TR** 41917 green+brown - *62-70*	20	35
R560	**TR** 23127 green+brown - *62-70*	20	35
R5600	**TR** 41917 black+yellow - *not made*	NA	NA

Track cleaning car [WT15]

WT17. Side-Tipping Car

This model came in an attractive presentation box with its grey ramp and dark brown bin. The latter was missing when the model returned in 1974.

R345	**TR** TR2549 salmon + 3 plastic logs + ramp + bin - *65-69*	20	50
R345	red + 3 plastic pipes + ramp - *74-75*	15	40

WT18. Old Time Caboose

This was a small 4-wheel model.

R449	**Transcontinental** TR449 red - *65-68*	20	30

WT19. Giraffe Car

Based on the stock car (but with fixed doors), this was an idea borrowed from Lionel and is remembered by many with affection. It came in an attractive presentation box.

R348	**TR** TR937 yellow Giraffe Car, mast, rail, clips - *65-72*	20	60

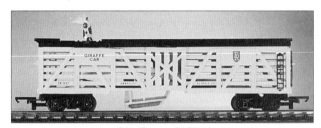

Giraffe car [WT19]

WT20. Fourgon (Continental Brake Van)

R262	**SNCF** M921452 brown - *63-65*	30	45

WT21. Australian Z Brake Van

R331	**VR** 739ZL orange (Australia) - *77*	10	15
R331	**VR** 683ZL maroon (Australia) - *77*	18	25

ACCESSORIES

Rovex, more than any other British manufacturer, supported their trains with plenty of lineside accessories so that a complete scene could be created. Once again it would be impossible to list them all here but the following are particularly sought after:

Water troughs (£75), pack of double space sleepers (£10), metal badge (£35), Pullman train boards (£50), Golden Arrow coach stickers and headboard (£50), coach train boards (£20), railway sounds record (£25), former Hornby-Dublo covered station (£160), extension to covered station (£195), former H-D island platform (re-boxed) (£30), track packs (£10-£35), olive green foot bridge, river bridge or level crossing (£20 each), early foot bridges or station buildings with uncommon posters (£10), Arkitex Ultra Modern Station (£300), pack of unpainted passengers and staff (£15), brown large girder bridge (£150), orange-red small girder bridge (£10), orange-red catenary mast (£8), brick bridge with graffiti, (£15), freight depot (ex-Minic) (£20), home maintenance kit (£20), power cleaning brush (£20) and service boxes (£70).

SETS

Since 1952 about 500 sets have been released by this company. Most of these worth only as much as their contents but a few are worth more as sets. Here are some of them:

Original Rovex set (picture box (£120) label box (£100), No4 or No5 set (£100)), Gamages Rovex set, (£200), Gamages Tri-ang set (£150), Blundells set (£120), Old Smoky set (£120), Dutch Primary sets (£120 each), Canadian assembled sets (£100-£200), Miniville sets (£80), clockwork toy train wholesale sets (£80), R6 Rich Uncle set (£180), RF EMU set (£100), R3P and R3Q sets (£80 each), RS7 unlisted set (£80), RS8 or RS28 large Lord of the Isles set (£250), RS16 and RS17 Battle Space sets (£100 each), RS30 Crash Train set (£100), RS36 Highwayman set (£450), RS37 The Frontiersman (£120), RS38 Snow Rescue set (£120), RS48 Lord of the Isles set (£80), RS44 The Picador (£150), RS47 Monster Double set (£250), RS62 Car-a-Belle set (£100), RS65 The Conqueror (£120), RS74 export military set (£120), RS105 Diesel Freight set (£80), R346 Rocket presentation pack (£120), French version (£120), RS602 Senior Freightliner set (£100), RS603 Local Diesel set (£90), RS606 Express Goods set (£80), RS607 Local Passenger set (£170), RS615 The Railway Children set (£120), French version of the R640 Lord of the Isles' presentation set (£180), RMA, RMB, RMC (£450) and RMD Motorail sets (£95). This list is not exhaustive.

Re-writing the book on detail

Join today and receive a FREE 0-4-0 Hornby locomotive, exclusive to Hornby Collectors Club members

How do I join?...

Complete the form below and send it with your subscription fee to:
The Hornby Collectors Club, PO Box 18, Melton Mowbray,
Leics, LE13 1ZF.

One year's membership to the Hornby Collectors' Club is

☐ £19 UK ☐ £23 Europe ☐ £25 Rest of the world

Name .... Age ....

Address ....

.... Post Code ....

Date of Birth .... Male ☐ Female ☐

Existing Membership No. (if applicable) ....

Telephone (daytime) ....

Email address ....

I enclose cheque/postal order for £ ....

Cheques from outside the United Kingdom must be drawn against a
London bank in £ sterling and made payable to **Hornby Hobbies Ltd.**
Please note we are no longer able to accept Eurocheques.

or Please debit £ .... sterling to my

☐ Visa ☐ MasterCard ☐ Delta
☐ Switch Switch Issue No. ☐☐

Card no. ☐☐☐☐ ☐☐☐☐ ☐☐☐☐ ☐☐☐☐

3-Digit Security No. (to be found on the back of your credit/debit card) ☐☐☐

Valid from ☐☐ ☐☐

Signature .... Date ....

Please quote **Ref. JR04** when responding. A photocopy of this form
is acceptable.   Prices and offer are correct at time of print

Join now

and look forward to:

- 6 full colour Hornby Collector magazines during your subscription year, of interest to both adult and junior collectors.

- Free 0-4-0 Hornby Locomotive exclusive to Hornby Collector Club Members

- Club competitions with fantastic prizes in every issue of Hornby Collector.

- An opportunity to come aboard the Hornby Roadshow vehicle in your area.

www.hornby.com

Tri-ang Big Big
(including Novo and Red Rocket)

HISTORY

Big Big was the idea of W.Moray Lines, the then Chairman of Lines Bros. Ltd, and was developed at the Tri-ang Research Centre at Canterbury and then handed to Rovex Scale Models Ltd for tooling and production.

The idea was to involve children in copious play participation which could involve the outdoors as well as the house. The plan was that the track could be laid from the house into the garden and a child could send trains outside while staying indoors himself even if it was raining. With this in mind, the system was designed to withstand all weathers. This principle was illustrated in the 4 page coloured leaflet produced to launch the system which showed children playing with a set in this way.

In July 1966 the model railway press carried advertisements for Big Big under the heading 'Model or Toy'. They extolled its virtues referring to safety, authentic detail and suitability for outdoor use. Apparently its pliable polypropylene track took the ups and downs of a garden layout in its stride. The trip switch was illustrated as too were the two sets available at that time; one had the Blue Flyer and two trucks and the other the Blue Flyer and four trucks. In attempting to appeal to children, the bright colours were not to everyone's taste but the serious modeller could always paint them.

Big-Big was discontinued in 1972. In the final years various new models were considered using parts for which tools already existed. One of these was a low steel wagon with two cable drums and another was a steel covered wagon. While a nice product, Big-Big was not really profitable due to the heavy tooling costs. Although large quantities were exported, these had a low profit margin - a common problem with exporting.

Eventually the tools were sold to Russia and used to make the Novo train sets that were available in the UK in the late 1970s.

Novo - Dunbee-Combex-Marx, who had acquired Rovex Ltd at the break-up of the Lines Group in 1971, entered into an agreement with the Soviet Ministry of Light Industries in 1975 under which various factories in the Soviet Union would manufacture kits and toys using tools and materials supplied by DCM. The finished products would be packaged under the Novo name and be delivered to DCM without charge in payment for the tools. Amongst the tools cleaned up and test run for this deal were Frog aircraft kits, Tri-ang TT and Tri-ang Big Big. I understand that linked to this, Russia also supplied stamps which were offered in thematic packs by Hornby Hobbies in 1976.

Novo Toys Ltd was set up in 1975 by DCM as a British company, based in Peterborough, with the sole purpose of handling this business. Once the agreed number of Novo kits, toys etc. had been delivered the tools became the property of the Russians and no further toys were supplied.

With the demise of Dunbee-Combex-Marx in 1980, Novo Toys Ltd went first into receivership and then was wound up when a buyer for the company could not be found.

Imitations - While the system had a reasonable reception in the

UK it sold well on the Continent. In 1967 the concept was sold to Lima in exchange for a deal to supply Wrenn with N gauge trains. Lima tooled up their own version of Big-Big under the name Jumbo. Later they went onto a more realistic 0-gauge model railway system using power from the track.

Big-Big was also sold to the American Machine & Foundry Co. (AMF) who tooled up their own version. This was where the idea of the caboose came from.

Red Rocket - Yet another version was made in Hong Kong for an Australian store but this was a pirate. it was sold as the 'Red Rocket Set' possibly in the early 1980s. The set included the Hymek in red with a white roof and carrying raised white letters giving the name 'Red Rocket' in the same style as the original 'Blue Flier'. The cab windows, unlike those on the Tri-ang and Novo versions, were glazed. The other contents were mineral wagons, side tipping wagons, switches and an oval of track in dark blue plastic instead of red. The couplings were the Peco type and the only inscription carried on the parts was 'Made in Hong Kong'. The mineral wagons differed from the Rovex ones in having domed buffers.

The box was white with the train flying out of a scenic picture circled in track. The box carried a sticker with the name 'Artin' on it and a racing car logo.

Couplings - The models were fitted with a coupling similar to the Peco type used on the Hornby-Dublo locos and rolling stock. They were at first attached with a brass screw into a type of heli-coil fixed to the chassis. In 1968 the type of fixing changed to the more familiar brass eyelet.

Packaging - Big-Big solo models were packed in yellow cardboard boxes. Initially, these were individually printed with a picture of the contents and the name 'Big-Big Trains' between two heavy black lines. Later, the boxes depicted the contents only on the end flaps and the logo took on a different style with the heavy lines being dropped.

With an uncertain future, in 1971 a number of models were sold in other yellow boxes with a label stuck over the printing or in temporary white boxes when stocks of the normal packaging ran out. These had a printed label stuck on the box ends describing the contents; the labels being produced on a small printing machine in the factory.

Dates: Dates quoted in the tables below are mostly those when factory records indicate that batches of the models were made or, in the case of Novo products, when stock entered the store.

LOCOMOTIVES
The locomotives were all battery powered having batteries inside each model rather than within a remote control module.

Cat.No.	Colour and Dates	£	£
L1. Small Tank Engine 0-4-0T			
Powered by four 1.5v HP11/U11 batteries.			
RV276	red - *68-69*	10	20
RV276	yellow - *68-69*	10	20
RV276A	blue - *70-71*	10	20
L2. USA Tank 0-6-0T			
Powered by four 1.5v HP11/U11 batteries.			
RV262	green - *71-72*	20	30

L3. Ruston Diesel Shunter 0-4-0DS

Powered by four 1.5v HP11/U11 batteries.

Cat.No.	Colour and Dates	£	£
RV272	yellow - 67-69	10	20
RV272A	blue - 70-71	10	20

'Red Rocket' Hymek [L4]

L4. Class 35 'Hymek' Diesel Hydraulic Bo-Bo

Powered by four 1.5v HP2/U2 batteries.

Cat.No.	Colour and Dates	£	£
RV256	'Blue Flier' blue with white roof - 67-69	10	20
RV256A	yellow with black roof - 70-71	25	30
-	blue with white roof (Novo) - 75-80	10	NA
-	'Red Rocket' red with white roof* - ?	40	NA

* See 'History' notes above.

COACHES

Cat.No.	Colour and Dates	£	£

C1. Mk2 Composite

RV257	blue + white - 68-71	8	15
RV257	blue + white (Novo) - 75-80	8	15

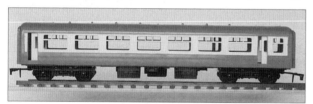

M2 composite coach [C1]

C2. US Style Coach

This was the same as the Mk2 coach but had corrugated sides.

RV274	yellow - 68-71	20	25

WAGONS

Cat.No.	Colour and Dates	£	£

W1. Steam Roller Wagon

A flat wagon with depressions in the deck to take the steam roller from the Minic range.

RV275	red + blue steam roller - 67-68, 71	15	25
RV275	red + pink steam roller - ?	15	25

W2. Cable Drum Wagon

This would have been a steel open wagon with two cable Drums from the Minic Push-and-Go Series.

?	planned but not made	NA	NA

W3. Steel Mineral Wagon

RV258	green - 67-70	10	14
RV258	red - 67-70	8	12
RV258	blue - 70-71	8	12
-	yellow (ex Red Rocket set) - ?	15	NA

W4. Covered Steel Wagon

This was the steel mineral wagon with a top making it look like a Presflow wagon.

?	planned but not made	NA	NA

W5. Side Tipping Wagon

RV273	red - 66-71	6	10
RV273	green - 66-71	6	10
-	green (Novo) - 75-80	6	NA
-	green (ex Red Rocket set) - ?	7	NA

W6. Zoo Cage Wagon

A 4-wheel flat wagon carrying a circus cage containing an animal.

RV283	red cage with yellow roof - 71	15	25

W7. Crane Truck

It was intended that this wagon would carry the Dinky Toys crane.

?	planned but not made	NA	NA

W8a. Caboose

RV298	green - 70-71	10	15

W8b. Message Carrier

Based on the caboose, it had a slot in the roof for posting letters.

RV330	green - 72?	20	30

W9. Bogie Zoo Cage Wagon

A bogie flat wagon carrying two circus cages each containing an animal.

RV?	red cages with yellow roofs - 71	25	NPG

W10. Gondola

American style bogie steel open wagon without buffers.

RV259	blue - 67-71	10	14
RV259	yellow - 67-71	10	14

W11. 3-Section Change-a-Truck

This was a kit of bits which made a bogie out of three 10' base sections joined together and various tops added.

RV297	in sets only - ?	15	25

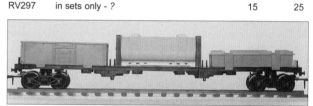

3-section Change-a-truck [W11]

W12. 4-Section Change-a-Truck

This was a kit of bits which made a bogie out of four 10' base sections joined together and various tops added.

RV277	various colours - 70-71	20	30

SETS

There was a good range of train sets in Tri-ang Big Big and the following may be found along with the dates when they were made:

RV266	Train Set No1 (2 trucks)	66
RV267	Train Set No2 (4 trucks)	67?
RV278	Yellow Shunter Train Set (freight)	67-68
RV279	Blue Flier Train Set No.3 (freight)	67-68
RV280	Big-Big Passenger Set	68-70
RV281	Mixed Traffic Train Set	68-70
RV282	Goods Train Set	68-70
RV320	Express Train Set	70-7
RV321	Lumber Camp Train Set	70-71
RV322	Goods Train Set	70
RV323	Mining Depot Train Set	70-71
RV324	Freight Yard Train Set	70-71
RV325	Zoo Train Set	71
RV326	Local Goods Train Set	71

Tri-ang TT

HISTORY

In the 1930s there had been experiments in 2.5 mm : 1 ft scale on 12.2 mm gauge track but, while the gauge was successful, the scale was found to be too cramped.

Following the Second World War, HP of America produced a TT system in 2.5 mm scale and in 1950 the German Rokal system was developed in a slightly larger scale. Rokal was imported into Britain in 1951 and this rekindled interest in TT scale in Britain. While Peco produced their Minilay track, few others responded. It needed a major company to show its faith in the scale.

In 1953, Walter Lines, chairman of the toy manufacturing giant Lines Bros. Ltd, returning from a trip to the Continent, brought back a train set manufactured by Wesa of Switzerland. He gave instruction that Rovex Scale Models Ltd., who were manufacturing the Tri-ang Railways 00 system, were to start work immediately on a Tri-ang TT system.

The command from above was not well received at Rovex where management were struggling to keep their heads above water with the staggering success of their 00 system. Despite this, someone was put on TT development as soon as the Company moved into its new factory at Margate in the Summer of 1954.

Milestones
1951 Rokal TT imported into Britain.
1953 Lines Bros. examine a Wesa TT set.
1954 Work on a Tri-ang TT system has started.
1957 Tri-ang TT launched at Toy Fair.
1959 Merchant Navy model launched.
1959 B type track introduced.
1960 'Britannia' released.
1961 Gold plated set appears.
1962 Production of Continental range of Tri-ang TT starts in France.
1963 French tools transferred to Margate.
1964 Last catalogue is released.
1967 A special run of models made.
1967 A few blue and grey coaches made.
1968 Wrenn acquire outstanding TT stock.

Many of the TT tools were made in the factory at Margate and the system was launched at the Toy Fair in the Spring of 1957 where the first two sets were displayed.

All locomotives and rolling stock were fitted with tension-lock couplings which had not yet appeared on the Tri-ang Railways 00 system. To distinguish it from the larger gauge system, the new TT products were packaged in yellow boxes with red printing and these would soon become a very familiar sight in model shops. Sets were available either with a battery box or a mains controller. The latter carried an 'X' suffix to their code.

At last the market had the impetus it needed to see TT taken as a serious scale for modelling. Other manufacturers quickly jumped on the band wagon producing accessories in the scale. For many this meant just producing smaller versions of existing models but track, card buildings, wagon kits and lineside accessories quickly appeared. Peco even produced a more detailed 10' chassis and supplied with Tri-ang bodies by Rovex, sold their TT chassis with a Tri-ang body fitted.

As with many of their ventures, Lines Bros. were determined to give their new baby a fighting chance. This meant producing a sizeable range of models to demonstrate their confidence in the system. Only by doing this could they persuade both the public and retailers that Tri-ang TT was here to stay and therefore worth buying.

1962 saw models of French prototypes added to the TT range. In order to access the European Common Market, which Britain had not yet joined, Lines Bros. built a factory in Calais. Various toy ranges were transferred there and one which the Company hoped to introduce to France was Tri-ang Railways TT. While other product lines from the Calais factory succeeded, the TT venture was not a success and the Continental tooling was sent to the Margate factory to be used there.

Tri-ang's eighth edition TT catalogue showed a system in decline with a number of models now missing from the range. Sales of the TT system had been falling sharply since 1960. In just two years the sales figures for sets halved. By 1964, total sales were just one sixth of what they had been in 1960.

By 1968, G&R Wrenn, who were another member of the Lines Group, had acquired the remaining stock of Tri-ang TT and were selling it as Wrenn Table Top Railways. According to a tool inventory, carried out in the early '90s, the bulk of the tools for the TT system stayed at Margate or, at least, those for the British range did.

Thus passed Britain's only TT scale system, but it was not the end of TT. It has remained one of the scales still modelled today and much of its success should be laid at the door of the 3 mm Society who have concentrated their energies on the production of models and materials to meet their members' needs.

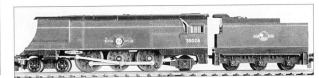

Merchant Navy Class 'Clan Line' [L4]

Further Reading

There is, as yet no definitive book on this subject although there is coverage in the first volume of Pat Hammond's trilogy, 'The Rovex Story'. The book concerned is *'Volume 1 - Tri-ang Railways'*. There are a few additional notes in *'Volume 2 - Tri-ang Hornby'*. The subject was also covered in a three part article in the *'Model Railway Collector'* magazine *Volume 7 numbers 2-4* (Feb-Apr 2000).

Collectors Club

We would also like to recommend the Tri-ang Society which caters for collectors of a wide range of Tri-ang toy products. The Society has a quarterly newsletter, called *Tri-ang Telegraph*, which contains a number of original articles by well known collectors. Details of the Tri-ang Society may be obtained from the Miles Rowland on Tel: 0161 9765059. Tri-ang TT is also sometimes covered in the magazine of the Train Collectors Society (details at the front of the book).

Dates - It is difficult to be completely accurate with production dates and those given should be treated as a guide, only.

Listing - The locos are listed in order of size starting with tank engines followed by tender locos and ending with diesels and multiple units. Wagons are listed in the order of: flats, open wagons, hoppers, tanks, vans, brake vans and bogie stock.

LOCOMOTIVES

Transfers - Early models had forward facing lions on their BR decals but on later ones the lions all faced to the left.

Cat.No.	Number, Company, Colour, Dates	£	£

British Locomotives

L1. Jinty 0-6-0T
There were two similar but different body moulds used at the same time. It could have been a two impression mould producing two bodies with each shot.

T90	**34171** BRc unlined black, plastic centre wheels, number transfers - *57*	30	35
T90	as above but heat printed - *58*	20	25
T90	as above but all metal wheels - *59-61*	20	25
T90S	**4171** BRc lined black + smoke - *62*	40	55
T90	as above without smoke - *62-68*	25	30

L2. GWR Class 61XX Prairie 2-6-2T
This used a modified Castle chassis and wheels. Both solid and open spoke wheels may be found on this models, the latter being introduced in 1964. The numbers were usually in yellow but white ones exist.

T99	**6157** BRc lined black, copper chimney top and dome - *61-67*	55	65
T99	**6157** BRc lined black, unpainted chimney top and dome - *61-64*	55	65
T99	ditto with open spoke wheels - *64-65*	60	70

GWR prairie 2-6-2 tank [L2]

L3. Castle Class 4-6-0
Both solid and open spoked (introduced in 1964) wheels may be found on 'Tintagel Castle'. Early locos were gloss green.

T91/92	**4082 'Windsor Castle'*** BRc green versions plastic centre wheels - *57*	35	40
T91/92	as above but all metal wheels - *58-61*	35	40
T91/92	**5011 'Tintagel Castle'** BRc green, black nameplate - *62-64*	40	45
T91/92	**5011 'Tintagel Castle'** BRc green, green nameplate - *62-64*	40	45
T91/92	ditto with open spoke wheels - *64-65*	50	60

* Two different fonts were used for the nameplate.

L4. Non-Rebuilt Merchant Navy 4-6-2
The model had metal nameplates.

T93/94	**35028 'Clan Line'** BRc green* - *59-64*	50	55
(T43)	**'Clan Line'** BRc gold from Ltd Edn T43 Kays set - *61*	80	NA

* Lining varies in shade between yellow and orange and both gloss (early) and matt finishes may be found.

L5. Britannia Class 4-6-2

T97/98	**70000 'Britannia'** BRc green - *60-61*	50	55
T97/98	as above with open spoke wheels - *67*	65	80
T97S/98	**70036 'Boadicea'** BRc green + smoke generator - *62-64*	70	75
T97/98	As above but no smoke - *62-64, 67*	55	70
T97/98	as above with open spoke wheels - *64*	65	80

L6. Diesel Shunter 0-6-0DS
This used the Jinty chassis.

T95	**13007** BRc green - *59-61*	25	30

T95	**D3115** BRc green - *62-67*	25	30
T95	**D3117** BRc green - *62-67*	25	30

L7. Class 30/31 Diesel A1A-A1A
Early models had brass gears but plastic ones were used later. Early examples had wire handrails but later models had moulded ones. The blue version came in a box marked 'Loco Electrique Habille Bleu'.

T96	**D5501** BRc green, wire handrails - *59-?*	30	35
T96	**D5501** BRc green moulded rails - *?-68*	30	35
T96	**D5501** BRc blue made in France - *67?*	400	500

L8. Diesel Multiple Unit

T190	**M50421** BRc green power car - *63-67*	35	40
T137	**M59133** green centre car - *63-67*	30	35
T136	**M50425** BRc green trailer car - *63-67*	25	30

Diesel multiple unit [L8]

Continental Locomotives

L9. Continental 0-6-0T

T590	**4711** black - *63-64*	80	120
T590	**4711** black unpainted rear lights - *63-64*	80	120

L10. Est Class 231D 4-6-2
Both solid and open spoke wheels may be found on these models, the latter being introduced in 1964.

T591	**1401** AL S16 black - *62-68*	60	80
T591S	**1401** AL S16 black + smoke - *62-68*	80	100

L11. Continental EMU

T594/595	silver - *not made*	-	-

COACHES
The body was a single moulding with a separate roof, underframe, bogies and buffers and the window glazing was strips or sheets of clear plastic inside the coach. Most of the coaches fell into two categories - suburbans and mainline. From January 1960, roofs were screw fixed and interior units could be bought and added. Examples with seats usually sell for £2-3 more. Early suburban coaches had roundish windows while late ones had squarer ones and are rarer. The rarest and most sought after mainline coaches are blue and grey. There are a lot of minor variations in common main line coaches including different running numbers, class lines and shades of plastic used in their construction.

Cat.No.	Company, Number, Colour, Date	£	£

C1a. Suburban Composite
sfr = screw fixed roof. ov = oval windows. sq = squared windows. rn = raised number (others are heat printed).

T80	**BR** M41006 maroon ov rn - *57-58*	8	12
T80	**BR** M41007 maroon ov - *58-60*	10	15
T80	**BR** 41007 maroon ov sfr - *60-61*	10	15
T80	**BR** 41007 maroon sq sfr - *62-65*	10	15
T130	**BR** S3153S green ov sfr - *59-61*	10	15
T130	**BR** S3153S green ov sfr - *61*	10	15
T130	**BR** S3153S green sq sfr - *62*	15	20

C1b. Suburban Brake 2nd
sfr = screw fixed roof. ov = oval windows. sq = squared windows. rn = raised number (others are heat printed).

T81	**BR** M34000 maroon ov rn - *57-58*	8	12
T81	**BR** M53171 maroon ov - *58-60*	10	15

T81	BR 53171 maroon ov sfr - *60-61*	10	15
T81	BR 53171 maroon sq sfr - *62-65*	10	15
T131	BR S4718S green ov - *59-61*	10	15
T131	BR S4718S green ov sfr - *61*	10	15
T131	BR S4718S green sq sfr - *62*	15	20

Suburban composite coach [C1a]

C2a. Main Line Composite

From January 1960, roofs were screw fixed and interior units could be bought and added. Examples with seats usually sell for £2-3 more. sfr = screw fixed roof. cl = yellow class line over 1st class section.

T82	BR W.15732 bright maroon - *57*	8	12
T82	BR W15732 bright maroon- *57-59*	8	12
T82	BR 24011 bright maroon- *59*	8	12
T82	BR 24011 maroon sfr - *60*	8	12
T82	BR 24010 maroon sfr - *60-63*	8	12
T82	BRc 24010 maroon sfr cl - *63-66*	8	12
T132	BR S15021 green - *59*	8	12
T132	BR S15021 green sfr- *60-62*	8	12
T132	BRc S15021 green sfr- *63-64*	8	12
T182	BR W15773 brown+cream - *59*	8	12
T182	BR W15773 brown+cream sfr - *60-63*	8	12
T182	BR W15772 brown+cream sfr - *60-63*	8	12
T182	BRc W15772 brown+cream sfr cl - *60-63*	8	12
T87	BR S15021 blue+grey sfr - *67-68*	35	40

C2b. Main Line Brake 2nd

From January 1960, roofs were screw fixed and interior units could be bought and added. Examples with seats usually sell for £2-3 more. sfr = screw fixed roof.

T83	BR W.53111 bright maroon - *57*	8	12
T83	BR W53111 bright maroon - *57-59*	8	12
T83	BR 34001 bright maroon - *59*	8	12
T83	BR 34001 maroon sfr - *60-66*	8	12
T133	BR S4718S green - *59*	8	12
T133	BR S34245 green - *59*	8	12
T133	BR S4718S green sfr - *60*	8	12
T133	BR S34245 green sfr - *60-62*	8	12
T133	BRc S34245 green sfr - *63-64*	8	12
T183	BR W21134 brown+cream - *59*	8	12
T183	BR W34150 brown+cream sfr - *60-63*	8	12
T183	BRc W34150 brown+cream sfr - *60-63*	8	12
T88	BR S34245 blue+grey sfr - *67-68*	35	40

C2c. Restaurant Cars

The restaurant cars had blue (bc) or white (wc) curtains.

T84	BR W307 bright maroon bc - *58-59*	8	12
T84	BR 11005 bright maroon bc - *59-66*	8	12
T84	BRc 11005 maroon wc - *59-66*	8	12
T134	BR S1771 green bc - *59-64*	8	12
T134	BR S1771 green wc - *59-64*	8	12
T184	BR W301 brown+cream bc - *59-63*	8	12
T184	BR W301 brown+cream wc - *59-63*	8	12
T89	BR S1771 blue+grey - *67-68*	35	40

C3. Sleeping Cars

T86	BR 2510 maroon - *61-65*	13	15
T86	BR 2510 dark maroon - *61-65*	13	15

C4. Utility Vans

T85	BR S224S maroon - *61*	13	15
T85	BR S227S maroon - *61*	13	15
T135	BR S2278 green - *61-67*	13	15
T135	BR S227S green - *61-67*	13	15

C5. DMU Centre Car

The roof (painted grey) and sides were a single moulding. The underframe and bogies were from the DMU power cars.

T137	BRc M59133 green centre car - *63-67*	30	35

C6. Pullman Cars

These were 1st class kitchen cars. The screw-fixed roof was a separate moulding which was usually cream but white ones may be found. The printed curtains were blue and it was always sold with an interior unit.

T185	'Snipe' brown+cream - *61-67*	30	35
T185	'Falcon' brown+cream - *61-67*	30	35
T185	'Eagle' brown+cream - *61-67*	30	35

Pullman car 'Eagle' [C6]

C7. Continental Stock

Special bogies were made for the Continental coaches.

T580	stainless steel car, silver - *62-65*	25	30
T581	generator/baggage blue - *not made*	NA	NA
T582	Wagon-Lits blue sleeper - *not made*	NA	NA
T583	Wagon-Lits Pullman car blue+cream - *not made*	NA	NA
T584	SNCF 1471 forestiere green - *65?*	45	60

WAGONS

These had diecast chassis with moulded plastic bodies. They were joined together by four pins on the casting which located four holes in the moulding. There are examples of unusual plastic colours that are worth looking out for and these often sell at much higher rates. Some colours, such as grey, brown and maroon, turn up in a range of different shades. As it is practically impossible to determine which shade was available when, the period during which it may have occurred is given.

Peco fitted their more detailed 10' chassis to four Tri-ang TT bodies supplied by Rovex. These were the 13T steel low-sided wagon, mineral wagon, cattle wagon and 12T goods van.

Loads: It seems that each of the mouldings for the loads was produced in a twin impression mould resulting in there being two versions of each load to be found in equal quantities and in each colour variation.

Cat.No.	Company, Number, Colour, Date	£	£

British Wagons

W1. 14T Flat Wagon with 3 'L' Type Containers

The L type containers (3 per wagon) may be a dark greenish grey or a paler translucent grey.

T276	BR B530258 red-brown + load - *60-67*	8	10
T276	BR B530258 dark brown + load - *60-67*	8	10

W2. 12T 6-Plank Open Truck

Timber loads, of which there were two versions, were cream or tan and drum loads were black, maroon, brown, grey or cream. The heat printing was white.

T176	BR 17351 green - *59-67*	25	30
T176	BR 17351 yellow brown - *59-67*	5	7
T176	BR 17351 red-brown - *59-67*	5	7
T176	BR 17351 dark yellow brown - *62*	8	10
T176	BR 17351 maroon - *59-67*	8	10
T177	any of the above + timber - *59-61*	8	10
T178	any of the above + drums - *59-61*	8	10

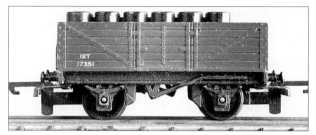

12T 6-plank open wagon + drum load [W2]

W3. 13T Steel Low-Sided Wagon

plank = planked interior. plain = plain interior. The load was a plastic moulding representing granite chips. Two different mouldings of this exist.

T172	**BR** B9325 grey plank - *58-67*	5	7
T273	as above with load - *60-61*	8	10
T172	**BR** B9325 light grey plank - *58-67*	5	7
T273	as above with load - *60-61*	8	10
T172	**BR** B9325 grey plain - *58-67*	5	7
T273	as above with load - *60-61*	8	10
T172	**BR** B9325 light grey plain - *58-67*	5	7
T273	as above with load - *60-61*	8	10
-	**BR** grey fitted to Peco chassis - *58-62*	10	20

W4. 16T Mineral Truck

This had raised numbers etc. and two versions of the coal/ore load moulding may be found. Quite a variety of shades of grey exist.

T70	**BR** B44821 grey - *57-68*	5	7
T179	as above + coal - *59-61*	8	10
T270	ditto + iron ore - *59-61*	8	10
T70	**BR** B44821 light grey - *57-68*	5	7
T70	**BR** B44821 translucent grey - *57*	7	9
T70	**BR** B44821 duck egg blue - *59-61*	15	20
T179	as above + coal - *59-61*	15	20
T270	ditto + iron ore + ore - *59-61*	15	20
-	**BR** B44821 fitted to Peco chassis - *57-62*	10	20

W5. 21T Ore Wagon

On some, the number was printed directly onto the moulded body but later it was printed onto a black panel. The body was also printed in white with 'Bulk Ore'.

T170	**BR** lt.grey no markings - *58-59*	5	7
T170	**BR** B41429 light greenish-grey - *59-68*	5	7
T170	**BR** B41429 bluish-grey - *59-68*	5	7
T271	any above + bauxite load - *59-61*	8	10
T274	any above + iron ore load - *60-61*	8	10
T170	**BR** B41429 green - *?*	25	30

W6. 20T Bulk Grain Wagon

This model used the body of the ore wagon with a matching top and was produced in similar shades to the ore wagon. On some, the number was printed directly onto the moulded body but later it was printed onto a black panel. The position of this panel varies: A = last section on left, B = first section in on left.

T171	**BR** B85040 A grey - *58-59*	5	7
T171	**BR** B85040 A grey - *60-64*	5	7
T171	**BR** B85040 B grey - *60-64*	5	7

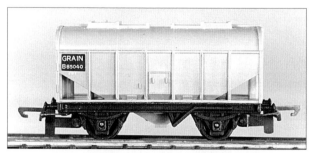

Bulk grain wagon [W6]

W7. 20T Presflo

The printing on both was white.

T278	**BR** B887812 red, Cement - *61-64*	10	12
T279	**BR** B888185 dark green, Salt - *61-64*	10	12

W8. Tar Tank Track Cleaning Wagon

This had a special diecast lwb chassis incorporating an internal tanks to hold the cleaning fluid. A felt strip was used as a wick to transfer the liquid to the track. The body was printed in white - 'Permanent Way Dept'.

T146	**BR** DS4020 black tar tank - *63-66*	12	15

W9a. Tank Wagon

The silver tank wagon originally had heat printed red 'Shell' on one side and a green 'BP' on the other. A later version had four Shell logos - two on each side and a red line on the chassis side. T75 was heat printed in white and T76 in red and black.

T73	**Shell BP** silver black solebar - *57-61*	5	7
T73	**Shell BP** silver red solebar - *57-61*	5	7
T73	**Shell** 5056 silver logos - *62-67*	18	20
T75	**Shell BP** black fuel oil - *57-64*	5	7
T76	**Shell Lubricating Oil** yellow - *57-66*	5	7

Tank wagon - Shell [W9a]

W9b. Milk Tank Wagon

Physically this was the same as W9a but had a ladder each side. It was heat printed in red.

T74	**UD** white - *57-64*	5	7

W10. 8T Cattle Wagon

This used the roof from the goods van and this was either white or cream coloured.

T77	**BR** B3778 yellow-brown - *58-64*	5	7
T77	**BR** B3778 red-brown - *58-64*	5	7
T77	**BR** B3778 green - *58-64*	25	30
-	**BR** brown fitted to Peco chassis - *58-62*	10	20

W11. Horse Box

The position of the inscription 'Return to Depot' varies: A below door, B below door window and C on upper door, These are sometimes found with grey roofs. Printing was in yellow.

T78	**BR** W2483 maroon A - *58-64*	5	7
T78	**BR** W2483 maroon B - *58-64*	5	7
T78	**BR** W2483 maroon C - *58-64*	5	7

W12. Fruit Van

This model had white or yellow lettering and a cream or white roof.

T79	**BR** W2460 yellow brown - *58-64*	5	7
T79	**BR** W2460 dark yellow brown - *62*	8	10
T79	**BR** W2460 maroon - *?*	16	20

W13. 12T Goods Van/ Meat Van

The same moulding was used for the goods van and the meat van. It had raised numbers etc.. The roof of the van was white.

T71	**BR** B875550 dark grey - *57-68*	5	7
T71	**BR** B875550 brown - *57?*	8	10
T71	**BR** B875550 green-grey - *57-68*	6	8
T71	**BR** B875550 light grey - *58-66*	8	10
T175	**BR** B875550 white - *58-66*	5	7
-	**BR** B875550 fitted to Peco chassis - *57-62*	10	20

W14. 16T Toad Brake Van

This used the same chassis as the standard BR brake van and printing was white.

T370	**BR** W56423 greenish grey - *61-64*	10	12
T370	**BR** W56423 grey - *61-64*	10	12

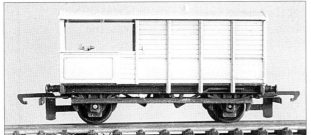

Toad brake van [W14]

W15. BR Standard Brake Van

This had a special chassis made for it which had decked platforms at both ends. Some platforms have a patterned surface and the sides had full-length step boards. It usually had a white roof.

T72	**BR** B9514 brown - *57-68*	5	7
T72	**BR** B9514 red brown - *57-68*	5	7
T72	one of the above but grey roof - *57-68*	8	10

W16. Bogie Well Wagon

Single body moulding with coach buffers attached and cast bogies. Printed in white.

T173	**BR** S61077 dark grey - *58-64*	5	7
T173	**BR** S61077 light grey - *58-64*	6	8
T173	**BR** S61077 green* - *58-64*	25	30

* Southern coach green.

W17. 30T Bogie Bolster C

The timber load was a single cream coloured moulding.

T174	**BR** B940050 grey - *58-61*	5	7
T277	**BR** B940050 grey + timber - *60-65*	8	10

W18. Bogie Caustic Tank Wagon

This had plastic body and frame and metal bogies.

T272	**ICI** 355 bright red - *59-65*	8	10
T272	**ICI** 355 darker red - *59-65*	8	10
T275	**Liquid Chlorine** T204 cream - *60-65*	12	15
T275	**Murgatroyds** T27 white - *60-61*	15	18
T275	**Murgatroyds** T227 white - *62-65*	14	17

Bogie caustic wagon [W18]

Continental Wagons

A special diecast long wheelbase chassis (with no hand brake handle) was tooled up for these wagons. The fixing of the body to the chassis was the same as for the British wagons. Unlike the British range, the Continental wagons had no identification markings on the underside of the body.

W19. French Mineral Wagon

Heat printed in white.

T574	**SNCF** 76923 brown - *62-64*	25	30

W20. French Grain Wagon

Heat printed in red and white.

T571	**SNCF** T502/84 CTC grey - *63-65*	22	28

W21. French Petrol Tank Wagon

T572	**Primagaz** white - *63-64*	20	25

W22. French Cattle Wagon

The roof was bonded to the body and heat printing was white.

T573	**SNCF** K dark blue - *63-64*	25	30
T573	**SNCF** K black - *63-64*	25	30

W23. French Brake Van (Fourgon)

Heat printing was in white except for the tail lights which were red.

T570	**SNCF** 92145 black - *63-65*	22	28

ACCESSORIES

The Tri-ang TT system had the benefit of a good range of attractive lineside accessories. The station was available both as the T31 main set (£30-35) and T32 island set (£25-30) and as loose items (£1 to £10 depending what they are). Other accessories included signal boxes and water towers (£8-10), engine and diesel sheds (£10-12), level crossings (£5-6), fuelling depots (£20-25), goods sheds (£65-70), girder bridges (£15-18), girder bridge presentation sets (£30-35), cattle docks (£40-70), signal gantries (£65-70), track foundations, incline pier sets, high levels supports, telegraph poles (all £2-3), lineside hut sets (£9-10), footbridges (£7-8) and signals (£3-5). The rarest item in the British range is the rubber tunnel (made by associate company Young & Fogg) for which we have no example of a price. The French accessories consisted of a signal box, water tower, engine shed and goods depot all of which are rare and for which we have no established prices.

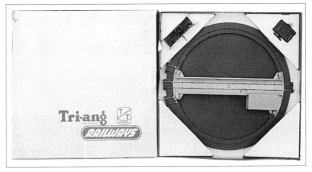

Trix (British)

This includes Trix Twin Railway, British Trix, Trix Trains and Liliput UK

HISTORY

The history of the Trix model railway system is very complicated and, with its twists and turns, it is a fascinating one to study. It started out as a 3-rail 14V AC coarse scale system and finished up 2-rail fine scale with 12V DC operation. At times its owners could not decide whether it was an 00 or an H0 scale and the confusion did nothing to improve sales. The company changed hands many times and the product was renamed on almost as many occasions. The story is further complicated by its links with the German Trix system and Liliput of Austria.

The Trix Twin Railway took its name from the fact that one could operate two trains on the same piece of track. This was achieved by having three rail track with the centre rail acting as a common return. The left-hand outer rail was then used by one locomotive to collect current and the right outer rail by another loco. When overhead catenary was introduced it became possible to run three trains on the same track!

Trix was a system invented and initially made in Germany but, soon afterwards, made in Britain through the involvement of W.J.Bassett-Lowke.

Stephan Bing left the famous family toy making firm and, in 1928, purchased the toy making business of Andreas Fortner. Bing brought to his new venture a number of colleagues including Siegfried Kahn who became his general manager and designer of his new range of toys. A construction toy, along the lines of Meccano, was launched in 1930 under the name of Trix and proved very successful. In order to make this system in Britain, Trix Ltd

Milestones
1928 Stephan Bing buys Andreas Fortner.
1930 Trix construction toy launched.
1932 Trix Ltd formed in UK. with W.J.Bassett-Lowke as a director.
1932 Franz Bing joins Trix Ltd.
1935 Trix Express is launched in Germany and imported and sold by Trix Ltd.
1936 Trix Twin, made by Winteringham Ltd, is launched by Trix Ltd.
1937 Wholesale expansion of Trix Twin on the back of early high volume sales.
1937 First issue of The TTR Gazette printed.
1938 First Pacific locomotives arrive.
1938 Launch of Hornby Dublo hits sales.
1940 Death of Stephan Bing.
1941 Trix Ltd and Winteringham Ltd form Precision Models Ltd.
1942 Trix Ltd take control of Precision Models Ltd.
1946 Post-war production starts.
1948 Models designed for the American market.
1950 BR liveries introduced.
1950 First post-war edition of The TTR Gazette.
1951 Winteringham Ltd wound up.
1952 German company sells its Trix Ltd shares.
1953 Death of W.J.Bassett-Lowke.
1955 The first 12V DC train set is produced.
1957 Ewart Holdings Ltd buy Trix.
1957 Fibre base track introduced.
1958 Ewart Holdings bankrupt and Trix and PML assets are acquired by Dufay Ltd.
1958 Trix Products Ltd formed.
1960 Trix production moved to Birmingham.
1961 Ernst Rozsa joins Trix Products Ltd.
1961 Production of Trix ceases.
1963 Trix sold to British Celanese Ltd and moved to Wrexham.
1965 Courtaulds offer Trix to Lines Bros..
1967 Production of British Minitrix starts at Wrexham.
1968 Trix sold to German Trix and production restarted at Wrexham through Thernglade Ltd.
1971 Decision taken to phase out Trix production.
1973 Thernglade factory closes. Rozsa acquires British Trix spares and stock, Liliput buy tooling.
1973 Rovex Ltd take over marketing of British outline Minitrix models as Hornby Minitrix.
1974 Rosza forms Liliput Model Railways (UK) Ltd.
1992 Ernst Rosza ceases production.
1993 Kader buy Liliput and thereby acquire Trix Trains tools.

was formed in 1932.

The actual manufacture took place at Winteringham Ltd; an associate company of Bassett-Lowke Ltd. The MD at the factory was James Mackenzie and he had as his assistant Robert Bindon Blood, a keen model railway man who was responsible for the design of some of the finest locomotives made by Bassett-Lowke Ltd.

In 1932 Stephan Bing's son Franz emigrated to Britain and joined the fledgling company, organising sales. About this time Mettoy Ltd, another toy manufacturer who would later be remembered for Corgi toys and Playcraft model railways, started up in the basement of Winteringham Ltd with Winteringham doing the manufacturing for them. In 1935, a new 00 scale model railway system called Trix Express was launched in Germany by Stephan Bing and, by the end of the year, was being imported to the UK by Trix Ltd. Initially it was sold here as 'Bassett-Lowke Twin-Train Table Railway' and production of a British version was soon started at Winteringham Ltd in Northampton and launched by Trix Ltd in time for Christmas 1936.

Like the German version, design was built around an 0-4-0 14V AC electric mechanism. The locomotives had diecast bodies while rolling stock was tinplate and wood was largely used for lineside buildings.

1937 saw considerable expansion of the Trix Twin Railway and, to keep the public informed, The TTR Gazette was published from late 1937. The first Pacific locomotives arrived in 1938 but this was the year the rival Hornby Dublo system was launched with its better looking models.

Anti-Semitic legislation in Germany forced Stephan Bing and his partners to sell their German company. Their associate Ernst Voelk, who had also bought the Distler toy company in Nuremberg, purchased it. The partners and Kahn emigrated to Britain.

War halted production as Winteringham Ltd transferred its attention to the war effort. In 1941, Winteringham Ltd got together with Trix Ltd and formed Precision Models Ltd to take over the production of the Trix range. The following year, Trix Ltd took a

Trix (British)

controlling interest in Precision Models Ltd and effectively separated the former Winteringham factory from Bassett-Lowke's control.

The Trix trains were not to reappear until 1948 and by then had the Peco type automatic couplings fitted. It was at this time that the fateful decision was made to stick with 14V AC 3-rail operation and coarse wheels, for the sake of existing customers; a decision that was to condemn Trix to a very slow death and to bankrupt companies along the way.

Export was the first priority after the war and American outline models were produced. However, shortage of materials was the company's biggest problem. Ahead of their rivals, Trix adopted the new BR liveries in 1950 but the public wanted more realism in model design. They were getting it from Hornby Dublo and Tri-ang but not from Trix. In 1952 the German company decided it was time to pull out of its involvement with Trix Ltd and sold its shares. The following year W.J.Bassett-Lowke resigned from the boards of both Trix Ltd and Precision Models Ltd.

Trix Ltd limped along but with very low profits there was no money to invest in the new models needed to reform the system. They managed to produce a 12V DC junior train set in 1955 but a complete 12V DC system was needed. By the end of 1956 the financial problems peaked and there was no way out but to sell the company. In February 1957 the Trix group was bought by Ewart Holdings Ltd.

From 1957 both Trix Ltd and Precision Models Ltd had a completely new board of Directors and a fresh start was feasible. The conversion to 12V DC continued, fibre base track was introduced and an excellent range of new locomotives was designed. The only problem was: they were to be in the smaller HO scale! Furthermore, 3-rail operation was retained and so too were those horrible coarse wheels.

New models needed new capital and money was borrowed. With insufficient money coming in the financial position worsened and in 1958 Ewart Holdings collapsed. A major creditor was Dufay Ltd who in November 1958 acquired the assets of Trix Ltd and Precision Models Ltd. Trix Products Ltd took over the design and marketing of the Trix range and in 1960 Dufay moved Trix production to Birmingham.

In 1958 Ernst Rozsa had established a company to import Liliput models from Austria. His company was called Miniature Constructions and assembled some of the Austrian models in the UK. He persuaded Liliput to make an 00 model of the Class AL1 E3000 for them. Rozsa joined Trix in 1961 and took with him the E3000 model.

Poor sales in 1960 and 1961 lead to Dufay closing down Trix production in order to save damaging the rest of their group and Trix was prepared for sale. In 1962 the company was sold to Alvus Investments & Trading Ltd who planned to restart production of Trix in High Wycombe but only the coach moulding tools were made. At about this time it was reported that Trix models were produced to a scale of 3.89mm to the foot.

In April 1963 British Celanese (part of the Courtaulds Group) formed British Trix Ltd and purchased the goodwill and patents of Trix Products Ltd for £1 and a production base was set up at the British Celanese factory in Wrexham. Ernst Rozsa was placed in charge of design and development but later took full responsibility for production. The decision was taken to dump the stocks of tinplate and 14V AC models and they were buried in a large hole on the Wrexham factory site.

To swell the range quickly a lot of models were bought in from Continental manufacturers and repackaged. 1964 was a good year but by 1965 Courtaulds were inviting Lines Bros. to take Trix off their hands. Lines Bros. turned down the offer. Kit locomotives and rolling stock were introduced that year and sold well and in 1967 N gauge Minitrix models for the British market were being made in the Wrexham factory.

Despite a number of successes, the financial problems continued and at the end of 1967 the plug was once again pulled. Quickly the German Trix company acquired the assets of British Trix and a company called Thernglade Ltd was acquired to take over production. Rozsa was a Director of the new company and the product was renamed 'Trix Trains'. This period was famed for the excellent LNER Pacific locomotives they produced in 00 scale.

A number of German toy company ownership changes lead to a decision to phase out model railway production at Wrexham from 1971. The Minitrix tools were bought by the German Trix company and in 1973 Rovex Ltd became the importers of the range which was renamed Hornby Minitrix. Meanwhile Thernglade continued toy production until the factory closed in 1973.

Rozsa had salvaged the model railway side of the business and purchased stock and spares. He set up a mail order business under the name Berwyn Hobbies Supplies while Liliput of Austria purchased the British model tools owned by Trix of Germany. In 1974 Rozsa formed Liliput Model Railways (UK) Ltd and continued to assemble former British Trix models from parts supplied by Liliput. This continued until 1992 when the supply of parts finally dried up. Some parts and tools were acquired by Dapol Ltd and others were retained by Liliput which was bought by Kader in 1993. Kader, a Chinese company who owned the American Bachmann company, had established Bachmann Industries Europe Ltd in Britain to market British outline models made from the former Mainline Railways tools which it owned. With the Liliput tools now in their possession, the former British Trix A4 model formed the basis of the Class A4 models currently sold by Bachmann.

As we said at the beginning, Trix has a very complicated history!

Further Reading

The excellent book *'The History of Trix H0/00 Model Railways in Britain'* by Tony Matthewman, which formed the basis of the above potted history, is strongly recommended to anyone wishing to study the subject. It was published by New Cavendish Books

(ISBN 0-904568-76-8).

Collectors Clubs

The Trix Twin Railway Collectors Association (TTRCA) was founded in 1975 and caters for enthusiasts of Trix Twin, Trix Express, Trix Trains and the models of Liliput UK. It publishes a quarterly magazine called 'Trix Twin Gazette' and offers a spares service to its members. For enquiries concerning membership, telephone: 0116 271 5943.

Couplings - These provide a means of distinguishing between pre- and post-war models. The pre-war coupling (referred to as 'PW' in the tables) was non-automatic and consisted of a cast (or tinplate) hook and a wire loop. The post-war couplings came into use in 1948 and were the Peco style automatic ones also used by Meccano Ltd on Hornby Dublo stock. Pre-war couplings were used after the war during 1946 and 1947 but only small quantities of certain models were being made.

Dates - Where a model was available with a variety of numbers, it is hard to say which numbers were being carried at any one time. The dates quoted in the following tables, therefore, normally apply to the model form and not the number.

Listing - The locos are listed in order of size in each section starting with tank engines followed by tender locos and ending with diesels, electrics and multiple units. Wagons are listed in the order of: flats, open wagons, hoppers, tanks, vans, brake vans and bogie stock.

LOCOMOTIVES

White Numbers - A lot of people are mystified by white numbers printed on the underside of locomotives (and other electrical equipment) made after 1948. These numbers indicate the month and year that the model was made. The months were lettered 'A' for January, 'B' for February, and so on, while the year was represented by the last digit (sometimes last two digits). Thus 'C3' was March 1953. This provides us with a very useful way of dating much post-war Trix electrical equipment up until 1960 when the system was dropped. Incidentally the letter 'I' was not used and so September was 'J'.

A single 'R' on a chassis means that it went back to the factory at some time for a repair and 'M' was applied to chassis in 1948, indicating modification.

Voltage - The Trix Twin Railway system initially operated on a 14V AC power supply but later manufacturers used 12V DC as it was more controllable. Trix were tied to their AC system but eventually had to change over to 12V DC as the market demanded. The DC system was introduced in 1956. Some of the locomotives listed below were made only for an AC supply and some only for DC. Four models may be found with either AC or DC mechanisms and these are clearly marked in the respective tables. The models that were available only with AC mechanisms are those listed in tables L1, L4 - L15 unless otherwise stated.

Cat.No.	Number, Company, Colour, Dates	£	£

1st Series of Locomotives

L1. 0-4-0 Tank

Tank engines bearing the wording on the back of the bunker 'Patents TTR Pending' were made before mid-1937 while those with 'British TTR Patents 465168 469656 Patented Abroad' were made between 1937 and circa 1950. They were not to be found on BR models.

	prewar couplings		
2/510	**91, 121, 141, 191** LMS lined black - 36-39,46	30	50
2/515	**5, 20, 31, 91, 121** LMS unlined black - 36-39,46	30	50
2/515	**39, 58, 62** LMS unlined blk - 36-39,46	40	60
2/515	**58** LMS lined black - 36-39,46	40	60
2/515	**11** LMS unlined black - 47-52	30	50
4/510	**2901, 9276** LNER lined black - 36-39,46	50	70
4/515	**2901, 6178, 7693, 8403** LNER unlined black - 36-39,46	50	70
5/510	**520** Southern lined green - 37-39,46	150	200
5/515	**951** Southern lined black - 37-39,46	150	200
	postwar couplings		
2/515	**5, 11, 20, 31** LMS unlined black - 47-52	30	50
2/515	**30, 62** LMS unlined black - 47-52	40	60
2/515	**63** LMS lined black - 47-52	40	50
2/515	**68** LMS unlined black - 47-52	40	50
2/515	**91** LMS lined or unlined black - 47-52	30	40
2/515	**97** LMS unlined black - 47-52	25	35
2/515	**98** LMS unlined black - 47-52	40	45
2/515	**781, 914, 1109** LMS unlined black - 47-52	35	40
4/510	**396** LNER lined black - 47-52	40	60
4/515	**298, 605, 7693, 8403** LNER unlined black - 47-52	40	60
5/510	**1923** Southern lined green - 47-52	150	200
5/515	**91** Southern lined or unlined black - 47-52	100	150
1/510	**40, 63** BRb lined black - 47-52	30	40
1/510	**63** BRb unlined black - 47-52	30	40
1/510	**48, 50, 85** BRb lined black - 50-55	25	35

L2. 0-4-0 Tank with Plastic Body

Distler motor.

1/515	**59, 85** BRb lined black 14vAC - 56-57	35	45
1/510	**84** BRb unlined black 14vAC - 56-57	35	45
1/510	**85** BRc lined black 14vAC - 56-57	35	45
1/515	**98, 30951** BRc unlined black 14vAC - 56-57	35	45
210	**84** BRc unlined black 12vDC - 55-61	25	35
210	**30951, 41218** BRc unlined black 12vDC - 58-61	25	35
210	**67611** BRc unlined black 12vDC - 58-61	40	60

L3. 2-4-2 Tank

This was planned for 1940 based on the German 2-4-2 chassis but was dropped because of the war.

2/514	LMS - not made	NA	NA
4/514	LNER - not made	NA	NA
5/514	Southern - not made	NA	NA

L4. 0-4-0 with Tender

This was the first loco in the Trix range being originally released with 'Trix Express' on the tender. PW = pre-war couplings. dlt = double lining on tender. slt = single lining on tender.

-	**5391** TRIX EXPRESS lined green, disc wheels - 36	500	NPG
-	**5391** TRIX EXPRESS unlined black, disc wheels - 36	500	NPG
-	TRIX TWIN on tender unlined green demonstration model PW - 46?	600	NPG
-	TRIX TWIN on tender unlined black demonstration model PW - 46?	600	NPG
	prewar couplings		
2/520	**5647, 5670, 5724 , 6138, 6200** LMS lined maroon - 36-39,46	80	100
2/525	**5049, 6138, 8046, 8067, 8209** LMS lined black - 36-39,46	60	80
4/520	**2581** LNER lined light green - 36-39,46	80	100
4/520	**4472** LNER lined light green - 36-39,46	60	80
4/525	**2394, 3451** LNER lined black - 36-39,46	40	60
4/525	**4472** LNER lined black - 36-39,46	80	100
5/520	**763** Southern lined green - 37-39	200	250
5/525	**498** Southern lined black tender - 37-39,46	180	250
	postwar couplings		
2/520	**5647** LMS lined maroon - 47-52	80	100

2/520	**6138** LMS lined v.dark maroon - *47-52*	80	100
2/525	**6138, 8209** LMS lined black front boiler band and tender - *47-52*	40	60
2/525	**6138** LMS lined black front boiler band - *47-52*	40	60
2/525	**5124** LMS unlined black - *47-52*	40	60
2/525	**8032** LMS unlined black - *47-52*	30	50
4/520	**2876** LNER lined light green - *47-52*	80	100
4/520	**2876** LNER lined dark green - *47-52*	80	100
4/520	**693** LNER lined light green, black cylinders - *47-52*	80	100
4/520	**103, 447, 465** LNER lined green - *47-52*	100	120
4/520	**2876** LNER lined green - *47-52*	80	100
4/525	**2394, 3451** LNER lined black - *47-52*	40	60
4/525	**2394, 3451** LNER lined black on tender only - *47-52*	40	60
4/525	**4472** LNER lined black on tender only - *47-52*	80	100
4/525	**103, 620, 693** LNER unlind black - *47-52*	60	80
4/525	**4472** LNER unlined black - *47-52*	80	100
4/525	**5124, 8032** LNER unlined black - *47-52*	60	80
5/520	**763** Southern lined green - *48-50?*	250	NPG
5/525	**498** Southern lined black tender - *47-52*	180	220
1/520	**46231** BRb lined light blue - *50-51*	100	120
1/520	**46256, 60100** BRb light blue lined - *50-51*	80	100
1/520	**46256, 60100** BRb dark blue lined - *51-52*	80	100
1/520	**30782, 46256, 46258, 60089** BRb lined green dlt black cylinders - *52-58*	40	60
1/520	**60100** BRb lined green dlt green cylinders - *51-52*	60	70
1/520	**73029** BRb lined green dlt green or black cylinders - *52-53*	60	70
1/520	**30782, 60089** BRb lined green slt black cylinders - *52-58*	40	60
1/520	**46258** BRb lined green slt black cylinders - *52-58*	30	50
1/525	**48427** BRb lined black front boiler band and cylinders - *52-58*	30	50
1/525	**48152** BRb lined black front boiler band only - *52-58*	30	50
1/525	**2750, 6201** BRb unlined black - *50-58*	30	50
1/525	**30846, 31829** BRb unlined black - *50-58*	25	40
1/525	**46201** BRb unlined black - *50-58*	50	70
1/525	**48427** BRb unlined black - *50-58*	30	50
1/525	**63950** BRb unlined black - *50-58*	25	40

0-4-0 tender loco [L4]

L5. Midland Compound 4-4-0

dlt = double lined tender. slt = single lining on tender.

2/536	**1168** LMS lined maroon PW - *39,46*	250	350
2/536	**1168** LMS lined black PW - *39,46*	150	250
2/536	**1168** LMS lined maroon - *47-52*	300	400
2/536	**1168** LMS lined matt black - *49-52*	100	200
2/536	**41062 41128 41135** BRb black dlt - *50-56*	80	120
2/536	**41162** BRb black dlt- *50-56*	60	90
2/536	**41128** BRb black slt - *50-52?*	80	120
2/536	**41135** BRc black dlt- *56-58*	80	120
2/536	**41162** BRc black dlt- *56-58*	60	90
2/536	**41162** BRb green dlt- *53*	400	600
2/536	**62750** BRb green dlt, factory mistake (only one) - *53*	NPG	NPG
F101	**1168, 41168** BRc black 12vDC - *59-60*	120	150

L6. Hunt Class 4-4-0

dlt = double lining on tender. slt = single lining on tender.

'Pytchley'

4/536	**298** LNER lined green PW 14vAC - *39*	400	500
4/536	**298** LNER lined green 14vAC - *47-48*	500	600
4/536	**2750** LNER lined green 14vAC - *48-52*	500	600
4/536	**2750** LNER lined matt black 14vAC - *49-52*	200	300
4/536	**62750, 62750** BRb green dlt 14vAC - *53-58*	80	100
4/536	**62750** BRb black dlt 14vAC - *50*	120	150
4/536	**62750** BRb black slt 14vAC - *50*	120	150
230	**62750** BRc green 12vDC - *57-60*	80	100
235	**62750** BRc black 12vDC - *57-60*	80	100

Hunt Class 4-4-0 [L6]

L7. Schools Class 4-4-0

The Schools Class locomotive was planned for 1940 and an order placed but the war intervened. The project was then shelved until the late 1950s when it was released as a 12v DC model with a new casting.

5/536	**911 'Dover'** Southern green - *not made*	NA	NA
5/364	**911 'Dover'** Southern green set in wooden presentation box with 3 coaches - *not made*	NA	NA
F100	**30911 'Dover'** BRc green 12vDC - *59-60*	200	300

L8. Princess 4-6-2

The chassis were made in Germany. The tooling became damaged beyond economic repair and so the model was not reintroduced after the war.

2/540	**6201 'Princess'** LMS maroon - *38-39*	375	475
2/344	**6201 'Princess'** LMS maroon set in wooden presentation box with 3 coaches - *38-39*	525	1000

'Princess' 4-6-2 [L8]

L9. Coronation 4-6-2

After the war, with the streamlining being removed from the real locomotives, the model was thought to be out of date and not worth reintroducing.

6220 'Coronation'

2/542	LMS maroon - *39*	600	800
2/347	LMS maroon set in wooden presentation box with 3 coaches - *39*	800	1500
2/347	LMS maroon set in dark green wooden presentation box with 3 coaches - *39*	800	1500

L10. A3 4-6-2

The chassis were made in Germany. PW = pre-war couplings. dlt = double lined tender.

4472 'Scotsman'

4/540	LNER green PW - *38-39*	600	800
4/344	LNER green in wooden presentation box with 3 coaches PW - *38-39*	800	1000
4/540	LNER green PW black cylinders - *39*	600	800
4/540	LNER black PW - *c42?*	NPG	2000
1/540	BRb dark blue single lined tend - *51-52*	300	400
1/540	BRb green single lined tender - *52-53*	300	375
1/540	BRb green dlt silver nameplate - *53-54*	300	375
1/540	BRb green dlt orge nameplate - *55-58*	300	375

L11. American 0-4-0 with Tender

This looked similar to the next model but had a larger square backed tender and a hooded lamp in the centre of the smokebox door. 'Trix Twin' on tender

9/519	**4638, 4762** black no light - *48-49*	60	80
9/520	**4826** black - *48-49*	60	80
9/520	**4638, 4762, 5986, 8612** black - *50-56*	60	80

L12. American 0-4-0 Switcher with Tender

This looked similar to the last model but had a smaller tender with a sloping back and a lamp above the smokebox door. Both were produced as part of a post-war export drive.

9/524	**3747, 3812, 5986, 8612** black no light - *48-49*	60	80
9/525	**2690, 4681** black - *48-49*	60	80
9/525	**3747, 3812, 4701, 5647, 5986, 8612** black - *50-56*	60	80
81/50	kit for export with DC motor - *51*	100	160
81/51	kit without lamp - *51*	100	160

L13. LT 0-4-0 Electric

This was an adaptation from a German model with pantographs removed etc.

7/530	**19** London Transport maroon- *37-38*	350	450
7/530	**17** London Transport maroon- *not made*	NA	NA

L14. Meteor Diesel Express

377	**1394** red 3-car 14vAC - *55-58*	140	200
277	**1394, 2602** red 3-car 12vDC - *57-61*	140	200
277	**2602, 2782** blue 3-car 12vDC - *58-61*	160	220

L15. Southern EMU

This model was made in Germany with the exception of the tinplate body which was produced in the UK. Several shades of green may be found.

5/375	**11081** Southern Railway green 3-car set - *37-39*	400	700
5/530	**11081** Southern Railway green power car only - *37-39*	200	400

Southern EMU [L15]

2nd Series of Locomotives

L16. Class E2 0-6-0T (H0)

1107	**32103** BRc black 2-rail (F107) - *61-72*	20	25
1108	**32103** BRc black 3-rail (F107) - *61-66*	20	25

L17. Collett Class 5600 0-6-2T (H0)

This was wrongly called a Class 66XX by Trix. conw = convertible wheels. sw = 'scale' wheels.

6664 BRc			
F103B	black 3-rail conw (1101) - *59-63*	40	60
F103B	black 2-rail conw - *59-60*	45	60
F103B	black 2-rail sw (1102) - *60-64*	45	60
F103G	green 3-rail conw (1105) - *59-63*	50	75
F103G	green 2-rail conw - *60*	50	75
F103G	green 2-rail sw (1106) - *60-64*	50	75

L18. Britannia Class 4-6-2 (H0)

'Scale' wheels fitted from 1960 had smaller flanges so that they could run on 2-rail track but the wheels were still thick. Many, however, were converted to run on universal tack, after purchase.

70000 'Britannia' - green			
236	BRc coarse wheels - *59*	60	90
1109	BRc 'scale' wheels 2/3-rail - *60-65*	60	90
1110	BRc 'scale' wheels 3-rail - *63*	60	90
1111	BRc 'scale' wheels 2-rail - *63-65*	60	90
2111	Footplateman construction kit - *66, 69*	60	90

L19. Standard Class V 4-6-0 (H0)

'Scale' wheels fitted from 1960 had smaller flanges so that they could run on 2-rail track but the wheels were still thick. Many, however, were converted to run on universal tack, after purchase. sw = 'scale' wheels. cw = coarse wheels. The Footman kits were unlined.

237G	**73000** BRc green cw - *59*	70	100
237G	**73001** BRc green cw - *59*	100	150
237B	**73000** BRc black cw - *59*	60	90
1115	**73000** BRc green sw 2/3-rail (also 237G) - *60-65*	70	100
1112	**73000** BRc black sw 2/3-rail (also 237B) - *60-66*	60	90
1117	**73000** BRc green sw 2-rail - *63-65*	70	100
1114	**73000** BRc black sw 2-rail - *63-66*	60	90
1113	**73000** BRc green sw 3-rail - *63-64*	70	100
1116	**73000** BRc black sw 3-rail - *63-64*	60	90
2113	**73000** green Footplateman kit - *66, 69*	NPG	110
2116	**73000** black Footplateman kit - *66, 69*	NPG	110

L20. Ruston Hornsby 0-6-0DS + Shunter's Truck (H0)

244	green - *58-61*	85	110

L21. Warship Type 4 Diesel Hydraulic B-B (H0)

'Vanguard' had red nameplates while the others had black ones. conw = convertible wheels. sw = 'scale' wheels.

D801 'Vanguard'			
1119	BRc green 2-rail conw (F106) - *60-64*	50	65
1120	BRc green 2-rail sw (F106) - *60-71*	50	65
1118	BRc green 3-rail sw (F106) - *60-66*	50	65
1122	BRc maroon 2-rail sw - *66-69*	70	90
1119	BRc maroon 3-rail sw - *66*	70	90
1123	BRc blue 2-rail sw - *67-71*	70	90
D809 'Champion'			
1120	BRc green 2-rail sw - *66-70*	70	90
1118	BRc green 3-rail sw - *66*	70	90
1122	BRc maroon 2-rail sw - *66-69*	70	90
1119	BRc maroon 3-rail sw - *66*	70	90
1123	BRc blue 2-rail sw - *67-71*	70	90
D811 'Daring'			
1120	BRc green 2-rail sw - *66-70*	70	90
1118	BRc green 3-rail sw - *66*	70	90
1122	BRc maroon 2-rail sw - *66-69*	70	90
1119	BRc maroon 3-rail sw - *66*	70	90
1123	BRc blue 2-rail sw - *67-71*	70	90
D828 'Magnificent'			
1120	BRc green 2-rail sw - *66-70*	90	110
1118	BRc green 3-rail sw - *66*	90	110
1122	BRc maroon 2-rail sw - *66-69*	80	110
1119	BRc maroon 3-rail sw - *66*	80	110
1123	BRc blue 2-rail sw - *67-71*	80	110
D844 'Spartan'			
1120	BRc green 2-rail sw - *66-70*	70	90
1118	BRc green 3-rail sw - *66*	70	90
1122	BRc maroon 2-rail sw - *66-69*	70	90
1119	BRc maroon 3-rail sw - *66*	70	90
1123	BRc blue 2-rail sw - *67-71*	70	90

L22. EM1 Bo-Bo (H0)

conw = convertible wheels. sw = scale wheels.

F105B	**26010** BRc black conw (1122) - *59-63*	100	170
F105B	**26010** BRc black 2-rail sw (1123) - *60-64*	100	170
F105G	**26056 'Triton'** BRc green conw - *60-61*	120	200
F105G	**26056 'Triton'** BRc green 2-r sw - *60-61*	120	200

Trix (British)

F105G	**26056** BRc green conw (1125) - *62-63*	120	190
F105G	**26056** BRc green 2-rail sw (1125) - *62-64*	120	190

Black EMI [L22]

3rd Series of Locomotives

L23. 0-4-0 Southern Tank
Illustrated in the 1964 catalogue but not made.

1165	black 2-rail - *not made*	NA	NA
1166	black 3-rail - *not made*	NA	NA

In 1965, a Royal Scot, a Black 5 and a 9F were planned but none of these came to fruition.

L24. Class A2 4-6-2
This used a Trix Express/International chassis made in Germany with other parts manufactured by Liliput of Austria but assembled by Thernglade Ltd at Wrexham in Wales. The body tool was made by British Lego which was another member of the Courtaulds Group. From 1974 these models were Liliput UK products (see 'History' above). The model was not released in 3-rail versions but they could be made to order as too could ones with Trix coarse scale wheels. A small batch of A2 kits was released by Ernst Rosza in 1995. Today the tools that remained in the UK are owned by Dapol Ltd. Some very late A2s were released in plain white boxes but stamped with the Liliput UK name and address.

	LNER 525 'A.H.Peppercorn'		
1186	green - *70-73*	90	140
1060	green - *74-92*	90	140
1062	green tender drive - *78-92*	90	140
1160	green EMS equipment fitted - *82-84*	NPG	NPG
1187	532 'Blue Peter' * LNER green as preserved loco - *?*	185	NPG
	NE 'A.H.Peppercorn'		
1064	wartime black - *82-92*	160	200
1065	wartime black tender drive - *82-92*	160	200
	BRc 60525 'A.H.Peppercorn'		
1185	green - *71-73*	100	160
1061	green - *74-92*	100	165
1063	green tender drive - *78-92*	100	165
1161	green EMS equipment fitted - *82-84*	NPG	NPG

* 12 Code 3 models of this exists which were made for the BBC 'Blue Peter' programme.

L25. Class A3 4-6-2
The body was tooled by British Lego and the model manufactured by Liliput of Austria but assembled by Thernglade Ltd at Wrexham in Wales. From 1974 these models were Liliput UK products. Production of 3-rail models ceased in 1970 although they were available by special order until 1972.

	LNER 4472 'Flying Scotsman'		
1180	very pale apple green - *68*	50	90
1180	correct apple green 2-rail - *68-70*	50	90
1181	as above 3-rail - *68-70*	60	80
1180	green, front handrails on tender 2-rail - *70-73*	60	100
1181	as above 3-rail - *70*	70	90
1180	green, motor in tender - *70-73*	50	70
1071	green, static model - *75, 90*	NPG	NPG
1130	green, EMS equipment fitted - *82-84*	NPG	NPG
1180DT	2 tenders very pale apple green coal top on both tenders - *68*	50	100
1180DT	as above but apple green 2-rail - *68-70*	50	100
1181DT	as above 3-rail - *68-70*	50	100
1180DT	green 2 tenders, water tender now with correct top and front handrail fitted to both tenders 2r - *70-73*	70	90
1181DT	as above 3-rail - *70*	70	90
1035	green, 2 tenders - *74-87*	50	90
1075	green, 2 tenders static model - *75, 90*	NPG	NPG
1183	NER black, red buffer beams and running plate edges Ltd Edn - *69?*	NPG	NPG
1183	'Flying Scotsman' black, red buffer beams and running plate edges 2-rail - *69-73*	90	110
1183	as above motor in tender - *70-73*	90	110
1039	as above without lights - *74-87*	90	110
1035T	4472 LNER water tender in apple green on its own - *76, 79*	20	30
1071			
1070	water tender black fitted with red snow plough on its own - *78-87*	100	220
	BRc 60103 'Flying Scotsman'		
1182	green 2-rail - *70-73*	90	110
1182/3	as above 3-rail - *70*	100	120
1182	green motor in tender - *70-73*	90	110
1030	green (also 1037) - *74-87*	90	110
1031	green without lights (also 1038) - *74-75*	90	110
1078	green static model - *75, 90*	NPG	NPG
1137	green EMS equipment fitted - *82-84*	NPG	NPG

Class A3 'Flying Scotsman' [L25]

L26. Class A4 4-6-2
Tooled and manufactured by Liliput of Austria but assembled by Thernglade Ltd at Wrexham in Wales. From 1974 these models were Liliput UK products. 3-rail versions were not available. v = with valances down over the wheels. op = optional name to order.

	4468 'Mallard'		
1190	LNER blue v - *70-73*	60	90
1045	LNER blue v - *74-87*	60	90
1085	LNER blue v static model - *75, 90*	NPG	NPG
1045	LNER blue v with fire glow - *78*	80	100
1140	LNER blue v EMS equip fitted - *82-84*	NPG	NPG
1046	NE wartime black - *78-87*	120	160
1046	NE wartime black with fire glow - *78*	120	160
	2509 'Silver Link'		
1188	LNER grey v - *71-73*	60	90
1040	LNER grey v - *74-87*	60	90
1080	LNER grey v static model - *75, 90*	NPG	NPG
1040	LNER grey v with fire glow - *78*	80	100
1145	LNER grey v EMS equip fitted - *82-84*	NPG	NPG
	60027 'Merlin'		
1195	BRc green - *71-73*	50	75
1050	BRc green - *74-87*	50	75
1090	BRc green static model - *75, 90*	NPG	NPG
1050	BRc green with fire glow - *78*	70	90
1150	BRc green EMS equip fitted - *82-84*	NPG	NPG
1047	**4498 'Sir Nigel Gresley'** LNER blue v op - *74-87*	NPG	NPG
1048	**7 'Sir Nigel Gresley'** LNER blue op - *74-87*	NPG	NPG
1041	**2512 'Silver Fox'** LNER grey v op - *74-87*	NPG	NPG
1042	**2511 'Silver King'** LNER grey v op - *74-87*	NPG	NPG
1043	**2510 'Quicksilver'** LNER grey v op - *74-87*	NPG	NPG
1051	**60025 'Falcon'** BRc green op - *74-87*	NPG	NPG
1052	**60030 'Golden Fleece'** BRc green op - *74-87*	NPG	NPG
1053	**'Golden Shuttle'** * BRc green op - *74-87*	NPG	NPG
1054	**'Kestrel'** * BRc green op - *74-87*	NPG	NPG
1055	**60033 'Seagull'** BRc green op - *74-87*	NPG	NPG

* No BR liveried real A4s carried these names!

L27. Brush-Sulzer Type 4 Class 47 Co-Co

1170	green - *not made*	NA	NA
1171	blue - *not made*	NA	NA

L28. Western Diesel Hydraulic C-C (H0)

This model was developed and tooled by Liliput in Austria to a design by Ernst Rozsa. Route codes on these models vary as the model was supplied with a sheet of self-adhesive labels as well as yellow cab front panels (with earlier releases) for the purchaser to apply. All models made after 1966 were 2-rail. From 1974 these were Liliput UK models, manufactured in Austria and assembled in Wales.

D1002 'Western Explorer'

1165	BRc green 2-rail - *65-73*	55	75
1166	BRc green 3-rail - *65-66*	55	75
1163	BRe blue - *67-73*	55	75
1010	BRe blue yellow cab fronts - *74-87*	55	75
1011	BRc green yellow cab fronts - *74-87*	55	75
1013	BRc green yellow cab fronts no lights - *77-87*	55	75
1017	BRe green yellow cab fronts 2 motor bogies - *79-81*	80	100

D1004 'Western Crusader'

1165	BRc green 2-rail - *65-73*	55	75
1166	BRc green 3-rail - *65-66*	55	75
1163	BRe blue - *67-73*	55	75
1010	BRe blue yellow cab fronts - *74-87*	55	75
1011	BRc green yellow cab fronts - *74-87*	55	75
1013	BRc green yellow cab fronts no lights - *77-87*	55	75
1017	BRe green yellow cab fronts 2 motor bogies - *79-81*	80	100

D1000 'Western Enterprise'

1164	BRc maroon 3-rail 2 motor bogies - *65-66*	80	100
1167	BRc maroon 2-rail - *65-73*	55	75
1168	BRc maroon 3-rail - *65-73*	55	75
1169	BRc maroon 2-rail 2 motor bogies - *65-73*	80	100
1163	BRe blue - *67-73*	55	75
1010	BRe blue yellow cab fronts - *74-87*	55	75
1012	BRc maroon yellow cab fronts - *74-87*	55	75
1009	BRc sand changing lights - *79-87*	160	200

D1067 'Western Vanguard'

1164	BRc maroon 3-rail 2 motor bogies - *65-66*	55	75
1167	BRc maroon 2-rail - *65-73*	55	75
1168	BRc maroon 3-rail - *65-68*	55	75
1169	BRc maroon 2-rail 2 motor bogies - *65-73*	80	100
1163	BRe blue - *67-73*	55	75
1010	BRe blue yellow cab fronts - *74-87*	55	75
1012	BRc maroon yellow cab fronts - *74-87*	55	75
1013	BRc maroon fitted with track cleaning device - *82*	200	30

D1038 'Western Sovereign'

1167	BRc maroon 2-rail - *65-73*	55	75
1168	BRc maroon 3-rail - *65-68*	55	75
1169	BRc maroon 2-rail 2 motor bogies - *65-73*	80	100
1164	BRc maroon 3-rail 2 motor bogies - *65-66*	80	100
1163	BRe blue - *67-73*	55	75
1010	BRe blue yellow cab fronts - *74-87*	55	75
1012	BRc maroon yellow cab fronts - *74-87*	55	75

D1045 'Western Viscount'

1167	BRc maroon 2-rail - *65-73*	55	75
1168	BRc maroon 3-rail - *65-68*	55	75
1169	BRc maroon 2-rail 2 motor bogies - *65-73*	80	100
1164	BRc maroon 3-rail 2 motor bogies - *65-66*	80	100
1163	BRe blue - *67-73*	55	75
1010	BRe blue yellow cab fronts - *74-87*	55	75
1012	BRc maroon yellow cab fronts - *74-87*	55	75

various

1014	BRe blue yellow cab fronts kit - *74-76*	55	75
1015	BRe blue yellow cab fronts 2 motor bogies - *74-81*	55	75
1016	BRe blue yellow cab fronts changing lights - *75-77*	55	75
1013	BRe blue yellow ends no lights - *76-87*	55	75
1013	BRc maroon yellow ends no lights - *77-87*	55	75
1017	BRe maroon yellow cab fronts 2 motor bogies - *79-81*	80	100
1110	EMS various equipment fitted - *82-83*	55	75
-	various unmade kits of these models	NA	200

Many other variations were advertised but only those known to have been made are listed above.

L29. Class AL1 Bo-Bo Electric

This model was initially manufactured and partly finished by Liliput in Austria and imported by Miniature Construction Ltd who fitted the pantographs and put it on the market in 1960. In 1962, Trix bought the model from Miniature Construction Ltd to adapt and sell as a Trix product. From 1974 they were assembled and sold by Liliput Model Railways (UK) Ltd. After 1966, all models were 2-rail.

E3001 - blue

1128	BRd (moulding) 2-rail - *63-64*	100	150
1127	BRd (moulding) 3-rail - *63-64*	100	150
1128	BRd (transfers) 2-rail improved pantograph yellow panels - *64-72*	100	150
1127	as above but 3-rail - *64-66*	100	150
1130	BRd (transfers) 2-rail 2 motors - *65-68*	100	150
1129	as above but 3-rail - *65-66*	100	150
2128	BRd 2-rail Footplateman kit - *65-71*	NA	120
2127	as above but 3-rail - *65-66*	NA	120
1128	BRd one pantograph - *72*	100	150
1001	BRd one pantograph - *74-76*	100	150
1002	ditto but changing headlights - *74-83*	100	150
1003	ditto but no lights - *74-88*	100	150
1004	BRd kit - *not made*	100	150
1002	BRd 2 motor bogies - *76-82*	100	150
1001/0	BRd 2 pantographs - *84-88*	100	150
1001	BRd 1 pantograph - *84-88*	100	150
1005	**81007** BRe blue yellow front - *77-88*	100	150
1005	**81014** BRe blue yellow front - *77-88*	100	150
1100	various models fitted with EMS train control blue - *82-85*	100	150
1001/0	**E3012** BRd blue 2 pants - *84-88*	100	150
1001	as above but 1 pantograph - *84-88*	100	150
1001/0	**E3018** BRd blue 2 pants - *84-88*	100	150
1001	as above but 1 pantograph - *84-88*	100	150

L30. Class 124 Trans-Pennine DMU (H0)

Based on BR 6-car units built at Swindon for the Hull-Manchester route, the model was partly tooled by Liliput of Austria with a German Trix motor bogie fitted. A choice of headcodes and front yellow panels were provided for the purchaser to attach. From 1974 the model was assembled and sold by Liliput UK and these models may be identified by grey (instead of cream) interiors. No 3-rail versions were made after 1970.

Green NE51953/NE51954

1178	BRc 2-rail 2 car set - *66-73*	100	120
1179	BRc 3-rail 2 car set - *66-70*	100	120
1175	BRc 2-rail 2 car without lights - *67-73*	100	120
1176	BRc 3-rail 2 car without lights - *67-68*	100	120
1025	BRe 2 car without lights - *74-88*	100	120
1025	BRe 2 car with route lights - *74-88*	100	120
1027	BRe 2 car with route lights 2 motors - *74-88*	100	120
1125	BRc 2 car EMS equipment fitted - *82-85*	100	120

Blue and Grey 51960/51960

1174	BRe 2 car without lights - *67-73*	100	120
1177	BRe 2-rail 2 car with lights - *67-73*	100	120
1173	BRe 3-rail 2 car without lights - *68-70*	100	120
1173/3	BRe 3-rail 2 car with lights - *68-73*	100	120
1020	BRe 2 car without lights - *74-84*	100	120
1021	BRe 2 car with route lights - *74-84*	100	120
1022	BRe 2 car with route lights 2 motors - *74-84*	100	120
1120	BRe 2 car EMS equipment fitted - *82-85*	100	120

COACHES

Trix coaches fall into two distinct categories - tinplate and plastic.

Cat.No.	Company, Number, Colour, Date	£	£

Tinplate Coaches

The very first coaches sold in Britain were Trix Express ones. The British range of tinplate coaches, which were made from the start up of Trix Twin Railway production until the early 1960s, came in three sizes. The smallest were short 4-wheeled suburban stock which were shorter than the Trix Express ones, available in LNER or LMS livery and were available in composite and brake versions.

Trix (British)

The standard coaches were short bogie main line stock of three types - composite (all 3rd for SR), brake end and restaurant car and in three pre-nationalisation liveries and three BR ones. These were made up to the end of 1939 and resumed for two years in 1946 before the Peco coupling was introduced.

For the 'scale' models such as the 'Scotsman', 'Princess' and 'Coronation' there were tinplate bogie coaches of nearer scale length (8.5" long) and in a similar range of liveries except that when it came to producing BR versions, BR(SR) green ones were not produced but BR(WR) chocolate and cream coaches later were. Late in the day, interiors were fitted greatly improving their appearance. Post-war LNER scale coaches had elliptical roofs giving them a Gresley appearance.

For the 'Coronation' train set, 'scale' coaches were specially liveried for 'The Royal Scot'. There was also a Pullman parlour car which carried 'TRIX TWIN' on its sides in place of a name, although authentic parlour car names were adopted in the early '60s.

Pre-war coaches all had diecast and wire non-automatic couplings (PW) while those made after the war had the Peco type fitted. All coaches were glazed but, with time, the celastoid glazing strips have shrunk. This glazing had window dividing bars printed on them up until 1937, but from then on the printing could be found on only the 'scale' coaches (even these were unprinted in 1948 for one year only).

C1a. 4-Wheel Suburban Coach

2/550	LMS 3012 maroon PW - *36-39*	20	30
4/550	LNER 3120 teak PW - *36-39*	25	35
5/550	SR green - *not made*	NA	NA

C1b. 4-Wheel Suburban Luggage Van

2/555	LMS 7401 maroon PW - *36-39*	20	30
4/555	LNER 3316 teak PW - *36-39*	25	35
5/555	SR green - *not made*	NA	NA

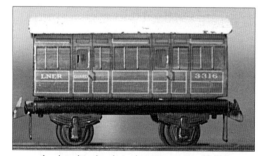

4-wheel suburban luggage van [C1b]

C2a. Short Coach 1st

2/560	LMS 7495 maroon PW - *36-47*	15	20
2/560	LMS 7495 brown - *48-49*	8	12
2/560	LMS 7495 maroon - *50*	10	15
4/560	LNER 1134 gloss teak PW - *36-47*	15	20
4/560	LNER 1134 matt teak - *48*	8	12
4/560	LNER 1134 gloss teak - *49-50*	10	15
5/560	SR 12232 gloss green PW* - *37-48*	25	30
-	TTR 1st, 2nd or 3rd class green demonstration coach - *46?*	35	50
-	as above but later couplings - *48*	40	60
1/560	BR 4135 red+cream dull - *51*	5	8
1/560	BR 4135 red+cream - *52-58*	8	12
1/561	BR 4135 maroon - *57-62*	8	12
5/560	BR green no markings - *59*	30	NPG
5/560	BR green markings no number - *60*	30	NPG
5/560	BR S31595 (transfer) green - *61-62*	30	NPG

* some were made with PW couplings in 1946-47 for export only.

C2b. Short Brake 3rd (2nd)

2/570	LMS 5542 maroon PW - *36-47*	15	20
2/570	LMS 5542 brown - *48-49*	8	12
2/570	LMS 5542 7495 maroon - *50*	10	15
4/570	LNER 1263 gloss teak PW - *36-47*	15	20
4/570	LNER 1263 matt teak - *48*	8	12
4/570	LNER 1263 gloss teak - *49-50*	10	15
5/570	SR 11012 gloss green PW* - *37-48*	25	30
1/570	BR 27104 red+cream dull - *51*	5	8
1/570	BR 27104 red+cream - *52-58*	8	12
1/571	BR 27104 maroon - *57-62*	8	12
5/570	BR green no markings - *59*	20	25
5/570	BR green markings no number - *60*	20	25
5/570	BR S31595 (transfer) green - *61-62*	20	25

* some were made with PW couplings in 1946-47 for export only.

C2c. Short Dining/Restaurant Car

This used the same body pressing as the 1st class coach.

2/580	LMS 2074 maroon PW - *36-47*	15	20
2/580	LMS 2074 brown - *48-49*	8	12
2/580	LMS 2074 7495 maroon - *50*	10	15
4/580	LNER 1433 gloss teak PW - *36-47*	15	20
4/580	LNER 1433 matt teak - *48*	8	12
4/580	LNER 1433 gloss teak - *49-50*	10	15
4/580	SR 7621 gloss green PW* - *37-48*	25	30
1/580	BR 19 red+cream dull - *51*	5	8
1/580	BR 19 red+cream - *52-58*	8	12
1/581	BR 19 maroon - *57-62*	8	12

* some were made with PW couplings in 1946-47 for export only.

C2d. Short All 3rd

This used the same body pressing as the 1st class coach.

5/590	SR 10055 green PW - *37-39*	25	30

C3a. Parcel Van/Whistle Coach

1/557	BR 7055 red - *55-57*	12	15
1/558	BR 7055 maroon - *57-62*	12	15
(274)	BR 7055 red + whistle without windows in end ex set - *55*	18	NA
(274)	BR 7055 red + whistle with windows in end ex set - *56-58*	15	NA

C3b. Bogie Suburban Composite Coach

Aluminium underframe and roof. The Engineer's coach was made by respraying surplus red or maroon ones.

1/553	BR 6301 red - *55-59*	12	15
1/554	BR 6301 maroon - *57-62*	12	15
1688	BR Engineer's ED94528 black - *61-63*	25	30
1688	as above but blue - *not made*	NA	NA

C4a. Scale 1st Coach

2/567	LMS 7652 maroon PW- *38-39*	30	40
2/567	LMS 7652 maroon - *48-51*	25	35
4/567	LNER 31876 teak PW- *38-39*	30	40
4/567	LNER 31876 pale matt teak - *48*	25	35
4/567	LNER 31876 gloss teak - *49-51*	25	35
5/567	SR green - *not made*	NA	NA
1/567	BR 3963 red+cream - *51-52*	20	25
1/568	as above + lights - *53-60*	25	30
1/569	BR 3963 maroon + lights - *57-61*	25	30
1/562	BRc as above + interior - *60-62*	25	30
FL1/562	as above + lights + interior - *60-62*	30	35
1/569	BR brown+cream + lights - *59-60*	30	35
1/563	BRc as above + interior - *60-62*	30	35
FL1/563	as above + lights + interior - *61-62*	35	40

C4b. Scale Brake 3rd (2nd)

2/577	LMS 5772 maroon PW- *38-39*	30	40
2/577	LMS 5772 maroon - *48-51*	25	35

4/577	**LNER** 4942 teak PW- *38-39*	30	40
4/577	**LNER** 4942 pale matt teak - *48*	25	35
4/577	**LNER** 4942 gloss teak - *49-51*	25	35
5/577	**SR** green - *not made*	NA	NA
1/577	**BR** 27316 red+cream - *51-52*	20	25
1/578	as above + lights - *53*	25	30
1/578	as above + tail light - *54-58*	30	35
1/579	**BR** 27316 maroon + lights - *57-61*	25	30
1/572	**BRc** as above + interior - *60*	25	30
1/572	as above but with luggage in guard's section - *61-62*	25	30
FL1/572	as above + lights + interior - *60-62*	30	35
1/579	**BR** brown+cream + lights - *59*	25	30
1/573	**BRc** as above + interior - *60-62*	30	35
FL1/573	as above + lights + interior - *61-62*	35	40

C4c. Scale Restaurant Car

2/587	**LMS** 243 maroon PW - *38-39*	30	40
2/587	**LMS** 243 maroon - *48-51*	25	35
4/587	**LNER** 3587 teak PW- *38-39*	30	40
4/587	**LNER** 3587 pale matt teak - *48*	25	35
4/587	**LNER** 3587 gloss teak - *49-51*	25	35
1/587	**BR** 23 red+cream - *51-52*	20	25
1/588	as above + lighting - *53-58*	25	30
1/589	**BR** 23 maroon + lights - *57-62*	25	30
1/582	as above + interior - *60-62*	25	30
FL1/582	as above + lights + interior - *60-62*	30	35
1/583	**BRc** brown+cream + interior - *60-62*	30	35
FL1/583	as above + lights + interior - *61-62*	35	40

C5. Pullman Car

598	'Trix Twin' dark brown+cream PW - *39*	40	50
598	as above post-war couplings grey roof, heavy poor printing - *50-52*	20	25
599	as above but + lights and improved fine printing, white roof - *53-59*	25	35
599	as above + interior, no lights - *60-61*	25	30
FL599	as above + interior + lights - *60*	30	35
599	'Zena' as above no lights - *61-62*	35	40
599	'Sheila' as above no lights - *61-62*	35	40
599	No.34 as above no lights - *61-62*	35	40

C6a. Coronation Coach

2/568	**LMS** 56001 maroon+yellow PW - *39*	30	45
2/568	**LMS** 56001 v.dark maroon+yellow PW - *39*	30	45

C6b. Coronation Brake End

2/578	**LMS** 56501 maroon+yellow PW - *39*	30	45
2/578	**LMS** 56501 v.dark maroon+yellow PW - *39*	30	45

C7. Meteor Centre Car

597	red - *56-63*	20	30

Plastic Coaches

With new locomotives like Britannia and the Standard 5 in H0 scale, and the intention of offering the new coaches in the German Trix Express catalogue, when it came to designing the new range of plastic coaches in 1961, it was decided to produce them in a scale of 3.8mm to the foot. This proved to be an unfortunate decision as it tied Trix to the less popular scale for subsequent models. The coaches were very attractive, all having interior units, and quickly replaced the tinplate ones. They were also available in kit form.

Some coaches were also used as trailer cars for the Trans-Pennine DMU and, as such, were released in Brunswick green and in blue and grey. These had printing on the solebars until around 1970 after which the solebars were left unprinted.

Less attractive was the later use of the coaches in pre-Nationalisation liveries including GWR and LMS during the Liliput UK period. The Trix LMS and GWR coaches may be found with black or white roofs but Liliput (UK) ones had white on the GWR and black on the LMS coaches. During the Trix period the coaches had self coloured plastic but during the Liliput UK days they were moulded in black plastic and sprayed the required colour.

An unfurnished (no interior unit) range was advertised in 1962 and 1963 but these were never made; nor were the interior units sold on their own as planned. Coaches with a space between the prefix letter of the running number and the number itself date from 1966 where as those without the gap probably predate that. Composite brakes carrying the words 'Load 1 Ton Evenly Distributed' were made during 1965. Light grey roofs were moulded during the Liliput (UK) period when Trix roofs had run out.

C8a. Mk1 Composite Corridor

1901	**BRc** M16171 maroon - *64-72*	8	12
1905	as above + lights 2-rail - *65-67*	13	17
1908	as above + lights 3-rail - *66-67*	13	17
1201	as 1901 by Liliput (UK) - *74-88*	10	15
1911	**BRc** W16198 brown+cream - *62-71*	10	15
1915	as above + lights 2-rail - *65-67*	15	20
1918	as above + lights 3-rail - *66-67*	15	20
1211	as 1911 by Liliput (UK) - *74-88*	12	18
1921	**BRc** S15900 green - *64-72*	10	15
1925	as above + lights 2-rail - *65-67*	15	20
1928	as above + lights 3-rail - *66-67*	15	20
1221	as 1921 by Liliput (UK) - *74-88*	12	18
1951	**BRc** M16171 blue+grey - *66-72*	12	18
1251	as 1951 by Liliput (UK) - *74-88*	12	18
1971	**BRc** NE59766 dark green DMU trailer- *67-72*	15	20
1271	as 1971 by Liliput (UK) - *74-88*	15	20
1291	as above + lights - *78-85*	20	25
1975	**BR** NE59766 blue+grey DMU trailer- *67-71*	15	20
1275	as 1975 by Liliput (UK) - *74-88*	15	20
1295	as above + lights - *78-85*	20	25
1932	**LMS** 1670 maroon - *71-72*	8	12
1232	as 1932 by Liliput (UK) - *74-83*	8	12
1935	**GWR** 2017 brown+cream - *71-72*	8	12
1235	as 1935 by Liliput (UK) - *74-87*	8	12
	Coachbuilder kits		
1941	**BRc** M16171 maroon - *65-72*	8	12
1944	**BRc** W16198 brown+cream - *65-72*	10	15
1947	**BRc** S15900 green - *65-72*	10	15
1954	**BR** S15900 blue - *68-70*	20	25
1956	**BRc** M16171 blue+grey - *66-72*	12	18
1959	**BRc** W? blue+grey - *68-69*	NPG	NPG
	Coachbuilder De Luxe kits		
1961	**BRc** M16171 maroon - *67-68*	8	12
1966	**BRc** M16171 blue+grey - *67-68*	12	18

Mk1 composite WR [C8a]

C8b. Mk1 Composite Brake End

1902	**BRc** M21240 maroon - *64-72*	8	12
1906	as above + lights 2-rail - *65-67*	13	17
1909	as above + lights 3-rail - *66-67*	13	17
1981	**BRc** M21240 maroon + tail light - *67*	NPG	NPG
1202	as 1902 by Liliput (UK) - *74-88*	10	15
1912	**BRc** W21194 brown+cream - *62-71*	10	15

1916	as above + lights 2-rail - *65-67*	15	20
1919	as above + lights 3-rail - *66-67*	15	20
1212	as 1912 by Liliput (UK) - *74-88*	12	18
1922	**BRc** S2301 green - *62-71*	10	15
1926	as above + lights 2-rail - *65-67*	15	20
1929	as above + lights 3-rail - *66-67*	15	20
1222	as 1922 by Liliput (UK) - *74-88*	12	18
1952	**BRc** M21240 blue+grey - *66-72*	12	18
1252	as 1952 by Liliput (UK) - *74-88*	12	18
1982	as above + tail light* - *67*	NPG	NPG
1972	**BRc** NE57976 dark green DMU trailer- *67-72*	15	20
1272	as 1972 by Liliput (UK) - *74-88*	15	20
1293	as above + lights - *78-85*	20	25
1976	**BR** NE51970 blue+grey DMU trailer- *67-72*	15	20
1276	as 1976 by Liliput (UK) - *74-88*	15	20
1297	as above + lights - *78-85*	20	25
1252	**BR** M16171 blue/grey - *74-88*	15	20
1933	**LMS** 5531 maroon - *71-72*	8	12
1233	as 1933 by Liliput (UK) - *74-79*	8	12
1936	**GWR** 3148 brown+cream - *71-72*	8	12
1236	as 1936 by Liliput (UK) - *74-79*	8	12
	Coachbuilder kits		
1942	**BRc** M21240 maroon - *65-72*	8	12
1945	**BRc** W21194 brown+cream - *65-72*	10	15
1948	**BRc** S2301 green - *65-72*	10	15
1955	**BR** S2301 blue - *68-70*	20	25
1957	**BRc** M21240 blue+grey - *66-72*	12	18
	Coachbuilder De-Luxe kits		
1963	**BRc** M21240 maroon - *67-68*	8	12
1967	**BRc** M21240 blue+grey - *67-68*	12	18

* very rare as only a handful were made due to the high cost of the Trix Express light units used.

C8c. Mk1 Miniature Buffet

1903	**BRc** M1820 maroon - *64-72*	8	12
1907	as above + lights 2-rail - *65-67*	13	17
1910	as above + lights 3-rail - *66-67*	13	17
1203	as 1903 by Liliput (UK) - *74-88*	10	15
1913	**BRc** W1816 brown+cream - *62-71*	10	15
1917	as above + lights 2-rail - *65-67*	15	20
1920	as above + lights 3-rail - *66-67*	15	20
1213	as 1913 by Liliput (UK) - *74-88*	12	18
1923	**BRc** S1852 green - *62-71*	10	15
1927	as above + lights 2-rail - *65-67*	15	20
1930	as above + lights 3-rail - *66-67*	15	20
1223	as 1923 by Liliput (UK) - *74-88*	12	18
1953	**BRc** M1820 blue+grey - *66-72*	12	18
1253	as 1953 by Liliput (UK) - *74-88*	12	18
1973	**BRc** NE59774 dark green DMU trailer - *67-72*	15	20
1273	as 1973 by Liliput (UK) - *74-88*	15	20
1977	**BR** NE59744 blue+grey DMU trailer- *67-72*	15	20
1277	as 1977 by Liliput (UK) - *74-88*	15	20
	Coachbuilder kits		
1943	**BRc** maroon - *65-72*	8	12
1946	**BRc** brown+cream - *65-72*	10	15
1949	**BRc** green - *65-72*	10	15
1958	**BRc** blue+grey - *66-71*	12	18
	Coachbuilder De-Luxe kits		
1964	**BRc** maroon - *67-68*	8	12
1968	**BRc** blue+grey - *67-68*	12	18

C9. Pullman 1st Class Kitchen Car

Pullman brown+cream

1931	'Pullman' printed on + interior, names also printed on - *62-?*	20	25
1931	as above but blank + sheet of names supplied - *?-70*	15	20
1931	as above but 'Pullman' now also applied as transfers - *71-72*	15	20
1938	as 1931 but with lights - *66-67*	25	30
1278	as 1931 by Liliput (UK) - *74-85*	20	25
1950	Coachbuilder Series kit - *65-72*	15	20

Pullman grey+blue

1960	Coachbuilder Series kit- *68-72*	20	25
1978	342 assembled - *71-72*	25	30
1279	as 1978 by Liliput (UK) * - *74-85*	25	30
	names carried by Pullman cars		
	'Adrian', 'Aries', 'Carina', 'Eagle', 'Hawk',	-	-
	'Heron', 'Ibis', 'Joan', 'Lydia', 'Orion',		
	'Raven', 'Plato', 'Robin', 'Snipe', 'Wren'		

* E3000 loco roof plugs fitted as table lamps in later ones.

C10. Mk2 Stock

These were planned in 1968.

| 1906 | **BR** 2nd open blue+grey - *not made* | NA | NA |
| 1907 | **BR** M5070 blue+grey - *not made* | NA | NA |

C11. Grey & Blue Pullman Stock

Mk1 miniature buffet [C8c]

These were planned in 1968.

1933	**BR** parlour car 1st class - *not made*	NA	NA
1934	**BR** parlour brake car - *not made*	NA	NA
1935	**BR** parlour kitchen car - *not made*	NA	NA

WAGONS

Like the coaches, the wagons started life as tinplate models and plastic was not adopted until the 1960s; and even then the transition was gradual. Originally most wagons were on a short wheel base with a slightly longer one for brake vans, tanks and cattle wagons. They were initially printed with large company lettering but, even pre-war, changed to small letters in the bottom left hand corner of the wagon side. The open wagon also appeared quite early on in a private owner liveries as well as those of 'Trix' and 'Bassett-Lowke'. The most striking wagon was the breakdown crane which consisted of two short four wheel trucks one of which contained a working diecast crane and the other a jib cradle.

After the war the wagon range looked very much the same and by 1948 was being fitted with Peco style couplings. These simple tinplate wagons adopted BR liveries around 1951, received a diecast chassis in 1954 and had cheap versions made of some of them, of which some were made for Cadet starter sets from 1957. A very attractive Weltrol wagon was released in 1953 with a variety of well designed loads. This was diecast as were the lighted brake van and the tipping hopper wagon that were released about the same time.

In the 1960s we saw the introduction of plastic for wagon production but unlike Meccano Ltd with their Hornby Dublo range, Trix did not initially appreciate the possibilities of the new material. The first series of plastic wagons had embossed numbers and looked little better than the tinplate wagons they replaced. This quickly changed when the first private owner open wagons appeared followed by a series of plastic tank wagons and the BRT bulk grain wagon with a large range of adverts. Some wagons were also available in kit form. From 1974 the wagon range was reintroduced under the Liliput UK name and many remained available until the mid '80s.

| Cat.No. | Company, Number, Colour, Date | £ | £ |

Tinplate Wagons

The tinplate series of wagons started with the launch of the system in the mid 1930s and survived into the 1960s. Around 1954 the tinplate chassis used for most wagons was replaced with a diecast (die1) one, with tinplate brake gear, in an attempt at improving the appearance of the models. This itself was replaced with another diecast chassis around 1960. The new chassis had cast brake gear but as a new range of plastic wagons came in at the same time, very few tinplate wagons received the new chassis (die2). The Cadet set wagons introduced in 1957 had tinplate chassis but with no axlebox detail.

W1. Timber Wagon

662	flat + 29 plank load with cross strapping PW - *36-37*	10	14
662	same without cross-strapping - *37-38*	10	14
662	flat + 25 plank load with 2 card straps PW - *38-39*	10	14
657	post-war couplings - *48-50*	8	12

W2a. 3-Plank Platform Truck

600	**LMS** 472870 dark brown PW - *37-39*	15	20
600	**LMS** 472870 dark brown - *48-51*	10	15
600	**BR** 49736 grey - *51-53*	NPG	NPG
600	**BR** 481760 red-brown - *51-53*	8	12
600	**BR** 481760 grey - *51-59*	5	7
630	as above but die1 chassis - *54-59*	6	9
-	as above but Cadet chassis - *57-61*	5	NA

W2b. 3-Plank Container Wagon

612	**LMS** 472870 dark brown PW + Carter Paterson container - *38-39*	18	22
612	**LMS** 472870 dark brown + Carter Paterson container - *48-51*	15	20
612	**BR** 481760 grey + Carter Paterson container - *48-51*	8	12
612	**BR** 481760 red-brown + Carter Paterson container - *48-51*	10	14
639	as above but die1 chassis - *55-59*	10	14

W3a. 4/5-Plank Open Wagon

	pre-war open wagon		
2/601	**LMS** 247185 grey PW - *36-38*	15	20
2/601	**LMS** 33550 dark brown PW - *37-39*	15	20
4/601	**NE** 140721 red-brown PW - *36-38*	15	20
4/601	**NE** 174651 red-brown PW - *37-39*	15	20
	pre-war wagon with ballast		
609	any wagon + grey load PW - *37-38*	18	22
609	same but blue-grey load - *38-39*	18	22
	post-war open wagon		
2/601	**LMS** 33550 dark brown - *48-51*	8	12
4/601	**NE** 174651 red-brown - *48-51*	8	12
1/601	**BR** 183724 red-brown - *51-59*	5	7
623	same but die1 chassis - *54-60*	5	7
	post-war wagon with coal		
608	**LMS** 33550 dark brown + coal - *48-51*	10	14
608	**NE** 174651 red-brown + coal - *48-51*	10	14
608	**BR** 183724 red-brown + coal - *51-54*	6	9
	post-war wagon with ballast		
609	**LMS** 33550 dark brown + ballast - *48-51*	10	14
609	**NE** 174651 red-brn + ballast - *48-51*	10	14
609	**BR** 183724 red-brown + ballast - *51-54*	6	9
638	same but die1 chassis - *54-59*	6	9

W3b. Tarpaulin Wagon

	5-Plank Wagon		
660	**LMS** 33550 dark brown PW + tarpaulin LMS 304721 - *37-39*	18	22
660	same with post-war couplings - *48-51*	12	15
660	**NE** 140721 red-brown PW + tarpaulin NE 270341 - *36-39*	18	22
660	same with post-war couplings- *48-51*	12	15
660	**BR** 183724 red-brown + tarpaulin - *51-54*	10	14
662	as above but die1 chassis - *54-60*	10	14
	7-Plank Wagon		
660	**LMS** 604707 dark brown + tarpaulin LMS 304721- *48-49*	12	15
660	**NE** 10687 grey + tarpaulin NE 270341- *48-51*	12	15
660	**BR** 168723 grey + tarpaulin - *51-54*	10	14
662	same but die1 chassis - *54-60*	10	14
660	**BR** 12738 grey + tarpaulin - *51-54*	10	14
662	same but die1 chassis - *54-60*	10	14
	BR tarpaulin numbers: 278304, 287430, 317420, 317521 and 321704		

Tarpaulin wagons [W3b]

W4. 7-Plank Open Wagon

	pre-war open wagon		
2/603	**LMS** 93631 grey Loco PW - *36-38*	15	20
2/603	**LMS** 604707 dark brown PW - *38-39*	15	20
2/603	**LMS** 53084 dark brown Loco PW - *38-39*	15	20
4/603	**NE** 142690 grey PW - *36-38*	15	20
4/603	**NE** 171312 grey PW - *38-39*	15	20
4/603	**NE** 10687 grey PW - *38-39*	15	20
5/603	**SR** 40037 dark brown PW - *37-39*	15	20
604	**Trix** 7372 yellow PW - *36-39*	30	35
605	**Bassett-Lowke** 6285 grey+yellow PW - *36-37*	25	30
605	same but dark grey + yellow - *37-39*	25	30
607	**Hinchliffes** 236 red PW - *37-39*	15	20
607	**Charringtons** 451 red PW - *37-39*	15	20
	pre-war wagon with ballast		
609	**LNER** + blue-grey load PW - *38-39*	18	22
	pre-war wagon with coal		
606	any wagon + coal PW - *36-39*	18	22
	post-war open wagon		
2/603	**LMS** 604707 dark brown - *48-49*	8	12
2/603	**LMS** 53084 dark brown Loco - *49-50*	8	12
4/603	**NE** 171312 grey - *48-51*	8	12
4/603	**NE** 10687 grey - *48-51*	8	12
5/603	**SR** 40037 dark brown - *48-51*	12	15
607	**Hinchliffes** 236 red - *48-54*	8	12
607	**Charringtons** 451 red - *48-54*	8	12
1/603	**BR** 168732 grey - *51-59*	5	7
634	same but die1 chassis - *54-59*	6	8
634	same but Cadet chassis - *57-61*	5	NA
1/603	**BR** 12738 grey - *51-59*	5	7
634	same but die1 chassis - *54-59*	6	8
	post-war wagon with ballast		
609	**NE** 171312 grey + ballast - *48-51*	10	14
609	**NE** 10687 grey + ballast - *48-51*	10	14
609	**BR** 168732 grey + ballast - *51-59*	6	9
638	same but die1 chassis - *54-59*	7	10
609	**BR** 12738 grey + ballast - *51-59*	6	9
638	same but die1 chassis - *54-59*	7	10
	post-war wagon with coal		
2/606	any wagon + coal - *48-54*	10	14
606	**BR** 12738 grey + coal - *51-59*	6	9
606	**BR** 168732 grey + coal - *51-59*	6	9
637	same but die1 chassis - *54-59*	7	10

Trix (British)

W5. Small Tank Wagon

pre-war

640	**Esso** yellow PW small black cap - *36-38*	15	20
640	same but large yellow cap - *38-39*	15	20
643	**Shell Oil** red PW small black cap - *36-38*	15	20
643	same but large red cap - *38-39*	15	20
645	**UD** green PW small black cap - *36-38*	15	20
645	same but large green cap - *38-39*	15	20

post-war

640	**Esso** yellow large yellow cap - *48-49*	8	12
640	same but black cap - *49-50*	8	12
640	**Esso** 1591 silver - *51-53*	12	15
640	**Esso** 2591 silver - *53*	6	9
641	same but die1 chassis - *54-59*	7	10
-	same but Cadet chassis - *57-61*	5	NA
P646	same but die2 chassis* - *60-65*	10	14
643	**Shell Oil** red large red cap - *48-49*	8	12
643	same but black cap - *49-54*	8	12
646	same but die1 chassis - *57-60*	8	12
-	same but Cadet chassis - *57-61*	6	NA
P641	same but die2 chassis* - *60-65*	10	14
643	**Shell** silver - *51-54*	6	9
643	same but die1 chassis - *54-59*	5	7
-	same but Cadet chassis - *57-61*	5	NA
P644	same but die2 chassis* - *60-65*	10	14
645	**UD** green large black cap - *48-51*	12	15

* These were strictly speaking in the plastic wagon series and although they had the old tinplate tank barrel, they now had a plastic gantry (of sorts) on top.

Small tank wagon [W5]

W6. Cattle Truck

627	**LMS** 14549 dark brown PW - *37-39*	15	20
627	same but post-war couplings- *49-50*	5	7
627	**BR** 15263 red-brown white roof - *50-51*	7	10
636	same but grey - *50-51*	7	10
627	same but red brown and die 1 chassis - *54-60*	7	10
627	**BR** 14263 grey, grey roof - *52-59*	6	9
627	same but red-brn - *52-59*	6	9
636	as above but die1 chassis - *54-60*	7	10

W7a. Covered Van

2/621	**LMS** 81548 grey PW - *37-38*	18	22
2/621	**LMS** 61253 dark brown PW - *38-39*	18	22
2/621	same but post-war couplings - *48-51*	12	15
4/621	**NE** 24296 red-brown PW - *36-39*	18	22

W7b. Refrigerator Van

661	**SR** 50165 cream PW - *36-39*	18	22

W8. LMS/LNER Goods Brake Van

pre-war

2/650	**LMS** 134900 grey PW - *36-37*	15	20
2/650	**LMS** 730274 dark brown PW - *38-39*	15	20
4/650	**NE** 140351 red-brown PW - *36-37*	15	20
4/650	**NE** 141578 red brown PW - *38-39*	15	20

post-war

2/650	**LMS** 730274 dark brown grey roof - *48-49*	6	8
2/650	same with white roof - *49-51*	8	10
4/650	**NE** 141578 red brown - *48-51*	6	8
1/650	**BR** 743126 grey - *51-59*	5	7
651	same but die1 chassis* - *54-59*	5	7
1/650	same but red-brown - *51-59*	5	7
651	as above but die1 chassis* - *54-59*	5	7
-	as above but Cadet chassis - *57-61*	5	NA

* no brake gear fitted to these models.

Goods brake van [W8]

W9. SR Goods Brake Van

5/650	**SR** 56130 dark brown PW - *37-39*	18	22
5/650	same with post-war couplings - *48-50*	12	15

W10a. 20T Bogie Bolster Wagon

671	6713 black PW - *38*	12	15
671	46713 black PW - *39*	12	15
671	no number black - *48-50*	8	12
671	46713 black - *54-59*	10	15
671	58209 black - *54-59*	10	15
671	59382 black - *54-59*	10	15
671	no number black embossed sides (later 1671) - *59-63*	8	10

W10b. Bogie Timber Wagon

673	6713 black + 20 planks PW - *38*	15	20
673	46713 black + 25 planks PW - *39*	15	20
673	no number black +20 planks - *48-54*	10	14
673	46713 black +20 planks - *54-59*	12	15
673	58209 black +20 planks - *54-59*	12	15
673	59382 black +20 planks - *54-59*	12	15
673	no number black embossed sides black +20 planks (later 1673) - *59-63*	8	12

W11a. Bogie Brick Wagon

675	**NE** 163551 red-brown PW - *38-39*	20	25
675	same with post-war couplings - *48-50*	12	15
675	**BR** 164132 red-brown - *51-62*	12	15

Bogie brick wagon [W11a]

W11b. 30T Bogie High Capacity Wagon

676	**LMS** 10468 dark brown PW - *38-39*	20	25
676	same with post-war couplings- *48-50*	12	15
676	**BR** 12640 grey - *51-59*	12	15

W12. Breakdown Crane

This consisted of two tinplate 3-plank wagons, one carrying a diecast crane and the other acting as the match truck with a jib rest.

615	**Eng Dept** 83610/49736 dark grey - *39*	25	30
615	sprayed dark grey no markings - *46-48*	25	30
615	**Eng Dept** 83610/49736 dark grey - *48-52*	15	20
615	**Eng Dept** 83610/49736 grey - *52-55*	15	20
615	same but die1 chassis - *56-61*	15	20

Diecast Wagons

W13. 20T Tipping Hopper Wagon (Dump Car)

666	**BR** grey - *53-63*	12	15

W14. Goods Brake Van

This model had an internal light and tail lamp. die = diecast chassis.

653	**BR** 31595 grey tinplate chass - *53-61*	9	12
P621	same but die2 chassis - *60-62*	10	14
P622	as above but red-brown - *60-62*	15	20

W15. Weltrol Bogie Well Wagon

677	**BR** 41900 grey - *53-54*	10	14
677	**BR** 41900 black orange print - *53-54*	9	13
677	same with white print- *53-54*	8	12
677	**BR** 41900 black *55-65*	8	12
678	**BR** 41900 grey + boiler - *53-54*	15	20
678	same but black - *54-65*	13	18
679	**BR** 41900 black + transf'mer - *54-60*	13	18
680	**BR** 41900 grey + cable drum - *53-54*	15	20
680	same but black- *54-65*	13	18
P674	**BR** 41900 black + granite - *60-63*	20	25

Plastic Wagons

With the new plastic wagons which started to arrive at the end of the 1950s came a new design of diecast chassis (die2) marked 'TTR made in England'. This was available in two sizes and with or without a vacuum tank beneath. In 1964 a plastic chassis came into use. Where there is no indication of chassis type in the following tables, it should be assumed that the 4-wheel models have plastic chassis. In 1974, Liliput Model Railways UK took over stock and tools for the Trix range and once stocks of parts were used up, new supplies were produced. Plastic chassis with the Trix name removed will have been produced by Liliput UK. From 1978 the earlier plastic wagons were made to order only.

'L' in the following tables means that the model was assembled by Liliput UK and sold in their packaging.

W16. Container Flat A

P616	**BR** B735103 brown die2 - *60-64*	6	8
P617	**BR** B735103 brown + maroon standard container die2 - *60-64*	7	9
P618	same but white container - *60-64*	7	9
1617	**BR** B735103 brown + maroon standard container - *65-71*	7	9
1618	same but white container - *65-72*	7	9
2017	**BR** B735103 brown + maroon standard container kit - *65-71*	NA	10
2018	same but white container - *65-71*	NA	10

W17. Container Flat B

P619	**BR** B740367 brown + 2 Birds Eye containers die2 - *60-64*	8	10
1619	**BR** B740367 brown + 2 Birds Eye containers - *65-69*	8	10
2019	same but kit - *66-69*	NA	12
1623	**BR** B740367 brown + Speedfreight container - *66-71*	8	1
2023	same but kit - *68-69*	NA	12

Container flat B [W17]

W18a. 3-Plank Platform Truck

die1 = first style diecast chassis.

630	**BR** B457434 light grey die1 - *59*	7	9
630	same but medium grey - *60*	7	9
P601	**BR** B457434 brown die2 - *60-64*	6	8
P602	same but light grey - *60-64*	6	8
2001	**BR** B457434 brown kit - *65-66*	NA	10
2002	same but light grey - *65-66*	NA	10
1301	**BR** B457434 brown L - *74-88*	9	12
1302	same but light grey L - *74-88*	9	12

W18b. Plate Wagon

P603	**BR** B457434 light grey die2 + trestle + plate - *60-64*	10	15

W19. Shunter's Truck

620	**BR** grey die1 - *58-62*	8	12
1620	same but die2 - *63-65*	8	12

W20. 7-Plank Wagon

1657	**Spiers** 347 yellow - *67-71*	8	10
2057	same but kit - *68-70*	NA	12
1357	same but L - *74-83*	9	12
1658	**Maltby** 11 brown - *67-72*	8	10
1358	same but L - *74-83*	9	12
1659	**Salter** 122 brown - *67-72*	8	10
1359	same but L - *74-83*	9	12
1661	**Young** 25 dark brown - *67-72*	8	10
2061	same but kit - *68-71*	NA	12
1361	same but L - *74-78*	9	12
1662	**Ocean** 17107 black - *67-72*	8	10
2062	same but kit - *68-70*	NA	12
1362	same but L - *74-83*	9	12
1664	**Hall & Co** 510 grey - *67-72*	8	10
2064	same but kit - *68-71*	NA	12
1364	same but L - *74-78, 84-88*	9	12
1665	**ICI** 326 red - *67-72*	8	10
2065	same but kit - *68-71*	NA	12
1365	same but L - *74-83*	9	12
1666	**Blue Circle** 173 yellow - *67-71*	8	10
1366	same but L - *74-78, 84-88*	9	12
1667	**Charringtons** 257 brown - *67-72*	8	10
1367	same but L - *74-83*	9	12
1668	**Isaac Wilkinson** 35 red - *67-72*	8	10
1368	same but L - *74-83*	9	12
1669	**Abbott** 3510 black - *67-72*	8	10
2069	same but kit - *68-71*	NA	12
1369	same but L - *74-78, 84-88*	9	12
1670	**Stewart & Lloyds** 6534 dark green - *67-71*	8	10
1370	same but L - *74-78*	9	12
1671	**Chubb** 181 brown - *68-72*	8	10
1371	same but L - *74-78, 84-88*	9	12
1672	**Wm Gordon Jamesons** 51 yellow - *68-72*	8	10
1372	same but L - *74-78, 84-88*	9	12

1673	**Roberts Jenks** 100 black - *68-72*	8	10
1373	same but L - *74-78, 86-88*	9	12
1674	**Sutton Manor** 1075 grey - *68-72*	8	10
1374	same but L - *74-84*	9	12
1675	**Nicholsons** 1 black - *68-72*	8	10
1375	same but L - *74-78, 84-88*	9	12
1631	**LMS** 259484 brown - *71-72*	12	15
1346	same but L - *75-76*	9	12
1632	**GWR** 109453 v.light grey - *71-72*	12	15
1348	same but L - *75-76*	9	12
1632	**GWR** 109453 medium grey - *71-72*	12	15
1633	**SR** 32277 medium grey - *71-72*	12	15
1633	same but v.light grey - *71-72*	12	15
1349	as above L - *75-76*	9	12
1634	**NE** 91528 brown - *71-72*	12	15
1347	same but L - *75-76*	9	12
1656	no number matt black - *72*	12	15
1356	same but L - *74-85*	9	12

7-plank wagon [W20]

W21.   20T Pig Iron Wagon

P604	**BR** B744083 brown die2 - *60-64*	7	9
P605	same but grey - *60-64*	7	9
2004	**BR** B744083 brown kit - *65-66*	NA	10
2005	same but grey - *65-66*	NA	10

W22a.   16T Mineral Wagon
open wagon

P606	**BR** B68174 grey die2 - *60-64*	6	8
P607	same but brown - *60-64*	6	8
1606	**BR** B68174 grey - *65-71*	7	10
1606	same but no diag lines - *71-72*	8	10
1607	**BR** B68174 brown - *65-72*	8	10
2006	same but grey kit - *65-70*	NA	10
2007	same but brown kit - *65-71*	NA	10
1307	**BR** B68174 grey L - *74-85*	9	12
1306	same but brown - *74-?*	9	12
1306	same but grey painted brown - *?-85*	12	15
	open wagon with coal		
P608	**BR** B68174 grey + coal die2 - *60-64*	6	8
P612	same but brown - *60-64*	6	8
2008	same but grey kit - *65-66*	NA	10
	open wagon with iron ore		
P609	**BR** B68174 grey + ore die2 - *60-64*	6	8
2009	same but kit - *65-66*	NA	10
	open wagon with ballast		
P611	**BR** B68174 brown + ballast die2 - *60-64*	6	8
2011	same but kit - *65-66*	NA	10
2011	**BR** B68174 brown or grey + load kit - *68-70*	NA	10

W22b.   Tarpaulined Mineral Wagon

P660	**BR** B68174 grey die2 - *60-64*	8	10
	BR tarpaulin numbers: 278304, 287430, 317420 and 321704		

W23a.   Open Hopper Wagon
This was formed from the bottom of the bulk grain wagon.

1692	**BR** grey - *67-68*	15	20

W23b.   BRT Bulk Grain Hopper Wagons

1680	**Johnnie Walker** 5817, 5820, 5822, 5825, 5829, 5833, 5837, 5842, 5846, 5847, 5850, 5853, 5854, 5857, 5858, 5859, 5860, 5861 blue - *67-72*	9	12
2080	same but kit - *68-69*	NA	12
1380	same but L - *74-83*	9	12
1681	**Haig** 5815, 5823, 5826, 5830, 5834, 5839, 5843, 5862, 5863, 5864, blue - *67-72*	9	12
2081	same but kit - *68-69*	NA	12
1381	same but L - *74-83*	9	12
1683	**Vat** 69 5814, 5819, 5824, 5827, 5831, 5835, 5840, 5844, 5848, 5851 blue - *67-69*	9	12
2083	same but kit - *68-69*	NA	12
1383	same but L - *74-85*	9	12
1684	**King George IV** 5816, 5878 blue - *67-69*	9	12
2084	same but kit - *68-69*	NA	12
1384	same but L - *74-85*	9	12
1685	**Dewer's** 5810, 5811, 5812, 5838 blue - *67-72*	9	12
2085	same but kit - *68-69*	NA	12
1385	same but L - *74-85*	9	12
1686	**Crawfords** 5899 blue - *67-71*	9	12
2086	same but kit - *68-69*	NA	12
1386	same but L - *74-85*	9	12
1687	**White Horse Whisky** 5813, 5818, 5821, 5828, 5832, 5836, 5841, 5845, 5849, 5852, 5855, 5856 blue - *67-72*	9	12
2087	same but kit - *68-69*	NA	12
1387	same but L - *74-83*	9	12
1688	**Jamie Stuart** any numbers blue - *67-72*	9	12
2088	same but kit - *68-69*	NA	12
1388	same but L - *74-85*	9	12
1689	**The Maltsters Association** of Great Britain any numbers yellow - *67-72*	9	12
2089	same but kit - *68-69*	NA	12
1389	same but L - *74-83*	9	12
1690	**Abbot's Choice** any numbers blue - *67-71*	9	12
2090	same but kit - *68-69*	NA	12
1390	same but L - *74-83*	9	12
1691	**BR** any numbers grey - *67-71*	9	12
2091	same but kit - *68-69*	NA	12
1391	same but L - *74-85*	9	12

W24.   Small Tank Wagon

1638	**Regent** grey - *66-69*	10	12
1639	same but black - *66*	12	14
1640	**Shell** silver - *66*	12	14
1340	**Shell** red L - *74-83*	10	12
1641	**Shell** BP red - *66-72*	10	12
1642	same but black - *66*	12	14
2025	same but black kit - *66*	NA	12
1644	**Esso** silver - *66-72*	10	12
1643	same but black - *66*	12	14
2026	same but black kit - *66*	NA	12
1344	same but silver L - *74-83*	10	12
1645	**BP** green - *66-72*	10	12
1646	same but black - *66*	12	14
2030	same but black kit - *66*	NA	12
1345	same but L - *74-83*	10	12
1647	**Fina** silver - *66-69*	10	12
1670	same but black - *66*	12	14
2027	same but black kit - *66*	NA	12
1648	**Total** grey - *66-71*	10	12
2028	same but kit - *66-71*	NA	12
1649	**Mobil** silver - *66-69*	10	12
2029	same but black - *66*	12	14
2024	**Regent** or Total black kit - *67-71*	NA	14
2025	**Shell** BP, Fina, Esso or Mobil black kit - *67-71*	NA	15

W25.   12T Covered Van with Sliding Doors

P613	**BR** B753500 brown die2 - *60-64*	6	8
P614	same but grey - *60-64*	6	8

1613	**BR** B753500 brown - *65-72*	6	8
1614	same but grey - *65-72*	6	8
2013	**BR** B753500 brown kit - *65-71*	NA	10
2014	same but grey - *65-70*	NA	10
1313	**BR** B753500 brown L - *74-84*	9	12
1314	same but grey L - *74-84*	9	12

W26. Goods Brake Van

P621	**BR** M731528 grey die2 - *60-64*	6	8
P622	same but brown - *60-64*	6	8
1621	**BR** M731528 grey - *65-72*	6	8
1622	same but brown - *65-72*	6	8
1653	**BR** M731528 grey + lights 2-rail - *66-69*	10	12
1654	same but brown + lights 3-rail - *66*	10	12
2021	**BR** M731528 brown kit - *66-71*	NA	10
2022	same but grey - *66-71*	NA	10
1321	**BR** M731528 brown L - *74-90*	9	12
1322	same but grey - *74-90*	9	12

W27. Breakdown Crane

| 615 | 2 plastic bodied 3-plank wagons grey - *61-62* | 18 | 20 |
| 615 | same but brown - *61-62* | 18 | 20 |

ACCESSORIES

The first lineside buildings were made of wood and painted cream with grey roofs and red bases. most impressive of these was a terminus station with all-over glazed cover. The footbridges had very steep steps. The buildings developed into the Many-Ways station system which reflected W.J.Bassett-Lowke's interest in modern architecture. The building was modular, allowing the modeller to make up any one of a number of complex designs. Some parts were diecast and heavy, especially the central clock tower. Others, including water towers, gantry signal boxes, engine and carriage sheds, remained in wood until they were dropped from the range. The stations over-all roof and windows were printed acetate sheet.

Trix bought in some items including station figures, luggage and platform accessories from Britains and containers for trucks from Kenlow who manufactured similar ones for MasterModels. An attractive and popular lineside accessory in pre- and post-war years was the derelict coach hut which used the body of the 4-wheel coach, in either teak or maroon finish, mounted on a base. Other small accessories included diecast signs, telegraph poles and yard lamps; the last two being mounted on similar large square bases. Single, double and junction signals were made and a tinplate signal box which concealed a whistle.

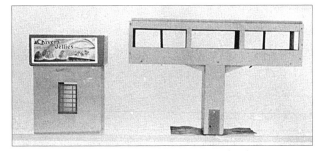

Wooden water tower and signal cabin

The most famous of all the Trix lineside accessories was the working coal conveyor which allowed tipping hopper wagons to dump coal in a bin from which it was carried up an elevator onto a conveyor belt and emptied into another waiting truck - all operated electrically. The largest accessory came in the '50s and was a ready wired table top, which was covered with green flock and made by the furniture manufacturers Vono Ltd.

SETS

The first train sets were copies of the German Trix Express sets but with British coloured coaches. These had long shiny red boxes in which trains included either three coaches or four wagons. They also contained an oval of bakelite track and a square power controller. Another feature was the bottle of Trix Shell oil and the brass plugs for fitting onto the end of your connecting wire to attach the controller to the track.

The near square hinged lid set box came in after the war and survived through the 1950s . A feature of it was the space marked as being for your second train. They were really train packs rather than train sets as they contained no track or controls. This would have kept the cost down making an otherwise expensive system look better against rival makes which did include track etc.

At the end of the '50s the sets changed again to include track and incorporate cheaper boxes with lift-off lids and a more attractive printed top. These were redesigned in the '60s with the introduction of plastic coaches; the box top picture showing 'family involvement'.

There was a large range of train sets and train packs made over a period of 35 years and these are sought by some collectors. The most common, and therefore the least interesting, are those in the red hinged top boxes of the 1950s.

Wrenn

HISTORY

George and Richard Wrenn established their company, G&R Wrenn, at Lee Green at Blackheath, London, in the 1950s and there made track for railway modellers not satisfied with existing proprietary brands. They were later to be joined by their brother Cedric. In 1955 they moved to an industrial unit at 11 Honeywood Road, Basildon, Essex where they had room to expand their activities. By the early 1960s they were offering at least 120 items of 00 and TT track and had developed their own slot-car racing system called Formula 152 which had been launched in 1960.

They had developed a number of other mechanical toys and one, a unique design of motor, caught the eye of a representative of the giant toy makers, Lines Bros. Ltd., better known for their Tri-ang trade mark. Lines bought a controlling interest in G&R Wrenn in the early 1960s and thus it became part of the Lines Bros. Group and was placed under the wing of Rovex Scale Models Ltd who made Tri-ang Railways.

Following the take-over of Meccano Ltd. by Lines Bros. in 1964, George Wrenn successfully purchased some of the redundant Hornby-Dublo tools from the Meccano factory in Liverpool in 1966. He relaunched the system under the name Tri-ang Wrenn and for the next few years felt the benefit of the large Tri-ang sales network. On the break-up of the Lines Bros. empire in 1971, he bought back from the receiver the shares in his company that had been held by Lines and changed the name of his railway system to Wrenn Railways. From the start of 1973 Wrenn was no longer marketed by Rovex and by the mid 1970s Airfix and Palitoy were providing a new higher quality product being demanded by modellers. Wrenn's sales were also affected by Hornby's development of new models of better quality which included competing subjects such as the A4 and Duchess.

The range of models produced by Wrenn in the '70s and '80s was quite considerable and included four new model locomotive designs. However, the volumes produced were low and getting lower. By the late '80s many short runs and limited editions reached the market and Wrenn had become manufacturers of collectables.

In 1992 George Wrenn retired and sold his equipment, stock and the Wrenn intellectual assets to Dapol. However, a quirk of fate at this time was to make Wrenn models even more highly

Milestones
1950s G&R Wrenn established as track makers.
1955 The Company moves to Basildon.
1960 Formula 152 racing system launched.
1964 Lines Bros. take over Meccano Ltd.
1964 Lines Bros. buy control of the Company.
1966 Wrenn purchase former Hornby Dublo tools.
1966 Wrenn advertise their first ex-Hornby Dublo product - 'Cardiff Castle'.
1967 First Wrenn locos released.
1967 Wrenn enter into an agreement to market Lima N gauge in Britain.
1968 First Tri-ang Wrenn wagons released.
1968 The Company sells-off remainder Tri-ang TT stock.
1971 Wrenn buy back their shares
1972 The product renamed 'Wrenn Railways'.
1972 Further wagon tools bought from Meccano Ltd
1973 Wrenn take over the marketing of their own products from Rovex and release 1st full-colour catalogue.
1980 1st new locomotive.
1984 last new locomotive.
1992 George Wrenn retires and sells his business to Dapol Ltd in 1993.
1995 Dapol restart Wrenn production at Llangollen.
2001 G&R Wrenn Ltd bought by Mordvale Ltd of Cheshunt.
2002 1st Cheshunt model.

collectable.

As we have seen, demand for Wrenn had been falling during the 1980s and various limited edition locomotives rarely received enough orders to require completion of the proposed batch. Added to this George Wrenn's dogged determination to clear the decks as far as possible before he left the business, many unfinished models were produced in the final days in order to use up the stock of parts. This meant, for example, normally lined locomotives going out with only a part or none of their lining. Thus, in a few weeks many future 'rarities' were produced and these more than anything else drew the interest of collectors in the years ahead. This phenomenon was further extended by Dapol who assembled further models from parts that they inherited.

A disastrous fire at the Dapol headquarters at Winford destroyed and damaged much of the paperwork and pre-production models causing Dapol to abandon plans to open a Wrenn museum. No new Wrenn locomotive models have been produced since then except, perhaps, from the stock of parts acquired with the Company, but Dapol absorbed a number of the former Wrenn wagon models into their own range, giving them new chassis.

Having extracted from the Wrenn tooling those items that Dapol felt were commercially viable, the remainder of the tooling, outstanding stock of parts and the surviving Wrenn archive were sold in 2001 to Mordvale Limited along with the intellectual assets of G&R Wrenn Ltd. The new owner was a company set up by three Wrenn collectors to trade under the G&R Wrenn name and reintroduce Wrenn models including wagons and coaches.

Early track made by Wrenn

Further Reading

With the company archives in his hands, Maurice Gunter has written a comprehensive history of the Wrenn range of models and a history of the company. The book was published by Irwell Press (ISBN 1903266424) early in 2004 and is called 'The Story of Wrenn'. The book includes production numbers and values.

Packaging: More than with any other make of model, the value of Wrenn items depends on the packaging they are in and the above book describes the models under the different phases of box used. Thus any model may appear several times in the book with the value changing according to the box it is in. In quoting prices we have chosen the lowest in each case but the same model in a rarer box could increase its value by as much as three times.

Prices: Those included below have been much revised, since the third edition of this catalogue, to bring them into line with those quoted in Maurice Gunter's book but they will be revised over the next two years as auction prices come in. In general it is thought

Wrenn

that Wrenn has peaked and that prices are now falling. This means that they will be dropping below those quoted in this chapter, particularly for the more common items, and the prices shown here should be used only to make comparisons between different models.

Collecting Club

We are indebted to the Wrenn Railways Collectors Club for their considerable help with advice and proof reading during the original preparation of this section. The Club publishes a bimonthly newsletter, called *Wrenn Tracker*, and also commissions the occasional special edition wagon. Anyone interested in further information about this organisation should contact Barry Fentiman on Tel: 01628 488455 or visit the Club's Web site at http//www.wrennrail.freeserve.co.uk

Dates - Providing dates to indicate availability of Wrenn models has always been difficult as they were produced in small batches sometimes with breaks between. Introduction dates were also convoluted as new models were frequently added to the catalogue and price list several years before they were ready for release. Dates quoted here have been mostly taken from Maurice Gunter's book. A span of dates should not be interpreted as meaning that the model was made, or even available, every year between those dates.

In the case of wagons, it is often not possible to date when plastic shades or stock numbers changed and so the dates covering the run of a model irrespective of any changes have been put against just one of the variations and question marks against the others. If anyone has more precise information about when variations occurred, the Editor would be interested to hear from them.

Numbers Made - Only where the quantity of a model made is small have they been quoted in the text. However, this information is not known in all cases. The numbers quoted are not always the complete picture as production figures are missing from the archive for at least three years. However, with such small numbers produced in each batch, the missing information should not dramatically change the result.

Listing - The locos are listed in order of size starting with tank engines followed by tender locos and ending with diesels, electrics and multiple units. Wagons are listed in the order of: flats, open wagons, hoppers, tanks, vans and brake vans.

LOCOMOTIVES

Late Issues - Locomotives produced late in the history of the Basildon based company are usually scarcer than those produced in the early years and it is useful to be able to recognise them. The boxes were generally a darker grey or even greeny-grey (make sure that this was not due to exposure to sunlight). The contents description on the end of the box could be either rubber stamped of a sticky label with typed print. The last five locos made (W2312 to W2316) had typed labels. The base of the box was stamped with a five or six figure code; two of the figures indicating the year of production (in 1990 and 1991 it was the first two figures but in 1992 this changed to the last two).

The models themselves received improvements which included better lining and larger driving wheels.

Suffixes - Some models were later fitted with 5-pole motors and these generally received a 'M2' or '5P' suffix to their catalogue number and, on the whole, at auction fetch a higher price (as do

any of the later models).

Mk1 and Mk2 Chassis - The Hornby Dublo A4 and Duchess had undersize wheels and so when Wrenn revised these chassis to take the 5-pole motor from 1983, they took the opportunity to also change the wheels using the larger ones from the Castle. They, at the same time, did away with the flange-less centre wheels and used flanged ones instead. This was called the Mk2 chassis and there were other improvements on the Mk2 such as more power collectors. In the case of the Duchess, there was added cab detail. 'M2' meant a Mk2 chassis, however, not all A4s and Duchesses with Mk2 chassis are fitted with 5-pole motors although these are the exception. The locos fitted with Mk2 chassis could not negotiate 1st radius curves and so A4s and Duchesses with Mk1 chassis remained in production.

Flaking Paint - Due to a bad lot of varnish used in the factory, some of the last models made (including some of the rarest) suffer from flaking paint. This makes them a questionable investment.

'Khaki' Models - Around 1984/85, a number of locomotives, supposedly BR Brunswick green, were sold with correct coloured tenders but with the paintwork on the loco body in different shade. This was a khaki green and may have resulted from over cooking in the stove enamelling oven. Paradoxically, these faulty models are now worth more than correct ones.

Cat.No.	Number, Company, Colour, Dates	£	£

L1. Adams Tank 4-4-2

W3003	**52** LSWR light green - *not made*	NA	NA

Class R1 0-6-0 tank [L2]

L2. Class R1 Tank 0-6-0T (ex-Hornby Dublo)

This loco shared a chassis block with the 0-6-2T but the tool for this was lost in 1990 and, as a result, few R1 tanks were produced after 1989.

W2201	**38** Esso blue 336 made - *80*	70	100
W2201	as above but unfinished body* - *92-93*	NPG	NA
W2201	**69** SE&CR green 241 made - *88-92*	150	225
W2202	**56** NTG (North Thames Gas) yellow c600 made - *79-80*	60	90
W2202	as above but unfinished body* - *92-93*	NPG	NA
W2203	**Shell** silver - *78-83*	50	75
W2204	**7420** LMS red - *74-89*	35	55
W2205	**31337** BRc black - *68-92*	35	50
W2205	**31340** BRc black - *68-71, 91-92*	40	100
W2206B	**31337** BRc black also W2206(B) - *79-82*	35	50
W2205A	**31047** BRb black 210 made - *85-88*	140	250
W2206	**31337** BRc green - *68-88*	100	150
W2206	**31337** BRb dark green - *?*	250	300
W2206A	**31128** BRb green 95 made - *85-88*	200	300
W2206	**31340** BRc green also W2206(G) - *69-71*	40	60
W2206A	**31340** BRc green also W2206(G) - *77-78*	40	50
W2206C	chassis and motor only - *69-76*	NA	125
W2207	**1127** Southern green - *72-90*	45	75
W2207A	**1152** Southern green 156 made - *86-92*	200	250
W2408	non-powered 24ct gold plated Jubilee tank	250	375

	Ltd Edn 149 with stand - *88-89*		
W2410	**1047** Southern olive green Ltd Edn 71 with stand - *89-92*	600	900
-	**GWR** clear plastic body Sp Edn as display item - *?*	500	NA

Maurice Gunter's book suggests that these were not officially released by the factory but were unfinished bodies sold by Dapol and fitted to a chassis by the purchaser.

L3. Class N2 Tank 0-6-2T (ex-Hornby Dublo)

This loco shared a chassis block with the 0-6-0T but the tool for this was lost in 1990 and, as a result, few N2 tanks were produced after 1989.

W2214	**2274** LMS plain red - *78-87*	70	110
W2215	**2385** LMS plain black - *72-87*	45	70
W2216	**69550** BRc lined black - *69-92*	60	85
W2216	as above but no boiler bands - *84-85*	180	250
W2216	**69550** BRc maroon - *?*	500	620
W2216A	**69496** BRb black 111 made* - *85-88*	320	480
W2217	**9522** LNER light green - *69-89*	35	55
W2217A	**2690** (number on tank) LNER plain black c130 made - *82-84*	300	450
W2217A	**2690** (number on bunker) LNER plain black 43 made - *88*	450	600
W2280	**8230** GWR green 98 made - *88-89*	320	480
W2292	**2752** SR malachite green 23 made - *89*	620	950
W2292	**2752** SR olive green 25 made - *90*	600	950

* Two types of transfer used (with serifs and san-serifs).

L4. Class 45XX Prairie Tank 2-6-2T

W3001	**4528** GWR green - *not made*	NA	NA

L5. 4MT Standard Tank 2-6-4T (ex-Hornby Dublo)

W2218	**80033** BRc lined black, numbers various shades of yellow - *67-92*	60	95
W2218	same but, gold+red transfers - *late 70s*	120	175
W2218A	**80064** BR lined black c560 made - *85-92*	150	225
W2218	**80079** BR lined black - *84*	160	195
W2219	**2679** LMS lined maroon - *72-90*	65	95
W2219	**2679** LMS maroon bright yellow lining c50 made - *91-92*	200	225
W2219	**2679** LMS unlined maroon c15 made - *91*	1000	1100
-	**2679** maroon Silver Jubilee 1977 Basildon Sp Edn 51 (Basildon Dev. Corp) - *77*	2500	3000
W2219	**2642** LMS maroon - *not made*	NA	NA
W2220	**8230** GWR green - *73-92*	100	150
W2245	**1927** SR lined green - *78-88,*	100	150
W2245	**1927** SR unlined green 20 made - *92*	950	1000
W2246	**2085** CR lined blue - *79-89*	180	275
W2246	**2079** CR lined blue - *not made*	NA	NA
W2270	**80135** BRc lined green c630 made - *83-92*	160	250
W2271	**9025** LNER lined green 144 made - *83-89*	260	400
W2271	**9025** LNER partially lined or unlined green 20 made - *92*	950	1000
W2279/5P	**80151** BRb lined black 518 made - *87-92*	160	250
W2307	**80079** BRb unlined black 59 made - *91-92*	550	800
W2406	**80120** BR lined black Ltd Edn 283 with stand - *88-89*	250	375

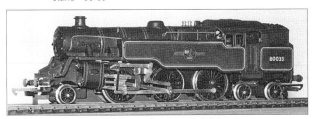

4MT standard tank [L5]

L6. Castle Class 4-6-0 (ex-Hornby Dublo)

W2221	**4075 'Cardiff Castle'** BRc green - *67-71, 76-89*	80	120
W2221	**4075 'Cardiff Castle'** BRc green in white temporary packaging - *67*	NA	500
W2221	**4075 'Ludlow Castle'** BRc green Cardiff Castle number (an error but about 50 made) - *69?*	410	450
W2221A	**7013 'Bristol Castle'** BRc green improved lining c350 made - *80-82, 88-89*	210	325
W2221	**5023 'Brecon Castle'** BRb experimental green - *74-82*	100	150
W2221B	**5023 'Brecon Castle'** BRb experimental green - *91-92*	100	390
W2221K	**4075 'Cardiff Castle'** BRc green kit - *69-70*	NA	800
W2222	**7002 'Devizes Castle'** G()W green - *71-77,84*	75	105
W2222	**7002 'Devizes Castle'** G()W green improved lining - *82-84*	70	100
W2223	**4082 'Windsor Castle'** BRb blue - *75-82*	90	135
W2247	**7029 'Clun Castle'** Great()Western green (number on buffer beam) - *78-80, 83-92*	110	165
W2247A	**7029 'Clun Castle'** BR green (number on smokebox door) 104 made - *86-87, 91-92*	280	425
W2284	**5090 'Neath Abbey'** BR green 139 made - *90-92*	280	425
W2400	**7007 'Great Western'** BRb green Ltd Edn 250 with stand - *85-87*	330	500
W2417	**5034 'Corfe Castle'** BRb green Ltd Edn 132 with stand - *91-92*	400	600

Castle Class 'Corfe Castle' [L6]

L7. Class 6P (Royal Scot) 4-6-0

W2260	**6100 'Royal Scot'** LMS maroon (cat. error W3002) - *81-82*	140	210
W2260/5P	**6100 'Royal Scot'** LMS maroon 80 made - *86-88*	225	380
W2260A	**6141 'Caledonian'** LMS maroon c250 made - *82-90*	220	350
W2261	**6102 'Black Watch'** LMS black - *81-92*	140	210
W2261	**6102 'Black Watch'** LMS black 4 boiler bands - *?-91*	NPG	NPG
W2261/5P	**6102 'Black Watch'** LMS black 61 made - *86-87*	230	390
W2261A	**6160 'Queen Victoria's Rifleman'** LMS lined black c200 made - *82-83*	260	395
W2262	**46110 'Grenadier Guardsman'** BRb green - *81-92*	160	250
W2262	**'khaki model'** (see notes) - *84-85*	280	320
W2262/5P	**46110 'Grenadier Guardsman'** BRb green 86 made - *86-87*	260	400
W2262A	**46148 'The Manchester Regiment'** BR green c200 made - *82-83*	165	250
W2262A/5P	**46148 'The Manchester Regiment'** BR green 72 made - *89*	270	420
W2273	**46159 'The Royal Air Force'** BRb blue c150 made - *83-92*	290	450
W2274/5P	**6125 'Lancashire Witch'** LMS maroon c300 made - *84-92*	260	400
W2288	**46159 'The Royal Air Force'** BR green 112 made - *89-92*	330	500
W2293	**6141 'Caledonian'** LMS unlined gloss black - *89-92*	450	675
W2293	**6141 'Caledonian'** LMS unlined matt black - *89-92*	450	675
W2298	**46100 'Royal Scot'** BR green - *89-92*	440	650
W2403	**6146 'The Rifle Brigade'** LMS black Ltd Edn 243 with stand - *87-90*	330	500

Wrenn

Class 6P Royal Scot [L7]

L8. Princess Coronation (Duchess) 4-6-2
(ex-Hornby Dublo)

Large wheels on locos with 3-pole motors were introduced around 1986/87. In 1989 all Duchesses received the larger driving wheels on both Mk1 and Mk2 chassis.

W2226	**46245 'City of London'** BRc maroon - *69-80, 86-90*	80	120
W2226	**46245 'City of London'** BRc maroon, lined tender - *?*	210	250
W2226M2	**46245 'City of London'** BRc maroon Mk2 chassis 118 made - *88-89*	80	120
W2226	**46245 'City of London'/ 'City of Birmingham'** BRc maroon factory error with different name on each side - *?*	310	350
W2226A	**46238 'City of Carlisle'** BRc maroon 322 made - *80-88*	230	350
W2226AM2	**46238 'City of Carlisle'** BRc maroon Mk2 chassis 168 made - *85-88*	350	500
W2227	**6254 'City of Stoke on Trent'** LMS lined black - *70-76, 79-89*	80	115
W2227	as above but Mk2 chassis - *90-92*	460	500
W2227A	**6256 'Sir William Stanier'** LMS lined black c500 made - *80-83, 88-92*	150	225
W2227AM2	**6256 'Sir William Stanier'** LMS lined black Mk2 chassis c100 made - *84-87*	365	550
W2228	**46235 'City of Birmingham'** BRc green - *73-91*	100	145
W2228M2	**46235 'City of Birmingham'** BRc green Mk2 chassis c100 made - *84-86*	400	600
W2228A	**46241 'City of Edinburgh'** BRc green 400+ made - *80-84*	200	300
W2228AM2	**46241 'City of Edinburgh'** BRc green Mk2 chassis 87 made - *87-90*	330	500
W2229	**46242 'City of Glasgow'** BRc blue - *not made*	NA	NA
W2229	**46242 'City of Glasgow'** BRb blue - *73-81*	90	135
W2229A	**46246 'City of Manchester'** BRb blue 360+ made - *80-84*	220	325
W2241	**6229 'Duchess of Hamilton'** LMS lined black no smoke deflectors - *77-86*	110	165
W2241	**6229 'Duchess of Hamilton'** LMS lined black Mk1 but large wheels 10 made - *92*	950	1000
W2241M2	**6229 'Duchess of Hamilton'** LMS black 123 made Mk2 chassis - *87-92*	330	500
W2241A	**6225 'Duchess of Gloucester'** LMS lined black c150 made - *82-85*	300	450
W2241AM2	**6225 'Duchess of Gloucester'** LMS black Mk2 chassis 122 made - *86-92*	330	500
W2242	**6247 'City of Liverpool'** LMS maroon - *78-92*	110	165
W2242	as above but larger wheels - *89-92*	220	350
W2242	**6247 'City of Liverpool'** LMS maroon extended lining on tender - *90-92*	245	300
W2242	**6247 'City of Liverpool'** LMS maroon no lining on tender 26 made - *89*	245	300
W2264	**46229 'Duchess of Hamilton'** BRc maroon c300 made, there are many variations to this model - *81-86*	350	375
W2264	**46229 'Duchess of Hamilton'** BRc maroon Mk1 chassis but large wheels, 10 made - *92*	350	375
W2285	**6221 'Queen Elizabeth'** LMS maroon, Mk1 chassis with large wheels, 243 made - *89-92*	270	400
W2286	**46252 'City of Leicester'** BR ex LNWR black 182 made - *89-92*	320	475
W2294	**6234 'Duchess of Abercorn'** LMS	430	650

	experimental grey 151 made - *90-92*		
W2299	**46221 'Queen Elizabeth'** BRc green 145 made - *91-92*	400	600
W2304	**46244 'King George VI'** BRc maroon with optional **'Leeds City'** etched metal plates 166 made - *91-92*	370	550
W2311	**46244 'City of Leeds'** BRb unlined black 69 made - *91-92*	520	800
W2311	**46244 'City of Leeds'** BRc unlined black very few made - *91-92*	1000	1200
W2312	**46245 'City of London'** BR green 40+ made, larger wheels - *92*	520	800
W2313	**46234 'Duchess of Abercorn'** BR green 10+ made - *92*	600	900
W2314	**46256 'Sir William Stanier'** BRc green 26+ made - *92*	600	900
W2315	**46242 'City of Glasgow'** BRc maroon 43+ made - *92*	520	800
W2316	**46242 'City of Glasgow'** BR green 22+ made - *92*	600	900
W2401	**6223 'Princess Alice'** LMS maroon Ltd Edn 345 with stand Mk2 chassis but usually a 3-pole motor - *86-87*	330	500
W2405	**46231 'Duchess of Atholl'** BRc green Ltd Edn 249 with stand - *88*	330	500
W2414	**6251 'City of Nottingham'** BRb ex LNWR black Ltd Edn 182 with stand - *90-92*	400	600

'Princess Alice' [L8]

L9. Streamlined Princess Coronation 4-6-2

These used the Mk2 chassis with white-metal loco and tender bodies produced by N&KC Keyser Ltd.

W2300	kit with R-T-R chassis - *not made*	NA	NA
W2301	**6221 'Queen Elizabeth'** LMS blue 200 made - *83-87*	300	450
W2301A	**6220 'Coronation'** LMS blue 80 made - *86-87*	500	750
W2302	**6244 'King George VI'** LMS maroon c200 made - *83-87*	310	475
W2302A	**6228 'Duchess of Rutland'** LMS maroon c100 made - *86-87*	500	750
W2303	**6237 'City of Bristol'** LMS unlined black c15 made by Dapol, sold unboxed - *c85*	1000	NA

L10. Class A4 4-6-2 (ex-Hornby Dublo)

From 1989 all A4s received the larger driving wheels on both Mk1 and Mk2 chassis. The M2 versions listed below did not have a cab interior. Models with 3-pole motors and larger wheels are scarce.

W2209	**4482 'Golden Eagle'** LNER green - *78-92*	85	130
W2209A	**4495 'Great Snipe'** LNER green c420 made - *80-92*	185	275
W2209AM2	**4495 'Great Snipe'** LNER green Mk2 chassis c60 made - *87-88*	380	575
W2210	**4468 'Mallard'** LNER blue - *79-85*	85	125
W2210AM2	**4495 'Golden Fleece'** LNER blue Mk2 chassis, etched brass nameplate 118 made - *88-90*	340	525
W2211	**60022 'Mallard'** BRc green - *69-79, 83-91*	80	115
W2211A	**60014 'Silver Link'** BR green c550 made - *80-92*	170	255
W2212	**7 'Sir Nigel Gresley'** LNER blue - *70-92*	80	115
W2212A	**4498 'Sir Nigel Gresley'** LNER blue - *79-89*	100	145
W2212AM2	**4498 'Sir Nigel Gresley'** LNER blue Mk2 chassis 170 made - *87-90*	290	425

Cat No	Description		
W2213	**4903 'Peregrine'** NE black - *74-90*	100	145
W2213	as above but larger wheels - *90-92*	100	150
W2213A	**4900 'Gannet'** NE wartime black - *80-89*	190	295
W2282	**4463 'Sparrow Hawk'** NE wartime black Mk1 with large wheels c100 made - *89-92*	350	550
W2283	**4489 'Woodcock'** LNER workshop grey Mk1 with large wheels 173 made - *89-92*	350	550
W2295M2	**4489 'Dominion of Canada'** LNER blue 90 made Mk2 chassis - *90-92*	460	700
W2306	**60010 'Dominion of Canada'** BRc green 76 made - *91-92*	500	750
W2310	**4498 'Sir Nigel Gresley'** LNER (silver) (preserved) blue 53 made - *91-92*	535	850
W2404	**4468 'Mallard'** LNER blue ,etched metal plates, Mk2 chassis but usually a 3-pole motor Ltd Edn 252 with stand - *88*	330	500
W2413	**4464 'Bittern'** LNER Ltd Edn 142 with stand green - *90-92*	400	600

Class A4 'Woodcock' [L10]

L11. Streamlined Bullied Pacific 4-6-2

The late streamlined Bulleid Pacifics have a satin sheen paintwork and are lined with a finer orange/black/orange lining (as opposed to a pale yellow lining). In 1990, some were released with old lining on the loco and new lining on the tender.

Cat No	Description		
W2265	**34051 'Winston Churchill'** BRc green - *82-90*	200	300
W2265	as above but with later lining - *90-92*	300	400
W2265	'khaki model' (see notes) - *84-85*	380	480
W2265A	**21C155 'Fighter Pilot'** Southern green Golden Arrow c550 made - *84-90*	285	425
W2265A	as above but with later lining - *90-92*	330	470
W2265AX	**21C155 'Fighter Pilot'** Southern green c250 made - *84-90*	300	450
W2265AX	as above but with later lining - *90-92*	300	440
W2266	**21C103 'Plymouth'** Southern green - *82-90*	225	340
W2266	as above but with later lining - *90-92*	220	335
W2266A	**34092 'City of Wells'** BRc green Golden Arrow c800 made - *85-90*	260	390
W2266A	as above but with later lining - *90-92*	260	400
W2266A	'khaki model' (see notes) - *84-85*	380	480
W2266AX	**34092 'City of Wells'** BRc green c650 made - *85-92*	265	410
W2266AX	as above but with later lining - *90-92*	265	410
W2266AX	'khaki model' (see notes) - *84-85*	380	500
W2267	**35026 'Lamport and Holt Line'** BRb blue (cat. error W3000) c850 made - *82-85*	280	425
W2267A	**35026 'Lamport and Holt Line'** BRc green 82 made - *88-89*	600	900
W2268	**34004 'Yeovil'** BRb blue c230 made - *83-89*	330	500
W2268/5P	**34004 'Yeovil'** BR blue '5 Pole Motor' on box 57 made - *87-88*	340	550
W2268A	**34004 'Yeovil'** BRb green 165 made - *88-92*	565	850
W2268A	**34004 'Yeovil'** BRc green with later lining 12 made - *92*	1100	1200
W2275/5P	**34065 'Hurricane'** BRc green c300 made - *84-90*	330	500
W2275/5P	as above but with later lining - *90-92*	530	700
W2275/5P	'khaki model' (see notes) - *84-85*	600	780
W2276	**21C101 'Exeter'** Southern green 50 made - *89*	660	1000
W2276/5P	**21C101 'Exeter'** Southern green Golden Arrow 103 made - *86-89*	600	900
W2276X/5P	**21C101 'Exeter'** Southern green 185 made - *86-89*	365	550
W2277	**34066 'Spitfire'** BR green 140 made - *86-91*	435	650
W2278	**21C13 'Blue Funnel Line'** SR wartime	320	475

Cat No	Description		
	black 346 made - *85-91*		
W2278	as above but with later lining - *90-92*	400	550
W2278A	**21C13 'Blue Funnel Line'** SR malachite green 83 made - *88-89*	600	900
W2278A	as above but Golden Arrow version - *?*	800	1000
W2289	**21C5 'Canadian Pacific Line'** SR wartime black c100 made - *89-90*	500	750
W2289	as above but with later lining - *90-92*	500	750
W2290	**21C5 'Canadian Pacific Line'** SR malachite green c60 made - *89-90*	500	750
W2290	as above but with later lining - *90-92*	620	770
W2290	**21C5 'Canadian Pacific Line'** SR malachite green unlined tender c40 made - *89*	670	850
W2291	**34010 'Sidmouth'** BRb green 165 made - *89-90*	330	500
W2291	as above but with later lining 35 made - *90-92*	355	525
W2305	**21C107 'Wadebridge'** SR green 93 made - *91-92*	565	850
W2407	**21C111 'Tavistock'** SR green Ltd Edn 248 with stand - *88-89*	250	370
W2407	as above but with later lining - *90-91*	315	470
W2407	as above but Golden Arrow version - *?*	800	1000
W2411	**35003 'Royal Mail Line'** BRb blue Ltd Edn 248 with stand - *89-92*	400	600
W2411	as above but with later lining - *90-92*	500	700
W2412	**34020 'Seaton'** BRb green Ltd Edn 196 with stand - *89-92*	400	600
W2416	**34057 'Biggin Hill'** BRc green Ltd Edn 171 with stand - *90-92*	400	600

* This was not a standard issue and may have been made to order or from a Golden Arrow kit that was available.

Streamlined Bullied Pacific [L11]

L12. Rebuilt Bullied Pacific 4-6-2
(ex-Hornby Dublo)

The late rebuilt Bulleid Pacifics have a satin sheen paintwork and are lined with a finer orange/black/orange lining (as opposed to a pale yellow lining). On some, the green paint on the sides of the footplate runs the entire length of the loco instead of ending at the smoke deflectors (as was the case even with the earlier Hornby Dublo locomotives).

Cat No	Description		
W2235	**34005 'Barnstaple'** BRc green - *68-92*	120	175
W2236	**34042 'Dorchester'** BRc green - *70-92*	115	170
W2236A	**34016 'Bodmin'** BRc green, black nameplates - *80*	285	425
W2236A	**34016 'Bodmin'** BRc green, red nameplates - *80-88*	215	325
W2236A	'khaki model' (see notes) - *84-85*	300	400
W2237	**21C109 'Lyme Regis'** SR malachite green - *73-90*	125	190
W2237	**21C109 'Lyme Regis'** SR malachite green more orange transfers 58 made - *91-92*	950	1000
W2237	**21C109 'Lyme Regis'** SR blue over green - *?*	265	400
W2238	**35015 'Rotterdam Lloyd'** BR green planned for '76 but replaced by 'Clan Line' - *not made*	NA	NA
W2238	**35028 'Clan Line'** BRc green - *77-88*	100	190
W2238	**35028 'Clan Line'** BRc green etched brass nameplates - *88-92*	215	325
W2239	**34028 'Eddystone'** BRc green - *79-88, 92*	170	275
W2269	**34053 'Hurricane'** BR green Golden Arrow planned for '83 - *not made* **	NA	NA
W2269	**34053 'Sir Keith Park'** BRc green Golden Arrow 512 made - *84-92*	265	395
W2269	as above but with later lining - *90-92*	270	400
W2269X	**34053 'Sir Keith Park'** BRc green 270 made - *83-92*	315	475

Wrenn

W2269X	'khaki model' (see notes) - *84-85*	400	550
W2287	**34036 'Westward Ho'** BRc green 280 made - *89-92- 90-92*	300	450
W2296	**34021 'Dartmoor'** BRc green gold+black lining* 141 made - *90-92*	465	600
W2296	**34021 'Dartmoor'** BRc green orange-red + black lining* - *92*	265	400
W2297	**35010 'Blue Star Line'** BRc green 152 made - *90-92*	360	550
W2309	**34036 'Westward Ho'** BRc unlined green 280 made - *89-92*	330	500
W2309	**34036 'Westward Ho'** BRb unlined black no smoke deflectors 34 made (beware of repaints!) - *91-92*	560	850
W2402	**34090 'Sir Eustace Missenden'** BRc green Ltd Edn 250 with stand - *87-88*	360	550
W2415	**34052 'Lord Dowding'** BRc green Ltd Edn 182 with stand - *90-92*	400	600

* A total of 300 of both types made but how many of each is not known.   ** This was demonstrated at the 1983 Toy Fair before it was discovered that 'Hurricane' was not rebuilt!.

Rebuilt West Country [L12]

L13.   Class 8F 2-8-0 (ex-Hornby Dublo)

W2224	**48073** BRc plain black - *67-81*	55	85
W2224	**48109** BR plain black - *67-69*	370	400
W2224A	**48290** plain black c450 made - *83-92*	185	250
W2225	**8042** LMS plain black - *70-80*	55	80
W2225A	**8233** LMS plain black, transfers gold shaded red, c400* made - *80-89*	165	250
W2225A	as above but unshaded yellow transfers	190	275
?	**8431** LMS plain black - *84-88*	330	500
W2240	**3144** LNER plain black, transfers gold shaded red - *77-79*	80	180
W2240	as above but yellow transfers - *78-80*	80	120
W2272	**8016** LMS maroon c270 made - *83-92*	250	375
W2281	**302** WD grey 207 made - *88-92*	385	550
W2281	as above but grey front end and smaller transfers, 8 made - *92*	900	1000
W2308	**48290** BRc plain green 58* made - *91-92*	460	700
W2308	as above but numbered 48102 - *91-92*	560	800
W2409	**48102** BRc plain black Ltd Edn 151 with stand - *89-91*	330	500

* this figure includes the version below it.

Class 8F [L13]

L14.   Class 08 Diesel Shunter 0-6-0DS
(ex-Hornby Dublo)

This model's body was retooled by Wrenn as Meccano Ltd had altered the original tool to produce their 0-4-0 diesel shunter. The two bodies differ in that the Wrenn one has no manufacturer's name inside. A quantity of bodies were taken over by Dapol and these may account for a number of unusual variations, including part finished ones, which turn up.

W2231	**D3763** BRc green - *75-90*	45	70
W2231	**D3768** BRc green - *86*	280	400

W2231NP	**D3768** BRc green non-powered 57 made - *82-85*	250	375
W2231NP	black non-powered - *82?*	250	370
W2232	**D3464** BRe blue - *75-90*	45	70
W2232	**D3523** BRe blue - *86*	280	400
W2232NP	**D3523** BRe blue non-powered 55 made - *82-85*	250	375
W2232A	**08 762** BRe blue - *made?*	NPG	NPG
W2233	**7124** LMS black - *76-88*	80	120
W2233	**7124** LMS green - *92*	260	300
W2234	**72** NCB red* - *78-80*	75	110
W2243	Dunlop yellow c400 made - *80*	90	140

* Some have moulded red plastic bodies while others have black ones sprayed red.

L15.   Class 20 Diesel Bo-Bo (ex-Hornby Dublo)

It seems that the Hornby Dublo body tool was not available and a new tool had to be made for this model. This would explain why it was a late addition to the range. In the 1980s, press-fitted bogie sideframes were gradually replaced by screw fitted ones.

W2230	**D8017** BRc green - *77-89*	50	75
W2230NP	**D8010** BRc green non-powered 323 made - *80-87*	185	275
W2230	**20 008** BRe blue (also) - *88-89*	125	150
W2230B	as above but different number on box	145	225
W2230	**8003** BRe blue - *77-89*	50	75
W2230BNP	**D8015** BRe blue non-powered 415 made - *80-88*	165	250
W2230RF	**20 132** BReLL grey early Railfreight livery 116 made - *88-89*	235	350

Class 20 diesel Bo-Bo [L15]

L16.   Pullman EMU Brighton Belle

	blue+grey		
W3005	**S291S** BRe dummy car 9 made - *80-81*	NA	500
W3004/5	**S290S+S291S** BRe 2-car set - *80-92*	155	250
	as above but sold in 2 loco boxes - *91-92*	NA	450
W3004/5A	**S290S+S291S** BRe 2-car set in 2 loco boxes 150 Years 1841-1991 Ltd Edn 11 made - *92*	500	750
W3006/7A	as above but wrong catalogue number	NA	1500
	brown+cream		
W3007	**91** dummy car sold singly 40 made - *80-81*	NA	350
W3006/7	**3052 (90+91)** 2-car set brown tables - *79-85*	170	220
W3006/7	as above but white tables - *86-91*	100	275
W3006/7	same packed in 2 loco boxes - *91-92*	NA	450
W3006/7	same packed in 2 coach boxes - *92*	NA	500
W3006/7A	**3051 (88+89)** 2-car set, 246 made - *80-83*	380	575
W3006/7A	same packed in 2 coach boxes - *92*	NA	500
W3006/7A	**3051 (90+89)** 2-car set in 2 loco boxes, 150 years 1841-1991, Ltd Edn 40 - *91-92*	500	750

L17.   Former Hornby Dublo EMU

W3008/9	**65320** BRc maroon - *not made*	NA	NA
W3010/11	**S66238?** BRc green - *not made*	NA	NA

COACHES

The Wrenn range of coaches was limited to those that could be produced from the former Hornby-Dublo tools for the Pullman cars. Those produced included some impossible liveries namely those of LMS and the Southern Railway.

In the mid 1980s detailing changed to tampo printing and at this time the coat-of-arms on the brown and cream Pullmans changed to full colour.

There had been the intention to produce come of the tinplate coaches and the Stove was even illustrated in one catalogue but these were not proceeded with.

Cat.No.	Company, Number, Colour, Date	£	£

C1a. Pullman Cars (ex-Hornby Dublo)

These were based on 1928 vehicles built for LNER use. The prototypes were transferred to steam-hauled services on the Southern Region in the 1950s. bt = brown tables. wt = white tables. White table versions tend to attract a higher price and so it is important to be sure that they have been painted white in the factory.

Pullman car No 87 [C1a]

	Pullman brown+cream		
W6001	No 73 2nd bt - 77-86	20	30
W6001	No 73 2nd wt c560 made - 86-92	60	75
W6001C	No.83 parlour car Ltd Edn 350 - 91-92?	55	80
W6001AG	'Agatha' parlour c600 made wt - 86-92	80	125
W6001S	'Sheila' parlour c150 made wt - 91-92	85	160
W6001U	'Ursula' parlour c110 made wt - 90-91	95	175
W6002	'Aries' 1st bt - 79-86	20	30
W6002	'Aries' 1st wt c570 made - 86-92	60	75
W6002B	'Belinda' 1st kitchen 150 made wt - 91-92	105	160
W6102E	'Evadne' 1st kitchen wt Ltd Edn 84 sold - 90	150	225
W6002E	'Evadne' 1st kitchen wt * 6 sold - 92	150	400
W6102C	No.83 parlour wt Ltd Edn 88 sold - 90	70	225
W6001C	No.83 parlour wt * 13 sold - 92	70	350
W6002C	'Carina' 1st kitchen 100 made wt - 91-92	125	185
	Brighton Belle brown+cream		
W6001A	No.87 parlour 3052 c330 made bt - 82-86	35	50
W6001A	No.87 parlour 3052 c500 made wt - 86-92	60	80
W6001/B	No.86 parlour 3051 bt - 83-86	50	75
W6001/B	No.86 parlour 3051 wt - 86-92	70	100
W6002A	'Audrey' 1st 3052 bt - 79-86	30	50
W6002A	'Audrey' 1st 3052 c650 made wt - 86-92	60	80
W6002A	'Vera' 1st 3052 bt - 79-81	30	50
W6002V	'Vera' 1st 3052 c360 made bt - 81-86	30	60
W6002V	'Vera' 1st 3052 c600 made wt - 86-92	85	110
W6002/D	'Doris' 1st 3051 c270 made bt - 82-86	90	130
W6002/D	'Doris' 1st 3051 c460 made wt - 86-92	85	120
W6002/H	'Hazel' 1st 3051 c230 made bt - 82-86	90	130
W6002/H	'Hazel' 1st 3051 c500 made wt - 86-92	85	120
	Golden Arrow brown+cream		
W6012	'Pegasus' (+ alternative name transfers) 1st c750 made bt - 82-86	25	85
W6012	'Pegasus' (+ alternative name transfers) 1st c325 made wt - 86-92	40	135
-	'Perseus' transfer on the above - 86-84	30	NA
-	'Phoenix' transfer on the above - 86-84	30	NA
-	'Cygnus' transfer on the above - 86-84	30	NA
W6012A	'Cecilia' 1st 400 made wt - 85-92	35	125
W6012B	'Aries' 1st 270 made wt - 86-92	35	160
W6012C	'Cygnus' 1st parlour c100 made wt - 91-92	130	200
W6105P	'Phoenix' Ltd Edn 60 - 02	150	175
	BR blue+grey		
W6004	S302S 2nd wt - 76-81, 87-92	25	35
	as above but no number **	NPG	NPG
	Brighton Belle blue+grey		
W6004A	S287S parlour car wt - 76-81, 85-92	35	50
W6004A	S302S parlour car wt - 76-92	100	150
W6005A	S280S 1st wt - 79-81, 90-92	45	70
W6005A	S284S 1st wt - 79-81, 90-92	45	70
	Golden Arrow blue+grey		
W6005	S301S 1st wt - 79-80, 90-92	35	50
W6005	S280S 1st wt - 79-80, 90-92	100	150

	Non-Authentic Liveries		
W6007	SR 2523 green 2nd wt - 78-84	35	50
W6008	SR 1245 green 1st wt - 78-84	35	50
W6010	LMS 3459 red 2nd class wt - 78-84	30	45
W6011	LMS 1046 red 1st class wt - 78-84	30	45

* These were limited edition coaches which did not sell and so were re-boxed and sold as non-limited editions. ** Possibly made from unfinished body at end of production.

C1b. Pullman Brake 2nd Cars (ex-Hornby Dublo)

These were based on 1928 vehicles built for LNER use. The prototypes were transferred to steam-hauled services on the Southern Region in the 1950s. bt = brown tables. wt = white tables. White table versions tend to attract a higher price and so it is important to be sure that they have been painted white in the factory.

	Pullman brown+cream		
W6000	**Pullman** No 77 bt - 72-86	20	30
W6000	**Pullman** No 77 wt c600 made - 86-92	45	60
W6000A	**Pullman** No 79 390 made wt - 88-?	NPG	NPG
W6003	**BR** S308S blue+grey wt - 76-80, 90-92	25	35
	as above but no number	NPG	NPG
W6006	**SR** 1708 green wt - 78-84	35	50
W6009	**LMS** 2370 red wt - 78-84	30	45

C2. Former Hornby Dublo Super Detail Coaches

W6006	**BR** maroon+cream corr comp - not made	NA	NA
W6007	**BR** maroon+cream corr brk 2nd - not made	NA	NA
W6008	**BR** maroon corridor comp - not made	NA	NA
W6009	**BR** maroon corridor brake 2nd - not made	NA	NA
W6010	**BR** green suburban brake 2nd - not made	NA	NA
W6011	**BR** green suburban comp - not made	NA	NA
W6012	**BR** maroon suburban brake 2nd - not made	NA	NA
W6013	**BR** maroon suburban comp - not made	NA	NA
W5014	**BR** maroon M32598 stove 6-wheel brake - not made	NA	NA

WAGONS

A large range of wagons was produced and these may be quickly distinguished from Hornby-Dublo ones by their tension-lock couplings.

Special Edition wagon bodies released through the Wrenn Railways Collectors Club were supplied by Dapol and appear in the Dapol wagon listing.

Great care should be taken in buying supposedly rare models as they may have been assembled in the Dapol factory from leftover parts or by others.

Cat.No.	Company, Number, Colour, Date	£	£

W1. Lowmac Machine Wagon (ex-Hornby Dublo)

W4652	**BR** B904631 brown Lowmac WBB dark axle-hangers - 73-92	10	15
W4652	as above but nickel axle-hangers - 82-92	60	85
W4652A	**GW** 43260 grey Loriot dark axle-hangers - 81-90	12	20
W4652A	as above but nickel axle-hangers* - 90-92	60	85
W4652A	**GW** 43260 brown Loriot dark axle-hangers - 81-90	130	200
W4652A	as above but nickel axle-hangers - 90-92	130	200
W4652P	**Auto Distributors** BR brown + Minix Anglia and caravan - 70-79	130	195
W5103	**BR** B904631 brown dark axle hangers + Cement body load 174 made - 89-92	100	145
W5103	**BR** B904631 brown bright axle hangers + Cement body load 98 made - 89-92	115	175

* The last ones made were brown mouldings painted grey.

W2. Low Sided Wagon

W5059	**Auto Spares** 115 red-brown load of 4 large tyres - 80	20	30
W5060	**BR** B459325 grey - 80-81	25	35

Wrenn

W3. 5-Plank Open Wagon (ex-Hornby Dublo)

W4635P	**Higgs** 85 beige + coal, cream and thick red letters - *70-71*	30	45
W4635P	same with white and thin red letters - *70-71*	30	45
W4635P	**Higgs** 85 dark brown + coal - *69-71*	20	30
W4635P	**Higgs** 85 dark grey + coal - *69-71*	12	18
W4635P	**Higgs** 85 light grey + coal - *69-85, 92*	12	18
W4635P	**Higgs** 85 grey + coal, also W4635 - *73-80*	12	18
W4635P	**Higgs** 85 blue-green + coal - *70-80*	30	45
W4660P	**Twining** 95 beige - *68-71*	30	45
W4660P	**Twining** 95 red-brown - *68-72**	10	15
W5075	**Twining** 95 dark brown shaded black letters + coal 759 made *82-92*	25	40
W5075	as above but shading missing ** - *82-92*	50	75
W5000	**J.Bly** 15 dark green + coal - *71-74, 86-92*	13	20
W5008	**S.Harris** 14 black + coal - *71-92*	13	20
W5032	**LMS** 314159 red + white load - *?*	NPG	NPG
W5032	**LMS** 24361 red + white load - *74-77*	10	15
W5032	**LMS** 24361 orange-red + black load - *74-77*	12	18
W5043	**Ayr Co-op** 67 black - *77-87*	12	17
W5048	**Cranston** 347 red-brown + coal - *78-83*	12	17
W5067	**Amos Benbow** 3 grey + coal - *81-90*	20	30
W?	**BR** B478038 grey - *?*	NPG	NPG
W5069	**British Soda** 14 red + grey load 679 made - *82-88*	25	40
W5069	as above but white load** - *89-92*	35	50
W5074	**Bassetts** 77 painted dark grey + coal 696 made - *82-88*	25	40
W5500	**Barnsley Collieries** 350 brown + load Ltd Edn 314 - *89-91*	50	80
W5109	overrun of W5500 (above) - *92*	140	225
W5096	**A Bramley** 6 brown + coal 413 made- *88-92*	40	60
W5096	As above but black shading missing** - *92*	65	95
W5097	**Webster** 47 grey 378 made - *88-92*	65	70
W5107	**Consolidated Fisheries** 76 grey + load 140 made - *91-92*	100	140

* pre-production model seen at 1968 Toy Fair. **production figures included in the figure above.

5-plank open wagon [W3]

W4. High-Sided Wagon
This was the body of the gunpowder van without a roof.

W5106	**Hughes Minerals** 29 grey 129 made - *91-92*	110	170

W5. Steel Sided Wagon (ex-Hornby Dublo)
Tool bought in 1972.

W4660	**Twining** B486865 brown - *not made*	NA	NA
W5034	**NTG** B486863 yellow + load - *74-79*	12	18
W5034	**NTG** B486863 buff + load - *73-80*	13	20
W5034	as above with white edged transfers - *80*	30	45
W4640	**BR** B466865 brown - *73-92*	10	15
W4640	**BR** B466865 red-brown - *73-92*	10	15
W4640	**BR** B466865 buff - *73-80*	35	50
W5073	**BAC** 4253 red-brown 461 made - *82-92*	40	60

W6. 16T Mineral Wagon (ex-Hornby Dublo)
Tool bought in 1972.

W4655	**BR** B54884 grey - *78-92*	8	13
W4655L	**BR** B54884 grey + coal - *79-82*	15	25
W4655A	**BR** B550200 brown* - *81-88*	15	25
W4655A	**BR** B54884 brown 260 made - *88-92*	60	90
W5029	**GW** 110265 dark grey - *74-78*	10	16
W5029L	**GW** 110265 dark grey + mineral load - *74-79*	13	20
W5029	**GW** 110265 light grey - *87-88*	55	85
W5026	**Park Ward** 7 brown - *74-80, 87*	10	15
W5051	**Shell** silver - *78-79*	16	25
W5051A	**Esso** blue or silver 357 made - *88-89*	50	75

* Early examples were grey mouldings painted brown.

W7. 21T Hopper Wagon (ex-Hornby Dublo)
Tools bought in 1972.

W4644	**BR** B413021 light grey - *81-92*	35	50
W4644	**BR** B413021 dark grey - *81-92*	60	95
W4644	**BR** B414029 light grey - *73,78-92*	10	15
W4644L	**BR** B414029 light grey + load - *78-83*	13	20
W5035	**Simpson** 72 light grey - *not made*	NA	NA
W5036	**Hoveringham** 230 red-brown - *83*	10	16
W5036	as above but no number - *80-86*	35	50
W5035	**NCB** 128 dark grey + load - *86-92*	10	16
W5056	**Tarmac** M82 beige - *79-92*	16	25
W5068	**Charringtons** B421818K grey 696 made - *82-90*	35	50
W5079	**NE** 174369 dark grey 679 made - *83-92*	30	45
W5079	**NE** 174369 light grey * - *83-92*	40	65
W5502	**Weaver Transport** 152 brown + load Ltd Edn 277 - *89-91*	60	90
W5111	overrun of W5502 (above) - *92*	140	225
W5082	**Sykes** 7 light grey 451 made - *87-90*	45	70
W5088	**British Gas** 142 dark grey 488 made - *87-92*	40	65
W5098	**British Steel** 28 brown 358 made - *88-92*	50	75

* production figures included in the figure above.

W8a. Hopper Wagon (grain wagon body)

W5078	**Wilton Quarry** 95 red-brown + load - *not made*	NA	NA

W8b. Grain Wagon (ex-Hornby Dublo)
Tools bought in 1972.

W4625	**BR** B885040 light grey - *73-92*	8	13
W5020	**Kelloggs** B885040 grey - *74-76*	12	18
W5020	as above but no numbers - *74-84*	12	18
W5045	**Quaker Oats** red-brown - *77-80*	13	20
W5071	**Bass Charrington** 24 maroon 296 made - *82-83*	45	70

W9a. Ore Wagon (Presflo body)
This was the Presflo without its top and is thought to be fictitious.

W4600P	**Clay Cross** light grey, grey board - *69-70*	17	25
W4600P	as above but orange board - *70-*	12	18
W5503	**Clay Cross** black Ltd Edn 175 - *90-91*	45	95
W5112	overrun of W5530 (above) - *92*	140	225
W5006	**Southdown** 17 grey, green board + chalk load - *71-80, 88-90*	17	25
W5006	same but green label on grey boards - *71-82*	10	15
W5006	same but yellow label 200 made - *88*	50	75
W5006	**Southdown** 17 blue + chalk - *?*	NPG	NPG
W5015	**Hinchley** 14 blue + chalk - *74-80*	13	20
W5015	**Hinchley** 14 grey + chalk - *?*	NPG	NPG
W5017	**Pycroft Granite** black, black boards + granite load - *74-83*	13	20
W5017	**Pycroft Granite** light green, green boards + granite load - *73-80*	12	17
W5025	**Wm.Carter** 7 black + gravel - *74-81*	12	18

W9b. Presflo Wagon (ex-Hornby Dublo)
YbG = yellow background on grey plastic boards, YbB = yellow background on blue plastic boards, BbB = blue background on blue plastic boards,

W4626P	**Blue Circle** dark grey YbG - *68-71*	13	20

W4626P	as above but grey BbB - *70-71*	17	25
W4626P	as above but pale grey YbG - *68-69*	17	25
W4626P	as above but dark blue-green YbB - *68-69*	17	25
W4626P	as above but dark blue BbB - *70-71*	22	35
W5016	**Blue Circle** pale yellow paper labels - *73-80*	12	17
W5016	as above but darker colours on boards	12	17
W5016	**Blue Circle** dark yellow paper labels - *74-82*	12	18
W5016	**Blue Circle** painted bright yellow with tampo detail 251 made - *90-92*	40	60
W5072	**Blue Circle** grey Bulk Loaded - *82-89*	20	30
W5072	**Blue Circle** bright yellow Bulk Loaded - *90-92*	40	60
W4627P	**Cerebos Salt** blue-black also W4627 - *68-71**	27	40
W4626P	as above but dark blue-green	20	30
W4626P	as above but grey	17	25
W5021	**Cerebos Salt** red - *74-79*	10	16
W5021	as above but tampo printed - *86-92*	30	45
W5021	**Cerebos Salt** red - *74-79*	10	16
W5005	**Tunnel Bulk** grey, red board paper label - *71-92*	10	15
W5005	the same tampo printed - *85-92*	35	50
W5005	**Tunnel Bulk** red - *?*	NPG	NPG
W5080	**Rugby** 17 grey - *85-92*	22	37
W5080	**Rugby** 17 light grey - *85-92*	37	50
W5081	**BR** 72 brown Presflo - *86-92*	22	35
W5005X	grey 20T 12-17 - *72-76*	17	25
W5005X	same but no markings at all - *72-76*	20	30
W5084	**Bulk Cement** 52 red-brown c550 made - *87-92*	35	50
W5084	**Bulk Cement** 52 buff c20 made - *92*	115	175
W5092	**Ready Mix** 68 grey 413 made - *88-91*	40	60

* pre-production model seen at 1968 Toy Fair.

Presflo wagon - Cerebos Salt [W9b]

W10.   Prestwin Silo Wagon (ex-Hornby Dublo)

W4658	**Fisons** B873000 red-brown - *71-84*	9	13
W4658X	**BR** B873000 brown 466 made - *87-92*	40	60

Prestwin silo wagon [W10]

W11.   Salt Van (ex-Hornby Dublo)

This was the old salt wagon with a pitched roof.

W4665P	**Saxa Salt** 248 dark orange - *68-92*	10	15

W4665P	**Saxa Salt** 248 light orange - *68-71*	10	15
W4665P	**Saxa Salt** 248 pale lemon - *73-81*	10	15
W4665P	**Saxa Salt** 248 pale lemon (darker red) - *73-80*	10	15
W4666	**Sifta** Table Salt 125 blue - *71-77*	13	20
W4666	as above but bright blue - *73-77*	30	45
W5018	**Star** Salt 105 red, white letters - *74-84*	10	15
W5018	**Star** Salt 105 red, black letters - *74-80*	17	25
W5024	**Jas. Colman** 15 pale green, white lettering - *74-79*	40	60
W5024	same with black lettering - *74-79*	13	20
W5024	**Jas. Colman** 15 yellow - *73-80*	12	18
W5024	**Jas. Colman** 15 pale yellow - *73-80*	30	45
W5070	**DCL** 87 blue mouldings painted grey 388 made - *82-83*	30	45
W5070	**DCL** 87 grey mouldings 200 made - *84-90*	30	45
W5101	**ICI** Bulk Salt 25 light grey 377 made - *89-91*	48	70
W5101	same but brown body painted grey* - *91-92*	48	70

* production figures included in the above figure.

W12.   Short Tank Wagon

W5039	**Esso** 3300 dark blue green star and writing - *80-90*	20	30
W5039	as above but yellow star and writing - *80-90*	20	30
W5040	**Shell** yellow small star 896 made - *80-90*	20	30
W5040	as above but large star * - *80-90*	30	45
W5040	as above but with white background to the star * - *90-92*	50	75
W5040	**Shell** yellow, white missing from printing - *80-86*	NPG	NPG
W5041	**Mobil** red - *80-92*	22	35
W5042	**Esso** silver large emblems - *80-81*	20	30
W5042	as above small emblems 66 made - *91-92*	80	125
W5061	**Shell** BP Motor Spirit 1265 stone - *80-84*	30	45
W5062	**Royal Daylight** black - *81-92*	26	40
W5076	**Power Ethyl** green 576 made - *82-91*	42	65
W5077	**United Molasses** 18 purple-brown 487 made - *82-91*	45	70
W5501	**British Sugar** 23 red Ltd Edn 284 - *89-91*	55	80
W5110	overrun of W5501 (above) - *92*	140	225
W5093	**ICI** Chlorine 163 black 520 made - *88-92*	40	60
W5104	**Bulk Flour** 20 white 187 made - *90-92*	65	100

* production figures included in the figure quoted above.

W13.   6-Wheel Tank Wagon (ex-Hornby Dublo)

W4657	**UD** white also W4657P - *70-92*	12	18
W5003	**Guinness** silver paper label - *71-81*	12	18
W5003	same tampo printed - *90-92*	80	125
W5013	**St Ivel** white+orange - *73-83*	12	18
W5013	**St Ivel** white+red-brown - *80-86*	22	35
W5013	**St Ivel** Gold white - *91-92*	80	125
W5023	**Milk Marketing Board** blue - *74-92*	17	22
W5066	**Skol Lager** red 675 made - *81-82*	37	55
W5044	**Double Diamond** red-brown - *77-78*	18	28
W5086	**Co-op** 172 white 650 made - *87-92*	40	60
W5091	**Unigate** 220 white 427 made - *88-92*	50	80
W5095	**Express Dairies** 50 blue 469 made - *88-92*	50	80

UD 6-wheel tank wagon [W13]

Wrenn

W14. Gunpowder Van (ex-Hornby Dublo)

W4313	**BR** B887002 brown - *68?*	37	55
W4313P	**Standard Fireworks** B887002 brown - *68-70**	40	60
W4313	as above but no letter shading	50	75
W4313	as above but cream lettered name	50	75
W4313	as above but name missing	20	30
W4313P	**Standard Fireworks** B887002 dark green - *68*	22	35
W5009	**BSA** B887002 red brown - *71-75*	12	17
W5009	**BSA** B887002 brown - *71-75*	12	17
W5057	**GW** W105780 black red X - *79-92*	16	25
W5102	**BR** B887002 brown 192 made - *90-91*	100	150
W5102	**BR** W105780 brown only about 5 made - *91*	335	500

* pre-production model seen at 1968 Toy Fair.

W15. Cattle Wagon (ex-Hornby Dublo)

Tools bought in 1972.

W4630	**BR** B893344 brown - *71-92*	10	15
W4630A	**GW** 103240 grey - *87-92*	26	40
W5504	**Manor Farm** brown 50 Ltd Edn 226 - *90-91*	60	95
W5113	overrun of W5504 (above) - *92*	140	225

W16. BR Standard Horse Box (ex-Hornby Dublo)

W4315P	**Roydon Stables** E96435 SR green Foxhunter Championships Oct 6-11 Wembley - *70-71, 74-90*	22	35
W4315P	same but lime green label	35	50
W4315	**Roydon Stables** E96435 green Foxhunter Championships - *81-90*	60	90
W4315X	**BR** E96435 green Foxhunter Championships 193 made - *90-92*	80	125
W4315X	same but no poster* - *90-92*	80	125
W4316	**BR** E96435 maroon no label - *72-90*	26	40
W5002	**Selsdon Stables** E96435 maroon Foxhunter Championships Oct 6-11 Wembley - *71-74*	35	50

* The number made is included in the figure above.

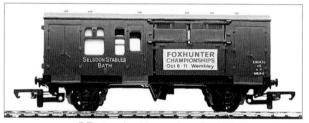

BR standard horse box [W16]

W17. 8T Fruit Van

This model represents one of 130 cattle vans converted to fruit vans by the GWR in 1939.

W5058	**GW** 38200 light grey - *80-92*	16	25
W5058	**GW** 38200 dark grey - *80-92*	22	35
W5083	**BR** B872181 brown 680 made - *86-92*	28	40
W5083A	**BR** B872181 grey 25 made - *91-92*	130	200

W18. Passenger Fruit Van (ex-Hornby Dublo)

W4305P	**Babycham** maroon* W2910 - *70-74, 79-80*	20	30
W4305P	as above but paper labels for advert	18	25
W4305X	**BR** W2910 maroon (shades) - *74-92*	10	15
W4305X	as above but no numbers	30	45
W5049	**GW** (yellow) 27614 dark brown - *78-86*	12	18
W5049	**GW** (white) 27614 dark brown - *88-92*	60	95
W5055	**BR** W28720 blue - *79-92*	13	20
W5108	**BR** B517112 grey 75 made - *91-92*	120	175

* Roof colour varies.

W19. Yellow Spot Banana Van (ex-Hornby Dublo)

W4301P	**Fyffes** B881867 brown also W4301 - *68-71**	10	15

W4301P	**Fyffes** B881867 green - *68-*	12	18
W5022	**Fyffes** B881867 pale yellow - *73-80*	10	15
W5022-	**Fyffes** B881867 yellow - *73-80*	10	15
W5022	**Fyffes** B881867 dark yellow - *86-92*	30	45
W5022	**Fyffes** B87023 yellow - *74-79, 86-88*	NPG	NPG
W5022A	**Fyffes** B881867 brown 426 made - *87-90*	42	65
W5007	**Geest** B881867 brown - *71-88*	12	18
W5007	as above but khaki spot - *71-80*	13	20
W5007	as above but no yellow spot - *71-80*	10	15
W5007	**Geest** B881902 brown - *90-92*	60	95
W5007A	**Geest** B881902 grey 171 made - *90-92*	80	125
W5007X	**BR** B881867 brown - *81-92*	50	75
W5007X	**BR** B881902 brown no yellow spot - *81-92*	50	75
W5028	**NE** 159611 grey - *74-76*	12	18
W5063	**Tropical Fruits** M40 grey - *80-84*	20	30
W5105	**Jaffa** B881902 grey 124 made - *91-92*	115	175

* pre-production model seen at 1968 Toy Fair.

Yellow spot banana van [W19]

W20. Ventilated Van (ex-Hornby Dublo)

?	**Cinzano** white displayed at 1968 Toy Fair - *not made*	NA	NA
W4318	**Walls** DE545523 red - *68-72**	13	20
W4318P/A	**Peak Freans** DE545533 brown - *71-90*	30	45
W4318	**Peak Freans** B757051 brown - *81*	40	60
W4318P/A	**Peak Freans** 757051 brown - *73-80*	13	20
W4318P/A	**Peak Freans** DE545523 brown - *68-72**	12	18
W4318P/A	**Peak Freans** DE545523 dark grey - *68-*	12	18
W4318P/A	**Peak Freans** DE545533 dark grey - *70-*	30	45
W4318P/A	as above but blue-grey *70-*	30	45
W4318P/A	**Peak Freans** B757051 grey - *?*	NPG	NPG
W4318X	**BR** B757051 brown also W5011X - *73-92*	10	15
W4318X	**BR** 57 brown - *80-92*	35	50
W4318X	**BR** B545523 brown - *80-92*	40	55
W4318X	**BR** DE545533 bright red - *?*	NPG	NPG
W5011X	**BR** DE545523 red - *73-75*	18	27
W5011X	**BR** B757051 bright red - *?*	NPG	NPG
W5007X	**BR** B881902 brown - *81-92*	50	75
W5007X	**BR** B881867 brown - *81-92*	50	75
W5094	**BR** W145207 grey 453 made - *89-92*	40	60
W5094	**BR** W145207 painted grey on a red moulding - *92*	65	100
W4325P	**OXO** DE545533 white - *68-72**	12	18
W4325P	same but no running no. - *?*	40	55
W4325P	**OXO** DE545523 white - *70-**	26	40
W5004	**Dunlop** DE545543 yellow - *71-81*	13	20
W5004	**Dunlop** DE545523 dark yellow - *73-84*	12	18
W5004	**Dunlop** DE545523 dark yellow slogan reversed - *73-80*	26	40
W5004	**Dunlop** B757051 pale yellow - *73-80*	10	15
W5004	**Dunlop** B757051 yellow - *73-80*	10	15
W5010	**Robertson's** B757051 light grey, white roof - *73-80*	12	18
W5010	same with grey roof - *73-80*	30	45
W5010	**Robertson's** B757051 blue-grey, grey roof - *71-83*	28	40
W5010	**Robertson's** B757051 dark grey - *73-80*	12	18
W5010	**Robertson's** B757051 brown - *73-80*	20	30
W5010	**Robertson's** 57 brown - *73-80*	20	30

W5010	**Robertson's** B545533 dark brown - ?	NPG	NPG
W5011	**Watney's** B757051 red - 73-77	11	17
W5011	**Watney's** B881867 red - ?	NPG	NPG
W5030	**LMS** 59673 red - 74-76	12	18
W5033	**SR** 41596 dark brown - 74-81	12	18
W5046	**Walls** Bacon 57 dark brown - 78-84	30	45
W5046	**Walls** Bacon B757051 red-brown - 78-83	17	25
W5046	**Walls** Bacon DE545523 brown - 78-83	NPG	NPG
W5047	**Bisto** 25 beige - 77-84	13	20
W5047	**Bisto** 25 dark brown - 87-88	80	120
W5054	**Decca** DE545543 yellow - 79-80	28	40
W5100	**Wrenn Railways** W145207 grey 532 made - 89-92	55	85
W5100A	**Wrenn Railways** W145207 brown 89 made - 90-92	100	150

* pre-production model seen at 1968 Toy Fair.

W21. SR Utility Van (ex-Hornby Dublo)

W4323P	**SR** S2380S green yellow letters - 70-90	13	20
W4323P	as above but white letters - 70-90	35	50
W4323	**SR** S2371S green - 91	80	125
W4323	**BR** S2380S green no lettering - 80-90	35	50
W4324	**BR** S2380S blue - 73-90	12	17
W4324	**BR** S2371S blue - 91-92	115	175
W5053	**BR** E37232 brown - 79-90	28	40
W5085	**LMS** M527071 maroon 543 made - 86-89	42	65

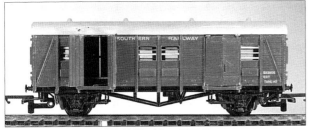

SR Utility Van [W21]

W22. 6T Mica B Refrigerator Van (ex-Hornby Dublo)

W4320P	**Eskimo** W59850 white also W4320 - 68-81*	10	15
W4320X	**BR** W59850 white Mica B - 73-75	80	125
W5019	**GW** 59828 white Mica B - 74-92	10	15
W5019X	**BR** W145207 white Mica B c200 made - 88-92	80	125
W5019X	**BR** W59850 white Mica B 96 made - 87	120	175
W5027	**Carr & Co** pale green W59850 - 73-90	10	16
W5052	**Young's** 78 white - 79-92	13	20
W5065	**Birds Eye** 312 blue - 80-90	20	30
W5089	**BR** 105721 white 512 made- 87-92	40	60

* pre-production model seen at 1968 Toy Fair.

W23. Blue Spot Fish Van/Parcels Van
(ex-Hornby Dublo)

W4300P	**Findus** E87231 white also W4300 - 69-71	12	18
W5001	**Ross** E87231 cream or white - 72-92	10	15
W5012	**BRe** E87003 blue Express Parcels - 73-89	10	14
W5001X	**BR** E87231 white Insulfish - 73-86	10	15
W5001X	**BR** E87502 white Insulfish - 88-91	45	70
W5050	**North Sea Fish** E67840 blue - 78-81	17	25
W5064	**BRe** BRT E67840 beige - 80-84	22	35
W5087	**Red Star** E87003 blue 580 made - 87-92	40	60

W24. WR Goods Brake Van (ex-Hornby Dublo)
Tools bought in 1972. Mould faulty listed 1974-77

W4312	**BR** W35247 brown - *not made*	NA	NA
W5037	**GW** 17575 grey - *not made*	NA	NA

W25. LMS Goods Brake Van (ex-Hornby Dublo)

W4311P	**LMS** M730973 brown* also W4311- 69-90	10	15
W4311X	**BR** M730973 brown - 78-90	13	20

W4311X	**BR** M730973 grey - ?	13	20
W5090	**BR** B950127 grey 338 made - 88-92	55	80
W5090	**BR** M730012 grey - 88-94	13	20

* Roof colour varies.

W26a. BR Standard Goods Brake Van
(ex-Hornby Dublo)
Tools bought in 1972.

W4310	**BR** B950350 grey - 70-	10	15
W4310	**BR** B950350 brown - 73-92	NPG	NPG
W4310	**BR** B932103 brown - 81-91	12	18
W5038	**SR** 32831 dark brown - 74-80	13	20

W26b. BR Standard Goods Brake Van
(short wheel base) (ex-Hornby Dublo)

W5031	**NE** 128105 light grey - 74-77	12	18
W5099	**BR** B950231 brown 263 made - 89-92	60	90
W5099A	**BR** B932103 grey 321 made - 89-92	60	95

Wrenn wagons sold after 1993 were produced by Dapol in their factory in Llangollen and will be found in the Dapol section of this catalogue. Those numbered with a 'WR1' prefix were sold in Wrenn boxes but all others had Dapol packaging.

ACCESSORIES

Of particular interest to collectors are the diesel horn sets made by Wrenn in the late 1960s. These contained either a Hymek or a Class 37 diesel locomotive, supplied by Rovex from their Tri-ang Hornby range, and a Wrenn horn sound unit. One sold at auction in 1998 for £260.

SETS

Initially Wrenn made up train sets to use up the remnant stocks of Hornby-Dublo that they acquired in the mid '60s. After that there were three Wrenn sets numbered 001 to 003. The first two sell at around £250 each while 003 could cost you about twice that.

Code 3 Models

BACKGROUND

A Code 3 model is one that has been finished (or, as is usually the case, refinished) outside the factory by a secondary 'manufacturer'. These are often retailers who buy a quantity of a certain model and re-release them in modified form. To count as a Code 3, a model has to have been produced in the modified form in quantity and to a common specification. This means that one-off modifications do not count. Batches of 50 or more are usual. These should have a numbered certificate to authenticate them and to indicate how many of them were modified.

Code 3 models have their own niche market.

This subject is likely to be a minefield for us to list as there has been little recording of Code 3 models until recent times. Consequently, there may be many in existence that we should be listing but of which we know nothing. Obviously, numbered certificates with models are good evidence that a model should be included. Care, however, should be taken not to assume that the maximum production figure quoted (the figure just before the dates in each entry) was necessarily achieved. As Code 3 models were/are often produced on demand it is possible that the actual number made fell short of the set target.

EX- HORNBY MODELS

Cat.No.	Number, Company, Colour, Dates	£	£

The Model Centre

All have etched brass nameplates and a numbered certificate.

TH1. Schools Class 4-4-0

Some of the Schools Class locomotives, besides new names and numbers, have been fitted with large chimneys for the Lemaitre exhaust (lc). dm = darkened metalwork.

SR Black			
TMC6	**904 'Lancing'** 250 - *99-02*	85	100
TMC2	**922 'Marlborough'** 50 - *99*	100	100
TMC136	**931 'King's Wimbledon'** lc 100 - *00-02*	NPG	100
TMC137	**933 'King's Canterbury'** lc 100 - *00-02*	NPG	100
SR Olive Green			
TMC303	**938 'St Olaves'** 250 - *02*	NPG	100
SR Malachite Green			
TMC102	**901 'Winchester'** dm lc 100 - *00-02*	NPG	100
TMC184	**903 'Charterhouse'** 250 - *01-02*	NPG	100
TMC8	**907 'Dulwich'** lc dm 250 - *00-02*	85	100
TMC105	**909 'St.Paul's'** dm lc 100 - *00-02*	NPG	100
TMC181	**911 'Dover'** 250 - *01-02*	NPG	100
TMC140	**913 'Christ's Hospital'** lc 250 - *00-02*	NPG	100
TMC106	**915 'Brighton'** dm lc 100 - *00-02*	NPG	100
TMC220	**916 'Whitgift'** dm 250 - *01-02*	NPG	100
TMC104	**920 'Rugby'** dm lc 100 - *00-02*	NPG	100
TMC30	**926 'Repton'** 250 - *00-02*	NPG	100
TMC35	**930 'Radley'** dm lc 250 - *00-02*	NPG	100
TMC330	**932 'Blundells'** 250 - *02*	NPG	100
TMC103	**933 'King's Canterbury'** dm lc 100 - *00-02*	NPG	100
TMC221	**934 'St Lawrence'** dm lc 250 - *01-02*	NPG	100
TMC145	**937 'Epsom'** lc 100 - *00-02*	NPG	100
TMC20	**938 'St.Olave's'** dm lc 250 - *00-02*	NPG	100
BR Brunswick Green			
TMC178	**30901 'Winchester'** BRc dm lc 250 - *01-02*	NPG	100
TMC182	**30904 'St Paul's'** BRc dm lc 250 - *01-02*	NPG	100
TMC225	**30905 'Tonbridge'** BRc 250 - *01-02*	NPG	100
TMC110	**30906 'Sherbourne'** BRc dm 100 - *00-02*	NPG	100
TMC196	**30907 'Dulwich'** BRc dm lc 250 - *01-02*	NPG	100
TMC111	**30910 'Merchant Taylors'** BRc dm 100 -	NPG	100

	00-02		
TMC108	**30911 'Dover'** BRc dm 100 - *00-02*	NPG	100
TMC109	**30913 'Christ's Hospital'** BRc dm - *00-02*	NPG	100
TMC183	**30915 'Brighton'** BRc dm lc 250 - *01-02*	NPG	100
TMC107	**30916 'Whitgift'** BRc dm 100 - *00-02*	NPG	100
TMC177	**30920 'Rugby'** BRc dm lc 250 - *01-02*	NPG	100
TMC123	**30926 'Repton'** BRc dm - *00-02*	NPG	100
TMC179	**30930 'Radley'** BRc dm lc 250 - *01-02*	NPG	100
TMC222	**30931 'Kings Wimbledon'** BRc lc 250 - *01-02*	NPG	100
TMC138	**30933 'King's Canterbury'** BRc dm lc 250 - *00-02*	NPG	100
TMC142	**30937 'Epsom'** BRc dm lc 250 - *00-02*	NPG	100
TMC144	**30938 'St Olaves'** BRc dm lc 250 - *01-02*	NPG	100
BR Black			
TMC36	**30900 'Eton'** BRb or BRc lc 250 - *00-02*	NPG	100
TMC91	**30913 'Christ's Hospital'** BRb 250 - *00-02*	NPG	100
TMC143	**30932 'Blundells'** BRb 100 - *00-02*	NPG	100
TMC37	**30933 'King's Canterbury'** BRb 250 - *00-02*	NPG	100
TMC7	**30935 'Sevenoaks'** BRb 250 - *99-02*	80	100
TMC141	**30938 'St Olave's'** BRb 250 - *00-02*	NPG	100

Hornby Schools class 'Marlborough' in SR black [TH1]

TH2. Castle Class 4-6-0

Darkened metalwork.

	Limited to 250 of Each		
	BRb or BRc Brunswick Green		
TMC61	**5014 'Goodrich Castle'** - *00-02*	NPG	95
TMC62	**5087 'Tintern Abbey'** - *00-02*	NPG	95
TMC130	**7037 'Swindon'** - *01-02*	NPG	95

TH3. King Class 4-6-0

The models used were R2119 'King Henry VII' (X1).

	Limited to 250 of Each		
TMC60	**6000 'King George V'** GWR grn - *00*	NPG	95
TMC176	**6008 'King James II'** GWR grn - *00*	NPG	95

TH4. Princess Royal Class 4-6-2

We understand that R2070 'Princess Louise' was used for early models marked X1 while for the rest super detailed models were used.

	Limited to 250 of each		
	LMS Crimson Lake		
TMC331	**6200 'The Princess Royal'** - *02*	NPG	100
TMC332	**6201 'Princess Elizabeth'** - *02*	NPG	100
TMC333	**6203 'Princess Margaret Rose'** - *02*	NPG	100
TMC334	**6204 'Princess Louise'** - *02*	NPG	100
TMC335	**6205 'Princess Victoria'** - *02*	NPG	100
TMC336	**6206 'Princess Mary Louise'** - *02*	NPG	100
TMC337	**6207 'Princess Arthur of Connaught'** - *02*	NPG	100
TMC338	**6208 'Princess Helena Victoria'** - *02*	NPG	100
TMC339	**6209 'Princess Beatrice'** - *02*	NPG	100
TMC340	**6210 'Lady Patricia'** - *02*	NPG	100
TMC341	**6211 'Queen Maud'** - *02*	NPG	100
TMC342	**6212 'Duchess of Kent'** - *02*	NPG	100
BR Brunswick Green			
TMC320	**46200 'The Princess Royal'** - *02-03*	NPG	100
TMC321	**46201 ' Princess Elizabeth'** - *02-03*	NPG	100
TMC22A	**46203 'Princess Margaret Rose'** BRb green X1 Ltd Edn - *02*	NPG	100
TMC322	**46204 'Princess Louise'** - *02-03*	NPG	100
TMC323	**46205 'Princess Victoria'** - *02-03*	NPG	100
TMC324	**46206 'Princess Mary Louise'** - *02-03*	NPG	100
TMC129A	**46207 'Princess Arthur of Connaught'** BRb green X1 - *00-03*	NPG	100
TMC325	**46208 'Princess Helena Victoria'** - *02-03*	NPG	100
TMC326	**46209 'Princess Beatrice'** - *02-03*	NPG	100

TMC327	46210 'Lady Patricia' - *02-03*	NPG	100
TMC328	46211 'Queen Maud' - *02-03*	NPG	100
TMC329	46212 'Duchess of Kent' - *02-03*	NPG	100

Hornby 'Duchess of Hamilton' [TH5a]

TH5a. Duchess 4-6-2 (1977 model)

Shed codes were provided to the purchaser's requirements. dc = double chimney.

Limited to 250 of each (except TMC1)
BR Brunswick Green

TMC148	46220 'Coronation' BRc - *00-02*	NPG	90
TMC149	46221 'Queen Elizabeth' BRb or BRc - *00-02*	NPG	90
TMC150	46222 'Queen Mary' BRb or BRc - *00-02*	NPG	90
TMC237	46222 'Queen Mary' BRb dc - *02*	NPG	100
TMC151	46223 'Princess Alice' BRb or BRc - *00-02*	NPG	90
TMC238	46223 'Princess Alice' BRb dc - *02*	NPG	100
TMC152	46224 'Princess Alexandra' BRb or BRc - *00-02*	NPG	90
TMC239	46224 'Princess Alexandra' BRb dc - *02*	NPG	100
TMC240	46227 'Duchess of Devonshire' BRb dc - *02*	NPG	100
TMC1	46229 'Duchess of Hamilton' BRb Ltd Edn 50 - *99*	100	120
TMC153	46235 'City of Birmingham' BRb or BRc - *00-02*	NPG	90
TMC241	46235 'City of Birmingham' BRb dc - *02*	NPG	100
TMC41	46236 'City of Bradford' BRb - *00-02*	NPG	90
TMC42	46237 'City of Bristol' BRc - *00-02*	NPG	90
TMC38	46238 'City of Carlisle' BRb - *00-02*	NPG	90
TMC154	46240 'City of Coventry' BRc - *00-02*	NPG	90
TMC156	46241 'City of Edinburgh' BRc - *00-02*	NPG	90
TMC39	46242 'City of Glasgow' BRc - *00-02*	NPG	90
TMC157	46243 'City of Lancaster' BRc - *00-02*	NPG	90
TMC158	46244 'King George VI' BRc - *00-02*	NPG	90
TMC162	46253 'City of St.Albans' BRb or BRc - *00-02*	NPG	90
TMC242	46254 'City of Stoke on Trent' BRb dc - *02*	NPG	100
TMC163	46255 'City of Hereford' BRb or BRc - *00-02*	NPG	90

BR Maroon

TMC3	46229 'Duchess of Hamilton' BRc - *99-01*	75	90
TMC147	46236 'City of Bradford' BRc - *00-02*	NPG	90
TMC146	46238 'City of Carlisle' BRc - *00-02*	NPG	90
TMC155	46240 'City of Coventry' BRc - *00-02*	NPG	90
TMC159	46244 'King George VI' BRc - *00-02*	NPG	90
TMC45	46245 'City of London' BRc - *00-02*	NPG	90
TMC46	46246 'City of Manchester' BRc - *00-02*	NPG	90
TMC160	46247 'City of Liverpool' BRc - *00-02*	NPG	90
TMC161	46248 'City of Leeds' BRc - *00-02*	NPG	90
TMC49	46249 'City of Sheffield' BRc - *00-02*	NPG	90

TH5b. Duchess 4-6-2 (2001 model)

These are based on the Hornby Super Detail model of 2001. Shed codes were provided to the purchaser's requirements. dc = double chimney. wt = welded tender

Limited to 250 of Each
LMS Maroon

TMC243	6230 'Duchess of Buccleugh' dc - *02*	NPG	100
TMC244	6231 'Duchess of Atholl' dc - *02*	NPG	100
TMC245	6232 'Duchess of Montrose' dc - *02*	NPG	100
TMC246	6233 'Duchess of Sutherland' dc - *02*	NPG	100
TMC247	6234 'Duchess of Abercorn' dc - *02*	NPG	100

LMS Wartime Black

TMC380	6231 'Duchess of Atholl' dc - *02-03*	NPG	120
TMC381	6232 'Duchess of Montrose' dc - *02-03*	NPG	120
TMC382	6249 'City of Sheffield' dc - *02-03*	NPG	120
TMC383	6250 'City of Lichfields' dc - *02-03*	NPG	120
TMC384	6251 'City of Nottingham' dc - *02-03*	NPG	120
TMC385	6252 'City of Leicester' dc - *02-03*	NPG	120

LMS Lined Black
with sloping smokebox top

TMC425	6220 'Coronation' dc - *04*	NPG	110
TMC426	6221 'Queen Elizabeth' dc - *04*	NPG	110
TMC427	6222 'Queen Mary' dc - *04*	NPG	110
TMC428	6223 'Princess Alice' dc - *04*	NPG	110
TMC429	6224 'Princess Alexandra' dc - *04*	NPG	110
TMC430	6225 'Duchess of Gloucester' dc - *04*	NPG	110
TMC431	6227 'Duchess of Devonshire' dc - *04*	NPG	110
TMC432	6228 'Duchess of Rutland' dc - *04*	NPG	110
TMC433	6229 'Duchess of Hamilton' dc - *04*	NPG	110
TMC434	6235 'City of Birmingham' dc - *04*	NPG	110
TMC435	6236 'City of Bradford' dc - *04*	NPG	110
TMC436	6237 'City of Bristol' dc - *04*	NPG	110
TMC437	6238 'City of Carlisle' dc - *04*	NPG	110
TMC438	6239 'City of Chester' dc - *04*	NPG	110
TMC439	6240 'City of Coventry' dc - *04*	NPG	110
TMC440	6241 'City of Edinburgh' dc - *04*	NPG	110
TMC441	6243 'City of Glasgow' dc - *04*	NPG	110
TMC442	6244 'King George VI' dc - *04*	NPG	110
TMC443	6245 'City of London' dc - *04*	NPG	110
TMC444	6246 'City of Manchester' dc - *04*	NPG	110
TMC445	6247 'City of Liverpool' dc - *04*	NPG	110
TMC446	6248 'City of Leeds' dc - *04*	NPG	110

BRb blue
with sloping smokebox top

TMC588	46220 'Coronation' dc - *04*	NPG	105
TMC589	46221 'Queen Elizabeth' dc - *04*	NPG	105
TMC590	46222 'Queen Mary' dc - *04*	NPG	105
TMC591	46223 'Princess Alice' dc - *04*	NPG	105
TMC592	46224 'Princess Alexandra' dc - *04*	NPG	105
TMC593	46225 'Duchess of Gloucester' dc - *04*	NPG	105
TMC594	46226 'Duchess of Norfolk' dc - *04*	NPG	105
TMC595	46227 'Duchess of Devonshire' dc - *04*	NPG	105
TMC596	46228 'Duchess of Rutland' dc - *04*	NPG	105
TMC597	46229 'Duchess of Hamilton' dc - *04*	NPG	105
TMC598	46235 'City of Birmingham' dc - *04*	NPG	105
TMC599	46237 'City of Bristol' dc - *04*	NPG	105
TMC600	46239 'City of Chester' dc - *04*	NPG	105
TMC601	46240 'City of Coventry' dc - *04*	NPG	105
TMC602	46241 'City of Edinburgh' dc - *04*	NPG	105
TMC603	46242 'King George VI' dc - *04*	NPG	105

BRc Brunswick Green

TMC447	46220 'Coronation' dc - *04*	NPG	110
TMC448	46221 'Queen Elizabeth' dc - *04*	NPG	110
TMC449	46222 'Queen Mary' dc - *04*	NPG	110
TMC450	46223 'Princess Alice' dc - *04*	NPG	110
TMC451	46224 'Princess Alexandra' dc - *04*	NPG	110
TMC452	46226 'Duchess of Devonshire' dc - *04*	NPG	110
TMC453	46235 'City of Birmingham' dc - *04*	NPG	110
TMC454	46237 'City of Bristol' dc - *04*	NPG	110
TMC455	46239 'City of Chester' dc - *04*	NPG	110
TMC456	46241 'City of Edinburgh' dc - *04*	NPG	110
TMC457	46242 'City of Glasgow' dc - *04*	NPG	110

BRb Brunswick Green
with sloping smokebox top

TMC400	46220 'Coronation' 100 Royal Scot headboard - *04*	NPG	115
TMC420	46220 'Coronation' dc wt - *04*	NPG	110
TMC421	46221 'Queen Elizabeth' dc wt - *04*	NPG	110
TMC304	46222 'Queen Mary' dc - *02-03*	NPG	100
TMC305	46223 'Princess Alice' dc - *02-03*	NPG	100
TMC306	46224 'Princess Alexandra' dc - *02-03*	NPG	100
TMC422	46225 'Duchess of Gloucester' dc wt - *04*	NPG	110
TMC423	46226 'Duchess of Norfolk' dc wt - *04*	NPG	110
TMC307	46228 'Duchess of Rutland' dc - *02-03*	NPG	100
TMC308	46229 'Duchess of Hamilton' dc - *02-03*	NPG	100
TMC309	46236 'City of Bradford' dc - *02-03*	NPG	100
TMC310	46237 'City of Bristol' dc - *02-03*	NPG	100
TMC311	46238 'City of Carlisle' dc - *02-03*	NPG	100
TMC312	46239 'City of Chester' dc - *02-03*	NPG	100
TMC424	46240 'City of Coventry' dc wt - *04*	NPG	110
TMC313	46241 'City of Edinburgh' dc - *02-03*	NPG	100

TMC314	**46243 'City of Lancaster'** dc - *02-03*	NPG	100
TMC315	**46244 'King George VI'** dc - *02-03*	NPG	100
TMC316	**46245 'City of London'** dc - *02-03*	NPG	100
TMC317	**46246 'City of Manchester'** dc - *02-03*	NPG	100
TMC318	**46247 'City of Liverpool'** dc - *02-03*	NPG	100
TMC319	**46248 'City of Leeds'** dc - *02-03*	NPG	100
TMC386	**46235 'City of Birmingham'** dc - *02*	NPG	100

TH6. Streamlined Coronation 4-6-2 (2001 model)

These are based on the scale length Coronation model released by Hornby in 2001 and all have darkened metalwork. dc = double chimney.

Limited to 250 of each
LMS Blue

TMC226	**6220 'Coronation'** - *01-03*	NPG	95
TMC227	**6221 'Queen Elizabeth'** - *01-03*	NPG	95
TMC388	**6221 'Queen Elizabeth'** dc - *04*	NPG	110
TMC228	**6222 'Queen Mary'** - *01-03*	NPG	95
TMC389	**6222 'Queen Mary'** dc - *04*	NPG	110
TMC229	**6223 'Princess Alice'** - *01-03*	NPG	95
TMC390	**6223 'Princess Alice'** dc - *04*	NPG	110
TMC230	**6224 'Princess Alexandra'** - *01-03*	NPG	95
TMC391	**6224 'Princess Alexandra'** dc - *04*	NPG	110

LMS Maroon

TMC79	**6225 'Duchess of Gloucester'** - *00-03*	NPG	94
TMC395	**6225 'Duchess of Gloucester'** dc - *04*	NPG	110
TMC80	**6226 'Duchess of Norfolk'** - *00-03*	NPG	94
TMC396	**6226 'Duchess of Norfolk'** dc - *04*	NPG	110
TMC81	**6227 'Duchess of Devonshire'** - *00-03*	NPG	94
TMC397	**6227 'Duchess of Devonshire'** dc - *04*	NPG	110
TMC82	**6228 'Duchess of Rutland'** - *00-03*	NPG	94
TMC398	**6228 'Duchess of Rutland'** dc - *04*	NPG	110
TMC83	**6229 'Duchess of Hamilton'** - *00-03*	NPG	94
TMC399	**6229 'Duchess of Hamilton'** dc - *04*	NPG	110
TMC392	**6235 'City of Birmingham'** dc - *04*	NPG	110
TMC393	**6236 'City of Bradford'** dc - *04*	NPG	110
TMC394	**6236 'City of Bristol'** dc - *04*	NPG	110
TMC231	**6238 'City of Carlisle'** dc - *01-03*	NPG	95
TMC232	**6239 'City of Chester'** dc - *01-03*	NPG	95
TMC233	**6240 'City of Coventry'** dc - *01-03*	NPG	95
TMC234	**6241 'City of Edinburgh'** dc - *01-03*	NPG	95
TMC235	**6242 'City of Glasgow'** dc - *01-03*	NPG	95
TMC236	**6243 'City of Lancaster'** dc - *01-03*	NPG	95
TMC378	**6244 'King George VI'** dc - *02*	NPG	100

LMS Black

TMC401	**6221 'Queen Elizabeth'** dc - *04*	NPG	110
TMC402	**6222 'Queen Mary'** dc - *04*	NPG	110
TMC403	**6223 'Princess Alice'** dc - *04*	NPG	110
TMC404	**6224 'Princess Alexandra'** dc - *04*	NPG	110
TMC405	**6225 'Duchess of Gloucester'** dc - *04*	NPG	110
TMC406	**6226 'Duchess of Norfolk'** dc - *04*	NPG	110
TMC407	**6227 'Duchess of Devonshire'** dc - *04*	NPG	110
TMC408	**6228 'Duchess of Rutland'** dc - *04*	NPG	110
TMC409	**6229 'Duchess of Hamilton'** dc - *04*	NPG	110
TMC410	**6235 'City of Birmingham'** dc - *04*	NPG	110
TMC344	**6236 'City of Bradford'** dc - *02-03*	NPG	100
TMC411	**6237 'City of Bristol'** dc - *04*	NPG	110
TMC412	**6238 'City of Carlisle'** dc - *04*	NPG	110
TMC413	**6239 'City of Chester'** dc - *04*	NPG	110
TMC414	**6240 'City of Coventry'** dc - *04*	NPG	110
TMC415	**6241 'City of Edinburgh'** dc - *04*	NPG	110
TMC416	**6242 'City of Glasgow'** dc - *04*	NPG	110
TMC417	**6243 'City of Lancaster'** dc - *04*	NPG	110
TMC418	**6244 'King George V1'** dc - *04*	NPG	110
TMC419	**6245 'City of London'** dc - *04*	NPG	110
TMC345	**6246 'City of Manchester'** dc - *02-03*	NPG	100
TMC346	**6247 'City of Liverpool'** dc - *02-03*	NPG	100
TMC347	**6248 'City of Leeds'** dc - *02-03*	NPG	100

TH7. A3 Class 4-6-2

sc = single chimney. dc = double chimney. GN = GNR style tender. dm = darkened metalwork. gsd = German smoke deflectors. nct = non-corridor tender.

LNER Apple Green

TMC19	**2506 'Salmon Trout'** sc GN 250 - *00-02*	NPG	95
TMC21	**2507 'Singapore'** sc GN 250 - *00-02*	NPG	95
TMC29	**2508 'Brown Jack'** sc GN 250 - *00-02*	NPG	95

LNER Black
Limited to 100 of Eac

TMC298	**74 'Harvester'** sc GN - *02*	NPG	100
TMC299	**80 'Shotover'** sc GN - *02*	NPG	100
TMC297	**90 'Grand Parade'** sc GN - *02*	NPG	100
TMC300	**82 'Neil Gow'** sc GN - *02*	NPG	100

NE Black
Limited to 100 of Each

TMC296	**105 'Victor Wild'** sc GN - *02*	NPG	100
TMC295	**2502 'Hyperion'** sc GN - *02*	NPG	100
TMC294	**2505 'Cameronian'** sc GN - *02*	NPG	100
TMC293	**2550 'Blink Bonny'** sc GN - *02*	NPG	100
TMC291	**4474 'Victor Wild'** sc GN - *02*	NPG	100
TMC292	**4479 'Robert the Devil'** sc GN - *02*	NPG	100

BR Brunswick Green

TMC5	**60035 'Windsor Lad'** BRc dc nct 250 - *00-02*	80	95
TMC99	**60037 'Hyperion'** BRb dm GN sc 50 - *00-02*		NPG	95
TMC120	**60037 'Hyperion'** BRc dm GN gsd dc 50 - *00-02*		NPG	95
TMC174	**60040 'Cameronian'** BRb GN sc 250 - *01-02*		NPG	95
TMC40	**60040 'Cameronian'** BRc dc dm gsd GN 250 - *00-02*		NPG	95
TMC100	**60041 'Salmon Trout'** BRb dm GN sc 250 - *00-02*		NPG	95
TMC121	**60041 'Salmon Trout'** BRc dm GN gsd dc 250 - *00-02*		NPG	95
TMC101	**60042 'Singapore'** BRb dm GN sc 250 - *00-02*		NPG	95
TMC122	**60042 'Singapore'** BRc dm GN gsd dc 250 - *00-02*		NPG	95
TMC197	**60043 'Brown Jack'** BRb GN sc 250 - *01-02*		NPG	95
TMC57	**60049 'Galtee More'** BRb dm sc GN sc 250 - *00-02*		NPG	95
TMC115	**60049 'Galtee More'** BRc dm GN gsd dc 50 - *00-02*		NPG	95
TMC4	**60051 'Blink Bonny'** BRc dc nct 250 - *00-02*	80	95
TMC302	**60055 'Woolwinder'** BRc dc GN 250 - *02*	80	95
TMC116	**60056 'Centenary'** BRc dm GN gsd dc 50 - *00-02*		NPG	95
TMC58	**60056 'Centenary'** BRb dm sc GN 50 - *00-02*		NPG	95
TMC59	**60065 'Knight of the Thistle'** BRb dm sc GN sc 250 - *00-02*		NPG	95
TMC117	**60078 'Night Hawk'** BRc dm GN gsd dc 250 - *00-02*		NPG	95
TMC95	**60078 'Night Hawk'** BRb dm sc GN 50 - *00-02*		NPG	95
TMC96	**60082 'Neil Gow'** BRb dm GN sc 50 - *00-02*		NPG	95
TMC98	**60088 'Book Law'** BRb dm GN sc 50 - *00-02*		NPG	95
TMC119	**60088 'Book Law'** BRc dm GN gsd dc 50 - *00-02*		NPG	95
TMC97	**60090 'Grand Parade'** BRb dm GN sc 50 - *00-02*		NPG	95
TMC118	**60090 'Grand Parade'** BRc dm GN gsd dc 50 - *00-02*		NPG	95
TMC92	**60092 'Fairway'** BRb dc nct 50 - *00*		NPG	95
TMC186	**60096 'Papyrus'** BRb GN sc 250 - *01-02*		NPG	95
TMC266	**60100 'Spearmint'** BRb GN sc 250 - *01-02*		NPG	95
TMC43	**60102 'Sir Frederick Banbury'** BRb GN sc 50 - *00-02*		NPG	95
TMCSE	**60103 'Flying Scotsman'** BRc dm nct gsd dc Special Edition - *?*		NPG	110
TMC44	**60105 'Victor Wild'** BRb dm sc GN sc 50 - *00-02*		NPG	95
TMC112	**60105 'Victor Wild'** BRc dm GN gsd dc 50 - *00-02*		NPG	95
TMC113	**60106 'Flying Fox'** BRc dm GN gsd dc 250 - *00-02*		NPG	95
TMC47	**60106 'Flying Fox'** BRb dm sc GN sc 250 - *00-02*		NPG	95
TMC48	**60110 'Robert the Devil'** BRb dm sc GN sc		NPG	95

Code 3 Models

	50 - *00-02*		
TMC114	**60110 'Robert the Devil'** BRc dm GN gsd dc 250 - *00-02*	NPG	95

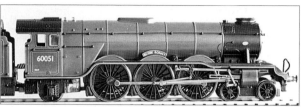

Hornby A3 'Blink Bonny' [TH7]

TH8. A4 Class 4-6-2

dc = double chimney. sc = single chimney. ct = corridor tender. nct = non-corridor tender.

Limited to 250 of each
LNER

TMC139	**4488 'Kingfisher'** blue sc ct - *00-02*	NPG	95
TMC458	**4902 'Seagull'** black no valances - *04*	NPG	95
	BR Brunswick Green		
TMC71	**60001 'Sir Ronald Mathews'** BRc nct - *01-02*	NPG	95
TMC24	**60003 'Andrew K McCosh'** BRb sc ct - *00-02*	NPG	95
TMC28	**60004 'William Whitelaw'** BRc dc ct - *00-02*	NPG	95
TMC25	**60007 'Sir Nigel Gresley'** BRc dc ct - *00-02*	NPG	95
TMC26	**60008 'Dwight D Eisenhower'** BRb sc ct - *00-02*	NPG	95
TMC72	**60011 'Empire of India'** BRc dc ct - *00-02*	NPG	95
TMC173	**60019 'Bittern'** BRc dc nct - *00-02*	NPG	95
TMC354	**60022 'Mallard'** BR dc nct - *00-02*	NPG	95
TMC73	**60024 'Kingfisher'** BRc - *03-04*	NPG	95
TMC74	**60025 'Falcon'** BRc dc ct - *00-02*	NPG	95
TMC75	**60027 'Merlin'** BRc dc ct - *00-02*	NPG	95
TMC76	**60028 'Walter K.Whigham'** BRc dc ct - *00-02*	NPG	95
TMC77	**60029 'Woodcock'** BRc dc ct - *00-02*	NPG	95
TMC23	**60031 'Golden Plover'** BRc dc ct - *00-02*	NPG	95
TMC78	**60032 'Gannet'** BRc dc ct - *00-02*	NPG	95
TMC34	**60034 'Lord Faringdon'** BRc dc ct - *00-02*	NPG	95
	BR Express Blue		
TMC25	**60007 'Sir Nigel Gresley'** BRb dc ct 50 made - *04*	NPG	95

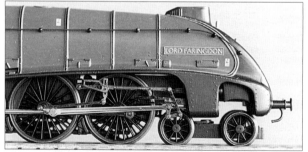

Hornby class A4 'Lord Faringdon' [TH8]

TH9. Bulleid Light Pacifics 4-6-2

All of these are based on the retooled model of 2001. HS = high sided tender. CD = cut-down tender.

Limited to 250 of each
SR Malachite Green

TMC478	**21C104 'Yeovil'** HS - *04*	NPG	110
TMC485	**21C151 'Winston Churchill'** HS - *04*	NPG	110
TMC486	**21C153 'Sir Keith Park'** HS - *04*	NPG	110
TMC487	**21C154 'Lord Beaverbrook'** HS - *04*	NPG	110
TMC488	**21C155 'Fighter Pilot'** HS - *04*	NPG	110

TMC489	**21C157 'Biggin Hill'** HS - *04*	NPG	110
TMC490	**21C159 'Sir Archibald Sinclair'** HS - *04*	NPG	110
TMC491	**21C164 'Fighter Command'** HS - *04*	NPG	110
TMC492	**21C165 'Hurricane'** HS - *04*	NPG	110
TMC493	**21C166 'Spitfire'** HS - *04*	NPG	110
TMC494	**21C167 'Tangmere'** HS - *04*	NPG	110
TMC495	**21C168 'Kenley'** HS - *04*	NPG	110
TMC496	**21C169 'Hawkinge'** HS - *04*	NPG	110
TMC497	**21C170 'Manston'** HS - *04*	NPG	110
	BRa Malachite Green		
TMC498	**s21C149 'Anti Aircraft Command'** HS - *04*	NPG	110
TMC499	**s21C150 'Royal Observer Command'** HS - *04*	NPG	110
TMC500	**s21C157 'Biggin Hill'** HS - *04*	NPG	110
TMC501	**s21C158 'Sir Frederick Pile'** HS - *04*	NPG	110
TMC502	**s21C159 'Sir Archibald Sinclair'** HS - *04*	NPG	110
TMC503	**s21C169 'Hawkinge'** HS - *04*	NPG	110
TMC504	**s21C170 'Manston'** HS - *04*	NPG	110
TMC479	**34026 'Yes Tor'** HS - *04*	NPG	110
TMC480	**34031 'Torrington'** HS - *04*	NPG	110
TMC481	**34033 'Chard'** HS - *04*	NPG	110
TMC482	**34037 'Clovelly'** HS - *04*	NPG	110
TMC483	**34042 'Dorchester'** HS - *04*	NPG	110
TMC484	**34048 'Crediton'** HS - *04*	NPG	110
TMC505	**34049 'Anti Aircraft Command'** HS - *04*	NPG	110
TMC506	**34050 'Royal Observer Command'** HS - *04*	NPG	110
TMC507	**34051 'Winston Churchill'** HS - *04*	NPG	110
TMC508	**34052 'Lord Dowding'** HS - *04*	NPG	110
TMC509	**34053 'Sir Keith Park'** HS - *04*	NPG	110
TMC510	**34054 'Lord Beaverbrook'** HS - *04*	NPG	110
TMC511	**34055 'Fighter Pilot'** HS - *04*	NPG	110
TMC512	**34057 'Biggin Hill'** HS - *04*	NPG	110
TMC513	**34058 'Sir Frederick Pile'** HS - *04*	NPG	110
TMC514	**34059 'Sir Archibald Sinclair'** HS - *04*	NPG	110
TMC515	**34060 '25 Squadron'** HS - *04*	NPG	110
TMC516	**34061 '73 Squadron'** HS - *04*	NPG	110
TMC517	**34062 '17 Squadron'** HS - *04*	NPG	110
TMC518	**34063 '229 Squadron'** HS - *04*	NPG	110
TMC519	**34064 'Fighter Command'** HS - *04*	NPG	110
TMC520	**34065 'Hurricane'** HS - *04*	NPG	110
TMC521	**34066 'Spitfire'** HS - *04*	NPG	110
TMC522	**34067 'Tangmere'** HS - *04*	NPG	110
TMC523	**34068 'Kenley'** HS - *04*	NPG	110
TMC524	**34069 'Hawkinge'** HS - *04*	NPG	110
TMC525	**34070 'Manston'** HS - *04*	NPG	110
	BRb or BRc Brunswick Green		
TMC250	**34002 'Salisbury'** BRc - *01-03*	NPG	110
TMC459	**34009 'Wadebridge'** BRc CD - *04*	NPG	110
TMC251	**34011 'Tavistock'** BRc - *01-03*	NPG	110
TMC252	**34015 'Exmouth'** BRc - *01-03*	NPG	110
TMC460	**34019 'Bideford'** BRc CD - *04*	NPG	110
TMC253	**34021 'Seaton'** BRc - *01-03*	NPG	110
TMC288	**34023 'Blackmoor Vale'** BRc- *02-03*	NPG	110
TMC461	**34030 'Watersmeet'** BRc CD - *04*	NPG	110
TMC462	**34035 'Shaftsbury'** BRc CD - *04*	NPG	110
TMC463	**34038 'Lynton'** BRc CD - *04*	NPG	110
TMC286	**34041 'Wilton'** BRc- *02-03*	NPG	110
TMC254	**34043 'Coombe Martin'** BRc - *01-03*	NPG	110
TMC581	**34049 'Anti Aircraft Command'** BRc CD - *04*	NPG	110
TMC464	**34049 'Anti Aircraft Command'** BRb HS - *04*	NPG	110
TMC465	**34050 'Royal Observer Command'** BRb HS - *04*	NPG	110
TMC258	**34051 'Winston Churchill'** BRc - *01-03*	NPG	110
TMC364	**34051 'Winston Churchill'** BRc CD - *04*	NPG	110
TMC466	**34052 'Lord Dowding'** BRb HS - *04*	NPG	110
TMC467	**34053 'Sir Keith Park'** BRb HS - *04*	NPG	110
TMC582	**34054 'Lord Beaverbrook'** BRc CD - *04*	NPG	110
TMC468	**34054 'Lord Beaverbrook'** BRb HS - *04*	NPG	110
TMC259	**34055 'Fighter Pilot'** BRc - *01-03*	NPG	110
TMC365	**34055 'Fighter Pilot'** BRc CD - *04*	NPG	110
TMC469	**34056 'Croydon'** BRb HS - *04*	NPG	110

TMC260	34057 'Biggin Hill' BRc - *01-03*	NPG	110
TMC366	34057 'Biggin Hill' BRc CD - *04*	NPG	110
TMC470	34058 'Sir Frederick Pile' BRb HS - *04*	NPG	110
TMC471	34059 'Sir Archibald Sinclair' BRb HS - *04*	NPG	110
TMC472	34060 '25 Squadron' BRb HS - *04*	NPG	110
TMC583	34061 '73 Squadron' BRc CD - *04*	NPG	110
TMC473	34061 '73 Squadron' BRb HS - *04*	NPG	110
TMC474	34062 '17 Squadron' BRb HS - *04*	NPG	110
TMC584	34063 '229 Squadron' BRc CD - *04*	NPG	110
TMC475	34063 '229 Squadron' BRb HS - *04*	NPG	110
TMC585	34064 'Fighter Command' BRc CD - *04*	NPG	110
TMC476	34064 'Fighter Command' BRb HS - *04*	NPG	110
TMC261	34065 'Hurricane' BRc - *01-03*	NPG	110
TMC367	34065 'Hurricane' BRc CD - *04*	NPG	110
TMC262	34066 'Spitfire' BRc - *01-03*	NPG	110
TMC368	34066 'Spitfire' BRc CD - *04*	NPG	110
TMC285	34067 'Tangmere' BRc - *02*	NPG	110
TMC586	34067 'Tangmere' BRc CD - *04*	NPG	110
TMC263	34068 'Kenley' BRc - *01-03*	NPG	110
TMC369	34068 'Kenley' BRc CD - *04*	NPG	110
TMC587	34069 'Hawkinge' BRc CD - *04*	NPG	110
TMC477	34069 'Hawkinge' BRb HS - *04*	NPG	110
TMC290	34070 'Manston' BRb- *02-03*	NPG	110
TMC374	34070 'Manston' BRc CD - *04*	NPG	110
TMC604	34071 '601 Squadron' BRb HS - *04*	NPG	110
TMC289	34072 '257 Squadron' BRb - *02-03*	NPG	110
TMC373	34072 '257 Squadron' BRc CD - *04*	NPG	110
TMC605	34072 '257 Squadron' BRb HS - *04*	NPG	110
TMC264	34073 '249 Squadron' BRc - *01-03*	NPG	110
TMC370	34073 '249 Squadron' BRc CD - *04*	NPG	110
TMC606	34073 '249 Squadron' BRb HS - *04*	NPG	110
TMC607	34074 '46 Squadron' BRb HS - *04*	NPG	110
TMC608	34075 '264 Squadron' BRb HS - *04*	NPG	110
TMC609	34076 '41 Squadron' BRb HS - *04*	NPG	110
TMC610	34077 '603 Squadron' BRb HS - *04*	NPG	110
TMC611	34078 '222 Squadron' BRb HS - *04*	NPG	110
TMC612	34079 '141 Squadron' BRb HS - *04*	NPG	110
TMC613	34080 '74 Squadron' BRb HS - *04*	NPG	110
TMC287	34081 '92 Squadron' BRb- *02-03*	NPG	110
TMC372	34081 '92 Squadron' BRc CD - *04*	NPG	110
TMC614	34081 '92 Squadron' BRb HS - *04*	NPG	110
TMC615	34082 '615 Squadron' BRb HS - *04*	NPG	110
TMC265	34083 '605 Squadron' BRc - *01-03*	NPG	110
TMC371	34083 '605 Squadron' BRc CD - *04*	NPG	110
TMC616	34083 '605 Squadron' BRb HS - *04*	NPG	110
TMC617	34084 '253 Squadron' BRb HS - *04*	NPG	110
TMC618	34085 '501 Squadron' BRb HS - *04*	NPG	110
TMC619	34086 '219 Squadron' BRb HS - *04*	NPG	110
TMC620	34088 '145 Squadron' BRb HS - *04*	NPG	110
TMC621	34088 '213 Squadron' BRb HS - *04*	NPG	110
TMC622	34089 '206 Squadron' BRb HS - *04*	NPG	110
TMC387	34091 'Weymouth' BRb - *02-03*	NPG	110
TMC255	34092 'City of Wells' BRc - *01-03*	NPG	110
TMC256	34105 'Swanage' BRc - *01-03*	NPG	110
TMC257	34107 'Blandford Forum' BRc - *01-03*	NPG	110
TMC623	34109 'Sir T L Mallory' BRb HS - *04*	NPG	110
TMC624	34110 '66 Squadron' BRb HS - *04*	NPG	110

TH10. Rebuilt Merchant Navy 4-6-2

Darkened metalwork.

Limited to 250 of Each
BR Brunswick Green

TMC274	35010 'Blue Star' BRb - *01*	NPG	110
TMC248	35014 'Nederland Line' BRc - *01-03*	NPG	110
TMC63	35021 'New Zealand Line' BRc - *00-03*	NPG	110
TMC64	35022 'Holland America Line' BRc - *00-03*	NPG	110
TMC273	35023 'Holland Afrika Line' BRb - *01-02*	NPG	110
TMC65	35024 'East Asiatic Company' BRc - *00-03*	NPG	110
TMC66	35025 'Brocklebank Line' BRc - *00-03*	NPG	110
TMC249	35027 'Port Line' BRc - *01-03*	NPG	110
TMC67	35028 'Clan Line' BRc - *00-03*	NPG	110
TMC68	35030 'Elder Dempster Lines' BRc - *00-03*	NPG	110

TH11a. Britannia Class 4-6-2

dm = darkened metalwork. st = small tender. lt = large tender.

BR Brunswick Green Small Tender

TMC70	70000 'Britannia' BRb dm 50 - *00-02*	NPG	90
TMC135	70000 'Britannia' BRc dm 250 - *00-02*	NPG	95
TMC189	70001 'Lord Hurcomb' BRb dm 250 - *01-02*	NPG	95
TMC188	70002 'Geoffrey Chaucer' BRb dm 250 - *01-02*	NPG	95
TMC187	70003 'John Bunyan' BRb dm 250 - *01-02*	NPG	95
TMC69	70004 'William Shakespeare' BRb dm 250 - *00-02*	NPG	90
TMC190	70005 'John Milton' BRb dm 250 - *01-02*	NPG	95
TMC191	70006 'Robert Burns' BRb dm 250 - *01-02*	NPG	95
TMC84	70007 'Coeur-de-Lion' BRb dm 50 - *00-02*	NPG	90
TMC192	70008 'Black Prince' BRb dm 250 - *01-02*	NPG	95
TMC85	70009 'Alfred the Great' BRb dm 50 - *00-02*	NPG	90
TMC134	70010 'Owen Glendower' BRc dm 250 - *00-02*	NPG	95
TMC185	70010 'Owen Glendower' BRb dm 250 - *01-02*	NPG	95
TMC180	70013 'Oliver Cromwell' BRb dm 50 - *01-02*	NPG	95
TMC86	70014 'Iron Duke' BRb dm 50 - *00-02*	NPG	90
TMC87	70015 'Apollo' BRb dm 50 - *00-02*	NPG	90
TMC133	70017 'Arrow' BRc dm 250 - *00-02*	NPG	95
TMC93	70020 'Mercury' BRb dm 250 - *00-02*	NPG	90
TMC301	70020 'Mercury' BRc dm 250 - *00-02*	NPG	90
TMC94	70021 'Morning Star' BRb dm 50 - *00-02*	NPG	90
TMC88	70024 'Vulcan' BRb dm 50 - *00-02*	NPG	90
TMC219	70027 'Rising Star' BRb dm 250 - *01-02*	NPG	95
TMC132	70029 'Shooting Star' BRc dm 250 - *00-02*	NPG	95
TMC193	70030 'William Wordsworth' BRb dm 250 - *02*	NPG	90
TMC89	70031 'Byron' BRb dm 50 - *00-02*	NPG	90
TMC33	70033 'Charles Dickens' BRb dm 250 - *00-02*	NPG	90
TMC194	70034 'Thomas Hardy' BRb dm 250 - *01-02*	NPG	95
TMC90	70036 'Boadicea' BRb dm 50 - *00-02*	NPG	90
TMC175	70037 'Hereward the Wake' BRb dm 50 - *01-02*	NPG	95
TMC174	70040 'Clive of India' BRc dm 250 - *01-02*	NPG	95

BR Brunswick Green Large Tender

TMC9	70045 'Lord Rowallan' BRc 250 - *00-02*	NPG	90
TMC10	70046 'Anzac' BRc 250 - *00-02*	NPG	90
TMC11	70047 BRc 250 - *00-02*	80	90
TMC12	70048 'The Territorial Army 1908-1958' BRc 250 - *00-02*	80	90
TMC13	70049 'Solway Firth' BRc 250 - *00-03*	NPG	90
TMC14	70050 'Firth of Clyde' BRc 250 - *00-03*	NPG	90
TMC15	70051 'Firth of Forth' BRc 250 - *00-03*	NPG	90
TMC16	70052 'Firth of Tay' BRb or BRc 250 - *00-03*	NPG	90
TMC17	70053 'Moray Firth' BRc 250 - *00-03*	80	90
TMC18	70054 'Dornoch Firth' BRc 250 - *00-03*	80	90

Hornby Britania class 'The Territorial Army 1908-1958' [TH11a]

TH11b. Britannia Class 4-6-2 (2000 model)

BR Brunswick Green

TMC267	70011 'Hotspur' BRc dm 250 - *01-02*	NPG	95
TMC526	70015 'Apollo' SD 50 - *04*	NPG	110
TMC527	70016 'Ariel' SD 50 - *04*	NPG	110
TMC528	70018 'Flying Dutchman' SD 50 - *04*	NPG	110
TMC529	70019 'Lightning' SD 50 - *04*	NPG	110
TMC530	70022 'Tornado' SD 50 - *04*	NPG	110
TMC531	70023 'Venus' SD 50 - *04*	NPG	110

Code 3 Models

TMC532	**70025 'Western Star'** SD 50 - *04*	NPG	110
TMC533	**70026 'Polar Star'** SD 50 - *04*	NPG	110
TMC534	**70027 'Rising Star'** SD 50 - *04*	NPG	110
TMC268	**70030 'William Wordsworth'** BRc dm 250 - *02*	NPG	95
TMC269	**70035 'Rudyard Kipling'** BRc dm 250 - *01-02*	NPG	95
TMC270	**70039 'Sir Christopher Wren'** BRc dm 250 - *01-02*	NPG	95
TMC131	**70037 'Hereward the Wake'** BRc dm 250 - *00-02*	NPG	95
TMC271	**70041 'Sir John Moore'** BRc dm 250 - *01-02*	NPG	95
TMC272	**70044 'Earl Haig'** BRc dm 250 - *01-02*	NPG	95

TH12. 9F Class 2-10-0

The models used are 'Evening Star' R2187 (X1). Production is limited to 250.

TMC128	**92220 'Evening Star'** BRc green - *00*	NPG	90

TH13. Class 25 Diesel

The models have been profesionally weathered.

TMC?	**25033** BRe blue weathered - *02*	NPG	60
TMC?	**25056** BRe blue weathered - *02*	NPG	60

TH14. Speed Kings Double Pack

The models are from the TMC Code 3 range and came in a rosewood presentation box with a special certificate and information Production is limited to 50.

TMC?	**4468 'Mallard'** LNER blue + **6220 'Coronation'** LMS blue - *02*	NPG	250

Train Trading Post

PH1. Bullied Pacific

Repainted with engraved brass nameplates and numbered certificate.

-	**35029 'Ellerman Lines'** BRb blue ex- 'Lord Beaverbrook' (R310) Ltd Edn 50 - *95*	120	150

Hornby Merchant Navy 'Elleman Lines' in BR blue [PH1]

Frizinghall Model Railways

All come fitted with etched brass nameplates (where named) and renumbered and issued with a certificate.

FH1. J94 Class 0-6-0ST

Based on the Hornby Class J94.

FMR12A	**118 'Brussels'** LMR blue ex- R2151 Ltd Edn 100 - *00*	NPG	50
FMR12B	**196 'Errol Lonsdale'** LMR blue ex- R2151 Ltd Edn 100 - *00*	NPG	50

FH2. Class 56 Diesel Co-Co

Based on the Hornby Class 56 (R2074).

FMR14A	**56074 'Kellingley Colliery'** Load Haul black+orange Ltd Edn 100 - *00*	NPG	55
FMR14B	**56110 'Croft'** LoadHaul black+ orange Ltd Edn 100 - *00*	NPG	55

FH3. Classes 41XX, 51XX and 61XX Prairie Tank 2-6-2T

Sprayed black. Based on the Hornby Class 61XX (R2098A). Various numbers used. Production limited to 100 of each.

FMR13A	BRb black Class 41XX - *00*	NPG	60
FMR13B	BRb black Class 51XX - *00*	NPG	60
FMR13C	BRb black Class 61XX - *00*	NPG	60

FH4. B17 Class 4-6-0

Based on the Hornby Class B17.

FMR17B	**2853 'Huddersfield Town'** LNER lt.green Ltd Edn 100 - *00-01*	NPG	75
FMR17A	**2868 'Bradford City'** LNER lt.green Ltd Edn 100 - *00-01*	NPG	75

FH5. Patriot Class 4-6-0

Based on the Hornby Patriot.

FMR16	**45516 'The Bedfordshire and Hertfordshire' Regiment'** LMS/BR maroon Ltd Edn 100 - *01*	NPG	70

FH6. Duchess Class 4-6-2

Based on the Hornby super detail Duchess.

FMR?	**46236 'City of Bradford'** LMS black - *03*	NPG	100
FMR?	**46241 'City of Edinburgh'** BRc green - *03*	NPG	100

Miscellaneous

MH1. Class 86 Electric

Based on the Hornby Class 86.

-	**86220 'The Round Tabler'** InterCity grey ex-R333 etched nameplates Ltd Edn 1267 (Round Table) - *90*	50	75

MH2. Holden Tank 0-4-0T

Based on the Hornby Holden 0-4-0T.

-	**30** blue ex-R796 (Pendle Forest Model Rly Soc)* Ltd Edn 150 - *94*	40	50

* Transfers

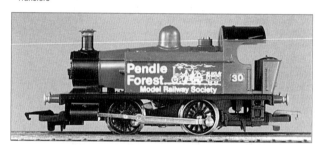

Hornby Holden tank for Pendle Forest MRS [MH2]

MH3. Patriot Class 4-6-0

Based on the Hornby Patriot.

-	**5538 'Giggleswick'** LMS maroon Ltd Edn 50 (Giggleswick School) - *99*	90	180
-	**45538 'Giggleswick'** BR green Ltd Edn 50 (Giggleswick School) - *99*	90	180
	45538 'Giggleswick' BR black Ltd Edn 10? (Giggleswick School) - *99*	100	200

MH4. Class 90 Electric

Based on the Hornby Class 90.

-	**DC230 ST 'Connectivity'** red Digital X Systems Ltd Edn 60 (Xerox) - *98*	NPG	NPG

This was finished by Western Resprays

EX- BACHMANN MODELS
Trafford Model Centre

All have etched brass nameplates and a numbered certificate.

TB1. Patriot Class 4-6-0

Based on the Bachmann Patriot.

TMC353	**45528 'REME'** BRb green Ltd Edn 250 - *01*	NPG	70

TB2. Jubilee Class 4-6-0

Each of these came with a certificate and brief history of the locomotive. They all had darkened wheels and other metalwork, sprung buffers and were available with a choice of early or late decals (except 'Gold Coast'). Ft = Fowler tender. St = Stanier tender.

LMS Lined Black Green
Limited to 25 of each

TMC577	5563 'Australia' Ft - 04	NPG	110
TMC578	5711 'Courageous' Ft - 04	NPG	110
TMC579	5712 'Victory' Ft - 04	NPG	110
TMC580	5717 'Dauntless' Ft - 04	NPG	110

BR Brunswick Green
Limited to 50 of each

TMC198	45567 'South Australia' Ft - 01-02	NPG	90
TMC199	45608 'Gibraltar' BRb or BRc St - 01-02	NPG	90
TMC217	45610 'Gold Coast' BRb St - 01-02	NPG	90
TMC218	45610 'Ghana' BRc St red nameplate - 01-02	NPG	90
TMC201	45667 'Jellicoe' BRb or BRc St - 01-02	NPG	90
TMC202	45682 'Trafalgar' BRb or BRc St - 01-02	NPG	90
TMC200	45688 'Polyphemus' BRb or BRc St - 01-02	NPG	90
TMC203	45689 'Ajax' BRb or BRc St - 01-02	NPG	90
TMC204	45693 'Agamemnon' BRb or BRc St large numbers - 01-02	NPG	90
TMC205	45694 'Bellerophon' BRb or BRc, St - 01-02	NPG	90
TMC206	45695 'Minotaur' BRc Ft - 01-02	NPG	90
TMC207	45697 'Achilles' BRc Ft large numbers - 01-02	NPG	90
TMC208	45718 'Dreadnought' BRc Ft - 01-02	NPG	90
TMC209	45723 'Fearless' BRb or BRc St - 01-02	NPG	90
TMC210	45727 'Inflexible' BRb or BRc St large number - 01-02	NPG	90
TMC211	45728 'Defiance' BRc Ft - 01-02	NPG	90
TMC212	45729 'Furious' BRb St large numbers - 01-02	NPG	90
TMC213	45734 'Meteor' BRb or BRc St - 01-02	NPG	90
TMC215	45737 'Atlas' BRb or BRc St - 01-02	NPG	90
TMC216	45738 'Samson' BRb or BRc St - 01-02	NPG	90
TMC214	45739 'Ulster' BRb or BRc St - 01-02	NPG	90

TB3. Rebuilt Royal Scot Class 4-6-0

Based on the Bachmann Rebuilt Scot with a Stanier tender.

BR Green
Limited to 25 of each

TMC540	46103 'Royal Scots Fusilier' - 04	NPG	110
TMC541	46105 'Cameron Highlander' - 04	NPG	110
TMC542	46115 'Scots Guardsman' - 04	NPG	110
TMC543	46117 'Welsh Guardsman' - 04	NPG	110
TMC544	46120 'Royal Inniskilling Fusilier' - 04	NPG	110
TMC545	46127 'Old Contemptibles' - 04	NPG	110
TMC546	46128 'The Lovat Scout' - 04	NPG	110
TMC547	46131 'The Royal Warwickshire Regiment' - 04	NPG	110
TMC548	46133 'The Green Howards' - 04	NPG	110
TMC549	46136 'The Border Regiment' - 04	NPG	110
TMC550	46139 'The Welch Regiment',- 04	NPG	110
TMC551	46150 'The Life Guardsman' - 04	NPG	110
TMC552	46158 'The Loyal Regiment' - 04	NPG	110
TMC553	46161 'Kings Own'- 04	NPG	110
TMC554	46166 'The Londopn Rifle Brigade' - 04	NPG	110

TB4. Peppercorn A1 Class 4-6-4

Blackened metalwork. rt = riveted tender. wt = welded tender.

BRb Express Blue
Limited to 25 of each

TMC555	60114 'W P Allen' - 04	NPG	110
TMC556	60115 'Meg Merrilies' - 04	NPG	110
TMC557	60116 'Hal o' The Wynd' - 04	NPG	110
TMC558	60117 'Biois Roussel' - 04	NPG	110
TMC559	60118 'Archibald Sturrock' - 04	NPG	110
TMC560	60119 'Patrick Stirling' - 04	NPG	110
TMC561	60120 'Kittiwake' - 04	NPG	110
TMC562	60121 'Silurian' - 04	NPG	110
TMC563	60122 'Curlew' - 04	NPG	110
TMC564	60123 'H A Ivatt' - 04	NPG	110

TMC565	60125 'Scottish Union' - 04	NPG	110
TMC566	60126 'Sit Vincent Raven' - 04	NPG	110
TMC567	60128 'Bongrace' - 04	NPG	110
TMC568	60129 'Guy Mannering' - 04	NPG	110
TMC569	60153 'Flamboyant' - 04	NPG	110
TMC570	60154 'Bon Accord' - 04	NPG	110
TMC571	60155 'Borderer' - 04	NPG	110
TMC572	60156 'Great Central' - 04	NPG	110
TMC573	60157 'Great Eastern' - 04	NPG	110
TMC574	60158 'Sberdonian' - 04	NPG	110
TMC575	60159 'Bonnie Dundee' - 04	NPG	110
TMC576	60161 'North British' - 04	NPG	110
TMC350	60161 'North British' rt 100 - 02	NPG	115

BR Brunswick Green
Rivited Tender Limited to 100

TMC275	60116 'Hal o' the Wynd' BRc - 01-02	NPG	110
TMC276	60118 'Archibald Sturrock' BRc - 01-02	NPG	110
TMC277	60119 'Patrick Stirling' BRc - 01-02	NPG	110
TMC352	60123 'A.A.Ivatt' BRc - 02	NPG	110
TMC278	60125 'Scottish Union' BRc - 01-02	NPG	110
TMC279	60126 'Sir Vincent Raven' BRc - 01-02	NPG	110
TMC348	60147 'North Eastern' BRc - 02	NPG	110
TMC280	60156 'Great Central' BRc - 01-02	NPG	110
TMC281	60157 'Great Eastern' BRc - 01-02	NPG	110
TMC351	60158 'Aberdonian' BRc - 02	NPG	110
TMC282	60159 'Bonnie Dundee' BRc - 01-02	NPG	110
TMC283	60160 'Auld Reekie' BRc - 01-02	NPG	110
TMC284	60161 'North British' BRc - 01-02	NPG	110

Welded Tender Limited to 250

TMC349	60130 'Kestrel' BRc - 02	NPG	115
TMC356	60131 'Osprey' BRc - 02	NPG	115
TMC357	60134 'Foxhunter' BRc - 02	NPG	115
TMC358	60138 'Boswell' BRc - 02	NPG	115
TMC359	60139 'Sea Eagle' BRc - 02	NPG	115
TMC360	60140 'Balmoral' BRc - 02	NPG	115
TMC361	60146 'Peregrine' BRc - 02	NPG	115
TMC362	60151 'Midlothian' BRc - 02	NPG	115
TMC363	60152 'Holyrood' BRc - 02	NPG	115

TB5. A4 Class 4-6-2

All have the double chimney and darkened metalwork. ct = corridor tender. nct = non-corridor tender.

LNER Blue

TMC536	13 'Dominion of New Zealand' 50 - 04	NPG	110
TMC537	21 'Wild Swan' 50 - 04	NPG	110
TMC538	20 'Gullemot' 50 - 04	NPG	110
TMC539	32 'Gannet' 50 - 04	NPG	110
TMC535	4496 'Dwight D Eisenhower' 50 - 04	NPG	110

BR Brunswick Green
Limited to 250 of each

TMC126	60003 'Andrew K McCosh' BRc nct - 00-02	NPG	95
TMC124	60004 'William Whitelaw' BRc ct - 00-02	NPG	95
TMC355	60007 'Sir Nigel Gresley' BRc ct dc - 02	NPG	95
TMC223	60008 'Dwight D Eisenhower' BRc ct - 00-02	NPG	95
TMC195	60011 'Empire of India' BRc ct - 00-02	NPG	95
TMC170	60016 'Silver King' BRc ct - 00-02	NPG	95
TMC169	60018 'Sparrow Hawk' BRc nct - 00-02	NPG	95
TMC27	60022 'Mallard' BRb or BRc ct - 00-02	NPG	95
TMC172	60023 'Golden Eagle' BRc nct - 00-02	NPG	95
TMC164	60024 'Kingfisher' BRc ct - 00-02	NPG	95
TMC166	60025 'Falcon' BRc ct - 00-02	NPG	95
TMC171	60026 'Miles Beevor' BRc nct - 00-02	NPG	95
TMC165	60027 'Merlin' BRc ct - 00-02	NPG	95
TMC167	60028 'Walter K Whigham' BRc ct - 00-02	NPG	95
TMC168	60029 'Woodcock' BRc ct - 00-02	NPG	95
TMC125	60031 'Golden Plover' BRc ct - 00-02	NPG	95
TMC31	60032 'Gannet' BRc ct - 00-02	NPG	95
TMC224	60034 'Lord Faringdon' BRc ct - 00-02	NPG	95

Code 3 Models

TB6. WD 2-8-0

Blackened metalwork. Shed plates fitted to customer's choice.

TMC32	**90732 'Vulcan'** BRb or BRc black Ltd Edn 1000 - *00-02*	NPG	110

Limited editions of 100

TMC53	**90000** BRb or BRc black - *00-02*	NPG	95
TMC54	**90085** BRb or BRc black - *00-02*	NPG	95
TMC52	**90146** BRb or BRc black - *00-02*	NPG	95
TMC50	**90245** BRb or BRc black - *00-02*	NPG	95
TMC127	**90266** BRb or BRc black - *00-02*	NPG	95
TMC56	**90464** BRb or BRc black - *00-02*	NPG	95
TMC51	**90503** BRb or BRc black - *00-02*	NPG	95
TMC55	**90566** BRb or BRc black - *00-02*	NPG	95

WD 2-8-0 'Vulcan' [TB6]

TB7. Class 55 Deltic Co-Co

Based on the Bachmann model.

BRc Green

TMC017	**D9000 'Royal Scots Grey'** - *04*	NPG	90
TMC018	**D9001 'St Paddy'** - *04*	NPG	90
TMC019	**D9002 'The King's Own Yorkshire Light Infantry'** - *04*	NPG	90
TMC020	**D9003 'Meld'** - *04*	NPG	90
TMC021	**D9004 'Queen's Own Highlander'** - *04*	NPG	90
TMC022	**D9005 'The Prince of Wales's Own Regiment of Yorkshire'** - *04*	NPG	90
TMC023	**D9006 'The Fife & Forfar Yeomanry'** - *04*	NPG	90
TMC024	**D9007 'Pinza'** - *04*	NPG	90
TMC025	**D9008 'The Green Howards'** - *04*	NPG	90
TMC026	**D9009 'Alycidon'** - *04*	NPG	90
TMC027	**D9010 'The King's Own Scottish Borderer'** - *04*	NPG	90
TMC028	**D9011 'The Royal Northumberland Fusiliers'** - *04*	NPG	90
TMC029	**D9012 'Crepello'** - *04*	NPG	90
TMC030	**D9013 'The Black Watch'** - *04*	NPG	90
TMC031	**D9014 'The Duke of Wellington's Regiment'** - *04*	NPG	90
TMC032	**D9015 'Tulyar'** - *04*	NPG	90
TMC033	**D9016 'Gordon Highlander'** - *04*	NPG	90
TMC034	**D9017 'The Durham Light Infantry'** - *04*	NPG	90
TMC035	**D9018 'Ballymoss'** - *04*	NPG	90
TMC036	**D9019 'Royal Highland Fusiliers'** - *04*	NPG	90
TMC037	**D9020 'Nimbus'** - *04*	NPG	90
TMC038	**D9021 'Argyll and Sutherland Highlander'** - *04*	NPG	90

Frizinghall Model Railways

All come fitted with etched brass nameplates and renumbered and issued with a certificate.

FB1. Parallel Boiler Royal Scot Class 4-6-0

Renamed and renumbered. Blackened wheels but not valve gear.

FMR15C	**46137 'The Prince of Wales Volunteers'** BRb green Ltd Edn 100 - *00-01*	NPG	65
FMR15A	**46142 'The York & Lancaster Regiment'** BRb green Ltd Edn 100 - *00-01*	NPG	65
FMR15B	**46163 'Civil Service Rifleman'** BRb green Ltd Edn 100 - *00-01*	NPG	65

FB2. B1 Class 4-6-0

Repainted.

FMR11A	**8302 'Eland'** NE black Ltd Edn 100 - *00*	NPG	70
FMR11B	**8306 'Bongo'** NE black Ltd Edn 100 - *00*	NPG	70

FB3. A4 Class 4-6-2

Repainted.

FMR10A	**60003 'Andrew K.McCosh'** BRa garter blue, cream lettering Ltd Edn 100 - *00*	NPG	90
FMR10B	**60004 'William Whitelaw'** BRa garter blue, cream lettering Ltd Edn 100 - *00*	NPG	90

EX-TRIX MODELS

Miscellaneous

MT1. A2 Class 4-6-2

These were supplied to a Mr Fox who was responsible for the BBC 'Blue Peter' model railway layout. It is understood that the new number transfers were applied at the factory and Mr Fox had the nameplates and double chimney done. In the spring of 1998, 7 of these came on the market.

-	**532 'Blue Peter'** LNER green, double chimney Ltd Edn 12? - *00*	150	NPG

Trix A2 'Blue Peter' [MT1]

EX-LIMA MODELS

Howes of Oxford

HL1. Class 47 Diesel

-	**47910 'Howes of Oxford'** gold, to Celebrate our 50th Anniversary, plinth + track - *?*	NPG	100

Miscellaneous

ML1. Class 92 Electric

-	**92? 'Silverstone'** LMS Coronation livery of blue livery with silver stripes Digital X Ltd Edn 25 (Xerox) - *?*	NPG	NPG

This was finished by Western Resprays

Guide to Advertisers

- Ace Trains, London — page 3a, first colour section which follows page 96
- Andrew Clark , Shipley, W. Yorks — page 22
- Barry Potter Auctions, Model Toy & Train Auctioneers - outside rear cover
- Bonham's Auctioneers, Toys and Trains Auctions, London — page 25a,
  second colour section which follows page 288
- British Railway Modeller Magazine — inside rear cover
- Capes Dunn Auctioneers, Manchester — page 104
- Christie's Auctioneers, Toy and Model Trains Auctions, London — page 1a, first colour section
  which follows page 96
- Collector's Gazette - for Toy Collectors Worldwide - inside rear cover
- Hornby Collectors' Club - how to join and membership benefits - page 312
- Lacy, Scott & Knight, Model Toy & Train Auctioneers, Bury St Edmunds, Suffolk - page166
- LOCOREPAIR, Bristol - page 22
- Models & Hobbbies, Steyning, W. Sussex, - page 214
- Modelfair.com - page 27a, second colour section which follows page 288
- K.H.Norton Group — (Wholesalers, Leicester) - page 214
- Park Trains and Models at the Old Toy Shop, Southampton - page 104
- Rolling Stock, North Shields, Tyne & Wear - page 104
- Ron's Model Rail & Diecast, Rochester, Kent - page 234
- Sandown Park Toyfair Dates 2005 (Barry Potter) - page 242
- Scale Model Railways - page 27a, second colour section which follows page 288
- Square Wheels, Mayfield, East Sussex - page 234
- 4th edition - Ramsay's 'British Model Trains Catalogue' - page 214
- 10th edition - Ramsay's 'British Diecast Model Toys Catalogue' - page 28
- Terry Durrant, (Layout Planning) - page 22
- The Model Centre, Leeds, Liverpool, Manchester, Nottingham, Sheffield - page 24a, first colour
  section which follows page 96
- The Rovex Story by Pat Hammond - page 348
- Train Collectors Society, London - page 214
- Trix Twin Railway Collectors' Association, Leicester - page 214
- Vectis Auctions Ltd, Collectable Toy Specialists, Stockton-on-Tees - inside front cover
- Vectis Auctions Ltd incorporating Barry Potter Auctions   - outside rear cover
- Wallis & Wallis, International Toy & Model Auctioneers, Lewes, Sussex - page 320
- Wrenn Railways Collectors' Club, Marlow, Bucks - page 336

The Guide to Advertisers has been compiled as an extra service for Catalogue users. Whilst every care has been taken in compiling
the listing, the publishers cannot accept responsibility for any errors or omissions. Similarly, the publishers cannot accept
responsibility for errors in the advertisements or for unsolicited photographs or illustrations.

Notes

4th Edition
'British Model Trains Catalogue'

Reader Survey

Whether you are a collector or trader, we would greatly value your views on this new Edition and would ask you to kindly complete and return this questionnaire.

We hope to publish the results of this survey, and for the three most constructive and helpful replies that we receive, we shall be giving a year's free subscription to the collecting magazine or newspaper of their choice. If necessary, do please use a photocopy of this form or a seperate sheet of paper for your response. Thank you.

1   What do you like MOST about the Catalogue?_____
_____

2   What do you like LEAST about the Catalogue? _____
_____

3   What improvements or additions would you like to see?_____
_____

4   Would you like the Catalogue to be published yearly or every two years?_____
_____

If you have model information not currently included in the Catalogue - do please send it to us. Your costs will be fully refunded.

Name and Address (BLOCK CAPITALS, please)_____
_____
_____
_____

Kindly send your response to:
Swapmeet Publications, PO Box 47, Felixstowe, Suffolk, IP11 7LP.

Scales and Gauges

**'Scale' refers to the linear scale of the model,
for example: 4mm to 1 foot (the '00' scale measurement).
'Gauge' refers to the distance between the running rails of the track.**
listed here are a few of the more common scales and gauges.

Gauge name	Scale	Gauge distance
'N' (British)	2mm to 1 foot	9mm
'000'	2mm to 1 foot	9.5mm
'TT' (British)	3mm to 1 foot	12mm
'HO'	3.5mm to 1 foot	16.5mm
'00'	4mm to 1 foot	16.5mm
'EM'	4mm to 1 foot	18mm
'0' (British)	7mm to 1 foot	32mm
'No.1'	10mm to 1 foot	45.45mm
'No.2'	7/16inch to 1 foot	51mm
'No.3'	17/32", 1/2" or 14mm to 1 foot	63.5mm

**The illustrations below are only approximately to scale to give
some idea of the difference in size between the various gauges.**

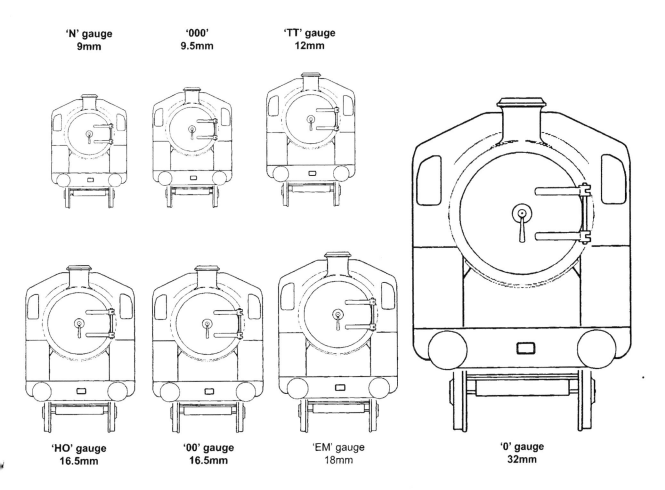

'N' gauge	'000'	'TT' gauge
9mm	9.5mm	12mm

'HO' gauge	'00' gauge	'EM' gauge	'0' gauge
16.5mm	16.5mm	18mm	32mm

Sale and Purchase Record

Dates	Models bought and sold	Price